ANNUAL REVIEW OF
PHYSIOLOGY

ANNUAL REVIEW OF PHYSIOLOGY

I. S. EDELMAN, *Editor*
Columbia University College of Physicians and Surgeons

STANLEY G. SCHULTZ, *Associate Editor*
University of Texas Medical School

VOLUME 43

1981

ANNUAL REVIEWS INC.   4139 EL CAMINO WAY   PALO ALTO, CALIFORNIA 94306 USA

ANNUAL REVIEWS INC.
Palo Alto, California, USA

REPRINTS   The conspicuous number aligned in the margin with the title of each article in this volume is a key for use in ordering reprints. Available reprints are priced at the uniform rate of $2.00 each postpaid. The minimum acceptable reprint order is 5 reprints and/or $10.00 prepaid. A quantity discount is available.

International Standard Serial Number: 0066-4278
International Standard Book Number: 0-8243-0343-1
Library of Congress Catalog Card Number: 39-15404

Annual Reviews Inc. and the Editors of its publications assume no responsibility for the statements expressed by the contributors to this Review.

PRINTED AND BOUND IN THE UNITED STATES OF AMERICA

PREFACE

Volumes 41 (1979) and 42 (1980) of the *Annual Review of Physiology* established a new format for the series, which the present volume continues. The *Review* is organized into eight sections, each under the editorship of a noted specialist in one of the major fields of physiology: Gastrointestinal Physiology (Section Editor Stanley G. Schultz, Section Organizer Norman Weisbrodt), Respiratory Physiology (Section Editor Alfred P. Fishman), Endocrinology and Metabolism (Section Editor Dorothy T. Krieger), Comparative and Integrative Physiology (Section Editor William Dawson), Cardiovascular Physiology (Section Editor Robert M. Berne), Cell and Membrane Physiology (Section Editor John Gergely), Renal and Electrolyte Physiology (Section Editor Thomas E. Andreoli), and the Special Topic Section: Neuronal Plasticity (Section Editor Gerald Fischbach).

In previous prefaces the forces that led to the introduction of the sectional format were described and discussed. The considerations noted there—especially the progressive specialization within physiology—continue to justify the use of both sectional and thematic principles in the present volume. There is, of course, a continuing appreciation of the underlying unity of the discipline of physiology and of the need not to lose sight of this basic unity.

As always, the ultimate value of these reviews is a consequence of the scholarly efforts of our authors, for which we and our readers are grateful. Key elements in the success of the present *Annual Review of Physiology* derive from the insights and the leadership of our Section Editors, all of whom merit our wholehearted appreciation. Dr. Stanley G. Schultz has earned special commendation for his outstanding contributions to the *ARP* over a span of five years (two years as a Member of our Editorial Committee, and three years in the combined roles of Section Editor for Gastrointestinal Physiology and Associate Editor). At Dr. Schultz's retirement from service we are pleased to welcome Dr. Robert M. Berne as Associate Editor.

The Annual Reviews staff, represented by R. L. Burke, continues to provide a stable foundation for our efforts.

I. S. EDELMAN, EDITOR

SOME RELATED ARTICLES IN OTHER *ANNUAL REVIEWS*

Annual Review of Physiology
Volume 43, 1981

CONTENTS

ANNUAL REVIEWS INC. is a nonprofit corporation established to promote the advancement of the sciences. Beginning in 1932 with the *Annual Review of Biochemistry,* the Company has pursued as its principal function the publication of high quality, reasonably priced *Annual Review* volumes. The volumes are organized by Editors and Editorial Committees who invite qualified authors to contribute critical articles reviewing significant developments within each major discipline. Annual Reviews Inc. is administered by a Board of Directors, whose members serve without compensation.

Publications

Annual Reviews of Anthropology, Astronomy and Astrophysics, Biochemistry, Biophysics and Bioengineering, Earth and Planetary Sciences, Ecology and Systematics, Energy, Entomology, Fluid Mechanics, Genetics, Materials Science, Medicine, Microbiology, Neuroscience, Nuclear and Particle Science, Nutrition, Pharmacology and Toxicology, Physical Chemistry, Physiology, Phytopathology, Plant Physiology, Psychology, Public Health, and *Sociology.*

Special Publications: *History of Entomology* (1973), *The Excitement and Fascination of Science* (1965), *The Excitement and Fascination of Science, Volume Two* (1978), *Annual Reviews Reprints: Cell Membranes, 1975–1977* (published 1978), *Annual Reviews Reprints: Immunology, 1977–1979* (published 1980), and *Intelligence and Affectivity: Their Relationship During Child Development,* by Jean Piaget (1981).

For the convenience of readers, a detachable order form/envelope is bound into the back of this volume.

Victor E Hall

Ralph R. Sonnenschein

Ann. Rev. Physiol. 1981. 43:1-5

THE *ANNUAL REVIEW* OF *PHYSIOLOGY:* PAST AND PRESENT

❖1293

Victor E. Hall and Ralph R. Sonnenschein

Department of Physiology, University of California, Los Angeles, School of Medicine, Los Angeles, California 90024

When Isidore Edelman invited us to write an introductory chapter for this volume of the *Annual Review of Physiology,* we were delighted with the opportunity to give some of our thoughts and reminiscences about the *Review.* Our combined span of service as editors covered about 40 years, nearly the entire lifetime of the *Review.* Each of us had his own experiences and point of view, so rather than attempt a single presentation we have written the following separate sections.

I. (V.E.H.)

One day in 1938 Dr. J. Murray Luck burst into my office in the Department of Physiology at Stanford University with an invitation to become Associate Editor of the new *Annual Review of Physiology,* which he had recently set in motion with the cooperation of the American Physiological Society. I immediately accepted and soon was involved in the delightful efforts of the *Review* and its staff. And in 1947 I was made Editor, replacing Dr. Luck. At that time the Editorial Committee was impelled to "seize the occasion to acknowledge Dr. Luck's services as founder, editor and business manager to which a considerable measure of the success of the Review has been due." In those activities he had the successful example of the *Annual Review of Biochemistry,* the format and procedures of which were closely followed in the new review.

In the ensuing years the meetings of the *Review's* Editorial Committee were most exciting events. Here were assembled a potent group of senior physiologists appointed by the Society: A. J. Carlson, J. F. Fulton, M. H. Jacobs, F. C. Mann, and W. S. Meek. At one meeting I presented a scheme

1

0066-4278/81/0315-0001$01.00

for dividing coverage of the functions of the nervous system so as to provide a more systematic treatment of the autonomic nervous system. Carlson immediately turned his well-known satire on me and blurted out, "Hall, that won't do. Authors will set their own boundaries." I was duly chastened. But Ajax and I became friends, and one day when the Committee's meeting at Stanford was over he asked me if I had a family. I confessed I did, and he demanded to see them. So I drove him to my home and introduced him to my wife and children. He immediately took to them with enthusiasm and they loved him! He was a powerful and helpful member of the Committee. The other members savored his knowledge and enjoyed his salty wisdom and humor. His term ended in 1948 and the Committee was never the same again.

Of all the members the courtly and quiet Walter Meek was the most helpful to me as Associate Editor for many years; J. F. Fulton was a delightful gentleman, as was F. C. Mann.

Early on it was the custom to hold the meetings of the Committee in the afternoon of Registration Day of the Federation. But many members thought other appointments more important. On one occasion only Dr. Mann and I were present, so we made up the list of topics and authors for the next volume of the *Review* without help. This led after many years to our holding meetings in August in various places, campuses and resorts. In the late 1960s we met, among many places, at the Marine Laboratory in Woods Hole, in a ski lodge at Aspen, and in the ancient hotel in Santa Fé. This earned our Committee the undivided attention of all its members.

In 1962 the American Physiological Society discontinued its role in the affairs of the *Review,* most importantly the appointment of Editorial Committee members. Each year thereafter the Committee nominated its own successors, which the Board of Annual Reviews almost always approved. The quality of topic and author choices remained high. The *Review* no longer needed the formal support of the Society, it had earned its own place!

From its beginning the planners of the *Review* assigned to each of its authors the task of preparing "a critical appraisal of the contemporary field, an analysis and interpretation of the most significant contributions." It was their hope that no national boundaries would restrict inclusion of either research in our field or the enrollment of authors from outside North America.

The outbreak of World War II shortly after the launching of the *Annual Review* seriously interfered with the hopes of international representation. However, during these years citation of *Pflügers Archiv* and the *Ergebnisse der Physiologie* continued to appear in our pages, though less frequently.

In the period 1940–1944 we had two authors from England, three from Sweden, and two from Argentina. It was not until 1947 that Bremer was appointed as our first contributor from continental Europe.

A few words on the modus operandi of the Editorial Committee. The Editor, aided by the highly competent staff of the central office of Annual Reviews, among whom Joann Huddleston deserves to be remembered, prepared a document showing for every standard chapter a list of those who had already written on that topic, those who had refused invitations, the suggestions gathered from the then current author, and suggestions from various outside sources. At the meeting of the Committee, names suggested as authors were noted and included in the document for the next year's meeting. With this information the Committee made first, second, and third choices for each topic. The central staff took the decisions of the Committee, mailed invitations to the first choices, and if not successful in obtaining commitments to write, followed up by calling on the second choice. Finally, if all such efforts failed, the Editor was forced to act on his own.

We had a very high acceptance rate, but all too often some calamity prevented an author from sending a completed manuscript. For one early volume (1941) when the author of the chapter on circulatory physiology failed to deliver, I wrote one to take its place. It was apparently good enough. In all my twenty years as Editor I had to reject only one manuscript —on the ground that it consisted almost entirely of long quotations from another review the author had recently written. In several cases I made extensive changes—for example, one chapter consisted of a collection of paragraphs in no apparent order. I rearranged them into groups on topics and gave these groups headings. The author not only accepted the change but was kind enough to say I had much improved the chapter. In only one case did the author object to my changes and I immediately restored his original text.

The innovation that gave me the most satisfaction was the addition to each volume of a "Prefatory Chapter" to be written by a senior physiologist, perhaps concerning his or her personal attitudes and activities, perhaps dealing with the history, organization, and sociology of physiology. The first, by my greatly esteemed friend Eugene Dubois, set an excellent example for the many who followed him. The practice of including such chapters has been adopted by many of the other *Annual Reviews*.

Finally, I must pay tribute to the Associate Editors who shared my editorial efforts: Arthur Giese, Jefferson Crismon and, longest and particularly helpful, Ralph Sonnenschein. By assigning each chapter to that one of us who was most familiar with the field of discourse, we assured the chapters the best available editorial study. These physiologists together with our highly effective technical staff gave the *Review* a good working menage!!

II. (R.R.S.)

As Associate Editor of the *Annual Review of Physiology* from 1962 to 1977, I had the rare opportunity of working with Victor Hall until his retirement in 1971. Victor's leadership over some 20 years brought the *Annual Review* to eminence in the physiological community. Aided by distinguished colleagues on the Editorial Committee, he brought to bear his breadth of knowledge and critical ability, as well as his affection for the *Review* that he nurtured for so long. His frankness, consideration, and sense of humor kept the wheels oiled and made working with him a delight.

Under Victor's editorship, increasing emphasis was placed on presenting reviews that were selective, critical appraisals, rather than mere annotated bibliographies. To be sure, this resulted sometimes in rather idiosyncratic coverage of a topic. But this was a natural result of the continuous attempt to select the most competent authors, the people with ideas. A roster of authors over the years would read like a "Who's Who in Physiology." It must be admitted, though, that eminence in physiology is no guarantee of ability to write clearly: We editors often had more rewriting to do on chapters from our compatriots than on those submitted by our foreign colleagues.

As the *Review* attempted over the years to be of greatest service to the physiological community, it was faced with two sorts of problems. First, should its chapters be addressed to the specialists in the several areas, or rather to the teachers and researchers who would want to be kept abreast of general developments in fields other than their own specialties? Generally, the latter direction was taken, so that ideally any reader with a reasonably broad background in physiology should be able to benefit from any of the chapters in each volume. As composition of the Editorial Committee changed from year to year, however, different views emerged and at times, as in the most recent volumes, the specialist became the preferred audience. No doubt, such policy, like trends in research, will continue to show the "pendulum effect," swinging periodically around some optimal point.

The second concern of the *Review* arose from the nature of physiology as a discipline. With growth of the field, areas originally subsumed by physiology broke off and regrouped. The development of biophysics and bioengineering, both with one foot in physiology and one in the physical sciences, led inevitably to establishment of new professional societies and journals, and perforce to the *Annual Review of Biophysics and Bioengineering,* whose first volume appeared in 1972. The same trend was reflected in the initiation of the *Annual Review of Neuroscience* in 1978.

Minutes of meetings of the Editorial Committee of the *Annual Review of Physiology* reflect concern over the effects of the new review series. Would there be a fall-off in readership of *Physiology?* (This has in fact not occurred.) Since often a topic of interest to one individual might appear in two or more *Reviews,* how could the effect of this "splintering" be best counteracted? (In fact, of course, the reader of *Physiology* might find pertinent articles as well in the *Annual Reviews of Pharmacology, Medicine, Biochemistry* and others.) As this problem became increasingly evident under the editorship of Julius Comroe (1971–1975) and later of Ernst Knobil (1975–1978) and Isidore Edleman (1978 to the present), a number of solutions were suggested. One, quickly perceived as impractical, was to enlarge the scope of *Physiology* to encompass all the "physiological sciences," bringing the errant children back into the fold. Another, pressed repeatedly by the Committee, was to offer the reader collections of chapters from the several series dealing with a single topic area. For example, articles on the cardiovascular or the renal system appearing over a 2- or 3-year period in the *Annual Reviews of Physiology, Pharmacology, Medicine,* and *Biophysics* might be so collated. The directors of Annual Reviews, Inc. were unfortunately unable to support a trial of this idea at the time.

The *Annual Review of Physiology* has made a change in recent years, under Isidore Edelman's editorship, in the direction of recognizing the increasing specialization within the discipline. The division of the *Review* into sections, each with its own editor, allows treatment in more detail than was formerly the case of each of the major areas: Cell & Membrane Physiology, Endocrinology, Respiration, etc. This is an exciting and promising venture aimed at maintaining and improving the usefulness of the *Review* to the ever-changing field of physiology.

With remarkable prescience, Victor Hall wrote in the Preface to the *Annual Review of Physiology,* Volume 23, 1961, about the day to come when the physiologist could pursue a literature search through automated retrieval systems, with rapid display of abstracts of all papers pertinent to his interest. With such computerized systems at hand, would the *Annual Review* still have a useful place in the working library of the physiologist? Well, the day has arrived, and Victor's answer, which I quote here, is as applicable today as it was clear and insightful then: "The *Review* will still be there, and with a more clear-cut function than it now possesses. It will no longer even try to help the specialist find new material in his field, but will continue to do something beyond the foreseeable ability of computers: to sift the excellent from the merely good, to recognize and evaluate new trends in physiological thought, to warn against blind fashion, and to keep the enduring questions concerning the function of living matter firmly before us. To do these things has always been one of our purposes. We welcome the pressures of the future which will make them our sole purpose."

GASTROINTESTINAL AND NUTRITIONAL PHYSIOLOGY

Introduction, Norman W. Weisbrodt,
Section Organizer

GASTROINTESTINAL MOTILITY

Normal digestion and absorption of foodstuffs by the gastrointestinal tract are dependent on the orderly and controlled transit of intraluminal contents. Coordinated movements of the tongue, pharynx, and esophagus propel substances into the stomach, where they are mixed with the digestive secretions of the stomach, broken down into smaller particles, and finally emptied into the small intestine in a regulated manner. Once in the small intestine, the contents are mixed with the digestive secretions of the pancreas, biliary tract, and intestine, circulated so that they are brought into contact with the absorptive cells of the mucosa, and propelled in a net aboral direction. From the small bowel, the unabsorbed contents are passed through the ileocecal junction into the large intestine. Here they are mixed and circulated so that they come into contact with the absorptive cells of the mucosa. The ever-decreasing volume of contents is propelled toward the rectum. There they are stored until defecation, an act involving both voluntary and involuntary movements of the colon, the anal sphincters, and muscles of the pelvic floor, abdomen, and chest.

All of the above-mentioned processes, along with the structures and events that effect and control them, can be discussed under the heading "Gastrointestinal Motility." In this section, we stress one aspect of this subject—intestinal propulsion. Several different approaches have been used to investigate propulsion, and the data are beginning to form a coherent picture. Furthermore, the concepts and methods used to study intestinal propulsion have been or can be applied to other apsects of motility and to the functions of other organ systems.

7

In the following chapters, Dr. Weems first defines propulsion and then discusses concepts and techniques used to study the propulsive capabilities of the intestine; he presents some of the data generated by in vitro studies of the intestine. In the second chapter, I describe some of the patterns of intestinal contractile activity recorded from intact, unanesthetized animals (including humans). Progress in this area now permits well-defined patterns to be compared and propulsive activities to be estimated. Studies on the control of these patterns have emphasized the importance of neural and humoral mechanisms. Thus in the third chapter, Dr. Wood describes the structure and function of the "intrinsic" nervous system of the bowel. Intrinsic neurons are of several functional types and are arranged such that integration of information and regulation of muscle contractions are possible. In the fourth chapter, Dr. Szurszewski points out the complexities of the prevertebral ganglia and the probable function of these structures in integrating neural and humoral information and in controlling various patterns of motility.

Since all aspects of gastrointestinal motility are not considered, the interested reader is referred to the following recent (last five years) reviews on gastrointestinal motility (1, 3, 6), esophageal motility (5, 8), the physiology and pharmacology of intestinal smooth muscle (2, 4, 10), and the effects of gastrointestinal hormones on motility (7, 9).

Literature Cited

1. Atanassova, E., Papasova, M. 1977. Gastrointestinal motility. *Int. Rev. Physiol.* 12:35–69
2. Bortoff, A. 1976. Myogenic control of intestinal motility. *Physiol. Rev.* 56: 418–34
3. Cohen, S., Long, W. B., Snape, W. J. Jr. 1979. Gastrointestinal motility. *Int. Rev. Physiol.* 19:107–149
4. Daniel, E. E., Sarna, S. 1978. The generation and conduction of activity in smooth muscle. *Ann. Rev. Pharmacol. Toxicol.* 18:145–66
5. Diamant, N. E., El-Sharkawy, T. Y. 1977. Neural control of esophageal peristalsis. A conceptual analysis. *Gastroenterology* 72:546–56
6. Gabella, G. 1979. Innervation of the gastrointestinal tract. *Int. Rev. Cytol.* 59:129–93
7. Glass, G. B. 1980. *Gastrointestinal Hormones.* NY: Raven Press. 1032 pp.
8. Goyal, R. K. 1976. Symposium on esophageal motility. *Arch. Int. Med.* 136:511–601
9. Johnson, L. R. 1977. Gastrointestinal hormones and their functions. *Ann. Rev. Physiol.* 39:135–58
10. Prosser, C. L. 1978. Rhythmic potentials in intestinal muscle. *Fed. Proc.* 37:2153–57

Ann. Rev. Physiol. 1981. 43:9–19
Copyright © 1981 by Annual Reviews Inc. All rights reserved

THE INTESTINE AS A FLUID PROPELLING SYSTEM

❖1294

William A. Weems

Department of Physiology, The University of Texas Medical School, Houston, Texas 77030

INTRODUCTION

The intestine orchestrates a variety of fluid movements within its lumen in order to both mix and move intestinal content along its length. Geometrically the intestine is basically a fluid-containing tube. As a fluid-propelling unit, however, it is an extremely complex system. Physiologists have traditionally viewed the intestine as a system composed of many interacting elements or components and have in general appreciated the fact that the motions of the intestinal wall, which transfer energy to the luminal fluid, result from a variety of interactions among both these components and extrinsic control systems (1, 18). This widespread recognition that fluid motion within the intestine is produced and controlled by movements of the intestinal wall spawned the extensive investigation of intestinal motility mentioned by Dr. Weisbrodt in the introduction to this section. These studies have focused on a variety of aspects associated with intestinal wall motions and their control. Only a few, however, have directly evaluated the ability of intestinal segments to produce and control fluid propulsion.

PROPULSION AS A CONCEPT

The concept of propulsion has its origins in the physical science of mechanics. Mechanics is concerned with the study of the motion of objects and traditionally views motion as having two different aspects—kinematic and dynamic (17, 19). The subspeciality of mechanics called kinematics describes the motion of an object relative to a reference frame and is not concerned with the forces that act on the object to alter its motion. Velocity and acceleration are two examples of kinematic quantities.

9

A number of studies have considered the motion of intestinal content from a basic kinematic viewpoint. Studies of intestinal transport (7, 12, 14, 31, 36) are in effect kinematic in nature. An example of such a study is when radioactive or radiopaque particles are placed in the intestinal lumen and the time required for various amounts of these particles to move a given distance is determined (12, 14, 36). Procedures of this general type permit kinematic quantities such as average velocity to be obtained but provide no information regarding the dynamic aspects of the transport process.

The subspeciality of mechanics called dynamics, on the other hand, deals with motion relative to the forces associated with it and to the properties (e.g. mass, volume, and density) of the moving object. One of the fundamental problems of dynamics is to determine how an object will move when we know the forces that act on it. Inherent in this problem is the idea that a system imparts motion to an object by the application of a force referred to as a propulsive force. The propulsive ability of any system can thus be regarded as that system's ability to produce and apply propulsive forces.

The first study to provide information regarding the intestinal system's ability to do propulsive work on fluid loads was conducted by Trendelenburg (38) in 1917. He demonstrated that in vitro segments of guinea pig ileum have the intrinsic ability to propel luminal fluid up a pressure gradient when intraluminal pressure was initially set at a value of 1–2 cm of water. This primarily qualitative observation was confirmed by Kosterlitz, Pire & Robinson (23) when they employed Trendelenburg's basic method to begin a semi-quantitative evaluation of some of the intrinsic capabilities of the guinea pig ileum to propel luminal fluid. These investigators examined maximal intraluminal pressure and volume of fluid ejected from the aboral end of segments as functions of the external resistance through which the fluid was expelled and the initial airspace present in a closed reservoir into which fluid was extruded. Since the reservoir was closed, the pressure gradient against which the segment did propulsive work increased as the volume of fluid ejected increased. The capacitance of the reservoir under these conditions was not constant but decreased nonlinearly with increasing volumes of extruded fluid. Under the conditions specific to this study, the volume of fluid ejected decreased and maximal intraluminal pressure increased as the volume of the initial airspace decreased. Progressive increases in output resistance resulted in maximal intraluminal pressure increasing to a peak value and then decreasing. Uncertainties regarding some of the physical properties of this reservoir system make a precise interpretation of these data in dynamic terms impossible. The ability of these segments to produce net fluid movement in either the oral or aboral direction also cannot be evaluated from studies using this general method since in the basic Trendelenburg preparation the oral end of the intestinal segment being studied is tied closed.

Several other investigators have employed the basic Trendelenburg method to demonstrate qualitatively the existence of the peristaltic reflex in isolated ileal segments from animals other than the guinea pig and to study the effects of various agents on the peristaltic reflex (10, 15, 16, 29, 39). Bulbring, Crema & Saxly (9) modified the Trendelenburg method so that the oral end of the segment received fluid at constant pressure. The aboral end was connected to a reservoir of effectively infinite capacitance and the volume of fluid extruded was measured by counting the number of times a 1 ml container was filled by the outflow. A similar technique developed by Bennett, Eley & Scholes (3) was used to investigate qualitatively the role of prostaglandins in controlling motility of rat and guinea pig ileum and colon (4). These and other studies that employ similar methods and concepts have not, however, attempted to investigate intestinal propulsion as a phenomenon in dynamic terms.

THEORETICAL APPROACHES TO INTESTINAL PROPULSION

Studies of intestinal propulsion of fluid, per se, have not progressed technically and conceptually much past those of Trendelenburg (38) and Kosterlitz et al (22, 23) because a general theoretical framework of principles underlying the production of fluid flow in tubes solely by movements of the surrounding wall has only recently begun to be developed. Without such a conceptual framework, derived from analyses of simpler systems with one or more similar functional properties, it is difficult to know what questions should be asked experimentally of a complex tubular system such as the intestine and how the required data are to be operationally obtained. It was for need of similar theoretical guidelines that Poiseuille, in 1840, developed the theoretical concepts describing the flow of Newtonian fluids through cylindrical tubes so he could study the relation between "the force of the heart" and the "amount of circulation" (32). This theoretical work formed a major portion of the conceptual framework on which the relatively exact science of modern hemodynamics is based.

Until the early 1960s, most theoretical work regarding flow in flexible tubes was designed to analyze flow in passive, viscoelastic tubes under specified flow and pressure conditions. Most of these analyses considered passive flow in nonridged tubes and were related to blood circulation in the vascular system. They were summarized in a review by Rudinger (33). The effects of intestinal motility on the passive flow of luminal fluid induced by external pressure gradients applied to intestinal segments have been examined (6, 18, 31). Such studies are extremely useful in determining the output conditions into which the stomach or a certain region of the intestine propels its fluid load. These studies do not, however, investigate the ability of an intestinal segment actively to produce fluid flow and hence do propulsive work.

Manor & Popper (27) published a theoretical study of fluid transfer by progressive transverse waves in 1964. Since then a number of analytical studies of active tube flow produced by motions in the surrounding walls have been published (2, 20, 24, 26, 30, 34, 44). These studies have considered only relatively simple tubular and channel-type models that contain a Newtonian fluid under conditions for which the relevant Reynolds number is small enough for inertial effects to be negligible. The wall motions are also usually taken to be axisymmetric, peristaltic, and of a simple wave form. Lew, Fung & Lowenstein (24), for example, have used such a model to address directly the question of how peristalsis produces propulsive work on a Newtonian fluid within the intestinal lumen. Their general solution to the problem results in the following two fundamental and independent solutions: (*a*) peristalsis of pure transport, which creates only mass transport without inducing a net pressure rise from one end of the segment to the other end; and (*b*) peristalsis of pure compression, which induces a net pressure gradient in the same direction as the direction of node propagation without an accompanying net mass flow. Physically, peristalsis of pure transport corresponds to the peristaltic motion in a tube connecting two reservoirs of equal pressure. Peristalsis of pure compression corresponds to the peristaltic motion in a tube connecting two filled and sealed tanks. By using a linear combination of the above two fundamental solutions, the peristaltic flow under a general type of end-to-end condition (e.g. prescribed pressure at both ends or prescribed volume flow for a given peristalsis) was obtained. Both the effectiveness of pure transport and of pure compression, for a given input-output condition, were found to decrease as the distance between contractions increased and to increase as the depth of wall constriction increased. The results of this simulation may be relevant to the study in which Code, Szurszewski, Kelly & Smith (11) determined the wave length of pacesetter potentials (slow waves or control potentials) along the small intestine of dogs and found that the wavelength decreased from approximately 45 cm in the duodenum to approximately 4.6 cm in the ileum. Since these potentials contribute to the temporal and spatial distribution of contractions along the gut, it must be assumed that the capacity exists for the number of contractile rings per unit length to increase as the distance from the pylorus increases. In view of the theoretical findings of Lew and coworkers (24), it would seem reasonable to ask if this change in the wavelength of the pacesetter potential might produce a difference in the ability of various regions of the intestine to do propulsive work.

In the physiological state, propulsion of intestinal fluid is probably never that of pure transport or compression but varies at different regions of the intestine and as a function of the input-output conditions imposed on a given intestinal region by adjacent regions of the gastrointestinal system. For example, ileal propulsion may be shifted toward pure compression when the ileocecal valve remains closed while duodenal propulsion may approach that of pure transport when aboral regions of the intestine are relatively empty and relaxed.

OPERATIONAL EVALUATION OF INTESTINAL PROPULSION

The theoretical studies reviewed in the preceding section have made significant contributions to our conceptual understanding of how fluid flow is produced and controlled in tubes by transverse oscillation of their walls. That these studies are conducted on extremely simple tubular systems and consider only wall motions of a simple peristaltic nature emphasizes the conceptual and computational difficulties associated with this approach. Attempts to construct an analytical model that adequately simulates the propulsive characteristics of the intestinal system are also hampered by the lack of quantitative information that precisely describes the temporal and spatial aspects of intestinal wall motions (35).

Although a complete dynamic or kinematic description of fluid motion at all points within the intestinal lumen is well beyond present theoretical and technical capabilities, operationally useful descriptions of intestinal propulsive performance can be obtained. Such descriptions are based on viewing the intestine as though it were composed of a series of "propelling" and "receiving" segments (41, 42). This conceptual approach permits the ability of intestinal segments to propel fluid to be evaluated in terms of the work that must be done on adjoining segments to effect fluid transfer. Ideally one might like to designate a given length of intact intestine as a "propelling" segment and then measure the propulsive work done by that segment as it transports fluid into or receives fluid from adjacent intestinal regions. Technical limitations presently preclude this. One can, however, attach an in vitro segment of intestine to a propulsive evaluation system that will impose on it physically well-defined input-output conditions; these predetermine the propulsive work necessary to effect fluid transfer into or out of the segment. The propulsive work done in expelling fluid in either the oral or aboral direction can be obtained from monitoring changes in physical quantities produced within the evaluation system by a segment's propulsive activity. By altering the configuration of the attached propulsion evaluating system, one can impose on an intestinal segment a variety of input-output conditions. These conditions may be static in that they do not change as functions of time or intestinal activity, or they may be permitted to vary during an evaluation period.

Our laboratory has recently evaluated the propulsive performance of intestinal and colonic segments in vitro under input-output conditions of negligible resistance and constant capacitance (40, 42). We found that segments of terminal ileum from cats are intrinsically capable of two propulsive states. In the net propulsive state, these segments can spontaneously and repetitively eject fluid from their aboral ends at an average interval of 8 minutes. The average maximal amount of propulsive work done per complex in the aboral direction was 63,650 ergs when initial intraluminal pressure was set at 5 cm of H_2O and capacitance was 0.025 ml (cm of $H_2O)^{-1}$. Ileal segments not in the net propulsive state produce simultaneous ejections of equal fluid volumes from both their oral and aboral ends at a frequency of 8 per minute. Segments of proximal duodenum and mid-jejunum do not intrinsically produce net, aborally directed transport when evaluated under similar conditions. Preliminary studies (40) designed to evaluate the intrinsic propulsive ability of cat colonic segments under identical conditions indicate that the feline colon also has an intrinsic capability to do net hydrostatic work on fluid loads in the aboral direction. It appears, however, that this ability is significantly less than that of ileal segments and that the average interval between propulsive complexes is approximately 4 minutes.

Our research has evaluated regional intestinal performance only under the static evaluation conditions described above. A variety of both static and variable conditions must be used to evaluate thoroughly the propulsive capabilities of intestinal regions. Projected experiments fall into two general categories (41). The first includes experiments designed to evaluate the propulsive capability of a segment under physiological input-output conditions; the second category includes experiments in which input-output conditions perturb an intestinal segment in order to obtain information about the functional organization and interaction of intrinsic segment subsystems.

PROPULSION AS A SYSTEM PROPERTY

The methods and concepts described in the preceding section enable one to characterize the propulsive performance of intestinal segments in dynamic terms. The propulsive state or performance being characterized in turn arises from the interplay among the many components comprising the intestinal segment under investigation. Since intestinal propulsion results from these interactions within the intestinal system, understanding of how the intestinal system operates to produce net fluid transport along its lumen can be obtained only by investigating the behavior of the entire system.

Several years ago Leon Harmon (21) noted that since the "staggering problems" that face neurophysiology range from the molecular to the behavioral, it would be useful to ask the question: What exactly is meant by the wish to understand the brain? Because the problems facing investigators of intestinal function also range from the molecular to the behavioral (i.e. intestinal behavior), the question of what it means to understand a complex system is also applicable to our research endeavors and follies. Harmon approached the question by using an analogy: If your task were to develop a thorough understanding of a computer system being maintained in perfect working order on an island by an unseen group of caretakers, you would have to develop an "understanding" on at least three levels. First you would have to comprehend how to operate the computer and discern its gross input-output functions. A second and quite different level of understanding would require you to learn the functional organization of the computer. A complete understanding at this level would enable you to design a similar but not identical machine using the same principles of subsystem organization, operation, and interaction. The third level of understanding would require a determination of how the elemental components of each subsystem operate. A thorough understanding on this level would enable you to produce a complete equivalent circuit diagram of all components within the computer.

Experience in applying procedures of system analysis to a variety of man-made and naturally occurring systems has demonstrated that logical and causal relationships exist among all three levels and that useful extrapolation can occur between levels. Extrapolation between levels is, however, markedly direction-sensitive (21, 25, 28). Knowledge at the first level may readily help one develop strategy for investigations at a lower level, but extrapolation in the other direction is often more difficult because knowledge of the structure and function of a component or a subsystem does not yield a prediction of behavior at a higher level (21, 25). This direction sensitivity between levels is apparent in the context of understanding the intestinal system when one notes that our finding of an 8 minute period between the occurrence of ileal propulsive complexes (42) was not predictable from the present knowledge of components, subsystems, and control interactions within ileal segments. Thus knowledge about the intrinsic propulsive behavior of an intestinal segment will be invaluable in helping elucidate how intestinal subsystems and components interact to produce propulsive behavior.

Figure 1 is a schematic depiction of three intestinal segments broken down into a simplistic set of subsystems. The luminal content of segment B, which is also designated as a propelling segment, interacts directly with the myogenic and neurogenic subsystems and with the receiving segments, A and C, via fluid coupling. The myogenic and neurogenic subsystems interact and are in turn influenced by physical and chemical properties of the luminal content. Adjacent segments can also be expected to interact both mechanically and electrically via components of the myogenic subsystem (8, 13) and neurally via components of the intrinsic neurogenic subsystems (8, 43). The subsystems of each segment are also influenced by extrinsic neural and hormonal control systems whose output can vary as a function of information received by them from the intestinal system (5, 22, 37).

The fluid interactions (depicted in Figure 1) that occur between segments are also a potential controlling input to any given segment because properties of the receiving segments (*a*) determine the amount of propulsive work a propelling segment must do on its surroundings to transfer a given fluid load and (*b*) determine to a large extent what volume-pressure conditions exist within the lumen of a propelling segment during a given sequence of wall movements. If these pressure-volume conditions within the lumen of the propelling segments influence its contractile pattern, then the physical properties of the receiving segments can contribute to the regulation of the propelling segment. This regulation may occur, in part, because the work demand placed on the propelling segment exceeds the segment's energy transfer capability; it may also result from the responses of intrinsic and extrinsic control mechanisms within the segment to specific volume and pressure conditions within its lumen (41).

In the chapters that follow, Dr. Wood considers the behavior of the neurogenic subsystem and its components and Dr. Szurszewski deals with certain aspects of the extrinsic control systems. In a general sense, these chapters focus on the second and third levels of understanding developed in the computer analogy presented above. Along with this chapter, Dr.

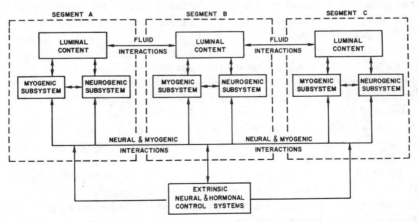

Figure 1 Diagram illustrating the subsystems and associated interactions that control fluid propulsion by an intestinal segment. For the purpose of evaluating propulsive performance, segment B can be viewed as a "propelling" segment and segments A and C as "receiving" segments (41, 42). See text for further details.

Weisbrodt's chapter deals with an emergent property of the intestinal system in that the mechanical and electrical signals and patterns discussed form an output from the myogenic subsystem that reflects the integrated activity of the system as whole.

SUMMARY

The ability of intestinal segments to propel fluid from their lumens can be characterized in dynamic terms by measuring the movement of luminal fluid ejected into attached systems that predispose the amount of work the segment must do to affect fluid transfer. Studies employing this approach have demonstrated that the propulsive capability intrinsic to intestinal and colonic segments is not uniform along the bowel. Differences in propulsive behavior observed to occur solely as the result of the operation of subsystems intrinsic to particular intestinal regions suggest (a) that external control inputs can alter the propulsive state of a region, and (b) that this altered state may exist for hours after the external input to the system is terminated. Consideration of the propulsive performance of segments as an emergent property of interactions among intrinsic subsystems has contributed to the formalization of precise questions heretofore not asked about the organization and function of intestinal subsystems and their associated interactions. Knowledge of propulsive behavior and its control is still in its infancy. Further studies employing basic concepts and procedures similar to those reviewed above will advance our understanding of intestinal propulsion and of the intestine as a complex system.

ACKNOWLEDGMENT

The research of the author described in this article was supported by National Institute of Health Grant AM23038.

Literature Cited

1. Alvarez, W. C. 1968. Early studies of the movements of the stomach and bowel. In *Handbook of Physiology, Section 6, Alimentary Canal, Vol. IV*, ed. C. F. Code, pp. 1573–78. Washington DC: Am. Physiol. Soc. 2343 pp.
2. Barton, C., Raynor, S. 1968. Peristaltic flow in tubes. *Bull. Math. Biophys.* 30:663–80
3. Bennett, A., Eley, K. G., Scholes, G. B. 1968. Effect of prostaglandins E_1 and E_2 on intestinal motility in the guinea-pig and rat. *Brit. J. Pharmacol.* 34:639–47
4. Bennett, A., Eley, K. G., Stockley, H. L. 1976. Inhibition of peristalsis in guinea-pig isolated ileum and colon by drugs that block prostaglandin synthesis. *Br. J. Pharmacol.* 57:335–40
5. Bloom, S. R., ed. 1978. *Gut Hormones.* Edinburgh: Churchill Livingston. 664 pp.
6. Bortoff, A. 1975. Electrical activity of gastrointestinal muscle. In *Functions of the Stomach and Intestine*, ed. M. H. F. Friedman, pp. 17–30. Baltimore: University Park Press. 469 pp.
7. Bueno, L., Fioramonti, J., Ruckebusch, Y. 1975. Rate of flow of digesta and electrical activity of the small intestine in dogs and sheep. *J. Physiol. London* 249:69–85

8. Bueno, L., Praddaude, F., Ruckebusch, Y. 1979. Propagation of electrical spiking activity along the small intestine: intrinsic versus extrinsic neural influences. *J. Physiol. London* 292:15–26

9. Bülbring, E., Crema, A., Saxby, O. B. 1958. A method for recording peristalsis in isolated intestine. *Brit. J. Pharmacol.* 13:440–43

10. Bülbring, E., Lin, R. C. Y., Schofield, G. 1958. An investigation of the peristaltic reflex in relation to anatomical observations. *Q. J. Exp. Physiol.* 43:26–37

11. Code, C. F., Szurszewski, J. H., Kelly, K. A., Smith, I. B. 1968. A concept of control of gastrointestinal motility. See Ref. 1, pp. 2881–96

12. Cramer, C. F. 1959. Movement of radiostrontium through intestinal tract of fed or fasted rats. *Proc. Soc. Exp. Biol. Med.* 102:511–12

13. Daniel, E. E., Sarna, S. 1978. The generation and conduction of activity in smooth muscle. *Ann. Rev. Pharmacol. Toxicol.* 18:145–66

14. Derblom, H., Johansson, H., Nylander, G. 1966. A simple method of recording quantitatively certain gastrointestinal motility functions in the rat. *Acta Chir. Scand.* 132:154–65

15. Feldberg, W., Lin, R. C. Y. 1949. The action of local anaesthetics and d-tubocurarine on the isolated intestine of the rabbit and guinea-pig. *Brit. J. Pharmacol.* 4:33–44

16. Fontaine, J., Van Nueten, J. M., Janssen, P. A. J. 1973. Analysis of the peristaltic reflex in vitro: effects of some antagonists. *Arch. Int. Pharmacodyn.* 203:396–99

17. Fox, R. W., McDonald, A. T. 1973. *Introduction to Fluid Mechanics,* pp. 203–84. NY: Wiley. 630 pp.

18. Gregory, R. A. 1950. Some factors influencing the passage of fluid in intestinal loops in dogs. *J. Physiol. London* 111:119–37

19. Halliday, D., Resnick, R. 1966. *Physics,* pp. 32–149. NY: Wiley. 1214 pp.

20. Hanin, M. 1968. The flow through a channel due to transversally oscillating walls. *Israel J. Technol.* 6:67–71

21. Harmon, L. D. 1970. Neural subsystems: an interpretive summary. In *The Neurosciences: Second Study Program,* ed. F. O. Schmidt, pp. 486–94. NY: Rockefeller Univ. Press. 1068 pp.

22. Kosterlitz, H. W. 1968. Intrinsic and extrinsic nervous control of motility of the stomach and the intestines. See Ref. 1, pp. 2147–71

23. Kosterlitz, H. W., Pire, V. W., Robinson, J. A. 1956. The mechanism of the peristaltic reflex in the isolated guinea-pig ileum. *J. Physiol. London* 133:681–94

24. Lew, H. S., Fung, Y. C., Lowenstein, C. B. 1971. Peristaltic carrying and mixing of chyme in the small intestine (an analysis of a mathematical model of peristalsis of the small intestine). *J. Biomech.* 4:297–315

25. Lewis, E. R. 1970. Neural subsystems: goals, concepts and tools. See Ref. 21, pp. 384–96

26. Liron, N. 1976. On peristaltic flow and its efficiency. *Bull. Math. Bio.* 38:574–96

27. Manor, H., Popper, J. B. 1964. Fluid transfer by means of progressive transverse waves. *Israel J. Technol.* 2:278–80

28. Marmarelis, P. Z., Marmarelis, V. Z. 1978. *Analysis of Physiological Systems,* pp. 1–8. NY: Plenum. 487 pp.

29. McDougal, M. D., West, G. B. 1954. The inhibition of the peristaltic reflex by sympathomimetic amines. *Brit. J. Pharmacol.* 9:131–37

30. Melville, J., Macagno, E., Christensen, J. 1975. Longitudinal contractions in the duodenum: their fluid-mechanical function. *Am. J. Physiol.* 228:1887–92

31. Nakayama, S. 1962. Movements of the small intestine in transport of intraluminal contents. *Jpn. J. Physiol.* 12:522–33

32. Poiseuille, J. L. M. 1846. Recherches experimentales sur le mouvement des liquids dans les tubes de tres-petits diametres. *Mem. Pres. Divers Savants, Acad. Sci. France* 9:433–49

33. Rudinger, G. 1966. Review of current mathematical methods for the analysis of blood flow. *Proc. Biomedical. Fluid Mechs. Symp.* NY: Am. Soc. Mech. Eng.

34. Shapiro, A. H., Jaffrin, M. Y., Weinberg, S. L. 1969. Peristaltic pumping with long wavelengths at low Reynolds number. *J. Fluid. Mech.* 37:799–825

35. Singerman, R. B., Macagno, E. O., Glover, J. R., Christensen, J. 1975. Stochastic model of contractions at a point in the duodenum. *Am. J. Physiol.* 229:613–17

36. Summers, R. W., Kent, T. H., Osborne, J. W. 1970. Effects of drugs, ileal obstruction, and irradiation on rat gastrointestinal propulsion. *Gastroenterology* 59:731–39

37. Szurszewski, J. H., Weems, W. A. 1976. Control of gastrointestinal motility by prevertebral ganglia. In *Physiology of Smooth Muscle,* ed. E. Bülbring, M. F.

Shuba, pp. 313–19. NY: Raven Press. 438 pp.

38. Trendelenburg, P. 1917. Physiologische und pharmakologische Versuche über die Dunndarmperastaltik. *Arch. Exp. Pathol. Pharmak.* 81:55–129

39. VanNueten, J. M., Geivers, H., Fontaine, J., Janssen, P. A. J. 1973. An improved method for studying peristalsis in the isolated guinea-pig ileum. *Arch. Int. Pharmacodyn.* 203:411–14

40. Weems, W. A., Seygal, G. E. 1979. Intrinsic abilities of cat colon to do propulsive work on fluid loads. *Fed. Proc.* 38:960

41. Weems, W. A., Seygal, G. E. 1980. Intestinal propulsion: studies employing a method for its quantitative evaluation. In *Proc. 7th Int. Symp. Gastrointest. Motil.*, ed. J. M. Christensen. NY: Raven Press

42. Weems, W. A., Seygal, G. E. 1980. Fluid propulsion by cat intestinal segments under conditions requiring hydrostatic work. *Am. J. Physiol.* In press

43. Wood, J. C. 1979. Neurophysiology of the enteric nervous system. In *Integrative Functions of the Autonomic Nervous System,* ed. C. McC. Brooks, K. Koezeimi, A. Sato, pp. 177–93. Amsterdam: Elsevier/North Holland. 508 pp.

44. Yin, F., Fung, Y. C. 1969. Peristaltic waves in circular cylindrical tubes. *J. Appl. Mech.* 36:579–87

Ann. Rev. Physiol. 1981. 43:21–31

PATTERNS OF INTESTINAL MOTILITY

❖1295

Norman W. Weisbrodt

Departments of Physiology and Pharmacology, The University of Texas
Medical School at Houston, Houston, Texas 77025

Introduction

In the preceding chapter Dr. Weems considered the propulsive characteristics of the small intestine studied in vitro. This chapter is concerned with the patterns of contractile activity recorded in vivo. These patterns are important for at least two reasons. First, they are responsible for propulsion of intraluminal contents in vivo. Thus, any propulsive characteristics determined in vitro must ultimately be related to the patterns of contractions seen in vivo. Second, these patterns represent one measurement of the net output of all the integrative subsystems that control motility. (Some of these subsystems are considered in the following chapters.) Thus findings on these subsystems must ultimately be integrated to explain the patterns seen in vivo.

Most experiments on intestinal motility performed before the 1960s were concerned with the shape of individual contractions and their relation to movement of luminal content. Much effort was spent on the classification of contraction waves into four types, and many attempts were made to assign a specific function (i.e. transporting or mixing) to each wave. Few studies were designed to determine the spatial and temporal relationships of contractions that occurred at one or more loci. In one of the more important studies on G.I. motility, Cannon (6) used radiographic techniques to follow the progression of bismuth through the small intestine of fed cats. He surmised that the different patterns of movement of intraluminal contents were caused by definite patterns of contractions of the intestinal muscle. He described two basic movements, segmentation and peristalsis. Segmentation was thought to be due to stationary ring contractions that would divide the contents but would cause no net movement in either the

0066-4278/81/0315-0021$01.00

oral or aboral direction. Peristalsis was thought to be due to ring contractions that occurred in an aboral sequence, thus propelling intraluminal contents in that direction. Other important early studies (2, 9, 15, 34) noted temporal patterns in the contractions recorded from fasted unanesthetized animals; patterns changed upon feeding. Since 1960 there has been marked interest in (a) the temporal and spatial distribution of contractile activities in the small intestine and (b) the effects these distributions have upon the movement of intraluminal contents. It is with these studies that the rest of this chapter is concerned.

Anatomical and Methodological Considerations

The small intestine is a long tubular structure composed of four layers: mucosa, submucosa, muscularis externa, and serosa. Propulsion of intraluminal contents results principally from contractions of the smooth muscle cells that comprise the muscularis externa. These cells are arranged in two layers, a thicker inner layer in which the long axis of the cells is oriented in the circular direction and an outer thinner layer in which the long axis of the cells is oriented in the longitudinal direction. Movements of intraluminal contents probably are affected by activities of both muscle layers. Although data on the point are meager, it is my impression that contractions of the circularly oriented muscle are the more important. Thus, this review concentrates on activities of only this layer.

Neural tissue can be found throughout the various layers of the intestine. Most of this tissue is organized into plexuses. As far as motility is concerned the major plexuses are the myenteric (located between the two muscle layers of the muscularis externa) and the submucosal. This "intrinsic" nervous system is discussed in this volume by Dr. Wood. The intestine also is innervated by both divisions of the autonomic nervous system. Some of the properties and functions of these "extrinsic" nerves are discussed in the present volume by Dr. Szurszewski.

Contractions of the circularly oriented layer in unanesthetized animals can be monitored in a number of different ways. Three of the most popular use small balloons or open-tipped catheters to monitor intraluminal pressure, strain gauge transducers to monitor contractions of the muscle directly, and electrodes to monitor myoelectric activity of the muscle. For purposes of this chapter, I assume that all three methods yield equivalent information.

Migrating Motility Complex (MMC)

The renewed interest in intestinal motility during the last twenty years has resulted in the clear recognition of a distinct pattern of contractions. Jacoby et al (26), Reinke et al (35), and Carlson et al (8) described a cycle of contractile activity that could be recorded from any site on the small bowel of dogs that had been fasted for twelve hours or more. In each cycle a period of around 50 minutes without contractions was followed by a period of 10–20 minutes of seemingly random contractions: these built up to a 10–20 minute period of large-amplitude contractions at the maximum frequency seen in that portion of the small bowel. These ended abruptly and the cycle started again. Szurszewski (44) recorded the myoelectric counterpart of these contractions and further observed that the period of intense contractile activity appeared to begin in the upper duodenum and then to migrate slowly down the bowel. The velocity of migration was not constant throughout the intestine. In the orad area velocity ranged between 3 and 6 cm min^{-1} while in the caudal areas velocity ranged between 1 and 2 cm min^{-1}. The velocity was such that the time to migrate from duodenum to ileum was similar to the interval between intense periods of activity at any one site. Carlson et al (7) and Code & Marlett (12) further described this cyclical activity and named it the interdigestive myoelectric complex. They divided each complex into four phases. Phase I equaled the phase of no activity. Phase II was the period of seemingly random activity. Phase III equaled the period of intense activity. Finally, phase IV was the transition period between phases III and I.

Since the MMC sweeps down the bowel, phase III activity is present over a definite length of bowel at all times. The length of bowel involved in phase III activity at any one time has been calculated to range from 40–60 cm in the duodenum to 5–10 cm in the distal ileum. Contractions at any locus in such a segment occur at the maximum frequency of that area of intestine. Also, contractions occur with a proximal-to-distal phase lag that results in multiple propulsive contractions.

Shortly after description of these events in the dog intestine, Ruckebusch and his co-workers (3, 36, 37, 39) reported similar activity in rabbits, sheep, rats, guinea pigs, pigs, cattle, and horses. Although the general description of activity was similar in all species, one major difference became obvious. In some species (e.g. the ruminants and the pig) complexes were seen in both fasted animals and those feeding ad lib. In the rat, as in the dog, complexes were seen only in the fasted state. Recent studies (19, 46) have shown that cyclical activity occurs in the small intestine of man. As in the dog and rat, these cycles were seen only in the fasted state.

Not all investigators have used the same terminology to describe the MMC and its various phases. Thus a few comments are in order. Since the first clearly described cyclical activities were recorded from fasted dogs, the term interdigestive myoelectric (or motor) complex was applied. The term "interdigestive," however, cannot be applied universally because the pattern is seen in some animals feeding ad lib. Thus this term is falling out of use as a general descriptor. Also, the terms myoelectric and motor may be too specific since activity can be recorded a number of ways. Perhaps a better general term for this activity is "migrating motility complex" (MMC). "Migrating" is appropriate since no matter how recordings are made, the complexes do appear to migrate down the intestine. "Motility" is appropriate since it is a general term used to describe contractile activity of the gut no matter how it is recorded. "Complex" is appropriate since the cyclical activity is composed of several phases. Perhaps more complicated are the names applied to the various phases of the MMC. Table I lists some of the equivalent terms used by various investigators. Hopefully, no new terms will be introduced.

There is a relationship between the various phases of the MMC and the movement of intraluminal contents. Reinke et al (35) noted that mucus was expelled from a cannula placed in the small intestine of the dog when phase III activity was present orad to the cannula. Thus, phase III activity appears to be propulsive. A more thorough study by Code & Schlegel (13) found that barium injected into the lumen of a loop of bowel during phase I activity simply stayed in place. If, however, the barium was placed in the intestine during phase III activity, it was swept aborally through the bowel at high velocity. In view of this highly propulsive nature of phase III activity, Code has called it the "intestinal housekeeper." Bueno et al (3) found essentially the same relationships between contractile activity and fluid movement in the sheep, an animal that shows MMCs in the nonfasted state. Additionally, they determined that intraluminal contents were moved during phase II activity and that the majority of propulsion of material already present in the bowel took place during the transition from phase II to phase III activity.

The purpose of the MMC in animals in which it occurs during the fasted state is unknown. One interesting proposal has been put forth by Vantrappen et al (46). They found that many of their patients who had bacterial overgrowth of the small intestine also had gross abnormalities of their

Table 1   Terms used to describe the various phases of the MMC

Author	Period of no activity	Period of random activity	Period of intense activity	Transitional period
Carlson et al (8)	Basal	Pre burst	Burst	
Code & Marlett (12)	Phase I	Phase II	Phase III or Activity front	Phase IV
Bueno et al (3)	Inactivity	Irregular activity	Regular activity	
Fleckenstein (19)	Phase I	Phase II	Phase III or Active phase	

MMCs. Thus, MMCs may be necessary to prevent bacterial overgrowth of the small intestine during fasting.

The subsystems that control the MMC have not been elucidated; however, various proposals have been made. Since the complexes recur at fairly regular intervals, factors that initiate them have been sought. Several reports have implicated the gastrointestinal hormone motilin. Itoh et al (24) first reported that intravenous infusions of motilin caused the premature appearance of phase III activity in the stomach and upper intestine. These premature phases were similar to the naturally occurring ones in duration, intensity, and migration. Since this study, Itoh and others (25, 27, 45, 47) have demonstrated that plasma levels of motilin fluctuate at approximately the same frequency as the cycles of phase III activity. Additionally, phase III activity was seen during or shortly after the peaks in plasma motilin levels. Initiation of complexes does not appear to depend critically upon extrinsic innervation since neither transection of the vagus nerve (5, 10, 28, 40, 50) nor removal of the celiac and superior mesenteric ganglia (29) abolished the appearance of MMCs. Although MMCs still occurred after extrinsic denervation, they were not as regular. Thus the timing of MMC may depend in part on these nerves.

Since each phase of the complex migrates aborally from the upper small intestine, there must be factors responsible for controlling this orderly migration. Carlson et al (7) and Grivel & Ruckebusch (22) studied segments of intestine that had been removed from continuity with the rest of the bowel but still maintained all mesenteric attachments (blood vessels and extrinsic nerves). They found that MMCs still could be recorded from all areas of the small intestine, including the isolated segments. In many (30–75%) instances, migration of the various phases of the complex over the isolated segments occurred as if the segments were still in normal continuity with the rest of the bowel. Thus these results indicate that neither continuity of the bowel wall nor propulsion of intraluminal contents is absolutely necessary for coordinated migration of the complex. Furthermore, they suggest that coordination of activity can be provided by hormones and/or extrinsic nerves. More recent experiments have provided further support for the role of extrinsic nerves, since denervation of these isolated loops resulted in a loss of coordinated activity (4, 52). Although extrinsic nerves can suffice, recent results indicate that continuity of the bowel wall is necessary for normal activity. Some investigators have restudied the activity of isolated segments of bowel and found that more often than not, activity of these segments was independent of the rest of the bowel even though extrinsic nerves were intact (32, 33). Also, Bueno et al (4) found that simple transection and reanastomosis of the bowel resulted in a 38% decrease in the number of complexes that migrated beyond the anastomosis. These results taken together probably indicate that no one subsystem totally controls MMC activity. Intrinsic or extrinsic factors alone may suffice under certain conditions while under others both may be required.

Fed Pattern

In dog, rat, and human, feeding disrupts the pattern of MMCs and initiates a different pattern (8, 36, 46). This new pattern although definitely different from the MMC is not a discrete one and therefore is difficult to characterize. There are no distinct phases and it appears impossible to predict the sequence of contractions at any one locus or between any two adjacent loci. The temporal distribution of contractions at any one locus appears much more uniform in the fed condition. In humans, contractions of the duodenum occur in groups of 1–3 sequential contractions separated by periods of 5–40 sec (11). In the dog, similar activity occurs such that when contractile activity is analyzed in two minute intervals, a fairly uniform distribution of contractions over time becomes evident. A recent study by Dusdieker & Summers (16) indicated that 44% of the contractions in the fed animal are segmental in that they are not associated with immediate activity above or below the locus monitored. The rest of the contractions were associated with activity above and below such that groups of 3–6 seemingly propagated contractions were distributed evenly over time. Although these contractions were apparently propulsive, 90% propagated less than 30 cm. Thus, the intestine of the fed animal exhibits both segmental and peristaltic contractions as originally described by Cannon.

Even though contractions during the fed state are less distinct and have yet to be characterized completely, they do result in propulsion of intraluminal contents. In fact, results of some studies indicate that net aboral transport of content in the fed state is just as rapid as that occurring during phase III of the MMC.

The duration of the fed state depends upon the amount and composition of the food ingested (14, 42, 52). In general, the larger the amount ingested, the longer the period of fed activity. Not all foodstuffs, however, are equally effective. Equicaloric amounts of peptides and glucose caused much shorter fed periods than did an equicaloric amount of lipid. Also, the duration of the fed state appears to depend upon the species. In dogs, a normal meal induces a fed pattern for approximately 12–14 hr (8). In humans, a normal meal causes disruptions of MMCs of 3–4 hr (46). Thus there probably are shifts in motility patterns in humans during the day as well as at night.

Several factors could control the change in pattern seen with feeding. Since ingestion of food causes an increase in intraluminal contents and an increase in circulating products of digestion, either one or both of these factors could be responsible for the change in pattern. The influence of intraluminal contents has been investigated in those animals provided with isolated loops of intestine. In these animals, ingestion of a meal brought about a change in pattern in both the isolated loop and the intestine in continuity (9, 15, 33, 34, 52). Thus intraluminal contents do not appear critical. Likewise, circulating products of digestion do not seem to be the answer. Dogs maintained on total parenteral nutrition for up to 12 weeks demonstrated MMCs during the entire investigation (51). Thus, digestive levels of glucose and amino acids are not responsible for the conversion seen with feeding.

Since ingestion of food also brings about alterations in the hormonal state and neural activities, these factors may be responsible for the change in pattern. Several gastrointestinal hormones infused intravenously into unanesthetized dogs can affect the fasted pattern. Pentagastrin (28, 53), insulin (5), and cholecystokinin (31) all disrupted the MMCs and induced patterns resembling those seen during the fed state. Thus these hormones have been implicated. Not all data, however, fit this postulate. Several foodstuffs brought about a change in pattern without causing an increase in circulating levels of either gastrin or insulin (17). Additionally, the patterns induced by these hormones may not be identical to the pattern induced by feeding (55, 56). As pointed out by Wingate (54), however, plasma levels of the various hormones may not be as important as local concentrations if these hormones have a "paracrine" action.

Few studies have investigated the role of extrinsic and intrinsic nerves in the conversion to a fed pattern. Transection of the vagus nerves had only a slight effect on the response to feeding (5, 28, 40, 50). Although after transection it took somewhat larger amounts of food to cause disruption, this could have been due to the effects of vagotomy on gastric emptying. Activation of intrinsic factors can alter the pattern of motility since perfusion of isolated loops in dogs with glucose solutions disrupted the occurrence of MMCs on the loop (18). This was a local effect since MMCs still appeared on the rest of the bowel. Whether these local factors were neural or chemical was not determined. Thus the change in pattern induced by feeding may be brought about by several interacting factors. Hormones and/or extrinsic nerves may mediate the change at distant loci of the bowel. The local response, however, may then be modified by intraluminal contents that act via intrinsic nerves or locally released chemicals.

Other Patterns

Two other patterns of motility have been observed in "normal" animals. Recordings from the cat indicated that MMCs may not occur (48). Instead, prolonged individual contractions lasting 4–16 seconds were seen periodically in the fasted animal. Often these contractions migrated along the intestine. Thus they may represent a variation of the MMC even though their timing and behavior are not as constant. Some investigators have described a pattern they call "minute rhythm" in humans, healthy dogs, and sheep (20, 22). This pattern consists of a few contractions that appear in the upper small intestine and then migrate for varying distances. They occur at intervals of around 1 minute and migrate much more rapidly than the phase III activity seen during an MMC. Not all investigators have recorded such activity; their importance and function are not known.

Patterns have also been described in animals during certain pathological states (1, 38, 41). During diarrheal states induced by a number of agents and procedures, MMCs were disrupted. During the disruption, recurrent groups of 3–15 contractions were recorded at multiple loci. These groups migrated aborally along the bowel at a velocity much higher than the phase III activity seen during an MMC. Although measurements of propulsion have not been made, these contractions give the impression of being intensely propulsive.

The patterns of contractions discussed thus far suggest or result in an aboral movement of intestinal contents. A specific pattern suggesting oral movement of contents has been seen in cats, dogs, and perhaps humans shortly before emesis (23, 30, 43, 49). Stewart et al (43) recorded from conscious cats and found that injection of an emetic agent initiated an intense burst of spike potentials that appeared first at an electrode in the mid or distal small intestine and then spread orally at a velocity of 2–3 cm sec^{-1}. These bursts would reach the upper duodenum just seconds before the animals began to retch and vomit. Control of such emetic responses may involve extrinsic nerves. Gregory (21) recorded motor activity from isolated loops of intestine in unanesthetized dogs and found that subcutaneous injection of an emetic caused a change in motility of the loops before but not after extrinsic denervation of the loops. Likewise, the emetic response was inhibited after bilateral vagotomy. Stewart et al (43) found that the emetic response could be initiated by stimulation of structures within the central nervous system. Injection of emetic drugs into the lateral cerebral ventricles of unanesthetized cats caused appearance of orally migrating bursts of contractile activity. These drugs were active in dosages that had no effect when given systemically. Furthermore, the intestinal motility phase of the emetic response may contain a cholinergic pathway since atropine would inhibit the intestinal contraction but not emesis.

Summary

The small intestine in vivo is capable of a variety of patterns of contraction. Many of these patterns can result in the propulsion of intestinal contents. In the healthy human, dog, and rat propulsion is caused by at least two different patterns. One pattern seen in the fasted animal results in the intermittent movement of material out of any given segment of bowel and then the steady movement of this material down the bowel. In the fed state, there is a more or less uniform net aboral movement of contents. Although there are two distinct patterns, the net effect, in the rat at least, is that over long periods of time propulsion is of equal velocity in the two conditions. In certain disease states, other patterns of motility can be responsible for propulsion. These patterns can propel material orally as well as aborally.

In light of these contractile patterns, it would not be surprising to find that propulsion in isolated segments can be effected by several different patterns of activity. Also, it would not be surprising to find that the various subsystems controlling motility can be integrated in several different modes to produce such patterns.

Literature Cited

1. Atchison, W. D., Stewart, J. J., Bass, P. 1978. A unique distribution of laxative-induced spike potentials from the small intestine of the dog. *Am. J. Dig. Dis.* 23:513–20
2. Boldyreff, W. 1911. Einige neue Seiten der Tätigkeit des Pankreas. *Ergeb. Physiol.* 11:121–217
3. Bueno, L., Fioramonti, J., Ruckebusch, Y. 1975. Rate of flow of digesta and electrical activity of the small intestine in dogs and sheep. *J. Physiol. London* 249:69–85
4. Bueno, L., Praddaude, F., Ruckebusch, Y. 1979. Propagation of electrical spiking activity along the small intestine: intrinsic versus extrinsic neural influences. *J. Physiol. London* 292:15–26
5. Bueno, L., Ruckebusch, M. 1976. Insulin and jejunal electrical activity in dogs and sheep. *Am. J. Physiol.* 230:1538–44
6. Cannon, W. B. 1902. The movements of the intestines studied by means of the rontgen rays. *Am. J. Physiol.* 6:251–77
7. Carlson, G. M., Bedi, B. S., Code, C. F. 1972. Mechanism of propagation of intestinal interdigestive myoelectric complex. *Am. J. Physiol.* 222:1027–30
8. Carlson, G. M., Ruddon, R. W., Hug, C. C., Bass, P. 1970. Effects of nicotine on gastric antral and duodenal contractile activity in the dog. *J. Pharmacol. Exp. Ther.* 172:367–76
9. Castleton, K. B. 1934. An experimental study of the movements of the small intestine. *Am. J. Physiol.* 107:641–46
10. Catchpole, B. N., Duthie, H. L. 1978. Postoperative gastrointestinal complexes. In *Gastrointestinal Motility in Health and Disease,* ed. H. L. Duthie,

pp. 33–41. Lancaster, England: MTP Press
11. Christensen, J., Glover, J. R., Macagno, E. O., Singerman, R. B., Weisbrodt, N. W. 1971. Statistics of contractions at a point in the human duodenum. *Am. J. Physiol.* 221:1818–23
12. Code, C. F., Marlett, J. A. 1975. The interdigestive myoelectric complex of the stomach and small bowel of dogs. *J. Physiol. London* 246:289–309
13. Code, C. F., Schlegel, J. F. 1974. The gastrointestinal housekeeper. In *Gastrointestinal Motility,* ed. E. E. Daniel, pp. 631–33. Vancouver: Mitchell Press
14. DeWever, I., Eeckhout, C., Vantrappen, G., Hellemans, J. 1978. Disruptive effect of test meals on interdigestive motor complex in dogs. *Am. J. Physiol.* 235:E661–65
15. Douglas, D. M., Mann, F. C. 1939. An experimental study of the rhythmic contractions in the small intestine of the dog. *Am. J. Dig. Dis.* 6:318–22
16. Dusdieker, N. S., Summers, R. W. 1979. Patterns of smooth muscle contractions in the jejunum. *Gastroenterology* 76:1126
17. Eeckhout, C., DeWever, I., Peeters, T., Hellemans, J., Vantrappen, G. 1978. Role of gastrin and insulin in postprandial disruption of migrating complex in dogs. *Am. J. Physiol.* 235:E666–69
18. Eeckhout, C., DeWever, I., Vantrappen, G., Hellemans, J. 1979. Local disorganization of the interdigestive migrating motor complex (MMC) by perfusion of a Thirty-Vella loop. *Gastroenterology* 76:1127

19. Fleckenstein, P. 1978. Migrating electrical spike activity in the fasting human small intestine. *Am. J. Dig. Dis.* 23:769–75

20. Fleckenstein, P., Oigaard, A. 1978. Electrical spike activity in the human small intestine. *Am. J. Dig. Dis.* 23:776–80

21. Gregory, R. A. 1947. The nervous pathways of intestinal reflexes associated with nausea and vomiting. *J. Physiol. London* 106:95–103

22. Grivel, M. L., Ruckebusch, Y. 1972. The propagation of segmental contractions along the small intestine. *J. Physiol. London* 227:611–25

23. Ingelfinger, F. J., Moss, R. F. 1942. The activity of the descending duodenum during nausea. *Am. J. Physiol.* 136:561–66

24. Itoh, Z., Honda, R., Hiwatashi, K., Takeuchi, S., Aizawa, I., Takayanagi, R., Couch, E. F. 1976. Motilin-induced mechanical activity in the canine alimentary tract. *Scand. J. Gastroent.* 118 Suppl. 39, pp. 93–110

25. Itoh, Z., Takeuchi, S., Aizawa, I., Mori, K., Taminato, T., Seino, Y., Imura, H., Yanashara, N. 1978. Changes in plasma motilin concentration and gastrointestinal contractile activity in conscious dogs. *Dig. Dis. Sci.* 23:929–35

26. Jacoby, H. I., Bass, P., Bennett, D. R. 1963. In vivo extraluminal contractile force transducer for gastrointestinal muscle. *J. Appl. Physiol.* 18:658–65

27. Lee, K. Y., Chey, W. Y., Tai, H. H., Yajima, H. 1978. Radioimmunoassay of motilin: validation of studies on the relationship between plasma motilin and interdigestive myoelectric activity of the duodenum of dog. *Am. J. Dig. Dis.* 23:789–95

28. Marik, F., Code, C. F. 1975. Control of the interdigestive myoelectric activity in dogs by the vagus nerves and pentagastrin. *Gastroenterology* 69:387–95

29. Marlett, J. A., Code, C. F. 1979. Effects of celiac and superior mesenteric ganglionectomy on interdigestive myoelectric complex in dogs. *Am. J. Physiol.* 237:E432–36

30. Monges, H., Salducci, J., Naudy, B. 1974. Electrical activity of the gastrointestinal tract in dog during vomiting. See Ref. 13, pp. 479–84

31. Mukhopadhyay, A. K., Thor, P. J., Copeland, E. M., Johnson, L. R., Weisbrodt, N. W. 1977. Effect of cholecystokinin on myoelectric activity of small bowel of the dog. *Am. J. Physiol.* 232:E44–47

32. Ormsbee, H. S., Telford, G. L., Mason, G. R. 1979. Mechanism of propagation of canine migrating motor complex—a reappraisal. *Gastroenterology* 76:1212

33. Pearce, E. A., Wingate, D. C. 1979. The role of the myenteric plexuses. *Gastroenterology* 76:1215

34. Puestow, C. B. 1932. The activity of isolated intestinal segments. *Arch. Surg.* 24:565–73

35. Reinke, D. A., Rosenbaum, A. H., Bennett, D. R. 1967. Patterns of dog gastrointestinal contractile activity monitored in vivo with extraluminal force transducers. *Am. J. Dig. Dis.* 12:113–41

36. Ruckebusch, M., Fioramonti, J., 1975. Electrical spiking activity and propulsion in small intestine in fed and fasted rats. *Gastroenterology* 68:1500–8

37. Ruckebusch, Y., Bueno, L. 1973. The effect of weaning on the motility of the small intestine in the calf. *Br. J. Nutr.* 30:491–99

38. Ruckebusch, Y., Bueno, L. 1975. Electrical activity of the ovine jejunum and changes due to disturbances. *Am. J. Dig. Dis.* 20:1027–34

39. Ruckebusch, Y., Bueno, L. 1976. The effect of feeding on the motility of the stomach and small intestine in the pig. *Br. J. Nutr.* 35:397–405

40. Ruckebusch, Y., Bueno, L. 1977. Migrating myoelectrical complex of the small intestine. *Gastroenterology* 73:1309–14

41. Schanbacher, L. M., Nations, J. K., Weisbrodt, N. W., Castro, G. A. 1978. Intestinal myoelectric activity in parasitized dogs. *Am. J. Physiol.* 234:R188–95

42. Schang, J. C., Dauchel, J., Sava, P., Angel, F., Bouchet, P., Lambert, A., Grenier, J. F. 1978. Specific effects of different food components on intestinal motility. *Eur. Surg. Res.* 10:425–32

43. Stewart, J. J., Burks, T. F., Weisbrodt, N. W. 1977. Intestinal myoelectric activity after activation of central emetic mechanism. *Am. J. Physiol.* 233:E131–37

44. Szurszewski, J. H. 1969. A migrating electrical complex of the canine small intestine. *Am. J. Physiol.* 217:1757–63

45. Thomas, P.A., Kelly, K. A., Go, V. L. W. 1976. Does motilin regulate interdigestive gastric motility. *Dig. Dis. Sci.* 24:577–82

46. Vantrappen, G., Janssens, J., Hellemans, J., Ghoos, Y. 1977. The interdigestive motor complex of normal subjects and patients with bacterial over-

growth of the small intestine. *J. Clin. Invest.* 59:1158–66

47. Vantrappen, G., Janssens, J., Peeters, T. L., Bloom, S. R., Christofides, N. D., Hellemans, J. 1979. Motilin and the interdigestive migrating motor complex in man. *Dig. Dis. Sci.* 24:497–500

48. Weisbrodt, N. W. 1974. Electrical and contractile activities of the small intestine of the cat. *Am. J. Dig. Dis.* 19:93–99

49. Weisbrodt, N. W., Christensen, J. 1972. Electrical activity of the cat duodenum in fasting and vomiting. *Gastroenterology* 63:1004–10

50. Weisbrodt, N. W., Copeland, E. M., Moore, E. P., Kearley, R. W., Johnson, L. R. 1975. Effect of vagotomy on electrical activity of the small intestine of the dog. *Am. J. Physiol.* 228:650–54

51. Weisbrodt, N. W., Copeland, E. M., Thor, P. J., Dudrick, S. J. 1976. The myoelectric activity of the small intestine of the dog during total parenteral nutrition. *Proc. Soc. Biol. Med.* 153:121–24

52. Weisbrodt, N. W., Copeland, E. M., Thor, P. J., Mukhopadhyay, A. K.,

Johnson, L. R. 1976. Nervous and humoral factors which influence the fasted and fed patterns of intestinal myoelectric activity. In *Proc. Int. Symp. G.I. Motil., 5th,* ed. G. Vantrappen, pp. 82–87. Belgium: Typoff-Press

53. Weisbrodt, N. W., Moore, E., Kearley, R., Copeland, E. M., Johnson, L. R. 1974. Effects of pentagastrin on the myoelectric activity of the small intestine. *Am. J. Physiol.* 227:425–29

54. Wingate, D. 1976. The eupeptide system: a general theory of gastrointestinal hormones. *Lancet* 1:529–32

55. Wingate, D. L., Pearce, E. A., Hutton, M., Dand, A., Thompson, H. H., Wunsch, E. 1978. Quantitative comparison of the effects of cholecystokinin, secretin, and pentagastrin on gastrointestinal myoelectric activity in the conscious fasted dog. *Gut* 19:593–601

56. Wingate, D. L., Pearce, E., Ling, A., Boucher, B., Thompson, H., Hutton, M. 1979. Quantitative effect of oral feeding on gastrointestinal myoelectric activity in the conscious dog. *Dig. Dis. Sci.* 24:417–23

Ann. Rev. Physiol. 1981. 43:33–51

INTRINSIC NEURAL CONTROL OF INTESTINAL MOTILITY

❖1296

J. D. Wood

Department of Physiology, School of Medical Sciences, University of Nevada, Reno, Nevada 89557

THE LITTLE BRAIN CONCEPT

The structure, synaptic chemistry, and functional properties of the myenteric and submucosal plexuses closely resemble the central nervous system. This consensus emerges from recent reviews of histoanatomical, immunocytochemical, and electrophysiological studies (16, 29, 62, 64). The enteric ganglia are no longer conceived to be simple relay centers that function solely in distribution and divergence of parasympathetic outflow to gastrointestinal effector systems. The intrinsic nervous system is now perceived as a "little brain" that communicates with the central nervous system but that also possesses independent integrative circuitry programming and coordinating activity of the gastrointestinal effector systems.

NEUROPHYSIOLOGY OF THE ENTERIC BRAIN

Results From Extracellular Recording

Spontaneous and stimulus-evoked patterns of action potential discharge have been recorded extracellularly from neurons within myenteric and submucosal ganglia of intestinal segments from several mammalian species in vitro (14, 43, 49, 57, 60, 64–66, 74, 75) and from rabbits in vivo (42). Three kinds of neuronal units—burst-type units, mechanosensitive units, and single spike units—can be distinguished on the basis of pattern and properties of action potential discharge.

BURST-TYPE UNITS Burst-type units discharge periodic bursts of spikes with silent interburst intervals (57, 60). The ongoing discharge of the burst-type units reflects intrinsic neuronal activity that is not due to electrode-induced mechanical irritation as suggested by other authors (38). Evidence for this is: (*a*) the discharge continues unchanged for many hours; (*b*)

33

distortion of the ganglion produced by movement of the recording electrode does not alter the pattern of discharge; (c) burst activity can be recorded extracellularly with fine tipped (1 μm) NaCl-filled micropipettes; and (d) electrical stimulation of synaptic input to the cell elicits spike bursts that are similar to spontaneous bursts (10).

Burst-type units are distinguished as either steady bursters or erratic bursters on the basis of regularity of interburst time intervals. Steady bursters discharge with low statistical variance of interburst interval. Erratic bursters are characterized by irregular interburst intervals and by periodic conversion to continuous discharge of either single spikes or spike doublets. Erratic burst-type discharge requires synaptic input to the cell, whereas burst pattern generation in the steady bursters is independent of synaptic input and seems to involve an endogenous pacemaker mechanism (61).

Focal application of single electrical shocks to either the ganglionic surface or to an interganglionic connective evokes a burst of spikes that resembles the spontaneously occurring bursts in erratic bursters (10). This is a synaptic event; however, the neurotransmitter is unidentified. It is not acetylcholine, norepinephrine, serotonin, or an opioid peptide.

The steady bursters are thought to be continuously running oscillators, the erratic bursters to be follower neurons driven by synaptic input from the steady bursters (62).

MECHANOSENSITIVE UNITS   Three kinds of myenteric units respond to mechanical distortion of the ganglion. One of these behaves like a typical slowly adapting mechanoreceptor, another behaves like a fast-adapting mechanoreceptor, and the third is activated by mechanical stimulation to discharge prolonged trains of spikes of up to 40 sec duration (35, 57). The receptive fields of the mechanosensitive neurons are limited to the region of the ganglia and do not extend to the fiber tracts (43).

The third kind of mechanosensitive unit has been called a tonic-type mechanosensitive neuron (35). These neurons are thought to be interneurons activated by input derived from mechanoreceptors (60).

SINGLE SPIKE UNITS   These units discharge single spikes at relatively low frequencies with no consistent pattern. The ongoing discharge is sometimes altered but never blocked by elevated Mg^{2+}, indicating that it is not dependent on synaptic input (61).

Results From Intracellular Recording

MEMBRANE PROPERTIES OF ENTERIC NEURONS   Intracellular studies show two distinct types of myenteric ganglion cells based on the electrical behavior of the somal membranes. The first type was referred to as an AH neuron by Hirst et al (22) and as a Type 2 neuron by Nishi & North (38); the second type was called an S cell by Hirst et al and a Type 1 neuron by Nishi & North. The terms AH/Type 2 and S/Type 1 will be used here to distinguish the two kinds of ganglion cells. Most of the information for the following discussion was obtained from myenteric neurons in guinea-pig small bowel; preliminary intracellular studies indicate generally similar properties of myenteric neurons in cat small intestine (63).

The distinguishing characteristics of AH/Type 2 neurons are: (a) a high resting membrane potential relative to S/Type 1 neurons; (b) low input resistance relative to S/Type 1 neurons; (c) discharge of one or two spikes only at the onset of intrasomal injection of prolonged depolarizing current pulses; (d) no anodal-break excitation at the termination of intracellularly injected hyperpolarizing current pulses; (e) action potentials followed by prolonged hyperpolarizing after-potentials; (f) tetrodotoxin-resistant action potentials.

The distinguishing characteristics of the S/Type 1 neurons are: (a) a low resting membrane potential relative to AH/Type 2 neurons; (b) high input resistance relative to AH/Type 2 neurons; (c) discharge of spikes throughout a prolonged depolarizing current pulse with frequency of discharge a direct function of current intensity; (d) anodal-break excitation at the termination of intracellularly injected hyperpolarizing current pulses; (e) no hyperpolarizing after-potentials; (f) tetrodotoxin sensitive action potentials.

The earlier workers (22, 38) claimed that the AH/Type 2 neurons did not receive synaptic input and proposed that they were sensory neurons. This was shown to not be the case by subsequent workers who demonstrated both fast and slow synaptic events in the AH/Type 2 neurons (20, 67, 68).

About one fourth of the myenteric neurons display higher resting potentials and lower input resistances than AH/Type 2 neurons and, when first impaled with the electrode, cannot be induced to discharge by depolarizing current. These cells were presumed to be glial cells by Hirst et al (22) and Nishi & North (38); however, 20–30 min after impalement many of these initially inexcitable cells turn out to be AH/Type 2 neurons (28). Also, intrasomatic injection of the fluorescent dye, Lucifer yellow, reveals that many of these inexcitable cells are neurons (S. Erde, J. D. Wood, unpublished observations).

The prolonged hyperpolarizing potentials that follow spike discharge in AH/Type 2 cells are of important functional significance in the neurophysiology of the system. About 35% of the myenteric neurons show hyperpolarizing after-potentials, whereas this behavior is seldom encountered in the submucosal plexus. The hyperpolarizing after-potentials last up to 20 sec, and their amplitude summates as a direct function of the number of spikes discharged. An inward calcium current appears to contribute to the rising phase of the action potential in AH/Type 2 neurons, and this calcium triggers an increase in membrane potassium conductance which accounts for the postspike hyperpolarization (27, 39). The functional significance of the postspike hyperpolarization is that the decreased membrane resistance and hyperpolarization from spike threshold decrease the excitability of the cell body and prevent repetitive spike discharge.

TOPOGRAPHIC HETEROGENEITY   Unipolar neurons are present in enteric ganglia; nevertheless, most of the ganglion cells are multipolar. Several lines of evidence suggest that the multipolar neurons are multifunctional integrative units with distinct kinds of integrative functions occurring in different topographic regions of the same neuron.

Although it has not been possible to distinguish histologically or electrophysiologically between axons and dendrites, it is clear that the membrane properties of the cell soma and the attached processes of myenteric neurons are distinctly different. The processes are readily excitable, as evidenced by electrotonic invasion of the soma by stimulus-evoked spikes in the processes, at times when the somal membranes are relatively inexcitable (68). Tetrodotoxin, which blocks sodium-dependent spikes, always abolishes action potentials in the processes, but often does not block somal spikes.

The spike bursts of extracellularly recorded erratic burst-type neurons do not originate in the cell body. They originate in regions of the neuropil remote from the soma and are observed as electrotonic potentials that invade the soma from its processes (70). This also is an indication of multiple sites of spike initiation in these neurons.

AH/Type 2 neurons are multipolar as indicated by focal electrical stimulation at several points around the cells and the resulting electrotonic spread of spikes from the processes into the soma. They probably correspond to Dogiel Type II neurons. The initial segment of the processes of the neurons appear to have a much greater safety factor for spike discharge than the cell body, because intrasomatic injection of depolarizing current often fires the initial segment but not the somal membrane. The low safety factor of the multipolar soma of these cells effectively isolates the initial segments of each of the processes so that spike discharge by one initial segment does not influence spike activity of another at an opposite pole of the soma. If independent excitatory synaptic input occurs within the neuropil and at the initial segments, as is indicated by ultrastructural and electrophysiological studies, this would permit independent spike initiation in each of the cell's processes. This is adaptive in terms of neural economy because one neuron can function as several different neurons depending upon the number of processes. Independent operation of the cell's processes appears to be characteristic of one specific functional state of the multipolar AH/Type 2 neuron. These neurons show a second state in which augmented excitability of the somal membrane insures that all of the processes fire synchronously.

Discussion of synaptic transmission (below) will show how slow synaptic excitation of the cell soma greatly augments somal excitability and provides a mechanism for synchronization of the processes by the soma.

CHEMICAL NEUROTRANSMISSION   Both "fast" and "slow" synaptic potentials occur in enteric ganglion cells. The fast synaptic potentials are less than 50 msec long, whereas the slow synaptic potentials last for several seconds. Excitatory postsynaptic potentials (EPSPs) and inhibitory post-synaptic potentials (IPSPs) can be recorded in enteric neurons. Both may occur spontaneously, and both can be evoked by electrical stimulation of presynaptic fibers.

FAST EPSPs   Fast EPSPs occur in neurons of the myenteric and sub-mucosal plexuses. They are most prominent in S/Type 1 neurons, but occur in AH/Type 2 neurons also. Fast EPSPs usually have smaller amplitudes in AH/Type 2 neurons than in S/Type 1 cells (20). This is probably a reflection of synaptic input distal to the recording site in the soma, perhaps at the cone-like initial segments from which multiple processes are observed to arise in ultrastructural studies (15).

All of the fast EPSPs recorded in somata of cat (63) and guinea-pig enteric neurons (22, 38) appear to be mediated by nicotinic-cholinergic receptors. Choline esterase inhibitors prolong the EPSPs, and drugs such as hexamethonium and d-tubocurarine reduce or abolish them.

A noteworthy characteristic of fast EPSPs is a tendency for the amplitude to become progressively smaller when they are evoked repetitively by electrical stimulation of the ganglion. This rundown in amplitude occurs at frequencies as low as 0.1 Hz, and the rate of rundown is a direct function of stimulus frequency. A postsynaptic mechanism does not account for the rundown because no rundown occurs during repeated iontophoretic application of acetylcholine. Rundown is probably a reflection of presynaptic inhibition of acetylcholine release by other transmitter substances released within the ganglion by the electrical stimulus (see the section on ileus, below) and may be an experimental aberration.

Multiple cholinergic inputs converge on the ganglion cells and both spatial and temporal summation of the inputs occur. These inputs appear to project from widespread sites within the plexus because in some neurons an EPSP can be evoked by electrical stimulation of each of as many as five different connectives that enter the ganglion.

SLOW EPSPs   Slow EPSPs are recorded mainly in AH/Type 2 myenteric neurons (67, 68, 70). They are evoked by application of either single or multiple electrical stimuli to interganglionic connectives and can be demonstrated in about 38% of the AH/Type 2 neurons. The slow EPSPs are prolonged for 10–88 sec after termination of the stimulus and are associated with increased resistance and augmented excitability of the somal membrane. The augmented excitability has the following characteristics: (a) the somal membrane discharges a prolonged train of spikes that continues for several seconds after termination of stimulation; (b) the safety factor of the somal membrane is greatly increased; (c) electrotonic spike potentials invading the soma from the processes trigger somal spikes; and (d) the characteristic postspike hyperpolarizing protentials of the AH/Type 2 cells are greatly reduced or abolished.

The prolonged trains of spikes during the slow EPSPs are reminiscent of the spike trains recorded extracellularly in the tonic-type mechano-sensitive neurons, suggesting that the AH/Type 2 neurons are the intracellularly recorded counterpart of the tonic-type units.

Serotonin satisfies virtually every criterion for function as the neurotransmitter for the slow EPSP (71).

Substance P also mimics some aspects of the slow EPSP in AH/Type 2 neurons (18, 32); however, it does not appear to be the transmitter for the slow EPSP because drugs that block both the slow EPSP and the action of serotonin do not affect the action of substance P (18).

A major component of the ionic mechanism of the slow EPSP is a decrease in calcium-dependent potassium conductance of the somal membrane. AH/Type 2 neurons are like some invertebrate ganglion cells in which the membrane permeability for potassium is a direct function of the concentration of free cytoplasmic calcium (9, 36). Multivalent cations (e.g. Mn^{2+} and Mg^{2+}), which impede transmembrane movement of calcium and block calcium-dependent processes, reduce potassium conductance and mimic both the stimulus-evoked slow EPSP and the action of exogenous serotonin in AH/Type 2 neurons (19).

The somata of AH/Type 2 neurons function between extremes of low and high excitability. Low excitability is related to high resting membrane conductance for potassium that is dependent upon the availability of cytoplasmic calcium. The probability of occurrence of an action potential in this state is low; if a spike should occur, additional calcium enters the cell during the rising phase of the action potential and further activates potassium conductance. This, in turn, generates hyperpolarizing after-spike potentials that restrict excitability and repetitive spike discharge. The neuron is converted to the high excitability extreme by serotonin, which acts to reduce the level of free intracellular calcium and secondarily to reduce both the resting potassium conductance and the postspike increase in potassium conductance.

The functional significance of the slow EPSP in AH/Type 2 neurons has two major aspects. The first is the significance intuitively attributed to an excitatory synapse—i.e. increased probability of spike discharge in the postsynaptic neuron, which is then transformed into excitation or inhibition at either the next order neuron or an effector. Intestinal motility patterns require sustained discharge by some type of enteric neuron in order to account for the delays of several seconds between stimulus and coordinated contractile responses and also to account for sustained neural influence at the effector. The slow EPSP no doubt functions to produce prolonged excitation and/or inhibition at neuronal and neuro-effector junctions within the gut wall. Serotonin is a potent releasor of acetylcholine from the myenteric plexus (56), and it is probable that AH/Type 2 neurons either are cholinergic motor neurons or provide synaptic drive to the cholineric motor neurons. The train-like discharge of AH/Type 2 neurons is not associated with poststimulus rebound excitation of guinea-pig circular muscle, and it does not appear to influence the activity of the intrinsic inhibitory neurons (55).

The behavior of the cell soma of AH/Type 2 neurons also provides a mechanism by which the soma of the multipolar neuron gates the spread of excitation between the processes that arise from opposite poles of the soma (64, 70). Intracellular recordings from the soma show that electrical stimulation of the cell's processes evokes spikes that electrotonically invade the soma and that spontaneously occurring spike patterns in the processes spread electrotonically into the soma (68). The probability that the passive current flow from the spike in the processes will trigger a somal action potential is low in the absence of the neurotransmitter for the slow EPSP and is greatly increased during the augmented excitability of the slow EPSP. Thereby, spike activity associated with information processing in the synaptic neuropil is restricted to single cell processes in the absence of the slow EPSP, whereas during the slow EPSP the soma relays spike information from any one neurite to all other processes arising from other poles of the cell. If more than one of the cell's processes were axons, discharge of all axons would be synchronized during the slow EPSP. The specialized properties of the AH/Type 2 neurons and their synaptic input thus provide a mechanism whereby information processing by the ganglion cell is restricted to the neuropil of its ganglion during one functional state and is permitted to spread to adjacent ganglia in a second functional state. The second functional state (slow EPSP) permits interganglionic spread of neural information within the plexus and may underlie propagated peristaltic events; the first state may be associated with localized motility patterns— i.e. segmentation (see below).

INHIBITORY POSTSYNAPTIC POTENTIALS   IPSPs have been recorded in both myenteric and submucosal ganglion cells of guinea-pig small bowel (25, 68). Stimulus-evoked IPSPs have been reported for both myenteric and submucosal neurons; spontaneously occurring IPSPs have been reported only for myenteric neurons. IPSPs are evoked by electrical field stimulation in about 30% of submucosal neurons (25) and are observed much less often in myenteric neurons.

IPSPs in submucosal neurons are slowly developing hyperpolarizing potentials that persist 1–5 sec after termination of the stimulus. They occur in S/Type 1 neurons and result from a single synaptic input to the cell. As is the case for the slow EPSP, "single input" may be a misnomer because these potentials might result from en passant release of transmitter from several synaptic varicosities of a single axon entwined around the cell soma. The putative neurotransmitter is a catecholamine released by intrinsic neurons with cell bodies of unknown location in the submucosal and/or myenteric plexus (26).

Hirst & McKirdy (23) suggested that the functional significance of the submucosal IPSP is to delay the onset of descending excitation of cholinergic motor neurons during the peristaltic reflex. Slow synaptic inhibition may function to check the spread of neural information along the bowel, whereas the slow EPSP has the opposite function of opening gates for the spread of neural signals.

Neurophysiological studies on the submucosal plexus do not support the classical view that only sensory ganglion cells are present there. The submucosal plexus no doubt contains integrative circuitry that combines with the myenteric plexus in a single integrative unit.

NEUROPHYSIOLOGY AND INTESTINAL MOTOR FUNCTION

The main goal of gastrointestinal neurophysiology is to understand how the enteric brain controls gastrointestinal effector function, including motility. Significant advances in knowledge of the intestinal nervous system have resulted from application of electrical recording techniques; however, much remains unknown. For example, the functional identity of neurons from which recordings have been made (i.e. whether they are sensory neurons, interneurons, excitatory motor neurons, or inhibitory motor neurons) is unknown. Likewise, the particular effector system with which the recorded neural activity is associated is unknown. It is not known whether separate ensembles of neurons and their synaptic circuitry control separate functions such as motility, local blood flow, and secretion, or whether individual ganglion cells are multifunctional and influence associated processes of more than one effector system. In spite of the large gaps in knowledge, specific relationships between the neurophysiology, smooth muscle physiology, and organ-level motility emerge and define conceptual boundaries within which intestinal motor function may be considered. Here I review these emergent relationships among neurophysiology, muscle physiology, and intestinal motility patterns.

General Properties of Motor Control Systems

Small intestinal motor activity is characterized by cyclic, repeating movements. Intestinal motility, in this respect, is the same as the stereotyped locomotor movements generated by the spinal cord of vertebrates and the central ganglia of invertebrates. All kinds of cyclic motor behaviors (e.g. mammalian respiration, walking in spinal cats, insect flight, and swimming movements in leeches) are accounted for by similar neural mechanisms. A common component of all of these motor systems is a central pattern generator comprised of a neural network that generates a detailed motor output timed for appropriate spatial and temporal activation of groups of muscles to produce a specific sequence of movements. The patterned movements of these systems are different from polysynaptic chained reflexes in that they are not dependent upon sensory signals. Sensory input in these systems functions to tune the central program. That is, sensory feedback provides information for control of the duration of different phases of the motor pattern, for control of the amplitude during each phase, and for anticipatory compensation for external perturbances. A second general characteristic of these systems is that activation of a single "command neuron" elicits the entire preprogrammed sequence of rhythmic motor behavior. A third similarity between these systems is that the motor neurons are not part of the central pattern generator. They represent final common pathways that may be driven by any one of several central motor programs.

The universal presence of central pattern generators in nervous systems that generate repetitive motor activity suggests that pattern-forming circuitry within the synaptic networks of the enteric system may account for rhythmic motility patterns of the intestine. The results of electrophysiological recording of neural activity within enteric ganglia (see above) are consistent with this suggestion. Burst-type spike patterns are characteristic of both the enteric nervous system and other motor systems that are driven by central pattern generators. Hirst & McKirdy (23) reported that inflation of a stationary intraluminal balloon evoked a sequence of descending neural events that did not require continuous distension of the balloon in guinea-pig small bowel. This indicates that the neural circuitry does not require sensory information on forward movement of the intraluminal bolus nor on the continuous presence of the stimulus in order to initiate sequentially timed events 5–7 cm below the distended area. The system behaves as if "hardwired" circuitry for the complete motor sequence, analogous to polysynaptic spinal reflex circuitry, is present. Input from distension receptors appears to switch on the preprogrammed circuitry for the stereotyped sequence of motor events below the point of stimulation; once the command is received, the program continues to completion without further sensory input.

Small Intestinal Motility Patterns

The enteric brain controls two distinct patterns of small intestinal motor activity, with the particular pattern dictated by the digestive state. The predominant postprandial pattern is rhythmic segmentation (7); the inter-digestive pattern in dogs and humans is one of cyclic propulsive waves reflected by migration of a myoelectric complex throughout the intestine (7, 51), referred to as the "bowel's housekeeper" by C. F. Code (8). Each of these two motor patterns can be thought of as representing outflow from a specific pattern-generating circuit that is redundant along the length of the intestine. Commands from the central nervous system, circulating hormones, and sensory input are command mechanisms by which one or the other of the pattern-forming circuits may be selected.

Neural mechanisms account also for a third motor state, referred to as ileus, in which there is no contractile activity of the intestinal musculature.

Functional Properties of the Muscularis Externus Related To Nervous Control of Motility Patterns

The following functional properties and structural organization of the intestinal musculature are factors that limit hypotheses invoked to explain neural involvement in intestinal motor function.

CIRCULAR MUSCLE   Two physiological properties of the circular muscle must be considered in any explanation of its neural control. First, the muscle is functionally an electrical syncytium because of electrical coupling between the constituent smooth muscle fibers (31, 37, 47, 52). In the absence of nervous influence, the syncytial properties account for the three-dimensional spread of excitation and associated contraction that occurs throughout an intestinal segment when a stimulus is applied at any point on the segment. Second, organized excitation of the network of electrically coupled cells is initiated by rhythmic myogenic pacemaker mechanisms (electrical slow waves) in virtually all mammalian species except the guinea pig. The electrical slow waves occur in phase around the bowel's circumference and are out of phase along the longitudinal axis; that is, a single slow wave occurring instantaneously around the bowel appears to travel longitudinally along the gut. In the absence of neural influence, the circular muscle is highly excitable and responsive to the pacemaker so that each slow wave cycle triggers a synchronous circumferential contraction that propagates along the length of the bowel.

These properties of the circular muscle preclude a mechanism of neural control that relies only on excitatory neural input to the muscle for coordination of the contractile pattern. Excitatory motor neurons cannot control the spread of excitation within the muscular syncytium, and observations that excitability of the muscle is greatly increased when neuronal activity is experimentally abolished (3, 58) indicate that excitatory nerves do not control the responsiveness of the muscle to the pacemaker. Control of both the responsiveness of the muscle to the pacemaker and of spread of excitation within the syncytium require modulation of continuously active inhibitory innervation of the muscle. Continuously active inhibitory efferent neurons are required to explain: (a) why each and every electrical slow wave does not trigger action potentials and associated contractions in the circular muscle [only one third of the slow waves trigger spikes in vivo and the slow waves rarely trigger spikes in circular muscle of equilibrated small intestinal segments in vitro, whereas every slow wave cycle triggers spikes after blockade of the ongoing activity of the inhibitory motor neurons (2, 58)]; (b) why each slow wave does not elicit a muscle contraction of maximal strength, as is the case after nervous blockade; and (c) why excitation usually does not spread over great extents of the conductile syncytium when spikes occur in a localized region as is the case when the segmentation motility pattern occurs.

The presence of an effective myogenic activating mechanism brings to question whether excitatory motor neurons are at all necessary to evoke the phasic contractile responses associated with segmentation and peristaltic motility in the circular muscle. Excitatory junction potentials, evoked by massive electrical field stimulation, can be recorded in some circular muscle fibers; nevertheless, they occur less often than in the longitudinal muscle, are species dependent, and could reflect overflow of transmitter from myenteric ganglia rather than release at nerve-muscle appositions (13). Cholinergic junction potentials seem to be more readily recorded in guinea-pig circular muscle than in circular muscle of other species. This raises the unanswered question of whether the stronger cholinergic excitatory component of the guinea-pig circular muscle is related to absence of a myogenic pacesetting system (electrical slow waves) in the guinea pig.

LONGITUDINAL MUSCLE   The longitudinal muscle, unlike the circular, is strongly influenced by excitatory motor neurons and does not appear to receive any input from intrinsic inhibitory neurons. Nerve-mediated release of acetylcholine may be a necessary part of the mechanism of activation of the longitudinal muscle. This is suggested by failure of electrical field stimulation to evoke contractile responses in strips of longitudinal muscle after removal of the myenteric plexus and prevention of acetylcholine release (45).

Consistent with this are the observations that the longitudinal muscle contains ten times more muscarinic receptors than the remainder of the bowel (73), and that the contractile sensitivity of the longitudinal muscle to acetylcholine is very high relative to the circular muscle (13, 21). Electrical field stimulation and balloon distension of isolated segments of small bowel consistently evoke inhibitory junction potentials in fibers of the circular, but not the longitudinal, muscle layer. This indicates that the longitudinal muscle is not innervated by inhibitory motor neurons (13, 23, 33).

CIRCULAR-LONGITUDINAL INTERACTION The circular and longitudinal muscle layers are antagonistic muscles because of their anatomical arrangement within the intestinal wall. An intestinal segment geometrically is a constant surface area cylinder; therefore, shortening of the length must be accompanied by an increase in the diameter of the segment and vice versa. Consequently, when one of the muscle layers contracts, it produces forces that oppose shortening of its counterpart (72). These physical properties of the external muscularis make it likely that mechanisms that prevent simultaneous activation of the two muscle layers exist within the neural control circuitry.

Segmentation Motility Pattern

The segmentation motility pattern at any instant of time consists of narrow annular contractions interposed between relaxed segments of bowel. Moments later, the contracted annuli relax while previously relaxed intersegments contract. These cycles of reciprocal contraction-relaxation of adjacent segments accomplish mixing of intraluminal content and continue until digestion is complete. Segmentation movements occur at the same frequency as the electrical slow waves or at a multiple of the slow wave interval. The forces for mixing are exerted by the circular muscle, and contractile activity of the longitudinal muscle probably does not contribute to the mechanical forces required for mixing action.

Segmentation must involve reciprocal neural inhibition and disinhibition of adjacent segments of the circular muscle; otherwise, excitation of the contracting segment would spread within the syncytium to the adjacent relaxed segment and as a consequence a long length of intestine would contract simultaneously. The system behaves as if a central pattern generator periodically turns off the inhibitory neurons to a narrow band of circular muscle. When this occurs, the omnipresent electrical slow waves trigger contraction of the disinhibited band of muscle. The strength of the segmental contraction will depend on the number of muscle fibers in parallel that are disinhibited within the active segment. It is unclear whether cholinergic input to the disinhibited segment of muscle reinforces excitation. This may be true in the guinea pig where there are no electrical slow waves and where cholinergic junction potentials can be evoked in the circular muscle by experimentally distending an adjacent segment (23). On the other hand, in many species, segmentation contractile activity of the circular muscle is enhanced when acetylcholine release is reduced in the presence of morphine (11).

It is likely, although unproven, that the cyclical inhibition-disinhibition of a given segment of bowel is preprogrammed in the internuncial circuitry of the enteric system, and that the precisely timed discharge of the steady burst-type neurons is the clock for the program.

In view of the recent results on the presence of opioid peptides in, and the action of these substances on, enteric neurons, it should be considered that an endogenous opioid substance could be one of the messengers that commands the segmentation motility pattern (40, 41). Morphine and opiate-like substances increase both phasic contractile activity and contractile tone of the circular muscle in situ (2, 6, 11, 12, 54). It is dogma that the action of morphine on guinea-pig small bowel differs from other species in this respect (50). This view is derived from the observations of the blocking action of morphine on electrically stimulated contractions of the longitudinal muscle, on release of acetylcholine from the myenteric plexus, and on the peristaltic reflex. It cannot necessarily be concluded from these results that morphine suppresses the segmentation motility pattern in guinea pig. In dogs, cats, humans, and a number of other species, the action of opiates is to lock the intestine into a continuous segmentation pattern that is non-propulsive and constipating (11).

The action of morphine on myenteric neurons is suppression of excitability of S/Type 1 neurons in both guinea pig and cat (41, 63). This suggests that the action of morphine on segmentation motility is related to decreased release of neurotransmitters from the opiate-sensitive neurons and that the spasmogenic action on intestinal circular muscle cannot be explained by activation of excitatory motor neurons to the muscle. It suggests also that the segmentation motility pattern is associated with low excitability of the somas of S/Type 1 neurons. Prevention of release of acetylcholine from the myenteric plexus by morphine is well established (44). North & Tonini (41) have argued that this can be attributed to the hyperpolarizing action of morphine on the myenteric neurons. If some of the neurons that are hyperpolarized by morphine were intrinsic inhibitory neurons, then tonic release of the inhibitory transmitter at the muscle would be reduced by morphine. This could account for the morphine-induced increase in circular muscle contractile activity because disinhibition of the muscle would increase its responsiveness to the myogenic pacemaker. This has been proposed to be the case in rat large bowel (17). Morphine may mimic an endogenous opioid functioning as a neuromodulator that tones down the activity of both the intrinsic inhibitory neurons to the circular muscle and cholinergic excitatory neurons to the longitudinal muscle during the segmentation motility pattern. Contractile activity of the longitudinal muscle probably does not contribute to the mechanical forces required for mixing action. Since acetylcholine release is the principal mechanism for contracting the longitudinal muscle, suppression of acetylcholine release from motor neurons to the longitudinal muscle during segmentation makes functional sense. On the other hand, longitudinal muscle contraction is an integral part of peristaltic propulsion (see below) and consequently, suppression of acetylcholine release disrupts this motility pattern.

Peristaltic Motor Pattern

Peristalsis accomplishes mass propulsion of intraluminal contents in either the oral or aboral direction along the intestine. Although retropulsion is rare and usually limited to abnormal functional states, its occurrence indicates existence of neural circuits that can control for both ortho- and retroperistalsis.

Sequentially timed contractions of the circular and longitudinal muscle coats appear to be necessary for peristaltic propulsion, and the neural program may, therefore, be more complex than for the segmentation motility pattern. Both nerve-mediated shortening of the longitudinal muscle and inhibition of the circular muscle occur ahead of the advancing bolus. Circular muscle shortening associated with a relaxed longitudinal muscle occur within the intestinal segment immediately behind the bolus. Shortening of the longitudinal muscle and inhibition of the circular muscle ahead of the bolus expand the lumen and decrease intraluminal pressure in the path of the advancing bolus. Since the intestine behaves geometrically as a cylinder with constant surface area, shortening of the long axis of the cylinder increases the radius and expands the lumen, and inhibition of the circular muscle in the same segment insures that circular muscle contraction does not oppose this action of the longitudinal muscle. Contraction of the circular muscle behind the bolus increases intraluminal pressure and propels the bolus forward into the expanded lumen. Activation of the longitudinal muscle ahead of the advancing bolus is produced by activation of cholinergic motor neurons. Relaxation of the circular muscle results from increased discharge of the intrinsic inhibitory neurons. The mechanism that initiates the circular muscle contraction behind the bolus is unclear and may be species-dependent. This activation of the circular muscle could be: (*a*) a myogenic event triggered by an electrical slow wave coordinated with inhibition of continuously active inhibitory neurons: (*b*) cholinergic excitatory input coupled with disinhibition of the muscle; (c) postinhibitory rebound excitation; and (d) combinations of these factors. The observations of Hirst & McKirdy on distension-evoked inhibitory junction potentials (23) suggest that postinhibitory rebound is not a factor in circular muscle activation in guinea-pig small bowel.

Hirst & McKirdy (23) devised a preparation of guinea-pig small bowel that permitted study of neural activity in response to inflation of an intraluminal balloon. The preparation is a 5 cm segment of intestine in continuity with a strip of longitudinal muscle on which the myenteric plexus is exposed by dissection of the mucosa and circular muscle. Intracellular electrodes record from myenteric neurons on the longitudinal strip. Distension of a balloon within the segment activates neural pathways that project into the plexus on the longitudinal strip and initiate synaptic potentials in the ganglion cells. The delays of the EPSPs are then compared with the timing of occurrence of junction potentials in the longitudinal and circular muscle layers of separate preparations. Distension of the balloon elicits two distinct patterns of fast cholinergic EPSPs in neurons on the longitudinal strip aboral to the distended segment. One group of neurons shows a transient burst of EPSPs within 0.2–1.2 sec after balloon distension; this latency corresponds in time with transient inhibitory junction potentials that appear in the circular muscle after balloon distension. A second population of neurons shows EPSPs with a much longer latency of 2–11 sec. These long-latency EPSPs correspond in time with excitatory junction potentials in both longitudinal and circular layers.

Hirst & McKirdy's (23) short-latency pathway fits well the timing required for descending inhibition of the circular muscle, and the long-latency path is well timed for circular muscle excitation. However, their report that distension-evoked excitatory junction potentials occurred with the same long latency in both muscle coats is puzzling because it seems that the longitudinal and circular muscle coats should contract out of phase during peristalsis. Otherwise, the two layers would produce opposing contractile forces (see above). Electrical records from the muscle layers, ciné-films of peristaltic propulsion in mouse intestine (4, 59), and studies of the peristaltic reflex in guinea-pig small bowel (34) show that shortening of the longitudinal muscle precedes contraction of the circular.

Several lines of circumstantial evidence indicate that serotonin and substance P should receive consideration as possible messengers involved in initiation and maintenance of the peristaltic motility pattern. Enterochromaffin cell tumors in the gastrointestinal tract and other parts of the body synthesize and release large amounts of serotonin and substance P into the portal and systemic circulations (1, 46). The high levels of serotonin and substance P are often associated with increased propulsive motility and diarrhea in people with these carcinoid tumors. This raises the question of whether increased propulsive motility of carcinoid syndrome reflects the action of serotonin as the mediator for the slow EPSP in myenteric neurons. Serotonin enhances the excitability of the cell soma and in effect opens the somal gate for interganglionic transfer of information. Serotonin lowers the threshold for the peristaltic reflex in isolated segments of intestine (5), and it activates the release of acetylcholine from myenteric neurons (56). In these respects, the action of serotonin is opposite to that of the opioid peptides because accumulation of endogenous opioid substances within the intestinal wall in vitro prevents the peristaltic reflex (48, 53).

Hirst & McKirdy (23) never observed slow EPSPs in response to distension in their preparation; however, this laboratory also did not report slow EPSPs in response to electrical field stimulation. With respect to the Hirst-McKirdy preparation, it must be considered that even though radial distension is the stimulus for peristalsis in segments of intestine in vitro, the same kind of stimulation also occurs during the segmentation motility pattern. That is, segmentation normally occurs in a partly distended intestine. It may be that the particular pattern of motility evoked by mechanical distension is determined by the presence of hormonal and/or neuromodulatory factors associated with the existing digestive state of the intestinal lumen.

Ileus

Ileus is a state of no motor activity. It exists in fresh segments of small intestine equilibrated at 37°C in vitro and is a well-defined entity produced by peritoneal irritation and a variety of other causes in the intact animal. This paralysis of the bowel both in vitro and in vivo probably reflects unremitting activity of the intrinsic inhibitory neurons. Commands transmitted along sympathetic pathways are the signals that initiate the shutdown of motility in situ. Direct electrical recordings from myenteric neurons show that part of the mechanism of sympathetic shutdown is mediated by noradrenergic input that acts on presynaptic terminals to prevent release of excitatory transmitter substances.

Electrical stimulation of guinea-pig perivascular nerves inhibits cholinergic synaptic transmission between myenteric neurons but does not alter the electrical properties of the postsynaptic neurons (24, 30, 38). Application of norepinephrine blocks both the fast and slow EPSPs in guinea-pig myenteric neurons induced by electrical stimulation of interganglionic fiber tracts but does not block the action of exogenous acetylcholine or serotonin (24, 38, 69). This indicates that norepinephrine acts presynaptically to prevent release of acetylcholine and serotonin. Prevention of release of these excitatory transmitters appears to inactivate the neural circuits of the segmentation and peristaltic programs but permits continuous activity of the intrinsic inhibitory neurons. In this circumstance the cholinergic motor neurons to the longitudinal muscle cannot be activated, the circular muscle cannot respond to the myogenic pacemaker, and paralysis ensues.

Literature Cited

1. Alumets, J., Hakanason, R., Ingemansson, S., Sundler, F. 1977. Substance P and 5-HT in granules isolated from an intestinal argentaffin carcinoid. *Histochemistry* 52:217–22
2. Bass, P. 1968. In vivo electrical activity of the small bowel. In *Handbook of Physiology, Section 6, Alimentary Canal*, ed. C. F. Code, 4:2051–74. Washington DC: Am. Physiol. Soc. 2343 pp.
3. Bortoff, A., Miller, R. 1975. Stimulation of intestinal muscle by atropine, procaine and tetrodotoxin. *Am. J. Physiol.* 229:1609–13
4. Brann, L., Wood, J. D. 1976. Motility of the large intestine of piebald lethal mice. *Am. J. Digest. Dis.* 21:633–40
5. Bülbring, E., Lin, R. C. Y. 1958. The effects of luminal application of 5-hydroxytryptamine and 5-hydroxytryptophan on peristalsis: the local production of 5-HT and its release in relation to intraluminal pressure and propulsive activity. *J. Physiol. London* 140:381–407
6. Burks, T. F. 1973. Mediation by 5-hydroxytryptamine of morphine stimulant actions in dog intestine. *J. Pharmacol. Exp. Ther.* 185:530–39
7. Cannon, W. B. 1912. Peristalsis, segmentation and the myenteric reflex. *Am. J. Physiol.* 30:114–28
8. Code, C. F. 1979. The interdigestive housekeeper of the gastrointestinal tract. *Perspect. Biol. Med.* 22:549–55
9. Connor, J. A. 1979. Calcium current in molluscan neurones: measurement under conditions which maximize its visibility. *J. Physiol. London* 286:41–60
10. Cooke, A. R., Athey, G. F., Wood, J. D. 1979. Synaptic activation of burst-type myenteric neurons in cat small intestine. *Fed. Proc.* 28:959
11. Daniel, E. E. 1968. Pharmacology of the gastrointestinal tract. See Ref. 2, pp. 2267–324
12. Daniel, E. E., Sutherland, W. H., Bogoch, A. 1959. Effects of morphine and other drugs on the motility of the terminal ileum. *Gastroenterology* 36:510–23
13. Daniel, E. E., Taylor, G. S., Daniel, V. P., Holman, M. E. 1977. Can nonadrenergic inhibitory varicosities be identified

structurally? *Can. J. Physiol. Pharmacol.* 55:243–50
14. Dingledine, R. A., Goldstein, A., Kendig, J. 1974. Effects of narcotic opiates and serotonin on the electrical behavior of neurons in the guinea-pig Auerbach's plexus. *Life Sci.* 14:2299–309
15. Gabella, G. 1972. Fine structure of the myenteric plexus in the guinea-pig ileum. *J. Anat.* 111:69–97
16. Gershon, M. D. 1977. Biochemistry and physiology of serotonergic transmission. In *Handbook of Physiology, Section 1, the Nervous System*, ed. E. R. Kandel, 1:573–623. Washington DC: Am. Physiol. Soc. 717 pp.
17. Gillan, M. G. C., Pollock, D. 1976. Investigation of the effects of drugs on morphine induced contractions of the isolated colon of the rat. *Br. J. Pharmacol.* 57:P444–45
18. Grafe, P., Mayer, C. J., Wood, J. D. 1979. Evidence that substance P does not mediate slow synaptic excitation within the myenteric plexus. *Nature* 279:720–21
19. Grafe, P., Mayer, C. J., Wood, J. D. 1980. Synaptic modulation of calcium-dependent potassium conductance in myenteric neurons. *J. Physiol. London.* 305:235–48
20. Grafe, P., Wood, J. D., Mayer, C. J. 1979. Fast excitatory postsynaptic potentials in AH (Type 2) neurons of guinea-pig myenteric plexus. *Brain Res.* 163:349–52
21. Harry, J. 1963. The action of drugs on the circular strip from the guinea-pig isloated ileum. *Br. J. Pharmacol.* 20:399–417
22. Hirst, G. D. S., Holman, M. E., Spence, I. 1974. Two types of neurons in the myenteric plexus of duodenum in the guinea-pig. *J. Physiol. London* 236:303–26
23. Hirst, G. D. S., McKirdy, H. C. 1974. A nervous mechanism for descending inhibition in guinea-pig small intestine. *J. Physiol. London* 238:129–44
24. Hirst, G. D. S., McKirdy, H. C. 1974. Presynaptic inhibition at a mammalian peripheral synapse. *Nature* 250:430–31

25. Hirst, G. D. S., McKirdy, H. C. 1975. Synaptic potentials recorded from neurones of the submucous plexus of guinea-pig small intestine. *J. Physiol. London* 249:369–85

26. Hirst, G. D. S., Silinski, E. M. 1975. Some effects of 5-hydroxytryptamine, dopamine and noradrenaline on neurones in the submucous plexus of guinea-pig small intestine. *J. Physiol. London* 251:817–32

27. Hirst, G. D. S., Spence, I. 1973. Calcium action potentials in mammalian peripheral neurones. *Nature* 243:54–56

28. Hodgkiss, J. P., Lees, G. M. 1978. Correlated electrophysiological and morphological characteristics of myenteric neurons. *J. Physiol. London* 285:P19–20

29. Holman, M. E., Hirst, G. D. S. 1977. Junctional transmission in smooth muscle and the autonomic nervous system. See Ref. 16, pp. 417–61

30. Holman, M. E., Hirst, G. D. S., Spence, I. 1972. Preliminary studies of the neurones of Auerbach's plexus using intracellular microelectrodes. *Aust. J. Exp. Biol. Med.* 50:795–801

31. Holman, M. E., Neild, T. O. 1979. Membrane properties. *Br. Med. Bull.* 35:235–41

32. Katayama, Y., North, R. A. 1978. Does substance P mediate slow synaptic excitation within the myenteric plexus? *Nature* 274:387–88

33. Kitamura, K. 1978. Comparative aspects of membrane properties and innervation of longitudinal and circular muscle layers of rabbit jejunum. *J. Physiol. Jpn.* 28:583–601

34. Kosterlitz, H. W., Pirie, V. W., Robinson, J. A. 1956. The mechanism of the peristaltic reflex in the isolated guinea-pig ileum *J. Physiol. London* 133:681–94

35. Mayer, C. J., Wood, J. D. 1975. Properties of mechanosensitive neurons within Auerbach's plexus of the small intestine of the cat. *Pflügers Arch.* 357:35–49

36. Meech, R. W. 1974. The sensitivity of *Helix aspera* neurones to injected calcium ions. *J. Physiol. London* 237:259–77

37. Nagai, T., Prosser, C. L. 1963. Electrical parameters of smooth muscle cells. *Am. J. Physiol.* 204:915–25

38. Nishi, S., North, R. A. 1973. Intracellular recording from the myenteric plexus of the guinea-pig ileum. *J. Physiol. London* 231:471–91

39. North, R. A. 1973. The calcium-dependent slow after-hyperpolarization in myenteric plexus neurones with tetrodotoxin-resistant action potentials. *Br. J. Pharmacol.* 49:709–11

40. North, R. A., Katayama, Y., Williams, J. T. 1979. On the mechanism and site of action of enkephalin on single myenteric neurons. *Brain Res.* 165:67–77

41. North, R. A., Tonini, M. 1977. The mechanism of action of narcotic analgesics in the guinea-pig ileum. *Br. J. Pharmacol.* 61:541–49

42. Nozdrachev, A. D. 1978. *Vegetativnaya Reflektornaya Duga.* Leningrad: Akademiya Nauk USSR. 232 pp. (In Russian)

43. Ohkawa, H., Prosser, C. L. 1972. Electrical activity in myenteric and submucous plexuses of cat intestine. *Am. J. Physiol.* 222:1412–19

44. Paton, W. D. M. 1957. The action of morphine and related compounds on contraction and on acetylcholine output of coaxially stimulated guinea-pig ileum. *Br. J. Pharmacol. Chemother.* 12:119–27

45. Paton, W. D. M., Zar, M. A. 1968. The origin of acetylcholine released from guinea-pig intestine and longitudinal muscle strips. *J. Physiol. London* 194:13–33

46. Powell, D., Cannon, D., Skrabanek, P., Kirrane, J. 1978. The pathophysiology of substance P in man. In *Gut Hormones,* ed. S. R. Bloom, pp. 524–29. NY: Churchill Livingstone. 664 pp.

47. Prosser, C. L., Bortoff, A. 1968. Electrical activity of intestinal muscle under in vitro conditions. See Ref. 2, pp. 2025–50

48. Puig, M. M., Gascon, P., Musacchio, J. M. 1978. Electrically induced opiate-like inhibition of the guinea-pig ileum: cross tolerance to morphine. *J. Pharmacol. Exp. Ther.* 206:289–392

49. Sato, T., Tankayanagi, I., Takagi, K. 1973. Pharmacological properties of electrical activities obtained from neurons in Auerbach's plexus. *J. Pharmacol. Jpn.* 23:665–71

50. Schulz, R. 1978. The use of isolated organs to study the mechanism of action of narcotic analgesics. In *Developments in Opiate Research,* ed. A. Herz, pp. 241–77. NY: Marcel Dekker. 432 pp.

51. Szurszewski, J. H. 1969. A migrating electric complex of the canine small intestine. *Am. J. Physiol.* 217:1757–63

52. Tomita, T. 1970. Electrical properties of mammalian smooth muscle. In *Smooth Muscle,* ed. E. Bülbring, A. F. Brading, A. W. Jones, T. Tomita, pp.

197–243. Baltimore: Williams & Wilkins. 676 pp.

53. Van Nueten, J. M., van Ree, J. M., Vanhoutte, P. M. 1977. Inhibition by met-enkephalin of peristaltic activity in the guinea-pig ileum, and its reversal by naloxone. *Eur. J. Pharmacol.* 41: 341–42

54. Vaughn-Williams, E. M., Streeten, D. H. P. 1950. Action of morphine, pethidine and amidone upon intestinal motility of conscious dogs. *Br. J. Pharmacol.* 5:584–603

55. Vermillion, D., Gillespie, J., Cooke, A. R., Wood, J. D. 1979. Does 5-hydroxytryptamine influence purinergic inhibitory neurons in the intestine? *Am. J. Physiol.* 237:E198–202

56. Vizi, V. A., Vizi, E. S. 1978. Direct evidence for acetylcholine releasing effect of serotonin in the Auerbach plexus. *J. Neurol. Trans.* 42:127–38

57. Wood, J. D. 1970. Electrical activity from single neurons in Auerbach's plexus. *Am. J. Physiol.* 219:159–69

58. Wood, J. D. 1972. Excitation of intestinal muscle by atropine, tetrodotoxin and xylocaine. *Am. J. Physiol.* 222:118–25

59. Wood, J. D. 1973. Electrical activity of the intestine of mice with hereditary megacolon and absence of enteric ganglion cells. *Am. J. Digest. Dis.* 18:477–88

60. Wood, J. D. 1973. Electrical discharge of single enteric neurons in guinea-pig small intestine. *Am. J. Physiol.* 225:1107–13

61. Wood, J. D. 1975. Effects of elevated magnesuim on discharge of myenteric neurons of cat small bowel. *Am. J. Physiol.* 229:657–62

62. Wood, J. D. 1975. Neurophysiology of Auerbach's plexus and control of intestinal motility. *Physiol. Rev.* 55:307–24

63. Wood, J. D. 1979. Intracellular study of effects of morphine on electrical activity of myenteric neurons in cat small intestine. *Fed. Proc.* 38:959

64. Wood, J. D. 1979. Neurophysiology of the enteric nervous system. In *Integrative Functions of the Autonomic Nervous System,* ed. C. McC. Brooks, K. Koizumi, A. Sato, pp. 177–193. Amsterdam: Elsevier/North Holland. 508 pp.

65. Wood, J. D., Mayer, C. J. 1973. Patterned discharge of six different neurons in a single enteric ganglion. *Pflügers Arch.* 338:247–56

66. Wood, J. D., Mayer, C. J. 1974. Discharge patterns of single enteric neurons of the small intestine of the cat, dog and guinea-pig. In *Proc. 4th Int. Symp. Gastrointest. Motil.,* ed. E. E. Daniel, pp. 387–408. Vancouver: Mitchell Press. 690 pp.

67. Wood, J. D., Mayer, C. J. 1978. Electrical activity of myenteric neurons: comparison of results obtained with intracellular and extracellular methods of recording. In *Gastrointestinal Motility in Health and Disease,* ed. H. Duthie, pp. 311–20. Lancaster, Engl: MTP Press Ltd. 684 pp.

68. Wood, J. D., Mayer, C. J. 1978. Intracellular study of electrical activity of Auerbach's plexus in guinea-pig small intestine. *Pflügers Arch.* 374:265–75

69. Wood, J. D., Mayer, C. J. 1979. Adrenergic inhibition of serotonin release from neurons in guinea-pig Auerbach's plexus. *J. Neurophysiol.* 42:594–693

70. Wood, J. D., Mayer, C. J. 1979. Intracellular study of tonic-type enteric neurons in guinea-pig small intestine. *J. Neurophysiol.* 42:569–81

71. Wood, J. D., Mayer, C. J. 1979. Serotonergic activation of tonic-type enteric neurons in guinea-pig small intestine. *J. Neurophysiol.* 42:582–93

72. Wood, J. D., Perkins, W. E. 1970. Mechanical interactions between longitudinal and circular axes of the small intestine. *Am. J. Physiol.* 218:762–68

73. Yamamura, H. I., Snyder, S. H. 1974. Muscarinic cholinergic receptor binding in the longitudinal muscle of the guinea-pig ileum with [3H] quinuclidinyl benzilate. *Mol. Pharmacol.* 10:861–67

74. Yokoyama, S. 1966. Aktionpotentials der Ganglienzelle des Auerbachschen Plexus in Kaninchen Dünndarm. *Pflügers Arch.* 288:95–102

75. Yokoyama, S., Ozaki, T. 1978. Polarity of effects of stimulation of Auerbach's plexus on longitudinal muscle. *Am. J. Physiol.* 235:E345–53.

Ann. Rev. Physiol. 1981. 43:53–68

PHYSIOLOGY OF MAMMALIAN PREVERTEBRAL GANGLIA

❖1297

Joseph H. Szurszewski

Department of Physiology and Biophysics and Department of Pharmacology, Mayo Clinic and Foundation, Rochester, Minnesota 55901

INTRODUCTION

Modulation of visceral function is achieved through activity in noradrenergic neurons located in the abdominal prevertebral ganglia. This brief review examines the electrophysiological properties of these neurons, mechanisms available for modulation of synaptic transmission through these ganglia, and participation of these ganglia in reflex arcs outside the central nervous system. This review is limited to my interest in how autonomic ganglia modulate gastrointestinal motility. I emphasize prevertebral ganglia of guinea pigs and cats. Brief historical reviews are provided when background literature is required.

Anatomy

The abdominal prevertebral ganglia in mammals consist of the celiac, superior, and inferior mesenteric ganglia, and the hypogastric-pelvic plexus (pelvic plexus). The individual ganglia vary from an amorphous mass of cells spread out through the mesentery (guinea pig pelvic plexus) to ovoid lobes joined together by interconnecting fibers forming commissures (cat inferior mesenteric ganglion). The intermesenteric nerve connects the solar plexus (celiac and superior mesenteric ganglia) to the inferior mesenteric ganglion; the hypogastric nerves connect this mesenteric ganglion to the pelvic plexuses. Detailed anatomical descriptions of guinea pig and cat prevertebral ganglia have been published (15, 48, 67, 73, 74, 80).

General Morphology

PRINCIPAL GANGLION CELLS   The principal ganglion cells in the same ganglion and different prevertebral ganglia range in diameter from 20–30 μm. In guinea pig pelvic plexus, the intracapsular dendritic processes are

53

far less numerous and extensive than in the inferior mesenteric ganglion (4, 32, 33). This difference in morphology may reflect differences in function. The pelvic plexus functions as a simple relay; the inferior mesenteric ganglion functions as an integrator. The cytoplasm of the principal ganglion cell contains small agranular vesicles around 500 μm in diameter and larger vesicles around 900 μm in diameter filled with a granule of variable density (4, 31). Except in the pelvic plexus, the vast majority of principal ganglion cells in the prevertebral ganglia are noradrenergic cells. Some noradrenergic ganglion cells also contain peptides (11, 41). Fifty percent of the noradrenergic ganglion cells in the guinea pig celiac-superior mesenteric ganglion (11, 40) and most ganglion cells in the inferior mesenteric ganglion (11) contain a somatostatin-like peptide. A small proportion of ganglion cells in the celiac-superior mesenteric ganglia and a larger proportion in the pelvic plexus contain VIP immunoreactivity (11). In the pelvic plexus, the VIP-like peptide may be contained in cholinergic ganglion cells (12). The prevertebral ganglia in the guinea pig contain a vast network of peptide immuno-reactive fibers (11, 41). The inferior mesenteric ganglion of the guinea pig has a dense network of enkephalin (11, 41), VIP (11, 41), Substance P (11, 40) and gastrin/CCK and bombesin (12) immunoreactive fibers. The physiological role of these peptides is not known. They may act as neurotransmitters, trophic factors, or factors involved in long-term modulation.

GLIAL CELLS   Glial cells (or capsule cells) encapsulate the principal ganglion cells. Their cytoplasm is less densely stained and contains thin filaments (4).

SIF CELLS   The SIF (small intensely fluorescent) cells (35) contain granules approximately 1500 μm in diameter (4, 31). These cells usually cluster to form paraganglia around entering or leaving axon bundles and around small blood vessels. In the guinea pig prevertebral ganglia, these cells contain norepinephrine, not dopamine (34). Some of the SIF cells also contain enkephalin immunoreactivity (11).

ELECTRICAL PROPERTIES OF PREVERTEBRAL NEURONS

Glial Cells

The resting membrane potential ranges from 70–80 mV (4, 15); the input resistance is 5 MΩ or less (4, 15). These cells cannot fire an action potential during passage of intracellular depolarizing current or stimulation of preganglionic nerve trunks. In this sense they are inexcitable and probably are similar to "silent," "idle," "unresponsive," and "inexcitable" cells described by others in mammalian and nonmammalian ganglia (19, 51, 52). Repetitive preganglionic nerve stimulation produces a frequency-dependent depolarization (15). This depolarization is probably due to accumulation of potassium in the intercellular space between the principal ganglion cell and glial cell.

Principal Ganglion Cells

The resting membrane potential as measured by different investigators ranges from 50–70 mV (4, 14, 15, 48, 49, 76–79); the input resistance from 30–120 MΩ (4, 15, 48, 79). Assuming spherical cells with an average diameter of 30 μm and negligible contribution of cell processes to the surface area, the resistance for a unit area of membrane ranges from 2,000–10,000 Ω cm^2 and the capacitance for a unit area of membrane from 2–6 μF cm^{-2} (4). Threshold current for a 5–8 ms pulse of constant depolarizing current ranges from 0.2 to 0.4 nA (4, 15, 48, 79); threshold depolarization for initiation of an action potential ranges from 10–20 mV (4, 15, 48, 79). The overshoot of the action potential ranges from 10–20 mV. Constant depolarizing current pulses several seconds long reveal two types of neurons: neurons that fire action potentials for the duration of the depolarizing current and neurons that fire a burst of action potentials only at the onset of the depolarizing current. These have been referred to as tonic-discharging neurons and phasic-discharging neurons, respectively (79). There is no preferential distribution of either type; in the ganglia tested, half of the neurons are tonic-discharging, the other half phasic-discharging (44, 48, 79). The occurrence of a phasic- or a tonic-discharging neuron has not been correlated with the location of the neuron in the ganglion or with the neuron's resting membrane potential, input resistance, or pattern of preganglionic synaptic input (48, 79). The percentage of neurons in the pelvic plexus that demonstrate a phasic or tonic response has not been determined. In vivo, the duration of control of end organ activity might be different when these two types of noradrenergic neurons fire action potentials in response to preganglionic input. In the case of phasic-discharging neurons, maintenance of preganglionic synaptic input current for periods greater than the duration of the initial burst would result in cessation of action potentials. Output firing frequency of these postganglionic prevertebral neurons would decrease to zero even though preganglionic input to it were continuous. Structures innervated by these prevertebral neurons would be under neural control for only brief periods. In the case of tonic-discharging neurons, output firing frequency is maintained at an adaptive firing frequency for as long as preganglionic synaptic input current maintains the membrane potential above threshold for rhythmic firing (79). Structures innervated by these prevertebral neurons would be under neural control for the duration of the neuron's threshold preganglionic input.

In mammalian prevertebral ganglia two processes regulate the excitability and firing frequency of the neuronal membrane. One increases membrane excitability (15, 79). It is a slow, long-lasting depolarization of the membrane potential that follows the after-spike hyperpolarization. It can last as long as 15 sec and have an amplitude as large as 10 mV. Although synaptically activated (79), it is unaffected by α- and β-adrenoceptor blocking agents and variably affected by atropine (W. A. Weems, J. H. Szurszewski, unpublished observations). When it occurs, it can convert a subthreshold synaptic input to an action potential. From a functional point of view, it is analogous to the slow EPSP seen in rabbit superior cervical ganglion (60–62). However, dopamine may not be the transmitter involved because exogenous dopamine does not induce a depolarization of the membrane (J. H. Szurszewski, unpublished observations). The other process decreases membrane excitability. It is referred to as the after-spike hyperpolarization and is intrinsic to the ganglion cell membrane (79). No synaptic currents are associated with its generation (79). The duration of the after-spike hyperpolarization ranges from 100–500 msec; the mean duration is 175 msec; the amplitude varies from 5–10 mV (79). A single spike does not maximally activate the intrinsic properties responsible for the after-spike hyperpolarization because the amplitude of this potential increases when the interspike interval of a second following spike is less than the duration of the after-spike hyperpolarization. This indicates that the mechanism of the after-spike hyperpolarization once activated can be further activated by a subsequent spike if it occurs prior to complete deactivation of the mechanism. Since the after-spike hyperpolarization is reversed in the range of voltage of −75 to −90 mV and is reversed by elevated potassium and increased in amplitude in potassium-deficient solution, it appears likely that the after-spike hyperpolarization results from a transient increase in potassium conductance (79). The membrane excitability is reduced for the duration of the after-spike hyperpolarization. This feature of decreased excitability following the spike and lasting for the duration of the after-spike hyperpolarization is analogous to similar periods of reduced excitability associated with after-spike hyperpolarizations in spinal motorneurons (5, 42, 53) and Clarke's column neurons (30). There are no inhibitory postsynaptic potentials in any of the abdominal prevertebral ganglia. The after-spike hyperpolarization is the primary mechanism regulating firing frequency.

GANGLIONIC TRANSMISSION IN AUTONOMIC GANGLIA

In the early 18th century, Francois Pourfoit du Petit considered ganglia to be "little brains" that receive signals, integrate them, and organize a response (20). Although the idea was rejected at that time, it is meeting with greater acceptance today (see 3, 73, 75, 77). A brief review of the history of transmission through peripheral ganglia will provide perspective on how this "new" idea grew out of old concepts.

In 1935, Eccles published a series of papers on electrical recording from the surface of the rabbit superior cervical ganglion (21–23). The complex electrical record he obtained in response to maximal stimulation of the cervical sympathetic nerve contained 4 distinct peaks. Increasing the strength of nerve stimulation once the threshold value to record the first peak had been obtained resulted in the successive appearance of the other 3 peaks at progressively longer latencies. This response was followed immediately by a long period of opposite polarization of the ganglion (up to 0.5 sec), which Eccles called the late-positive, or P wave. Eccles interpreted the four peaks of the electrical response recorded from the ganglion (or four "S" waves as he called them) as being produced by four groups of ganglion cells that were excited to discharge by four corresponding groups of preganglionic fibers (21). He thought that there was no appreciable overlap between the various groups of preganglionic fibers and that each group served a different physiological function; however, he was unable to prove this. Eccles concluded that the "S" waves were not due to the repetitive discharge of impulses from ganglion cells, although his experiments showed that ganglion cells could receive more than one preganglionic fiber, usually from fibers within the same "S" group. This was the first evidence that ganglia could modify the frequency of impulses as they passed from preganglionic to postganglionic fibers, an idea put forward earlier by Cannon (12).

In a series of experiments on the inferior mesenteric ganglion, Lloyd (64) was able to examine in more detail some of the conclusions drawn from the studies on the superior cervical ganglion. The inferior mesenteric ganglion has a number of preganglionic nerve trunks, not just one as in the case of the superior cervical ganglion. Lloyd established that the after-potential following the ganglion cell discharge was a fundamental reaction of the ganglion cell and that the excitability cycle of the ganglion cell followed closely the course of the after-potential. Eccles had previously discussed this possibility (21, 24).

Bronk and co-workers studied the stellate ganglion (2, 7). They stimulated the preganglionic nerve trunk to the stellate ganglion while recording from the cardiac (postganglionic) nerves (8). They concluded that the function of this sympathetic ganglion was to transmit impulses from the preganglionic to the postganglionic fibers without altering their frequency. However, Bronk later questioned the suitability of using whole nerve trunk stimulation to investigate the properties of transmission in ganglia and decided that "the suggestion that a sympathetic ganglion may modify the

frequency of impulses coming from the central nervous system is undoubtedly correct" (6). Thus, by 1939 the mammalian ganglia had proved more
complex than was envisaged by Langley (57). Ganglion cells in the superior
cervical ganglion had been shown to receive more than one preganglionic
fiber and were thought to discharge usually by the summation of two or
more preganglionic impulses. This ruled out Langley's (57) idea that
ganglia acted as simple relay stations between pre- and post-ganglionic
fibers.

Using surface recording techniques, Rosamand M. Eccles (25, 26)
recorded the action potentials from the isolated cat superior cervical ganglion and the effect of various curarizing agents upon it. She found that
preganglionic fibers besides being excitatory also exerted inhibitory actions
on neurons in this ganglion. When the ganglion was curarized, a single
stimulus or a train of stimuli evoked a local negative potential—the N wave.
This was followed by a positive potential—P wave—and after the P wave
a later negative wave—LN wave. Eccles & Libet (29) studied the origin and
genesis of these potential changes. They suggested that the N wave represented activity at nicotinic cholinergic synapses. The P wave resulted from
activity at preganglionic fibers on chromaffin (SIF) cells. The release of a
catecholamine from the chromaffin cell caused a hyperpolarization of the
ganglion cell membrane (P wave). The LN wave was due to the activity of
muscarinic cholinergic receptors. The paper by Eccles & Libet became a
forerunner of a series of papers by Libet and his colleagues (60–62) dealing
with the features, electrogenesis, and physiological significance of slow
synaptic potentials in autonomic ganglia. Recently, an excellent summary
of slow postsynaptic potentials has been published (60). In the middle fifties,
the intracellular recording technique was applied to mammalian ganglion
cells. The intracellularly recorded potentials corresponding to the N, P, and
LN waves were called the EPSP, slow IPSP, and slow EPSP, respectively
(62; see also 60).

In one of the first intracellular studies of mammalian peripheral autonomic ganglia, Rosamand M. Eccles (27, 28) recorded the in vitro response
of single cells in the rabbit superior cervical ganglion to preganglionic nerve
stimulation. She showed that ganglion cell excitation was achieved by
means of a synaptic potential that reached a threshold for action potential
initiation. This synaptic potential was depressed by the curare-like substance, dihydro-β-erythroidine. Although she found that some cells could
receive more than one preganglionic fiber, she did not conclude that this was
a regular feature of ganglion innervation.

Erulkar & Woodward (36) made a major intracellular study of mammalian ganglia. They did not remove the superior cervical ganglion from
the animal (rabbit) as Eccles had done but recorded from it in vivo. For the

first time ganglion cells were shown to be capable of discharging more than one action potential in response to a preganglionic stimulus. (The recordings of Eccles had shown only multiple synaptic potentials.) Like Eccles they interpreted this to represent the convergence of a number of preganglionic fibers onto each ganglion cell, although they did not give any estimate of the number of fibers each cell could receive. An estimate of the number of preganglionic fibers that synapsed on a ganglion cell was given by Libet & Tosaka (62) from an intracellular study of the rabbit superior cervical ganglion in vitro. They estimated that three or four preganglionic fibers ordinarily appear to converge on a cell, but that there could be seven or more in some cases (62).

In the late 1960s and early 1970s, intracellular recording techniques were used to investigate transmission in mammalian abdominal prevertebral ganglia. In small discrete ganglia located along the hypogastric and pelvic nerves (4) and in the pelvic-hypogastric plexus (15), each neuron received 1–3 strong synapses; that is, the threshold response to each was a postsynaptic spike thus ensuring a direct connection to the central nervous system. In these ganglia, there was no evidence of a slow IPSP or a slow EPSP. There is one additional feature worth noting about ganglion cells in the pelvic ganglia. Many receive preganglionic input from both the sympathetic hypogastric and parasympathetic pelvic nerves. These inputs are not *en passant* synapses due to fibers passing through the ganglion on their way from one nerve trunk to the other. Rather, these ganglion cells represent the final common pathway for impulses arriving by both of these nerve trunks. This dual innervation is not confined to these ganglia because a few ganglion cells in the inferior mesenteric ganglion also receive preganglionic input from the parasympathetic and sympathetic branches of the autonomic nervous system (15). The functional significance of this dual innervation is not presently understood.

In contrast to the preponderance of strong synapses in pelvic ganglia, preganglionic fibers synapsing on ganglion cells in the inferior mesenteric ganglion of the guinea pig form weak synapses (15, 79). A weak synapse is one at which the preganglionic fiber produces an EPSP of insufficient voltage to attain threshold for generating an action potential (75). Activation of fibers preganglionic to the inferior mesenteric ganglion produced an EPSP smaller than the voltage change needed to reach threshold for an action potential. There was marked convergence of weak synapses. It was estimated that ganglion cells in the inferior mesenteric ganglion receive at least 40 converging preganglionic fibers (15). Marked convergence also occurs in the guinea pig superior mesenteric and celiac ganglia (48), cat inferior mesenteric ganglion (44), and renal ganglion (17). In the guinea pig celiac ganglion (48) and cat inferior mesenteric ganglion (44), there was no evidence for a slow IPSP. The occurrence of a slow EPSP in the ganglia is variable (Y. Julé, J. H. Szurszewski, unpublished observations).

The observations on synaptic transmission in peripheral autonomic ganglia made during the past four decades lead to the following generalizations. First, for a ganglion to integrate, mechanisms are needed within the ganglion that can organize preganglionic input into output responses. These mechanisms may take the form of a fast IPSP or a fast subthreshold EPSP of the usual duration for a fast postsynaptic potential. There is no evidence for the occurrence of fast IPSP activity in mammalian prevertebral ganglia or the superior cervical ganglion. The integrating mechanisms may also take the form of long-lasting hyperpolarizations or depolarizations lasting several seconds. Although both types of slow synaptic potentials occur in the superior cervical ganglion, the situation in abdominal prevertebral ganglia is different. The slow IPSP is absent. The important process that reduces membrane excitability and limits firing frequency is the after-spike hyperpolarization (79). The slow EPSP occurs consistently in the guinea pig inferior mesenteric ganglion, inconsistently in other prevertebral ganglia in the guinea pig and cat. When it does occur, it can convert subthreshold fast EPSP into action potentials (15, 79). Second, when integration occurs in abdominal prevertebral ganglia it is achieved mainly through spatial and temporal summation of subthreshold EPSP arriving in the ganglion from central and peripheral sources. Postsynaptic spikes are generated when responses to convergent stimuli sum to threshold to fire the neuron. And third, when a ganglion is not capable of integration, there are no slow synaptic potentials and the threshold response to preganglionic nerve stimulation is nearly always an action potential. On this basis, the pelvic ganglia of the guinea pig does not seem to be capable of integration.

PERIPHERAL REFLEXES BETWEEN PREVERTEBRAL GANGLIA AND THE GI SYSTEM

Prevertebral ganglia are important for normal motor function of the gastrointestinal tract. Under normal conditions, these ganglia together with the central sympathetic outflow exert a restraining action on the motor elements of the gastrointestinal tract. In the frog (39), destruction of the spinal cord or of the ganglia and mesenteric nerves increased motor activity. In dogs (13) and rabbits (66) ileus (absence of propulsion) is relieved or prevented by section of the splanchnic nerves. Popielski (68) found that removal of the prevertebral ganglia in dogs resulted in severe chronic diarrhea associated with increased motor activity. Lium (63) recorded an increase in motor activity of the rectum after extirpation of the inferior mesenteric ganglion. Gary (38) in his studies on the cat colon and Lawson & Holt (58) in their studies on the colon of the anesthetized and unanesthetized dog found that colonic tone increased following removal of the inferior mesenteric ganglion. Learmonth & Markowitz (59) found an increase in intracolonic pressure after section of the lumbar colonic nerves.

Prevertebral ganglia contain synapses that arise from axons whose cell bodies are located in the enteric plexuses. There is histological evidence for such synapses. Kuntz (54) and Kuntz & Saccomanno (55) found in the cat inferior mesenteric ganglion that terminal branches of axons remained intact following degeneration of all preganglionic fibers of spinal origin. They observed intact nerve fibers in the distal segment of the lumbar colonic nerve after the fibers that grow distalward had degenerated. These observations were confirmed earlier by Kuz'mina (56) and more recently by Bulygin & Archakova (10). McLennan & Pascoe (65) found intact c fibers in the rat ascending mesenteric nerve after decentralization of the inferior mesenteric ganglion, splanchnicotomy, bilateral sympathectomy, and bilateral vagotomy. Ross (69) found that 30% of the small fibers running between the superior mesenteric ganglion and the small intestine remained intact after fibers extending distalward had degenerated. Schofield (71) found in the cat and rat mesenteric fasciculi nerve fibers that were centripetal processes of intact neurons in the bowel wall.

There is also physiological evidence of synaptic connections between enteric neurons and prevertebral neurons. Kuntz (54) and Kuntz & Saccomanno (55) found that distention of one segment of the intestine inhibited another even after the associated prevertebral ganglia had been decentralized and all the associated visceral afferent fibers issuing from the dorsal root had been cut. Semba (72) confirmed these observations. Koch (46) found that cutting the splanchnic nerves did not abolish the intestinointestinal reflex, but the nerve ramifications along the mesenteric vascular branches must be left intact for the reflex to occur. Schapiro & Woodward (70) demonstrated that the gastric inhibitory effect of acid in the duodenum, the enterogastric reflex, persisted in dogs after chronic bilateral supradiaphragmatic vagotomy and bilateral thoracolumbar sympathectomy. However, following celiac ganglionectomy, the enterogastric reflex was completely abolished, which suggested that sensory fibers in the duodenum make synaptic contact with postganglionic sympathetic neurons in the celiac ganglion.

Electrophysiological recordings from nerve filaments attached to the prevertebral ganglia support the concept that peripheral autonomic pathways exist outside the central nervous system and that there are interactions between the different prevertebral ganglia. Brown & Pascoe (9) found that stimulation of the rabbit intermesenteric nerve produced an efferent volley back out the same nerve trunk. This reflex was blocked when nicotinic blocking agents were applied to the inferior mesentric ganglion. Bulygin & Archakova (10) recorded afferent impulses traveling from the intestine to the inferior mesenteric ganglion in the lumbar colonic nerves. Recently, Davison & Hersteinsson (16) reported that, except for the inferior splanchnic nerves, all peripheral nerve trunks attached to the inferior mesenteric ganglion of the guinea pig contain postganglionic fibers that can be excited reflexly by stimulation of any of the peripheral nerve trunks. When considered together, the combined weight of morphological and physiological evidence suggests that the prevertebral ganglia can receive synaptic input from the gastrointestinal tract and that they participate in reflex activity modulating intestinal motor activity close to and distant from the point of initiation of the reflex.

The first direct electrophysiological evidence for reflex activity and synaptic input from enteric neurons to ganglion cells in a prevertebral ganglion was obtained by Crowcroft et al (14). Using intracellular electrophysiological techniques, they found in the guinea pig that neurons in the inferior mesenteric ganglion received excitatory synaptic input from axons coming from the distal colon. The synaptic input took the form of EPSPs that occasionally summed to fire an action potential. The synaptic input to noradrenergic neurons in the inferior mesenteric ganglion resulted from activity of slowly adapting colonic mechanoreceptors that monitor the mechanical state of the colon (75). The level of synaptic afferent input is directly proportional to physiological levels of intraluminal pressure and varies with propulsive motor activity (77). Pelvic nerve stimulation and excitatory agents that increase smooth muscle colonic motility increased the level of synaptic input whereas inhibitory agents decreased it (75). Excitation of neurons in the inferior mesenteric ganglion by stimulation of any of its peripheral or central nerve trunks inhibited motor activity and discharge of the mechanoreceptors into the prevertebral ganglion (14, 74, 75). This inhibition by the efferent noradrenergic neurons is due to the inhibitory action of noradrenaline on the activity of the cholinergic motor neuron, the contractility of smooth muscle, and the mechanosensitivity of the afferent pathway (75). It remains to be determined whether the output of each noradrenergic neuron mediates all three of these inhibitory functions or whether each function is independently controlled by separate populations of neurons within the ganglion.

Ganglion cells in the celiac ganglion and superior mesenteric ganglion also receive excitatory synaptic input from colonic mechanoreceptors. Neurons in the celiac ganglion receive synaptic input from mechanosensory neurons located in the orad colon (48, 49); in contrast, the inferior mesenteric ganglion receives input from the caudad colon. The superior mesenteric ganglion, anatomically situated between the celiac and inferior mesenteric ganglia, receives about equal mechanosensory input from orad and caudad regions of the colon (49). Thus there is an orad-caudad distribution in the prevertebral ganglia of synaptic inputs from mechanoreceptors located in the wall of the colon. In parallel to this afferent distribution, there is also a viscerotopic distribution of efferent noradrenergic output (48). Stimulation of the sympathetic outflow from the celiac ganglion primarily inhibits contraction of the orad colon whereas stimulation of the outflow from the inferior mesenteric ganglion primarily inhibits contractions in the caudad colon (48). Recently, the horseradish peroxidase (HRP) technique was used to label mammalian neurons in vitro (50). HRP placed on the inferior celiac nerves and superior celiac nerves marked separate pools of neurons in the celiac ganglia and a few neurons in the more caudad inferior mesenteric ganglion. HRP placed on the more caudad lumbar colonic nerves marked almost all ganglion cell bodies in the inferior mesenteric ganglion. Many neurons in the superior mesenteric ganglia were also marked while a few neurons were marked in the more orad celiac ganglia. These morphological data provide the structural framework for the electrophysiological observations.

The orad and caudad colon are in neural communication through the intermesenteric nerve (49). Recent observations have shown that a physiological increase in intraluminal pressure in the orad colon reduces the intraluminal pressure in the caudad colon. An increase in pressure in the caudad colon reduces the pressure in the orad colon. This bi-directional reflex is abolished when the intermesenteric nerve is sectioned. These data provide evidence for a colo-colonic inhibitory reflex mediated through the prevertebral ganglia and independent of central nervous system activity.

The celiac ganglion of the guinea pig is the anatomical pathway not only for the colo-colonic inhibitory reflex but also for a gastro-duodenal inhibitory reflex (47). Contractile activity in the stomach influences duodenal contractility such that when the pyloric antrum contracts, contractions in the duodenum are inhibited (43). Recent observations in the guinea pig indicated that this reflex is mediated through the pyloric branch of the gastroduodenal nerve and utilizes a pool of neurons in the celiac ganglion located at the base of the gastroduodenal nerve. The returning efferent noradrenergic fibers course through the gastroduodenal nerve back to the duodenum, where they inhibit duodenal motor activity (47). The participation of the celiac ganglion in the gastroduodenal reflex indicates that this prevertebral ganglia not only interfaces between two regions of the same organ (colo-colonic reflex) but also between functionally distinct organs.

A number of other reflexes may utilize the prevertebral ganglia. One example is the gastro-gastric reflex, in which activation of antral gastric mechanoreceptors or tension receptors inhibits corpus-fundus motility (1).

Both spinal and prevertebral reflex pathways are thought to be involved but the evidence is lacking. Another example is the enterogastric reflex, in which acid in the duodenum inhibits gastric antral motility. This reflex persists in dogs after chronic bilateral thoracolumbar sympathectomy (70). However, following celiac ganglionectomy, the enterogastric reflex was completely abolished, which suggested that sensory fibers in the duodenum may make synaptic contact with postganglionic sympathetic neurons in the celiac ganglion (70). In a like manner, hypertonic solutions in the duodenum inhibit antral emptying into the duodenum (37). For this reflex, the structural integrity of the celiac ganglion is essential. Single unit intracellular studies should be useful in deciphering the precise neural pathways and pools of neurons in the prevertebral ganglia utilized by these reflexes.

SUMMARY

When assessing the physiological role of the prevertebral ganglia, the following should be considered. Ganglion cells in these ganglia receive continuous excitatory synaptic input from peripheral sensory mechanoreceptors and central preganglionic neurons. The latter may result from sensory afferents projecting from the gastrointestinal tract to spinal preganglionic neurons or as a result of endogenous oscillator activity located in the spinal cord (18) or within the ganglion (45). Peripheral and spinal reflex pathways probably do not operate as separate, independent pathways. Rather, they must be considered functionally integrated in the prevertebral ganglia. Because of continuous synaptic input, the prevertebral neuron operates at some level of "neurogenic tone" that provides capabilities for bi-directional responses. An increase in spinal or peripheral synaptic input will be matched by a proportional increase in output firing. The functional effect of spatial summation of peripheral and central input is to prime the prevertebral neuron so that adjustments in its firing frequency can be made without the lag inherent in building up a response in a quiescent system.

Not all prevertebral ganglia participate in reflex activity. It may be that reflex activity between prevertebral ganglia and visceral smooth muscle depends upon the nature of the mechanical activity of the muscle. For example, the mechanical activity of smooth muscle of the vas deferens is not characterized by spontaneous, myogenic, regularly occurring contractions. Mechanical activity in this organ occurs in bursts. There is no evidence to suggest that sensory fibers project from the wall of the vas deferens to the hypogastric plexus thereby forming a peripheral reflex arc. Contraction of the smooth muscle of the vas deferens is brought about by bursts of nerve impulses through simple relay connections in the pelvic plexus. Smooth muscles supplied by this ganglion have a direct line to the central nervous system and are secured by a "fail-safe" system. In contrast, the mechanical activity of the gastrointestinal system is characterized by slow spontaneous myogenic activity. Pattern formation of motor activity is achieved by reflex activity within the enteric plexuses. Extrinsic alteration of the nature and pattern of contraction of smooth muscle of the gastrointestinal tract would be best served by prevertebral ganglia that modulate and adjust motor function by continuous integration of convergent weak synaptic input emanating from the peripheral and central nervous systems. When a prevertebral neuron is part of a peripheral reflex loop, its physiological role may be to modulate end organ activity; when it does not participate in a peripheral reflex loop, its role may be to relay CNS input and initiate end organ activity.

ACKNOWLEDGMENTS

I thank Jacob Krier and James C. Lynch for many helpful discussions during preparation of this manuscript. I am grateful to Jan Applequist for her careful assistance in the preparation of this manuscript. This work was supported by a grant from the National Institutes of Health (AM 17632).

Literature Cited

1. Abrahamsson, H. 1971. Vago-vagal gastro-gastric relaxation. *Rendic. Roman. Gastroenterol.* 3:114–15
2. Adrian, E. D., Bronk, D. W., Phillips, G. 1932. Discharges in mammalian sympathetic ganglia. *J. Physiol. London* 74:115–33
3. Blackman, J. G. 1974. Function of autonomic ganglia. In *The Prevertebral Nervous System*, ed. J. I. Hubbard, pp. 257–76. NY: Plenum
4. Blackman, J. G., Crowcroft, P. J., Define, C. E., Holman, M. E., Yonemura, K. 1969. Transmission from preganglionic fibers in the hypogastric nerve to peripheral ganglia of male guinea pigs. *J. Physiol. London* 201:723–43
5. Brock, L. G., Coombs, J. S., Eccles, J. C. 1953. Intracellular recording from antidromically activated motorneurons. *J. Physiol. London* 122:429–61
6. Bronk, D. W. 1939. Synaptic mechanisms in sympathetic ganglia. *J. Neurophysiol.* 2:280–401
7. Bronk, D. W., Ferguson, L. F., Margaria, R., Solandt, D. 1936. The activity of cardiac sympathetic centers. *Am. J. Physiol.* 117:237–49
8. Bronk, D. W., Tower, S. S., Solandt, D. Y., Larrabee, M. 1938. The transmission of trains of impulses through a sympathetic ganglion and in its post-ganglionic nerves. *Am. J. Physiol.* 122:1–15
9. Brown, G. L., Pascoe, J. E. 1952. Conduction through the inferior mesenteric ganglion of the rabbit. *J. Physiol. London* 118:113–23
10. Bulygin, I. A., Archakova, L. I. 1971. Electron-microscopic analysis of synapses in caudal mesenteric sympathetic ganglion in afferent link of sympathetic reflexes. *Neirofiziologiia* 3:84–88
11. Burnstock, G., Hökfelt, T., Gershon, M. D., Iversen, L. I., Kosterlitz, H. W., Szurszewski, J. H. 1979. Non-adrenergic, non-cholinergic autonomic neurotransmission mechanisms. *NRP Bull.* 17:379–519
12. Cannon, W. B. 1914. The interrelations of emotions as suggested by recent physiological researches. *Am. J. Psychol.* 25:256–82
13. Cannon, W. B., Murphy, F. T. 1906. The movements of the stomach and intestine in some surgical conditions. *Ann. Surg.* 43:512–36
14. Crowcroft, P. J., Holman, M. E., Szurszewski, J. H. 1971. Excitatory input from the distal colon to the inferior mesenteric ganglion in the guinea-pig. *J. Physiol. London* 219:443–61

15. Crowcroft, P. J., Szurszewski, J. H. 1971. A study of the inferior mesenteric and pelvic ganglia of guinea-pigs with intracellular electrodes. *J. Physiol. London* 219:421–41

16. Davison, J. S., Hersteinsson, P. 1975. Functional organization of the guinea-pig inferior mesenteric ganglion. *J. Physiol. London* 250:27P–28P

17. Decktor, D. L., Weems, W. A. 1980. An intracellular characterization of neurons in cat renal ganglia and their preganglionic inputs. *Fed. Proc.* 39:363

18. de Groat, W. C., Krier, J. 1979. The central control of the lumbar sympathetic pathway to the large intestine of the cat. *J. Physiol. London* 289:449–68

19. Dennis, M. J., Gerschenfeld, H. M. 1969. Some physiological properties of identified mammalian neurological cells. *J. Physiol. London* 203: 211–22

20. du Petit, F. P. 1979. Cited in *Integrative Functions of the Autonomic Nervous System,* ed. C. McC. Brooks, K. Koizumi, A. Sato, p. 493. Tokyo: Univ. Tokyo Press

21. Eccles, J. C. 1935. The action potential of the superior cervical ganglion. *J. Physiol. London* 85:179–206

22. Eccles, J. C. 1935. Facilitation and inhibition in the superior cervical ganglion. *J. Physiol. London* 85:207–38

23. Eccles, J. C. 1935. Slow potential waves in the superior cervical ganglion. *J. Physiol. London* 85:464–500

24. Eccles, J. C. 1937. Synaptic and neuromuscular transmission. *Physiol. Rev.* 17:538–55

25. Eccles, R. M. 1952. Action potentials of isolated mammalian sympathetic ganglia. *J. Physiol. London* 117:181–95

26. Eccles, R. M. 1952. Responses of isolated curarized sympathetic ganglia. *J. Physiol. London* 117:196–217

27. Eccles, R. M. 1955. Intracellular potentials recorded from mammalian sympathetic ganglia. *J. Physiol. London* 130:572–84

28. Eccles, R. M. 1963. Orthodromic activation of single ganglion cells. *J. Physiol. London* 165:387–91

29. Eccles, R. M., Libet, B. 1961. Origin and blockade of the sympathetic responses of curarized sympathetic ganglia. *J. Physiol. London* 157:484–503

30. Eide, E., Fedina, L., Jansen, J., Lundberg, A., Vyklicky, L. 1969. Properties of Clarke's column neurones. *Acta Physiol. Scand.* 77:125–44

31. Elfvin, L. G. 1971. Ultrastructure studies on the synaptology of the inferior mesenteric ganglion of the cat. I. Observations on the cell surface of the postganglionic perikarya *J. Ultrastruct. Res.* 37:411–25

32. Elfvin, L. G. 1971. Ultrastructure studies on the synaptology of the inferior mesenteric ganglion of the cat. II. Specialized serial neuronal contacts between preganglionic end fibers. *J. Ultrastruct. Res.* 37:426–31

33. Elfvin, L. G. 1971. Ultrastructural studies on the synaptology of the inferior mesenteric ganglion of the cat. III. The structure and distribution of the axodendritic and dendrodendritic contacts. *J. Ultrastruct. Res.* 37:432–48

34. Elfvin, L. G., Hökfelt, T., Goldstein, M. 1975. Fluorescence microscopical, immunohistochemical and ultrastructural studies on sympathetic ganglia of the guinea pig with special reference to the SIF cells and their catecholamine content. *J. Ultrastruct. Res.* 51:377–96

35. Eränkö, O. 1976. SIF Cells. In *Structure and Function of the Small Intensely Fluorescent Sympathetic Cells.* (Fogarty Int. Cent. Proc. No. 30) Washington DC: USGPO

36. Erulkar, S. D., Woodward, J. K. 1968. Intracellular recording from mammalian superior ganglion in situ. *J. Physiol. London* 199:189–203

37. Furness, J. B., Costa, M. 1974. The adrenergic innervation of the gastrointestinal tract. *Ergebn. Physiol.* 69:1–51

38. Gary, R. C. 1933. The nervous control of the caudal region of the large bowel in the cat. *J. Physiol. London* 77:422–31

39. Goltz, F. 1872. Studien über die Bewegungen der Speiserohre und des Magens des Frosches. *Pflügers Arch.* 6:616–42

40. Hökfelt, T., Elfvin, L. G., Elde, R., Schultzberg, M., Goldstein, M., Luft, R. 1977. Occurrence of somatostatin-like immunoreactivity in some peripheral sympathetic noradrenergic neurons. *Proc. Natl. Acad. Sci. USA* 74:3587–91

41. Hökfelt, T., Johansson, O., Ljungdahl, Å., Lundberg, J. M., Schultzberg, M. 1980. Peptidergic neurones. *Nature* 284:515–21

42. Ito, M., Oshima, T. 1962. Temporal summation of after-hyperpolarization following a motorneuron spike. *Nature* 195:910–11

43. Joseph, D. R., Meltzer, S. J. 1910–1911. Inhibition of the duodenum coincident with the movements of the pyloric part of the stomach. *Am. J. Physiol.* 27:XXXi–XXXii

44. Julé, Y., Szurszewski, J. H. 1979. Distribution of peripheral inputs to neurons in the inferior mesenteric ganglion of the cat. *Fed. Proc.* 38:959

45. Julé, Y., Szurszewski, J. H. 1979. Occurrence of spontaneous oscillatory neurons in the cat inferior mesenteric ganglion: Relationship to ileus? *Gastroenterology* 76:1163

46. Koch, N. G. 1959. An experimental analysis of mechanisms engaged in reflex inhibition of intestinal motility. *Acta Physiol. Scand.* 164:Suppl. 47, pp. 1–54

47. Kreulen, D. L., Muir, T. C., Szurszewski, J. H. 1979. The influence of extraspinal reflex pathways on gastroduodenal activity in the guinea pig. *Gastroenterology* 76:1177

48. Kreulen, D. L., Szurszewski, J. H. 1979. Nerve pathways in celiac plexus of the guinea pig. *Am. J. Physiol.* E90–E97

49. Kreulen, D. L., Szurszewski, J. H. 1979. Reflex pathways in the abdominal prevertebral ganglia: evidence for a colo-colonic inhibitory reflex. *J. Physiol. London* 295:21–32

50. Kreulen, D. L., Szurszewski, J. H. 1979. Electrophysiological and morphological basis for organization of neurones in prevertebral ganglia. In *Frontiers of Knowledge in the Diarrheal Diseases,* ed. H. D. Janowitz, D. B. Sachar, pp. 211–26. NY: Projects in Health, Inc.

51. Kuffler, S. W., Nicholls, J. G. 1966. The physiology of neuroglial cells. *Ergebn. Physiol.* 51:1–90

52. Kuffler, S. W., Nicholls, J. G., Orkand, R. K. 1966. Physiological properties of glial cells in the nervous system of amphibia. *J. Neurophysiol.* 29:768–87

53. Kuno, M. 1959. Excitability following antidromic activation in spinal motorneurons supplying red muscles. *J. Physiol. London* 149:374–93

54. Kuntz, A. 1940. The structural organization of the inferior mesenteric ganglion. *J. Comp. Neurol.* 72:271–382

55. Kuntz, A., Saccomanno, C. J. 1944. Reflex inhibition of intestinal motility mediated through decentralized prevertebral ganglia. *J. Neurophysiol.* 7:163–70

56. Kuz'mina, S. V. 1963. Structural organization of the inferior mesenteric ganglion. *Arch. Anat. Histol. Embryol.* 45:T706–9

57. Langley, J. N. 1903. The autonomic nervous system. *Brain* 26:1–26

58. Lawson, H., Holt, J. P. 1937. The control of the large intestine by the decentralized inferior mesenteric ganglion. *Am. J. Physiol.* 118:780–85

59. Learmonth, J. R., Markowitz, J. 1930. Studies on the innervation of the large bowel. II. The influence of the lumbar colonic nerves on the distal part of the colon. *Am. J. Physiol.* 94:501–4

60. Libet, B. 1979. Slow postsynaptic actions in ganglionic functions. See Ref. 20, pp. 197–222.

61. Libet, B. 1970. Generation of slow inhibitory and excitatory postsynaptic potentials. *Fed. Proc.* 29:1945–56

62. Libet, B., Tosaka, T. 1969. Slow inhibitory and excitatory postsynaptic responses in single cells of mammalian sympathetic ganglia. *J. Neurophysiol.* 32:43–50

63. Lium, R. 1941. Peptic ulcer and diarrhea following the removal of the prevertebral ganglia in dogs; antispasmodic effects of magnesium sulfate, pentobarbital and atropine sulfate. *Surgery* 9:538–53

64. Lloyd, D. P. C. 1939. The origin and nature of ganglionic after potentials. *J. Physiol. London* 96:118–29

65. McLennan, H., Pascoe, J. E. 1954. The origin of certain non-medullated nerve fibers which form synapses in the inferior mesenteric ganglion of the rabbit. *J. Physiol. London* 124:145–56

66. Meltzer, S. J., Auer, J. 1907. Peristaltic movements of the rabbit's cecum and their inhibition. *Proc. Soc. Exp. Biol.* 4:37–40

67. Nozdrachev, A. D., Bezenkina, G. I., Efimova, N. I. 1970. Pathways of caudal mesenteric sympathetic ganglion. *Fiziol. Zh. SSR.* 56:543–51

68. Popielski, L. 1903. Zur Physiologie des Plexus Coeliacus. *Arch. Anat. Physiol., Physiol. Abt.* 338:360

69. Ross, J. G. 1958. On the presence of centripetal fibers in the superior mesenteric nerves of the rabbit. *J. Anat.* 92:189–98

70. Schapiro, H., Woodward, E. R. 1959. Pathway of enterogastric reflex. *Proc. Soc. Exp. Biol. N. Y.* 101:407–9

71. Schofield, G. C. 1960. Experimental studies on the innervation of the mucous membrane of the gut. *Brain* 83:490–514

72. Semba, T. 1954. Intestino-intestinal inhibitory reflexes. *Jpn. J. Physiol.* 4:241–45

73. Skok, V. I. 1973. *Physiology of Autonomic Ganglion,* p. 151. Tokyo: Igaku Shoin

74. Syromyantikov, A. V., Skok, V. I. 1968–1969. Pathways in the sympa-

thetic ganglia of cat solar plexus. *Neurosci. Transl.* 8:918–24

75. Szurszewski, J. H. 1977. Toward a new view of prevertebral ganglion. In *Nerves and the Gut,* ed. F. P. Brooks, P. W. Evers, pp. 244–60. Thorafare, NJ: Charles B. Slack

76. Szurszewski, J. H., Weems, W. A. 1976. A study of peripheral input to and its control by post-ganglionic neurones in the inferior mesenteric ganglion. *J. Physiol. London* 256:541–56

77. Szurszewski, J. H., Weems, W. A. 1976. Control of gastrointestinal motility by prevertebral ganglia. In *Physiology of Smooth Muscle,* ed. E. Bülbring, M. F. Shuba, pp. 313–19. NY: Raven

78. Weems, W. A., Szurszewski, J. H. 1977. Modulation of colonic motility by peripheral neural inputs to neurons of the inferior mesenteric ganglion. *Gastroenterology* 73:273–78

79. Weems, W. A., Szurszewski, J. H. 1978. An intracellular analysis of some intrinsic factors controlling neural output from inferior mesenteric ganglion of guinea pigs. *J. Neurophysiol.* 41:305–21

80. Wozniak, W., Skowronska, U. 1967. comparative anatomy of pelvic plexus in cat, dog, rabbit, macaque and man. *Anat. Anz.* 120:S457–73

RESPIRATORY PHYSIOLOGY

Introduction, Alfred P. Fishman, *Section Editor*

Breathing is an automatic process that fundamentally is designed for gas exchange. Normally it executes this function rhythmically, effortlessly, and efficiently in accord with the level of metabolic activity. But, the breathing apparatus also has responsibilities other than gas exchange. For example, the respiratory muscles are involved in maintaining posture. The capability of the system for automatic adjustments provides for these other obligations.

The automatic breathing pattern is subject to voluntary and involuntary interruption: Breathholding can be initiated and terminated at will; involuntary disturbances in breathing pattern are integral parts of certain behavioral responses, such as anger or fear. Each of these deviations from the fundamental breathing pattern is mediated by a distinct control mechanism, and all of the control circuits are interconnected. These connections among networks make it possible for some pathways to be engaged preferentially at one time and not at another, for coordinated responses to occur, and for interruptions to affect the gain of the inherent automatic system (1, 2).

Much more is known about the operation of the automatic system than about the other processes for which the respiratory apparatus has been co-opted. But even for the automatic system, knowledge is punctuated by large gaps. Best understood is the role of chemical stimuli, particularly pH, P_{CO_2}, and P_{O_2}, in the control of breathing. From preoccupation with arterial blood gas composition and acid-base balance, interest has enlarged to include the cerebrospinal fluid and tissues. Despite this wider scope of investigation, however, chemical stimuli do not account fully for the control of breathing—either at rest or during exercise.

The papers that follow concern nonchemical aspects of the control of breathing: neurophysiological, neuroanatomical, and neurohumoral. Each represents a leading edge in contemporary research.

The paper by Pack is concerned with sensory input into the central nervous system, particularly with afferent information carried by the vagus nerves. Vagal afferent input can increase the instantaneous magnitude of inspiratory neural output. The afferent information carried by the vagus nerves begins with mechanoreceptors in the lungs. Until a decade ago only specialists in the field of respiratory neurophysiology could decipher the various names applied to the receptors. Certain of the receptors had several pseudonyms. A giant step towards clarity—perhaps at the expense of precision—was made by sorting pulmonary mechanoreceptors into three categories: stretch, rapidly adapting (irritant), and juxtacapillary (J) receptors. Of the three, only the J receptors in the parenchyma have nonmyelinated C fibers. Pack speaks for a fourth set of receptors, lodged in the airways, that are also innervated by nonmyelinated C fibers. These do not fit comfortably under the now-conventional umbrella of "irritant fibers." As a result, it now seems necessary to enlarge the classification of pulmonary vagal receptors to four categories, two of which are innervated by myelinated fibers (stretch and rapidly adapting receptors) and two by nonmyelinated C fibers (bronchial and juxtacapillary). It is noteworthy that in this classification, the designation "irritant receptor" has been replaced by their original designation, "rapidly adapting receptors." Although it seems clear that these receptors can provide information to the medulla about mechanical events in the lungs, no specific stimulus for them has yet been identified nor is it understood how they operate. These mechanoreceptors do not operate independently of the more familiar chemoreceptors: The gain of the mechanoreceptor feedback loops is strongly influenced by the level of chemical drive.

A second focus of neurophysiological research in the control of breathing is on the central neural mechanisms that generate the respiratory rhythm. Both the neurons in the brain and the phrenic nerves are being scrutinized. From early descriptions of myriad groups of cells with various characteristics and unknown function, the search for neurophysiological bases of the control of breathing has progressed to models that provide a functional description of the brain stem oscillator. Current research aspires to define neural connections and to generate a "circuit diagram" of the oscillator. The paper by Cohen on central determinants of the respiratory rhythm deals with the various populations of respiratory neurons, their interplay, and their functional organization.

As though in response to Cohen's pleas for more neuroanatomical information, Kalia deals with the anatomical organization of the central respiratory neurons, seeking to uncover the structural bases for the respiratory control mechanisms. The techniques are complicated and still evolving. Nonetheless, she attempts to trace anatomical links from one end to the other, between the vagal nerves on the one hand and the phrenic nerves on the other. In doing so, she has reinforced observations made using the older degeneration techniques and has provided fresh insights into the links between afferent nerves in the lung parenchyma and their cell bodies in the central nervous system.

The final touch is provided by the fourth paper, in which Eldridge & Millhorn query the role of neurohumoral substances in the central nervous system as mediators of respiratory effects. The concern here is with longer-term regulatory mechanisms than those with which the respiratory physiologist usually deals. This provocative essay undoubtedly presages a large research effort that will seek to ascertain the role of neurochemicals in the control of breathing, with particular reference to the level and pattern of breathing, both at rest and during change in posture and activity, both in health and in disease.

Literature Cited

1. Purves, M. J. 1979. What do we breathe for? In *Central Nervous Control Mechanisms in Breathing,* ed. C. von Euler, H. Lagercrantz, pp. 7–12. Oxford: Pergamon

2. Wyke, B., ed. 1974. *Ventilatory and Phonatory Control Systems.* NY: Oxford Univ. Press. 531 pp.

Ann. Rev. Physiol. 1981. 43:73–90
Copyright © 1981 by Annual Reviews Inc. All rights reserved

SENSORY INPUTS TO THE MEDULLA

❖1298

A. I. Pack

Cardiovascular-Pulmonary Division, Department of Medicine, Hospital of the University of Pennsylvania, Philadelphia, Pennsylvania 19104

INTRODUCTION

Respiratory neurons in the medulla receive afferent information from many different sensory systems. Principal among these are the central and peripheral chemoreceptors, mechanoreceptors in the lung, and proprioceptors in the chest and abdominal wall. These sensory systems have been investigated with respect to both the information they provide to the medulla and the nature of their transduction mechanisms. This short review focuses on the pulmonary vagal receptors, and on literature that has appeared since the two most recent extensive reviews of this topic (32, 68); both the transduction mechanisms and reflex role of the receptors are considered. Other sensory systems—peripheral and central chemoreceptors—have been the subject of recent symposia (1, 51, 69).

PULMONARY VAGAL RECEPTORS

During the 1960s different names were employed by different investigators for essentially the same pulmonary vagal receptor. Once order was produced from relative chaos, it was agreed that there were three main pulmonary receptors—stretch, rapidly-adapting (or "irritant"), and J (juxta-capillary) receptors. The first two were innervated by myelinated fibers, the third by nonmyelinated. This classification has been used extensively, though it is now realized certain receptors in the bronchi, as well as the parenchyma, are innervated by nonmyelinated fibers (17). Thus we add a fourth group of receptors—bronchial receptors innervated by C fibers (17).

0066-4278/81/0315-0073$01.00

PULMONARY STRETCH RECEPTORS

From a functional point of view the main interest is in the stretch receptors (PSR). Evidence indicates that their afferent activity is involved in control of inspiratory and expiratory durations, and the instantaneous magnitude of neural output to a number of the main respiratory muscles.

Distribution of Stretch Receptors

Anatomical studies on the stretch receptors remain scarce although anatomical information on their distribution within the bronchial tree has been obtained by indirect physiological means (5, 57, 58). The receptors are thought to be situated in the bronchial smooth muscle. In the trachea, when the receptor is silenced by local dissection, the last piece of tissue to be removed is smooth muscle (5). The majority of the receptors (55.6%) are in the extrapulmonary airways (57). The total surface area of the extrapulmonary airways is orders of magnitude less than that of the intrapulmonary airways (98); this implies large differences in the density of these receptors (per unit surface area of bronchial wall) between the extra and intrapulmonary airways. This density of receptors in the extrapulmonary airways may however not reflect their functional significance (49, 50).

Within the intrapulmonary airways the receptors are also denser proximally (58). Such a distribution may have advantages, relating the distorting force on the bronchial wall more to the overall degree of lung inflation and being less influenced by local mechanical derangements.

A significant number of stretch receptors (of the order of 17% of the total) are located in the extrathoracic trachea (5). The mechanical forces on the extrathoracic trachea during ventilation are completely different from those on the intrathoracic airways. Transmural pressure, which distorts the wall, in the extrathoracic trachea is dependent on intratracheal pressure alone, whereas in the intrathoracic airways it reflects transpulmonary pressure. Since airflow is related to intratracheal pressure, the presence of receptors in this site may allow the control system to monitor airflow, thereby raising interesting possibilities with respect to overall control of ventilation (77). Such possibilities are at present largely theoretical; there has been little direct study of the role of the extrathoracic receptors in control of neural output (82).

Transduction Properties of Stretch Receptors

MECHANICAL   The relatively high density of receptors in the trachea has facilitated studies on their transduction mechanisms (6, 14, 61). The tracheal receptors are stimulated by both static increase in transmural pressure and marked decreases (61, 84). The firing increase when transmural pressure is significantly decreased is due to tension changes in the trachealis muscle as the posterior wall is drawn into the tracheal lumen (61). Indeed the firing of these receptors over the whole range tested correlates reasonably well with indirect calculations of tension changes within the muscle (61).

The firing of tracheal receptors seems largely to depend on variations in transverse rather than longitudinal dimensions of the posterial wall (86). Elongation of the trachealis muscle in vitro reduces the firing of the stretch receptors (14). However, local longitudinal stretch in the region of the receptor increases receptor firing (14). In systematic studies in vivo, Sant'Ambrogio et al (86) have shown no definite effect of variations in tracheal length on the response of PSR to transmural pressure, except at high pressures when the firing of the receptors was lower when the trachea was elongated.

These receptors respond not only to the overall degree of inflation (static component) but also to the rate of inflation (dynamic component). This was shown originally by Davis et al (26) and has been confirmed recently using frequency response methods (6). In these latter studies, which used an isolated tracheal segment preparation, the dynamic component seems larger than previously reported for PSR (26). However, the data from the isolated segment are difficult to relate to variables corresponding to overall inflation to the lung. The dynamic component of the receptors' response to changes in transmural pressure is in part related to the viscous properties of the trachealis muscle (61). However, the receptors' response still shows a dynamic component when compared with direct measurement of tension in the trachealis muscle in vitro (14).

The static responses of intrathoracic receptors have been studied, and two types of receptor have been identified (59). Type I receptors (40% of the total) saturate at a transpulmonary pressure of about 10 cm H_2O, while the firing of type II receptors (60% of total) does not reach a plateau (see Figure 1). These subtypes are not uniformly distributed throughout the bronchial tree; type I receptors predominate in the proximal airways, type II in the distal. The origin of this difference is not clear. It was first proposed that receptors of these different subtypes were arranged differently in the smooth muscle (59). Since the cross-sectional area of the larger bronchi increases little above a transmural pressure of around 10 cm H_2O (53) it was postulated that type I receptors were arranged in parallel in the smooth muscle (compare to muscle spindles) while the type II receptors were in series (compare to tendon organs). If receptors are in parallel, then contraction of smooth muscle should reduce activity, as seen with the muscle spindles' response following contraction of extrafusal muscle (54). However, isometric contraction of smooth muscle produces an increase rather than a decrease in the firing of all tracheal receptors (5). Thus the hypothesis of a parallel and series arrangement of the different subtypes is unsupported, and we do not know why such differences occur.

EFFECT OF CHANGES IN CO_2 CONCENTRATION   While PSR are primarily mechanoreceptors, their activity is also altered by variations in CO_2 in the airways; lowering of CO_2 increases their discharge (4, 13, 19, 62, 83, 88). This has stimulated much recent interest, although it may have little physiological relevance in mammals. This effect of CO_2 is primarily on the threshold of the receptors (13, 62); there is either no difference (62) or a minor change (13) in the slope of the relationship between receptor activity and transpulmonary pressure or volume. In consequence, while the effect of changes in CO_2 concentration on peak inspiratory activity is similar in absolute terms (impulses/sec) to its effect on end-expiratory activity (if present), proportionately its effects on end-expiratory activity are more marked (13, 19, 62, 83). Thus variations in lung CO_2 concentration without changes in arterial CO_2 produce alteration in expiratory rather than inspiratory duration (8).

The effects of changes in CO_2 concentration on the receptor are nonlinear, being more marked at lower CO_2 (19). The action of CO_2 is likely to be mediated by a hydrogen ion change within the bronchial wall, since it is blocked by the administration of a carbonic anhydrase inhibitor (83). The majority of evidence (13, 19, 62, 83) indicates that it is due to the direct

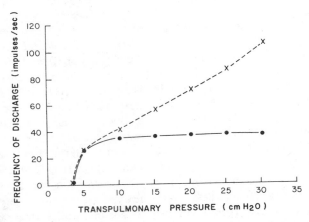

Figure 1   Relationship between activity of both the type I (−•−) and type II (x—x—x) pulmonary stretch receptors, and transpulmonary pressure during static inflations of the lung. [Redrawn from (59)]

effect of pH on neural tissue (97), rather than being secondary to the increase in smooth muscle tone produced by reduced CO_2 in the airways (95).

Change in airway CO_2 concentration does not alter the firing of receptors in all sites within the bronchial tree. The activity of tracheal receptors is unaffected by variations of CO_2 concentration within its lumen (4). Other extrapulmonary receptors do respond to changes in CO_2 concentration but more slowly than intrapulmonary receptors (83). This may reflect different concentrations of carbonic anhydrase in the walls of different bronchi, but there is no definitive information on this.

The physiological significance of this modulation of PSR activity by airway CO_2 is at present unknown, but it is unlikely to be important. In normal physiological conditions, airway CO_2 varies between zero and the end-tidal concentration. Whether such intra-breath variations in CO_2 affect receptor activity will depend on the dynamics of the response of the receptor to variations in CO_2 concentration, which may, at least for the intrapulmonary receptors, be sufficiently rapid (83). The inspiratory activity of the receptor depends primarily, however, on the mechanical stimulus, and is proportionately little affected by changes in airway CO_2 (13, 19, 62, 83). In expiration CO_2 can alter the activity significantly and produce reflex effects (8), but the normal end-tidal CO_2 (or higher) does not produce modulation of PSR firing (19). Thus any reflex effect of CO_2 on PSR activity is likely to be found only during profound hypocapnia, which will by this mechanism produce a reflex slowing of breathing.

In birds variations of intrapulmonary CO_2 concentration play a more important role in the normal control of ventilation (76); these animals have (a) pulmonary receptors sensitive to CO_2 (31, 74) and its rate of change (75) but not to mechanical stimuli (31, 74), and (b) mechanoreceptors sensitive to CO_2 (47).

Role of Stretch Receptors in Neural Control of Ventilation

Activity of PSR plays an important role in control of both inspiratory and expiratory durations (see M. I. Cohen, this volume). Changes in vagal afferent activity during inspiration alter its duration (T_I), although static increases in lung volume, in the absence of breathing, have no effect on T_I (7). From an extensive series of studies [for summary, see (34)] von Euler and his colleagues proposed that inspiration was terminated by an all-or-none off-switch mechanism, the final step of which involved the triggering of a group of high-threshold off-switch cells (12). [Inspiratory neurons with off-switch characteristics have been described by various laboratories (15, 52).] The vagal contribution to the off-switch was thought to be dependent solely on the magnitude of afferent activity at inspiratory termination (12).

Since the original proposal of this hypothesis (12), certain of its elements have been disproved. The switch is now known to have an initial reversible phase (103), and there is a period of graded inhibition of phrenic neural output before the rapid decline in its activity (103). The vagal contribution to the off-switch is not dependent solely on PSR firing at end inspiration (20, 22, 67). Central processing of PSR activity seems to involve a process akin to leaky integration, with the time constant of decay being of the order of several hundred milliseconds (20, 67).

In view of the partial dependence of PSR activity on rate of inflation (see above) it is surprising that changes in the rate of inflation seemed to have no effect on inspiratory duration (3). However, the study's design was based on the assumption that the vagal contribution to the off-switch was solely dependent on PSR activity at end inspiration. We have recently reinvestigated this question. Using a mechanical stimulus (high frequency oscillatory airflow) that will preferentially stimulate the dynamic component of vagal receptors, we have shown that the dynamic component from pulmonary receptors does affect the mechanisms controlling T_I (67).

Much attention has been paid to control of T_I, less to control of expiratory duration (T_E). This is surprising since in most species, including humans (36), changes in respiratory frequency are largely produced by changes in T_E. Increased PSR activity does significantly increase T_E, an effect present even when the lungs are static (7). Expiratory duration can be lengthened by inflations of the lung (43, 44) and reduced by deflations below FRC (43, 44). Vagal afferent information is stored centrally since pulses of inflation delivered only early in the expiratory period still affect T_E (43). In contrast, the terminal part of the expiratory period is insensitive to changes in vagal afferent activity. Volume delivered to the lung at this time has no effect on T_E (43, 44).

During expiration the instantaneous magnitude of peripheral expiratory activity is also altered by changes in PSR firing. While earlier work indicated that static increases in volume were excitatory to abdominal muscle activity [for summary see (11)], recent studies have shown that increased volume inhibits the initial phase of expiratory activity (45, 73). These data are not incompatible. Earlier studies largely concentrated on examination of the peak activity of the abdominal EMG. Recent studies using either EMG (73) or direct recording of neural activity (45) have, in contrast, measured the detailed time course of peripheral expiratory activity. Increased lung volume initially inhibits expiratory activity, though the activity rises to a greater level during the resultant prolonged T_E. Thus the previously described excitatory effect of volume may be a result of the prolongation of expiratory duration. The magnitude of this inhibitory effect of volume on peripheral expiratory activity decreases during hypercapnia (45)—i.e. there is evidence of adaptive control whereby the gain of mechanoreceptor feedback loops is altered by chemical stimuli. The concept of adaptive control is new to this area of physiology, though it has been demonstrated in control of skeletal muscle (93).

The function of this inhibitory effect of volume is not known. The data suggest that abdominal activity will be inhibited at high lung volume when the lung recoil force, which promotes expiratory airflow, is high and the requirement for expiratory muscle activity is less. As lung volume decreases the gradually reducing inhibition should allow greater abdominal muscle activity, thereby tending to preserve a constant expulsive force in the face of the declining magnitude of lung recoil.

PULMONARY RAPIDLY ADAPTING RECEPTORS

Receptors of the second main class, the pulmonary rapidly adapting receptors (RAR), remain an enigma. Originally described by Knowlton & Larrabee (42) and identified by their rapid adaptation to lung inflation, they have become known as "irritant" receptors, since they can be stimulated by a variety of irritants (55, 56); but there is no supporting evidence for the implication that their primary function is nocioceptive.

The concept that RAR are primarily "irritant receptors" has been recently challenged. Sampson & Vidruk (79) demonstrated that a minority of canine RAR responded to inhaled irritants. Studies in other species (2, 55) also indicate that response to irritants is not a universal feature of these receptors. The term "irritant receptor" is thus inappropriate; the term "pulmonary rapidly adapting receptor," used here, implies nothing about the receptors' function, which is still uncertain (see below).

Distribution of RAR Within the Airways

The nerve endings of the RAR are thought to be in the airway epithelium (see 101), though there is no direct evidence for this. As for PSR, recent studies (60, 85) on the relative distribution of RAR throughout the bronchial tree indicate that they are mostly situated in the major airways, 55–70% being found within 1 cm of the hilum (2, 60). Their distribution in the bronchial tree does not exactly parallel that of the PSR; the largest concentration of RAR is in the lobar bronchi (60). The distribution of RAR correlates with the limited information on the relative distribution of intraepithelial axons (23).

In extrapulmonary airways the RAR can be located at any point on the airway circumference (85). In contrast, stretch receptors in the trachea are only found in the smooth muscle in the posterior wall (5). This fact supports the concept that the endings are primarily intraepithelial.

Direct probing of the mucosa indicates that the receptive field of an individual receptor in the extrapulmonary airway is large—about 1 cm in diameter (85). Thus the areas of bronchial mucosa supplied by different afferent fibers overlap, and a single receptor must have multiple endings within the bronchial epithelium. The receptor may also have multiple endings in the submucosa. Resection of the mucosa by removing the airway epithelium with the submucosa left intact (confirmed histologically) abolished the response to touch but not to inflation (85).

Transduction Properties of RAR

While significant advances have been made in understanding the distribution of the receptors, there has been less progress in determining what the receptors sense. Earlier literature emphasized that the response of the receptors was related to the compliance of the lung (91). The mechanism for this was poorly understood, though it was attributed to an increased pull on the bronchial walls when the lungs were stiff (91).

One of the difficulties in understanding the transduction mechanisms of RAR was the almost complete lack, until recently, of quantitative information relating receptor activity to mechanical events in the lung. This was in part due to difficulties posed by the relatively irregular firing of the receptors. From averaging the receptors' response over the whole volume of the lung inflation, Sullivan & Read did show that there is a linear relationship between activity of RAR and airflow (94).

Recent work from this laboratory (28) has confirmed this observation, but the receptors' response is not simply dependent on airflow. In our studies, we averaged the receptors' response over multiple tests at constant rates of inflation, rather than over the whole volume of inflation. At any rate of inflation the receptors' response significantly varied between tests (Figure 2a) but averaged over multiple tests showed a relationship between receptor activity and lung volume (Figure 2a). At any constant airflow the receptors' response was not constant (Figure 2b). There was a threshold volume or pressure below which the receptors did not fire. Thereafter, at a constant rate of inflation, there was an exponential relationship between receptor activity and lung volume. The magnitude of the exponent increased with increasing rates of inflation. The receptors' response is significantly dependent on the rate of inflation—i.e. they have a marked dynamic sensitivity.

The marked dynamic sensitivity of the receptors has not yet been explained. It may, in part, be related to surface forces on the bronchial mucosa whose magnitude is dependent on airflow. There are concentrations of

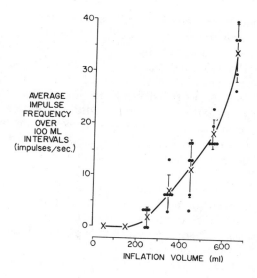

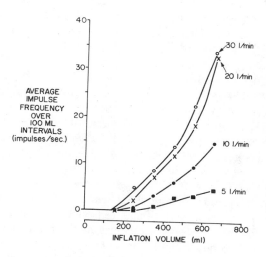

Figure 2 Relationship between activity of a pulmonary rapidly adapting receptor and lung volume during inflations of the lung at a constant rate. The inflations are divided into 100 ml volume increments, and the mean activity of the receptor over this volume increment is computed. In 2a (*top*) both the individual results (.) and the computed mean and SD of the responses (×) are shown for 6 identical tests at a single rate of inflation (20 l min⁻¹). In 2b (*bottom*) the computed mean responses from 6 identical tests at several different rates of inflation are shown.

receptors at bronchial branch points (85), at which significant surface forces on the mucosa occur [for summary see (72)]. The bifurcation disturbs the velocity profiles of gas flow such that there is high velocity of gas flow, and hence, shear on the inside wall following the bifurcation (89). In addition, gas impacts on the apex of the bifurcation causing a distorting force. The magnitude of this impact force depends on the velocity of airflow and is increased if there is particulate matter in the gas hitting the bronchial mucosa. Such mechanical considerations may explain the known effect of dust on the receptors' response (92). If so, the effect of dust on receptor activity should depend on flow-rate; this relationship has not been investigated.

While the receptors are primarily mechanoreceptors their response can be altered by chemical stimulation. This is particularly true for histamine, a potent stimulant of the receptors (29, 92, 96). In canine lungs, histamine may directly sensitize the receptors (96)—i.e. the response is not solely mediated by the bronchoconstriction produced by histamine. [Bronchoconstriction produced by any agent stimulates this receptor type (29).] For the direct effect of histamine there are three pieces of evidence: (a) Histamine produces more marked stimulation of the receptors than acetylcholine with comparable degrees of bronchoconstriction (29, 96); (b) histamine produces an increase in receptor activity even when changes in peak tracheal pressure are virtually abolished by prior administration of aerosolized isoproterenol (96); and (c) histamine produces an increase in some receptors' activity when applied locally to the receptor field, even after large doses of intravenous isoproterenol (96). This direct effect of histamine on canine RAR is mediated by H^1 receptors (81) and is species-dependent. In guinea pigs histamine produces no increase in RAR activity if changes in tracheal pressures are blocked by isoproterenol (10). Histamine primarily increases the response of the RAR to lung inflation, though in larger doses it may cause the RAR to fire tonically throughout the respiratory cycle (79).

Because of the presumed superficial location of the receptors in the epithelium of the major airways, their transduction properties may be altered by even minor pathological changes in the bronchial mucosa. For example, histamine produces more marked increases in RAR firing in dogs with upper respiratory tract infections than in normal control dogs (30). This may have pathophysiological significance (see below).

Physiological Function of RAR

While certain features of their transduction mechanism have been elucidated, the reflex role of the afferent activity from RAR remains disputed (see 71). Indeed it is still not certain whether these receptors have a significant role in the normal control of ventilation. The main difficulty in establishing their function lies in distinguishing effects due to RAR from those produced by PSR. Factors known to stimulate RAR—e.g. rapid large lung inflations (91), histamine (29, 96)—also alter the afferent input from PSR (99). Differential block of the vagus nerve by controlled hypothermia (63) or DC current (21) has been tried to distinguish the effects of the two receptor types, since the fibers from RAR tend to be smaller (68). However, the overlap in the conduction velocities of individual RAR and PSR fibers (68, 79) makes the data from such studies difficult to interpret.

Recently, a new technique has been introduced (25)—administration of SO_2 to the airways in rabbits—that almost completely abolishes the activity of PSR in this species. The evidence for this is partly derived from single-fiber recording studies and from the virtual abolition of the Hering-Breuer inflation reflex. This effect of SO_2 may be related to the acidic nature of the gas, the change in receptor activity being produced by changes in pH in the bronchial wall (25) (compare to the effect of CO_2 on PSR).

Data obtained with this technique suggest that activity of RAR may significantly alter respiratory timing mechanisms, particularly those concerned with control of T_E. SO_2 block produced a shortening of T_E compatible with the removal of expiratory activity of PSR (25). Subsequent vagotomy, which would have only additionally removed (at least as far as the lung is concerned) the afferent input from RAR and pulmonary/bronchial C fibers, produced a significant lengthening of expiratory duration. These data imply that activity from one of these receptor types [most likely the RAR, since the others are relatively inactive in eupneic breathing (17, 68)], plays a normal role in shortening expiratory duration. These data are compatible with those obtained by differential cooling of the vagus nerve (63) or DC block (21) and with the fact that chemical stimuli of RAR (e.g. histamine) produce tachypnea with shortening of both T_I and T_E (102). Neither the normal importance of RAR in determining expiratory duration nor how RAR interact with the PSR is known.

In certain circumstances the activity of RAR may also lead to an increase in phrenic neural output. Thus the receptors are thought to mediate the spontaneous augmented breath or sigh. As with other reflex actions of these receptors, the evidence is indirect. Augmented breaths occur only with intact vagus nerves (37), are more frequent when lung compliance is low (78) [which also stimulates RAR (91)], and still occur after SO_2 block of PSR (25). Whether in other circumstances RAR facilitate inspiration is uncertain. We have recently demonstrated that, in paralyzed dogs ventilated with a cycle-triggered ventilator with control of both the inflation and chemical status of the animal, both pneumothorax (66) and aerosolized histamine (39) cause an increase in the rate of rise of phrenic neural output. [In both states RAR are stimulated (90, 96).] This effect of histamine may, at least in part, explain the increase in inspiratory muscle activity in acute asthma (104).

Part of the difficulty in establishing the role of the receptors is that their central connections are at present unknown. In this laboratory we have obtained evidence that I beta cells in the NTS, which are stimulated by lung inflation, are not a homogeneous group of cells (52). The firing of a sub-group of I beta cells is markedly dependent on the rate of inflation. The dynamic sensitivity of this class of cells is much more marked than expected for cells connected to the PSR; they may connect to the RAR, which have a marked dynamic sensitivity (see above).

RAR activity may also cause reflex bronchoconstriction (56). Thus RAR could mediate the vagally mediated reflex bronchoconstriction, which oc-curs in the canine model of experimental asthma (38). As recently pointed out by Paintal (71), however, the evidence that RAR produce reflex bron-choconstriction is inconclusive. It is primarily based on the following indi-rect evidence: (a) Infusion of histamine into isolated bronchial arteries produces bronchoconstriction largely by a vagal reflex (27); and (b) in conditions in which RAR are stimulated, reflex bronchoconstriction is also found [e.g. dust administration (100), histamine administration (27), etc]. However, significant increases in RAR activity can occur without reflex bronchoconstriction (29). The situation is complicated by the fact that histamine stimulates both J receptors (70) and the recently described bron-chial C fibers (17), which are also supplied by the bronchial artery. Admit-tedly C-fiber stimulation is less intense than that of RAR.

Increased activity of RAR may help to explain the hyperreactivity of the airways in certain common airway diseases, in which aerosolized histamine produces more marked increases in airway resistance by a vagal reflex (30, 33, 46). This has been demonstrated, for example, in humans with colds (33), and following ozone exposure (46) or upper respiratory tract infections in dogs (30). There is no direct evidence that this vagal reflex involves RAR. RAR are more responsive to histamine in upper respiratory tract infections (30), but preliminary studies in dogs (80) indicate that ozone administration does not lead to sensitization of the receptor response to histamine, even though ozone does cause airway epithelial damage (87).

VAGALLY MEDIATED AUGMENTATION OF INSPIRATORY NEURAL OUTPUT

Difficulties are encountered in differentiating effects due to RAR from those due to PSR. This is illustrated by the recently rediscovered positive vagal feedback loop (9, 20, 41, 64). While increases in lung inflation cause an increase in phrenic motoneuron discharge, we do not know whether this is mediated by PSR or RAR. The augmentation of neural output is related to the dynamic events during inspiration that stimulate both receptors. In the absence of breathing movements, static changes in volume that stimulate only PSR do not alter the magnitude of phrenic nerve activity (7). The magnitude of the inspiratory facilitation correlates with the level of inspiratory airflow (64), if measured by changes in the rate of rise of phrenic neural output. Other stimuli that facilitate inspiration increase this neural variable. Alternatively, however, phrenic nerve output may follow the pattern of delivery of volume (20). The lung need not be hyperinflated to observe this phenomenon (64). While this is somewhat against the RAR mediating this effect, it does not exclude this possibility since certain of the RAR have relatively low thresholds (42). Phrenic augmentation has been demonstrated during both negative and positive pressure ventilation (64). Preliminary evidence suggests that this vagally mediated augmentation has more marked effects on intercostal than on phrenic output (35). The action of this particular feedback loop seems to vary among species (41).

The gain of this feedback loop is not constant, as it is increased by either hypercapnia or hypoxia (65). Thus in the interaction between chemical and mechanical control loops there is further evidence of adaptive control.

The central mechanisms underlying this loop are unknown. Lung inflation does produce a small excitatory effect on I alpha neurons (48), which are assumed to be the final motor output to phrenic motoneurons. This excitatory effect was demonstrated during dynamic inflations of the lung, and thus we cannot determine whether it is mediated by the afferent activity from PSR or RAR.

The function of this positive feedback loop is also unknown. Simulation studies of its action in our laboratory indicate that it both accelerates inspiratory volume change in the lung, thereby improving the overall dynamics of the response, and also helps to compensate for the declining efficiency of the diaphragm and increasing stiffness of the lung at higher volumes. This hypothesis has not yet been experimentally tested. Since the feedback loop is positive, an important functional consideration is whether, becoming unstable, it might lead to an explosive increase in lung volume. The system is, however, protected; the positive feedback loop is embedded within an overall negative feedback loop (the inspiratory off-switch), a feature it shares with other physiological positive feedback loops (24, 40).

RECEPTORS INNERVATED BY C FIBERS

Since earlier reviews on this topic (32, 68) the most significant finding in this area is that in addition to the J receptors in the parenchyma there are receptors in the bronchi innervated by C fibers (17). These receptors are perfused by the bronchial rather than pulmonary circulation (17). Thus they show short latency responses to left atrial injection of phenyl digua-

nide, which stimulates the receptors (17). The receptors are found throughout the bronchial tree but have little spontaneous activity during normal
breathing (17). They are not primarily mechanoreceptors since hyperinfla-
tion only minimally stimulates a minority of the receptors while forced
deflation is without effect (17). These receptors are stimulated by chemicals
released in the lung—e.g. histamine (17) and prostaglandins (16, 18). Even
when stimulated the receptors' activity shows no respiratory modulation.
The normal physiological role of these receptors is unknown.

CONCLUSION

Since the previous reviews on pulmonary vagal receptors (32, 68), significant progress has been made in understanding the transduction mechanisms
and reflex effects of the receptors. This progress has been the result of an
approach more quantitative than that of the past.

With respect to transduction mechanisms, studies are beginning to relate
receptor responses of PSR to mechanical events in the bronchial wall. The
studies are still somewhat crude, in that the mechanical variables generally
measured relate to the overall mechanical behavior of the lung. While it is
possible to improve on this in vitro (14), the normal mechanical events in
the airways are lost. These investigations are hampered by lack of information on receptor structure and orientation within the smooth muscle, on the
stresses within different parts of the bronchial tree, and on the distortion
of different components within the bronchial wall as the lungs are ventilated. A quantitative approach to the transduction properties of RAR,
which allows for their relatively poor signal-to-noise ratio, has also been
developed. The total population of receptors can provide information to the
medulla on mechanical events in the lung. There is evidence that the RAR
may have a normal role in control of ventilation.

Studies on vagal reflexes are now oriented to investigating them in detailed neurophysiological terms rather than studying crude overall responses—e.g. tachypnea. This quantitative neurophysiological approach
has been facilitated by studies in paralyzed animals using mechanical pumps
to control lung inflation in phase with the animal's neural respiration. This
approach has produced significant advances in understanding the mechanisms controlling inspiratory duration and is likely to prove equally valuable in investigating the other reflex effects.

ACKNOWLEDGMENT

I acknowledge the help of my colleagues, Dr. R. G. DeLaney, Dr. R. O.
Davies, and Dr. J. Ledlie, for helpful discussions in preparation of this
review. The original research reported is supported in part by grants HL–
08805 and HL–24542.

NOTE ADDED IN PROOF   With respect to vagally mediated augmentation of inspiratory neural output, there is evidence that static increases in lung volume can excite phrenic and intercostal nerve activity (Dimarco, A. F. et al. 1980. *Acta Physiol. Scand.* 109:343–44) and preliminary evidence that at least some I_β neurons have excitatory inputs to phrenic motoneurons (Lipski, J., Fedarko, L. 1980. *Proc. Int. Union Physiol. Sci.* XIV:550).

Literature Cited

1. Acker, H. et al. 1977. *Chemoreception in the Carotid Body.* Berlin: Springer
2. Armstrong, D. J., Luck, J. C. 1974. A comparative study of irritant and type J receptors in the cat. *Respir. Physiol.* 21:47–60
3. Baker, J. P. Jr., Remmers, J. E., Younes, M. K. 1979. Graded inspiratory inhibition: specific effects of flow rate. *J. Appl. Physiol.: Respir. Environ. Exer. Physiol.* 46:669–74
4. Bartlett, D. Jr., Sant'Ambrogio, G. 1976. Effects of local and systemic hypercapnia on the discharge of stretch receptors in the airways of the dog. *Respir. Physiol.* 26:91–99
5. Bartlett, D. Jr., Jeffery, P., Sant'Ambrogio, G., Wise, J. C. M. 1976. Location of stretch receptors in the trachea and bronchi of the dog. *J. Physiol. London* 258:409–20
6. Bartlett, D. Jr., Sant'Ambrogio, G., Wise, J. C. M. 1976. Transduction properties of tracheal stretch receptors. *J. Physiol. London* 258:421–32
7. Bartoli, A., Bystrzycka, E., Guz, A., Jain, S. K., Noble, M. I. M., Trenchard, D. 1973. Studies of the pulmonary vagal control of central respiratory rhythm in the absence of breathing movements. *J. Physiol. London* 230:449–65
8. Bartoli, A., Cross, B. A., Guz, A., Jain, S. K., Noble, M. I. M., Trenchard, D. W. 1974. The effect of carbon dioxide in the airways and alveoli on ventilation; a vagal reflex studied in the dog. *J. Physiol. London* 240:91–109
9. Bartoli, A., Cross, B. A., Guz, A., Huszczuk, A., Jefferies, R. 1975. The effect of varying tidal volume on the associated phrenic motoneurone output: studies of vagal and chemical feedback. *Respir. Physiol.* 25:135–55
10. Bergren, D. R., Sampson, S. R. 1980. Intrapulmonary rapidly-adapting receptors of the guinea pig. *Fed. Proc.* 39:831
11. Bishop, B. 1974. In *Ventilatory and Phonatary Control Systems*, ed. B. Wyke. London: Oxford Univ. Press.
12. Bradley, G. W., Euler, C. von, Marttila, I., Roos, B. 1975. A model of the central

and reflex inhibition of inspiration in the cat. *Biol. Cybernet.* 19:105–16
13. Bradley, G. W., Noble, M. I. M., Trenchard, D. 1976. The direct effect of pulmonary stretch receptor discharge produced by changing lung carbon dioxide concentration in dogs on cardiopulmonary bypass and its action on breathing. *J. Physiol London* 261:359–73
14. Bradley, G. W., Scheurmier, N. 1977. The transduction properties of tracheal stretch receptors in vitro. *Respir. Physiol.* 31:365–75
15. Cohen, M. I. 1979. Neurogenesis of respiratory rhythm in the mammal. *Physiol. Rev.* 59:1105–73
16. Coleridge, H. M., Coleridge, J. C. G., Ginzel, K. H., Baker, D. G., Banzett, R. G., Morrison, M. A. 1976. Stimulation of "irritant" receptors and afferent C-fibres in the lungs by prostaglandins. *Nature* 264:451–53
17. Coleridge, H. M., Coleridge, J. C. G. 1977. Impulse activity in afferent vagal C-fibres with endings in the intrapulmonary airways of dogs. *Respir. Physiol.* 29:125–42
18. Coleridge, J. C. G., Coleridge, H. M. 1977. Afferent C-fibers and cardiorespiratory chemoreflexes. *Am. Rev. Respir. Dis.* 115:251–60 (Suppl.)
19. Coleridge, H. M., Coleridge, J. C. G., Banzett, R. 1978. Effect of CO_2 on afferent vagal endings in the canine lung. *Respir. Physiol.* 34:135–51
20. Cross, B. A., Jones, P. W., Guz, A. 1980. The role of vagal afferent information during inspiration in determining phrenic motoneurone output. *Respir. Physiol.* 39:149–67
21. D'Angelo, E. 1978. Central and direct vagal dependent control of expiratory duration in anesthetized rabbits. *Respir. Physiol.* 34:103–19
22. D'Angelo, E. 1979. Mechanisms controlling inspiration studied by electrical vagal stimulations in rabbits. *Respir. Physiol.* 38:185–202
23. Das, R. M., Jeffery, P. K., Widdicombe, J. G. 1978. The epithelial innervation of

the lower respiratory tract of the cat. *J. Anat.* 126:123–31

24. Davie, E. L., Kirby, E. P. 1973. Molecular mechanisms in blood coagulation. *Curr. Top. Cell. Reg.* 7:51–86

25. Davies, A., Dixon, M., Callanan, D., Huszczuk, A., Widdicombe, J. G., Wise, J. C. M. 1978. Lung reflexes in rabbits during pulmonary stretch block by sulphur dioxide. *Respir. Physiol.* 34:83–101

26. Davis, H. L., Fowler, W. S., Lambert, E. H. 1956. Effect of volume and rate of inflation and deflation on transpulmonary pressure and responses of pulmonary stretch receptors. *Am. J. Physiol.* 187:558–66

27. DeKock, M. A., Nadel, J. A., Zwi, S., Colebatch, H. J. H., Olsen, C. R. 1966. New method for perfusing bronchial arteries: histamine bronchoconstriction and apnea. *J. Appl. Physiol.* 21:185–94

28. DeLaney, R. G., Pack, A. I., Fishman, A. P. 1980. Quantitation of pulmonary rapidly-adapting receptor function. *Fed. Proc.* 39:953

29. Dixon, M., Jackson, D. M., Richards, I. M. 1979. The effects of histamine, acetylcholine and 5-hydroxytryptamine on lung mechanics and irritant receptors in the dog. *J. Physiol. London* 287:393–403

30. Dixon, M., Jackson, D. M., Richards, I. M. 1979. The effect of a respiratory tract infection on histamine-induced changes in lung mechanics and irritant receptor discharge in dogs. *Am. Rev. Respir. Dis.* 120:843–48

31. Fedde, M. R., Gatz, R. N., Slama, H., Scheid, P. 1974. Intrapulmonary CO_2 receptors in the duck. I. Stimulus specificity. *Respir. Physiol.* 22:99–114

32. Fillenz, M., Widdicombe, J. G. 1972. Receptors of the lungs and airways. In *Handbook of Sensory Physiology, Vol. 3, Part 1, Enteroreceptors,* ed. E. Neil, pp. 81–112. Berlin: Springer

33. Empey, D. W., Laitinen, L. A., Jacobs, L., Gold, W. M., Nadel, J. A. 1976. Mechanisms of bronchial hyperreactivity in normal subjects after upper respiratory tract infection. *Am. Rev. Respir. Dis.* 113:131–39

34. Euler, C. von. 1977. The functional organization of the respiratory phase-switching mechanisms. *Fed. Proc.* 36:2375–80

35. Euler, C. von. 1980. Afferent input to the solitary tract respiratory neurons from pulmonary mechanoreceptors and from arterial chemoreceptors. In *The Role of Nuclei Tractus Solitarii in the Central Regulation of the Respiratory and Cardiovascular System.* Heidelberg: Int. Workshop

36. Gardner, W. N. 1977. The relation between tidal volume and inspiratory and expiratory times during steady-state carbon dioxide inhalation in man. *J. Physiol. London* 272:591–611

37. Glogowska, M., Richardson, P. S., Widdicombe, J. G., Winning, A. J. 1972. The role of the vagus nerves, peripheral chemoreceptors and other afferent pathways in the genesis of augmented breaths in cats and rabbits. *Respir. Physiol.* 16:179–96

38. Gold, W. M., Kessler, G. F., Yu, D. Y. C. 1972. Role of vagus nerves in experimental asthma in allergic dogs. *J. Appl. Physiol.* 33:719–25

39. Hertz, B. C., Ledlie, J. F., Murphy, D. M. F., Pack, A. I., Fishman, A. P. 1980. Histamine induced increases in respiratory output in the absence of changes in airway resistance. *Am. Rev. Respir. Dis.* 121:352 (Abstr.)

40. Hodgkin, A. L., Huxley, A. F. 1952. A quantitative description of membrane current and its application to conduction and excitation in nerve. *J. Physiol. London* 117:500–44

41. Huszczuk, A., Janowska, L., Kulesza, J., Ryba, M. 1977. Studies on reflex control of breathing in pigs and baboons. *Acta Neurobiol. Exp.* 37:275–98

42. Knowlton, G. C., Larrabee, M. G. 1946. A unitary analysis of pulmonary volume receptors. *Am. J. Physiol.* 147:100–14

43. Knox, C. K. 1973. Characteristics of inflation and deflation reflexes during expiration in the cat. *J. Neurophysiol.* 36:284–95

44. Knox, C. K. 1979. Reflex and central mechanisms controlling expiratory duration. In *Central Nervous Control Mechanisms in Breathing,* ed. C. von Euler, H. Lagercrantz, pp. 203–16. NY: Permagon

45. Ledlie, J. F., Ogilvie, M., Pack, A. I., Fishman, A. P. 1980. Effect of hypercapnia on inhibition by lung volume of the rate of rise of peripheral expiratory activity. *Fed. Proc.* 39:1075

46. Lee, L. Y., Bleecker, E. R., Nadel, J. A. 1977. Effect of ozone on bronchomotor response to inhaled histamine aerosol in dogs. *J. Appl. Physiol.: Respir. Environ. Exer. Physiol.* 43:626–31

47. Leitner, L. M. 1972. Pulmonary mechanoreceptor fibres in the vagus of the domestic fowl. *Respir. Physiol.* 16:232–44

48. Lipski, J., Trzebski, A., Kubin, L. 1979. Excitability changes of dorsal inspiratory neurons during lung inflations as studied by measurement of antidromic invasion latencies. *Brain Res.* 161:25–38

49. Lloyd, T. C. Jr. 1978. Reflex effects of lung inflation and inhalation of halothane, ether, and ammonia. *J. Appl. Physiol.: Respir. Environ. Exer. Physiol.* 45:212–18

50. Lloyd, T. C. Jr. 1979. Effects of extrapulmonary airway distension on breathing in anesthetized dogs. *J. Appl. Physiol.: Respir. Environ. Exer. Physiol.* 46:890–996

51. Loeschcke, H. H., ed. 1976. *Acid Base Homeostasis of the Brain Extracellular Fluid and the Respiratory Control System.* Stutgart: Thieme

52. Marino, P. L., Davies, R. O., Pack, A. I., Fishman, A. P. 1981. The responses of I beta cells to increases in the rate of lung inflation. *Brain Res.* (accepted for publication)

53. Martin, H. B., Proctor, D. F. 1958. Pressure volume measurements on dog bronchi. *J. Appl. Physiol.* 13:337–43

54. Matthews, B. H. C. 1933. Nerve endings in mammalian muscle. *J. Physiol. London* 78:1–53

55. Mills, J. E., Sellick, H., Widdicombe, J. G. 1969. Activity of lung irritant receptors in pulmonary microembolism, anaphylaxis, and drug induced bronchoconstriction. *J. Physiol. London* 203:337–57

56. Mills, J. E., Sellick, H., Widdicombe, J. G. 1970. Epithelial irritant receptors in the lungs. In *Ciba Foundation Symposium, Breathing: Hering-Breuer Centenary Symposium,* ed. R. Porter, pp. 77–92. London: Churchill

57. Miserocchi, G., Mortola, J., Sant'Ambrogio, G. 1973. Localization of pulmonary stretch receptors in the airways of the dog. *J. Physiol. London* 235:775–82

58. Miserocchi, G., Sant'Ambrogio, G. 1974. Distribution of pulmonary stretch receptors in the intrapulmonary airways of the dog. *Respir. Physiol.* 21:71–75

59. Miserocchi, G., Sant'Ambrogio, G. 1974. Responses of pulmonary stretch receptors to static pressure inflations. *Respir. Physiol.* 21:77–85

60. Mortola, J., Sant'Ambrogio, G., Clement, M. G. 1975. Localization of irritant receptors in the airways of the dog. *Respir. Physiol.* 24:107–14

61. Mortola, J. P., Sant'Ambrogio, G. 1979. Mechanics of the trachea and behavior of its slowly adapting stretch receptors. *J. Physiol. London* 286:577–90

62. Mustafa, M. E. K. Y., Purves, M. J. 1972. The effect of CO_2 upon discharge from slowly adapting stretch receptors in the lungs of rabbits. *Respir. Physiol.* 16:197–212

63. Nadel, J. A., Phillipson, E. A., Fishman, N. H., Hickey, R. F. 1973. Regulation of respiration by bronchopulmonary receptors in conscious dogs. *Acta Neurobiol. Exp.* 33:33–50

64. Pack, A. I., DeLaney, R. G., Fishman, A. P. 1981. Augmentation of phrenic neural activity by increased rate of inflation. *J. Appl. Physiol.: Respir. Environ. Exer. Physiol.* (In press)

65. Pack, A. I., DeLaney, R. G., Fishman, A. P. 1979. Interaction between chemical drive and airflow in determining phrenic neural output. *Fed. Proc.* 38:1299

66. Pack, A. I., DeLaney, R. G., Fishman, A. P. 1979. Phrenic neural output in pneumothorax. *Am. Rev. Respir. Dis.* 119:345 (Abstr.)

67. Pack, A. I., Davies, R. O., Marino, P. L., Fishman, A. P. 1980. Effects of high frequency oscillatory airflow on control of inspiratory duration. *Fed. Proc.* 39:1075

68. Paintal, A. S. 1973. Vagal sensory receptors and their reflex effects. *Physiol. Rev.* 53:159–227

69. Paintal, A. S., ed. 1976. *Morphology and Mechanisms of Chemoreceptors.* New Delhi: Vallabhbai Patel Chest Inst. Univ. Delhi

70. Paintal, A. S. 1974. Fluid pump of type J receptors of the cat. *J. Physiol. London* 238:53–54P

71. Paintal, A. S. 1977. The nature and effects of sensory inputs into the respiratory centers. *Fed. Proc.* 36:2428–32

72. Pedley, T. J., Schroter, R. C., Sudlow, M. F. 1977. Gas flow and mixing in the airways. In *Bioengineering Aspects of the Lung,* ed. J. B. West, pp. 163–265. NY: Marcel Dekker

73. Polacheck, J., Remmers, J., Younes, M. 1978. Effect of volume on expiratory neural output. *Fed. Proc.* 37:806

74. Osborne, J. L., Burger, R. E. 1974. Intrapulmonary chemoreceptors in *Gallus domesticus. Respir. Physiol.* 22:77–85

75. Osborne, J. L., Burger, R. E., Stoll, P. J. 1977. Dynamic responses of CO_2-sensitive avian intrapulmonary chemoreceptors. *Am. J. Physiol.* 233:R15–22

76. Osborne, J. L., Mitchell, G. S. 1977. Regulation of arterial pCO_2 during inhalation of CO_2 in chickens. *Respir. Physiol.* 31:357–64

77. Remmers, J. E., Bartlett, D. Jr. 1977. Reflex control of expiratory airflow and duration. *J. Appl. Physiol.* 42:80–87

78. Reynolds, L. D. 1962. Characteristics of an inspiration augmenting reflex in anesthetized cats. *J. Appl. Physiol.* 17:683–88

79. Sampson, S. R., Vidruk, E. H. 1975. Properties of "irritant receptors" in canine lung. *Respir. Physiol.* 25:9–22

80. Sampson, S. R., Vidruk, E. H., Bergren, D. R., Dumont, C., Lee, L. Y. 1978. Effects of ozone exposure on responsiveness of intrapulmonary rapidly adapting receptors to bronchoactive agents in dogs. *Fed. Proc.* 37:712

81. Sampson, S. R., Vidruk, E. H. 1979. The nature of the receptor mediating stimulant effects of histamine on rapidly adapting vagal afferents in the lungs. *J. Physiol. London* 287:509–18

82. Sant'Ambrogio, F., Sant'Ambrogio, G., Mortola, J. P. 1979. Reflex influences from the extrathoracic trachea during airway occlusion. *Respir. Physiol.* 36:327–36

83. Sant'Ambrogio, G., Miserocchi, G., Mortola, J. 1974. Transient responses of pulmonary stretch receptors in the dog to inhalation of carbon dioxide. *Respir. Physiol.* 22:191–97

84. Sant'Ambrogio, G., Mortola, J. P. 1977. Behavior of slowly adapting stretch receptors in the extrathoracic trachea of the dog. *Respir. Physiol.* 31:377–85

85. Sant'Ambrogio, G., Remmers, J. E., Groot, W. J. De, Callas, G., Mortola, J. P. 1978. Localization of rapidly-adapting receptors in the trachea and main stem bronchus of the dog. *Respir. Physiol.* 33:359–66

86. Sant'Ambrogio, G., Mortola, J. P., Sant'Ambrogio, F. B. 1980. Response of tracheal slowly adapting stretch receptors to longitudinal forces. *Respir. Physiol.* 41:323–32

87. Scheel, L. D., Dobrogorski, O. J., Mountain, J. T., Svirbely, J. L., Stokinger, H. E. 1959. Physiologic, biochemical, immunologic and pathologic changes following ozone exposure. *J. Appl. Physiol.* 14:67–80

88. Schoener, E. P., Frankel, H. M. 1972. Effect of hyperthermia and $PaCO_2$ on the slowly adapting pulmonary stretch receptor. *Am. J. Physiol.* 222:68–72

89. Schroter, R. C., Sudlow, M. F. 1969. Flow patterns in models of human bronchial airways. *Respir. Physiol.* 7:341–55

90. Sellick, H., Widdicombe, J. G. 1969. The activity of lung irritant receptors during pneumothorax, hyperpnoea and pulmonary vascular congestion. *J. Physiol. London* 203:359–81

91. Sellick, H., Widdicombe, J. G. 1970. Vagal deflation and inflation reflexes mediated by lung irritant receptors. *Q. J. Exp. Physiol.* 55:153–63

92. Sellick, H., Widdicombe, J. G. 1971. Stimulation of lung irritant receptors by cigarette smoke, carbon dust and histamine aerosol. *J. Appl. Physiol.* 31:15–19

93. Stein, R. B. 1974. Peripheral control of movement. *Physiol. Rev.* 54:215–43

94. Sullivan, C. E., Read, D. J. C. 1975. Pulmonary flow receptors—a new hypothesis for the regulation of breathing. *Proc. Aust. Physiol. Pharmacol. Soc.* 6:83

95. Tisi, G. M., Wolfe, W. G., Fallat, R. J., Nadel, J. A. 1970. Effects of O_2 and CO_2 on airway smooth muscle following pulmonary vascular occlusion. *J. Appl. Physiol.* 28:570–73

96. Vidruk, E. H., Hahn, H. L., Nadel, J. A., Sampson, S. R. 1977. Mechanisms by which histamine stimulates rapidly adapting receptors in dog lungs. *J. Appl. Physiol.: Respir. Environ. Exer. Physiol.* 43:397–402

97. Walker, J. L. Jr., Brown, A. M. 1970. Unified account of the variable effects of carbon dioxide on nerve cells. *Science* 167:1502–4

98. Weibel, E. R. 1963. *Morphometry of the Human Lung.* Berlin: Springer

99. Widdicombe, J. G. 1961. The activity of pulmonary stretch receptors during bronchoconstriction, pulmonary oedema, atelectasis and breathing against a resistance. *J. Physiol. London* 159:436–50

100. Widdicombe, J. G., Kent, D. C., Nadel, J. A. 1962. Mechanism of bronchoconstriction during inhalation of dust. *J. Appl. Physiol.* 17:613–16

101. Widdicombe, J. G. 1977. Studies on afferent airway innervation. *Am. Rev. Respir. Dis.* 115:99–105 (Suppl.)

102. Winning, A. J., Widdicombe, J. G. 1976. The effect of lung reflexes on the pattern of breathing in cats. *Respir. Physiol.* 27:253–66

103. Younes, M. K., Remmers, J. E., Baker, J. 1978. Characteristics of inspiratory inhibition by phasic volume feedback in cats. *J. Appl. Physiol.: Respir. Environ. Exer. Physiol.* 45:80–86

104. Zackon, H., Despas, P. J., Anthonisen, N. R. 1976. Occlusion pressure responses in asthma and chronic obstructive pulmonary disease. *Am. Rev. Respir. Dis.* 114:917–27

Ann. Rev. Physiol. 1981. 43:91–104

CENTRAL DETERMINANTS
OF RESPIRATORY RHYTHM

♦1299

Morton I. Cohen

Department of Physiology, Albert Einstein College of Medicine, Bronx,
New York 10461

In recent years there has been much interest in the central neural mechanisms that generate respiratory rhythm in the mammal; a 1978 symposium (84) reveals the current preoccupations of investigators. In the present paper, I consider selected aspects of the problem; more detailed discussions can be found in a recent comprehensive review (20).

Recordings of efferent phrenic discharge (the indicator of respiratory output most commonly used in neurophysiological studies) show several major features that require explanation [(20), Figure 1]: (*a*) the abrupt onset of phrenic activity marking the end of the expiratory (E) phase and the start of the inspiratory (I) phase; (*b*) the augmenting pattern of phrenic activity; and (*c*) the abrupt decline of phrenic activity marking the onset of the E phase. The augmenting pattern of I muscle activity results in a ramp waveform of tidal volume and intrapleural pressure. A similar augmenting pattern is seen in E nerve discharge (68).

Rhythmic discharge patterns such as those of respiratory neurons could arise from pacemaker cells, from network interactions, or from both. In order to determine if a cell has pacemaker properties it is necessary to isolate it completely from humoral and synaptic inputs (1, 16). Since this procedure is extremely difficult for cells in the mammalian nervous system, investigators have preferred the more tractable approach of analyzing possible network interactions that might produce respiratory rhythm.

Three types of interaction between respiratory neurons are suggested by experimental observations: (*a*) reciprocal inhibition, such as inhibition of E neurons by I neurons; (*b*) recurrent inhibition, such as might produce termination of I discharge by a negative-feedback loop involving I "off-switch" neurons; (*c*) recurrent excitation, such as might produce the augmenting discharge patterns of I and E neurons.

0066-4278/81/0315-0091$01.00

RESPIRATORY NEURON POPULATIONS

In order to ascertain which neuron populations are responsible for the properties of respiratory rhythm, microelectrode explorations have been made in different brain-stem regions. These have revealed the presence of different types of respiration-related neurons (RRN), defined as neurons whose spike activity has an oscillation linked to respiratory output (77). In several regions, RRNs are found in relatively high concentration [(20), Figure 5].

Dorsal Respiratory Group (DRG)

The DRG consists of a bilateral concentration of neurons, predominantly of inspiratory augmenting type (peak frequency at the end of I), found in a limited region of the dorsal medulla [0–2 mm rostral to the obex, 2.0–2.8 mm lateral to the midline, and 1.5–2.5 mm ventral to the medullary surface (7, 8, 12, 43, 70, 71, 74, 82)]. This region corresponds to the anatomically designated ventrolateral nucleus of tractus solitarius (vlNTS) (44). Most ($\sim 80\%$) of these neurons project contralaterally to cervical levels of the spinal cord (8, 12, 83), and some project to thoracic levels (12). Further, about two thirds of these I neurons monosynaptically excite contralateral phrenic motoneurons, as shown by crosscorrelation of unit vs phrenic activity (22, 29, 30).

The I neurons of the DRG have been classified into two functional populations on the basis of responses to pulmonary stretch receptor (PSR) activation produced by inflations delivered during either the E phase (8, 43, 80) or the I phase (21, 82). The latter type of experimental test, which preserves the normally occurring time relation between I discharge and lung volume increase, involves the use of a cycle-triggered pump system (26) where efferent phrenic discharge controls the delivery of lung inflation during the I phase in a paralyzed animal. With this system, the effects of PSR inputs during I are evaluated by withholding inflation or by changing the magnitude of inflation. (a) I_α neurons are not directly affected by inflation: when inflation is withheld, although there is a lengthening of burst duration (Breuer-Hering I-inhibitory reflex), there is no change in the slope of frequency augmentation for most of the I phase. In some cases, inflation tests reveal the existence of a graded inhibition by PSRs near the end of the I phase. These responses are similar to those observed in phrenic discharge. (b) I_β neurons are excited by PSR inputs, as shown by the reduction of their discharge frequency when inflation is withheld (21, 26). Thus, these neurons receive inputs from both PSRs and the central I pattern generator, since their discharges have an I pattern even in the absence of lung inflation. The

PSR input is probably monosynaptic, as indicated by the latency of the response to vagal electrical stimulation (61). On the basis of their responses to lung inflation, it has been suggested that the I_β neurons are inhibitory interneurons of the Breuer-Hering I-inhibitory reflex (81, 82).

A subpopulation of the I_β neurons, the late-firing I_β neurons (4, 21), start to fire a short time before the end of the I phase; when inflation is withheld, the time of onset of discharge is delayed concomitantly with the lengthening of I phase duration (T_I). On the basis of this response, it has been suggested that these neurons might function as I "off-switch" neurons.

Another population found in the DRG consists of the pump (P) neurons (8, 70, 71). The discharges of these neurons are completely determined by lung volume—i.e. they receive inputs from PSRs but receive no inputs from the central I pattern generator. They are not primary vagal afferents, since they can be excited synaptically by superior laryngeal afferents (8). Neurons of this type may function as summing points for diverse afferent inputs that influence respiratory rhythm.

Finally, about 5% of the DRG neurons have early-expiratory discharge patterns (8, 25, 82). These neurons start firing only after the cessation of phrenic discharge and reach their peak frequency early in the E phase; thereafter, discharge frequency diminishes to reach zero level before the end of the E phase. The rate of decrement of discharge is slowed during the lengthening of E phase duration (T_E) produced by two types of maneuver (25): (a) withholding of lung inflation during the preceding I phase; (b) delivery of lung inflation during the E phase. This association between increased discharge and lengthened T_E has led to the suggestion that such neurons may function to determine T_E by inhibiting the mechanisms that promote the onset of the I phase (25).

Ventral Respiratory Group (VRG)

The VRG consists of a continuous longitudinal bilateral column of densely packed RRNs, located in the ventrolateral region of the brain stem (3–4 mm lateral to the midline and 3–5 mm ventral to the surface) and extending from the level of the first cervical roots to the level of the middle pons (7, 12, 46, 47, 74, 78). In the region rostral to the obex, I neurons are more numerous than E neurons; however, an appreciable admixture of E neurons is found in the most rostral portion of the medulla, at the level of the retrofacial nucleus (12, 46). In the region around the obex there is a mixture of I and E neurons, while in the region caudal to the obex predominantly E neurons are found (46). Because of the large anatomical extent of the VRG column, it is likely that the I neurons, as well as the E neurons, comprise heterogeneous populations.

VRG I NEURONS   Three different populations of I neurons can be classified on the basis of antidromic stimulation and crosscorrelation studies:
(a) Vagal (V) motoneurons have been identified by antidromic stimulation
of the ipsilateral vagus or recurrent laryngeal nerves (12, 52). (b) As shown
by antidromic spinal cord stimulation, bulbospinal (BS) neurons project,
predominantly contralaterally, to cervical and thoracic levels (12, 46). By
use of crosscorrelation analysis, it has been found that some of these I
neurons excite phrenic motoneurons, others excite external intercostal
motoneurons, and still others project to both types of motoneuron (29).
Neurons of types (a) and (b) have been called I_γ neurons by Mitchell (51).
Lung inflation tests (J. L. Feldman & M. I. Cohen, unpublished observations) show that these neurons usually react to PSR inputs in a manner
similar to the I_α neurons of the DRG. (c) Propriobulbar (PB) neurons:
Spinal cord projections of these neurons cannot be demonstrated by antidromic stimulation. An interesting subclass of these neurons consists of the
"early-burst" I neurons (47) or I_δ neurons (52). These have their peak
discharge frequency at the start of the I phase, and thereafter the discharge
decrements to zero level before the end of the I phase. Lung inflation
produces a graded inhibition of their discharge [(21), Figure 2D]. Since the
discharge patterns of these neurons are similar to the hyperpolarization
patterns of caudal VRG E neurons (53), it has been suggested that they
function to inhibit E neurons (47).

ROSTRAL VRG E NEURONS   Although I neurons predominate in the
rostral VRG, an appreciable number of E neurons can be found (25, 46).
Some of these have early-E (decrementing) patterns, while others have
late-E (augmenting) patterns (peak frequency at the end of E). By use of
antidromic vagal stimulation, some of the early-E neurons can be identified
as vagal motoneurons (12, 46). In recent studies (42, 51), a concentrated
population of late-E neurons (dubbed the Bötzinger Complex), which
project to the contralateral DRG, has been found in the rostral VRG ($\sim$
3.5–4.5 mm rostral to the obex). In another study (25), the typical response
of these rostral late-E neurons to inflations applied during the E phase was
inhibition of activity.

CAUDAL VRG E NEURONS   The VRG region 1–5 mm caudal to the obex
contains predominantly late-E neurons (2, 3, 46). By spinal cord antidromic
stimulation, it has been shown that almost all these neurons project contralaterally to thoracic levels (46). Crosscorrelation analyses show that
many of these neurons monosynaptically excite internal intercostal
motoneurons (38), both ipsilaterally and contralaterally located (D. Sommer & M. I. Cohen, unpublished observations). The most common response

of the caudal medullary E neurons, as well as of internal intercostal motoneurons, to maintained lung inflation applied during E was inhibition of activity (reduction of the slope of frequency augmentation) together with prolongation of activity and higher peak frequency at the end of E (73); similar responses are observed in abdominal muscle and nerve activity (41, 58). In addition a "reversal effect" was observed: Application of smaller inflations during E did not produce inhibition, but rather produced a prolongation of activity with little or no change of slope of frequency augmentation; however the prolongation of T_E increased monotonically with degree of inflation (73). This dissociation between change of T_E and change of neuron discharge patterns suggests that this neuron population may not be primarily involved in determination of T_E.

Pneumotaxic Center (PC)

In the region of the dorsolateral rostral pons where lesions produce apneusis (27, 65), numerous RRNs can be recorded in vagotomized cats (9–11, 23). This region contains two anatomically designated nuclei. (*a*) The nucleus parabrachialis medialis (NPBM) contains mainly neurons with tonic discharge and superimposed respiratory modulation, e.g. a common pattern consists of a combination of augmenting higher-frequency discharge during I and steady lower-frequency discharge during E. In addition, the NPBM contains numerous neurons having phase-spanning patterns, in which peak discharge frequency is centered symmetrically around the I-E or E-I phase transition. These tonic and phase-spanning patterns contrast markedly with the patterns that are common in the medulla. (*b*) The more laterally located Kölliker-Fuse (KF) nucleus contains numerous I neurons with phasic discharge patterns similar to those of medullary and spinal I neurons.

After the initial report of the occurrence of numerous RRNs in the PC region (23), controversy arose; other investigators were unable to find such neurons (67). One possible explanation of this discrepancy was the use of deep anesthesia, which may have depressed activity in the region (85). However, the main factor probably responsible for difficulties in finding RRNs in the PC region is the recently discovered inhibition by PSR activity of the respiratory modulation of PC neurons (26). As a result of this influence, investigators who recorded in animals with intact vagi were unable to find respiratory-modulated neurons, whereas others found many such neurons in vagotomized animals, where this inhibition was removed.

Recently, two studies (45, 72) have reported recordings of RRNs in the NPBM of chronic animals. These were found in spite of the intactness of the vagi, a condition where afferent activity might have been expected to inhibit respiratory modulation. Presumably, other factors (such as state of arousal) may also affect the respiratory modulation of neurons in the NPBM.

Reticular Formation (RF)

In unanesthetized or lightly anesthetized animals, RRNs are found at widely scattered sites throughout the bulbopontine reticular formation (RF), i.e. the medial portion of the brain stem (78). In such preparations, administration of small doses of pentobarbital results in elimination or marked reduction of this activity (32, 33). In a comparison of recordings from unanesthetized vs lightly anesthetized animals, Caille et al (15) found that light barbiturate anesthesia markedly reduced the number of RRNs, as well as the degree of respiratory modulation, in the bulbopontine RF; it did not reduce respiratory-modulated activity in the NPBM, the DRG and VRG, and several cranial nerve (Vth and VIIth) nuclei; and in the KF nucleus it even increased respiratory modulation. On the basis of this observation, it was suggested (15, 31) that RRN activity in the RF produces facilitatory effects on the primary respiratory rhythm generator; this type of influence could account for the recovery from apneusis observed in chronic animals (66). In addition, changes of RRN activity in the RF could be the basis of the fluctuations of respiratory neuron activity in the NPBM (45, 72) and in the medulla (56) that are related to sleep-waking state.

Respiratory-modulated unit activity has also been observed in the diencephalon and mesencephalon (36, 79), including subthalamic and thalamic regions. Since section at the pontomesencephalic junction does not change respiratory rhythm, these rostral respiratory-modulated neurons are not involved in rhythm generation per se; rather they may function to coordinate respiration with locomotor and autonomic activities.

INTERACTIONS BETWEEN RESPIRATORY NEURONS

The connections and interactions between brain stem respiratory neurons have been studied by three methods: (a) histochemical (HRP or tritiated amino acid) labelling; (b) antidromic stimulation; (c) crosscorrelation analysis. The latter two methods have also been used to ascertain efferent projections of medullary I and E neurons.

PC-Medullary Connections

The connections between neurons in the PC region and neurons in medullary respiratory regions (DRG and VRG) have been studied by histochemical labelling. It has been found that afferent projections to NPBM and KF from the DRG (region of vlNTS) are sparse, but projections from the VRG region of the ventrolateral medulla are numerous (34). Similarly, efferent projections from the NPBM and KF regions to the DRG are much less numerous than those to the VRG (14, 24). In addition, fibers from the PC region project to the obex region of the medulla (59) and to the cervical spinal cord (40, 75).

DRG-VRG Connections

The connections between the DRG and VRG have been studied by Merrill using antidromic mapping (48). He found numerous projections, predominantly ipsilateral, from the NTS I neurons to the VRG region of I neurons, but found no projections in the reverse direction. However, in a study where HRP injections were made into DRG sites having dense I unit activity, Kalia et al (35) found labelling in an aggregate of cells located in the contralateral VRG about 3.5–4.5 mm rostral to the obex (region of the retrofacial nucleus). More recently, recordings in this region have revealed the presence of late-E neurons that send axons to the contralateral vlNTS region, as shown by antidromic stimulation; and this group of neurons has been dubbed the Bötzinger Complex (42, 51).

VRG Connections

Antidromic mapping has also revealed connections between neurons in different regions of the VRG [(50), Figure 2]. The early-I (decrementing) neurons of the rostral VRG project heavily to the contralateral caudal VRG, where E neurons are concentrated, as well as to sites in the rostral VRG. The augmenting I neurons found in the rostral VRG also project, both ipsilaterally and contralaterally, to rostral I regions and caudal E regions of the VRG. The existence of projections to the caudal E neurons from both the rostral VRG and the DRG has been demonstrated in a study where HRP injections were made at caudal sites having dense E neuron activity (M. Kalia et al, personal communication at the Workshop on Central Control of Circulation and Respiration, Heidelberg, March 1980). In that study, connections to contralateral caudal E neurons could not be found, confirming the failure to find such connections in an antidromic stimulation study (47).

Short Time Scale Interactions

The functional interactions between respiratory neurons have been studied by crosscorrelation between activities of pairs of neurons or between unit and population activities. The crosscorrelation histogram (CCH) gives the probability of occurrence of one signal at different times relative to the occurrence of the other; and various features of the CCH (peaks, troughs, periodicities) indicate functional relations between the sources of the two signals (37, 55, 57). This method has been applied to analysis of coupling between external intercostal motoneurons (39, 69) and betweeen phrenic motoneurons (30). In those studies, the frequent occurrence of a peak at zero lag in the CCH, indicating increased probability of coincident firings, showed that common inputs to different motoneurons of each population are ubiquitous. These common inputs are derived from descending medullary projections, as revealed by CCHs between medullary neuron and spinal motoneuron activities (22, 29, 30).

Since neurons in widely scattered medullary regions are synchronized on the time scale of the respiratory cycle (seconds) or on a time scale of tens of milliseconds, as revealed by high frequency oscillations (HFO) of I discharge having periods of 9–17 msec (17, 19), various investigators have looked for short time scale correlations between pairs of respiratory neurons of a similar type (e.g. pairs of I or E neurons). In a recent study (28), it was found that such correlations (indicated by a peak in the CCH in a zone of <5 msec duration near zero lag) were quite common for pairs of "adjacent" neurons (neurons recorded with the same microelectrode and therefore situated within 100 μm of each other), but they were rare for pairs of "distant" neurons (neurons recorded with separate microelectrodes on opposite sides of the medulla). A similar rarity of such correlations between distant ipsilateral pairs has been reported for caudal E neurons (49) and for rostral VRG I neurons (76). However, another study (G. Hilaire, personal communication) found that 10 of 25 ipsilateral pairs of DRG I neurons (recorded with separate electrodes) had significant peaks in their CCHs.

Since the various populations of respiratory neurons are synchronized on a long time scale (seconds) or an intermediate time scale (HFO), at least some pairs of distant I neurons or distant E neurons must be monosynaptically connected. The rarity of short time scale correlations suggests that such connections are not uniformly distributed but may involve specific subregions or subpopulations. In contrast, the high incidence of such correlations between neighboring neurons indicates that within a group of neurons there is a high degree of local interaction and/or locally shared inputs. This situation seems to be especially common for DRG I neurons and for caudal E neurons.

Reciprocal Inhibition

The observation that the firing patterns of I and E neurons are reciprocal has suggested that respiratory rhythm is generated in part by reciprocal inhibition (13). Indeed, intracellular recordings from medullary neurons show that I neurons are relatively depolarized during I and relatively hyperpolarized during E, while E neurons are relatively depolarized during E and relatively hyperpolarized during I (53, 54, 60–64).

In order to determine whether the hyperpolarization during the silent phase of a neuron is due to inhibition or disfacilitation, the reversal potential method has been used. It was found by Mitchell & Herbert (54) that intracellular application of hyperpolarizing current in E neurons caused a reversal of the hyperpolarization occurring during I to a depolarization, thus demonstrating that this hyperpolarization was due to IPSPs. However, a similar reversal during E could not be demonstrated in I neurons. More recently, Richter et al (60) found that prolonged chloride injection (20–40 min) produced reversal of the hyperpolarizing wave to a depolarizing wave in both I and E neurons. This effect was observed in 52 of 53 neurons tested, including vagal, BS, and PB neurons (of both I and E types) of the VRG, as well as BS and PB I neurons of the DRG. The reversal effect was particularly easy to obtain in I_β neurons of the DRG; in contrast, for most of the I BS neurons of the DRG and VRG, chloride injection had to continue for a long time before reversal occurred. This slow appearance of reversal was interpreted as indicating that post-synaptic inhibition acts at distant dendritic sites, so that reversal could occur only after a time sufficient for chloride to diffuse to these remote sites. The conclusion of Richter et al (60) was that "reciprocal inhibition between bulbar respiratory neurones does exist and is a general phenomenon."

The possible sources of these inhibitory effects have been suggested by studies of connections between different neuronal groups. The inhibition of caudal VRG E neurons during I could be due to projections, demonstrated by antidromic studies (50), from both the early-I (decrementing) and the late-I (augmenting) neurons of the rostral VRG, as well as due to projections from I neurons of the DRG, demonstrated by a recent HRP study (M. Kalia et al, personal communication, cited above). The sources of the inhibition of DRG I neurons during E have been more obscure. Although axons with augmenting E discharge patterns have been found in the DRG region (60), rostral projections from augmenting E neurons of the caudal VRG could not be demonstrated by antidromic studies (47, 50). Very recently, however, a group of E neurons with augmenting patterns, which project to the contralateral DRG region, has been found in the rostral VRG (42, 51). These neurons, which comprise the Bötzinger Complex, could furnish the inhibitory inputs to DRG I neurons.

Recurrent Inhibition

Reciprocal inhibition is not sufficient to explain the alternation of respiratory phases, since such action if unopposed would tend to keep the respiratory cycle fixed in one or the other phase. Moreover, the termination of activity of late-E neurons typically precedes (by $\sim$ 50 msec) the onset of phrenic activity [(18), Figure 10; D. Sommer & M. I. Cohen, unpublished observations], so that the switching off of these E neurons could not be due to I neurons that have patterns similar to phrenic discharge patterns. A similar situation holds for I termination: Since the discharge of early-E neurons starts after the decline of phrenic discharge (25), the termination of I activity could not be due to inhibition by these early-E neurons.

Therefore, in order to explain the abrupt phase transitions (I → E switching and E → I switching), it has been proposed that recurrent inhibitory actions are operative within each phase and reach critical levels shortly before the phase transition.

I → E SWITCHING   Several current hypotheses (21, 81) on the mechanisms of the I-E phase transition emphasize the role of a recurrent inhibitory loop between I_α and I_β neurons [(20), Figure 15]. These hypotheses are based mainly on the observation that I_β neuron discharge is increased concomitantly with reduction of T_I (produced, for example, by lung inflation). However, those I_β neurons that start firing early in the I phase apparently do not produce inhibitory actions, since the slopes of the phrenic neurogram and of I_α neurons' frequency augmentation during this part of the phase are not affected when I_β neuron firing is changed (21, 26). However, late in the I phase graded inhibition can be produced by lung inflation (5, 6, 86); this effect, as well as the subsequent sharp cutoff of I discharge, could arise from inhibitory actions by the late-onset I_β neurons. The discharge properties of the late I_β neurons (4, 21) are consistent with their being I off-switch neurons, but at present the evidence for such a role is purely correlational.

E → I SWITCHING   The mechanisms responsible for the E-I phase transition are more obscure. A recent plausible hypothesis (21, 25) states that there is a recurrent inhibitory loop between the early-E neurons and systems promoting the onset of the I phase. The discharge of early-E neurons is maximum at the start of E (perhaps partially due to post-inhibitory rebound) and thereafter the discharge decays towards zero level at the end of E. If such neurons exerted inhibitory actions on I neurons, the onset of I neuron discharge would occur when these inhibitory inputs declined sufficiently to allow effective depolarizing actions by excitatory inputs (tonic and/or phasic) to the I neurons.

It is apparent that our knowledge of the mechanisms of respiratory rhythm is still rather primitive. Further progress will undoubtedly rely on both electrophysiological and neuroanatomical methods. In electrophysiological systems analysis, it will probably be useful to frame questions in terms of such concepts as recurrent excitation, reciprocal inhibition, and recurrent inhibition.

Literature Cited

1. Alving, B. O. 1968. Spontaneous activity in isolated somata of *Aplysia* pacemaker neurons. *J. Gen. Physiol.* 51:29–45
2. Bainton, C. R., Kirkwood, P. A. 1979. The effect of carbon dioxide on the tonic and the rhythmic discharges of expiratory bulbospinal neurones. *J. Physiol. London* 296:291–314
3. Baker, J. P. Jr., Frazier, D. T., Hanley, M., Zechman, F. W. Jr. 1979. Behavior of expiratory neurons in response to mechanical and chemical loading. *Respir. Physiol.* 36:337–51
4. Baker, J. P. Jr., Remmers, J. E. 1979. Neuronal correlates of inspiratory off-switching. *Fed. Proc.* 38(3):1229 (Abstr.)
5. Baker, J. P. Jr., Remmers, J. E. 1980. Characteristics of sustained graded inspiratory inhibition by phasic lung volume changes. *J. Appl. Physiol.* 48:302–7
6. Baker, J. P. Jr., Remmers, J. E., Younes, M. K. 1979. Graded inspiratory inhibition: specific effects of flow rate. *J. Appl. Physiol.* 46:669–74
7. Barillot, J. C., Bianchi, A. L. 1979. Évolution de la latence d'envahissement antidromique des neurones respiratoires bulbaires. *J. Physiol. Paris* 75:783–803
8. Berger, A. J. 1977. Dorsal respiratory group neurons in the medulla of cat: spinal projections, responses to lung inflation and superior laryngeal nerve stimulation. *Brain Res.* 135:231–54
9. Bertrand, F., Hugelin, A. 1971. Respiratory synchronizing function of nucleus parabrachialis medialis: pneumotaxic mechanisms. *J. Neurophysiol.* 34:189–207
10. Bertrand, F., Hugelin, A., Vibert, J. F. 1973. Quantitative study of anatomical distribution of respiration related neurons in the pons. *Exp. Brain. Res.* 16:383–99
11. Bertrand, F., Hugelin, A., Vibert, J. F. 1974. A stereologic model of pneumotaxic oscillator based on spatial and temporal distributions of neuronal bursts. *J. Neurophysiol.* 37:91–107
12. Bianchi, A. L. 1971. Localisation et étude des neurones bulbaires respiratoires. Mise en jeu antidromique par stimulation spinale ou vagale. *J. Physiol. Paris* 63:5–40
13. Burns, B. D., Salmoiraghi, G. C. 1960. Repetitive firing of respiratory neurons during their burst activity. *J. Neurophysiol.* 23:27–46
14. Bystrzycka, E. K. 1980. Afferent projections to the dorsal and ventral respiratory nuclei in the medulla oblongata of the cat studied by the horseradish peroxidase technique. *Brain Res.* 185:59–66
15. Caille, D., Vibert, J. F., Bertrand, F., Gromysz, H., Hugelin, A. 1979. Pentobarbitone effects on respiration related units: selective depression of bulbopontine reticular neurones. *Respir. Physiol.* 36:201–16
16. Chen, C. F., von Baumgarten, R., Takeda, R. 1971. Pacemaker properties of completely isolated neurones in *Aplysia californica. Nature New Biol.* 233:27–29
17. Cohen, M. I. 1973. Synchronization of discharge, spontaneous and evoked, between inspiratory neurons. *Acta Neurobiol. Exp.* 33:189–218
18. Cohen, M. I. 1974. The genesis of respiratory rhythmicity. In *Central Rhythmic and Regulation,* ed. W. Umbach, H. P. Koepchen, pp. 15–35. Stuttgart: Hippokrates. 418 pp.
19. Cohen, M. I. 1976. Synaptic relations between inspiratory neurons. In *Respiratory Centres and Afferent Systems,* ed. B. Duron. *Colloq. Inst. Natl. Santé Recherche Méd.* 59:19–29
20. Cohen, M. I. 1979. Neurogenesis of respiratory rhythm in the mammal. *Physiol. Rev.* 59:1105–73
21. Cohen, M. I., Feldman, J. L. 1977. Models of respiratory phase-switching. *Fed. Proc.* 36:2367–74
22. Cohen, M. I., Piercey, M. F., Gootman, P. M., Wolotsky, P. 1974. Synaptic connections between medullary inspiratory neurons and phrenic motoneurons as revealed by cross-correlation. *Brain Res.* 81:319–24
23. Cohen, M. I., Wang, S. C. 1959. Respiratory neuronal activity in pons of cat. *J. Neurophysiol.* 22:33–50
24. Denavit-Saubié, M., Riche, D. 1977. Descending input from the pneumotaxic system to the lateral respiratory nucleus of the medulla. An anatomical study with the horseradish peroxidase techinque. *Neurosci. Lett.* 6:121–26
25. Feldman, J. L., Cohen, M. I. 1978. Relation between expiratory duration and rostral medullary expiratory neuronal discharge. *Brain Res.* 141:172–78
26. Feldman, J. L., Cohen, M. I., Wolotsky, P. 1976. Powerful inhibition of pontine respiratory neurons by pulmonary afferent activity. *Brain Res.* 104:341–46
27. Feldman, J. L., Gautier, H. 1976. Interaction of pulmonary afferents and pneumotaxic center in control of respir-

atory pattern in cats. *J. Neurophysiol.* 39:31–44

28. Feldman, J. L., Sommer, D., Cohen, M. I. 1980. Short time scale correlations between discharges of medullary respiratory neurons. *J. Neurophysiol.* 43:1284–95

29. Hilaire, G., Monteau, R. 1976. Connexions entre les neurones inspiratoires bulbaires et les motoneurones phréniques et intercostaux. *J. Physiol. Paris* 72:987–1000

30. Hilaire, G., Monteau, R. 1979. Facteurs déterminant l'ordre de recrutement des motoneurones phréniques. *J. Physiol. Paris* 75:765–81

31. Hugelin, A. 1977. Anatomical organization of bulbopontine respiratory oscillators. *Fed. Proc.* 36:2390–94

32. Hukuhara, T. Jr. 1973. Neuronal organization of the central respiratory mechanisms in the brain stem of the cat. *Acta Neurobiol. Exp.* 33:219–44

33. Hukuhara, T., Goto, K., Kiguchi, Y., Takano, K. 1979. Unterschiedliche Stabilität respiratorischer Einzelneuronenaktivität im Hirnstamm der Katze. *Jikeikai Med. J.* 26:245–61

34. Kalia, M. 1977. Neuroanatomical organization of the respiratory centers. *Fed. Proc.* 36:2405–11

35. Kalia, M., Feldman, J. L., Cohen, M. I. 1979. Afferent projections to the inspiratory neuronal region of the ventrolateral nucleus of the tractus solitarius in the cat. *Brain Res.* 171:135–41

36. Kastella, K. G., Spurgeon, H. A., Weiss, G. K. 1974. Respiratory-related neurons in anterior hypothalamus of the cat. *Am. J. Physiol.* 227:710–13

37. Kirkwood, P. A. 1979. On the use and interpretation of cross-correlation measurements in the mammalian central nervous system. *J. Neurosci. Meth.* 1:107–32

38. Kirkwood, P. A., Sears, T. A. 1973. Monosynaptic excitation of thoracic expiratory motoneurones from lateral respiratory neurones in the medulla of the cat. *J. Physiol. London* 234:87–89P (Abstr.)

39. Kirkwood, P. A., Sears, T. A. 1978. The synaptic connexions to intercostal motoneurones as revealed by the average common excitation potential. *J. Physiol. London* 275:103–34

40. Kuypers, H. G. J. M., Maisky, V. A. 1977. Funicular trajectories of descending brain stem pathways in cat. *Brain Res.* 136:159–65

41. Ledlie, J. F., Ogilvie, M., Pack, A. I., Fishman, A. P. 1980. Effect of hypercapnia on inhibition by lung volume of the rate of rise of peripheral expiratory activity. *Fed. Proc.* 39(3):1075 (Abstr.)

42. Lipski, J., Merrill, E. G. 1980. Electrophysiological demonstration of the projection from expiratory neurones in rostral medulla to contralateral dorsal respiratory group. *Brain Res.* 197:521–24

43. Lipski, J., Trzebski, A., Kubin, L. 1979. Excitability changes of dorsal inspiratory neurons during lung inflations as studied by measurement of antidromic invasion latencies. *Brain Res.* 161:25–38

44. Loewy, A. D., Burton, H. 1978. Nuclei of the solitary tract: efferent projections to the lower brain stem and spinal cord of the cat. *J. Comp. Neurol.* 181:421–50

45. Lydic, R., Orem, J. 1979. Respiratory neurons of the pneumotaxic center during sleep and wakefulness. *Neurosci. Lett.* 15:187–92

46. Merrill, E. G. 1970. The lateral respiratory neurones of the medulla: their associations with nucleus ambiguus, nucleus retroambigualis, the spinal accessory nucleus and the spinal cord. *Brain Res.* 24:11–28

47. Merrill, E. G. 1974. Finding a respiratory function for the medullary respiratory neurons. In *Essays on the Nervous System,* ed. R. Bellairs, E. G. Gray, pp. 451–86. Oxford: Clarendon

48. Merrill, E. G. 1974. Preliminary studies on nucleus retroambigualis—nucleus of the solitary tract interactions in cats. *J. Physiol. London* 244:54–55P (Abstr.)

49. Merrill, E. G. 1978. Absence of correlations between lateral expiratory neurones in cat. *J. Physiol. London* 276:33–34P (Abstr.)

50. Merrill, E. G. 1979. Is there reciprocal inhibition between medullary inspiratory and expiratory neurones? See Ref. 84, pp. 239–53

51. Merrill, E. G. 1980. Where are the *real* respiratory neurones? *Fed. Proc.* 39:In press

52. Mitchell, R. A. 1977. Location and function of medullary respiratory neurons. *Am. Rev. Resp. Dis.* 115:(Suppl.) 209–16

53. Mitchell, R. A., Herbert, D. A. 1974. The effect of carbon dioxide on the membrane potential of medullary respiratory neurons. *Brain Res.* 75:345–49

54. Mitchell, R. A., Herbert, D. A. 1974. Synchronized high frequency synaptic potentials in medullary respiratory neurons. *Brain Res.* 75:350–55

55. Moore, G. P., Segundo, J. P., Perkel, D. H., Levitan, H. 1970. Statistical signs of synaptic interaction in neurons. *Biophys. J.* 10:876–900

56. Orem, J. 1980. Medullary respiratory neuron activity: relationship to tonic and phasic REM sleep. *J. Appl. Physiol.* 48:54–65

57. Perkel, D. H., Gerstein, G. L., Moore, G. P. 1967. Neuronal spike trains and stochastic point processes. II. Simultaneous spike trains. *Biophys. J.* 7:419–40

58. Polachek, J., Remmers, J., Younes, M. 1978. Effect of volume on expiratory neural output. *Fed. Proc.* 37(3):806 (Abstr.)

59. Riche, D., Denavit-Saubié, M., Champagnat, J. 1979. Pontine afferents to the medullary respiratory system: anatomofunctional correlation. *Neurosci. Lett.* 13:151–55

60. Richter, D. W., Camerer, H., Meesmann, M., Röhrig, N. 1979. Studies on the synaptic interconnection between bulbar respiratory neurones of cats. *Pflügers Arch.* 380:245–57

61. Richter, D. W., Camerer, H., Röhrig, N. 1979. Monosynaptic transmission from lung stretch receptor afferents to R_β-neurones. See Ref. 84, pp. 267–70

62. Richter, D. W., Camerer, H., Sonnhof, U. 1978. Changes in extracellular potassium during the spontaneous activity of medullary respiratory neurones. *Pflügers Arch.* 376:139–49

63. Richter, D. W., Heyde, F. 1975. Accommodative reactions of medullary respiratory neurons of the cat. *J. Neurophysiol.* 38:1172–80

64. Richter, D. W., Heyde, F., Gabriel, M. 1975. Intracellular recordings from different types of medullary respiratory neurons of the cat. *J. Neurophysiol.* 38:1162–71

65. St. John, W. M., Glasser, R. L., King, R. A. 1971. Apneustic breathing after vagotomy in cats with chronic pneumotaxic center lesions. *Respir. Physiol.* 12:239–50

66. St. John, W. M., Glasser, R. L., King, R. A. 1972. Rhythmic respiration in awake vagotomized cats with chronic pneumotaxic area lesions. *Respir. Physiol.* 15:233–44

67. Salmoiraghi, G. C. 1963. Functional organization of brain stem respiratory neurons. *Ann. NY Acad. Sci.* 109: 571–82

68. Sears, T. A. 1964. Efferent discharges in alpha and fusimotor fibres of intercostal nerves of the cat. *J. Physiol. London* 174:295–315

69. Sears, T. A., Stagg, D. 1976. Short-term synchronization of intercostal motoneurone activity. *J. Physiol. London* 263:357–81

70. Sessle, B. J., Greenwood, L. F., Lund, J. P., Lucier, G. E. 1978. Effects of upper respiratory tract stimuli on respiration and single respiratory neurons in the adult cat. *Exp. Neurol.* 61:245–59

71. Shannon, R. 1980. Intercostal and abdominal muscle afferent influence on medullary dorsal respiratory group neurons. *Respir. Physiol.* 39:73–94

72. Sieck, G. C., Harper, R. M. 1980. Pneumotaxic area neuronal discharge during sleep-waking states in the cat. *Exp. Neurol.* 67:79–102

73. Sommer, D., Feldman, J. L., Cohen, M. I. 1979. Responses of caudal medullary expiratory neurons to lung inflation. *Fed. Proc.* 38(3):1144 (Abstr.)

74. Taylor, E. K., Duffin, J., Vachon, B. R., McCracken, D. H. 1978. The recruitment times and firing patterns of the medullary respiratory neurones of the cat. *Respir. Physiol.* 34:247–66

75. Tohyama, M., Sakai, K., Touret, M., Salvert, D., Jouvet, M. 1979. Spinal projections from the lower brain stem in the cat as demonstrated by the horseradish peroxidase technique. II. Projections from the dorsolateral pontine tegmentum and raphe nuclei. *Brain Res.* 176:215–31

76. Vachon, B. R., Duffin, J. 1978. Cross-correlation of medullary respiratory neurons in the cat. *Exp. Neurol.* 61:15–30

77. Vibert, J. F., Bertrand, F., Denavit-Saubié, M., Hugelin, A. 1976. Discharge patterns of bulbo-pontine respiratory unit populations in cat. *Brain Res.* 114:211–25

78. Vibert, J. F., Bertrand, F., Denavit-Saubié, M., Hugelin, A. 1976. Three dimensional representation of bulbo-pontine respiratory networks architecture from unit density maps. *Brain Res.* 114: 227–44

79. Vibert, J. F., Caille, D., Bertrand, F., Gromysz, H., Hugelin, A. 1979. Ascending projection from the respiratory centre to mesencephalon and diencephalon. *Neurosci. Lett.* 11:29–33

80. von Baumgarten, R., Kanzow, E. 1958. The interaction of two types of inspiratory neurons in the region of the tractus solitarius of the cat. *Arch. Ital. Biol.* 96:361–73

81. von Euler, C. 1977. The functional organization of the respiratory phase-

switching mechanisms. *Fed. Proc.* 36: 2375–80

82. von Euler, C., Hayward, J. N., Marttila, I., Wyman, R. J. 1973. Respiratory neurones of the ventrolateral nucleus of the solitary tract of cat: vagal input, spinal connections and morphological identification. *Brain Res.* 61:1–22

83. von Euler, C., Hayward, J. N., Marttila, I., Wyman, R. J. 1973. The spinal connections of the inspiratory neurones of the ventrolateral nucleus of the cat's tractus solitarius. *Brain Res.* 61:23–33

84. von Euler, C., Lagercrantz, H., eds. 1979. *Central Nervous Control Mechanisms in Breathing. Physiological and Clinical Aspects of Regular, Periodic and Irregular Breathing in Adults and in the Perinatal Period.* Oxford: Pergamon. 508 pp.

85. Wang, S. C., Ngai, S. H. 1963. Respiration coordinating mechanism of the brain stem—a few controversial points. *Ann. NY Acad. Sci.* 109:550–59

86. Younes, M. K., Remmers, J. E., Baker, J. 1978. Characteristics of inspiratory inhibition by phasic volume feedback in cats. *J. Appl. Physiol.* 45:80–86

Ann. Rev. Physiol. 1981. 43:105–120
Copyright © 1981 by Annual Reviews Inc. All rights reserved

ANATOMICAL ORGANIZATION OF CENTRAL RESPIRATORY NEURONS[1]

❖1300

Madhu P. Kalia

Department of Physiology and Biophysics, Hahnemann Medical College, Philadelphia, PA 19102, USA

Introduction

Most of our currently held views on the organization of central respiratory mechanisms are based on electrophysiological studies of "respiratory neurons," i.e. neurons that Salmoiraghi & Burns (66, 67) described as "producing periodic bursts of activity which are locked constantly to some phase of respiratory activity of the diaphragm." Neurons that show no sign of rhythmicity or have irregular bursting patterns that may play a part in the genesis of respiratory rhythm are excluded by such a definition. Recently, the search for these respiratory related units—RRUs (15)—has been intense and much of the conceptual framework of the organization of the respiratory centers is derived from these studies.

Electrophysiological studies, however, have limitations. For instance, during extracellular stimulation and recording it is not possible to know the exact morphology or location of the neuron being studied. Furthermore, since only spontaneously active units are sampled, it is possible to miss neurons that are silent under the condition of the experiment and that could have been activated under other conditions. Combinations of electrophysiological and neuroanatomical mapping techniques might result in a more meaningful map of the respiratory centers. However, it is rarely possible to do definitive anatomical mapping of respiratory control mechanisms because of heterogeneity in the neuronal populations involved.

[1]This study was supported by US Public Health Service grants HL-17800, HL23961 and a Research Career Development Award HL-00103 from the National Heart, Lung and Blood Institute.

This review is based on the significant rather than the total literature on the topic. Various data have recently become available that give us a better insight into the structural basis of the respiratory control mechanisms. I consider here both anatomical studies on the inputs to and interconnections between the respiratory nuclear groups and pertinent electrophysiological studies of anatomical pathways.

Projections to the Brain Stem Respiratory Neuronal Populations

Respiratory function requires an orderly recruitment of motoneurons of the phrenic and intercostal nerves. These motoneuron pools are under the control of brain stem respiratory neurons the axons of which project down to the spinal cord via bulbo-spinal pathways (8, 9, 32, 37, 38, 40, 51). Brain stem respiratory neurons in turn receive a variety of signals capable of influencing respiratory activity. The most prominent of these is from pulmonary afferents via the vagus nerve. When the vagus nerve is stimulated electrically, evoked potentials can be recorded from the dorsal surface of the medulla (57). Studies on the discharge properties of individual respiratory neurons in the dorsal medulla, in the region of the nucleus of the Tractus Solitarius (nTS), led von Baumgarten and co-workers (4) to conclude that this region contains exclusively inspiratory neurons. This was subsequently confirmed (3, 9, 10, 11, 18). The nTS is the primary site of termination of vagal afferents from a number of thoracic and abdominal viscera (16, 24–26, 61). In an attempt to correlate the inspiratory-inhibiting lung-inflation reflex (the Hering-Breuer reflex) with the firing pattern of medullary respiratory neurons in the nTS, von Baumgarten & Kanzow (5) described two types of inspiratory neurons in the dorsal medulla—the R_α (now designated as I_α) whose activity was inhibited by lung inflation, and the R_β (now designated as I_β) which were excited by lung inflation. These investigators concluded that the R_β neurons were an inhibitory interneuron that turned off the R_α neurons during inspiration. The physiological segregation of respiratory neurons in the nTS into two distinct populations led to the presumption that the R_α and R_β neurons are anatomically distinct and that input from pulmonary stretch receptors goes almost exclusively to R_β neurons (see 15, 18, 61). In conformance with this simplified classification of inspiratory neurons in the nTS, the inputs to this nucleus were simplified as well (55, 76). Thus although numerous investigations [see (55) for an excellent review] had indicated that the pulmonary vagus nerve consisted of a heterogeneous group of afferent fibers of varying thresholds and rates of adaptation, and that lung inflation stimulated a number of these sensory fibers (28, 55), most of this information was ignored and the subdivision of pulmonary afferent fibers into pulmonary stretch, irritant, and type J fibers emerged. The danger of oversimplification is evident when one tries to fit a given respiratory reflex into such a grouping. The Heads Paradoxical (inflation-excitatory) reflex has been of interest to respiratory neurophysiologists because it produces reflex responses similar to those of the R_α neurons (7). Often ignored is the fact that the receptors involved in this reflex belong to the group of pulmonary stretch receptors and that this reflex can only be elicited when the vagus is cooled to 4°C. Thus attempts precisely to correlate pulmonary afferent inputs with specific brain stem respiratory neurons have been largely unsuccessful. Unless newer techniques demonstrate the anatomical connections of physiologically identified fibers, it is unwise to implicate specific pulmonary afferent fibers in the physiological responses of respiratory neurons.

We are still left with the problem of defining the functions of the R_α and R_β neurons in the nTS. Golgi studies (13) (see Figure 1a) and recent studies with horseradish peroxidase (HRP) (see Figure 1b) have shown (a) the morphology of neurons in the nTS that have dendritic arborizations extending widely into surrounding regions, and (b) the intense and intricate terminal arborization of vagal afferent fibers over different subnuclei of the nTS. In light of such data it would be inappropriate to presume that one type of vagal afferent input would go exclusively to one functional type of neuron. It might be reasonable to assume at this stage that quantitative differences in the inputs to various respiratory neurons result in the production of varying patterns of responses. Lipski and co-workers (36) have recently provided the first physiological evidence against a clear cut differentiation between R_α and R_β cells as far as their respective inputs are concerned. These investigators used antidromic latency measurements as an indirect means of estimating fluctuations in the membrane potential and have ascertained the excitability of R_α and R_β neurons during the central inspiratory excitation (CIE) time and during lung inflation in expiration. Most R_α cells showed a shortening of the antidromic latency during lung inflation in expiration, which indicated a subthreshold depolarization. This contradicts the traditionally held view that a direct inhibitory input from R_β to R_α cells exists (14, 47, 60, 62, 63, 67), and indicates that the inhibition of R_α neurons during inspiration comes directly from a more generalized central inspiratory excitation. Thus, as far as the central terminations of pulmonary afferents are concerned, physiological evidence seems to indicate a generalized distribution of these afferents within the various neuronal populations in the nTS (15, 18, 29, 48, 50, 64). The functional responses of these neurons depends upon the level of lung inflation, the nature of the receptors being activated, and the existing membrane potential of the neuron in question. The membrane potential is in turn under the influence of ECF chemistry (P_{CO_2}, P_{O_2}, and pH) and the density of synaptic connections.

A recent study using a neuroanatomical tracing method of horseradish peroxidase (HRP) histochemistry (26) has shown that afferents from the lung parenchyma and airways terminate in many subnuclei of the nTS. A topographical organization between subnuclei of the nTS and individual end organs has been found (see Table 1). The vlnTS, which is the major subnucleus of the nTS containing respiration related units (RRUs), receives afferent projections from larynx, extrathoracic trachea, intrathoracic trachea, main bronchus, lung, and heart. The principal sensory receptors in the trachea are the stretch and irritant receptors (55, 68, 76); the stretch receptors are located in the posterior wall in the trachealis muscle and the irritant receptors are located under the mucosa of the trachea (68). These two groups of receptors terminated in the subdivisions of the nTS, the vlnTS receiving the heaviest projection. Afferent fibers from paired pulmonary viscera (bronchi and lungs) travel via both vagus nerves to the brain stem. This bilateral projection from the lungs is derived from communicating branches between the two vagus nerves in the pulmonary plexus; it was described by anatomists over 60 years ago (21, 33, 34). These anatomical observations having escaped attention, in recent studies on pulmonary reflexes it is often presumed that each vagus is involved in innervating the lung of the ipsilateral side (55, 69, 76). Thus in a series of studies unilateral vagotomy has been considered an acceptable means for denervating a lung (11, 17), and mechanical manipulations of this "denervated" lung are not considered to register in the central medullary respiratory apparatus. In view of this recent anatomical data, however, it would seem hazardous to presume that unilateral vagotomy would lead to sensory or motor denervation of either lung.

Medullary respiratory centers also receive projections from the cerebral cortex. Using the Marchi technique in the monkey, Mettler (43–46) described fibers from the pyramid terminating in brain stem nuclei. Brodal

---→

Figure 1   (a-top) An illustration from Cajal's work (1909) of a cross section through the medulla of a cat at the level of the hypoglossal nucleus showing the structures subjacent to the fourth ventricle. B: nucleus interstitialis (ni). C: tractus solitarius (TS). D: dorsal nucleus of the vagus nerve (dmnX). E: fibers of the vagus nerve (X). F: axons of the IX and X nerves. G: the fourth ventricle. b: large cells of the dmnX. c,d: small cells of the dmnX. The axons of cells are marked by the letter a.

(b-bottom) Dark field photomicrograph of the dorsal medulla of a cat that was sectioned coronally; dorsal is towards the top and medial is towards the right. The level of this section is +2.8. The right nodose ganglion was injected with HRP. Survival time is 46 hr. Retrograde labeling is seen in nerve fibers (X) and perikarya of the dmnX. Anterograde labeling in sensory fibers is seen in the TS as well as in the mnTS, nI, vlnTS, and vnTS. Labeled fibers can be seen skirting the nTS. Some can be seen leaving the TS and entering the nTS. In some instances, labeled fibers from the TS bifurcate (arrowhead) with each branch extending toward a different subnucleus. Labeled sensory fibers can be seen leaving the mnTS to enter the dmnX. Bar = 1 mm. [From (25)].

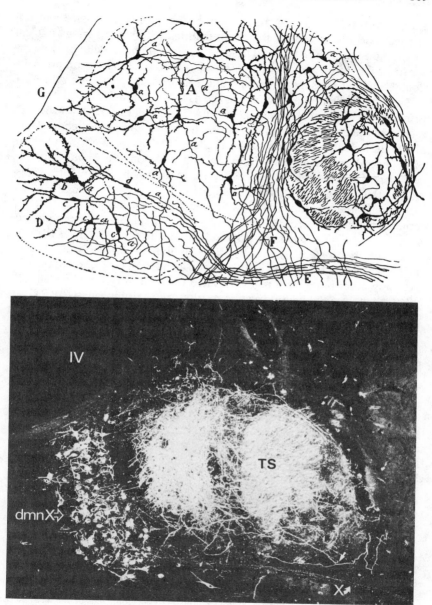

et al (12), using the Glees silver impregnation method in the cat, described fibers from widespread regions of the cortex to the nTS. These included the frontoparietal region, the motor area, the medial and basal surfaces of the cerebral hemispheres, and the occipital and temporal lobes. These corticofugal fibers to the brain stem respiratory centers are both crossed and un-crossed, and the pattern of their terminations within the various nuclear subdivisions of the nTS varies. These projections are believed to provide the substrate for the physiologically observed inhibition of the central propaga-tion of different messages at the site of the first sensory synapse in the nTS.

Evidence of afferent projections to the nTS from the spinal cord has been provided by many anatomists (49, 58, 65, 72). Spinal afferents to the nTS ascend in the dorsal columns and lateral funiculus and project contralater-ally to the dorsolateral region of the nTS (see 30). The possibility of overlap-ping central representations from visceral and somatic inputs must be considered, and the role of spinal afferents in modifying synaptic transmis-sion in this nucleus should be investigated.

Although the experimental work described above establishes the fact that inputs from visceral organs, cerebral cortex, and spinal cord can influence neurons in the nTS, our knowledge regarding the connections of the nTS with other brain stem respiratory nuclei is limited. Earlier studies using microstimulation techniques could not find an afferent projection to the nTS from any other brain stem regions related to respiratory function (38–42). What, then, was the neural basis of respiratory rhythmogenesis? RRUs in the vlnTS continued to show respiratory modulated activity even after the cortical and vagal inputs had been severed. This led to the logical conclusion that in the absence of cortical and vagal input to the vlnTS, respiratory related activity in this nucleus must be due to intrinsic properties of these

Table 1 Summary of labeling of the subnuclei of the NTS produced by injection of HRP into individual pulmonary visceral organs[a]

	LAR	ETT	ITT	RMB	LUN
dnTS[b]	+	++	++	+	+
dlnTS	++	++	+++	+	+++
mnTS	+	++	+	+	+
ncom	++	++	++	+	++
ni	+++	++	—	++	+
nI	—	+	+	++	+
sg	—	+	+	—	—
vlnTS	++	+++	++	+++	+++
vnTS	+	+	+	+	—
ap	—	—	—	+	+

[a] +++ > 10 grains of HRP label per 100 sq μ; ++ 2–9 grains of HRP label per 100 sq μ; + < 2 grains of HRP label per 100 sq μ. [Modified from (26)]

[b] Abbreviations—ap: area postrema; dlnTS: dorso-lateral subnucleus of the nTS; dnTS: dorsal subnucleus of the nTS; ETT: extra-thoracic trachea; ITT: intra-thoracic trachea; LAR: larynx; LUN: lung; mnTS: medial subnucleus of the nTS; ncom: nucleus commis-suralis; ni: interstitial subnucleus of the nTS; nI: intermediate subnucleus of the nTS; RMB: right main bronchus; sg: subnucleus gelatinosus of the nTS; vlnTS: ventrolateral subnucleus of the nTS; vnTS: ventral subnucleus of the nTS.

neurons (13). Kalia et al (24) recently used the neuroanatomical methods of HRP histochemistry to extend the search for brain stem regions sending afferent projections to the nTS. Following small localized iontophoretic injections of HRP into the inspiratory neuronal population in the vlnTS, retrogradely labeled neurons were found in the contralateral rostral nucleus retroambigualis (nRA) in the region of the retrofacial nucleus at a level 6 mm rostral to the obex. This region corresponds to the Bötzinger Complex (Böt.C.) (35). These neurons projecting to the inspiratory region in the vlnTS were not identified physiologically in this study. However, since this region corresponded closely with the region of the medulla where inspiratory activity had previously been reported (38), it was presumed that this projection from inspiratory neurons in the rostral ventral medulla to inspiratory neurons in the contralateral vlnTS represented a crossed connection between physiologically identical units. In a recent series of electrophysiological experiments Lipski & Merrill (35) have reexamined this contralateral input to the vlnTS from rostral medullary neurons in the region of the Böt.C. and have found that these neurons fired during the expiratory phase of respiration and not during the inspiratory phase as had been presumed earlier (24). This finding has provided a most significant missing link in our understanding of respiratory rhythmogenesis. Expiratory neurons projecting to inspiratory neurons within the brain stem could provide a precise mechanism for inactivating vlnTS inspiratory neurons during the expiratory phase of respiration.

Efferent Projections from the Dorsal Respiratory Group— Ventrolateral Nucleus of the Tractus Solitarius (vlnTS)

The majority of neurons in the vlnTS fire in synchrony with the inspiratory phase of the respiratory cycle (3, 4, 8, 9, 19, 47, 63, 77). Classical studies on the efferent connections of these inspiratory neurons done by anatomical degeneration and autoradiographic techniques and by electrophysiological antidromic cross-correlation experiments have clearly demonstrated that axons of cells in the vlnTS project mainly contralaterally to spinal respiratory motoneurons (6, 9, 18, 19, 37, 39, 40, 41, 49, 51, 73). These descending contralateral bulbo-spinal fibers travel predominantly in the lateral funiculus with a few fibers also traveling in the ventral funiculus (9, 10, 19, 38).

Using autoradiographic methods, Norgren (52) has recently shown more details of these anatomical connections of the nTS. Axons from various subdivisions of the nTS first ramify within various subnuclear groups of the nTS itself. This finding demonstrates that the segregation of small nuclear groups in the nTS into isolated functional centers was a misconception and that the control of respiratory, cardiovascular, digestive, and gustatory functions may involve interactions between the central neurons subserving these different functions. Efferents from the nTS also terminate in the various motor nuclear group in the medulla—i.e. the dorsal motor nucleus of the vagus (dmnX), the hypoglossal nucleus (nXII), the nucleus inter-calatus (nIC), the commissural nucleus (ncom), and the nucleus ambiguus (nA) at all levels. These projections are ipsilateral. They provide an anatomical substrate for the mediation of short latency visceral and somatic reflexes while also providing input from central regulatory mechanisms in the nTS to other respiratory nuclear groups for further processing. Output from the nTS also ascends to the rostral regions of the neuraxis. Using HRP and autoradiographic methods, recent investigators (32, 52, 59) have shown bilateral projections from the nTS to the pontine parabrachial areas. These axons ascend in the ipsilateral and contralateral tractus solitarius (TS) to terminate in the caudal regions of the pons (52). Using injections of HRP into the pontine parabrachial nuclei that have been associated with respiratory activity (74, 75)—i.e. the nucleus parabrachialis medialis (NPBM) and Kölliker Fuse nucleus (KF)—Kalia (23) found that a number of subnuclei of the nTS project to these pontine regions. Thus, second-order neurons in the nTS project to the pontine respiratory centers. Although these anatomical studies do not directly implicate respiratory neurons in the nTS projecting to the pons, a recent study on inhibition of pontine respiratory neurons by vagal afferents (20) indicates that such a short latency pathway between the vagus and the pons via the nTS must exist to make such precise control of pontine respiratory units possible. Norgren & Leonard (53), studying the rostral projections of the parabrachial nuclei, have described projections rostral to the ventrobasal hypothalamus, lateral hypothalamus, substantia innominata, central nucleus of amygdala, and bed nucleus of the stria terminalis. These findings further establish the existence of disynaptic afferent access to the highest autonomic integrative centers in the brain. In the rat, Ricardo & Koh (59) found that neurons in the nTS send projections directly to limbic forebrain structures. Whether such a direct pathway exists in other species as well is at present undetermined and must await more localized applications of tritiated amino acids or HRP and more sensitive histochemical methods.

Afferent and Efferent Connections of Pontine Respiratory Centers

In addition to receiving input from the nTS bilaterally, pontine respiratory nuclei (parabrachial nuclei) receive bilateral projections from the nucleus ambiguus (nA), nucleus Para Ambiguus (nPA), Bötzinger Complex (Böt.C.), and nucleus Retroambigualis (nRA) (see Figure 2). A column of neurons in the nA extending from 2 mm rostral to 5 mm caudal to the obex send projections to the parabrachial nuclei [see Figure 2, (23)]. Ricardo &

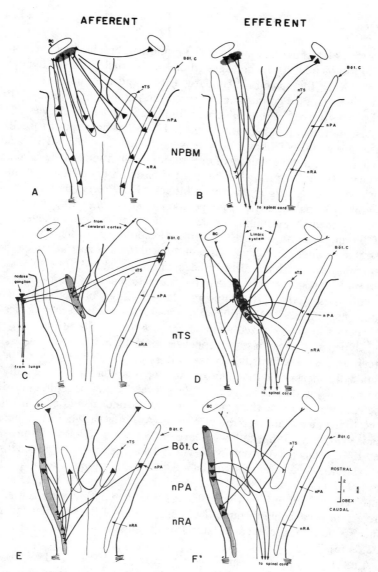

Figure 2 Drawings from horizontal sections of the medulla and pons showing the major regions associated with respiratory activity and their afferent and efferent connections as determined by anatomical tracing and electrophysiological mapping. Cell bodies are shown as filled triangles, axons and axon collaterals are shown as solid lines, and inverted "V's" represent axon terminations. Since the column of respiratory related neurons in the ventral medulla are associated with three physiologically distinct-subgroups, they are shown in sections E & F as components of the nucleus Ambiguus related region.

Abbreviations used: BC: Brachium Conjunctiuum; Böt. C.: Bötzinger Complex; nPA: nucleus Para Ambiguus; NPBM: Nucleus Para Brachialis Medialis; nRA: nucleus Retroambigualis; nTS: nucleus of the Tractus Solitarius.

Koh (59) also showed input to the pontine parabrachial region from the dorsal motor nucleus of the vagus (dmnX), the nucleus of the hypoglossal nerve (nXII), the nucleus intercalatus (nIC), and the nucleus gracilis (g). In addition crossed connections between the parabrachial nuclei (NPBM) of the two sides of the pons have been found (23). In a recent review, Cohen (15) has indicated that because the medial NTS has no respiratory cells and the ventrolateral NTS has a high density of I neurons, the NTS I neurons apparently are not the sources of respiratory modulation of PC neurons. We are currently in the process of finding the basic wiring of the pontomedullary nuclei subserving respiratory function. The precise pathway a given respiratory signal follows must depend on a variety of factors that can only be determined by examining processing at a single-neuronal level.

Efferent projections from the pontine respiratory nuclei travel in both rostral and caudal directions. The anatomical basis of rostral projections to the limbic system have already been discussed above. The influence of parabrachial respiratory centers in the generation of respiratory rhythm has recently been studied (70, 71) using bilateral lesions of the NPBM. It was found that these NPBM lesions did not change the pattern of generation of apneusis in vagotomized animals. Studies on the alterations of hypoxic and hypercapnic responses in apneusis seem to indicate that a feedback circuit between pontomedullary respiratory nuclei is necessary for the generation of apneusis and that hypoxia and hypercapnia can differentially alter apneusis by interacting at the medullary level. From this indirect evidence, one can presume that the pontine respiratory nuclei send efferent projections to the medullary respiratory centers. As far as the vlnTS is concerned, Kalia (23) showed that following large injections of HRP into the NPBM and KF, no labeled neurons in the vlnTS could be found. In a recent study on expiratory neurons in the caudal medulla in the region of the nRA, Kalia et al (27) have found a significant number of retrogradely labeled neurons in the NPBM and KF on the ipsilateral side. The pathway for this efferent projection is probably through the lateral region of the reticular formation since lesion in a discrete area lateral to the superior olive results in apnea (22 & 56).

A most prominent efferent projection from the NPBM and KF has been found recently by anatomical studies (2, 23, 31, 32) using horseradish peroxidase injections into the cervical, thoracic, and lumbar spinal cord. Retrogradely labeled neurons were found in a number of brain stem regions including the pontine parabrachial and KF areas [see Figure 2 in (31)]. This finding of a direct efferent projection from the pontine respiratory region to the spinal cord suggests that the brain stem respiratory nuclei do not have one output to the spinal cord that reflects the final integrated signal to respiratory motoneurons. Rather, since each of the three brain stem respiratory nuclear groups independently sends efferents to the spinal cord, the integration probably occurs on the "final common pathway," i.e. on the respiratory motoneuron itself. As Figure 2 illustrates, the pattern of efferent projections from the brain stem respiratory nuclei is very similar.

Afferent and Efferent Projections of the Nucleus Retroambigualis (nRA), Nucleus Para Ambiguus (nPA), and the Bötzinger Complex (Böt. C.)

Olszewski & Baxter (54) described the nRA as a "nucleus of unknown connections." Twenty-five years later, we not only know a great deal about its connections and functions but also have begun to use the term nRA as synonymous with the ventral respiratory group (VRG), a column of neurons in the ventral region of the medulla that fire in synchrony with respiration. These neurons were originally described by Archard & Bucher (1) and Batsel (3) and were found to lie in association with the nucleus ambiguus (nA). The studies of Merrill (38–42) and of Bianchi and co-workers (8–10) on this VRG identified the functional aspects of these neurons, which lay lateral to the nA. Olszewski & Baxter (54) had located the nRA in the caudal medulla extending to the caudal pole of the inferior olivary complex. They presumed that the nRA represented the oral extension of the intermedio-lateral cell column of the spinal cord. However, once the function of the nRA in the caudal medulla had been delineated and it had been found to have respiratory related activity (38–42), the VRG rostral to the caudal pole of the inferior olive, which showed similar respiratory activity, also began to be called nRA (24, 35, 38–40). The term was subsequently adopted for the entire VRG to distinguish it from the nA, which is predominantly a vagal motor nucleus and is not a part of the central respiratory network responsible for rhythm generation. Thus E. G. Merrill (personal communication) has modified Olszewski & Baxter's nRA to signify the wider physiologically functional system of neurons now associated with the VRG. Although it is necessary to differentiate respiratory neurons in the ventral medulla from laryngeal motoneurons lying in the same general region, the use of the term nRA for the entire VRG seems inappropriate since the nRA is a definite anatomical nucleus lying caudal to the obex. Since the rostrally located respiratory neurons in the VRG lie in association with the nA, the term nucleus Para Ambiguus (nPA) is used in this review to define respiratory neurons in the rostral VRG. At the most rostral end of this column a group of expiratory neurons has been defined (24, 35). These neurons have been found to lie in association with the Böt.C. (35). In this review the terms nRA, nPA, and Böt.C. signify these physiologically distinct subgroups of respiratory neurons in the VRG.

The afferent projections to the nRA, nPA, and Böt.C. have only recently begun to be examined. The results available therefore represent only a part of the total spectrum of projections. One of the reasons for the rather cautionary approach to this study of the afferent connections of the nRA, nPA, and Böt.C. is that, unlike the nTS and NPBM, the respiratory neurons in the nRA, nPA, and Böt.C. represent a functional entity rather than a discrete anatomical nucleus. Therefore, studies on the connections of these nuclei must be based on precise physiological localization. Using antidromic methods, Merrill (38, 40) found that a large population of respiratory neurons in the nTS sent projections to the nRA. This projection was easily demonstrated, extensive, and bilateral; the ipsilateral projection was the heaviest. Recently, Kalia et al (27), following small iontophoretic applications of HRP into the expiratory population in the caudal nRA, found that this region of the nRA receives afferent projections from contralateral and ipsilateral nTS (vlnTS and vnTS) (the contralateral projection being the heavier), the ipsilateral and contralateral rostral nRA (the ipsilateral projection being more prominent), and the ipsilateral and contralateral parabrachial region of the pons (ipsilateral projection being more intense). Although a careful search was made in this recent study for HRP-labeled neurons in the contralateral nRA at the same level as the injection site, none was found, thus confirming the observation of Merrill that expiratory neurons do not have medullary axon collaterals to the contralateral nRA at the same level.

The efferent projections of the nRA and nPA have been studied most extensively by Merrill (38, 40). Recent anatomical data support Merrill's antidromic studies and also extend the efferent connections to include pontine respiratory regions. Merrill has described a direct projection of axons from the nRA and nPA to the contralateral side of the spinal cord, terminating in spinal cord segments from first thoracic through third lumbar segments. Thus, neurons in this region are capable of driving both intercostal and abdominal respiratory motoneurons. Neurons in the nRA belong to both inspiratory and expiratory types of respiratory units. The concept that inspiratory units are located in the rostral part of the nPA and expiratory units are located in the caudal part of the nRA (38, 40) has recently been challenged by Lipski & Merrill (35), who found that the rostral part of the nPA (6 mm rostral to the obex) contains expiratory neurons that project to neurons in the caudal contralateral vlnTS. The spinal projections of respiratory neurons in the ventral medulla therefore cannot be divided into projections from inspiratory or expiratory populations. The problems associated with reconciling conflicting data from various laboratories on inhibition and excitation of respiratory neurons during various phases of the respiratory cycle still remain largely unresolved (14, 43). Part of the confusion has arisen from the assumption that at present all the data are available with which a reasonable model of the respiratory rhythm generator can be made. There are obvious problems with such an assumption since electrophysiological sampling studies are unable to provide a complete understanding of all the possible connectivity patterns between populations of neurons.

The efferent projection from the Böt.C. (retrofacial nucleus) to the vlnTS described by Kalia et al (24) anatomically, and recently confirmed physiologically by Lipski & Merrill (35), has shown direct connections between expiratory and inspiratory neurons in the medulla. Axons traveling from expiratory neurons in the Böt.C. to inspiratory neurons in the vlnTS must travel through many millimeters of the medulla and even cross over to the opposite side. How significant this expiratory input really is in determining the activity of neurons in the vlnTS is at present uncertain. Neurons in the nPA and Böt.C. also send efferent projections to the pons (23) bilaterally terminating in the region of the pontine respiratory nuclei.

Literature Cited

1. Archard, O., Bucher, V. M. 1954. Courants d'action bulbaires a rhythme respiratoire. *Helv. Physiol. Acta* 12: 265–83
2. Basbaum, A. I., Fields, H. L. 1979. The origin of descending pathways in the dorsolateral funiculus of the spinal cord of the cat and rat: Further studies on the anatomy of pain modulation. *J. Comp. Neurol.* 187:513–32
3. Batsel, H. L. 1964. Localization of bulbar respiratory center by microelectrode recording. *Exp. Neurol.* 9: 410–26
4. Baumgarten, R. von, Baumgarten, A. von, Schaefer, K. P. 1957. Beitrag zur Lokalizationsfrage bulboreticulärer respiratorischer Neurone der Katze. *Pflügers Arch.* 264:217–27
5. Baumgarten, R. von, Kanzow, E. 1958. The interaction of two types of inspiratory neurons in the region of the tractus solitarius of the cat. *Arch. Ital. Biol.* 96:361–73
6. Baumgarten, R. von, Nakayama, S. 1964. Spontane und reizbedingte Änderungen der antidromen Erregbarkeit von bulbaren respiratorischen Nervenzellen der Katze. *Pflügers Arch.* 281:245–58
7. Berger, A. J. 1977. Dorsal respiratory group neurons in the medulla of cat: Spinal projections, responses to lung inflation and superior laryngeal

nerve stimulation. *Brain Res.* 135: 231–54
8. Bianchi, A. L. 1971. Localisation et étude des neurones respiratoires bulbaires. Mise en jeu antidromique ou stimulation spinale ou vagale. *J. Physiol. Paris* 63:5–40
9. Bianchi, A. L. 1974. Modalités de décharge et propriétés anatomo-fonctionelles des neurones respiratoires bulbaires. *J. Physiol. Paris* 68:555–87
10. Bianchi, A. L., Barillot, J. C. 1975. Activity of medullary respiratory neurones during reflexes from the lungs in cats. *Respir. Physiol.* 25:335–52
11. Bouverot, P., Flandrois, R., Puccinelli, R., Dejours, P. 1965. Etude du role des chemorecepteurs arteriels dans la regulation de la respiration pulmonaire chez le chien eveille. *Arch. Int. Pharmacodyn.* 157:253–71
12. Brodal, A., Szabo, T., Torvik, A. 1956. Corticofugal fibers to sensory trigeminal nuclei and nucleus of solitary tract. An experimental study in the cat. *J. Comp. Neurol.* 106:527–55
13. Cajal, S. R. 1909. *Histologie due Systeme Nerveux de l'Homme et des Vertebres*, Vol. 1. Paris: A. Maloine
14. Camerer, H., Meesmann, M., Richter, D. W., Röhrig, N. 1978. Reciprocal inhibition of bulbar respiratory neurons in the cat. *J. Physiol. London* 284:80P
15. Cohen, M. I. 1979. Neurogenesis of res-

piratory rhythm in the mammal. *Physiol. Rev.* 59:1105–73

16. Cottle, M. K. 1964. Degeneration studies of primary afferents of IXth and Xth cranial nerves in the cat. *J. Comp. Neurol.* 122:329–45

17. Dejours, P. 1970. In *Breathing: Hering-Breuer Centenary Symposium,* ed. R. Porter, pp. 48–49. London: J. & A. Churchill

18. Euler, C. von, Hayward, J. N., Marttila, I., Wyman, R. J. 1973. Respiratory neurones of the ventrolateral nucleus of the solitary tract of cat: Vagal input, spinal connections and morphological identification. *Brain Res.* 61:1–22

19. Euler, C. von, Hayward, J. N., Marttila, I., Wyman, R. J. 1973. The spinal connections of the inspiratory neurones of the ventrolateral nucleus of the cat's tractus solitarius. *Brain Res.* 61:23–33

20. Feldman, J. L., Cohen, M. I., Wolotsky, P. 1976. Powerful inhibition of pontine respiratory neurons by pulmonary afferent activity. *Brain Res.* 104:341–46

21. Honjin, R. 1956. Experimental degeneration of the vagus and its relation to the nerve supply of the lung of the mouse, with special reference to the cross innervation of the lung by the vagi. *J. Comp. Neurol.* 106:1–19

22. Hugelin, A. 1977. Anatomical organization of bulbopontine respiratory oscillators. *Fed. Proc.* 36:2390–94

23. Kalia, M. 1977. Neuroanatomical organization of the respiratory centers. *Fed. Proc.* 36:2405–11

24. Kalia, M., Feldman, J. L., Cohen, M. I. 1979. Afferent projections to the inspiratory neuronal region of the ventrolateral nucleus of the tractus solitarius in the cat. *Brain Res.* 171:135–41

25. Kalia, M., Mesulam, M. M. 1980. Brain stem projections of sensory and motor components of the vagus complex in the cat. I. The cervical vagus and nodose ganglion. *J. Comp. Neurol.* 193:435–65

26. Kalia, M., Mesulam, M. M. 1980. Brain stem projections of sensory and motor components of the vagus complex in the cat. II. Laryngeal, tracheobronchial, pulmonary, cardiac and gastrointestinal branches. *J. Comp. Neurol.* 193:467–508

27. Kalia, M., Sommer, D., Cohen, M. I. 1980. Afferent projections to the expiratory neuronal population of the caudal medulla in the cat. *Brain Res.* In press

28. Knowlton, G. C., Larrabee, M. G. 1946. A unitary analysis of pulmonary volume receptors. *Am. J. Physiol.* 147:100–14

29. Kreuter, F., Richter, D. W., Camerer, H., Senekowitsch, R. 1977. Morphological and electrical description of medullary respiratory neurons of the cat. *Pflügers Arch.* 372:7–16

30. Kuru, M. 1956. The spino-bulbar tracts and pelvic sensory vagus. Further contributions to the theory of the sensory dual innervation of the viscera. *J. Comp. Neurol.* 104:207–32

31. Kuypers, H. G. J. M., Maisky, V. A. 1975. Retrograde axonal transport of horseradish peroxidase from spinal cord to brain stem cell groups in the cat. *Neurosci. Lett.* 1:9–14

32. Kuypers, H. G. J. M., Maisky, V. A. 1977. Funicular trajectories of descending brain stem pathways in cat. *Brain Res.* 136:159–65

33. Larsell, O. 1921. Nerve terminations in the lung of the rabbit. *J. Comp. Neurol.* 33:105–32

34. Larsell, O., Mason, M. L. 1921. Experimental degeneration of the vagus nerve and its relation to the terminations in the lung of the rabbit. *J. Comp. Neurol.* 33:509–16

35. Lipski, J., Merrill, E. G. 1980. Electrophysiological demonstration of the projection from expiratory neurons in rostral medulla to contralateral dorsal respiratory group. *Brain Res.* In press

36. Lipski, J., Trzebski, A., Kubin, L. 1979. Excitability changes of dorsal inspiratory neurons during lung inflations as studied by measurement of antidromic invasion latencies. *Brain Res.* 16:25–38

37. Loewy, A. D., Burton, H. 1978. Nuclei of the solitary tract: Efferent projections to the lower brain stem and spinal cord of the cat. *J. Comp. Neurol.* 181:421–50

38. Merrill, E. G. 1970. The lateral respiratory neurons of the medulla: Their association with nucleus ambiguus, nucleus retroambigualis, the spinal accessory nucleus and the spinal cord. *Brain Res.* 24:11–28

39. Merrill, E. G. 1972. Interaction between medullary respiratory neurones in cats. *J. Physiol. London* 226:72P–74P

40. Merrill, E. G. 1974. Finding a respiratory function for the medullary respiratory neurons. In *Essays on the Nervous System,* ed. R. Bellairs, E. G. Gray, pp. 451–86. Oxford: Clarendon

41. Merrill, E. G. 1975. Preliminary studies on nucleus retroambigualis—nucleus of

the solitary tract interaction in cats. *J. Physiol. London* 244:54P–55P

42. Merrill, E. G. 1979. Is there reciprocal inhibition between medullary inspiratory and expiratory neurones? In *Central Nervous Control Mechanisms in Breathing: Physiological and Clinical Aspects of Regular, Periodic and Irregular Breathing in Adults and in the Perinatal Period,* ed. C. von Euler, H. Lagercrantz, pp. 239–54. Oxford: Pergamon

43. Mettler, F. A. 1935. Corticofugal fiber connections of the cortex of *Macaca mulatta.* The occipital region. *J. Comp. Neurol.* 61:221–56

44. Mettler, F. A. 1935. Corticofugal fiber connections of the cortex of *Macaca mulatta.* The frontal region. *J. Comp. Neurol.* 61:509–42

45. Mettler, F. A. 1935. Corticofugal fiber connections of the cortex of *Macaca mulatta.* The parietal region. *J. Comp. Neurol.* 62:263–92

46. Mettler, F. A. 1935. Corticofugal fiber connections of the cortex of *Macaca mulatta.* The temporal region. *J. Comp. Neurol.* 63:25–48

47. Mitchell, R. A. 1977. Location and function of medullary respiratory neurons. *Am. Rev. Respir. Dis.* 115:209–16

48. Mitchell, R. A., Herbert, D. A. 1974. Synchronized high frequency synaptic potentials in medullary respiratory neurons. *Brain Res.* 75:350–55

49. Morest, D. K. 1967. Experimental study of the projections of the nucleus of the tractus solitarius and the area postrema in the cat. *J. Comp. Neurol.* 130:277–300

50. Nakayama, S., Baumgarten, R. von. 1964. Lokalisierung absteigender Atmungsbahnen im Ruckenmark der Katze mittels antidromer Reizung. *Pflügers Arch.* 281:231–44

51. Newsome-Davis, J., Plum, F. 1972. Separation of descending spinal pathways to respiratory motoneurons. *Exp. Neurol.* 34:78–94

52. Norgren, R. 1978. Projections from the nucleus of the solitary tract in the rat. *Neuroscience* 3:207–13

53. Norgren, R., Leonard, C. M. 1973. Ascending central gustatory pathways. *J. Comp. Neurol* 150:217–38

54. Olszewski, J., Baxter, D. 1954. *Cytoarchitecture of the Human Brain Stem.* Basel: S. Karger. 199 pp.

55. Paintal, A. S. 1973. Vagal sensory receptors and their reflex effects. *Physiol. Rev.* 53:159–227

56. Pitts, R. F., Magoun, H. W., Ranson, S. W. 1939. The origin of respiratory rhythmicity. *Am. J. Physiol.* 127:654–70

57. Porter, R. 1963. Unit responses evoked in the medulla oblongata by vagus nerve stimulation. *J. Physiol. London* 168:717–35

58. Ranson, S. W., Davenport, H. K., Doles, E. A. 1932. Intramedullary course of the dorsal root fibers of the first three cervical nerves. *J. Comp. Neurol.* 54:1–12

59. Ricardo, J. A., Koh, E. T. 1978. Anatomical evidence of direct projections from the nucleus of the solitary tract to the hypothalamus, amygdala and other forebrain structures in the rat. *Brain Res.* 153:1–26

60. Richter, D. W., Camerer, H., Meesmann, M., Röhrig, N. 1979. Studies on the synaptic interconnection between bulbar respiratory neurons of cats. *Pflügers Arch.* 380:245–57

61. Richter, D. W., Camerer, H., Röhrig, N. 1978. Medullary inspiratory interneurons receiving a monosynaptic input from lung stretch receptors. *Pflügers Arch.* 373:R75 (Suppl)

62. Richter, D. W., Heyde, F. 1974. Reciprocal innervation of medullary inspiratory and expiratory neurons. *Pflügers Arch.* 347:R39 (Suppl)

63. Richter, D. W., Heyde, F., Gabriel, M. 1975. Intracellular recordings from different types of medullary respiratory neurons of the cat. *J. Neurophysiol.* 38:1162–71

64. Richter, D. W., Seller, H. 1976. Response of medullary neurons to lung inflation and vagal nerve stimulation. *Pflügers Arch.* 362:R40

65. Rossi, G. F., Brodal, A. 1956. Spinal afferents to the trigeminal sensory nuclei and the nucleus of the solitary tract. *J. Anat. London.* 16:321–32

66. Salmoiraghi, G. C., Burns, B. D. 1960. Localization and patterns of discharge of respiratory neurones in brain stem of cat. *J. Neurophysiol.* 23:2–13

67. Salmoiraghi, G. C., Burns, B. D. 1960. Notes on mechanism of rhythmic respiration. *J. Neurophysiol.* 23:14–26

68. Sant'Ambrogio, G., Remmers, J. E., DeGroot, W. J., Callas, G., Mortola, J. P. 1978. Localization of rapidly adapting receptors in the trachea and main stem bronchus of the dog. *Respir. Physiol.* 31:359–66

69. Sellick, H., Widdicombe, J. G. 1970. Vagal deflation and inflation reflexes mediated by lung irritant receptors. *Q. J. Exp. Physiol.* 55:153–63

70. St. John, W. M. 1979. Differential alteration by hypercapnia and hypoxia of the apneustic respiratory pattern in decerebrate cats. *J. Physiol. London* 287:467–91

71. St. John, W. M., Wang, S. C. 1977. Alteration from apneusis to more regular rhythmic respiration in decerebrate cats. *Respir. Physiol.* 31:91–106

72. Torvik, A. 1956. Afferent connections to the sensory trigeminal nuclei, the nucleus of the solitary tract and adjacent structures. An experimental study in the rat. *J. Comp. Neurol.* 106:51–141

73. Torvik, A. 1957. The spinal projection from the nucleus of the solitary tract. An experimental study in the cat. *J. Anat.* 91:314–22

74. Vibert, J. F., Bertrand, F., Denavit-Saubié, M., Hugelin, A. 1976. Discharge patterns of bulbo-pontine respiratory unit projections in cat. *Brain Res.* 114:211–25

75. Vibert, J. F., Bertrand, F., Denavit-Saubié, M., Hugelin, A. 1976. Three dimensional representation of bulbo-spinal respiratory network architecture from unit density maps. *Brain Res.* 114:227–44

76. Widdicombe, J. G. 1974. Reflexes from the lungs in the control of breathing. *Recent Adv. Physiol.* 9:239–78

77. Wyman, R. J. 1977. Neural generation of the breathing rhythm. *Ann. Rev. Physiol.* 39:417–48

Ann. Rev. Physiol. 1981. 43:121–35

CENTRAL REGULATION OF RESPIRATION BY ENDOGENOUS NEUROTRANSMITTERS AND NEUROMODULATORS

❖1301

Frederic L. Eldridge and David E. Millhorn

Departments of Medicine and Physiology, University of North Carolina, Chapel Hill, N.C. 27514

INTRODUCTION

Although many excitatory and inhibitory neural inputs from central and peripheral sources including the chemoreceptors have been discovered, the elements essential for setting the level of resting ventilation have never been clearly identified, much less quantified. The traditional view has been that signals from the central and peripheral chemoreceptors are primarily responsible. However, despite over a century of studies, these traditional chemical stimuli (P_{CO_2}, pH, P_{O_2}) alone have not provided a full accounting of the level at which we breathe.

A change in respiratory drive may be produced by peripheral receptors other than chemoreceptors. Other mechanisms may involve poststimulation reverberation of activity, i.e. a sort of "memory," in neural networks in the brain stem. Involuntary influences from higher brain areas can also affect the automatic control system either by direct excitation or by activation or removal of inhibition.

A relatively new idea is that one or more of the array of chemicals known as neurotransmitters or neurohormones, manufactured and released by neurons in the brain, may have modulating effects on respiratory neurons either directly or through other central neuronal connections. Although considerable progress has been made in recent years in characterizing some of these agents, mapping their distribution, and elucidating some of their actions, relatively little has been done regarding their effects on respiration.

0066-4278/81/0315-0121$01.00

121

No evidence exists at present that specific agents are primarily responsible for neural transmission in the respiratory control system. On the other hand, there do appear to be endogenous substances that modify respiration. This review therefore examines studies of potential respiratory effects mediated by neurochemicals in the central nervous system. For the most part the evidence is incomplete and only suggestive. Nevertheless, a better understanding of the role these chemicals play is needed.

GENERAL CONSIDERATIONS

Central neurotransmitters are elaborated by neurons in the brain and then carried by their axons to target neurons where they act on specific receptor sites. They may act directly on rapidly responding receptors and have a short-lasting effect owing to rapid inactivation or removal. They can also have longer-lasting effects owing to activation of receptors that induce the formation of a second messenger, such as cyclic AMP, by which the effects of the transmitter are mediated inside the target neuron over a relatively long period. Some neurochemicals act like hormones in that they are delivered to target neurons by the circulation and may have very long-lasting effects.

Over 30 agents have been proposed as neurotransmitters. Only a few, acetylcholine and the monoamines, norepinephrine, dopamine, and serotonin, have been accepted as having fulfilled all the requirements for being so classed.

Several kinds of evidence have been used to determine the importance of a given neurochemical: demonstration by anatomical and histochemical means that it is present in areas and neurons related to the process under study; determination of the effect of ablation or the electrical stimulation of areas producing a specific neurochemical—e.g. the raphe nuclei, which produce serotonin; direct injection into the brain via the cerebral ventricles or placement near specific neurons by iontophoresis; and, administration of precursors or other nonphysiological agonists or antagonists in an attempt to mimic or block the effect of a specific substance. Although in a few instances particular neurotransmitters have been identified in areas traditionally associated with respiration, the bulk of the evidence for their role in the control of respiration involves giving the agent itself or testing the effect of a precursor, agonist, or antagonist. In some studies, the concentration of the chemical in brain tissue has been measured to confirm that an intervention has been successful.

Several potential problems in interpretation are inherent in the administration of agents. Systemic administration of agents that do not readily cross the blood-brain barrier, for example, cannot cause a respiratory effect by means of a central mechanism. Even for substances that do cross the blood-brain barrier, analysis of the results may be complicated. For example, some of the recognized peripheral neurotransmitters—e.g. norepinephrine, dopamine, serotonin, and histamine—act on peripheral receptors in both the lung and the carotid bodies. Therefore, after systemic administration of the substance under study to animals with intact carotid bodies and vagi, it is impossible to separate central from the peripheral components of the response. Indeed, in some cases, the two responses may be in opposite directions. In this review peripheral mechanisms are considered only when they might influence the interpretation of studies of centrally mediated effects.

It is often assumed that precursors of a neurotransmitter lead only to the accumulation of that transmitter, or antagonists to its depletion. However, substances along the whole metabolic pathway may also be affected, and one of these may cause an observed respiratory response. This problem may be compounded when an agent is given to block the primary catabolic pathways. In this case, production of a metabolite in a secondary unblocked pathway may increase. An example is the use of a monoamine oxidase (MAO) inhibitor, which inhibits catabolism and increases the serotonin (5-hydroxytryptamine) concentration but which also increases production of n,n-dimethytryptamine, a specific serotonin antagonist (10). Since MAO inhibitors also affect the catabolism of the catecholamines, the resulting change in catecholamine concentration further handicaps interpretation of such experiments. Under these circumstances, the sole finding that tissue concentration of serotonin has increased does not give the information necessary to make a valid interpretation of the experimental results, for the concentration of an agent is an imprecise measure of turnover, correlation with which would be far more significant.

The response to an exogenously administered transmitter, precursor, or antagonist—possibly through effects noted above—may be dose-dependent, so that opposite responses may occur with small and large doses (51). If one is looking for physiological respiratory responses, it would seem logical to suggest that the dose not be so large as to yield unphysiologically high concentrations in the brain.

Another problem is that some of the neurotransmitters have diverse effects on other central control mechanisms—e.g. temperature regulation and cardiovascular control. Changes in these mechanisms may affect respiration indirectly rather than through a direct effect on the respiratory control system. An example is the effect of serotonin on temperature control; it has been shown to cause increases of temperature in some species (65) but decreases in others (16). These differences may also depend on the route of administration and on the doses even in the same species (51).

Experiments in which the respiratory effect of a given agent is being studied should be performed under conditions of constant body temperature; temperature should at least be monitored.

Finally, studies under closed-loop chemical feed-back conditions require special precautions. One too common practice is the measurement of ventilation as output variable of the control system with no attempt to keep the arterial P_{CO_2} constant; in this circumstance, the ventilatory effects of a neural stimulus may be markedly reduced by the resulting change in P_{CO_2}. Both the ventilatory and blood-gas effects of small changes of neural stimuli, such as might occur during studies of neurotransmitters, may then be so small as to be masked by the noise of the experiment.

RESPIRATORY EFFECTS

Monoamines

Neurons of the central monoaminergic systems synthesize, store, and release either serotonin, dopamine, or norepinephrine. These systems are unique among those of the various neurotransmitters in that their central neuronal pathways are fairly well delineated (30). Their roles in certain autonomic functions and behavior are at least partially understood, but their role in the regulation of respiration has received relatively little attention.

SEROTONIN   Central serotoninergic neurons, whose cell bodies are localized within the raphe nuclei of the brain stem, send axons throughout the spinal cord and brain (30). The nucleus of the tractus solitarius in the medulla and the nucleus parabrachialis in the pons are among the structures that receive serotoninergic input (56). A functional relationship between the serotonin-dense raphe nuclei and the central respiratory controller has been demonstrated by Polc & Monnier (60), who found that electrical stimulation of the former causes an increase of respiratory activity in rabbits.

Serotonin has been implicated in several central control systems, the cardiovascular (9) and thermoregulatory (51), as well as sleep (38), so it has seemed reasonable to think that it should affect respiration as well. Since serotonin does not readily cross the blood-brain barrier, studies using systemic administration can be disregarded if one is looking for central effects. The straightforward approach would seem to be intracerebroventricular injection. Interestingly enough, however, the results of such studies are contradictory. Some have shown clear facilitatory effects on respiration following large doses of serotonin (60–600 μg) in awake (31) and anesthetized cats (25). Similar responses were found in oxen following injections of 500 μg of serotonin (26). In another study in cats (3), doses of 50 μg had facilitatory effects lasting 15 min but were followed by a prolonged depression. In rats, 5 μg led to a modest reduction of ventilation (40). Most of these studies can be criticized on various grounds. Body temperature was not controlled in any or even monitored in some (3, 25, 26). In none of the studies were baroceptors denervated, so cardiovascular changes could have affected respiration by this mechanism. In all of the studies, the doses of serotonin were large; even if uniformly distributed in the brain, the physiologic concentration of serotonin would have been exceeded. Responses to high concentrations may differ from those to more physiologic ones (51). The use of a monoamine oxidase inhibitor (3), which has a respiratory effect of its own, raises problems with secondary metabolites. In only one study (23) were all these problems addressed; in it vagotomized, paralyzed cats with their carotid bodies and baroreceptors denervated and their CO_2 and body temperature servocontrolled at constant levels were given small doses (1–2 μg) into the third ventricle. Significant increases of respiratory (phrenic) activity lasting up to 30 min were found in most cats; none developed inhibition of respiration following the exhibition of serotonin.

Several investigators have placed serotonin iontophoretically on brain stem neurons. Reticular units were stimulated in some cases and inhibited in others (37). In another study (6) serotonin caused prolonged excitatory responses in brain stem neurons. In a third (11), a number of neurons were excited but none inhibited by serotonin. Serotonin applied to respiratory-related units (13) excited more than half but depressed some.

The systemic administration of the precursors of serotonin, L-tryptophan and L-5-hydroxytryptophan (5-HTP) which cross the blood-brain barrier, has also led to opposing results. Bogdanski et al (7) noted that 5-HTP led to a marked increase in respiratory frequency in various species; in no instance did it inhibit frequency. Others have found an inhibitory effect on ventilation with (2, 42) and without (55) the ancillary use of a monoamine oxidase (MAO) inhibitor. These studies are difficult to evaluate because of systemic administration of the drugs to animals with intact carotid and pulmonary receptors, the use of MAO inhibitors, and because 5-HTP causes the central release of dopamine (53).

Antagonists of serotonin have been shown to affect respiration. Systemic administration of parachlorophenylalanine (PCPA) and other agents that inhibit synthesis of serotonin causes an increase in ventilation (55). Unfortunately these studies were also performed in rats with intact peripheral chemo- and pulmonary receptors. The interpretation is further complicated by the fact that the metabolite parachlorophenylethylalanine (PCPEA) is formed from PCPA for several days after its administration and stimulates the release of serotonin (67).

None of these studies proves that serotonin is a physiological modulator of respiration. However, destruction of serotonin neurons in rat by intracerebroventricular injections of 5,7-dihydroxytryptamine does lead to a persisting hypoventilation (55). Intravenous methysergide, an antagonist of serotonin receptors, causes an immediate decrease of respiration in cats (47). Stimulation of carotid body afferents uniquely activates a central neural mechanism that causes a long-lasting increase of respiration; serotonin antagonists block the ventilatory response (46, 47). These findings suggest that serotonin is indeed a tonic facilitatory modulator of respiration.

CATECHOLAMINES   The central catecholaminergic system includes both dopamine- and norepinephrine-containing neurons. Cell bodies of the former are found in the substantia nigra and hypothalamus, of the latter primarily but not exclusively in the locus coeruleus (69). Axonal pathways of these neurons are rather diffuse, but some have been shown to synapse directly on respiratory neurons in the brain stem (30).

Most of the available evidence suggests that the central catecholamines play an inhibitory role in modulating respiration. Increased norepinephrine receptor activity in rat brain has been associated with a decrease of respiratory frequency, and the central norepinephrine agonists clonidine and L-DOPA cause a decrease of frequency lasting up to an hour (8). Iontophoretic application of norepinephrine on respiratory-related neurons in the brain stem has led to decreased firing frequency in most units studied (13).

Lundberg et al (43) reported that systemically administered apomorphine (3 mg kg^{-1}), a dopamine agonist, stimulated respiration in rats. They concluded that this effect was central. However, their animals had intact carotid bodies. Since dopamine has been shown to stimulate carotid bodies in rats (48), the opposite of its effect in cats, it seems probable that the demonstrated effect was peripherally rather than centrally mediated. In a similar study, Bolme et al (9) also found that small quantities (3–10 μg) of apomorphine led to an increase in respiration when given intravenously to intact rats, but that the same doses given intracisternally consistently caused a dose-dependent decrease in respiratory frequency.

HISTAMINE   Histamine is ubiquitously distributed throughout the brain (69). Although its credentials for being a neurotransmitter are not as good as those of serotonin and the catecholamines, some observations show that it may fulfill many of the essential criteria. Applied to brain stem neurons (33) or cerebral cortex (34), histamine usually depresses excitability, though it stimulates hypothalmic neurons in rats (62). Its function in respiratory control is unknown, though it has been reported that intracerebroventricular injection causes not only hypothermia but also tachypnea lasting several hours (15). The possibility therefore exists that the central histaminergic system may be involved in the modulation of respiratory activity.

ACETYLCHOLINE   Much is known about the peripheral actions of acetylcholine. Evidence is also accumulating for its being a central neurotransmitter, in that microiontophoretic application leads to a relatively brief excitation of neurons in the cerebral cortex of cats, rabbits, and monkeys (39) and in the brain stem of cats (10).

Champagnat et al (13) found that acetylcholine excited more than half of the respiratory-related units to which it was applied in the brain stems of decerebrate cats. It also may be involved in neurotransmission within the central chemoreceptors. Dev & Loeschcke (20) induced hyperventilation by local application to chemosensitive zones on the ventral surface of the medulla. Application of atropine, an antagonist of acetylcholine receptors, reduced resting ventilation and the ventilatory response to CO_2. When physostigmine, a cholinesterase inhibitor, was applied to the same areas ventilation again increased.

Based on the brevity of acetylcholine's action at peripheral synapses and on central neurons, it is likely to be involved in rapid transmission of information between neurons but probably not in the mediation of long-lasting responses.

Neuropeptides

The number of chemical-messenger systems thought to exist in the brain has expanded considerably in recent years with the discovery of the neuropeptides. These molecules are chains of 2–39 amino acids; they have been localized within neurons and many are considered to be possible neurotransmitters.

ENDORPHINS AND ENKEPHALINS   The most recently discovered of the neuropeptides is the family of endogenous polypeptides, generically termed endorphins, that interact with opiate receptors in the brain (70). Current interest is primarily in two types of endorphins, the pentapeptides, leucine-enkephalin and methionine-enkephalin, and a larger peptide, β-endorphin.

Opiate receptors have a stereospecific affinity for the endorphins as well as for exogenous opiates and antagonists (58). The receptors are found in high concentration within hypothalamus, striatum, amygdala, midbrain, brainstem, and spinal cord (68). Within the brain stem they are found in areas classically associated with respiration, the nucleus of the tractus solitarius and the nucleus ambiguus (57).

It has been shown that endorphins mimic the analgesic and catatonic effects, and the respiratory depressant effects (64), of exogenous opiates and that these effects are blocked by naloxone, a potent opiate receptor antagonist (1). The endorphins function as inhibitory neurotransmitters or modulators of various neurons and neural systems, causing naloxone-reversible depression of test cells in most brain regions, including the reticular formation and lateral reticular nuclei of the brain stem (54).

In the case of respiration, Florez & Mediavilla (28) have shown that exogenous met-enkephalin applied directly to the brain stem depresses ventilation and that this effect is blocked by naloxone. Human β-endorphin injected intracisternally in lightly anesthetized dogs also causes marked respiratory depression that is reversed by intravenous administration of naloxone (49). Met-enkephalin has been shown to depress the spontaneous discharge of respiratory-related neurons in the pons and medulla when applied by iotophoresis (18). Again, the effect is antagonized by naloxone.

Thus, endorphins, like opiates, have a depressant effect on respiration that is due to stereospecific binding to opiate receptors. These findings do not prove that endogenous endorphins affect respiration; nevertheless, they could act tonically on central control neurons and exert a constantly modulating effect as they apparently do on other forms of behavior, such as the regulation of body temperature (36) and sexual behavior (32).

Relatively few studies have attempted to elucidate this question. All have involved the administration of the endorphin antagonist, naloxone, to animals or humans not pretreated with an opiate or opiate-like agent. Using intratracheal pressure changes as indicators of respiratory output in mature fetal lambs, Moss & Scarpelli (50) noted that naloxone (3 mg kg^{-1}) caused the initiation of fetal respiration, decreased CO_2 threshold, and increased the response to elevations of CO_2. They suggested that endogenous opiate may participate in the physiological suppression of breathing in fetal life. Endorphins also appear to affect anoxic and asphyxial respiration in newborn rabbit pups (14).

Belenky & Holaday (5) found that naloxone (1 mg kg^{-1}) pretreatment was associated with a significant elevation in respiratory frequency after electroconvulsive shock in adult rats and suggested a role for endorphin in the regulation of respiration, especially after stress. They did not find a significant change in respiration after naloxone had been given to unstressed rats. However, in this study the only measurement made was that of respiratory frequency, and no attempt was made to open the chemical (CO_2) or temperature feedback loops. A more complete study is that of Lawson et al (41) in which the experiments were performed in paralyzed adult cats in the absence of peripheral chemoreceptor or vagal input and with carefully servocontrolled and constant alveolar P_{CO_2} level and body temperature. In these experiments the intravenous administration of naloxone (0.4 mg kg^{-1}) always led to modest increases in respiratory output as reflected by phrenic nerve activity. The authors concluded that endorphin acts tonically to modulate respiration in adult animals. Since the results were similar in anesthetized animals with intact brains and in decerebrate unanesthetized animals, it was also concluded that the endorphin acts at levels no higher than the brain stem.

In human beings naloxone antagonizes the respiratory effects evoked by prior administration of opiates. Whether tonic endogenous endorphin modulation of respiration exists is, however, less certain. In one study (29) in ten anesthetized subjects, naloxone in small doses (0.005 and 0.01 mg kg^{-1}) caused some increase of tidal and minute volumes but the changes were not significant. Fleetham et al (27) infused large doses (50 mg) in seven normal awake men. Because ventilatory responses to inhaled CO_2 and hypoxia were not significantly changed, they concluded that endogenous opiates have no major influence on the control of breathing. Willer (73) gave small doses (about 0.02 mg kg^{-1}) of naloxone intravenously to awake men and women. Again, no significant effect was reported, although Pa_{CO_2} decreased by more than 1 torr 15 min after the drug was given. The interpretation that these studies really show a lack of tonic modulation of respiration by the endorphins in man is not completely convincing. In two of the studies (29, 73) the doses of naloxone were small. In none of the studies was P_{CO_2} kept constant after administration of naloxone, nor was body temperature monitored. Nevertheless, in all there were slight changes in the direction to be expected if naloxone were effective: an increase of tidal volumes in one (29), a decrease of P_{CO_2} in another (73), and an increase of ventilation of over 6 liters per minute at a P_{CO_2} of 55 torr in the third (27).

In summary, the evidence to date supports the idea that endorphins act on respiratory control in a manner similar to that of exogenous opiates. Animal studies support the idea that endogenous endorphins act to modulate respiration following certain kinds of stress and that they probably also act as a tonic modulator at all times. Insufficient evidence is currently available to settle whether they do so in human beings.

OTHER NEUROPEPTIDES   These short chains of amino acids have been found in brain and a variety of peripheral tissues. They appear to play a multiplicity of roles in different parts of the body. For example, they are involved in cardiovascular control and in such phenomena as thirst, pain, and sexual behavior. The group includes angiotensin, bradykinin, cholecystokinin, neurotensin, oxytocin, substance P, vasopressin, and vasoactive intestinal peptide.

Angiotensin II has been studied for its effect on respiration. In dogs whose peripheral buffer nerves had been cut, intravenous angiotensin II stimulated breathing. This effect appeared to be independent of its effect on blood pressure (61). Intracerebroventricular injection (10 μg) in cats led to a decreased respiratory rate, but no other measurements were made in that study (52). Rosendorff (63) gave smaller intraventricular doses (115 ng) in rabbits and found that both air flow rates and frequency increased. Vertebral artery infusions, on the other hand, failed to produce any respiratory response. While these results show that exogenous angiotensin can affect respiration to some extent, they are not adequate to define satisfactorily either the precise location or the mechanism of action.

In view of the convincing evidence for the involvement of endogenous endorphin it seems reasonable that other neuropeptides may also be involved in the tonic modulation of respiration. However, at present this remains an open question awaiting the demonstration of a respiratory response not only to the central administration of the substance but also to specific antagonists; the latter would indicate that the substance may be endogenously active.

Amino Acids

Several amino acids have profound effects on membrane potential when iontophoresed onto neurons. Glutamic acid and aspartic acid excite most neurons in the mammalian central nervous system (CNS); they may be the most common excitatory transmitters in the brain. Other amino acids, such as γ-aminobutyric acid (GABA), glycine, and taurine are generally found to exert powerful inhibitory effects on central neurons.

For the most part, these studies have been performed on unidentified hetrogeneous populations of neurons throughout the CNS. However, iontophoretically applied GABA and glycine have been found to inhibit medullary respiratory neurons (17, 71) and glutamic and aspartic acids to excite ongoing phasic neural activity of both inspiratory and expiratory neurons (71).

In an attempt to characterize the synaptic inputs involved in the rhythmic modulation of bulbar respiratory units, Denavit-Saubié et al (19) applied L-glutamate and GABA iontophoretically and found that these substances could mimic the effect of tonic excitations or inhibitions. They postulate that glutamate and GABA may be involved in the reciprocal innervation of respiratory neurons in the medulla.

It has also been postulated that GABA may play an important role in the mechanism of action of benzodiazepines. For example, diazepam is thought to act by enhancing GABA-mediated synaptic inhibition of central neurons (59). This may be the mechanism by which diazepam acts to depress respiration and lower arterial pressure.

Other Agents

PROSTAGLANDIN   Prostaglandins are cyclic fatty acids thought to function as mediators or modulators of neural transmission. Even though they are known to have greatly diversified physiological properties, their effects on the CNS have received little attention. However, iontophoretic application of prostaglandins has been shown to modify the firing of neurons in the brain stem (4), and there is evidence supporting the role of prostaglandins in fever (74) and central control of the cardiovascular system (35).

Evidence for the involvement of prostaglandins in the regulation of respiration is limited to several studies in which they were administered peripherally to intact guinea pigs (44) and humans (12). In both cases intravenous injections led to an increase of respiratory frequency. However, since the experiments were performed on intact individuals it is impossible to determine whether or not the effect was due to stimulation of central neurons. A more probable explanation is that the prostaglandins caused an increase in bronchial smooth muscle tone, thereby leading to an excitation of pulmonary stretch receptors that increases respiratory frequency. At present there is no evidence that prostaglandins are involved in the central modulation of respiration. However, since it has been shown that intraventricular injections of prostaglandin E_1 are associated with stupor, catonia, tremor, and disturbance of posture (21) it would be surprising if the prostaglandins did not affect respiration as well.

PROGESTERONE   Progesterone, a steroid derivative of cholesterol, is the major progestational hormone in primates. During pregnancy and the luteal phase of the menstrual cycle, the corpus luteum produces quantities of progesterone resulting in a marked increase in plasma progesterone. There seems to be ample evidence that the cyclic increases in endogenous progesterone are associated with an increase in ventilation (22) and a concomitant decrease in alveolar P_{CO_2} (24). Furthermore, the administration of exogenous progesterone has been shown to stimulate respiration in males as well as females (72). The site of action seems to be central since the carotid bodies are not essential to the response (45).

In a recent study, Skatrud et al (66) examined the time course of ventilatory, blood gas, and acid-base changes in male subjects following the oral administration of medroxyprogesterone acetate (MPA). They found that orally administered MPA was associated with a stimulation of respiration lasting for days. They also measured a substantial decrease in both arterial and cerebral spinal fluid (CSF) P_{CO_2} as well as an increase in arterial and CSF pH. They concluded that MPA causes a sustained stimulation of respiration independent of the action of hydrogen ion in the blood or CSF. The site of stimulation is not certain; however, MPA may at least in part act centrally since MPA-related materials can cross the blood-brain barrier.

ACKNOWLEDGMENTS

We are grateful to Ms. Camille Wheeler for her excellent assistance in preparing this manuscript. The work was supported by U.S. Public Health Service Grant HL-17689. Dr. Millhorn was supported by U.S. Public Health Service Pulmonary Training Grant HL-07106.

Literature Cited

1. Akil, H., Mayer, D. J., Liebeskind, J. C. 1976. Antagonism of stimulation produced analgesia by naloxone, a narcotic antagonist. *Science* 191:961–62
2. Armijo, J. A., Florez, J. 1974. The influence of increased brain 5-hydroxytryptamine upon the respiratory activity of cats. *Neuropharmacology* 13:977–86
3. Armijo, J. A., Mediavilla, A., Florez, J. 1979. Inhibition of the activity of the respiratory and vasomotor centers of centrally administered 5-hydroxytryptamine in cats. *Rev. Esp. Fisiol.* 35: 219–28
4. Avanzio, G. L., Bradley, P. B., Wolstencroft, J. H. 1966. Actions of prostaglandins E_1, E_2 and $F_{2\alpha}$ on brain stem neurons. *Br. J. Pharmacol.* 27:157–63
5. Belenky, G. L., Holaday, J. W. 1979. The opiate antagonist naloxone modifies the effects of electroconvulsive shock (ECS) on respiration, blood pressure and heart rate. *Brain Res.* 177:414–17
6. Boakes, R. J., Bradley, P. B., Briggs, I., Dray, A. 1970. Antagonism of 5-hydroxytryptamine by LSD 25 in the central nervous system: a possible neuronal basis of actions of LSD 25. *Br. J. Pharmacol.* 40:202–18
7. Bogdanski, D. F., Weissbach, H., Udenfriend, S. 1958. Pharmacological studies with the serotonin precursor, 5-hydroxytryptophan. *J. Pharmacol. Exp. Ther.* 122:182–94
8. Bolme, P., Fuxe, K. 1973. Pharmacological studies on a possible role of central noradreniline neurons in respiratory control. *J. Pharm. Pharmacol.* 25:351–52
9. Bolme, P., Fuxe, K., Hökfelt, T., Goldstein, M. 1977. Studies on the role of dopamine in cardiovascular and respiratory control. *Adv. Biochem. Psychopharmacol.* 16:281–90
10. Bradley, P. B., Briggs, I. 1974. Further studies on the mode of action of psychotomimetic drugs: antagonism of the excitatory actions of serotonin by methylated derivatives of tryptamine. *Br. J. Pharmacol.* 50:345-54
11. Bramwell, G. J., Bradley, P. B. 1974. Actions and interactions of narcotic agonists and antagonists on brain stem neurones. *Brain Res.* 73:167–70
12. Carlson, L. A., Ekelund, L.-G., Ord, L. 1969. Circulatory and respiratory effects of different doses of prostaglandin E_1 in man. *Acta Physiol. Scand.* 75:161–69
13. Champagnat, J., Denavit-Saubié, M., Henry, J. L., Leviel, V. 1979. Catecholaminergic depressant effects on bulbar respiratory mechanisms. *Brain Res.* 160:57–68
14. Chernick, V., Madansky, D. L., Lawson, E. E. 1980. Naloxone decreases the duration of primary apnea with neonatal asphyxia. *Pediatr. Res.* 14:357–59
15. Clark, W. G., Cumby, H. R. 1976. Biphasic changes in body temperature produced by intraventricular injections of histamine in the cat. *J. Physiol. London* 261:235–53
16. Crawshaw, L. I. 1972. Effects of intracerebral 5-hydroxtryptamine injec-

tion on thermoregulation in the rat. *Physiol. Behav.* 9:133–40

17. Denavit-Saubié, M., Champagnat, J. 1975. The effect of some depressing amino acids on bulbar respiratory and non-respiratory neurons. *Brain Res.* 97:356–61

18. Denavit-Saubié, M., Champagnat, J., Zieglgänsberger, W. 1978. Effect of opiates and methionine-enkephalin on pontine and bulbar respiratory neurones of the cat. *Brain Res.* 155:55–67

19. Denavit-Saubié, M., Champagnat, J., Velluti, J. C. 1979. The central transmission of respiratory signals: a pharmacological study. In *Central Nervous Control Mechanisms in Breathing,* ed. C. von Euler, H. Lagercrantz, pp. 255–60. NY: Pergamon. 508 pp.

20. Dev, N. B., Loeschcke, H. H. 1979. A cholinergic mechanism involved in the respiratory chemosensitivity of the medulla oblongata in the cat. *Pflügers Arch.* 379:29–36

21. Disiraju, T. 1973. Effects of intraventricular administered prostaglandin on the electrical activity of cerebral cortex and behavior in the unanesthetized monkey. *Prostaglandins* 3:859–70

22. Döring, G. K., Loeschcke, H. H., Ochwadt, B. 1949. Über die Blutgase in der Schwangerschaft unter besonder Berucksichtigung der arteriellen Sauerstoffsattigung. *Arch. Gynaekol.* 176:746–58

23. Eldridge, F. L., Millhorn, D. E., Waldrop, T. G. 1979. Respiratory effect of centrally injected serotonin. *Physiologist* 22:33 (Abstr.)

24. England, S. J., Farhi, L. E. 1976. Fluctuations in alveolar CO_2 and in base excess during the menstrual cycle. *Respir. Physiol.* 17:157–61

25. Feldberg, W., Sherwood, S. L. 1954. Injections of drugs into the lateral ventricle of the cat. *J. Physiol. London* 123:148–67

26. Findlay, J., Thompson, G. 1968. The effect of intraventricular injections of noradrenaline, 5-hydroxytryptamine, acetylcholine and trancylcypromine on the ox (*Bos taurus*) at different environmental temperatures. *J. Physiol. London* 194:809–16

27. Fleetham, J. A., Clark, H., Dhingra, S., Anthonisen, N. R., Chernick, V. 1978. Do endogenous opiates influence control of ventilation in man? *Clin. Res.* 26:A878 (Abstr.)

28. Florez, J., Mediavilla, A. 1977. Respiratory and cardiovascular effects of met-enkephalin applied to the ventral surface of the brain stem. *Brain Res.* 138:585–90

29. Foldes, F. F., Duncalf, D., Kuwabara, S. 1969. The respiratory, circulatory, and narcotic antagonistic effects of nalorphine, levallorphan, and naloxone in anaesthetized subjects. *Can. Anaesth. Soc. J.* 16:151–61

30. Fuxe, K. 1965. Evidence for the existence of monoamine neurons in the central nervous system. IV. Distribution of monoamine nerve terminals in the central nervous system. *Acta Physiol. Scand.* 64: Suppl. 247, pp. 39–85

31. Gaddum, J. H., Vogt, M. 1956. Some central actions of 5-hydroxytryptamine and various antagonists. *Br. J. Pharmacol.* 11:175–79

32. Gessa, G. L., Paglietti, E., Pellegrini Quarantatti, B. 1979. Induction of copulatory behavior in sexually inactive rats by naloxone. *Science* 204:203–5

33. Haas, H. L., Anderson, E. G., Hösli, L. 1973. Histamine metabolites: their effects and interactions with convulsants on brain stem neurones. *Brain Res.* 51:269–78

34. Haas, H. L., Bucher, V. M. 1975. Histamine H2-receptors on single central neurones. *Nature* 255:634–35

35. Hoffman, W. E., Schmid, P. G. 1979. Cardiovascular and antidiuretic effects of central prostaglandin E_2. *J. Physiol. London* 288:159–69

36. Holaday, J. W., Wei, E., Loh, H. H., Li, C. H. 1978. Endorphins may function in heat adaptation. *Proc. Natl. Acad. Sci. USA* 75:2923–27

37. Hösli, L., Tebecis, A. K., Schönwetter, H. P. 1971. A comparison of the effects of monoamines on neurones of the bulbar reticular formation. *Brain Res.* 25:357–70

38. Jouvet, M. 1974. The role of monoaminergic neurons in the regulation and function of sleep. In *Basic Sleep Mechanisms,* ed O. Petre-Quadeno, J. P. Schlag, pp. 207–36. NY: Academic. 459 pp.

39. Krnjevic, K., Phillis, J. W. 1963. Acetylcholine-sensitive cells in the cerebral cortex. *J. Physiol. London* 166:296–327

40. Lambert, G. A., Friedman, E., Buchwertz, E., Gershon, S. 1978. Involvement of 5-hydroxytryptamine in the central control of respiration, blood pressure and heart rate in the anesthetized rat. *Neuropharmacology* 17:807–13

41. Lawson, E. E., Waldrop, T. G., Eldridge, F. L. 1979. Naloxone enhances

respiratory output in cats. *J. Appl. Physiol* 47:1105–11

42. Lundberg, D. B. A., Breese, G. R., Mueller, R. A. 1978. Central serotoninergic and dopaminergic modulation of respiratory drive. *Neurosci. Abstr.* 4:277 (Abstr.)

43. Lundberg, D., Breese, G. R., Mueller, R. A. 1979. Dopaminergic interaction with the respiratory control system in the rat. *Eur. J. Pharmacol.* 54:153–59

44. McQueen, D. S. 1973. The effects of prostaglandin E_2, prostaglandin $F_{2\alpha}$, and polyphloretin phosphate on respiration and blood pressure in anesthetized guinea-pigs. *Life Sci.* 12:163–72

45. Mei, S., Gort, D., Kao, F. 1977. The investigation of respiratory effects of progesterone in cross-circulated dogs. *Fed. Proc.* 36:489 (Abstr.)

46. Millhorn, D. E., Eldridge, F. L., Waldrop, T. G. 1980. Prolonged stimulation of respiration by a new central neural mechanism. *Respir. Physiol.* 41:87–103

47. Millhorn, D. E., Eldridge, F. L., Waldrop, T. G. 1980. Prolonged stimulation of respiration by endogenous central serotonin. *Respir. Physiol.* 41:In press

48. Mishra, J., Sapru, H. N., Hess, A. 1979. Physiological effects of dopamine agonists and antagonists on rat carotid body. *Fed. Proc.* 38:143 (Abstr.)

49. Moss, I. R., Friedman, E. 1978. β-endorphin: Effects on respiratory regulation. *Life Sci.* 23:1271–76

50. Moss, I. R., Scarpelli, E. M. 1979. Generation and regulation of breathing in utero: fetal CO_2 response test. *J. Appl. Physiol.* 47:527–31

51. Myers, R., Waller, M. B. 1978. Thermoregulation and serotonin. In *Serotonin in Health and Disease. Vol II: Physiological Regulation and Pharmacological Action,* ed. W. B. Essman, pp. 1–67. NY: Spectrum. 443 pp.

52. Nashold, B. S., Mannarino, E., Wunderlich, M. 1962. Pressor-depressor blood-pressure responses in the cat after intraventricular injection of drugs. *Nature* 193:1297–98

53. Ng, L. K. Y., Chase, T. N., Colburn, R. W., Kopin, I. J. 1972. Release of [³H]dopamine by L-5-hydroxytryptophan. *Brain Res.* 45:499–505

54. Nicoll, R. A., Siggins, G. R., Ling, N., Bloom, F. E., Guillemin, R. 1977. Neuronal actions of endorphins and enkephalins among brain regions. A comparative microiontophoretic study. *Proc. Natl. Acad. Sci. USA* 74:2584–88

55. Olson, E. B. Jr., Dempsey, J. A., McCrimmon, D. R. 1979. Serotonin and control of ventilation in awake rats. *J. Clin. Invest.* 64:689–93

56. Palkovits, M., Brownstein, M., Saavedra, J. M. 1974. Serotonin content of the brain stem nuclei in the rate. *Brain Res.* 80:237–49

57. Pert, C. B., Kuhar, M. J., Snyder, S. H. 1976. Opiate receptor: autoradiographic localization in rat brain. *Proc. Natl. Acad. Sci. USA* 73:3729–33

58. Pert, C. B., Pasternak, G., Snyder, S. H. 1973. Opiate agonists and antagonists discriminated by receptor binding in the brain. *Science* 182:1359–61

59. Polc, P., Mohler, H., Haefely, W. 1974. The effect of diazepam on spinal cord activities: possible sites and mechanisms of action. *Arch. Pharmacol.* 284:319–37

60. Polc, P., Monnier, M. 1970. An activating mechanism in the ponto-bulbar raphe system of the rabbit. *Brain Res.* 22:47–61

61. Potter, E. K., McCloskey, D. I. 1979. Respiratory stimulation by Angiotensin II. *Respir. Physiol.* 36:367–73

62. Renaud, L. P. 1976. Histamine microiontophoresis on identified hypothalamic neurons: 3 patterns of response in the ventromedial nucleus of the rat. *Brain Res.* 115:339–44

63. Rosendorff, C., Lowe, R. D., Lavery, H., Cranston, W. I. 1970. Cardiovascular effects of angiotensin mediated by the central nervous system of the rabbit. *Cardiovasc. Res.* 4:36–43

64. Rossier, J., Bloom, F. 1979. Central neuropharmacology of endorphins. *Adv. Biochem. Psychopharmacol.* 20:165–85

65. Ruckebusch, Y., Grivel, M. L., Laplace, J. P. 1965. Variations interspecifiques des modifications de la température centrale liees a l'injection cérébroventriculaire de catecholamines et de 5-hydroxytryptamine. *C.R. Soc. Biol.* 159:1748–50

66. Skatrud, J. B., Dempsey, J. A., Kaiser, D. G. 1978. Ventilatory response to medroxyprogesterone acetate in normal subjects: time course and mechanism. *J. Appl. Physiol.* 44:939–44

67. Sloviter, R. S., Drust, E. G., Connor, J. D. 1978. Serotonin agonist actions of p-chlorophenylalanine. *Neuropharmacology* 17:1029–33

68. Smith, T. W., Hughes, J., Kosterlitz, H. W., Sosa, R. P. 1976. Enkephalins: isolation, distribution and function. In *Opiates and Endogenous Opioid Pep-*

tides, ed. H. W. Kosterlitz, pp. 57–62. Amsterdam: Elsevier. 456 pp.

69. Snyder, S. H. 1976. Catecholamines, serotonin and histamine. In *Basic Neurochemistry,* ed. J. Siegel, R. W. Albers, R. Katzman, B. W. Agranoff, pp. 203–17. Boston: Little, Brown. 825 pp.

70. Snyder, S. H., Simantov, R. 1977. The opiate receptor and opioid peptides. *J. Neurochem.* 28:13–20

71. Toleikis, J. R., Wang, L., Boyarsky, L. L. 1979. Effects of excitatory and inhibitory amino acids on phasic respiratory

neurons. *J. Neurosci. Res.* 4:225–35

72. Tyler, J. M. 1960. The effect of progesterone on the respiration of patients with emphysema and hypercapnia. *J. Clin. Invest.* 39:34–41

73. Willer, J. C., Boureau, F., Dauthier, C., Bonora, M. 1979. Study of naloxone in normal awake man: effects on heart rate and respiration. *Neuropharmacology* 18:469–72

74. Wolfe, L. S. 1976. Prostaglandins and synaptic transmission. See Ref. 69, pp. 263–75

ENDOCRINOLOGY AND METABOLISM

Introduction, Dorothy T. Krieger,
Section Editor

Endocrinology subsumes an understanding of the factors regulating the synthesis, secretion, and metabolism of hormones, and the action of such hormones on target tissues. In recent years, new basic insights have been obtained with the demonstration of hitherto unknown hormones, delineation of their physiological roles, and elucidation of the mechanisms of hormone action. These advances have been greatly aided by technological advances, notably in the fields of radioimmunoassay and radioreceptor assay, immunocytochemistry, fluorescent labeling, tissue culture, protein purification and synthesis, and microsurgery. In this year's section, the topics of (*a*) reproductive endocrinology, (*b*) factors regulating bone and mineral metabolism, (*c*) intracellular localization of peptides, and (*d*) recently characterized growth factors and endorphins have been chosen as compelling representatives of such recent advances. The reviews indicate the numerous questions raised by these findings and point out the direction of relevant future research.

In the field of reproductive endocrinology, two aspects have been emphasized. Newer insights have been obtained in the pathophysiology of male reproduction. The identification, testicular localization, and purification of androgen-binding protein and the demonstration of its bidirectional secretion into blood and testicular lumen raise questions of its role in spermatic function, its clinical utility as a marker of Sertoli-cell function, and its relation to testosterone-binding globulin in species where both are present. The other aspect concerns the fetal-placental unit. The two chapters on this subject discuss the known and unknown communications that exist among

137

the fetal, maternal, and placental compartments with regard to substrate exchange for steroidogenesis, possible effects of peptides and steroids produced in a given compartment on endocrine events in the other(s), and the regulation and functional role of the fetal adrenal. The demonstration of placental synthesis of many pituitary-like peptides and releasing factors raises questions about (a) the chemical identity of the placental forms with previously described peptides, and (b) the physiological role of the placental forms.

Consideration of the role of placenta in the maintenance and development of the fetus makes it apparent that other factors present initially in fetal life are also involved in the growth and development of fetal tissues. Epidermal growth factor and nerve growth factor are among the best-characterized of these. Regulation and expression of these factors in the neonate and their continued expression throughout growth require considerable further elucidation.

In the field of calcium regulation and bone metabolism, many new insights have arisen from studies in the biochemistry of vitamin D and parathormone, and from detailed in vitro studies of the factors involved in bone formation and resorption. The section's comprehensive review of vitamin D metabolism demonstrates that despite the vast amount of information available on its metabolites and their physiological role and alteration in disease, much remains to be done to further characterize additional metabolites, their functional roles, and the site and mechanisms of their action. Detailed studies of parathormone synthesis and metabolic action have (a) clarified structure-function relationships and elucidated the pathophysiology of states accompanied by elevated parathormone levels or resistance thereto, and (b) delineated the presence of metabolites that may have additional physiological roles. Investigation of the role(s) of the above-cited hormones and other steroid and peptide hormones, as well as prostaglandins, that are involved in bone formation and remodeling has provided basic data that should lead to clinical insights into metabolic bone diseases that have thus far resisted intervention.

A major advance in endocrinology has been the elucidation of mechanisms of hormone action. The classic concept that steroids act solely via intracellular receptors, whereas peptides assert their effects by membrane receptors, has recently been challenged by the finding that such membrane receptors are internalized. New questions thus arise about the role of such internalization, which is also observed for other substances such as LDL, toxins, viruses, and lysosomal enzymes.

Lastly, new hormones as well as new actions and new sites of production of previously described hormones remain to be discovered. The recent description of the endorphins has been chosen as an example of this aspect.

The "endorphins" have been defined as any ligand binding to an opiate receptor; for purposes of clarity, β-endorphin specifies only the 31 amino acid molecule derived from β-lipotropin. Much has been learned about the formation and actions of "endorphins," but their physiological role in health and disease requires further characterization.

The topics in this section illustrate the rapid advances in the elucidation of basic physiological processes in the field of endocrinology. In addition, the reviews delineate the new pathways for investigation that have resulted from these conceptual and methodological advances.

Ann. Rev. Physiol. 1981. 43:141–62
Copyright © 1981 by Annual Reviews Inc. All rights reserved

THE FETAL ADRENAL GLAND ❖1302

Maria Serón-Ferré and Robert B. Jaffe

Reproductive Endocrinology Center, Department of Obstetrics, Gynecology and
Reproductive Sciences, University of California, San Francisco, California 94143

Introduction

Attaining approximately twice the size of the fetal kidney in human fetuses
by midgestation, the fetal adrenal gland has occasioned much investigative
interest. In domestic and experimental animals, secretions of the fetal adrenal gland play a key role in the induction of enzymes in various organ
systems and in the initiation of parturition. Therefore, research now seeks
to assess the extent to which the adrenal gland subserves parallel roles in
the subhuman primate and human fetus. This review focuses upon the
development, function, and regulation of the fetal adrenal gland in monkeys
and humans. Studies of fetal adrenal function and regulation in other species are cited as appropriate.

Morphology and Development

During fetal life, the adrenal gland of most mammalian species lacks the
typical morphological zonation seen in the adult. In rodents, the cells
resemble those of the zona glomerulosa of the adult animal (43). In primates
and in some edentata (armadillo, sloth), the fetal adrenal gland possesses
a distinct inner zone, the fetal zone, that atrophies after birth. This zone is
composed of large eosinophilic cells with pale staining nuclei that have the
ultrastructural characteristics of steroid-secreting cells. The outer portion
of the gland, the definitive or adult zone, is composed of small basophilic
cells resembling those of the adult zona glomerulosa.

At approximately 6 weeks of gestation, the human fetal adrenal gland
appears as a condensation of coelomic epthelium at the cranial end of the
mesonephric kidney. At this stage, the gland is composed of large cells

141

0066-4278/81/0315-0141$01.00

similar to those of the fetal zone of older fetuses. A second proliferation of epithelial cells takes place at 8 weeks of gestation. These cells form a cap over the fetal zone; this spreads as a narrow rim that surrounds the fetal zone and forms the definitive, or adult, zone. The definitive-zone cells are small and have basophilic cytoplasm and darkly staining nuclei. The fetal-zone cells at this stage are large, polyhedral and possess acidophilic cytoplasm with large pale nuclei and distinct cell outlines. Neural elements penetrate the gland through the vascular pole, and clumps of medullary cells can be observed in the central portion of the gland (90).

The human fetal adrenal gland grows rapidly between 10 and 20 weeks of gestation. The combined fetal adrenal glands weigh less than 100 mg at 10 weeks and increase to approximately 2 g at 20 weeks (41). This increase in weight is achieved by an increase in size of both the fetal and definitive zones (88). At this time, the vasculature develops and sinusoidal plexuses appear. The number of medullary cells also increases.

Between 20 and 30 weeks of gestation the glands double in size (from 2 to 4 g). Assessment of the relative proportion of the different zones of the human fetal adrenal gland (88) in specimens obtained from 4 fetuses and 2 neonates indicates that the volume of the fetal zone increases 15% during this period, while the definitive zone and the medulla increase 700% and 400%, respectively. At 30 weeks, indications of adult-type zonation appear in the definitive cortex (87). Connective tissue stroma delineates the glomerulosa, and a columnar arrangement of cells begins to appear in the developing outer zona fasciculata. Human fetal adrenal weight doubles again from 30 weeks to term (4–8 g) (77). Fetal zone volume increases 4-fold, while that of the definitive zone and the medulla increase 20% and 40%, respectively (88). At term, the fetal zone comprises approximately 80% of the gland's volume. Given the size difference between fetal- and definitive-zone cells, however, the number of cells in each zone is probably not so disproportionate.

Decrease in weight and volume of the adrenal gland due to a decrease in size of the fetal zone after birth has been described (77, 88). Adrenal weight decreases from 8 g at 40 weeks to 5 g at a month of age. Volume decreases 50% (88).

Early workers attributed the regression of the fetal zone to necrosis of the fetal-zone cells (88, 90), but more recent work (87) has not confirmed this. The fetal zone disappears by the end of the first year of extrauterine life, while the definitive cortex and medulla continue to grow. The definitive cortex apparently gives rise to the three zones of the adult adrenal gland (reticularis, glomerulosa, fasciculata) during the first year of life. However, limited mitotic activity has been observed during this period in the definitive cortex (87).

In vitro studies indicate that dispersed fetal adrenal cells from 10–20 weeks' gestation lose their morphologic characteristics in culture, become epithelioid, and secrete cortisol (44, 74). Studies performed in the rhesus monkey (see below) suggest that the "atrophy" of the fetal zone after birth is really a remodeling into the zona fasciculata. The characteristic zonation of the adult adrenal gland appears between 1 and 3 years of life (22). A connective tissue band appears between the developing zona fasciculata and the medulla and remains until puberty (22). The zona reticularis appears poorly organized until 11 or 12 years of age, at which time it develops more fully. At this time, the connective tissue band between the medulla and the cortex breaks down. These events are associated with the increase in the secretion of adrenal androgens (adrenarche), particularly dehydroepiandrosterone sulfate (DHAS), that takes place shortly before puberty in humans (22).

Figure 1 depicts the increasing weight of the rhesus fetal adrenal throughout late gestation. No acute decrease in weight has been detected after birth (10). Systematic studies of the monkey adrenal gland throughout gestation indicate that its morphology is remarkably similar to that of the human during fetal life. After birth, the fetal zone gradually disappears. The absence of necrosis in this zone and of mitosis in the definitive zone suggests that, in the rhesus monkey at least, the fetal zone gradually becomes the zona fasciculata during the first year of extrauterine life (W. McNulty, personal communication). A connective tissue band replaces the fetal zone between the medulla and the developing cortex; unlike that of the human, it remains during adult life in the rhesus (35). Recent data from our laboratory show that the rhesus monkey does not have the prepubertal rise in the androgen DHAS that characterizes adrenarche in the human (46).

Cells that appear to be the morphologic and functional equivalent of the fetal zone of the adrenal are present in the fetal gonad of the horse (17, 70). These cells are prominent during fetal life and regress at the end of gestation (17). This striking similarity between the horse fetal gonad and the primate fetal adrenal suggests that some other species may have variable combinations of "fetal zones" in the adrenal or gonads or in both, contributing precursors for steroid synthesis to the placenta.

Adrenal Steroid Biosynthesis, Metabolism and Regulation

The two principal secretory products of the human fetal adrenal gland are DHAS and cortisol, DHAS being the most abundant. Recent studies (78) have demonstrated functional specialization: The definitive zone is the major source of cortisol, the fetal zone of DHAS.

DHAS can be synthesized de novo (40) or from cholesterol derived from circulating low-density lipoprotein (LDL) (12, 64). DHAS also can be

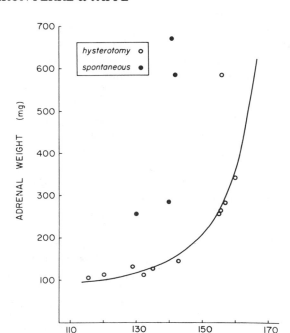

Figure 1 Weight of paired adrenal glands of the fetal rhesus monkey during the last third of gestation. Note the rapid increase in weight near term. (Mean gestational length = 168 days.) Note also the earlier increase in weight in those fetuses that delivered early following spontaneous premature labor (-•-) as compared with those delivered by hysterotomy (-o-).

formed by "direct conversion" of other steroid sulfates, without loss of the sulfate side chain (67)—i.e. via a pathway involving cholesterol sulfate→ pregnenolone sulfate→17 hydroxypregnenolone sulfate→DHAS. In vitro the human fetal adrenal can metabolize DHAS further to 16α-hydroxydehydroepiandrosterone sulfate (16-OH DHAS) (67). The relative contribution of the direct sulfate pathway to DHAS production in the fetus in vivo compared to formation via free (unconjugated) steroid intermediates or from LDL cholesterol has not been ascertained, although it has been suggested that LDL is the main substrate in vivo (64). The capacity for direct steroid sulfate conversion is present in neoplastic, but not in the normal adult human adrenal. Thus the neoplastic tissue may revert to a fetal metabolic mode.

DHAS is extensively metabolized to 16-OH DHAS by the fetal liver. Both DHAS and 16-OH DHAS can be hydrolyzed by the human placenta, which has abundant sulfatase activity (9). After hydrolysis, 16-OH DHAS is aromatized by the placenta to estriol, quantitatively the major estrogen present in the pregnant woman. After hydrolysis, DHAS is aromatized to estrone and estradiol. Sixteen hydroxylation in the fetal liver and adrenal, and estrogen formation by the placenta, then, are major routes of metabolism of the large quantities of DHAS formed in the fetal zone of the human fetal adrenal gland.

The interdependence of fetus, placenta, and mother in the formation of estrogens has led to the concept of the "fetoplacental unit" in which androgenic precursors (DHAS and 16-OH DHAS) of fetal and maternal adrenal origin are hydrolyzed and aromatized by the placenta with the subsequent formation of estrogens.

Cortisol, the major glucocorticoid elaborated by the human and monkey fetal adrenal gland, can be formed by de novo synthesis (78), from progesterone (86) or from lipoprotein-bound cholesterol. The extent to which these latter circulating precursors are used by the fetal adrenal gland in cortisol synthesis remains to be established.

It has been suggested that the human fetal adrenal gland has a deficiency in the 3β-hydroxysteroid dehydrogenase-isomerase enzyme complex. The inability to detect significant progesterone formation following midterm fetal perfusions with radiolabeled pregnenolone (39) may reflect the activity of the desmolase, sulfokinase, and 17-hydroxylase enzyme systems with resultant predominant formation of DHAS. It also is possible that, in vivo, steroids such as progesterone or estrogen suppress or mask the 3β-hydroxysteroid dehydrogenase system. However, most studies of the human fetal adrenal gland have been carried out prior to mid-gestation, and maturational events in enzyme activity very likely change the amount of cortisol and other Δ^4-3 ketosteroids produced toward the end of pregnancy. The pathways of hormone formation in the fetal adrenal gland are depicted schematically in Figure 2.

Cortisol has been found in significant amounts (282 ng/g fresh tissue) in the human fetal adrenal gland at 11 weeks of gestation (57). A high concentration of total corticosteroids, as measured by a competitive protein-binding assay, was detected even earlier in the adrenals of an 8½-week-old fetus (26 mg adrenal weight), but not in a 5½-week fetus, indicating that the capacity to synthesize corticoids appears in the human fetal adrenal soon after organogenesis.

The ability to produce cortisol has been detected in vitro as early as 10 weeks of gestation in the human (78). Both cortisol and DHAS have been shown to increase after ACTH stimulation (11, 78).

Fetal adrenal steroid production increases with age as indicated by the increase in circulating levels of cortisol from 6.9 ng/ml at 13 weeks to 15 ng/ml at 18.5 weeks, 22 ng/ml at 36 weeks, and the further rise to 70 ng/ml found in cord blood in fetuses that delivered spontaneously (57). The adre-

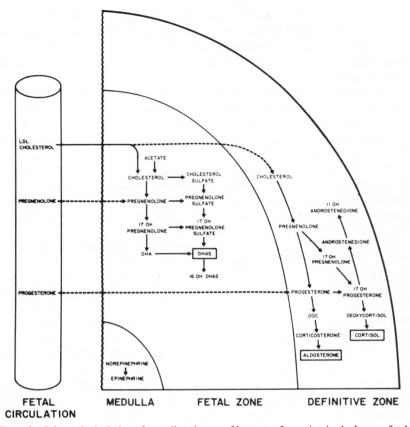

Figure 2 Schematic depiction of overall pathways of hormone formation in the human fetal adrenal gland.

nal origin of cortisol in the fetal circulation between 10 and 20 weeks is indicated by a difference in cortisol concentration between umbilical artery and vein (48, 58). This difference persists until term (59). DHAS levels increase from 60 ng/ml at 16 weeks (37) to 1–2 μg/ml at term (85). Similar values have been reported for 16-OH DHAS (24). A significant cord arteriovenous difference has been reported (85), indicating fetal origin of this steroid as well. Plasma DHAS concentrations remain high during the first week of extrauterine life and then decline (71), probably reflecting atrophy of the fetal zone cells. High plasma DHAS levels have been reported in premature infants (47, 71); some endocrine functions in the premature newborn follow the pattern corresponding to biologic age rather than postnatal age (68).

The human fetal adrenal gland secretes aldosterone (23), desoxycorticosterone (DOC), and corticosterone in vitro (11) between 10 and 20 weeks. At term, aldosterone and DOC are found in high concentrations in cord blood (7), and they respond to sodium-loading and depletion.

Both immunocytochemical and biochemical studies have shown that ACTH is present in the human fetal pituitary gland at 10 weeks of gestation (3, 5, 82). Mean plasma ACTH concentrations of 240 pg/ml have been found in cord blood samples obtained at 14–34 weeks in fetuses delivered by hysterotomy. A decrease to 160 pg/ml in plasma ACTH concentration occurs after 34 weeks. No differences in cord blood ACTH concentrations were detected between cesarean section and vaginally delivered fetuses in this study (93). Cord blood ACTH is of fetal origin as indicated by a difference between umbilical arterial and venous concentrations in samples obtained after spontaneous delivery (2). An increase in ACTH concentration in fetal scalp blood samples was observed during the first and second stages of labor (2). Plasma ACTH levels are low in anencephalic fetuses, although the fetal pituitary remnants contain ACTH that can be released by vasopressin (1). Thus in the normal fetus ACTH is under hypothalamic regulation. There is no transfer of ACTH across the placenta as shown by normal ACTH levels in an infant from a mother with Nelson's syndrome (1, 56) and low ACTH levels in infants of mothers treated with ACTH (85). There is evidence that the human placenta synthesizes ACTH (50) and ACTH-related peptides, including β-endorphin (36) and αMSH (50).

The chemical identity of the immunoreactive ACTH-like material found in the human fetal circulation has not been established. Silman et al found corticotropin-like intermediate lobe peptide (CLIP), αMSH, and ACTH in the human fetal pituitary (83); the proportion of ACTH relative to the other peptides increased with gestational age. This is of interest since it has been found that ACTH-related peptides may modulate the response of the fetal adrenal gland to ACTH in the fetal sheep (73). It is not known whether CLIP and αMSH are present in the human fetal circulation.

The pituitary-adrenal axis in the human fetus is functional as indicated by the suppression of cord blood cortisol and DHAS levels in preterm (4) and term (85) infants delivered after treatment of the mother with glucocorticoids. Treatment of the mother with ACTH also decreases fetal cord blood ACTH levels (85). Measurements using radiolabeled cortisol (6) indicate extensive transfer of cortisol across the placenta. During this transplacental passage, much of the cortisol is oxidized to cortisone that is transferred to the fetus, as shown by a gradient of cortisone between the umbilical vein and artery. The fetal circulation contains five to ten times the amount of cortisone present in the maternal circulation. Cortisol also passes from fetus to mother, as shown by normal corticosteroid excretion during pregnancy in a woman with Addison's disease (40a). The conversion of cortisol to cortisone is reversible. Several fetal tissues, including lung, kidney, amniotic membrane and liver, possess this 11-hydroxysteroid dehydrogenase (11-HDS) enzymatic capacity (60, 89). The relative direction of this interconversion changes with gestational age; at term the conversion of cortisone to cortisol has been postulated to be an important source of cortisol for the fetus (60) and to contribute to the increase of cortisol. An interesting hypothesis has been proposed by Murphy (61), who has evidence that 11-HSD can be regulated by a steroid (unidentified as yet) secreted by the fetal zone of the fetal adrenal gland.

The fetal adrenal gland in vitro responds to ACTH as early as 10 weeks of gestation. The detection of several ACTH-related peptides (αMSH, CLIP, β endorphin) in the human fetal pituitary has led to the suggestion that these peptides may be trophic for the fetal adrenal gland at particular times in gestation. αMSH has been shown to stimulate corticosteroid secretion in rodents and sheep (13, 51, 76). Moreover, in rodents αMSH stimulates DNA synthesis by the fetal adrenal, while ACTH does not (76). Human fetal adrenal cells in short-term cultures also increase glucocorticoid production in response to αMSH (30). Preliminary data from our laboratory indicate that αMSH also stimulates DHAS secretion under short-term culture conditions, but much less than ACTH. However, a lack of effect of αMSH in organ culture of human fetal adrenal tissue has been reported (11). CLIP and β-endorphin also have been found ineffective in this system (11). The physiologic importance of the fetal adrenal response to αMSH is not clear; the capacity of the fetal adrenal gland of most species, including the human, to respond to αMSH suggests maturational changes in the ACTH receptor during development, since the adult adrenal gland does not respond to αMSH. It also may indicate alternate pathways of steroidogenesis or secretion by a more primitive type of cell, since αMSH has been shown to stimulate steroid production preferentially in the zona glomerulosa of the adult rat (91).

Other pituitary hormones may also be adrenotropic in the human fetus. The increase in prolactin during gestation follows the pattern of fetal adrenal growth (94). Prolactin may stimulate cortisol production in dispersed fetal adrenal cells (30), but the data are not conclusive. Growth hormone increases incorporation of radioactive precursors into cholesterol in fetal adrenal minces between 10 and 20 weeks of gestation (38). That hCG increases DHAS secretion in vitro (80) supports the finding of a normal-sized fetal zone in anencephalic fetuses before 20 weeks (8). The maintenance of the definitive zone in the anencephalic fetus (8) suggests that a substance other than ACTH maintains the definitive zone of the adrenal gland but not normal cortisol secretion. Since angiotensin is present in the fetal circulation in high concentration (69) and is mitogenic for the adult adrenal (29), it, together with ACTH and other pituitary or placental peptides (e.g. fibroblast growth factor and epidermal growth factor) may play a trophic role in adrenal growth and regulation. The existence of yet other factors regulating the fetal adrenal is suggested by the observation that the capacity of the isolated fetal zone cells to secrete cortisol increases in culture. This suggests the removal of a block present in vivo. The decrease in production of DHAS after birth also supports this hypothesis and suggests that a steroid or peptide peculiar to pregnancy may also play a role in the regulation of DHAS.

The fetal adrenal gland of the rhesus monkey is similar morphologically to that of the human. There also are functional similarities: The fetal zone secretes DHAS while cortisol is secreted primarily by the definitive zone. In addition, both respond to ACTH (Figure 3). Steroid biosynthesis is similar to that in the human, although the rhesus monkey does not have 16-hydroxylating capacity in the adrenal or liver (81). We have studied the secretion of steroids by the fetal adrenal gland of the monkey utilizing adrenal minces in a superfusion system, from 90 days of gestation to term (mean gestational length = 168 days). In this in vitro system the monkey fetal adrenal gland secretes androstenedione, progesterone, aldosterone, and DOC, in addition to cortisol and DHAS. Secretion of all of these steroids, except aldosterone, is increased by ACTH. Progesterone and DOC secretion decreases with gestational age. In contrast, basal concentrations of androstenedione and the secretion of androstenedione in response to ACTH increase at the end of gestation. Cortisol secretion also increases with gestational age.

Our in vitro data indicate that substantial amounts of DOC and aldosterone are secreted by the rhesus monkey fetal adrenal gland between 130 days and term. DOC increases in response to ACTH, while aldosterone increases following increases in the concentration of potassium in the medium.

These data indicate that the fetal adrenal gland of the rhesus monkey is an active steroid-secreting organ. The decrease in progesterone and DOC with advancing gestation suggests a maturation of enzyme systems involved in the utilization of endogenous progesterone in the synthesis of cortisol, androstenedione, and aldosterone. These changes seem to occur after 150 days' gestational age, corresponding with a period of rapidly accelerating growth of the gland (Figure 1). The increases in cortisol and aldosterone production toward the end of gestation appear to presage the adult pattern of adrenal steroid production, perhaps in preparation for extrauterine life.

In the rhesus monkey fetal pituitary gland, as in the human, there is an increase in the proportion of ACTH to other ACTH-related peptides (αMSH, CLIP, β-endorphin) (83). In our studies, αMSH stimulated

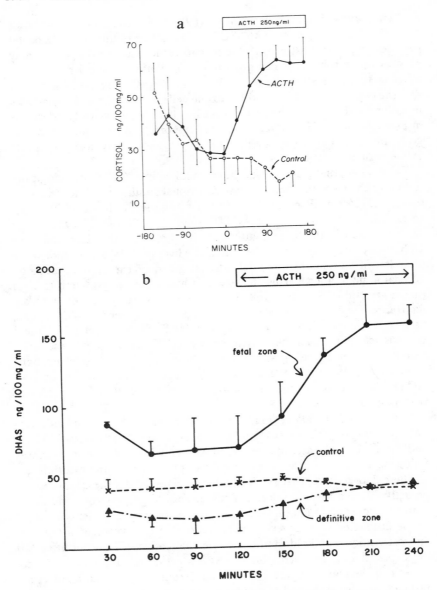

Figure 3 Corticosteroid and dehydroepiandrosterone sulfate (DHAS) responses to 250 ng/ml ACTH by minces of separated fetal and definitive zones of rhesus monkey fetal adrenal glands studied in a superfusion system. a. Cortisol responses. b. DHAS responses. Hormone levels obtained from superfusion of fetal adrenal minces to which no ACTH was added are included for comparison. Cortisol and DHAS were measured by radioimmunoassay.

cortisol in vitro, although to a lesser degree than ACTH. It is also less effective in the stimulation of DHAS and androstenedione and appears to have no effect on progesterone secretion by the rhesus monkey fetal adrenal in vitro. Thus the fetal adrenal of the rhesus monkey responds to αMSH, as has been documented in other species [human (30), sheep (51), rabbit, rat and guinea pig (76)].

The long-term catheterized rhesus monkey fetus has been used to study the factors that regulate the fetal adrenal gland in vivo in late gestation. Catheters are placed in the fetal circulation, the fetus remaining in utero, at 120–130 days of gestation (79, 92).

ACTH concentrations are lower in rhesus monkey than in human fetal circulation (79). This may indicate either a species difference or that the human data also reflect the measurement of other ACTH-related peptides because of cross-reaction with the antibody utilized for ACTH measurement. Treatment with high doses of dexamethasone suppresses 90% of the ACTH and cortisol in the monkey fetal circulation within 24 hr. Values return to normal after cessation of dexamethasone administration. Treatment with high doses of ACTH as a bolus or infusion (92) restores cortisol levels to pretreatment values in the dexamethasone-treated fetus. Treatment of nonsuppressed fetuses with ACTH does not increase cortisol levels, suggesting saturation of ACTH receptors in utero. αMSH also increases corticosteroids in dexamethasone-suppressed monkey fetuses, although the effect is much smaller and more short-lived than that brought about by ACTH. The study of cortisol secretion in vivo is complicated by the presence of other steroids in fetal plasma that can cross-react in most cortisol radioimmunoassays (16, 52). In our studies using extracted plasma, there was 10% contamination, measured by a radioimmunoassay utilizing an antibody against a 3-hemisuccinate of cortisol.

Cortisol concentration increases in the fetal circulation near term (79). We have detected a circadian variation of cortisol concentration in the fetal rhesus circulation, but this has not been found by other investigators, perhaps owing to methodologic differences. The factors that contribute to the regulation of circulating levels of cortisol include a high metabolic clearance rate and an efficient conversion of cortisol to cortisone (54, 55). The metabolic clearance rate of cortisol in the fetus (23 1/day or 86 1/kg/day) is significantly higher than in the mother or infant (11.9 and 27.1 1/kg/day, respectively) (54). The conversion of cortisone to cortisol accounts for approximately 40% of the cortisol present in the fetal circulation.

There is significant transplacental passage of cortisol. As shown in Figure 4, approximately 50% of fetal cortisol is of maternal origin. However, at 130 days the fetus secretes as much cortisol per unit weight as the mother, indicating a competent and active adrenal gland. The importance of the

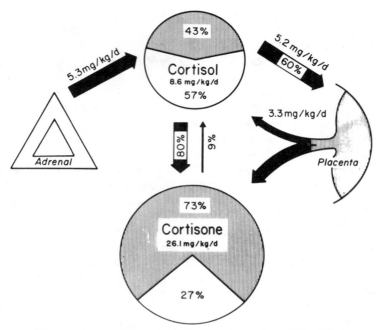

Figure 4 Schematic representation of overall production and metabolism of cortisol in the rhesus monkey fetus. Hatched areas represent maternal contribution and open areas represent fetal contribution.

fetal-maternal transport of cortisol in the regulation of fetal adrenal function is demonstrated by experiments (34) in which maternal hypophysectomy at 90 days resulted in fetal adrenal hypertrophy. The factor(s) that mediates maternal-fetal pituitary-adrenal interaction is not known. The data accumulated suggest that maternal cortisol crosses the placenta and suppresses the fetal pituitary gland. Changes in fetal ACTH following oscillations in maternal or fetal cortisol levels within the physiologic range have not been assessed. The concentration gradient of cortisol between the fetal and maternal circulation indicates that minor increases in the transfer of cortisol should suppress fetal ACTH. On the other hand, the amount of cortisol in the fetal compartment, because of the high cortisol production rate, is significantly greater than the production rate of cortisol in the adult (54). Therefore, the fetal hypothalamus and pituitary should be less sensitive to cortisol feedback. It is possible that steroids other than cortisol are also involved in feedback regulation of ACTH by the fetal pituitary. It is also possible that a portion of cortisol production is regulated independently of ACTH or the fetal pituitary; it may be determined by the placental clearance of cortisol and the regulation of the interconversion of cortisone to cortisol, perhaps by another steroid secreted by the fetal adrenal gland.

Mechanisms that regulate fetal cortisol in utero remain to be defined completely. The increase in cortisol after 150 days may be due to an increase in ACTH in the circulation, to a change in sensitivity of the adrenal to trophic stimulation, to adrenal maturation, to the increase in adrenal weight that takes place after 150 days (Figure 1), to changes in the metabolic clearance rate of cortisol, and/or to a greater conversion of maternal cortisone to cortisol. As with many other physiologic systems, it is likely that cortisol regulation is dependent upon more than one of these factors.

Circulating concentrations of DHAS in the fetal rhesus monkey are shown in Figure 5. DHAS levels remain constant, approximately 200 ng/ml, until 150 days. At this time, there is a sharp increase in DHAS concentration, and levels up to 5 μg/ml are observed in cord blood at term. The levels of DHAS are much higher in the neonate than in the fetus and, in contrast to the human, remain high for 2 to 3 months after birth. Circadian variation of DHAS has been observed, with evening levels being twice the morning values (16). We have found that suppression of ACTH by treatment with high doses of dexamethasone reduces plasma DHAS concentrations approximately 60% in 48 hr, while cortisol is suppressed 90% by this treatment. The partial suppression of DHAS by dexamethasone does not reflect an extended half-life of DHAS, since preliminary data from our laboratory indicate a half-life of 4–6 hr, while the persistence of 40% of DHAS at 48 hr requires a half-life of at least 20 hr. The incomplete suppression of DHAS by dexamethasone is in accord with the finding (15)

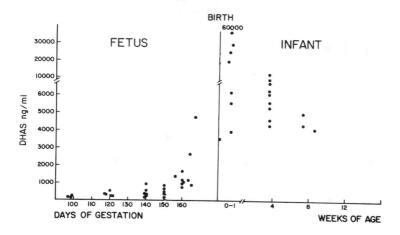

Figure 5 Concentrations of dehydroepiandrosterone sulfate (DHAS) in the circulation of the fetal and infant rhesus monkey.

of a partial suppression of androstenedione, estradiol, and estrone in the maternal circulation after long-term treatment with dexamethasone. The partial suppression of fetal DHAS with dexamethasone suggests that there may be another factor, in addition to ACTH, that could stimulate DHAS secretion in utero. This is further suggested by the increase in the ratio of DHAS to cortisol observed in the fetal circulation after 150 days (Figure 6). An adrenal androgen-stimulating hormone, distinct from ACTH, has been proposed to explain the dissociation between adrenal androgen (DHAS) and cortisol secretion observed in humans at puberty, with anorexia nervosa, and following treatment with dexamethasone (33, 65). In the fetus this factor might also stimulate preferential growth of the fetal zone at the end of gestation.

The Adrenal Medulla in the Fetus

While fetal adrenal cortical formation and regulation are relatively mature at term, the adrenal medulla is relatively immature, and medullary maturation continues during the first year of postnatal life (19, 20, 26). It may not be coincidental that the cortex surrounds the medulla, as adrenocortical steroids can stimulate the formation of epinephrine, a major product of the medulla, by effecting the conversion of norepinephrine to epinephrine (95).

The adrenal medulla in the fetus has been studied less extensively than the cortex. The medulla is well-formed in the human fetus by 10–12 weeks (20, 26, 32). Epinephrine was detected in the human fetal adrenal medulla as early as the 130-mm stage (31). However, most of the chromaffin tissue

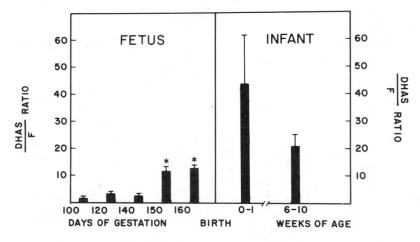

Figure 6   Ratio of dehydroepiandrosterone sulfate (DHAS) to cortisol (F) in the fetal and infant rhesus monkey.

in the fetus is represented by extramedullary, para-aortic paraganglia, which reach maximum size by 28 weeks of intrauterine life and then slowly regress (20, 26).

Both epinephrine and norepinephrine can be detected in the human adrenal medulla by 10–15 weeks of gestation (31, 62). In contrast, norepinephrine content predominates in the paraganglial tissue, including the organs of Zuckerkandl. The envelopment of the medulla by the cortex ensures a high corticosteroid environment, facilitating epinephrine formation by stimulating phenylethanolamine N-methyl transferase, which converts norepinephrine to epinephrine. In support of this thesis is the finding in rats that hypophysectomy of the fetus reduces epinephrine in the medulla while ACTH restores it (53).

The regulation of catecholamine secretion in the fetus has not been elucidated completely. Most work in this area to date has been carried out in the fetal lamb (18, 19, 42). To explore the role of the fetal adrenal medulla in the response to hypoxia, the content of epinephrine and norepinephrine in fetal adrenal glands of lambs removed after minimal trauma was compared with those after exposure to hypoxia (19). It was found that the fetal adrenals removed after minimal trauma contained approximately twice as much epinephrine and three times as much norepinephrine per unit weight of tissue as the corresponding glands removed after hypoxia. The total amounts of epinephrine and norepinephrine contained in the glands also differed in the two groups; after hypoxia, the amount of both epinephrine and norepinephrine was considerably lower at all ages than in the animals in which interference was kept to a minimum. In addition, in these animals there was a rapid increase in the norepinephrine content between 80 and 110 days which was barely seen after hypoxia. However, the major rise in epinephrine content occurred toward the end of pregnancy in both groups of animals. These experiments indicate that norepinephrine is released in response to hypoxia by the fetal lamb. Throughout pregnancy, no relation could be found between the weights of the fetal adrenal glands and the amounts of either epinephrine or norepinephrine contained in them. Thus at term the abrupt increase in the weight of the fetal adrenal glands was not accompanied by any comparable changes in catecholamine content; therefore, the increase in weight was ascribed to the growth of the adrenal cortex rather than the medulla.

The rate of release of epinephrine and norpinephrine rose sharply following splanchnic nerve stimulation from about 125 days until term; after 134 days the output of epinephrine was significantly higher than that of norepinephrine. The sudden change in the rate of epinephrine and norepinephrine output in response to splanchnic nerve stimulation at about 125 days was not accompanied by any corresponding change in the weight of the adrenal glands or in their pressor amine content. It seems probable, therefore, that the increased efficiency of this form of stimulus in late pregnancy was due to the development of the innervation of the adrenal medulla during this period. These studies demonstrated that the functional innervation of the adrenal medulla from the splanchnic nerves develops during the last 20 days of pregnancy in fetal lambs.

Comline & Silver called attention to the two components of response to hypoxia in the fetus, the direct response and the neural response (18). The direct response, which consists largely of secretion of norepinephrine, is confined to fetal life and differs in appearance and duration between lamb and calf. In the lamb, it is present at 80–90 days' gestation, reaches a maximum at 115–130 days, and declines with increasing rapidity, so that immediately before term it is small. In the calf, the direct response increases throughout gestation and does not decline until immediately after birth. The discharge of norepinephrine by the adrenal medulla is independent of innervation: It is found after cutting the splanchnic nerves, after the injection of hexamethonium, and after destruction of the spinal cord by pithing. In the fetal lamb, a substantial nervous response is found toward term, whereas in the calf this component is absent throughout gestation.

In a more recent study, plasma catecholamines in fetal and maternal sheep were measured (42). Fetal and maternal plasma catecholamine concentrations during and after hypoxia were quantified in chronically catheterized sheep 118–141 days pregnant. In most fetuses, the initial plasma catecholamine concentrations were less than 0.07 ng/ml. During hypoxia, plasma epinephrine and norepinephrine concentrations always rose to values higher than those found in the maternal circulation. The initial catecholamine concentration in the ewes was 0.05–2.3 ng/ml. The ewe, in contrast to the fetus, did not respond to hypoxia with an increase in epinephrine and norepinephrine.

The half-life of epinephrine and norepinephrine in the maternal and fetal circulation was 0.25–1.0 min. There was evidence of transfer of labeled catecholamine across the placenta. The clearance rates for the fetal and maternal circulation, calculated from infusion data, were 840 and 4200 ml/min, respectively. At a resting level of catecholamines in the fetal and maternal circulation of 50 pg/ml, their secretion rates would be 42 and 240 pg/min, respectively. These are comparable to the values reported by others for unstimulated adrenal glands.

Functions of the Fetal Adrenal Gland

The role of the fetal adrenal gland in the maintenance of intrauterine homeostasis is largely unknown. The fetus can survive in utero and continue to grow in the absence of a functional fetal adrenal gland, as in anencephalic human fetuses or decapitated monkey fetuses (63). However, these are extreme situations and do not rule out a contribution of the normal fetal adrenal to adaptation in utero. Moreover, anencephalic and decapitated fetuses do not represent instances in which there is an absolute absence of adrenocortical hormones; maternal contributions provide significant amounts of cortisol to the fetal circulation (25), and there may be varying degrees of steroid production by the fetal adrenal. Since the fetus lives in a restricted, relatively constant environment, it is possible that hormones play a more subtle or permissive role as homeostatic regulators in the fetus than they do in the adult.

It is possible that the pituitary gland of the primate fetus, like that of the sheep, can respond to hypoxia and hemorrhage with a release of ACTH. In the lamb, the adrenal gland does not respond to ACTH until the latter part of gestation (28, 51, 75); early in gestation, some of the extra-adrenal effects of ACTH, such as lipolysis, may be more important in adaptation to hypoxia or hemorrhage than the secretion of cortisol (41a). This also may be true in the primate.

In some species, glucocorticoids play an important role in the maturation of enzyme systems necessary for adaptation to extrauterine life. In the fetal sheep and rabbit, glucocorticoids induce maturation of the lung, liver, pancreas, small intestine, adrenal medulla, and thyroid (49). In the lung, glucocorticoids induce cytodifferentiation of Type II cells and increase synthesis and release of surfactant. In rabbits, glucocorticoids induce β-adrenergic receptors in the lung. Glucocorticoids may also increase lung compliance; however, this may not be a direct effect of glucocorticoids upon the lung (45).

Glucocorticoids increase glycogen deposition in the liver and heart. They also increase the insulin response to a glucose load and may stimulate maturation of pancreatic beta cells. Further, in the small intestine they increase the activity of disaccharidases and decrease the permeability of the gut mucosa to macromolecules such as immunoglobulins. Glucocorticoids also alter the metabolism of thyroxine and modulate the change from reverse T_3 to T_3 that is important for neonatal adaptation to cold.

In the sheep and certain other species, the adrenal gland of the fetus plays a key role in the initiation of parturition (49), presumably in the following manner: Increasing concentrations of cortisol toward the end of gestation induce an increase in the placental enzyme, 17-hydroxylase. This causes an increase in placental estrogen and a decrease in placental progesterone production (through 17-hydroxylation of progesterone and subsequent metabolism to estrogens). The increased estrogen : progesterone ratio leads to an increase in prostaglandin synthetase. The resultant increased prostaglandin production triggers uterine contractions leading to the initiation of labor. The extent to which the fetal adrenal gland in the human is involved in the initiation and/or timing of parturition is under investigation. That the timing of parturition in anencephalic fetuses is abnormal suggests that the fetal adrenal may be involved in its fine control.

The possible regulatory role of fetal mineralocorticoids in intrauterine life has not been explored in detail. The high mineralocorticoid secretion by the fetus may play a role in water and electrolyte balance. This is suggested by the demonstration of alterations in aldosterone and desoxycorticosterone in the fetus in response to sodium loading or depletion of the mother (7).

The role of the large concentrations of dehydroepiandrosterone sulfate (DHAS) during fetal life is less clear than that of cortisol. DHAS serves as a precursor for placental production of estrogens, which are important in the regulation of uterine blood flow (72). Modulation of uterine blood flow is important for fetal survival, and the fetus might play a role in the regulation of uterine and placental blood flow. DHAS may also serve as a "reservoir" for free (unconjugated) active steroids, following cleavage of the sulfate side chain.

That DHAS serves as a precursor of placental estrogens may provide the link by which the fetal adrenal gland participates in the initiation or timing of parturition, as increasing concentrations of estrogen seem to play an important role in this process. In the primate, however, the absence of a functional adrenal gland does not seem to prevent delivery, but rather inhibits the precise timing of delivery, increasing the number of both premature and post-term births. In primates, then, the primary contribution of the fetal adrenal gland to the initiation of labor may not be cortisol, as it is in sheep, but a precursor of estrogen, such as DHAS or androstenedione. As with many other aspects of intrauterine life, this intriguing hypothesis remains to be substantiated.

Literature Cited

1. Allen, J. P., Cook, D. M., Kendall, J. W., McGilvra, R. 1973. Maternal-fetal ACTH relationships in man. *J. Clin. Endocrinol. Metab.* 37:230–34
2. Arai, K., Yanaihara, T., Okinaga, S. 1976. Adrenocorticotropic hormone in human fetal blood at delivery. *Am. J. Obstet. Gynecol.* 125:1136–40
3. Baker, B. L., Jaffe, R. B. 1975. The genesis of cell types in the adenohypophysis of the human fetus as observed with immunocytochemistry. *Am. J. Anat.* 143: 137–62
4. Ballard, P. L., Gluckman, P. D., Liggins, G. C., Kaplan, S. L., Grumbach, M. M. 1980. Steroid and growth hormone levels in premature infants after perinatal betamethasone therapy to prevent respiratory distress syndrome. *Pediat. Res.* 14:122–27
5. Begeot, M., Dubois, M. P., Dubois, P. M. 1977. Growth hormone and ACTH in the pituitary of normal and anencephalic human fetuses: Immunocytochemical evidence for hypothalamic influences during development. *Neuroendocrinology* 24:208–20
6. Beitins, I. Z., Bayard, F., Ances, I. G., Kowarski, A., Migeon, C. J. 1973. The metabolic clearance rate, blood production, interconversion and transplacental passage of cortisol and cortisone in pregnancy near term. *Pediat. Res.* 7: 509–19

7. Beitins, I. Z., Bayard, F., Levitsky, L., Ances, I. G., Kowarski, A., Migeon, C. J. 1972. Plasma aldosterone concentration at delivery and during the newborn period. *J. Clin. Invest.* 51:386–94

8. Bernirschke, K. 1956. Adrenals in anencephaly and hydrocephaly. *Obstet. Gynecol.* 8:412–25

9. Bolté, E., Mancuso, S., Eriksson, G., Wiqvist, N., Diczfalusy, E. 1964. Aromatisation of C-19 steroids by placentas perfused *in situ. Acta Endocrinol.* 45:535–59

10. Bourne, G. H. 1975. In *The Rhesus Monkey. Vol I, Anatomy and Physiology,* ed. G. H. Bourne, pp. 1–64. New York/San Francisco/London: Academic

11. Branchaud, C. T., Goodyer, C. G., Hall, S. G. C., Arato, J. S., Silman, R. E., Giroud, C. J. P. 1978. Steroidogenic activity of ACTH and related peptides on the human neocortex and fetal adrenal cortex in organ culture. *Steroids* 31:557–72

12. Cacciari, E., Cicognani, A., Pirazzoli, P., Dallacasa, P., Mazzaracchio, M. A., Tassoni, P., Bernardi, F., Salardi, S., Zappulla, F. 1975. Plasma ACTH values during the first seven days of life in infants of diabetic mothers. *J. Pediat.* 87:943–45

13. Carr, B. R., Parker, C. R. Jr., Porter, J. C., MacDonald, P. C., Simpson, C. R. 1980. Regulation of steroid secretion by adrenal tissue of a human anencephalic fetus. *J. Clin. Endocrinol. Metab.* 50:870–73

14. Challis, J. R. G., Torosis, J. D. 1977. Is αMSH a trophic hormone to adrenal function in the fetus? *Nature* 269:818–19

15. Challis, J. R. G., Davies, I. J., Benirschke, K., Hendrickx, A. G., Ryan, K. J. 1975. The effects of dexamethasone on the peripheral plasma concentrations of androstenedione, testosterone and cortisol in the pregnant rhesus monkey. *Endocrinology* 96:185–91

16. Challis, J. R. G., Socol, M., Murata, Y., Manning, F.A., Martin, C. B. 1980. Diurnal variations in maternal and fetal steroids in pregnant rhesus monkeys. *Endocrinology* 106:1283–88

17. Cole, H. H., Hart, G. H., Lyons, W. R., Catchpole, H. R. 1933. The development and hormonal content of fetal horse gonads. *Anat. Rec.* 56:275–93

18. Comline, R. S., Silver, M. A. 1966. Development of activity in the adrenal medulla of the foetus and newborn animal. *Br. Med. Bull.* 22:16–20

19. Comline, R. S., Silver, M. A. 1961. The release of adrenaline and noradrenaline from the adrenal glands of the foetal sheep. *J. Physiol. London* 156:424–44

20. Coupland, R. E. 1952. The prenatal development of the abdominal para-aortic bodies in man. *J. Anat.* 86:357–72

21. Dawes, G. S., Mott, J. C., Shelley, H. J. 1959. The importance of cardiac glycogen for the maintenance of life in foetal lambs and new-born animals during anoxia. *J. Physiol. London* 146:516–38

22. Dhom, G. 1973. The prepuberal and puberal growth of the adrenal (adrenarche). *Beitr. Pathol. Bd.* 150:357–77

23. Dufau, M. L., Villee, D. B. 1969. Aldosterone biosynthesis by human fetal adrenal *in vitro. Biochem. Biophys. Acta* 176:637–41

24. Easterling, W. E. Jr., Simmer, H. H., Dignam, W. J., Frankland, M. V., Naftolin, F. 1966. C19-steroids and steroid sulfates in human pregnancy. II. Dehydroepiandrosterone sulfate, 16α hydroxydehydroepiandrosterone sulfate in maternal and fetal blood of pregnancies with anencephalic and normal fetuses. *Steroids* 8:157–78

25. Fencl, M. de, Osathanondh, R., Tulchinsky, D. 1976. Plasma cortisol and cortisone in pregnancies with normal and anencephalic fetuses. *J. Clin. Endocrinol. Metab.* 43:80–85

26. Fisher, D. A. 1979. Fetal endocrinology: endocrine disease and pregnancy. In *Endocrinology, Vol. 3,* ed. L. J. DeGroot, pp. 1649–63. NY: Grune & Stratton

29. Gill, G. N., Hornsby, P. J., Ill, C. R., Simonian, M. H., Weidman, R. E. 1978. In *The Endocrine Function of the Human Adrenal Cortex,* ed. V. H. T. James, M. Serio, G. Guisti, L. Martini, pp. 207–28. London/New York/San Francisco: Academic

30. Glickman, J. A., Carson, G. D., Challis, J. R. G. 1979. Differential effects of synthetic adrenocorticotrophic hormone 1–24 and α melanocyte-stimulating hormone on adrenal function in human and sheep fetuses. *Endocrinology* 104:34–39

31. Greenberg, R. E., Lind, J. 1961. Catecholamines in tissues of the human fetus. *Pediatrics* 27:904

32. Greenberg, R. E. 1969. The physiology and metabolism of catecholamines. In *Endocrine and Genetic Diseases of Childhood,* ed. L. I. Gardner, pp. 886–98. Philadelphia: Saunders

33. Grumbach, M. M., Richards, G. E., Conte, F. A., Kaplan, S. L. 1978. Pitui-

tary adrenal androgen-stimulating hormone. See Ref. 29, pp. 583–612

34. Hodgen, G. D., Gulyas, B. J., Tullner, W. W. 1975. Role of the primate placenta in cortisol secretion by the maternal adrenal. *Steroids* 26:233–40

35. Holmes, R. L. 1968. The adrenal glands of *Macaca mulatta*, with special reference to the cortico-medullary zone. *J. Anat.* 103:4711–77

36. Houck, J. C., Kimball, C., Chang, C., Pedigo, N. W. Yamamura, H. I. 1980. Placental β-endorphin-like peptides. *Science* 207:78–80

37. Huhtaniemi, I., Vihko, R. 1970. Determination of unconjugated and sulfated neutral steroids in human fetal blood of early and mid-pregnancy. *Steroids* 16:197–206

38. Isherwood, D. M., Oakey, R. E. 1976. Control of estrogen production during human pregnancy: effect of trophic hormones on steroid biosynthesis by the fetal adrenal gland *in vitro*. *J. endocrinol.* 68:321–29

39. Jaffe, R. B., Pion, R., Eriksson, G., Wiqvist, N., Diczfalusy, E. 1965. Studies on the aromatisation of neutral steroids in pregnant women. IV. Lack of oestrogen formation from progesterone. *Acta Endocrinol.* 48:413–22

40. Jaffe, R. B., Pérez-Palacios, G., Lamont, K. G., Givner, M. L. 1968. *De novo* steroid sulfate biosynthesis. *J. Clin. Endocrinol. Metab.* 28:1671–74

40a. James, V. H. T. 1966. Corticosteroid secretion by human placenta and fetus. *Eur. J. Steroids* 1:5–9

41. Jirasek, J. E. 1971. *Development of the Genital System and Male Pseudohermaphroditism.* Baltimore-London: Johns Hopkins Press, pp. 10–23

41a. Jones, C. T., Boddy, K., Robinson, J. S., Ratcliffe, T. F. 1977. Developmental changes in the response of the adrenal glands of fetal sheep to endogenous corticotropin as indicated by hormone responses to hypoxemia. *J. Endocrinol.* 72:279–92

42. Jones, C. T., Robinson, R. O. 1975. Plasma catecholamines in foetal and adult sheep. *J. Physiol. London* 248:15–33

43. Kahri, A. 1966. Histochemical and electron microscopic studies of the cells of the rat adrenal cortex. *Acta Endocrinol.* 52: Suppl. 108, pp. 1–96

44. Kahri, A. I., Huhtaniemi, I., Salmenpera, M. 1976. Steroid formation and differentiation of cortical cells in tissue culture in the presence and absence of ACTH. *Endocrinology* 98:33–41

45. Kitterman, J., Liggins, G. C., Campos, G., Forster, C., Creasy, R. 1979. Hormonal factors in lung maturation (LM) in fetal lambs. *Pediat. Res.* 13:537 (Abstr. 1269)

46. Koritnik, D. R., Jaffe, R. B. 1980. Evidence for the absence of adrenal androgen influence on the hypothalamo-pituitary-testicular axis of the neonatal and infant rhesus monkey. In *Adrenal Androgens.* NY: Raven Press

47. Korth-Schutz, S., Levine, L. S., New, M. I. 1976. Dehydroepiandrosterone sulfate (DS) levels, a rapid test for abnormal adrenal androgen secretion. *J. Clin. Endocrinol. Metab.* 42:1005–13

48. Leong, M. K. H., Murphy, B. E. P. 1976. Cortisol levels in maternal venous and umbilical cord arterial and venous serum at vaginal delivery. *Am. J. Obstet. Gynecol.* 124:471–73

49. Liggins, G. C. 1976. Adrenocortical-related maturational events in the fetus. *Am. J. Obstet. Gynecol.* 126:931–41

50. Liotta, A., Osathanondh, R., Ryan, K. J., Krieger, D. T. 1977. Presence of corticotropin in human placenta: demonstration of *in vitro* synthesis. *Endocrinology* 101:1552–58

51. Llanos, A. J., Ramachandran, J., Creasy, R. K., Rudolph, A. M., Serón-Ferré, M. 1979. α Melanocyte-stimulating hormone and adrenocorticotropin in the regulation of glucocorticoid secretion during the perinatal period in sheep. *Endocrinology* 105:613–17

52. Magyar, D. M., Elsner, C. W., Nathanielsz, P. W., Lowe, K. C., Buster, J. E. 1979. Specificity assessment of cortisol radioimmunoassays applied to fetal ovine plasma. 26th Ann. Meet. Soc. Gynecol. Invest., San Diego, Calif., Abstr. 318

53. Margolis, F. L., Roffi, J., Jost, A. 1966. Norepinephrine methylation in fetal rat adrenals. *Science* 154:275–76

54. Mitchell, B. F., Serón-Ferré, M., Hess, D., Jaffe, R. B. 1978. Cortisol metabolism during the perinatal period in the rhesus monkey. 60th Ann. Meet. Endocrine Soc., Miami, Fl., Abstr. 544

55. Mitchell, B. F., Serón-Ferré, M., Jaffe, R. B. 1979. Cortisol (F)metabolism in the fetal rhesus monkey *in utero*. 26th Ann. Meet. Soc. Gynecol. Invest., San Diego, Calif., Abstr. 254

56. Miyakawa, I., Ikeda, I., Maeyama, M. 1974. Transport of ACTH across human placenta. *J. Clin. Endocrinol. Metab.* 39:440–42

57. Murphy, B. E. P., Diez d'Aux, R. C. 1972. Steroid levels in the human fetus:

cortisol and cortisone. *J. Endocrinol. Metab.* 35:678–83

58. Murphy, B. E. P. 1973. Steroid arteriovenous differences in umbilical cord plasma: evidence of cortisol production by the human fetus in mid-gestation. *J. Clin. Endocrinol. Metab.* 35:678–83

59. Murphy, B. E. P. 1973. Does the human fetal adrenal play a role in parturition? *Am. J. Obstet. Gynecol.* 115:521–25

60. Murphy, B. E. P. 1977. Chorionic membrane as an extra-adrenal source of fetal cortisol in human amniotic fluid. *Nature* 266:179–81

61. Murphy, B. E. P. 1980. Mechanism of initiation of labor—A new hypothesis 62nd Ann. Meet. Endocrine Soc., Washington DC Abstr. 72

62. Niemineva, K., Pekkarinen, A. 1952. The noradrenaline and adrenaline content of human fetal adrenal glands and aortic bodies. *Ann. Med. Exper. Fenn.* 30:275–86

63. Novy, M. J., Walsh, S. W., Kittinger, G. W. 1977. Experimental fetal anencephaly in the rhesus monkey: Effect on gestational length and fetal and maternal steroids. *J. Clin. Endocrinol. Metab.* 45:1031–38

64. Parker, C. R. Jr., Simpson, E. R., Bilheimer, D. W. et al. 1980. Inverse relation between low-density lipoprotein-cholesterol and dehydroisoandrosterone sulfate in human fetal plasma. *Science* 208:512–13

65. Parker, L. N., Odell, W. D. 1979. Evidence for existence of cortical androgen-stimulating hormone. *Am. J. Physiol.* 236:616–20

66. Pepe, G. J., Titus, J. A., Townsley, J. D. 1977. Increasing fetal adrenal formation of cortisol from pregnenolone during baboon (Papio papio) gestation. *Biol. Reprod.* 17:701–5

67. Pérez-Palacios, G., Pérez, A., Jaffe, R. B. 1968. Conversion of pregnenolone-7 α-^{3}H-sulfate to other Δ^5-3β-hydroxysteroid sulfates by the human fetal adrenal *in vitro*. *J. Clin. Endocrinol. Metab.* 28:19–25

68. Perlman, M., Schenker, J., Glassman, M., Ben-David, M. 1978. Prolonged hyperprolactinemia in preterm infants. *J. Clin. Endocrinol. Metab.* 47:894–97

69. Pipkin, F. B., Symonds, E. M. 1977. Factors affecting angiotensin II concentrations in the human infant at birth. *Clin. Sci. Molec. Med.* 52:449–56

70. Raeside, J. I. 1976. Dehydroepiandrosterone in the fetal gonads of the horse. *J. Reprod. Fert.* 46:423–25

71. Reiter, E. O., Fuldauer, V. G., Root, A. W. 1977. Secretion of the adrenal androgen, dehydroepiandrosterone sulfate, during normal infancy, childhood, and adolescence in sick infants and in children with endocrinologic abnormalities. *J. Pediatr.* 90:766–70

72. Resnik, R., Killam, A. P., Battaglia, F. C., Makowski, E. L., Meschia, G. 1976. The effect of various vaso-active compounds upon the uterine vascular bed. *Am. J. Obstet. Gynecol.* 125:201–6

73. Roebuck, M. M., Jones, C. T., Holland, D., Silman, R. 1980. *In vitro* effects of high molecular weight forms of ACTH on the fetal sheep adrenal. *Nature* 284:616–18

74. Roos, B. A. 1974. Effect of ACTH and cAMP on human adrenocortical growth and function *in vitro*. *Endocrinology* 94:685–90

75. Rose, J. C., MacDonald, A. A., Heymann, M. A., Rudolph, A. M. 1978. Developmental aspects of the pituitary adrenal axis response to hemorrhagic stress in lamb fetuses *in utero*. *J. Clin. Invest.* 61:424–31

76. Rudman, D., Hollins, B. M., Lewis, N. C. et al. 1980. Effects of melanotropic peptides on fetal adrenal gland. *J. Clin. Invest.* 65:822–28

77. Schulz, D. M., Giordano, D. A., Schulz, D. H. 1962. Weights of organs of fetuses and infants. *Arch. Pathol.* 74:244–50

78. Serón-Ferré, M., Lawrence, C. C., Siiteri, P. K., Jaffe, R. B. 1978. Steroid production by the definitive and fetal zones of the human fetal adrenal gland. *J. Clin. Endocrinol. Metab.* 47:603–9

79. Serón-Ferré, M., Rose, J. C., Parer, J. T., Foster, D. B., Jaffe, R. B. 1978. *In vivo* regulation of the fetal rhesus monkey adrenal gland. *Endocrinology* 103:368–75

80. Serón-Ferré, M., Lawrence, C. C., Jaffe, R. B. 1978. Role of hCG in regulation of the fetal zone of the human fetal adrenal gland. *J. Clin. Endocrinol. Metab.* 46:834–37

81. Short, R. V., Eckstein, P. 1961. Oestrogen and progesterone levels in pregnant rhesus monkeys. *J. Endocrinol.* 22: 15–22

82. Silman, R. E., Chard, T., Lowry, P. J., Smith, I., Young, I. M. 1976. Human pituitary peptides and parturition. *Nature* 260:716–18

83. Silman, R. E., Holland, D., Chard, T., Lowry, P. J., Hope, J., Robinson, J. S., Thorburn, G. D. 1978. The ACTH "family tree" of the rhesus monkey

changes with development. *Nature* 276:526–28

84. Siler-Khodr, T. M., Morgenstern, L. L., Greenwood, F. C. 1974. Hormone synthesis and release from human fetal adenohypophysis *in vitro. J. Clin. Endocrinol. Metab.* 39:891–905

85. Simmer, H. H., Tulchinsky, D., Gold, E. M., Frankland, M., Greipel, M., Gold, A. S. 1974. On the regulation of estrogen production by cortisol and ACTH in human pregnancy at term. *Am. J. Obstet. Gynecol.* 119:283–97

86. Solomon, S., Bird, C. E., Ling, W., Iwamiya, M., Young, P. C. M. 1967. Formation and metabolism of steroids in the fetus and placenta. *Rec. Prog. Horm. Res.* 23:297–347

87. Sucheston, M. E., Cannon, M. S. 1968. Development of zonular patterns in the human adrenal gland. *J. Morphol.* 126:477–92

88. Swinyard, C. A. 1941. Growth of the human suprarenal glands. *Anat. Rec.* pp. 141–50

89. Tanswell, A. K., Worthington, D., Smith, B. T. 1977. Human amniotic membrane corticosteroid 11-oxidoreductase activity. *J. Clin. Endocrinol. Metab.* 45:721–25

90. Velican, C. 1946. Embryogenese de la surrenale humaine. *Arch. Anat. Microscop.* 36:316–33

91. Vinson, G. P., Whitehouse, B. J., Dell, A., Etienne, T., Morris, H. R. 1980. Characterisation of an adrenal zona glomerulosa-stimulating component of posterior pituitary extracts as αMSH. *Nature* 284:464–67

92. Walsh, S. W., Norman, R. L., Novy, M. 1979. *In utero* regulation of rhesus monkey adrenocorticotropin, thyrotropin-releasing hormone, prolactin, human chorionic gonadotropin and α melanocyte-stimulating hormone on fetal and maternal plasma steroids. *Endocrinology* 104:1805–13

93. Winters, A. J., Oliver, C., Colston, C., MacDonald, P. C., Porter, J. C. 1974. Plasma ACTH levels in the human fetus and neonate as related to age and parturition. *J. Clin. Endocrinol. Metab.* 39:269–73

94. Winters, A. J., Colston, C., MacDonald, P. C., Porter, J. C. 1975. Fetal plasma prolactin levels. *J. Clin. Endocrinol. Metab.* 41:626–29

95. Wurtman, R. J. 1966. Control of epinephrine synthesis in the adrenal medulla by the adrenal cortex: hormonal specificity and dose-response characteristics. *Endocrinology* 79:608–14

Ann. Rev. Physiol. 1981. 43:163–88
Copyright © 1981 by Annual Reviews Inc. All rights reserved

ENDOCRINE PHYSIOLOGY OF THE PLACENTA

❖1303

Evan R. Simpson and Paul C. MacDonald

The Cecil H. and Ida Green Center for Reproductive Biology Sciences and Departments of Biochemistry and Obstetrics and Gynecology, University of Texas Southwestern Medical School, Dallas, Texas 75235

INTRODUCTION

The alterations in hormone production that accompany human pregnancy are the most remarkable recorded in human physiology or pathophysiology. In pregnant women, at or near term, there is the daily production of 15–20 mg estradiol–17β (E2), 50–100 mg estriol (E3), 250–600 mg progesterone (P4), 1–2 mg aldosterone, and 3–8 mg deoxycorticosterone (DOC). Furthermore, there are strikingly increased levels of plasma renin, angiotensinogen, and angiotensin II, and the daily production of 1 g of human placental lactogen (hPL), massive quantities of human chorionic gonadotropin (hCG), and likely human chorionic thyrotropin (hCT), chorionic ACTH, and possibly chorionic TRH, LHRH, and somatostatin. The most remarkable physiologic phenomena of pregnancy may be the mechanisms by which the woman and her fetus adapt to this unusual endocrine milieu. Many of the hormones cited above are produced by the placenta. The placenta secretes large quantities of a variety of both steroid and polypeptide hormones. These are the topic of this review.

STEROID HORMONE PRODUCTION BY THE HUMAN PLACENTA

The human placenta produces two principal steroid hormones, progesterone and estrogen, primarily E3 but also E2 and estrone (E1). P4 is synthe-

163

0066-4278/81/0315-0163$01.00

sized from cholesterol, and estrogens are formed from circulating C_{19}-steroid precursors (13, 27, 153). Among steroidogenic tissues the human placenta is unusual in that it cannot convert C_{21}-steroids to C_{19}-steroids. This is in contrast to the placenta of the sheep, in which the capacity to effect this transformation appears to be induced by cortisol (7). Hence, the human placenta is not autonomous in terms of steroid hormone production since it relies on the fetal and maternal adrenals as sources of C_{19}-steroids for estrogen biosynthesis. The major source of cholesterol for P4 biosynthesis in the placenta is low-density lipoprotein (LDL) from the maternal circulation (189).

Steroid Production in Early Pregnancy

Blastocysts of several animal species synthesize steroids prior to implantation—e.g. P4 from pregnenolone and E2 from E1 (56). Formation of C_{19}-steroids and aromatization to estrogens by blastocysts also have been reported (65). Steroids, derived from the maternal compartment, or possibly synthesized de novo by the blastocysts, may play an important role in the implantation process and in embryological development (29, 148). The early placenta also synthesizes C_{21}-steroids from cholesterol and estrogen from C_{19}-steroids (71, 162, 166), but the human placenta does not become the dominant source of steroid hormones until the 8th week of gestation. Prior to this time, the primary source of P4 and E2 is the corpus luteum (50, 178, 195). The human trophoblast produces hCG, which maintains and stimulates the corpus luteum to produce P4 and E2 until at least 8 weeks of gestation (30, 178). For the first 4 weeks of pregnancy, the levels of P4 and 17α-hydroxyprogesterone in the maternal serum rise strikingly as a result of secretion by the corpus luteum (178). By the 5th week, the levels of 17α-hydroxyprogesterone (which is not synthesized in the placenta) begin to fall, signaling decline of corpus luteum function. Subsequently the placenta is dominant in the biosynthesis of P4 and estrogen. Interestingly, hCG levels rise rapidly after the 5th week and the maximum rate of secretion is attained around the 10th week of pregnancy (32, 106). Subsequently the level of hCG in serum declines from 100 IU ml^{-1} to about 10 IU ml^{-1}, a level maintained until delivery.

Progesterone Production by the Human Placenta

Late in pregnancy, the placenta secretes 250 mg or more of P4 per day. In some pregnancies involving multiple fetuses, 800 mg of P4 are formed per day. The first step in the biosynthesis of progesterone is the conversion of cholesterol to the C_{21}-steroid, pregnenolone, with loss of a 6-carbon fragment from the cholesterol side-chain. This reaction is known as cholesterol side-chain cleavage (CSCC), the first step in the biosynthesis of all steroid hormones and the step that ordinarily is rate-limiting in steroid biosynthesis. In other steroidogenic tissues, CSCC is stimulated by a trophic hormone —e.g. ACTH in adrenal and LH in ovary and testis. In placenta, however, a trophic stimulus for CSCC has not been identified. CSCC occurs exclusively in mitochondria of all steroidogenic tissues and is believed to involve a series of hydroxylation reactions in which molecular oxygen is incorporated into the steroid molecule with utilization of NADPH. CSCC involves a form of cytochrome P–450, namely P–450$_{scc}$ (86, 158, 187). P-450 is found in mitochondria of placental tissue (108, 109, 162). This species of P-450 was characterized by optical spectrophotometry and EPR spectrometry. It has the properties of P-450$_{scc}$—i.e. the g value of the low-field EPR spectrum at a temperature of 10°K is 8.2. This finding is indicative of the high-spin ferric form of P-450$_{scc}$—i.e. P-450$_{scc}$ bound to its substrate cholesterol. Placental mitochondria, reduced with dithionite, contain a signal with an EPR spectrum identical to that of the iron-sulphur protein that transfers electrons from NADPH to cytochrome P-450 in the mitochondria of other steroidogenic tissues (162). Placental CSCC-NADPH can be derived by the oxidation of Krebs cycle acids—e.g. isocitrate and citrate (109, 111). The concentration of P-450 and of the iron-sulphur protein in placental mitochondria is 0.1–0.2 nmoles mg^{-1} protein, about 1/10th the content in adrenal cortex mitochondria. However, the rate of CSCC in placental mitochondria, expressed as nmoles pregnenolone formed min^{-1} nmole^{-1} P-450, is similar to that in mitochondria from adrenal of ACTH-treated rats (161, 162).

Pregnenolone is converted to P4 in a reaction catalyzed by the enzymes 3β-hydroxysteroid dehydrogenase and Δ^5-Δ^4 isomerase. Originally it was believed that these enzymes were localized in the endoplasmic reticulum, but now it is established that mitochondrial fractions prepared from all steroidogenic tissues contain these enzymes (49, 104, 168). It is not known whether the enzymatic activity in mitochondrial fractions is due to contamination by microsomes. Where, then, does the cholesterol utilized by the placenta for P4 biosynthesis originate? Cholesterol could arise from two sources: de novo cholesterol synthesis within the trophoblastic cells, or the utilization of plasma cholesterol. The capacity of the placenta to synthesize cholesterol from 2-carbon units is limited (131, 183, 192, 202). The specific activity of 3-hydroxy-3-methyl glutaryl coenzyme A (HMG CoA) reductase, the rate limiting enzyme in cholesterol biosynthesis, is only 0.1 nmoles min^{-1} mg^{-1} protein in placental microsomes, a rate sufficient to provide only a small portion of the total progesterone produced (163). Indeed, progesterone formed by the human placenta is derived from the utilization of cholesterol in the maternal circulation (26, 53, 76), and the fetus does not contribute to P4 formation (41, 103). Following ligation of the umbilical cord with the fetus and placenta left in situ there was no immediate reduction in plasma P4 or in the levels of pregnanediol in the maternal urine. Following administration of radiolabeled cholesterol to a woman pregnant with an anencephalic fetus for a time sufficient to achieve steady-state conditions, the specific activity of plasma P4 and that of pregnanediol in maternal urine were similar to that of circulating cholesterol (76). These results indicate that maternal cholesterol is the principal precursor of placental P4. What, then, is the form of circulating cholesterol utilized by the placenta for P4 formation?

Trophoblastic cells in monolayer culture take up and degrade low-density lipoprotein (LDL) (188). LDL degradation is mediated by a saturable process suggestive of the binding of LDL to plasma membrane receptors. Degradation of LDL in trophoblastic cells was inhibited by chloroquine, an inhibitor of lysosomal degradative processes. These results indicate that LDL is metabolized by human trophoblast in a manner similar to that described for a number of human and nonhuman cells in culture by Goldstein & Brown (67). Trophoblastic cells, maintained in culture medium containing lipoprotein-poor serum (LPPS), produced P4 at a rate of about 150 ng 24 hr^{-1} mg^{-1} cell protein (189). When LDL was in the culture medium, P4 secretion was 2–3-fold greater. Thus following degradation of LDL, cholesterol from the lipoprotein serves as precursor for P4 biosynthesis. Upon incubation of trophoblastic cells with LDL, the rate of incorporation of [^{14}C]acetate into cholesterol was reduced drastically (189), indicating that LDL-cholesterol suppresses de novo synthesis of cholesterol. Trophoblastic cells did not degrade high-density lipoprotein (HDL), and HDL did not stimulate P4 biosynthesis except when present in the medium in very high concentrations (185, 189). Therefore the major source of cholesterol for P4 biosynthesis was maternal plasma LDL. LDL stimulates cholesteryl ester synthesis in trophoblastic cells as in other cell types (160, 165); however, the cholesterol ester content of placental tissue is extremely low (159). An explanation for this apparent paradox is found in the observation that P4 inhibits acyl CoA cholesterol:acyl transferase (ACAT) activity, the enzyme that catalyzes cholesteryl ester synthesis (159, 160). A concentration of P4 of 20 μM was required for half-maximal inhibition of ACAT activity. Such concentrations of P4 could exist in trophoblastic cells (159); therefore it is reasonable to conclude that P4 in high levels may be a factor in preventing cholesteryl ester synthesis in the placenta. Thus it is possible to explain the following facts regarding P4 biosynthesis in the placenta: (*a*) The principal source of cholesterol for P4 biosynthesis is LDL in maternal plasma; (*b*) de novo cholesterol synthesis in human placenta is limited; (c) the cholesteryl ester content of the placenta is extremely low.

REGULATION OF PROGESTERONE BIOSYNTHESIS Regulation of P4 biosynthesis in human placenta seems strictly autonomous. Evidence obtained earlier that hCG might stimulate cholesterol metabolism does not appear to have been substantiated (184). HCG, when added to culture medium of choriocarcinoma and trophoblastic cells, has little effect on P4 secretion, although hCG causes an increase in cAMP levels in placental tissue (55, 112). It is possible that the endogenous levels of hCG are so high at all times that additional hCG is ineffective in stimulating further P4 secretion. If this is so, then it was possible that addition of an antiserum to hCG might suppress P4 biosynthesis, but this was not the case (164). Another study (172) showed that neither hCG nor anti-hCG antibody had any effect on the conversion of pregnenolone to P4. However, since this reaction is subsequent to the CSCC reaction, it is not clear why it was supposed these agents would have any effect. Although the levels of P-450 in placental mitochondria are low, the specific activity of CSCC, expressed as nmoles pregnenolone formed min^{-1} $nmole^{-1}$ P-450, is as high as that found in mitochondria obtained from ACTH-stimulated rat adrenals, which suggests that CSCC is operating at a maximal rate in placenta (162). Thus the supply of cholesterol to the placental mitochondria appears rate-limiting for P4 biosynthesis. The concentration of LDL in maternal plasma is high; thus the rate of P4 biosynthesis may be determined ultimately by the number of LDL receptors on the surface of the trophoblast cells—i.e. placental mass (157).

Estrogen Production by the Human Placenta

During human pregnancy, large quantities of estrogen are produced. After the first three to four weeks of pregnancy, nearly all estrogens are produced in the trophoblast. The placenta lacks steroid 17α-hydroxylase activity and consequently cannot convert C_{21}-steroids to C_{19}-steroids. Nonetheless, placental tissue has a remarkable capacity for aromatization of C_{19}-steroids (13, 27, 153). Androstenedione, testosterone, and dehydroisoandrosterone (DHIA) are converted to E1 and E2 by placental microsomes. However, there is a disproportionate amount of E3 in the urine of pregnant women. In nonpregnant women the ratio of urinary E3 to E1 plus E2 is approximately 1, whereas in pregnant women this ratio is 10 or more. Thus, two questions were posed. First, what is the source of the C_{19}-steroids utilized by the placenta for estrogen biosynthesis? Second, what is the mechanism(s) whereby the disproportionate amount of estriol arises in pregnant women?

It seemed likely that the fetus was involved in placental estrogen biosynthesis since urinary estrogen levels declined to very low levels after fetal demise or upon ligation of the umbilical cord, and were very low in women pregnant with an anencephalic fetus. In 1963, several groups of investigators (13, 27, 153) demonstrated that the principal precursor of placental E2 is circulating DHIA-sulfate, and that the reason for the disproportionate amount of E3 in maternal plasma and urine was the secretion of E3 by the placenta. E3 is formed in the placenta by aromatization of circulating 16 α-OH-DHIA sulfate (154). DHIA sulfate, in both fetal and maternal plasma, is utilized by the placenta in the formation of E2. The product of aromatization of DHIA sulfate that enters the maternal compartment is principally E2. It is not yet clear whether the principal product entering the fetal circulation is E1 or E2. It appears that both E2 and E1 are secreted into the fetal compartment, or else E2 is converted to E1 by fetal erythrocytes. Near term, approximately half of E2 synthesized in placenta is derived from precursors in the fetal plasma and half is derived from precursors in maternal plasma. On the other hand, E3 is derived principally from 16α-OH-DHIA sulfate in fetal plasma. DHIA sulfate, secreted by the fetal adrenal cortex, is converted extensively to 16α-OH-DHIA sulfate, principally in fetal liver. It is likely that some 16α-OH-DHIA sulfate also is secreted by the fetal adrenal. It has been computed that approximately 90% of E3 excreted into maternal urine is derived from the placental aromatization of fetal plasma 16α-OH-DHIA sulfate (154). The first step in the conversion of DHIA sulfate or 16α-OH-DHIA sulfate to estrogens is removal of the sulfate moiety. Steroid sulfatase activity in placenta ordinarily is high (133, 185). Thus the entry of DHIA or 16α-OH-DHIA into trophoblasts as the sulfoconjugate presents no obstacle to the utilization of these precursors in estrogen biosynthesis. Cases of placental sulfatase deficiency have been reported (170) in which there is failure to hydrolyze DHIA sulfate or 16α-OH-DHIA sulfate, and a deficiency in estrogen formation by the placenta obtains. In such instances, the levels of E3 in the maternal plasma and urine are quite low. In some such pregnancies there is a delay in the onset of parturition and/or a refractoriness to the induction of labor by oxytocin administration. The infants born of such pregnancies usually are normal and all such infants have been boys.

The pathway of E2 formation in the placenta from DHIA is through androstenedione and E1 (8, 57); that of E3 synthesis from 16α-OH-DHIA is through 16α-hydroxyandrostenedione and 16α-hydroxyestrone. The conversion of DHIA and 16α-OH-DHIA to the corresponding androstenedione derivatives is catalyzed by placental 3β-hydroxysteroid dehydrogenase and Δ^5-Δ^4 isomerase in a reaction similar to that involving the conversion of pregnenolone to P4. Conversion of C_{19}-steroids to estrogens in placenta is catalyzed by the aromatase enzyme complex in the endoplasmic reticulum (138). However, aromatase activity also is found in mitochondrial preparations of placenta (4, 137, 147). Aromatase activity in mitochondria that were disrupted by treatment with a high concentration of calcium was similar to aromatase activity in intact mitochondria supported by a NADPH generating system (114). This finding is suggestive that aromatase activity of mitochondria was associated with the outer mitochondrial membrane. The properties of the aromatase system in the mitochondrial fraction of human term placenta are similar to those in the microsomal fraction in relative activities toward androstenedione, 19-nortestosterone, and 16α-hydroxytestosterone, sensitivity to carbon monoxide, and sensitivity to an antibody raised against hepatic microsomal NADPH-cytochrome c reductase (39). When inner and outer mitochondrial membrane subfractions were employed, aromatase activity was associated predominantly with outer membrane preparations (39). This subcellular localization differs from that of CSCC, which is in the inner mitochondrial membrane. When the total mitochondrial fraction was separated into heavy, light, and very light mitochondria (114), most of the aromatase activity was found in the very light mitochondrial fraction; little activity was found in heavy mitochondria. Thus aromatase activity in mitochondrial fractions may be due to contamination by endoplasmic reticulum vesicles. Nevertheless, when inosine diphosphatase activity was used as a marker for endoplasmic reticulum, the aromatase activity in mitochondrial membranes could not be accounted for by microsomal contamination (39).

The sequence of reactions in the biosynthesis of estrogens (69) involves three enzymatic hydroxylations. The first two take place on the C_{19}-methyl group, resulting in its conversion to an aldehyde. The final and rate-determining hydroxylation step occurs at the 2β position, subsequent to which the product rapidly and nonenzymatically collapses to estrogen. Aromatization requires molecular oxygen and NADPH. Thus the enzyme system is of the mixed function oxidase type. For every mole of estrogen formed, three moles of NADPH and three moles of oxygen are used, findings which are suggestive that three hydroxylation reactions are involved in this reaction sequence (175) (Figure 1).

ROLE OF CYTOCHROME P-450 IN ESTROGEN BIOSYNTHESIS   The question arose as to the involvement of P-450 and NADPH-P-450 reductase, enzymes which are present in placental microsomes, in the aromatase enzyme complex. The aromatization of 19-norandrostenedione and 19-nortestosterone is inhibited by carbon monoxide. Aromatization of

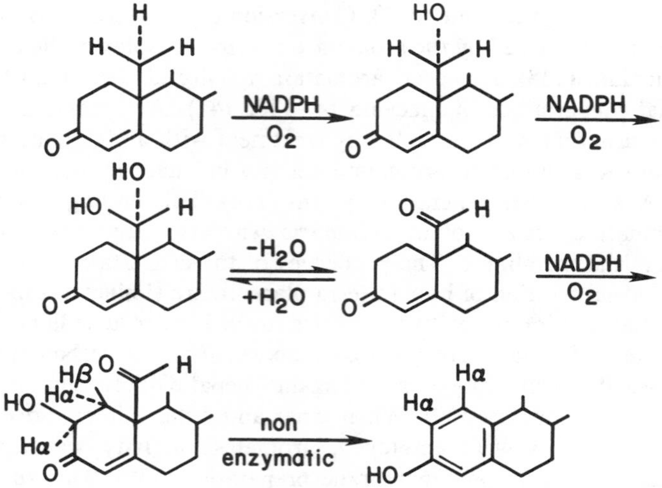

Figure 1 Pathway for the conversion of androgens to estrogens

androstenedione is insensitive to carbon monoxide (38, 43, 109, 110, 201) and is not inhibited by the P-450 inhibitor, metapyrone; it is, however, inhibited by the P-450 inhibitors, aminoglutethimide, SKF525-A, and an antibody raised against porcine hepatic NADPH-P-450 reductase. In addition, androstenedione and 19-nortestosterone interact with placental microsomes to form a type I optical difference spectrum, a finding that is indicative of substrate binding to low-spin ferric P-450 (174). The magnitude of the type I difference spectrum induced by androstenedione is almost equal to that of the reduced carbon monoxide difference spectrum of P-450 in placental microsomes (174). Although the extinction coefficients for these difference spectra in placental microsomes have not been computed, in other systems these are relatively similar.

Therefore it seems that substrates for aromatase also are substrates for P-450 of placental microsomes and that a substantial proportion of the P-450 in placental microsomes is involved in reactions involving these steroids. Furthermore, 19-nortestosterone is a competitive inhibitor of C_{19}-steroid aromatization and of the binding of androstenedione to P-450 (174). Other substrates for the aromatase enzyme complex, namely 19-hydroxyandrostenedione and 19-oxyandrostenedione, also form type I difference spectra with P-450, and competition for binding to P-450 exists among these substrates and androstenedione (174). These results are suggestive that all aromatization reactions may be carried out at the same active site and that a single enzyme complex is responsible for aromatization of all steroids.

How can aromatization of one substrate be CO-sensitive and another CO-insensitive? CO-sensitivity of a particular reaction, or lack of same, is an imperfect criterion of P-450 involvement in a particular reaction (58). In particular, CO-insensitivity can occur when the flow of reducing equivalents from NADPH to P-450 is limited—i.e. when formation of the ferrous P-450-substrate complex is rate-limiting for the overall reaction (58). The rate of aromatization of C_{19}-steroids, a CO-insensitive reaction, is 10–20 times the rate of aromatization of C_{18}-steroids, a CO-sensitive reaction (174). In the case of aromatization of C_{19}-substrates, the flow of reducing equivalents to P-450 may indeed be rate-limiting, a property that would render the overall reaction CO-insensitive. Interestingly, when aromatization of androstenedione is inhibited by 19-norandrostenedione, CO-sensitivity of aromatization of androstenedione develops (201). Moreover, this CO-sensitivity is reversed by light of 450 nm wavelength (201). However, another explanation for the failure of inhibition of aromatization of androstenedione by carbon monoxide is that androstenedione displaces CO from P-450 binding sites (91, 97, 199, 200). On the other hand, 19-norsteroids facilitate CO binding. However, it is difficult to imagine how a compound could cause displacement of carbon monoxide from its binding site on P-450 without also causing displacement of oxygen. In the purification of the aromatase enzyme complex from human placental microsomes utilizing digitonin solubilization followed by chromatography on BioGel P10 and DEAE-cellulose, the enzyme system was resolved into two components, both of which are required for activity. One component contained P-450 and the other NADPH-cytochrome c reductase (176).

REGULATION OF ESTROGEN BIOSYNTHESIS IN THE HUMAN PLACENTA   Stimulation of estrogen synthesis in granulosa cells by FSH and in Leydig cells by LH appears to be mediated through cyclic AMP. HCG stimulates the conversion of C_{19}-steroids to estrogens in perfused human placentas (6, 42, 177, 191). Aromatase activity of human choriocarcinoma cells is stimulated by dibutyryl cyclic AMP and theophyline (19), and the P-450 content of these cells increased following incubation with dibutyryl cyclic AMP (18). However, the P-450 and the aromatase activity were localized primarily in the $900 \times g$-10 min fraction of these cells instead of in the $106,000 \times g$-60 min fraction. The activity of the aromatase system may be regulated by a phosphorylation-dephosphorylation mechanism as for a number of other enzymes. Such a mechanism would seem entirely reasonable in view of the stimulation of estrogen formation and of aromatase activity by cyclic AMP. In vivo the capacity of placenta to convert androgens to estrogen is great, and the production of estrogens ordinarily is not limited by the activity of the aromatizing system in the placenta, but rather is dependent on the supply of precursor C_{19}-steroids. Consequently, the rate of placental estrogen formation is dependent on the activity of the fetal adrenal.

PROTEIN HORMONE PRODUCTION BY THE PLACENTA

Human Chorionic Gonadotropin (hCG)

STRUCTURE   HCG, in common with the other glycoprotein hormones, FSH, TSH, and LH, possesses a quaternary structure characterized by two dissimilar subunits, designated α and β (20, 37, 40, 130, 151, 152). The α-subunit of hCG has a mol wt of 10,200 (not including the carbohydrate contribution) and comprises 92 amino acids. The amino acid sequence is almost identical with that of the α-subunits of the other hormones listed above (20, 59, 83, 115, 134, 139, 140, 151). The β-chain has a mol wt of 15,500 (not including the carbohydrate residues) and comprises 145 amino acids (40, 48). There are sequence homologies between the various β-subunits, and between the α- and β-chains. For example, of the 115 amino acid residues of the β-chain of LH, 80 are identical to those of the β-chain of hCG (48). This family of hormones may have evolved from a single-chain ancestral protein by means of gene duplication and subsequent independent mutation of the individual genes (1). Thirty percent of the weight of hCG is comprised of carbohydrate (20, 37, 40). There are 4 asparagine-linked multiple-branched carbohydrate units at positions 52 and 78 of the α-subunit (20), and at positions 13 and 30 of the β-subunit (40). There also are 3 short linear serine-linked oligosaccharide units located only in the β-subunit. A typical monosaccharide sequence in a single branch of the complex oligosaccharide unit is NANA-Gal-GluNAc-Man (11). Asialo-hCG is almost as potent as hCG when assayed in vitro using testicular or ovarian cell suspensions (12, 118); however, in vivo it has a much shorter half-life (117, 182) because, in common with other glycoproteins with exposed galactose residues, it binds to the protein on the cell surface of hepatocytes that recognize terminal galactose residues (93). This interaction leads to internalization and degradation of the asialo-glycoproteins. A major function of the carbohydrate residues of hCG may be to prolong its half-life. The separated subunits of hCG are virtually devoid of biological activity (37, 116, 135). However, the biological activity characteristic of each hormone is determined by the structure of the β-subunit, since the α-subunits can be interchanged.

SECRETION   It is believed that hCG is secreted by syncytiotrophoblasts. HCG is concentrated in syncytiotrophoblasts (54, 80, 121, 194). Interestingly, the maximum rate of secretion of hCG coincides with the time that cytotrophoblasts are present in greatest abundance (32, 106). Since it is believed that the cytotrophoblast is the progenitor of the syncytiotrophoblast, it may be that the rate of formation and secretion of hCG is related more to the age of the syncytiotrophoblast than to a possible origin for hCG in the cytotrophoblast. On the other hand, LHRH is produced in cytotrophoblasts (155), and it is possible that LHRH of cytotrophoblasts stimulates syncytiotrophoblasts to secrete hCG in a manner similar to the hypothalamic control of pituitary LH secretion. Increased levels of hCG are found in women with multiple fetuses and in women with hydatidiform mole and choriocarcinoma. In fact, if the serum levels of hCG rise above 500 IU ml^{-1} plasma, the diagnosis of hydatidiform mole is virtually assured (51, 88, 128). Late in pregnancy, rising levels of hCG also may be observed in women with Rh-isoimmunization and an affected fetus (31, 113) and in some women with diabetes mellitus. Importantly, in these two circumstances a reappearance of cytotrophoblasts is found in the placenta late in gestation.

The role of hCG in human pregnancy is not fully defined. HCG is a luteotropin in the human and is believed to stimulate the fetal testes to secrete testosterone at a time prior to the secretion of LH by the fetal pituitary (3). It is possible that hCG stimulates P4 production by trophoblasts. Some investigators have envisioned a role for hCG in immunologic protection of the trophoblast (173); others have suggested this activity is due to a contaminant in hCG preparations (72, 102). Because of the biological and immunological similarity between hCG and LH, it was difficult previously to distinguish between these two gonadotropins. With the recognition that each is composed of an α- and β-subunit, and that the β-subunits of the two compounds differ, antibodies specific against the β-subunit of hCG were developed (179). The measurement of hCG, employing antibodies developed against the β-subunit, has facilitated the monitoring of subjects with hydatidiform mole and choriocarcinoma, and the monitoring of the efficacy of treatment of such persons. In addition to the production of hCG by the normal placenta, hydatidiform mole, and choriocarcinoma, hCG is present in the plasma of nonpregnant women and men and in normal human tissues (33, 196, 197). However, in sites other than malignant trophoblast hCG is believed to be nonglycosylated. In addition to the dimeric form of hCG, the plasma of pregnant women contains small amounts of free α-subunit that increase during pregnancy (9, 180), whereas the concentration of free β-subunit remains low and constant. Thus the synthesis of the α- and β-subunits of hCG may be controlled independently, with the β-subunit limiting the appearance of complete hCG molecules (4, 5).

BIOSYNTHESIS OF hCG   Like other protein hormones, hCG is synthesized on membrane-bound ribosomes. Apparently the α- and β-subunits are translated from separate mRNAs rather than synthesized in tandem from one mRNA. The rate of incorporation of [³H]leucine into hCG in cell-free systems has been studied by incubation with placental polyribosomes (45, 52, 23). The α- and β-subunits were precipitated by a specific antiserum and resolved on SDS polyacrylamide gels. Utilizing ribosomes prepared from first trimester placentas, it was found that the α- and β-subunits accounted for 5% and 4%, respectively, of total incorporation into protein but for only 1.3% and 0.6%, respectively, of incorporation by ribosomes of full term placentas (45). This reflects the declining maternal blood levels of hCG in late pregnancy. The change in the α/β-subunit ratio from 1.2 to 2.3 is suggestive of uncoordinated synthesis of the subunits and coincides in time (third trimester) with the appearance in plasma of free α-subunits (9, 180). It is suggestive further that the synthesis of the β-subunits is rate-limiting in the synthesis of the intact hCG in vivo. The major proteins synthesized in a wheat germ translation system by first trimester placental polyadenylated mRNA have mol wts estimated to be 13,000 and 16,000 (59). These proteins are produced only in trace amounts when full-term mRNA is utilized. These products are believed to be precursor forms of the α- and β-subunits of hCG (23), as the respective mol wts of the mature forms of these proteins are 10,200 and 15,500. When membranes are included in the in vitro translation system, species with higher mol wts are produced, an indication of glycosylation (24, 25, 59). Double-stranded cDNA has been synthesized from polyadenylated RNA from first trimester human placenta (59). A 621 base-pair fragment of this cDNA for the α-subunit of human chorionic gonadotropin was isolated by cloning in a plasmid vector; the complete nucleotide sequence was determined. The entire coding region and most of the untranslated regions of the mRNA were present in this fragment. The coding region includes a 24 amino acid presequence (25, 59) commencing with the initiating amino acid, methionine, and rich in hydrophobic amino acid residues.

CONTROL OF THE BIOSYNTHESIS OF hCG   Incubation of placental explants or choriocarcinoma cells with LHRH (94, 119), cyclic AMP, or its butyrated derivatives with and without phosphodiesterase inhibitors (74, 81, 82) or epidermal growth factor (21) results in an increased release of hCG. No such increase has been reported utilizing dibutyryl cyclic GMP,

AMP, insulin, P4, epinephrine, or prostaglandin (64, 126). Dopamine inhibited hCG secretion by human placental explants in vitro, whereas the dopaminergic antagonist, pimozide, caused a stimulation of hCG secretion (105). However, the physiological factors regulating hCG synthesis and release still are unknown.

Human Placental Lactogen (hPL)

STRUCTURE OF hPL   HPL is a single-chain polypeptide hormone with a mol wt of 22,300. It is composed of 191 amino acids and contains two intramolecular disulfide bridges (90) but contains no carbohydrate residues. Of the 191 amino acid residues, 162 (85%) are identical with the amino acids found in human pituitary growth hormone (75). The amino acid sequence of hPL is similar to that of human prolactin (22, 98). Because of the structural similarity among these three polypeptides, the genes of all three may have been derived from a common ancestral gene that divided to give rise to prolactin and another ancestral polypeptide, the latter subsequently giving rise to growth hormone and hPL through gene duplication and subsequent mutation of each independent gene (22). Within each polypeptide are four regions containing internally homologous sequences (122, 149), a finding which is suggestive that each of these polypeptides is formed by two duplications of a single primordial peptide of much smaller molecular weight. There is evidence of microheterogeneity in hPL samples from individual placentas (46). About 3% of the hPL in maternal serum and placental tissue exists in a dimeric form with a mol wt of 45,000 (141, 142). This is composed of two hPL chains that appear to be linked covalently by disulfide bridges (142). Thus it is not surprising that hPL shares some biological properties with growth hormone and prolactin—namely lactogenic and somatotrophic properties. HPL is only 1/100 as potent as pituitary GH in promoting growth; nonetheless, because it is produced in large quantities during human pregnancy, this hormone is believed to exert considerable physiological effects on the pregnant woman. Little hPL enters the fetus. The principal role of hPL in human pregnancy is believed to be mediated by its action as an insulin antagonist (15, 89), and it is believed that this action of hPL may be responsible for the development of diabetic ketoacidosis in pregnant women who were not known to have diabetes before they became pregnant and who do not require insulin after pregnancy. HPL can bring about a marked rise in fasting levels of plasma free fatty acids (62, 70). Since the most potent effect of placental lactogen in rodent appears to be luteotrophic, it has been suggested that regulation of the secretion of P4 in the maintenance of pregnancy might be the primary role of this hormone. However, there is little evidence that this is the case in humans. It remains to be proven that hPL is lactogenic in the primate. It is clear that hPL is not essential to a successful pregnancy since one pregnancy has been described in which the placenta did not produce hPL and the mother and infant did well (123).

PRODUCTION OF hPL   HPL can be detected by immunofluorescence in the syncytiotrophoblast five to ten days after implantation of the fertilized ovum (14, 143). The increase in maternal peripheral serum levels of hPL as pregnancy advances can be correlated directly with the mass of the placental tissue (144). The rate of secretion of hPL in pregnant women (1 g day^{-1}) is the greatest of any protein hormone in man and is a major placental secretory product accounting for 10% of all placental protein production at term (61, 169).

BIOSYNTHESIS OF hPL   HPL has been synthesized from radiolabeled amino acids in a cell-free wheat germ translation system utilizing placental polyadenylated mRNA (28, 44, 129). The predominant translation product of full-term placental mRNA, unlike mRNA obtained from first trimester placentas, is a protein that immunoprecipitates with antibody to hPL. By analysis of the immunoprecipitable products on SDS polyacrylamide gels two heavily radiolabeled bands were found with mol wts of 25,000 and 22,300 (129), the latter being the mol wt of native hPL. The product of higher molecular weight is known to be preplacental lactogen, which contains an extension of 25 amino acids at the N-terminal end of the molecule. Synthesis of the hormone was inhibited by 7-methylguanosine 5'-monophosphate, a finding that is suggestive of the presence of a 7-methylguanosine cap on the 5'-end of the mRNA for hPL (129). In the presence of triton X–100 in low concentrations, only pre-lactogen was detectable in the immunoprecipitate.

Utilizing polyadenylated mRNA from human placenta, a 550 base-pair fragment cDNA clone, coding for amino acids 24–191 of the hPL sequence, has been described (150). An analogous fragment coding for growth hormone also has been cloned. Restriction endonuclease fragments of human DNA containing hPL and growth hormone gene sequences were identified by hybridization with cDNA (60). By restriction endonuclease mapping it was shown that the growth hormone gene contains three intervening sequences interrupting the coding sequence. A detailed restriction map for the hPL gene has not been published but preliminary findings are suggestive that the pattern of intervening sequences is similar to that of the growth hormone gene (60).

REGULATION OF hPL SYNTHESIS BY THE HUMAN PLACENTA   Dibutyryl cyclic AMP and/or theophylline causes stimulation of hCG secretion by choriocarcinoma cells in culture but has little effect on the secretion of hPL (81, 82). However, in intact perfused placental lobules, dibutyryl cyclic AMP stimulated the release of hPL (186). Following the addition of calcium to the medium superfusing term placental fragments, hPL secretion was stimulated. E3 and P4 have been reported either to stimulate hPL secretion from placental explants (16) or to have no effect (96). PGE$_2$ has been found either to depress hPL secretion or to have no effect, whereas PGF$_{2\alpha}$ depresses hPL secretion by placental explants (64). PGF$_{2\alpha}$ administered intra-amniotically causes a rapid reduction in maternal serum hPL levels (167, 193). Glucose is essential for hPL secretion by placental explants; but when glucose was present in high concentrations in the medium, hPL secretion was apparently inhibited (17).

Placental ACTH

Pregnancy is associated with increased maternal plasma cortisol levels. Plasma ACTH levels in the pregnant woman increase throughout pregnancy but nonetheless are lower than those found in nonpregnant women and in men (63, 136). In contrast, umbilical cord plasma ACTH concentrations are high, averaging 241 pg ml^{-1} between 12–34 weeks of gestation (190). There is evidence that neither maternal nor fetal immunoreactive ACTH crosses the placenta in the human (5, 87, 113); thus the concentrations in the maternal and fetal compartments are reflective only of secretion from their respective sources. Maternal urinary excretion of free cortisol is relatively resistant to glucocorticosteroid negative feedback suppression, and the placenta may be involved in the secretion of ACTH in pregnant women. Several investigators have found bioactive and/or immunoreactive ACTH in placental extracts. Reports of ACTH-like activity in placental extracts first appeared in the 1950s (10, 85, 125); however, not until the advent of radioimmunoassay for ACTH and related peptides did studies of this placental activity advance (63). The ACTH-like material in human term placentas reacts with antisera raised to the N-terminal (1–24), midportion (13–18), and C-terminal of ACTH (136). Bioassayable ACTH is only about 1/5 to 1/3 that measured by radioimmunoassay. Dexamethasone administration does not alter significantly the levels of ACTH in placentas as measured by bioassay or by immunoassay (100). When homogenates of term placenta were treated by chromatography on Sephadex G-50, two fractions containing immunoreactive ACTH were eluted, one in the void volume and the other in the region of synthetic human ACTH (1–39). The mol wt of the material in the void volume was approximately

34,000. This material reacted with antisera raised against ACTH and against β-endorphin and thus is similar to the high molecular weight precursor of ACTH and endorphin in pituitary and hypothalamus.

Utilizing a combination of gel filtration chromatography in 1 M acetic acid to separate fractions by molecular weight, and specific antisera to assay separated fractions, it was shown that human placenta contains ACTH (1-39), β-lipotropin, β-endorphin, and α-MSH (47, 101, 120, 124). The relative proportions of these four peptides are more similar to those of the intermediate lobe of the pituitary and the hypothalamus than to those of the anterior lobe of the pituitary, in which the major end products are β-lipotropin and ACTH (1–39). Utilizing dispersed trophoblastic cells in monolayer culture, the incorporation of [^{35}S]methionine and [^{3}H]leucine into ACTH and related peptides was demonstrated (99). The results of pulse-chase studies are indicative of initial incorporation into a high molecular weight glycoprotein of ∼34,000 mol wt, similar to the ACTH, β-LPH precursor in the pituitary and hypothalamus. With longer incubation times, the radiolabel progressively disappeared from the high molecular weight species and appeared in smaller peptides containing ACTH or β-endorphin antigenic determinants according to the following scheme: (a) utilizing antisera to ACTH, high mol wt ACTH/β-endorphin → 22–17 K ACTH → 4.5 K ACTH → α-MSH; (b) utilizing antisera to β-endorphin, high mol wt ACTH/β-endorphin → β-lipotropin → β-endorphin (99). In similar experiments with human fetal pituitary tissue, ACTH and β-lipotropin were the major end products. Presently, the physiological role of placental ACTH and related peptides is unclear.

Human Chorionic Thyrotropin (hCT)

Several molecular species of hCT were isolated from extracts of placental and hydatidiform mole tissues (2, 77). These appear not to be identical to that of TSH of the human anterior pituitary. The principal component of hCT appears to be a glycoprotein with a mol wt of 28,000. Unlike hTSH, it does not cross-react with hCG (36, 78), but cross-reacts with antisera to TSH from various animal species, especially bovine and porcine, but not human. Injection of hypothalamic thyrotropin releasing hormone (TRH) causes an increase in blood concentrations of hTSH but not of hCT (92). The physiologic role of hCT is unclear. It has been reported that hCT concentrations rise from 7 μg ml^{-1} in early pregnancy to about 30 μg ml^{-1} in the third trimester, while maternal hTSH concentrations remain within the nonpregnant range (92). Large amounts of hCT are found in neoplastic trophoblastic tissue; in women with hydatidiform mole, the level of thyroxine in blood may be strikingly increased.

Luteinizing Hormone and Thyrotropin Hormone Releasing Hormones

Acetic acid extracts of human placentas contain material similar to TRH on the basis of immunological and biological activities (66, 145, 146, 198). The material was similar to synthetic TRH by four criteria. (a) Serial dilutions of placental extracts produced displacement curves parallel to those of synthetic TRH using an antiserum raised against synthetic TRH. (b) When chromatographed on Sephadex G-10, TRH in placental extracts and synthetic TRH were found in similar fractions on the basis of their TRH immunoreactivity. (c) Both placental extract and synthetic TRH stimulated TSH release from rat pituitaries in vitro. (d) Human serum degraded placental extract TRH and synthetic TRH in a qualitatively similar manner. On the other hand, by TLC the R_F values of synthetic TRH and placental TRH-like activity were different. Apparently TRH does not release chorionic TSH, hPL, or hCG. Thus it is yet to be established whether placental TRH has any relation to placental hormone secretion or relevance to the state of pregnancy.

The human placenta contains material that is immunologically indistinguishable from hypothalamic LHRH with biological activity similar to that of LHRH (95, 145, 155, 156). Placental LHRH appears to be localized in the cytotrophoblastic cells but not in the syncytiotrophoblast. Placental tissue fragments release LHRH-like activity into the culture medium. LHRH stimulates the release of hCG from placental tissue (94). This has led to the postulate that the cytotrophoblastic LHRH may regulate hCG secretion by syncytiotrophoblast.

Growth Factors and the Human Placenta

Membrane fractions from human placentas are a rich source of receptors for insulin (132, 127). Human placental membranes also contain receptors for somatomedins A and C, insulin-like growth factors 1 and 2, and multiplication-stimulating activity (34, 35, 79, 84, 107, 171, 181). On the basis of competition studies, it appears that all of the material possessing growth factor activity binds to closely related, if not identical, receptor populations. These receptors bind radiolabeled insulin-like substances with high affinity, but their affinity for insulin is low. In contrast, insulin appears to bind to a different receptor population that interacts with both insulin and insulin-like substances. Somatomedins appear to bind to water-soluble receptors in the cytosol of human placenta (73). The human placenta is also a source of a high molecular weight form of human nerve growth factor (NGF). Dissociation of this protein (mol wt 140,000) by acidic conditions gives biologically active NGF (68).

Thus the human placenta is not only the source of prodigious amounts of steroid hormones but in many ways behaves in a manner similar to the anterior pituitary in the secretion of a variety of polypeptide hormones. Moreover, the relationship between cytotrophoblasts and syncytiotrophoblasts may be analogous to that of the hypothalamus and pituitary. Indeed the finding of LHRH and TRH in cytotrophoblasts gives rise to speculation that there may be a hierarchy of control of syncytiotrophoblast function that is mediated by hormones produced in the cytotrophoblasts.

Literature Cited

1. Acher, R. 1976. Molecular evolution of the polypeptide hormones. *Ciba Found. Symp.* 41:31–55
2. Akasu, R., Kawahara, S., Ohki, H., Harano, M., Tejuna, Y. 1955. Thyroid stimulating hormone extracted from human placenta. *Endocrinol. Jpn.* 2:297–302
3. Albert, A. 1969. Follicle-stimulating activity of human chorionic gonadotropin. *J. Clin. Endocrinol. Metab.* 29:1504–9
4. Aleen, F. A., Valdivia, E., Colas, A. E. 1970. The aromatizing activity of placental mitochondrial and microsomal fractions. *Gynecol. Invest.* 1:277–87
5. Allen, J. P., Greer, M. A., McGilvra, R., Castro, A., Fisher, D. A. 1974. Endocrine function in an anencephalic infant. *J. Clin. Endocrinol. Metab.* 38:94–98
6. Alsat, E., Cedard, L. 1973. The stimulatory action of the prostaglandins on the production of oestrogens by the human placenta perfused in vitro. *Prostaglandins* 3:145–53
7. Anderson, A. B. M., Flint, A. P. T., Turnbull, A. C. 1975. Mechanism of action of glucocorticoids in induction of ovine parturition: effect on placental steroid metabolism. *J. Endocrinol.* 66:61–70
8. Anderson, N. G., Lieberman, S. 1980. C_{19} steroidal precursors of estrogens. *Endocrinology* 106:13–18
9. Ashitaka, Y., Nishimura, R., Futamura, K., Ohashi, M., Tojo, S. 1974. Serum and chorionic tissue concentrations of human chorionic gonadotropin and its subunits during pregnancy. *Endocrinol. Jpn.* 21:547–50
10. Assali, N. S., Hamermesz, J. 1954. Adrenocorticotropic substances from human placenta. *J. Clin. Endocrinol. Metab.* 14:781–82
11. Bahl, O. P. 1969. Human chorionic gonadotropin. I. Purification and physiochemical properties. *J. Biol. Chem.* 244:565–74
12. Bahl, O. P., Channing, C. P., Kammerman, S. 1973. Effects of hCG, asialo hCG, and the subunits of hCG upon luteinization of monkey granulosa cell cultures. *Endocrinol.* 93:1035–43
13. Baulieu, E. E., Dray, F. 1963. Conversion of ^{3}H-dehydroisoandrosterone (3β-hydroxy-Δ^5-androsten-17-one) sulfate to ^{3}H-estrogens in normal pregnant women. *J. Clin. Endocrinol. Metab.* 23:1298–301
14. Beck, J. S., Gordon, R. L., Donald, D., Melvin, J. M. O. 1969. Immunofluorescence studies with these sera on normal and pathological syncytiotrophoblast. *J. Pathol.* 97:545–55
15. Beck, P., Daughaday, W. H. 1967. Human placental lactogen: studies of its acute metabolic effects and disposition in normal man. *J. Clin. Inves.* 46:103–10
16. Belleville, F., Lasbennes, A., Nabet, P., Paysant, P. 1978. HCS-HCG regulation in cultured placenta. *Acta Endocrinol.* 88:169–81
17. Belleville, F., Lasbennes, A., Nabet, P., Paysant, P. 1979. HCS regulation in cultured placenta: action of glucose. *Acta Endocrinol.* 92:336–46
18. Bellino, F. L., Hussa, R. O. 1978. Trophoblastic estrogen synthetase stimulation by dibutyryl cyclic AMP and theophylline: increase in cytochrome P-450 content. *Biochem. Biophys. Res. Commun.* 85:1588–95
19. Bellino, F. L., Hussa, R. O., Osawa, Y. 1978. Estrogen synthetase in choriocarcinoma cell culture. Stimulation by dibutyryl cyclic adenosine monophosphate and theophylline. *Steroids* 32:37–44
20. Bellisario, R., Carlsen, R. B., Bahl, O. P. 1973. Human chorionic gonadotropin; linear amino acid sequence of the α-subunit. *J. Biol. Chem.* 248:6796–809

21. Benveniste, R., Speeg, K. V. Jr., Carpenter, G., Cohen, S., Lindner, J., Rabinowitz, D. 1978. Epidermal growth factor stimulates secretion of human chorionic gonadotropin by cultured human choriocarcinoma cells. *J. Clin. Endocrinol. Metab.* 46:169–72

22. Bewley, T. A., Li, C. H. 1974. Structural similarities between human pituitary growth hormone, human chorionic somatomammotropin, and ovine pituitary growth and lactogenic hormones. In *Lactogenic Hormones, Fetal Nutrition and Lactation,* ed. J. B. Josimovich, M.Reynolds, E. Cobo, p. 19. NY: Wiley

23. Bielinska, M., Boime, I. 1978. mRNA-dependent synthesis of a glycosylated subunit of human chorionic gonadotropin in cell-free extracts derived from ascites tumor cells. *Proc. Natl. Acad. Sci. USA* 75:1768–72

24. Bielinska, M., Boime, I. 1979. Glycosylation of human chorionic gonadotropin in mRNA-dependent cell-free extracts: post-translational processing of an asparagine-linked mannose-rich oligosaccharide. *Proc. Natl. Acad. Sci. USA* 76:1208–12

25. Birken, S., Fetherston, J., Desmond, J., Canfield, R., Boime, I. 1978. Partial amino acid sequence of the preprotein form of the alpha subunit of human choriogonadotropin and identification of the site of subsequent proteolytic cleavage. *Biochem. Biophys. Res. Commun.* 85:1247–53

26. Bloch, K. 1945. Biological conversion of cholesterol to pregnanediol. *J. Biol. Chem.* 157:661–66

27. Bolté, E., Mancuso, S., Eriksson, G. et al. 1964. Studies on the aromatization of neutral steroids in pregnant women. 1. Aromatization of C-19 steroids by placentas perfused *in situ. Acta Endocrinol.* 45:535–59

28. Boime, I., Boguslawski, S. 1974. The synthesis of human placental lactogen by ribosomes derived from human placenta. *Proc. Natl. Acad. Sci. USA* 71:1322–25

29. Borland, R. M., Erickson, G. F., Ducibella, T. 1977. Accumulation of steroids in rabbit preimplantation blastocysts. *J. Reprod. Fertil.* 49:219–24

30. Bradbury, J. T., Brown, W. E., Gray, L. A. 1950. Maintenance of the corpus luteum and physiologic actions of progesterone. *Rec. Prog. Horm. Res.* 5:151–94

31. Bradbury, J. T., Goplerud, C. P. 1963. Serum chorionic gonadotropin studies in sensitized Rh-negative patients. *Obstet. Gynecol.* 21:330–33

32. Braunstein, G. D., Grodin, J. M., Vaitukaitis, J. L., Ross, G. T. 1973. Secretory rates of human chorionic gonadotropin by normal trophoblast. *Am. J. Obstet. Gynecol.* 115:447–50

33. Braunstein, G. D., Rasor, J., Wade, M. E. 1975. Presence in normal human testes of a chorionic gonadotropin-like substance distinct from human luteinizing hormone. *N. Engl. J. Med.* 293:1339–43

34. Brinsmead, M. W., Liggins, G. C. 1978. A receptor assay for somatomedin-like activity using multiplication-stimulating activity (MSA) as radioligand. *Aust. J. Exp. Biol. Med. Sci.* 56:513–25

35. Brinsmead, M. W., Liggins, G. C. 1978. The binding of rat liver cell multiplication-stimulating activity (MSA) to human placenta and serum proteins. *Aust. J. Exp. Biol.* 56:524–44

36. Burger, A. 1967. Further studies on a thyroid stimulating factor in crude chorionic gonadotropin preparations and in urine. *Acta Endocrinol.* 55:600–10

37. Canfield, R. E., Morgan, F. J., Kammerman, S., Bell, J. J., Agosto, G. M. 1971. Studies of human chorionic gonadotropin. *Rec. Prog. Horm. Res.* 27:121–64

38. Canick, J. A., Ryan, K. J. 1976. Cytochrome P-450 and the aromatization of 16α-hydroxytestosterone and androstenedione by human placental microsomes. *Mol. Cell. Endocrinol.* 6:105–15

39. Canick, J. A., Ryan, K. J. 1978. Properties of the aromatase system associated with the mitochondrial fractions of human placenta. *Steroids* 32:499–509

40. Carlsen, R. B., Bahl, O. P., Swaminathan, N. 1973. Human chorionic gonadotropin. Linear amino acid sequence of the β-subunit. *J. Biol. Chem.* 248:6810–27

41. Cassmer, O. 1959. Hormone production of the isolated human placenta. *Acta Endocrinol.* 45:9–12 (Suppl)

42. Cedard, L., Alsat, E., Urtasun, M. J., Varangot, J. 1970. Studies on the mode of action of luteinizing hormone and chorionic gonadotropin on estrogenic biosynthesis and glycogenolysis by human placenta perfused *in vitro. Steroids* 16:361–75

43. Chakraboty, J., Hopkins, R., Parke, D. V. 1972. Binding of rat liver and hepatoma polysomes to stripped rough endoplasmic reticulum *in vitro. Biochem. J.* 130:19p–20p

44. Chattejee, M., Babiga, B. S., Munro, H. N. 1976. Synthesis of human placental lactogen and human chorionic gonadotropin by polyribosomes and messenger RNAs from early and full term placentas. *J. Biol. Chem.* 251:2945–51

45. Chattejee, M., Munro, H. N. 1977. Changing ratio of human chorionic gonadotropin subunits synthesized by early and full-term placental polyribosomes. *Biochem. Biophys. Res. Commun.* 77:426–33

46. Chattejee, M., Laga, E. M., Merrill, C. C., Munro, H. N. 1977. Microteterogeneity of human placental lactogen showing different patterns in individuals. *Biochim. Biophys. Acta* 493:332–39

47. Clark, D., Thody, A. J., Shuster, S., Bowers, H. 1978. Immunoreactive α -MSH in human plasma in pregnancy. *Nature* 273:163–64

48. Closset, J., Hennen, G., Lequin, R. M. 1973. Human luteinizing hormone. The amino acid sequence of the β-subunit. *FEBS Lett.* 29:97–100

49. Cowan, R. A., Grant, J. K., Gile, C. A., Biddlecombe, W. 1972. The intracellular distribution of adrenal 3β-hydroxysteroid dehydrogenase and 3-oxosteroid Δ⁴-Δ⁵-isomerase studied with the zonal rotor. *Abstr. Biochem. J.* 126:12

50. Csapo, A. I., Pulkkinen, M. O., Wiest, W. G. 1973. Effects of luteectomy and progesterone replacement in early pregnant subjects. *Am. J. Obstet. Gynecol.* 115:759–65

51. Curry, S. L., Hammond, C. B., Tyrey, L., Creasman, W. T., Parker, R. T. 1975. Hydatidiform mole: diagnosis, management and long-term follow-up of 347 patients. *Obstet. Gynecol.* 45:1–8

52. Daniels-McQueen, S., McWilliams, D., Birken, S., Canfield, R., Landefeld, T., Boime, I. 1978. Identification of mRNAs encoding the α-and β-subunits of human choriogonadotropin. *J. Biol. Chem.* 253:7109–114

53. Davis, E. M., Platz, E. J., LeRoy, G. V., Gould, R. G., Werbin, H. 1956. Hormones in human reproduction I. Metabolism of progesterone. *Am. J. Obstet. Gynecol.* 72:740–54

54. Deikonicoff, L. K., Cedard, L. 1973. Localization of human chorionic gonadotropic and somatomammotropic hormones by the peroxidase immunohistoenzymologic method in villi and amniotic epithelium of human placentas (from six weeks to term). *Am. J. Obstet. Gynecol.* 116:1124–32

55. Demers, L. M., Gabbe, S. G., Villee, C. A., Greep, R. O. 1973. Human chorionic gonadotropin mediated glycogenolysis in human placental villi. *Biochem. Biophys. Acta* 313:202–10

56. Dickmann, Z., Dey, S. K., Gupta, J. S. 1976. A new concept: control of early pregnancy by steroid hormones originating in the preimplantation embryo. *Vitam. Horm.* 34:215–42

57. Easterling, W. E., Simmer, H. H., Dignam, W. J., Frankland, M. V., Naftolin, F. 1966. Neutral C_{19} steroids and steroid sulfates in human pregnancy II. Dehydroepiandrosterone sulfate, 16α-hydroxydehydroepiandrosterone, and 16α-hydroxydehydroepiandrosterone sulfate in maternal and fetal blood of pregnancies with anencephalic and normal fetuses. *Steroids* 8:157–78

58. Estabrook, R. W., Franklin, M. R., Hildebrandt, A. G. 1970. Factors influencing the inhibitory effect of carbon monoxide on cytochrome P-450-catalyzed mixed function oxidation reactions. *Ann. N.Y. Acad. Sci.* 174:218–32

59. Fiddes, J. C., Goodman, H. M. 1979. Isolation, cloning and sequence analysis of the cDNA for the α-subunit of human chorionic gonadotropin. *Nature* 281:351–56

60. Fiddes, J. C., Seeburg, P. H., DeNoto, F. M., Hollewell, R. A., Baxter, J. D., Goodman, H. M. 1979. Structure of genes for human growth hormone and chorionic somatomammotropin. *Proc. Natl. Acad. Sci. USA* 76:4294–98

61. Friesen, H. G., Suwa, S., Pare, P. 1969. Synthesis and secretion of placental lactogen and other proteins by the placenta. *Rec. Prog. Horm. Res.* 25:161–205

62. Genazzani, A. R., Bennuzzi-Baldoni, M., Felber, J. P. 1969. Human chorionic somatomammotropin (hCSM): Lipolytic action of a pure preparation on isolated fat cells. *Metab. Clin. Exp.* 18:593–98

63. Genazzani, A. R., Fraioli, F., Hurlimann, J., Fioretti, P., Felber, J. P. 1975. Pattern of plasma ACTH, hGH and cortisol during normal menstrual cycle. *Clin. Endocrinol.* 4:1–14

64. Genbacev, O., Ratkovic, M., Kraincanic, M., Sulovic, V. 1977. Effect of prostaglandin F_{2a} on the synthesis of placental proteins and human placental lactogen. *Prostaglandins* 13:723–33

65. George, F. W., Wilson, J. D. 1978. Estrogen formation in the early rabbit embryo. *Science* 199:200–1

66. Gibbons, J. M., Mitnick, M., Chieffo, V. 1975. *In vitro* biosynthesis of TSH and LH-releasing factors by the human placenta. *Am. J. Obstet. Gynecol.* 121:127–31

67. Goldstein, J. L., Brown, M. S. 1974. Binding and degradation of low density lipoproteins by cultured human fibroblasts. *J. Biol. Chem.* 249:5153–62

68. Goldstein, L. D., Reynolds, C. P., Perez-Polo, J. R. 1978. Isolation of human nerve growth factor from placental tissue. *Neurochem. Res.* 3:175–78

69. Goto, J., Fishman, J. 1977. Participation of a nonenzymatic transformation in the biosynthesis of estrogens from androgens. *Science* 195:80–81

70. Grumbach, M. M., Kaplan, S. L., Abrams, C. L., Bell, J. J., Conte, F. A. 1966. Plasma free fatty acid response to the administration of chorionic "growth hormone-prolactin." *J. Clin. Endocrinol.* 26:478–83

71. Gunasegaram, R., Peh, K. L., Chew, P. C. T., Karim, S. M. M., Ratnam, S. S. 1978. Ability of molar trophoblasts to split the side-chain of [26-¹⁴C]cholesterol *in vitro. J. Endocrinol.* 79:409–10

72. Gundert, D., Merz, W. E., Hilgenfeldt, U., Brossmer, R. 1975. Inability of highly purified preparations of human chorionic gonadotropin to inhibit the phytohemagglutinin-induced stimulation of lymphocytes. *FEBS Lett.* 53:309–12

73. Guyda, H. J., Posner, B. I. 1977. Specific water-soluble binding factors for serum insulin-like activities in human and animal tissues. *Abstr., 59th Ann. Meet. Endocrine Soc.,* p. 138

74. Handwerger, S., Barrett, J., Tyrey, L., Schomberg, D. 1973. Differential effect of cyclic adenosine monophosphate on the secretion of human placental lactogen and human chorionic gonadotropin. *J. Clin. Endocrinol. Metab.* 36:1268–70

75. Handwerger, S., Sherwood, L. M. 1974. Comparison of the structure of human placental lactogenic hormone and human growth hormone. See Ref. 22, p. 33.

76. Hellig, H., Gattereau, D., Lefebvre, Y., Bolte, E. 1970. Steroid production from plasma cholesterol. I. Conversion of plasma cholesterol to placental progesterone in humans. *J. Clin. Endocrinol. Metab.* 30:624–31

77. Hennen, G. P. 1965. Detection and study of a human chorionic-thyroid-stimulating factor. *Arch. Int. Physiol. Biochim.* 73:689–95

78. Hennen, G. P., Freychet, P. 1974. Human chorionic thyrotropin. Its relation to thyroid stimulators from chorionic neoplasma and nonendocrine cancers. *Israel J. Med. Sci.* 10:1332–47

79. Horner, J. M., Hintz, R. L. 1979. Further comparisons of the [¹²⁵I]somatomedin A and the [¹²⁵I]somatomedin C radioreceptor assays of somatomedin peptide. *J. Clin. Endocrinol. Metab.* 48:959–63

80. Hoshina, M., Ashitaka, Y., Tojo, S. 1979. Immunohistochemical interaction on antisera to hCG and its subunits with chorionic tissue of early gestation. *Endocrinol. Jpn,* 26:175–84

81. Hussa, R. O., Pattillo, R. A., Ruckert, A. C. F., Scheuermann, K. W. 1978. Effects of butyrate and dibutyryl cyclic AMP on hCG-secreting trophoblastic and nontrophoblastic cells. *J. Clin. Endocrinol. Metab.* 46:69–76

82. Hussa, R. O., Story, M. T., Pattillo, R. A. 1974. Cyclic adenosine monophosphate stimulates secretion of human chorionic gonadotropin and estrogens by human trophoblast *in vitro. J. Clin. Endocrinol. Metab.* 38:338–40

83. Inagami, T., Murakami, K., Puett, D., Stockwell-Hartree, A., Nureddin, A. 1971. N-terminal amino acid sequence of the α-subunit of human pituitary luteinizing hormone. *Biochem. J.* 126:441–42

84. Jacobs, J. W., Mariz, I. K., Daughaday, W. H., Bradshaw, R. A. 1979. Characterization of the binding of a rat somatomedin to receptors in human placental membranes. *Biochem. Biophys. Res. Commun.* 86:869–76

85. Jailer, J. W., Knowlton, J. 1950. Stimulated adreno-cortical activity during pregnancy in an Addisonian patient. *J. Clin. Invest.* 19:1430–35

86. Jefcoate, C. R., Hume, R., Boyd, G. S. 1970. Separation of two forms of cytochrome P-450 from adrenal cortex mitochondria. *FEBS Lett.* 9:41–44

87. Jones, C. T., Luther, E., Ritchie, J. W. K., Worthington, D. 1975. Observations on facilitation of the preovulatory rise of LH by estrogen. *Endocrinology* 96:23–28

88. Jones, W. B., Lewis, J. L. Jr., Lehr, M. 1975. Monitor of chemotherapy in gestational trophoblastic neoplasm by radioimmunoassay of the beta-subunit of human chorionic gonadotropin. *Am. J. Obstet. Gynecol.* 121:669–72

89. Josimovich, J. B., Atwood, B. L. 1964. Human placental lactogen (hPL), a trophoblastic hormone synergizing with

chorionic gonadotropin and potentiating the anabolic effects of pituitary growth hormone. *Am. J. Obstet. Gynecol.* 88:867–79

90. Josimovich, J. B., Levitt, M. J. 1973. Human chorionic somatomammotropin (hCS). I. Purification and biochemical characterization In *Methods in Investigative and Diagnostic Endocrinology,* Vol. 2B, ed. S. A. Berson, R. S. Yalow, p. 787. Amsterdam; North-Holland

91. Juchau, M. R., Zachariah, P. K. 1975. Displacement of carbon monoxide from placental cytochrome P-450 by steroids: Antagonistic effects of androstenedione and 19-norandrostenedione. *Biochem. Biophys. Res. Commun.* 65:1026–32

92. Kanazawa, S., Nakamura, A., Saida, K., Tojo, S. 1976. Placento-thyroidal relationship in normal pregnancy. *Acta. Obstet. Gynecol. Scand.* 55:201–5

93. Kawasaki, T., Ashwell, G. 1976. Chemical and physical properties of a hepatic membrane protein that specifically binds asialoglycoproteins. *J. Biol. Chem.* 251:1296–302

94. Khodr, G. S., Siler-Khodr, T. M. 1978. The effect of luteinizing hormone-releasing factor on human chorionic gonadotropin secretion. *Fert. Steril.* 30:301–4

95. Khodr, G. S., Siler-Khodr, T. M. 1978. Localization of luteinizing hormone-releasing factor in the human placenta. *Fert. Steril.* 29:523–26

96. Lauritzen, C. L. 1975. Intraplacental regulations between steroid and peptide hormone (hCG and hPL) in pregnancy. *Acta Endocrinol.* 78: Suppl. 193, p. 46

97. Lee, Q. P., Zachariah, P. K., Juchau, M. R. 1975. Differential inhibition of androst-4-en-3,17-dione aromatization by carbon monoxide in the presence of estr-4-en-3,17-dione. *Steroids* 16: 571–78

98. Li, C. H., Dixon, J. S., Chung, D. 1971. Primary structure of the human chorionic somatomammotropin (hCS) molecule. *Science* 173:56–58

99. Liotta, A., Krieger, D. T. 1980. *In vitro* biosynthesis and comparative post-translational processing of immunoreactive precursor corticotropin/β-endorphin by human placental and pituitary cells. *Endocrinology* 106:1504–11

100. Liotta, A., Osathanondh, R., Ryan, K. J., Krieger, D. T. 1977. Presence of corticotropin in human placenta: Demonstration of *in vitro* synthesis. *Endocrinology* 101:1552–568

101. Liotta, A. S., Shickmanter, B., Krieger, D. T. 1979. Human placental synthesis of immunoreactive pro-opiocortin-like activity. *Clin. Res.* 27:256A

102. Loke, Y. W., Pepys, M. B. 1975. Effects of human chorionic gonadotropin preparations on complement *in vitro Am. J. Obstet. Gynecol.* 121:37–40

103. Lurie, A. O., Reid, D. E., Villee, C. A. 1966. The role of the fetus and placenta in maintenance of plasma progesterone. *Am. J. Obstet. Gynecol.* 96:670–75

104. McCure, R. W., Roberts, S., Young, P. L. 1970. Competitive inhibition of adrenal Δ^5-3β-hydroxysteroid dehydrogenase and Δ^5-3-ketosteroid isomerase activities by adenosine-3',5'-monophosphate. *J. Biol. Chem.* 245:3859–67

105. Macaron, C., Kyncl, M., Famuyiwa, O., Halpern, B., Brewer, J. 1979. *In vitro* effect of dopamine and pimozide on human chorionic gonadotropin secretion. *Am. J. Obstet. Gynecol.* 135:499–502

106. Marshall, J. R., Hammond, C. B., Ross, G. T., Jacobson, A., Rayford, P. L., Odell, W. D. 1968. Plasma and urinary chorionic gonadotropin during human pregnancy. *Obstet. Gynecol.* 32:760–64

107. Marshall, R. N., Underwood, L. E., Voina, S. J., Foushee, D. B., Van Wyk, J. J. 1974. Characterization of the insulin and somatomedin-C receptors in human placental cell membranes. *J. Clin. Endocrinol. Metab.* 39:283–92

108. Mason, J. I., Boyd, G. S. 1971. The cholesterol side chain cleavage enzyme system in mitochondria of human term placenta. *Eur. J. Biochem.* 21:308–21

109. Meigs, R. A., Ryan, K. J. 1968. Cytochrome P-450 and steroid biosynthesis in the human placenta. *Biochim. Biophys. Acta* 165:476–82

110. Meigs, R. A., Ryan, K. J. 1971. Enzymatic aromatization of steroids. *J. Biol. Chem.* 246:83–87

111. Meigs, R. A., Sheean, L. A. 1977. Mitochondria from human term placenta. III. The role of respiration and energy generation in progesterone biosynthesis. *Biochim. Biophys. Acta* 489:225–35

112. Menon, K. M. J., Jaffe, R. B. 1973. Chorionic gonadotropin sensitive adenylate cyclase in human placenta. *J. Clin. Endocrinol. Metab.* 36:1104–9

113. Miyakawa, I., Ikeda, I., Maeyama, M. 1974. Transport of ACTH across human placenta. *J. Clin. Endocrinol. Metab.* 39:440–42

114. Moorthy, K. B., Meigs, R. A. 1978. Aromatization of steroids by mitochondrial preparations from human term

placenta. *Arch. Biochim. Biophys.* 528:222–29

115. Morgan, F. J., Birken, S., Canfield, R. E. 1975. The amino acid sequence of human chorionic gonadotropin. *J. Biol. Chem.* 250:5247–58

116. Morgan, F. J., Canfield, R. E., Vaitukaits, J. L., Ross, G. T. 1974. Properties of the subunits of human chorionic gonadotropin. *Endocrinology* 94:1601–6

117. Morell, A. G., Gregoriadis, G., Scheinberg, I. H., Hickman, J., Ashwell, G. 1971. The role of sialic acid in determining the survival of glycoproteins in the circulation. *J. Biol. Chem.* 246:1461–67

118. Moyle, W. R., Bahl, O. P., Marz, L. 1975. Role of the carbohydrate of human chorionic gonadotropin in the mechanism of hormone action. *J. Biol. Chem.* 250:9163–89

119. Miura, S., Osathanondh, R., Makris, A., Todd, R. B., Levesque, L. A., Ryan, K. J. 1979. Effect of luteinizing-hormone-releasing factor on the concentrations of 3',5'-cyclic adenosine monophosphate and human chorionic gonadotropin in trophoblastic tissue in vitro. *Proc. 26th Ann. Meet. Soc. Gyn. Invest.*, p. 168

120. Nakai, Y., Nakao, K., Oki, S., Imura, H. 1978. Presence of immunoreactive β-lipotropin and β-endorphin in human placenta. *Life Sci.* 23:2013–18

121. Naughton, M. A., Merrill, D. A., McManus, L. M., Fink, L. M., Berman, E., White, M. J., Martinez-Hernandez, A. 1975. Localization of the β-chain of human chorionic gonadotropin on human tumor cells and placental cells. *Cancer Res.* 35:1887–89

122. Niall, H. D., Hogan, M. L., Sauer, R., Rosenbloom, L. Y., Greenwood, F. C. 1971. Sequences of pituitary and placental lactogenic and growth hormones: evolution from a primordial peptide by gene duplication. *Proc. Natl. Acad. Sci. USA* 68:866–70

123. Nielsen, P. V., Pedersen, H., Kampmann, E. M. 1979. Absence of human placental lactogen in an otherwise uneventful pregnancy. *Am. J. Obstet. Gynecol.* 135:322–26

124. Odagiri, E., Sherrell, B. J., Mount, C. D., Nicholson, W. E., Orth, D. N. 1979. Human placental immunoreactive corticotropin, lipotropin and β-endorphin: evidence for a common precursor. *Proc. Natl. Acad. Sci. USA* 76:2027–30

125. Opsahl, J. L., Long, R. C. 1951. Identification of ACTH in human placental tissue. *Yale J. Biol. Med.* 24:199–209

126. Osathanondh, R., Tulchinsky, D. 1980. Placental polypeptide hormones. In *Maternal-Fetal Endocrinology,* ed. D. Tulchinsky, K. J. Ryan, pp. 17–42. Philadelphia, London, Toronto: W. B. Saunders

127. Ozaki, S., Kalant, N. 1977. A radioreceptor assay for serum insulin. *J. Lab. Clin. Med.* 90:686–99

128. Pastorfide, G. B., Goldstein, D. P., Kosasa, T. S. 1974. The use of a radioimmunoassay specific for human chorionic gonadotropin in patients with molar pregnancy and gestational trophoblastic disease. *Am. J. Obstet. Gynecol.* 120:1025–28

129. Peeters, B., Mous, J., Van Bellegen, H., Rombauts, W. 1979. The wheat germ cell-free system possesses processing activity for the precursor of human placental lactogen. *Biochim. Biophys. Acta.* 561:502–16

130. Pierce, J. G. 1971. The subunits of pituitary thyrotropin. Their relationship to other glycoprotein hormones. *Endocrinology* 89:1331–44

131. Plotz, E. J., Kabara, J. J., Davies, M. E., LeRoy, G. V., Gould, R. G. 1968. Studies on the synthesis of cholesterol in the brain of the human fetus. *Am. J. Obstet. Gynecol.* 101:534–38

132. Posner, B. I., Kelly, P. A., Shiu, R. P. C. 1974. Studies of insulin, growth hormone and prolactin binding: tissue distribution, species variation and characterization. *Endocrinology* 95:521–31

133. Pulkkinen, M. O. 1961. Acylsulphatase and the hydrolysis of some steroid sulfates in developing organism and placenta. *Acta Physiol. Scand.* 52: Suppl. 180, pp. 1–92

134. Rathnam, P., Saxena, B. B. 1975. Primary amino acid sequence of follicle-stimulating hormone from human pituitary glands. *J. Biol. Chem.* 250:6735–46

135. Rayford, P. L., Vaitukaitis, J. L., Ross, G. T., Morgan, F. J., Canfield, R. E. 1972. Use of specific antisera to characterize biological activity of hCG β-subunit preparations. *Endocrinology* 91:144–46

136. Rees, L. H., Burke, C. W., Chard, T., Evans, S. W., Letchworth, A. T. 1975. Possible placental origin of ACTH in normal human pregnancy. *Nature* 254:620–22

137. Renwick, A. G. C., Oliver, J. F. 1973. The aromatization of [7-³H]androstenedione by human placental mitochondria. *Steroids* 22:123–32

138. Ryan, K. J. 1959. Biological aromatiza-

tion of steroids. *J. Biol. Chem.* 234:268–72

139. Sairam, M. R., Li, C. H. 1973. Human pituitary thyrotropin: isolation and chemical characterization of its subunits. *Biochem. Biophys. Res. Commun.* 51:336–42

140. Sairam, M. R., Papkoff, H., Li, C. H. 1972. Human pituitary interstitial cell stimulating hormone: primary structure of the α-subunit. *Biochem. Biophys. Res. Commun.* 48:530–37

141. Schneider, A. B., Kowalski, K., Buchman, G., Sherwood, L. M. 1977. Dimeric ('Big') human placental lactogen. Immunological and biological activity. *Biochim. Biophys. Acta* 493:69–77

142. Schneider, A. B., Kowalski, K., Russell, J., Sherwood, L. M. 1979. Identification of the interchain disulfide bonds of dimeric human placental lactogen. *J. Biol. Chem.* 254:3782–84

143. Sciarra, J. J., Kaplan, S. L., Grumbach, M. M. 1963. Localization of antihuman growth hormone serum within the human placenta: Evidence for a human chorionic "growth hormone-prolactin". *Nature* 199:1005–6

144. Sciarra, J. J., Sherwood, L. M., Varwa, A. A., Lundberg, W. B. 1968. Human placental lactogen and placental weight. *Am. J. Obstet. Gynecol.* 101:413–16

145. Shambaugh, G. E., Kubek, M., Wilber, J. F. 1977. Placenta: A newly identified source of thyrotropin-releasing hormone (TRH). *Abstr. Endocrinol.* 100:T24

146. Shambaugh, G., Kubek, M., Wilber, J. F. 1979. Thyrotropin-releasing hormone activity in the human placenta. *J. Clin. Endocrinol. Metab.* 48:483–86

147. Shaw, D. A., Dalziel, E. M., O'Donnell, V. J. 1969. Biogenesis of oestrogens from [^{14}C]testosterone in the mitochondrial fraction of the human placenta. *Biochem. J.* 113:737–39

148. Sherman, M. I., Atienza, S. B. 1977. Production and metabolism of progesterone and androstenedione by cultured mouse blastocysts. *Biol. Reprod.* 16:190–99

149. Sherwood, L. M., Handwerger, S., McLaurin, W. D., Lanner, M. 1971. Amino acid sequence of human placental lactogen. *Nature New Biol.* 233:59–61

150. Shine, J., Seeburg, P. H., Martial, J. A., Baxter, J. D., Goodman, H. M. 1977. Construction and analysis of recombinant DNA for human chorionic somatomammotropin. *Nature* 270:494–99

151. Shome, B., Parlow, A. F. 1974. Human follicle stimulating hormone (hFSH): first proposal for the amino acid sequence of the α-subunit (hFSHα) and first demonstration of its identity with the α-subunit of human luteinizing hormone (hLHα). *J. Clin. Endocrinol. Metab.* 39:191–202

152. Shome, B., Parlow, A. F. 1974. Human follicle stimulating hormone: first proposal for the amino acid sequence of the hormone-specific β-subunit (hFSHβ). *J. Clin. Endocrinol. Metab.* 39:203–5

153. Siiteri, P. K., MacDonald, P. C. 1963. The utilization of circulating dehydroisoandrosterone sulfate for estrogen synthesis during human pregnancy. *Steroids* 2:713–30

154. Siiteri, P. K., MacDonald, P. C. 1966. Placental estrogen biosynthesis during human pregnancy. *J. Clin. Endocrinol.* 26:751–61

155. Siler-Khodr, T. M., Khodr, G. S. 1978. Luteinizing hormone-releasing factor content of human placenta. *Am. J. Obstet. Gynecol.* 130:216–19

156. Siler-Khodr, T. M., Khodr, G. S. 1979. Extrahypothalamic luteinizing hormone-releasing factor (LRF): release of immunoreactive LRF *in vitro*. *Fert. Steril.* 32:294–96

157. Simpson, E. R., Bilheimer, D. W., MacDonald, P. C., Porter, J. C. 1979. Uptake and degradation of plasma lipoproteins by human choriocarcinoma cells in culture. *Endocrinology* 104:8–16

158. Simpson, E. R., Boyd, G. S. 1967. The cholesterol side-chain cleavage enzyme system of bovine adrenal cortex. *Eur. J. Biochem.* 2:275–85

159. Simpson, E. R., Burkhart, M. F. 1980. Acyl CoA : cholesterol acyl transferase activity in human placental microsomes: inhibition by progesterone. *Arch. Biochem. Biophys.* 200:79–85

160. Simpson, E. R., Burkhart, M. F. 1980. Acyl CoA : cholesterol acyltransferase activity in human choriocarcinoma cells in culture: effect of lipoproteins and progesterone on cholesteryl ester synthesis. *Arch. Biochem. Biophys.* 200:86–92

161. Simpson, E. R., McCarthy, J. L., Peterson, J. A. 1978. Evidence that the cycloheximide-sensitive site of adrenocorticotropic hormone action is in the mitochondria. *J. Biol. Chem.* 253:3135–39

162. Simpson, E. R., Miller, D. A. 1978. Cholesterol side-chain cleavage, cytochrome P-450, and iron-sulfur protein

in human placental mitochondria. *Arch. Biochem. Biophys.* 190:800–8

163. Simpson, E. R., Porter, J. C., Milewich, L., Bilheimer, D. W., MacDonald, P. C. 1978. Regulation by plasma lipoproteins of progesterone biosynthesis and 3-hydroxy-3-methyl glutaryl coenzyme A reductase activity in cultured human choriocarcinoma cells. *J. Clin. Endocrinol. Metab.* 47:1099–105

164. Simpson, E. R., Winkel, C. A., Unpublished observations

165. Simpson, E. R., Winkel, C. A. 1980. Regulation of cholesterol metabolism in human placental cells in primary culture. *Abstr. 27th Ann. Meet. Soc. for Gynecol. Invest.*, p. 17

166. Smith, S. W., Axelrod, L. R. 1969. Studies on the metabolism of steroid hormones and their precursors by the human placenta at various stages of gestation II. In vitro metabolism of 3β-hydroxyandrost-5-en-17-one. *J. Clin. Endocrinol.* 29:1182–90

167. Speroff, L., Caldwell, B. V., Brock, W. A., Anderson, G. G., Hobbins, J. C. 1972. Hormone levels during prostaglandin F$_{2\alpha}$ infusions for therapeutic abortion. *J. Clin. Endocrinol. Metab.* 34:531–36

168. Sulimovici, S., Bartoov, B., Lunenfeld, B. 1973. Localization of 3β-hydroxysteroid dehydrogenase in the inner membrane subfraction of rat testis mitochondria. *Biochim. Biophys. Acta* 321:27–40

169. Suwa, S., Friesen, H. G. 1969. Biosynthesis of human placental proteins and human placental lactogen (hPL) *in vitro.* I. Identification of [^{3}H]-labelled hPL. *Endocrinology* 85:1028–45

170. Tabei, T., Heinrichs, W. L. 1962. Diagnosis of placental sulfatase deficiency. *Am. J. Obstet. Gynecol.* 124:409–14

171. Takano, K., Hall, K., Fryklund, L., Holmgren, A., Sievertsson, H., Uthne, K. 1975. The binding of insulin and somatomedin A to human placental membrane. *Acta Endocrinol.* 80:14–31

172. Talwar, G. P. 1979. Human chorionic gonadotropin and ovarian and placental steroidogenesis. *J. Steroid Biochem.* 11:27–34

173. Teasdale, F., Adcock, E. W., August, C. S., Cox, S., Battaglia, F. C., Naughton, M. A. 1973. Human chorionic gonadotropin: inhibitory effect on mixed lymphocyte cultures. *Gynecol. Invest.* 4:263–69

174. Thompson, E. R. Jr., Siiteri, P. K. 1974. The involvement of human placental microsomal cytochrome P-450 in aromatization. *J. Biol. Chem.* 249:5373–78

175. Thompson, E. A. Jr., Siiteri, P. K. 1974. Utilization of oxygen and reduced nicotinamide adenine dinucleotide phosphate by human placental microsomes during aromatization of androstenedione. *J. Biol. Chem.* 249:5364–72

176. Thompson, E. A. Jr., Siiteri, P. K. 1976. Partial resolution of the placental microsomal aromatase complex. *J. Steroid. Biochem.* 7:635–39

177. Tominaga, T., Troen, P. 1967. Stimulation of aromatization in human placenta by human placental lactogen. *J. Clin. Invest.* 46:1124–28

178. Tulchinsky, D., Hobel, C. J. 1973. Plasma human chorionic gonadotropin, estrone, estradiol, estriol, progesterone and 17α-hydroxyprogesterone in human pregnancy. *Am. J. Obstet. Gynecol.* 117:884–93

179. Vaitukaitis, J. L., Braunstein, G. D., Ross, G. T. 1972. A radioimmunoassay which specifically measures human chorionic gonadotropin in the presence of human luteinizing hormone. *Am. J. Obstat. Gynecol.* 113:751–58

180. Vaitukaitis, J. L. 1974. Changing placental concentrations of human chorionic gonadotropin and its subunits during gestation. *J. Clin. Endocrinol. Metab.* 38:755–60

181. Van Buul-Offers, S., Van der Brande, J. L. 1979. Binding of somatomedin-A and -C, NSILA-S and insulin to human placental cell membranes. *Horm. Res.* 11:186–202

182. Van Hall, E. V., Vaitukaitis, J. L., Ross, G. T., Hickman, J. W., Ashwell, G. 1971. Effects of progressive desialylation on the rate of disappearance of immunoreactive hCG from plasma in rats. *Endocrinology* 89:11–15

183. Van Leusden, H., Villee, C. A. 1965. The de novo synthesis of sterols and steroids from acetate by preparations of human term placenta. *Steroids* 6:31–45

184. Villee, C. A., Van Leusden, H., Zelewski, L. 1966. The regulation of the biosynthesis of sterols and steroids in the placenta. *Adv. Enzyme Regul.* 4:161–79

185. Warren, J. C., Timberlake, C. E. 1962. Steroid sulphatase in the human placenta. *J. Clin. Endocrinol.* 22:1148–51

186. Welsch, F. 1979. Release of human chorionic somatomammotropin from isolated perfused lobules and superfused fragments of term placenta: spontaneous liberation and the effects of cholinergic drugs, dibutyrylcyclic adenosine monophosphate and calcium. *Res.*

Commun. Chem. Pathol. Pharmacol. 24:211–22

187. Wilson, L. O., Harding, B. W. 1970. Studies on adrenal cortical cytochrome P-450. III. Effects of carbon monoxide and light on steroid 11β-hydroxylation. *Biochemistry* 9:1615–20

188. Winkel, C. A., Simpson, E. R. 1979. Regulation of placental progesterone (P) secretion by low density lipoprotein (LDL) cholesterol (C). *Abstr. 61st Ann. Meet. Endocrine Soc.,* p. 79

189. Winkel, C. A., Snyder, J. M., MacDonald, P. C., Simpson, E. R. 1980. Regulation of cholesterol and progesterone synthesis in human placental cells in culture by serum lipoproteins. *Endocrinology* 106:1054–60

190. Winters, A. J., Oliver, C., Colston, C., MacDonald, R., Porter, J. C. 1974. Plasma ACTH levels in the human fetus and neonate as related to age and parturition. *J. Clin. Endocrinol. Metab.* 39:269–73

191. Wolf, A. S., Musch, K. A., Lauritzen, C. H. 1977. Effects of human choriogonadotropin on placental steroidogenesis in perfusions. *Acta Endocrinol. Copenhagen* 85: Suppl. 212 p. 33

192. Woolever, C. A., Goldfien, A., Page, E. W. 1961. Studies of the isolated perfused placenta. *Am. J. Obstet. Gynecol.* 81: 1137–39

193. Ylikorkala, O., Pennanen, S. 1973. Human placental lactogen (hPL) levels in maternal serum during abortion induced by intra- and extra-amniotic injection of prostaglandin $F_{2\alpha}$. *J. Obstet. Gynaecol. Br. Comm.* 80:927–31

194. Yorde, D. E., Hussa, R. O., Garancis, J. C., Pattillo, R. A. 1979. Immunocyto-chemical localization of human choriogonadotropin in human malignant trophoblast. *Lab. Invest.* 40:391–98

195. Yoshimi, T., Strott, C. A., Marshall, J. R., Lipsett, M. B. 1969. Corpus luteum function in early pregnancy. *J. Clin. Endocrinol. Metab.* 29:225–30

196. Yoshimoto, Y., Wolfsen, A. R., Hirose, F., Odell, W. D. 1979. Human chorionic gonadotropin-like material: presence in normal human tissues. *Am. J. Obstet. Gynecol.* 134:729–33

197. Yoshimoto, Y., Wolfsen, A. R., Odell, W. D. 1977. Human chorionic gonadotropin-like substance in normal human tissues. *Science* 197:575–77

198. Youngblood, W. W., Humm, J., Kizer, J. S. 1979. TRH-like immunoactivity in rat pancreas and eye, bovine and sheep pineals, and human placenta: non-identity with synthetic pyroGlu-His-Pro-NH_2(TRH). *Brain Res.* 163:101–10

199. Zachariah, P. K., Juchau, M. R. 1975. Interactions of steroids with human placental cytochrome P-450 in the presence of carbon monoxide. *Life Sci.* 10:1689–93

200. Zachariah, P. K., Lee, Q. P., Symms, K. G., Juchau, M. R. 1976. Further studies on the properties of human placental microsomal cytochrome P-450. *Biochem. Pharmacol.* 25:793–800

201. Zachariah, P. K., Juchau, M. R. 1977. Inhibition of human placental mixed function oxidation with carbon monoxide: reversal with monochromatic light. *J. Steroid Biochem.* 8:221–28

202. Zelewski, L., Villee, C. A. 1966. The biosynthesis of squalene, lanosterol and cholesterol by minced human placenta. *Biochemistry* 5:1805–14

Ann. Rev. Physiol. 1981. 43:189–98

EXTRACELLULAR ANDROGEN BINDING PROTEINS

❖1304

C. Wayne Bardin, Neal Musto, Glen Gunsalus, N. Kotite, S.-L. Cheng, F. Larrea, and R. Becker

The Population Council, The Rockefeller University, New York,
New York 10021

Over the past several years, extracellular androgen binding macromolecules have been identified that are distinct from the intracellular androgen receptors. The best characterized of these proteins are testosterone-estradiol binding globulin (TeBG) from serum and "androgen binding protein" (ABP) from testis. In addition, androgen binding proteins have been tentatively identified in a number of other organs.

TESTOSTERONE-ESTRADIOL BINDING GLOBULIN

Identification and Isolation

The demonstration of a plasma protein having high affinity for binding testosterone first appeared in 1965 (29). Subsequent investigators showed this binding protein is distinct from cortisol binding globulin (41, 48) and binds estrogens as well as androgens (8, 44). It was, therefore, given the name testosterone-estradiol binding globulin (8). Over the years several other names, including testosterone binding globulin and sex steroid binding globulin, have been suggested.

There are few studies of the species distribution of TeBG. Murphy (36) found androgen binding activity in the sera of human, cow, and frog, but not rat, rabbit, dog, or duck. Except for rabbit, these observations were similar to those of Corvol & Bardin (7), who identified TeBG in the plasma of 13 of the 21 animals examined using non-steady-state polyacrylamide gel electrophoresis (PAGE). Specifically, TeBG was found in primates, rabbits, goats, cows, sheep, reptiles, and amphibians and was missing in birds,

189

donkeys, cats, dogs, and rodents. It is perhaps significant that the electro-phoretic technique employed in this study would not detect TeBG in species whose binding protein exhibited rapid dissociation kinetics. The use of steady-state PAGE, which obviates this problem, subsequently permitted detection of a dog TeBG exhibiting androgen and estrogen affinities 20–80-fold lower than those observed in hTeBG (51). A low affinity TeBG was also identified in the cat (43). These observations emphasize that TeBGs in various species have a wide range of steroid affinities. We conclude that there has been less evolutionary pressure to retain a high affinity binding protein for androgens and estrogens in the extracellular compartment than in the cell where the androgen receptors serve as a mediator of hormone action. The divergence of TeBGs from one another is also suggested by their lack of common immunodeterminants. For example, antibodies to the hu-man protein cross-react with other primate TeBGs but not with those of the cat, dog, sheep, goat, or cow (43). Antibodies against rabbit TeBG cross-react with that of none of these species (4).

The demonstration of the stabilizing influence of calcium ions and devel-opment of effective androgen affinity chromatography allowed the isolation of active human TeBG (hTeBG) (32, 45). Rosner (45) reported that homo-geneous hTeBG had a molecular weight of 94,000 and no apparent subunit structure. Other investigators reported a dimeric structure for hTeBG with a minimum subunit size of 36,000–67,000 daltons as determined under denaturing conditions (31, 34). This discrepancy was partially resolved by Rosner, who now concludes that the TeBG isolated in his laboratory is composed of smaller units (personal communication). Recently, another group of investigators reported four subunits in highly purified hTeBG (23). Even though there is not uniform agreement regarding subunit size and composition, there is a consensus that TeBG is a glycoprotein with one binding site per native molecule (23, 45). The observed microheterogeneity of highly purified TeBG is likely due to sialic acid since only one isoelectric species is seen after treatment with neuraminadase (35).

Homogeneous TeBGs from rabbit (33), dog (51), and cow (49) have been prepared. The molecular weight, subunit structure, and amino acid compo-sition of rabbit TeBG (rbTeBG) were similar to those reported for hTeBG isolated by the same laboratory (34), even though the steroid binding affini-ties were lower (43). Canine TeBG, which like rbTeBG also has a much lower affinity for androgens than hTeBG, is also composed of dimers (51). By contrast, the native and subunit molecular weights of bovine TeBG (bTeBG) were reported to be 89,500 and 28,000, respectively, which sug-gests that this binding protein is composed of three subunits (49). Thus the TeBGs from the species so far examined are similar insofar as they are large glycoproteins ($\cong$ 80–90,000 mol wt) with a greater affinity for androgens than for estrogens. Although all of the highly purified TeBGs appear to have subunits, it is not possible to say whether a common number will be found in all.

Secretion and Metabolism of TeBG

Although not extensively studied, TeBG is believed to be synthesized in the liver of most species. The factors controlling the levels of this protein in blood have been studied most extensively in humans, where estrogens, thyroid hormone excess, and liver disease increase hTeBG concentrations and androgens and thyroid hormone deficiency decrease them (2). In some species the effects of these hormones differ from those in man. For example, in the rabbit, estrogen treatment has little effect on TeBG levels.

Little is known about the metabolism of TeBG. Suzuki & Sinohara (50) demonstrated that sialic acid on bTeBG prevents rapid removal from blood after its administration to rat. Following treatment with neuraminadase, asialo-bTeBG was cleared rapidly by the liver. Similar observations have been made on other asialo glycoproteins (1).

The Functions of TeBG

The fact that TeBG is absent in some species indicates that it is not absolutely essential for androgen action. Nonetheless, studies were performed to discern how this protein influences androgen action and metabolism in animals where it is present. A variety of in vivo studies have suggested that TeBG-bound testosterone is less available for expressing biological activity and for metabolism than is free steroid, since (a) in humans the rate of testosterone clearance is related to the TeBG levels in blood (53); and (b) in those animals possessing TeBG with high affinity for androgens, testosterone is cleared from the blood more slowly than androstenedione. This is in contrast to species without or with low affinity TeBG where both of these steroids are metabolized at the same rate (2). These considerations are compatible with the postulate that in species with high-affinity TeBG, testosterone leaves the blood at a slower rate.

In addition to its effects on the rate of androgen removal from blood, TeBG may also influence intracellular androgen metabolism. Recent immunohistochemical studies demonstrated TeBG uptake by androgen-responsive tissue (5). In these cells testosterone could be partitioned between the binding sites on TeBG, steroid metabolizing enzymes, and androgen receptors. Thus the amount of TeBG could influence the sensitivity of cells to androgens by altering the rate and pattern of hormone metabolism. That this is indeed the case was suggested by studies showing that the pattern of testosterone metabolism in human prostates perfused with TeBG differed from those perfused with albumin or buffer alone (30).

ANDROGEN BINDING PROTEIN

Identification and Isolation

Studies from several laboratories (20, 54) demonstrated that epididymal and testicular cytosol contained a heat-stable binding protein (ABP) with a high affinity for androgens and estrogens but not antiandrogens. In pubertal and adult animals, ABP is of Sertoli cell origin. Although ABP has been most extensively studied in rat, it or a similar protein has also been identified in either the epididymis or testis of other species (9, 13, 47, 55). The function of ABP is not known. Nonetheless, it has been used to study Sertoli cell physiology (11, 18). Decreased ABP activity in cryptorchidism (17), inherited seminiferous tubular failure (37), and other disorders (15, 19) suggests this protein may also be used as an index of testicular pathophysiology.

ISOLATION OF RAT ABP(rABP)   The isolation of rABP from testis and epididymis requires 55,000- and 6,400-fold purifications, respectively. In order to achieve this degree of purification, an affinity column was prepared with dihydrotestosterone-17α-hexanoic acid as the ligand. The attachment of the steroid via an alkyl side chain at the 17α position rather than the classical 17β-hemisuccinate ester bond resulted in a stable column with high affinity for androgen binding proteins (39, 40). This column was used to purify rABP more than 6,000-fold over crude homogenates with an overall recovery of 45% of the initial binding activity. An unambiguous purification of ABP from rat epididymis was possible because this species does not have detectable TeBG in plasma (7). When rABP was examined by SDS-PAGE, two major protein bands were observed that migrated with apparent molecular weights of 41,000 (41k) and 45,000 (45k) rather than the 90,000 observed for native rABP. These observations are consistent with a subunit structure for ABP (38). That 45k and 41k were present in a 3:1 ratio suggested rat ABP is a mixed hybrid system comprised of 45k-45k, 45k-41k, and 41k-41k dimers. Both species of monomer are secreted by Sertoli cells in culture, suggesting that heterogeneity is due to post-translational processing.

In addition to size heterogeneity of rABP monomers, a considerable microheterogeneity attributable to charged species was observed in the intact molecule. The heterogeneity varied in different portions of the male reproductive tract with a shift toward more basic species as it moved from testis to cauda epididymis (26).

ISOLATION OF RABBIT ABP (rbABP)   Androgen binding protein was first purified from rabbit epididymis by Weddington et al (56) using conventional procedures. One preparation was apparently homogeneous, but subsequent preparations were only 3–20% of theoretical purity. These authors concluded that rbABP is a single protein chain of 84,000 daltons. Recently Cheng et al (6) isolated rbABP by affinity chromatography and demonstrated that it was a dimeric protein with subunits of 43,000 and 47,000 daltons. As in rat, the relative amounts of rbABP subunits were unequal. Most of the physicochemical properties of rbABP were identical to those of rbTeBG, including K_d, heat stability, steroid specificity, binding kinetics, and molecular weight. A detailed comparison of rbTeBG and rbABP required that both these proteins be prepared free of one another, a problem not addressed in early studies (56). Cheng et al (6) obviated this problem by using concanavalin-A, which specifically and quantitatively binds rbTeBG. When highly purified binding protein from the rabbit epididymis was applied to concanavalin-A columns, 60% appeared in the void column, 20% was partially retarded, and 20% was specifically bound. The binding protein specifically bound to the concanavalin-A was assumed to be rbTeBG contaminants from blood; the protein not bound was defined as rbABP of Sertoli cell origin. At present it is not possible to determine whether rbTeBG and rbABP are similar but distinct proteins (such as hLH and hCG) or the same protein made in different tissues (such as conalbumin and transferin from chicken oviduct and liver, respectively). As noted below, a similar problem exists in humans.

IDENTIFICATION OF HUMAN ABP(hABP)   The studies in the rabbit are pertinent to observations on hABP. Vigersky et al (55) concluded that hABP could not be distinguished from hTeBG. Other studies suggested that a distinct testicular binding protein (hABP) could be distinguished from hTeBG by charge, binding kinetics, and pH optimum for binding (22). The fact that hTeBG is quantitatively adsorbed on concanavalin-A whereas hABP is only partially retained provides a method for assaying the latter protein in the testis. The concentration of hABP was found to vary directly as a function of testicular testosterone (27). The ultimate use of hABP, as well as rbABP, as markers for testicular function awaits the demonstration of how they are distinct from the TeBGs in the two species.

Synthesis and Metabolism of ABP

HORMONAL CONTROL OF ABP CONCENTRATIONS   Chronic FSH treatment of immature or long-term hypophysectomized adult rats increased testicular and epididymal ABP levels, suggesting that both synthesis and transport to the epididymis were stimulated (21, 46). These effects of FSH are similar in hypophysectomized or immature hormone-deficient animals. By contrast, acute effects of FSH on testicular ABP levels are not as clear. Tindall et al demonstrated that highly purified FSH (devoid of LH activity) failed to increase ABP in 1–2 hr after treatment of 31-day-old hypophysectomized rats; whereas FSH contaminated with LH, LH alone, or testosterone produced a rapid increase in testicular ABP binding activity within 1–2 hr (52). The fact that testosterone per se increased the recoverability of ABP from the testes of hypophysectomized rats seemed to provide an explanation for the effects of FSH and LH. However, other investigators, utilizing the 16-day-old intact animals, showed that rats treated with antibodies against LH respond within 2 hr to FSH by increasing ABP levels (25). In these studies, animals treated with anti-LH did not show increased testicular testosterone when exogenous LH was administered, thus indicating the effectiveness of the antibody treatment. These experiments suggested that FSH is capable of increasing acutely the amount of ABP. However, this observation still may be the result of testosterone, inasmuch as FSH, even in the presence of anti-LH, produces a slight rise in testicular androgens (25).

Testosterone treatment maintained ABP levels in hypophysectomized rat when administered immediately following surgery (10). In addition, when hypophysectomized animals were untreated until testicular regression was complete, subsequent testosterone administration increased ABP in animals 35 days old or older at the time of surgery (10). In this regard, it is of interest that FSH-responsive DNA synthesis in cultured Sertoli cells disappears after this age (12). These observations suggest that some differentiating event around 35 days of age results in altered hormonal responsiveness.

FSH and testosterone treatment of Sertoli cells in culture prevents the rapid decline in protein secretion that follows placement of these cells in culture (28). Additional studies have demonstrated that other substances (e.g. insulin, vitamin A), along with FSH and testosterone, can help to maintain the ability of the cultured Sertoli cell to secrete ABP (24).

PRODUCTION OF ABP BY FETAL RATS   Immunoreactive ABP was found in plasma and amniotic fluid of both male and female fetuses at 18 days of gestation (15). ABP levels in fetal tissues are similar to those in plasma in both sexes. Following birth, ABP plasma levels decrease until the fourth day of life, whereupon ABP in the male increases while it disappears from the female. The site(s) of origin and the function of ABP in the fetus are unknown.

METABOLISM OF ABP   Sertoli cells secrete most of their ABP into the tubular lumen; from there it is transported to the epididymis, where it is degraded. Immunohistochemical studies of the epididymis indicate that ABP is found in the apical cytoplasm of epithelial cells in caput but not other portions of the epididymis (42). These observations suggest a selective uptake of ABP into a relatively small portion of the epididymal epithelium. The purpose of this selective uptake remains to be established.

Little is known about the systemic metabolism of ABP. ABP secreted into blood disappears with a half-time of 18–19 hr. Its rate of metabolism is independent of age or hormonal status (3). The systemic site of ABP metabolism has yet to be determined.

BIDIRECTIONAL SECRETION OF RAT ABP   As noted above, the major portion of rABP is secreted into the seminiferous tubule (20) and into blood (14). Evidence from this and other laboratories suggests that ABP is not released into the blood from the lumen of the seminiferous tubule, the rete testis, or the epididymis (16). If this is true, then it is possible that a fraction of the ABP is released from the basal aspect of Sertoli cells. This has given rise to the concept that Sertoli cell proteins have a bidirectional release into testicular lymph (and blood) and into the seminiferous tubular lumen. In addition, the secretion into these two separate compartments appears to be under independent control; in many instances, most of the ABP in the blood appears to come from direct Sertoli secretion rather than from the epididymis. Studies supporting these considerations have been reviewed recently (16).

Recent studies have identified three conditions (uncontrolled diabetes, progestin treatment, and administration of LHRH agonists) in which the blood levels of ABP were not compatible with the simple bidirectional secretory model (C.W. Bardin, unpublished). In some of these conditions blood ABP levels rose during epididymal involution. Subsequent studies showed that ABP is released into blood from a regressing epididymis and that this loss can be reversed by androgen replacement (3). Thus ABP is released into the blood from the testes or the testes plus epididymides, depending upon hormonal states. The immunoassay for ABP has permitted insights into the complex secretion of a specific testicular protein. It is anticipated that this is the first of a series of such proteins that will be identified.

Function of ABP

The fact that ABP, like TeBG, cannot be identified in some species suggests that it cannot be essential for reproduction unless its function is subsumed by a protein without an androgen binding site. In spite of this consideration, ABP may influence androgen action or metabolism in species where it is present, particularly in the caput epididymis where it is present in high concentrations. This speculation is supported by the observations that physiological androgen concentrations in blood are insufficient to maintain this region of the epididymis once denied direct access to testicular androgens and proteins by ligation of the efferent ductules. It is, therefore, possible that one of the proteins of the testicular fluid, such as ABP, may facilitate the action of androgen on caput epididymis. In this regard the proximal caput epididymis is capable of concentrating ABP, thus raising the possibility that this protein might function as a transmembrane carrier protein for androgens (42).

ACKNOWLEDGMENT

This work was supported by NIH grants HD-13541 and HD-12976.

Literature Cited

1. Ashwell, G., Morell, A. G. 1974. The role of surface carbohydrates in the hepatic recognition and transport of circulating glycoproteins. *Adv. Enzymol.* 41:99–128
2. Bardin, C. W., Mahoudeau, J. A. 1970. Dynamics of androgen metabolism in women with hirsutism. *Ann. Clin. Res.* 2:251–62
3. Becker, R. R., Gunsalus, G. L., Musto, N. A., Bardin, C. W. 1980. Potential contribution of the epididymis to serum ABP. *Anat. Rec.* 196:15A (Abstr.)
4. Bordin, S., Lewis, J., Petra, P. H. 1978. Monospecific antibodies to the sex steroid-binding protein (SBP) of human and rabbit sera: Cross-reactivity with other species. *Biochem. Biophys. Res. Commun.* 85:391–401
5. Bordin, S., Petra, P. H. 1980. Immunocytochemical localization of the sex steroid-binding protein (SBP) of plasma in tissues of the adult monkey, Macacca Nemestrina. *Proc. Natl. Acad. Sci. USA* In press
6. Cheng, S. L., Musto, N. A., Gunsalus, G. L., Bardin, C. W. 1980. Purification and characterization of rabbit epididymal androgen binding protein (rbABP): Comparison with rat ABP. Presented at 62nd Meet. Endocrine Soc., Washington DC. Abstr. 246
7. Corvol, P., Bardin, C. W. 1973. Species distribution of testosterone-binding globulin. *Biol. Reprod.* 8:277–82
8. Corvol, P., Chrambach, A., Rodbard, D., Bardin, C. W. 1971. Physical properties and binding capacity of testosterone-estradiol-binding globulin in human plasma, determined by polyacrylamide gel electrophoresis. *J. Biol. Chem.* 246:3435–43
9. Danzo, B. J., Eller, B. C., Orgebin-Crist, M. C. 1974. Studies on the site or origin of the androgen binding protein present in epididymal cytosol from mature intact rabbits. *Steroids* 21:107–22
10. Elkington, J. S., Sanborn, B. M., Steinberger, E. 1975. The effect of testosterone propionate on the concentration of testicular and epididymal androgen binding activity in hypophysectomized rat. *Mol. Cell. Endocrinol.* 2:157–70
11. Fritz, I. B., Rommerts, F. G., Louis, B. G., Dorrington, J. H. 1976. Regulation of FSH and dibutyrylcyclic ABP of the formation of androgen binding protein in Sertoli cell-enriched cultures. *J. Reprod. Fert.* 46:17–24
12. Griswold, M. D., Solari, A., Tung, P. S., Fritz, I. B. 1977. Stimulation by FSH of DNA synthesis and of mitosis in cultured Sertoli cells prepared from testes of immature rats. *Mol. Cell. Endocrinol.* 7:151–65
13. Guerrero, R., Ritzen, E. M., Purvis, K., Hansson, V., French, F. S. 1975. Concentration of steroid hormones and androgen binding protein (ABP) in rabbit efferent duct fluid. In *Hormonal Regulation of Spermatogenesis,* ed. F. S. French, V. Hansson, E. M. Ritzen, S. N. Nayfeh, pp. 213–21. NY: Plenum
14. Gunsalus, G. L., Musto, N. A., Bardin, C. W. 1978. Immunoassay of androgen binding protein in blood: A new approach for study of the seminiferous tubule. *Science* 200:65–66
15. Gunsalus, G. L., Musto, N. A., Bardin, C. W. 1978. Factors affecting blood levels of androgen binding protein in the rat. *Int. J. Androl.* 2:482–93 (Suppl.)
16. Gunsalus, G. L., Musto, N. A., Bardin, C. W. 1980. Bidirectional release of a Sertoli cell product, androgen binding protein, into the blood and seminiferous tubule. In *Testicular Development, Structure* and *Function,* ed. A. Stein-

berger, E. Steinberger, pp. 291–97. NY: Raven

17. Hagenas, L., Ritzen, E. M. 1976. Impaired Sertoli cell function in experimental cryptorchidism in the rat. *Molec. Cell. Endrocrinol.* 4:25–34

18. Hagenas, L., Ritzen, E. M., Ploen, L., Hansson, V., French, F. S., Nayfeh, S. N. 1975. Sertoli cell origin of testicular androgen binding protein (ABP). *Molec. Cell. Endocrinol.* 2:339–350.

19. Hansson, V., Purvis, K., Attramadal, A., Torjersen, P., Andersen, D., Ritzen, E. M. 1978. Sertoli cell function in the androgen insensitive (TFM) rat. *Int. J. Androl.* 1:96–104

20. Hansson, V., Weddington, S. C., McLean, W. S., Smith, A. A., Nayfeh, S. N., French, F. S., Ritzen, E. M. 1975. Regulation of seminiferous tubular function by FSH and androgen. *J. Reprod. Fert.* 44:363–75

21. Hansson, V., Weddington, S. C., Naess, O., Attramadal, A., French, F. S., Kotite, N. J., Nayfeh, S. N., Ritzen, E. M., Hagenas, L. 1975. Testicular androgen binding protein (ABP)—A parameter of Sertoli cell secretory function. See Ref. 13, pp. 323–36.

22. Hsu, A-F., Troen, P. 1978. An androgen binding protein in the testicular cytosol of human testis. Comparison with human plasma testosterone-estrogen binding globulin. *J. Clin. Invest.* 61:1611–19

23. Iqbal, M. J., Johnson, M. W. 1979. Purification and characterization of human sex hormone binding globulin. *J. Steroid Biochem.* 10:535–40

24. Karl, A. F., Griswold, M. D. 1980. Actions of insulin and vitamin A on Sertoli cells. *Biochem. J.* 186:1001–3

25. Kotite, N. J., Nayfeh, S. N., French, F. S., Madhwa Raj, H. G., Purvis, K. 1979. Hormonal regulation of androgen binding protein and testosterone in the immature rat testis. Presented at 61st Meet. Endocrine Soc., Anaheim, Calif. Abstr. 710

26. Larrea, F., Musto, N. A., Gunsalus, G. L., Mather, J., Bardin, C. W. 1980. Heterogeneity of androgen binding protein (ABP) in the male reproductive tract of the rat as a cause for differences in binding and immulogiccal activities. Presented at Ann. Meet. Soc. Clin. Invest., Washington DC. Abstr.

27. Lee, J. A., Yoshida, K-I., Hosaka, M., Stratico, D., Hsu, A-F., Winters, S. J., Oshima, H., Troen, P. 1980. Studies of the human testis. XV. Androgen binding protein and function of Leydig cells

and tubules in aged men with prostatic carcinoma. *J. Clin. Endocrinol. Metab.* In press

28. Louis, B. G., Fritz, I. B. 1977. Stimulation by androgens of the production of androgen binding protein by cultured Sertoli cells *Mol. Cell. Endocrinol.* 7:9–16

29. Mercier-Bodard, C., Alfsen, A., Baulieu, E. E. 1965. A testosterone binding globulin. In *Proc. 2nd Symp. Steroid Hormones,* Ghent, p. 212. Excerpta Medica Found. Int. Congr. Ser. 101

30. Mercier-Bodard, C., Marchut, M., Perrot, M., Picard, M. T., Baulieu, E. E., and Robel, P. 1976. Influence of purified plasma proteins on testosterone uptake and metabolism by normal and hyperplastic human prostate in constant-flow organ culture. *J. Clin. Endocrinol. Metab.* 43:374–86

31. Mercier-Bodard, C., Renoir, J. M., Baulieu, E. E. 1979. Further characterization and immunological studies of human sex steroid binding plasma protein. *J. Steroid Biochem.* 11:253–59

32. Mickelson, K. E., Petra, P. H. 1975. Purification of the sex steroid binding protein from human serum. *Biochemistry* 14:957–63

33. Mickelson, K. E., Petra, P. H. 1978. Purification and characterization of the sex steroid-binding protein of rabbit serum. *J. Biol. Chem.* 268:5293–98

34. Mickelson, K., Teller, D. C., Petra, P. H. 1978. Characterization of the sex steroid binding protein of human pregnancy serum. Improvements in the purification procedure. *Biochemistry* 17:1409–15

35. Mischke, W., Weise, H. C., Graesslin, D., Rusch, R., Tamm, J. 1979. Isolation of highly purified sex hormone binding globulin (SHBG): Evidence for microheterogeneity. *Acta Endocrinol.* 90:737–42

36. Murphy, B. E. P. 1968. Binding of testosterone and estradiol in plasma. *Can. J. Biochem.* 46:299–302

37. Musto, N. A., Bardin, C. W. 1976. Decreased level of androgen binding protein in the reproductive tract of the restricted (H[re]) rat. *Steroids* 28:1–11

38. Musto, N. A., Gunsalus, G. L., Bardin, C. W. 1978. Further characterization of androgen binding protein in epididymis and blood. *Int. J. Androl.* 2:424–33 (Suppl.)

39. Musto, N. A., Gunsalus, G. L., Bardin, C. W. 1980. Purification and characterization of androgen binding protein from

the rat epididymis. *Biochemistry* 19:2853–59

40. Musto, N. A., Gunsalus, G. L., Miljkovic, M., Bardin, C. W. 1977. A novel affinity column for isolation of androgen binding protein from rat epididymis. *Endocrinol. Res. Commun.* 4: 147–57

41. Pearlman, W. H., Crepy, O. 1967. Steroid-protein interaction with particular reference to testosterone binding by human serum. *J. Biol. Chem.* 242:182–89

42. Pelliniemi, L. J., Dym, M., Gunsalus, G. L., Musto, N. A., Bardin, C. W., Fawcett, D. W. 1980. Immunocytochemical localization of androgen binding protein in the male rat reproductive tract. *Endocrinology.* In press

43. Petra, P. H. 1979. The serum sex steroid-binding protein. Purification, characterization and immunological properties of the human and rabbit proteins. *J. Steroid Biochem.* 11:245–52

44. Rosenbaum, W., Christy, N. P., Kelly, W. G. 1966. Electrophoretic evidence for the presence of an estrogen-binding β-globulin in human plasma. *J. Clin. Endocrinol. Metab.* 26:1399–403

45. Rosner, W., Smith, R. N. 1975. Isolation and characterization of the testosterone-estradiol-binding globulin from human plasma. Use of a novel affinity column. *Biochemistry* 14:4813–20

46. Sanborn, B. M., Elkington, J. S. H., Chowdhury, M., Tcholakian, K. R., Steinberger, E. 1975. Hormonal influences on the level of testicular androgen binding activity: Effect of FSH following hypophysectomy. *Endocrinology* 96:304–12

47. Sanborn, B. M., Elkington, J. S. H., Tcholakian, R. K., Steinberger, E. 1975. Some properties of androgen binding activity in rat testis. *Molec. Cell. Endocrinol.* 3:129–42

48. Steeno, O., Heyns, W., Van Baelen, H., DeMoor, P. 1968. Testosterone binding in human plasma. *Ann. Endocrinol.* 29: (*Suppl.*)141–48

49. Suzuki, Y., Itagaki, E., Mori, H., Hosoya, T. 1977. Isolation of testosterone-binding globulin from bovine serum by affinity chromatography and its molecular characterization. *J. Biochem.* 81:1721–31

50. Suzuki, Y., Sinohara, H. 1979. Hepatic uptake of desialylated testosterone-oestradiol-binding globulin in the rat. *Acta Endocrinol.* 90:669–79

51. Tabei, T., Mickelson, K. E., Neuhaus, S., Petra, P. H. 1978. Sex steroid binding protein (SBP) in dog plasma. *J. Steroid Biochem.* 9:983–88

52. Tindall, D. J., Mena, C. R., Means, A. R. 1978. Hormonal regulation of androgen binding protein in hypophysectomized rats. *Endocrinology* 103:589–94

53. Vermeulen, A., Verdonck, L., Straeten, M. V., Opie, N. 1969. Capacity of the testosterone-binding globulin in human plasma and influence of specific binding of testosterone on its metabolic clearance rate. *J. Clin. Endocrinol. Metab.* 29:1470–80

54. Vernon, R. G., Kopec, B., Fritz, I. B. 1974. Observations on the binding of androgens by rat testis seminiferous tubules and testis extracts. *Molec. Cell. Endocrinol.* 1:167–87

55. Vigersky, R. A., Loriaux, D. L., Howard, S. S., Hodgen, G. B. Lipsett, M. B., Chrambach, A. 1976. Androgen binding protein of testis, epididymis and plasma in man and monkeys. *J. Clin. Invest.* 58:1061–68

56. Weddington, S. C., Brandtzaeg, P., Sletten, K., Christensen, T., Hansson, V., French, F. S., Petrusz, P., Nayfeh, S. N., Ritzen, E. M. 1975. Purification and characterization of rabbit testicular androgen binding protein (ABP). See Ref. 13, pp. 433–51

Ann. Rev. Physiol. 1981. 43:199–209
Copyright © 1981 by Annual Reviews Inc. All rights reserved

RECENT ADVANCES IN THE METABOLISM OF VITAMIN D

❖1305

H. F. DeLuca

Department of Biochemistry, College of Agricultural and Life Sciences, University of Wisconsin, Madison, Wisconsin 53706

INTRODUCTION

During the past 15 years has come the elucidation of the vitamin D endocrine system. In this system it has been demonstrated that vitamin D first accumulates in the liver where it is converted to the major circulating form of vitamin D_3, 25-hydroxyvitamin D_3 (25-OH-D_3). This conversion takes place predominantly in the endoplasmic reticulum, but also occurs under conditions of large amounts of substrate in the mitochondrial fraction as well. The 25-OH-D_3 is not active directly under physiologic circumstances but must be further activated in the kidney where it is converted to the major vitamin D hormone, 1,25-dihydroxyvitamin D_3 (1,25-(OH)$_2$D$_3$). This reaction occurs exclusively in the kidney and exclusively in the mitochondrial fraction. The final hormone is then transported to the intestine, bone, and elsewhere in the kidney where it stimulates intestinal calcium absorption, intestinal phosphate absorption, the mobilization of calcium from bone, and possibly renal reabsorption of calcium. The 1,25-(OH)$_2$-D$_3$ functions in the mobilization of calcium from bone and possibly in the renal reabsorption of calcium by a process that requires the presence of parathyroid hormone. In these systems it is likely that the 1,25-(OH)$_2$D$_3$ hormone acts as a permissive agent while the parathyroid hormone provides the major adjustment of these processes. In the intestine, however, 1,25-(OH)$_2$D$_3$ appears to act by itself. The result of its actions is the elevation of plasma calcium and phosphorus to levels that support normal mineralization of bone and function of the neuromuscular system. Although some form of vitamin D may function at the bone site to promote mineralization, so far this has not been clearly demonstrated.

199

0066-4278/81/0315-0199$01.00

The production of the active form of vitamin D, namely 1,25-$(OH)_2D_3$, has been shown to be feedback-regulated, either directly or indirectly by plasma calcium concentration and the parathyroid hormone. Hypocalcemia triggers secretion of the parathyroid hormone that in turn functions to facilitate the conversion of 25-OH-D_3 to 1,25-$(OH)_2D_3$ in the kidney. In addition to this regulation, plasma phosphate influences the accumulation of 1,25-$(OH)_2D_3$ in the plasma. Sex hormones in the bird also either directly or indirectly stimulate the 25-OH-D-1α-hydroxylase. Thus the need for calcium and the need for phosphate as revealed by hypocalcemia or hypophosphatemia either directly or indirectly stimulates production of 1,25-$(OH)_2D_3$, which then accumulates in the target organs to facilitate active calcium transport or active phosphate transport.

Other metabolites of vitamin D have been isolated and identified. Among them are 24R,25-dihydroxyvitamin D_3 (24R,25-$(OH)_2D_3$), 1,24R,25-trihydroxyvitamin D_3 (1,24R,25-$(OH)_3D_3$), and 25S,26-dihydroxyvitamin D_3 (25S,26-$(OH)_2D_3$). These metabolites possess some biological activity and their function remains a matter of debate.

Readers are directed to recent reviews that summarize the above findings in the vitamin D system up to and including 1976 (11, 13–17, 31, 32, 35, 50). The present review focuses on newer developments in the metabolism of vitamin D at the basic level and excludes the many excellent clinical investigations that have been performed.

METABOLISM OF VITAMIN D

In attempts to learn whether it is active per se in intestine and bone to stimulate the calcium and phosphate transport systems or whether it must be metabolized further, 1,25-$(OH)_2D_3$ labeled with tritium in the 26 and 27 positions has been administered to animals. When target organs respond they are extracted and chromatographed to reveal the presence of any heretofore unknown metabolites. Two laboratories thereby demonstrated that 1,25-$(OH)_2D_3$ is the only chloroform-soluble metabolite found at the time the intestine and bone respond (22, 69). However, poor recoveries of tritium were experienced and led to the chemical synthesis of 25-OH-D_3 and 1,25-$(OH)_2D_3$ labeled with C-14 in the 26 and 27 positions (30). Administration of these compounds to vitamin D–deficient rats and chicks revealed a significant metabolism to an unknown side chain cleaved metabolite and a side chain piece oxidized to carbon dioxide and water. Nephrectomy prevented the metabolism of the 25-OH-D_3 to these products whereas it failed to prevent these reactions with 1,25-$(OH)_2D_3$. As much as 30% of the total injected 1,25-$(OH)_2D_3$ yielded its side chain ^{14}C as [14]CO_2 (44). Administration of [3α-^{3}H] and [26, 27-^{14}C]-1,25-$(OH)_2D_3$ to vitamin D–deficient animals revealed the presence of a major water-soluble metabolite of $1,25\text{-}(OH)_2D_3$ especially in liver and intestine (20). This metabolite is the major form of $1,25\text{-}(OH)_2D_3$ found in the intestine at the time it responds to $1,25\text{-}(OH)_2D_3$ (19). This compound has been isolated in pure form and its structure unequivocally identified as 1α-hydroxy-24,25,26,27-tetranor-vitamin D_3-23-carboxylic acid or calcitroic acid (20). It has been chemically synthesized and its biological activity determined (19). It is less than $1/100$ as active as $1,25\text{-}(OH)_2D_3$ in all of the systems known to be responsive to the vitamin. Evidence, therefore, suggests that this compound is an inactivation product and probably is not responsible for the intestinal responses to $1,25\text{-}(OH)_2D_3$.Calcitroic acid is the major biliary excretory product of $1,25\text{-}(OH)_2D_3$ and may be the end point of vitamin D metabolism through the $1,25\text{-}(OH)_2D_3$ hormone (51). Bile duct ligation does not totally eliminate the appearance of the calcitroic acid in the intestine, suggesting that some of it is made in that tissue. In addition to this, minor pathways of $1,25\text{-}(OH)_2D_3$ include conversion to $1,24R,25\text{-}(OH)_2D_3$ (17) and to $1,25S,26\text{-}(OH)_3D_3$ (Y. Tanaka, H. K. Schnoes, and H. F. DeLuca, unpublished).

An investigation into the metabolites present in human and chicken plasma that might interfere with the measurement of $24R,25\text{-}(OH)_2D_3$ revealed the presence of a major metabolite that comigrates with $24R,25\text{-}(OH)_2D_3$ not only on Sephadex LH-20 columns but also on straight phase silica high performance liquid chromatographic (HPLC) systems (56). This product was isolated from the plasma of chickens given either high or low doses of vitamin D_3 and its structure unequivocally identified by ultraviolet spectrophotometry, mass spectrometry, nmr spectrometry, and infrared spectrophotometry as $25\text{-}OH\text{-}D_3\text{-}26,23$-lactone (73). Since this compound has two chyral centers, four isomers are possible. Recently chemical synthesis of the four isomers has been completed, but the exact configuration of the natural product has yet to be determined (J. Wichmann, H. Paaren, H. Schnoes, and H. DeLuca, unpublished). Biological activity of this compound in calcium systems is minimal, but testing has not yet been completed. This metabolite appears in significant quantities of human plasma and chick plasma. It appears in all species tested when large doses of vitamin D are given (73). It certainly represents a major factor interfering with $24R,25\text{-}(OH)_2D_3$ determination, and its presence under certain pathological states may signal its importance in terms of function.

Metabolism of $24R,25\text{-}(OH)_2D_3$ in chick and rat kidney preparations has been studied. A major product has been produced by kidney homogenates; this product has been isolated and its structure identified as 25,26,27-trisnor-vitamin D_3-24-carboxylic acid or cholecalcioic acid (18). Its biological activity has not yet been deduced.

In studying the discrimination of chickens against vitamin D_2 as compared to vitamin D_3, it has been learned that vitamin D_2 is rapidly metabolized to biliary excretion products as compared to its vitamin D_3

counterpart, suggesting that the lack of effectiveness of these compounds at physiologic doses in the bird is the result of rapid metabolism and inactivation (38). A search of the metabolites of vitamin D_2 excreted into bile has revealed the presence of a major metabolite that upon mild acid hydrolysis or glucuronidase treatment yields 25-OH-D_3 (46). This metabolite has been isolated; by means of derivatization and mass spectrometric determinations, its structure has been identified as 25-OH-D_2-β-D-25-glucuronic acid (46). Thus the unexpected position of glucuronidation of vitamin D compounds for bile excretion is the 25-hydroxyl function. Thus the only major excretory forms of vitamin D that have been identified are the 25-glucuronide and the calcitroic acid. Figure 1 illustrates the known metabolism of vitamin D as presently elucidated.

Two vitamin D-25-hydroxylases are found in liver. One is a mitochondrial enzyme with a very high Michaelis constant for vitamin D_3 of the order of $10^{-6}M$ (3, 53). The hydroxylase found in the mitochondria is part of a three-component mixed function monooxygenase involving a flavoprotein, an iron-sulfur protein, and a cytochrome P-450. This enzyme may not be specific for the vitamin D molecule, since it hydroxylates cholesterol in the 25 and 26 positions. The major physiologically active enzyme is found

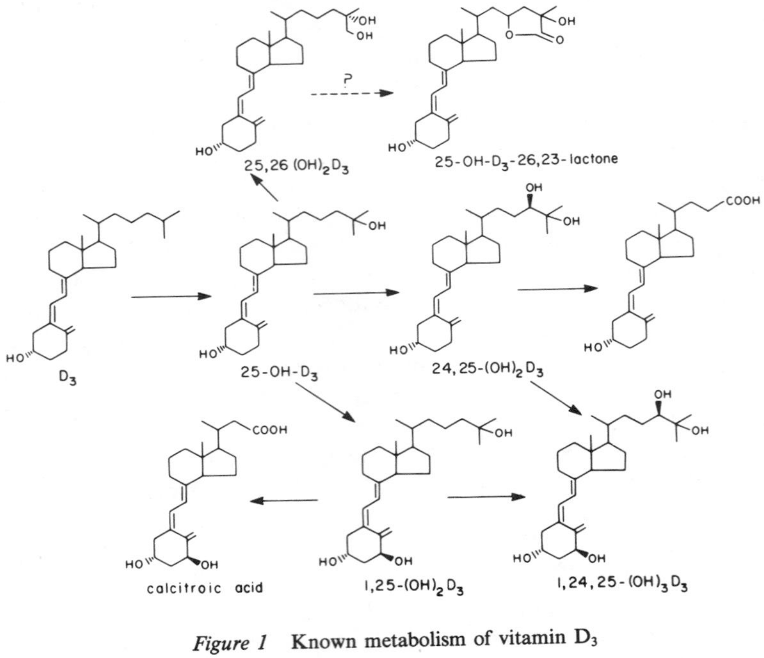

Figure 1   Known metabolism of vitamin D_3

in the microsomal fraction (2, 36, 47). It is a mixed function monooxygenase involving a flavoprotein and a cytochrome P-450 (76). Its Km for vitamin D_3 is 10^{-8}M. This system requires in addition to the two components found in the microsomes a cytoplasmic protein whose function is poorly understood. The microsomal 25-hydroxylase is suppressed by the preadministration of vitamin D to vitamin D–deficient animals (2, 37, 48). The microsomal enzyme is likely active at low and physiologic concentrations of vitamin D, whereas the mitochondrial enzyme carries out the conversions when pharmacological doses of the vitamin are employed.

Additional work has been carried out on the 25-OH-D_3-1α-hydroxylase. Previously this system had been solubilized and shown to be a three-component mixed function monooxygenase involving a flavoprotein, an iron-sulfur protein termed renal ferredoxin, and a cytochrome P-450 (24, 52). Of these, the iron-sulfur protein has been purified to homogeneity and separated from cytochrome b_5 (77). The iron-sulfur protein (11,800 mol wt) has been shown to be the specific electron donor in this system; cytochrome b_5 does not participate. The iron-sulfur protein contains a 2Fe2S cluster as revealed by cluster exchange reactions (78). Although the cytochrome P-450 fraction is present in kidneys of animals whose 1-hydroxylase is suppressed, it is inactive (24, 77). Whether or not the cytochrome P-450 that carries out the 1-hydroxylation is a major or minor component of the cytochrome P-450 fraction of mitochondria remains unknown. The nature of the regulation of this cytochrome P-450 enzyme is also a major biochemical problem remaining to be solved.

Pregnant nephrectomized rats produce 1,25-$(OH)_2D_3$ (28, 73) and therefore an extrarenal site of 1α-hydroxylation was sought. Placental homogenates contain the 25-OH-D-1α-hydroxylase (64), and placental cells also can produce the 1,25-$(OH)_2D_3$ (29).

Work on control of 1α-hydroxylation has been hampered because of an inability to measure the 25-OH-D-1α-hydroxylase in mammals (8). This is because contaminating plasma transport protein combines with a cytosol protein giving a large amount of a 6S binding protein (43, 71). This protein competes for substrate and is difficult to remove (7). Intact cell measurements have been reported (30), as have homogenate measurements in mammals using saturating amounts of substrate (70). The activity has been low and not easily reproducible in these systems. Additional work is needed on mammalian 1α-hydroxylase.

The 24R-hydroxylase of 25-OH-D_3 is found not only in kidney (41) but also in intestine (45) and cartilage tissue (23) and perhaps elsewhere. This enzyme is induced by some form of vitamin D (59), the most active being the 1,25-$(OH)_2D_3$ (65), which not only stimulates the 24R-hydroxylase but also suppresses the 25-OH-D-1α-hydroxylase (72). The nature of this regulation also remains unknown (12). Several groups have developed kidney cell cultures wherein the regulation of the hydroxylases can be approached (33, 39, 57, 68). So far these systems have revealed that $1,25-(OH)_2D_3$ directly suppresses the 1-hydroxylase and stimulates the 24-hydroxylase. However, the nature of regulation of the 1-hydroxylase by calcium, parathyroid hormone, and other hormonal substances has not been clarified by these systems. Recently it has been reported that parathyroid hormone can cause a small stimulation of 1-hydroxylase in renal cell cultures, although the presence of insulin seems to be required for this action (34).

25-OH-D-26-hydroxylase is found in the kidney (66), and its product is likely an intermediate in the synthesis of the 26,23-lactone. Certainly the kidney is the site of biogenesis of the lactone (47, 67). This enzyme also converts $1,25-(OH)_2D_3$ to the $1,25S,26-(OH)_3D_3$ (Y. Tanaka, H. K. Schnoes, and H. F. DeLuca, unpublished).

FUNCTION OF $24R,25-(OH)_2D_3$

Since its discovery and chemical synthesis there has been much interest in $24R,25-(OH)_2D_3$ (36). It is a major metabolite of vitamin D in animals and humans (27), its biogenesis is regulated by calcium and phosphorus status (9), and in mammals it possesses significant biological activity (60), although its activity in the intestine and bone is equal to but not greater than that of its precursor 25-OH-D₃. In vitamin D–deficient animals its activity appears to be primarily related to its 1α-hydroxylation and conversion to $1,24R,25-(OH)_3D_3$ (10). Thus nephrectomized rats do not respond to $24R,25-(OH)_2D_3$ whereas intact animals respond normally. It has been reported that $24R,25-(OH)_2D_3$ will stimulate intestinal calcium absorption in human subjects who do not have kidneys (40). In fact, it has been suggested that its biological activity is similar to that of $1,25-(OH)_2D_3$ in such subjects. It is difficult to understand why elaborate regulation of the 1α-hydroxylase and 24R-hydroxylase is found in the kidney if both compounds are equally active in the target organs. Other investigators have failed to demonstrate such a stimulation of intestinal calcium absorption in anephric humans (54). It therefore seems possible that the methods used have not been adequate to provide proof that $24R,25-(OH)_2D_3$ can specifically activate intestinal calcium absorption without 1-hydroxylation in humans. Other reports have suggested that $24R,25-(OH)_2D_3$ is more effective in mineralizing bone than is $1,25-(OH)_2D_3$ (4, 55). However, it is important to note that $1,25-(OH)_2D_3$ has a short lifetime in the body [on the order of a few hours (26)], whereas these investigators administered $1,25-(OH)_2D_3$ in relatively small doses three times weekly and for a period of only six weeks. It is unlikely that any compound having such pharmacological properties could function under this dosage protocol. Still another report has appeared regarding the possible special function of $24R,25\text{-}(OH)_2D_3$ in the mineralization of bone (25). Goodwin et al (25) have indicated that $1\alpha\text{-}OH\text{-}D_3$ or $1,25\text{-}(OH)_2D_3$ will not by itself mineralize bones of chicks and that full mineralization is realized only when $1,25\text{-}(OH)_2D_3$ is provided together with $24R,25\text{-}(OH)_2D_3$. Unfortunately, controls were not run in which $1\alpha\text{-}OH\text{-}D_3$ was administered alone and the dosage of $24R$, $25\text{-}(OH)_2D_3$ required for this response was not given. Several laboratories had already demonstrated that $1,25\text{-}(OH)_2D_3$ produces marked mineralization in the bones of chicks and rats when given at least once a day at reasonable doses (5, 49, 63). In fact, when given once daily, $1,25\text{-}(OH)_2D_3$ is ten times more active than vitamin D_3 in providing mineralization of rachitic rats (63). Both vitamin-D-dependency rickets of children and renal rickets have been healed by the administration of $1,25\text{-}(OH)_2D_3$ (1, 21). Because of the suggested importance of 24R-hydroxylation for the function of vitamin D, two research groups (42, 75) have synthesized 24,24-difluoro-25-OH-D_3. This compound cannot be 24R-hydroxylated—the fluoro groups, the size of hydrogen rather than hydroxyl, do not act as hydroxyls. 24,24-Difluoro-25-OH-D_3 is at least as active as 25-OH-D_3 in stimulating intestinal calcium transport, the elevation of plasma calcium and phosphorus, and the mineralization of rachitic cartilage and bone (61). Furthermore, histology shows these bones to be normally mineralized (S. Miller, W. Jee, unpublished). In an interesting mineralization model developed by Boris et al (6), no evidence for the role of $24,25\text{-}(OH)_2D_3$ could be obtained in the mineralization of bone. Therefore, the idea that $24R,25\text{-}(OH)_2D_3$ may play an important role in bone formation is speculative and requires much stronger verification than is currently available. The biological activity of $24,24\text{-difluoro-}1,25\text{-}(OH)_2D_3$ also fails to support the idea of the importance of 24-hydroxylation in the function of $1,25\text{-}(OH)_2D_3$ (62). Of great interest is the idea that $24,24\text{-difluoro-}1,25\text{-}(OH)_2D_3$ is as active as $1,25\text{-}(OH)_2D_3$ in binding to receptor proteins but is about five times more active than $1,25\text{-}(OH)_2D_3$ in the mineralization of bone, in stimulating intestinal calcium transport, and in the mobilization of calcium from bone (Y. Tanaka, S. Okamoto, H. DeLuca, unpublished).

ACKNOWLEDGMENTS

This work was supported in part by a program-project grant no. AM–14881 from the National Institutes of Health and by the Harry Steenbock Research Fund of the Wisconsin Alumni Research Foundation.

Literature Cited

1. Balsan, S., Garabedian, M., Sorgniard, R., Dommergues, J. P., Courtecuisse, V., Holick, M. F., DeLuca, H. F. 1975. Metabolites and analogs of vitamin D: Therapeutic effects in D-deficiency and "pseudo-deficiency" rickets. In *Vitamin D and Problems Related to Uremic Bone Disease,* ed. A. W. Norman, K. Schaefer, H. G. Grigoleit, D. von Herrath, E. Ritz, pp. 247–58. Berlin: de Gruyter

2. Bhattacharyya, M., DeLuca, H. F. 1974. Subcellular location of rat liver calciferol-25-hydroxylase. *Arch. Biochem. Biophys.* 160:58–62

3. Björkhem, I., Holmberg, I. 1978. Assay and properties of a mitochondrial 25-hydroxylase active on vitamin D_3. *J. Biol. Chem.* 253:842–49

4. Bordier, P., Zingraff, J., Gueris, J., Jungers, P., Marie, P., Pechet, M., Rasmussen, H. 1978. The effect of $1\alpha,25(OH)_2D_3$ on the bone in patients with renal osteodystrophy. *Am. J. Med.* 64:101–7

5. Boris, A., Hurley, J. F., Trmal, T. 1977. Relative activities of some metabolites and analogs of cholecalciferol in stimulation of tibia ash weight in chicks otherwise deprived of vitamin D. *J. Nutr.* 107:194–98

6. Boris, A., Hurley, J. F., Trmal, T., Mallon, J. P., Matuszewski, D. S. 1978. Evidence for the promotion of bone mineralization by $1\alpha,25$-dihydroxycholecalciferol in the rat unrelated to correction of deficiencies in serum calcium and phosphorus. *J. Nutr.* 108:1899–906

7. Botham, K. M., Ghazarian, J. G., Kream, B. E., DeLuca, H. F. 1976. Isolation of a potent inhibitor of 25-hydroxy-vitamin D_3-1-hydroxylase from rat serum. *Biochemistry* 15:2130–35

8. Botham, K. M., Tanaka, Y., DeLuca, H. F. 1974. 25-Hydroxy-vitamin D_3-1-hydroxylase. Inhibition in vitro by rat and pig tissues. *Biochemistry* 13:4961–66

9. Boyle, I. T., Gray, R. W., DeLuca, H. F. 1971. Regulation by calcium of in vivo synthesis of 1,25-dihydroxycholecalciferol and 21,25-dihydroxycholecalciferol. *Proc. Natl. Acad. Sci. USA* 68:2131–34

10. Boyle, I. T., Omdahl, J. L., Gray, R. W., DeLuca, H. F. 1973. The biological activity and metabolism of 24,25-dihydroxy-vitamin D_3. *J. Biol. Chem.* 248:4174–80

11. Coburn, J. W., Hartenbower, D. L., Brickman, A. S. 1976. Advances in vitamin D metabolism as they pertain to chronic renal disease. *Am. J. Clin. Nutr.* 29:1283–99

12. Colston, K. W., Evans, I. M. A., Spelsberg, T. C, MacIntyre, I. 1977. Feedback regulation of vitamin D metabolism by 1,25-dihydroxycholecalciferol. *Biochem. J.* 164:83–90

13. DeLuca, H. F. 1978. Vitamin D. In *Handbook of Lipid Research, Vol. II, The Fat-Soluble Vitamins,* ed. H. F. DeLuca, pp. 69–132. NY: Plenum

14. DeLuca, H. F. 1979. Vitamin D: Metabolism and function. In *Monographs on Endocrinology,* ed. F. Gross, M. M. Grumbach, A. Labhart, M. B. Lipsett, T. Mann, L. T. Samuels, J. Zander, 13:1–78. NY: Springer

15. DeLuca, H. F. 1979. The vitamin D system in the regulation of calcium and phosphorus metabolism. *Nutr. Rev.* 37:161–93

16. DeLuca, H. F. 1980. Some new concepts emanating from a study of the metabolism and function of vitamin D. *Nutr. Rev.* In press

17. DeLuca, H. F., Schnoes, H. K. 1976. Metabolism and mechanism of action of vitamin D. *Ann. Rev. Biochem.* 45:631–66

18. DeLuca, H. F., Schnoes, H. K. 1979. Recent developments in the metabolism of vitamin D. In *Vitamin D: Basic Research and Its Clinical Application,* ed. A. W. Norman, K. Schaefer, D. V. Herrath, H. G. Grigoleit, J. W. Coburn, H. F. DeLuca, E. B. Mawer, T. Suda, pp. 445–58. Berlin: de Gruyter

19. Esvelt, R. P., DeLuca, H. F. 1980. Calcitroic acid: Biological activity and tissue distribution studies. *Arch. Biochem. Biophys.* In press

20. Esvelt, R. P., Schnoes, H. K., DeLuca, H. F. 1979. Isolation and characterization of 1α-hydroxy-tetranor-vitamin D-23-carboxylic acid: A major metabolite of 1,25-dihydroxyvitamin D_3. *Biochemistry* 18:3977–83

21. Fraser, D., Kooh, S. W., Kind, H. P., Holick, M. F., Tanaka, Y., DeLuca, H. F. 1973. Pathogenesis of hereditary vitamin D dependent rickets: An inborn error of vitamin D metabolism involving defective conversion of 25-hydroxyvitamin D to $1\alpha,25$-dihydroxyvitamin D. *New Engl. J. Med.* 289:817–22

22. Frolik, C. A., DeLuca, H. F. 1971. 1,25-Dihydroxycholecalciferol: The metabolite of vitamin D responsible for in-

creased intestinal calcium transport. *Arch. Biochem. Biophys.* 147:143–47

23. Garabedian, M., Lieberherr, M., Nguyen, T. M., Corvol, M. T., Dubois, M. B., Balsan, S. 1978. In vitro production and activity of 24,25-dihydroxycholecalciferol in cartilage and calvarium. *Clin. Orthop. Rel. Res.* 135:241

24. Ghazarian, J. G., Jefcoate, C. R., Knutson, J. C., Orme-Johnson, W. H., DeLuca, H. F. 1974. Mitochondrial cytochrome P_{450}: A component of chick kidney 25-hydroxycholecalciferol-1α-hydroxylase. *J. Biol. Chem.* 249:3026–33

25. Goodwin, D., Noff, D., Edelstein, S. 1978. 24,25-Dihydroxy-vitamin D is a metabolite of vitamin D essential for bone formation. *Nature* 276:517–19

26. Gray, R. W., Caldas, A. E., Wilz, D. R., Lemann, J. Jr., Smith, G. A., DeLuca, H. F. 1978. Metabolism and excretion of ^{3}H-1,25-(OH)$_2$-vitamin D$_3$ in healthy adults. *J. Clin. Endocrinol. Metab.* 46:756–65

27. Gray, R. W., Weber, H. P., Dominguez, J. H., Lemann, J. Jr. 1974. The metabolism of vitamin D$_3$ and 25-hydroxyvitamin D$_3$ in normal and anephric humans. *J. Clin. Endocrinol. Metab.* 39: 1045–56

28. Gray, T. K., Lester, G. E., Lorenc, R. S. 1979. Evidence for extra-renal 1α-hydroxylation of 25-hydroxyvitamin D$_3$ in pregnancy. *Science* 204:1311–13

29. Gray, T. K., McAdoo, R., Pool, D., Williams, M. E., Jones, G. 1980. A radioimmunoassay for 1,25-dihydroxycholecalciferol. *Endocrine Soc. Abstr.,* p. 289

30. Harnden, D., Kumar, R., Holick, M. F., DeLuca, H. F. 1976. Side chain metabolism of 25-hydroxy-[26, 27-^{14}C]vitamin D$_3$ and 1,25-dihydroxy-[26, 27-^{14}C]vitamin D$_3$ in vivo. *Science* 193: 493–94

31. Haussler, M. R., McCain, T. A. 1977. Vitamin D metabolism and action (Second of two parts). *New Engl. J. Med.* 297:1041–50

32. Haussler, M. R., McCain, T. A. 1977. Vitamin D metabolism and action (First of two parts). *New Engl. J. Med.* 297:974–83

33. Henry, H. L. 1979. Regulation of the hydroxylation of 25-hydroxyvitamin D$_3$ in vivo and in primary cultures of chick kidney cells. *J. Biol. Chem.* 254:2722–29

34. Henry, H. L. 1980. Insulin permits parathyroid hormone stimulation of 25-hydroxyvitamin D$_3$-1-hydroxylase in kidney cell cultures. *Endocrine Soc. Abstr.,* p. 80

35. Holick, M. F., Clark, M. B. 1978. The photobiogenesis and metabolism of vitamin D. *Fed. Proc.* 37:2567–74

36. Holick, M. F., Schnoes, H. K., DeLuca, H. F., Gray, R. W., Boyle, I. T., Suda, T. 1972. Isolation and identification of 24,25-dihydroxycholecalciferol: A metabolite of vitamin D$_3$ made in the kidney. *Biochemistry* 11:4251–55

37. Horsting, M., DeLuca, H. F. 1969. In vitro production of 25-hydroxycholecalciferol. *Biochem. Biophys. Res. Commun.* 36:251–56

38. Imrie, M. H., Neville, P. F., Snellgrove, A. W., DeLuca, H. F. 1967. Metabolism of vitamin D$_2$ and vitamin D$_3$ in the rachitic chick. *Arch. Biochem. Biophys.* 120:525–32

39. Juan, D., DeLuca, H. F. 1977. The regulation of 24,25-dihydroxyvitamin D$_3$ production in cultures of monkey kidney cells. *Endocrinology* 101:1184–93

40. Kanis, J. A., Heynen, G., Russell, R. G. G., Smith, R., Walton, R. J., Warner, G. T. 1977. Biological effects of 24-25-dihydroxycholecalciferol in man. In *Vitamin D: Biochemical, Chemical and Clinical Aspects Related to Calcium Metabolism,* ed. A. W. Norman, K. Schaefer, J. W. Coburn, H. F. DeLuca, D. Fraser, H. G. Grigoleit, D. von Herrath, pp. 794–95. Berlin: de Gruyter

41. Knutson, J. C., DeLuca, H. F. 1974. 25-Hydroxyvitamin D$_3$-24-hydroxylase: Subcellular location and properties. *Biochemistry* 13:1543–48

42. Kobayashi, Y., Taguchi, T., Terada, T., Oshida, J., Morisaki, M., Ikekawa, N. 1979. Synthesis of 24,24-difluoro- and 24ξ-fluoro-25-hydroxyvitamin D$_3$. *Tetrahedron Lett.* 22:2023–26

43. Kream, B. E., DeLuca, H. F., Moriarity, D. M., Kendrick, N. C., Ghazarian, J. G. 1979. Origin of 25-hydroxyvitamin D$_3$ binding protein from tissue cytosol preparations. *Arch. Biochem. Biophys.* 192:318–23

44. Kumar, R., Harnden, D., DeLuca, H. F. 1976. Metabolism of 1,25-dihydroxyvitamin D$_3$: Evidence for side-chain oxidation. *Biochemistry* 15:2420–23

45. Kumar, R., Schnoes, H. K., DeLuca, H. F. 1978. Rat intestinal 25-hydroxyvitamin D$_3$- and 1α,25-dihydroxyvitamin D$_3$-24-hydroxylase. *J. Biol. Chem.* 253:3804–9

46. LeVan, L. 1980. *Biliary metabolites of vitamin D in the chick.* PhD thesis. University of Wisconsin, Madison.

208   DeLUCA

47. Littledike, E. T., Horst, R. L., Gray, R. W., Napoli, J. L. 1980. Impaired 24,25-(OH)$_2$D and 25-OHD$_3$-26,23 lactone (lactone) production in anephric man and pig. *Fed. Proc.* 39:662
48. Madhok, T. C., DeLuca, H. F. 1979. Characteristics of the rat liver microsomal enzyme system converting cholecalciferol into 25-hydroxycholecalciferol. Evidence for the participation of cytochrome P-450. *Biochem. J.* 184:491–99
49. McNutt, K. W., Haussler, M. R. 1973. Nutritional effectiveness of 1,25-dihydroxycholecalciferol in preventing rickets in chicks. *J. Nutr.* 103:681–89
50. Norman, A. W., Henry, H. L. 1974. 1,25-Dihydroxyvitamin D$_3$. A hormonally active form of vitamin D$_3$. *Rec. Progr. Horm. Res.* 30:431–80
51. Onisko, B. L., Esvelt, R. P., Schnoes, H. K., DeLuca, H. F. 1980. Metabolites of 1α,25-dihydroxyvitamin D$_3$ in rat bile. *Biochemistry.* In press
52. Pedersen, J. I., Ghazarian, J. G., Orme-Johnson, N. R., DeLuca, H. F. 1976. Isolation of chick renal mitochondrial ferredoxin active in the 25-hydroxyvitamin D$_3$-1α-hydroxylase system. *J. Biol. Chem.* 251:3933–41
53. Pedersen, J. I., Holmberg, I., Björkhem, I. 1979. Reconstitution of vitamin D$_3$ 25-hydroxylase activity with a cytochrome P-450 preparation from rat liver mitochondria. *FEBS Lett.* 98:394–98
54. Pierides, A. M., Aljama, P., Kerr, D. N. S., Scott, M., Norman, A. W. 1978. Effect of 1α-hydroxycholecalciferol, 1,25-dihydroxycholecalciferol, 3 deoxy-α-hydroxycholecalciferol, 24R,25-dihydroxycholecalciferol and successful renal transplantation on calcium absorption in haemodialysis patients. *Nephron* 20:203–11
55. Rasmussen, H., Bordier, P. 1978. Vitamin D and bone. *Metab. Bone Dis. Rel. Res.* 1:7–13
56. Shepard, R. M., DeLuca, H. F. 1980. Plasma concentrations of vitamin D$_3$ and its metabolites in the rat as influenced by vitamin D$_3$ or 25-hydroxyvitamin D$_3$ intakes. *Arch. Biochem. Biophys.* 202:43–53
57. Spanos, E., Brown, D. J., MacIntyre, I. 1979. Regulation of 25-OH-D$_3$ metabolism by parathyroid hormone in primary chick kidney cell cultures. *FEBS Lett.* 105:31–34
58. Talmage, R. V. 1969. Calcium homeostasis-calcium transport-parathyroid action. The effects of parathyroid hormone on the movement of calcium between bone and fluid. *Clin. Orthopaed. Rel. Res.* 67:210–24
59. Tanaka, Y., DeLuca, H. F. 1974. Stimulation of 24,25-dihydroxy-vitamin D$_3$ production by 1,25-dihydroxyvitamin D$_3$. *Science* 183:1198–200
60. Tanaka, Y., DeLuca, H. F., Ikekawa, N., Morisaki, M., Koizumi, N. 1975. Determination of stereochemical configuration of the 24-hydroxyl group of 24,25-dihydroxyvitamin D$_3$ and its biological importance. *Arch. Biochem. Biophys.* 170:620–26
61. Tanaka, Y., DeLuca, H. F., Kobayashi, Y., Taguchi, T., Ikekawa, N., Morisaki, M. 1979. Biological activity of 24,24-difluoro-25-hydroxyvitamin D$_3$. Effect of blocking of 24-hydroxylation on the functions of vitamin D. *J. Biol. Chem.* 254:7163–67
62. Tanaka, Y., DeLuca, H. F., Schnoes, H. K., Ikekawa, N., Kobayashi, Y. 1980. 24,24-Difluoro-1,25-dihydroxyvitamin D$_3$: in vitro production, isolation, and biological activity. *Arch. Biochem. Biophys.* 199:473–78
63. Tanaka, Y., Frank, H., DeLuca, H. F. 1973. Biological activity of 1,25-dihydroxyvitamin D$_3$ in the rat *Endocrinology* 92:417–22
64. Tanaka, Y., Halloran, B., Schnoes, H. K., DeLuca, H. F. 1979. In vitro production of 1,25-dihydroxyvitamin D$_3$ by rat placental tissue. *Proc. Natl. Acad. Sci. USA* 76:5033–35
65. Tanaka, Y., Lorenc, R. S., DeLuca, H. F. 1975. The role of 1,25-dihydroxyvitamin D$_3$ and parathyroid hormone in the regulation of chick renal 25-hydroxyvitamin D$_3$-24-hydroxylase. *Arch. Biochem. Biophys.* 171:521–26
66. Tanaka, Y., Shepard, R. M., DeLuca, H. F., Schnoes, H. K. 1978. The 26-hydroxylation of 25-hydroxyvitamin D$_3$ in vitro by chick renal homogenates. *Biochem. Biophys. Res. Commun.* 83:7–13
67. Tanaka, Y., Wichmann, J. K., DeLuca, H. F. 1980. Biogenesis of 25-hydroxyvitamin D-26,23-lactone in kidney preparations. *Proc. Natl. Acad. Sci. USA.* In press
68. Trechsel, U., Bonjour, J.-P., Fleisch, H. 1979. Regulation of the metabolism of 25-hydroxyvitamin D$_3$ in primary cultures of chick kidney cells. *J. Clin. Invest.* 64:206–17
69. Tsai, H. C., Wong, R. G., Norman, A. W. 1972. Studies on calciferol metabolism. IV. Subcellular localization of 1,25-dihydroxyvitamin D$_3$ in intestinal

mucosa and correlation with increased calcium transport. *J. Biol. Chem.* 247:5511–19

70. Turner, R. T., Bottemiller, B. L., Howard, G. A., Baylink, D. J. 1980. In vitro metabolism of 25-hydroxyvitamin D_3 by isolated rat kidney cells. *Proc. Natl. Acad. Sci. USA* 77:1537–40

71. Van Baelen, H., Bouillon, R., DeMoor, P. 1977. Binding of 25-hydroxycholecalciferol in tissues. *J. Biol. Chem.* 252:2515–18

72. Vieth, R., Fraser, D. 1979. Kinetic behavior of 25-hydroxyvitamin D-1-hydroxylase and -24-hydroxylase in rat kidney mitochondria. *J. Biol. Chem.* 254:12455–60

73. Weisman, Y., Vargas, A., Duckett, G., Reiter, E., Root, A. 1978. Synthesis of 1,25-dihydroxyvitamin D in the nephrectomized pregnant rat. *Endocrinology* 103:1992–98

74. Wichmann, J. K., DeLuca, H. F., Schnoes, H. K., Horst, R. H., Shepard, R. M., Jorgensen, N. A. 1979. 25-Hydroxyvitamin D_3 26,23-lactone: A new in vivo metabolite of vitamin D. *Biochemistry* 18:4775–80

75. Yamada, S., Ohmori, M., Takayama, H. 1979. Synthesis of 24,24-difluoro-25-hydroxyvitamin D_3. *Tetrahedron Lett.* 21:1859–62

76. Yoon, P. S., DeLuca, H. F. 1980. Resolution and reconstitution of soluble components of rat liver microsomal vitamin D_3-25-hydroxylase. *Arch. Biochem. Biophys.* In press

77. Yoon, P. S., DeLuca, H. F. 1980. Purification and properties of chick renal mitochondrial ferredoxin. *Biochemistry* 19:2165–71

78. Yoon, P. S., Rawlings, J., Orme-Johnson, W. H., DeLuca, H. F. 1980. Renal mitochondrial ferredoxin active in the 25-hydoxyvitamin D_3-1α-hydroxylase. Characterization of the iron-sulfur cluster using interprotein cluster transfer and EPR spectroscopy. *Biochemistry* 19:2172–76

Ann. Rev. Physiol. 1981. 43:211–23
Copyright © 1981 by Annual Reviews Inc. All rights reserved

REGULATION OF PARATHYROID HORMONE SECRETION AND BIOSYNTHESIS

♦1306

Joel F. Habener[1]

Laboratory of Molecular Endocrinology, Massachusetts General Hospital, and the Howard Hughes Medical Institute Laboratories at Harvard Medical School, Boston, Massachusetts 02114

INTRODUCTION

Parathyroid hormone increases the concentration of calcium in the extracellular fluid (ECF) through its effects on bone, kidney, and gut. An increase in ECF calcium in turn feeds back on the parathyroid gland to suppress secretion of the hormone (Figure 1). This negative-feedback inhibition is tightly controlled and contributes to the regulation of concentrations of ECF calcium within narrow limits.

Although calcium is the most potent known regulator of parathyroid hormone secretion (20) a number of other factors (magnesium, catecholamines, prostaglandins etc.) have been identified that appear to serve as modulators of hormone secretion, but their exact role in the physiologic functioning of the parathyroid gland is not fully understood. A brief discussion of these regulatory factors and a summary of current information regarding the biosynthetic and secretory pathways involved in the cellular production of parathyroid hormone is presented in this chapter.

BIOSYNTHETIC PATHWAY IN THE FORMATION OF PARATHYROID HORMONE

Parathyroid hormone (PTH) is a polypeptide of 84 amino acids. It is synthesized by way of two successive cleavages of NH_2-terminal sequences from a larger precursor, pre-proparathyroid hormone (Pre-ProPTH) of 115

[1]Acknowledgment: I thank Jeanne Sullivan for assistance in the preparation of this manuscript.

211

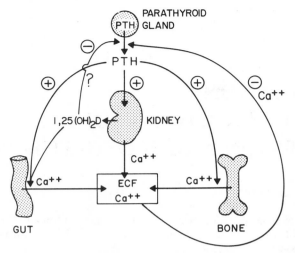

Figure 1   Regulation of parathyroid hormone secretion. Calcium is the principal regulator. The role of 1,25(OH₂)D as a regulator is uncertain. Note regulation occurs via a negative feed-back loop.

amino acids (38, 41, 43) (Figure 2). The earliest cleavage occurs co-translationally, in the rough endoplasmic reticulum (RER) and consists of the removal of an NH₂-terminal leader sequence of 25 amino acids, resulting in the formation of an intermediate precursor, proparathyroid hormone (ProPTH). In accord with the "signal hypothesis" (5, 38, 39, 41), the leader sequence of Pre-ProPTH appears to serve as a signal that functions in the establishment of a polyribosome/membrane junction via the attachment of the nascent polypeptide to a transport element, as yet unidentified, located in the lipid bilayer of the RER. The growing polypeptide chain is then transferred in a unidirectional manner into the cisterna of the RER (39). The second cleavage occurs in the Golgi complex 12–15 min later by removal of an NH₂-terminal sequence of six amino acids, resulting in the formation of PTH (19, 36, 54).

After release of the hormone from the gland into the circulation a third highly specific cleavage occurs in liver (14, 21) and perhaps in kidney (51, 59) resulting in proteolysis of the polypeptide between residues 33–34 and several other nearby sites toward the middle of the molecule (70) (Figure 2). The biological significance of this cleavage is at present unknown, but because the minimum amino terminal sequence required for expression of biological action (71) is apparently left intact, the peripheral cleavage might represent an activation step prior to action of the secreted peptide on target sites (58, 59). Fragments of hormone may also enter the circulation from proteolysis within the gland (30, 48, 62). These processes of late post-

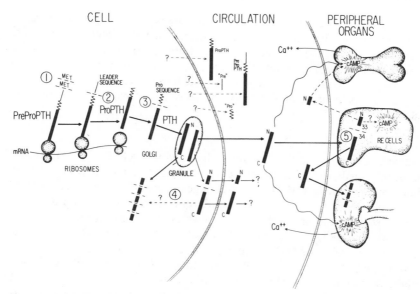

Figure 2 Schema showing extensive co- and post-transitional processing in the biosynthesis and metabolism of parathyroid hormone.

translational or post-secretory proteolysis seem responsible for the heterogeneity of circulating forms of immunoreactive hormone, a phenomenon that complicates interpretation of results achieved with immunoassays of hormone in blood in normal or pathophysiologic states (44).

CELLULAR MECHANISM OF HORMONE SECRETION

Calcium and Exocytosis

At least one of the cellular processes by which parathyroid hormone is released from the gland into the ECF is believed to involve exocytosis (36). The limiting membranes of granules or vesicles that contain hormone fuse with the plasma membrane, membrane lysis occurs, and the contents of the storage vesicle are released into the bloodstream. MacGregor et al (57) and Morrissey & Cohn (64) have suggested that more than one secretory pathway may operate in the parathyroid gland. These workers have found that newly synthesized hormone is released more rapidly from the gland than is mature or older hormone and further, that certain stimuli (such as dibutyryl cyclic AMP) preferentially release the hormone most recently synthesized.

With the apparent exception of the parathyroid gland, the processes of secretion via exocytosis in most secretory or endocrine glands is closely coupled to calcium influx into the cell; calcium serves as a "second messenger" and is required for secretion to occur; in the absence of adequate concentrations of calcium in the extracellular fluid all secretory activity ceases (68). The parathyroid gland, for reasons not understood, appears to behave paradoxically in this regard inasmuch as increases in calcium influx appear to result in an inhibition of the secretion of parathyroid hormone (8, 45).

Cyclic AMP

Adenylate cyclase and the product of the enzyme, cyclic 3' 5'-AMP, appear to be intermediates in the calcium control of PTH secretion (1, 8). Intracellular levels of cyclic AMP (cAMP) change in parallel with changes in PTH secretion effected by the secretagogues, epinephrine isopreteranol, dopamine, secretin, and prostaglandin E_2 as well as by hypocalcemia (1, 6, 8, 9, 12, 32). In addition agents that suppress secretion of PTH, such as α-adrenergic agonists (11) or prostaglandin $F_{2\alpha}$ (33), decrease intracellular levels of cAMP. Dibutyryl cyclic AMP (dbcAMP) and inhibitors of phosphodiesterase (aminophylline, theophyllines) mimic the effects of hypocalcemia in the elicitation of a parathyroid hormone secretory response in vitro (1). Several studies of the requirements for activity of adenylate cyclase prepared from parathyroid glands indicate that the enzyme is particularly sensitive to inhibition by calcium (8).

At the present the exact role of adenylate cyclase and the formation of cAMP in the secretory events involved in the release of parathyroid hormone remain unknown. The observation in vitro that cAMP is released concomitantly with the release of PTH in response to hypocalcemia (1) suggests that the formation of cAMP is closely linked to the process of exocytosis. One might speculate that cAMP is in some manner involved in the phosphorylation of a substrate protein in the parathyroid gland, perhaps a protein involved in the fusion of the secretory granule with the plasma membrane resulting in discharge of the granule contents of hormone into the extracellular space.

FACTORS THAT REGULATE HORMONE SECRETION

Catecholamines

Catecholamines are believed to modulate the secretion of PTH. Beta adrenergic agonists (epinephrine, isoproteranol) augment the secretion of hormone induced by hypocalcemia, and this augmentation of secretion can be inhibited by antagonists of β-adrenergic actions such as propranolol (10, 55). The effect of catecholamines on the secretion or PTH is associated with changes in intracellular levels of cAMP (8). In studies done in calves in vivo (6, 27, 61) the levels of epinephrine required to elicit secretory responses were similar to those found under normal physiologic circumstances. The effects of catecholamines on PTH secretion are additive to those of hypocalcemia, suggesting that two separate receptor-response systems may exist in the parathyroid gland—one sensitive to calcium and the other to catecholamines. Additional evidence in support of the existence of catecholamine receptors in the parathyroid gland comes from findings that propranolol inhibits the epinephrine but not the hypocalcemia-stimulating response on PTH secretion (6), and that repeated injection of epinephrine to calves in vivo leads to a diminishing PTH secretory response (6).

It should be emphasized that the catecholamines appear to serve as modulators of parathyroid hormone secretion only when secretion rates are greatly increased; they are not primary regulators. When hormone secretion is relatively suppressed, as it is under normal physiologic conditions of normocalcemia, epinephrine alters secretion rates of the hormone little if at all (6, 61).

Vitamin D Metabolites

The dihydroxylated metabolites of vitamin D, 1,25-dihydroxy vitamin D and 24,25-dihydroxy vitamin D, may regulate the activity of the parathyroid gland (see Figure 1). Nuclear and cytoplasmic binding components for $1,25(OH)_2D$ tentatively have been identified in cell-free extracts of parathyroid glands (13, 50, 52). These findings raise the possibility of the existence of a short-loop feedback system involving the metabolites of vitamin D and the secretion of PTH. Such a feedback loop theoretically could serve as a complement to the negative feedback loop on the parathyroid gland involving calcium and parathyroid hormone. Inasmuch as one of the physiologically important actions of parathyroid hormone is to increase the activity of the renal 25-hydroxy D hydroxylase and as a consequence the formation of $1,25(OH)_2D$ from its precursor 25(OH)D (24), $1,25(OH)_2D$ might be expected to feed back on the parathyroid gland to suppress hormone secretion.

Whether the hydroxylated metabolites of vitamin D actually exert regulatory actions on the parathyroid gland, however, is uncertain. A number of studies of the effects of the vitamin D metabolites on PTH secretion have been carried out both in vivo and in vitro and the results of the studies conflict. $1,25(OH)_2D$ is reported to suppress (18, 26), stimulate (15), or to have no effect (53) on the secretion of PTH in studies done in vivo (15, 53) and in vitro (26). $24,25(OH)_2D$, on the other hand, has been found to suppress hormone secretion in two studies (15, 16) and to have no effect on parathyroid gland function in another (26). In one in vivo study in the dog, suppression of PTH secretion into parathyroid effluent blood was observed within seconds after the injection of $24,25(OH)_2D$ into the thyroid artery (15). Thus, the establishment of a definite regulatory role for the hydroxylated metabolites of vitamin D must await the results of more definitive and conclusive studies.

Magnesium

Although calcium is the principal cation that influences PTH secretion, magnesium also can change rates of PTH secretion, but only at supraphysiological concentrations, two to three times those found in ECF under normal physiological conditions (40, 60). The contribution of magnesium compared to calcium is probably small under normal physiologic circumstances.

Magnesium, however, is essential for parathyroid gland functioning. In its absence, or when blood levels fall below a critical level, a marked inhibition of hormone secretion results (2, 17). The cellular basis for the inhibitory effects of hypomagnemia on PTH secretion is not known but may relate in some way to the formation of intraglandular cAMP and to the process of exocytosis by which hormone is transported via the secretory granules to the extracellular fluid.

Other Factors

Factors other than those indicated above have been reported to influence the secretion of parathyroid hormone. For the most part these studies have been carried out in vitro and the effects of the factors have been small. Whether or not they exert physiologically relevant regulatory effects on the parathyroid gland remains to be proven.

Calcitonin has been reported to stimulate directly the secretion of parathyroid hormone in studies using parathyroid explants in vitro (28). Some evidence, albeit indirect, suggests that calcitonin may stimulate PTH secretion physiologically in man (63). Calcium infusions given to patients with medullary carcinoma of the thyroid resulted not only in the expected rise in serum calcium and calcitonin but also in a paradoxical rise in blood levels of PTH rather than the expected suppression of PTH secretion (23). Although not shown directly in this study the results are consistent with a stimulation of PTH secretion by the large amounts of calcitonin released as a result of the calcium infusion.

Cortisol has been observed to produce elevated levels of serum PTH when administered in man (31) and in rats (72) or when exposed to rat parathyroid glands maintained in organ culture (3). Although the serum calcium levels measured in these studies remained within the normal range, the elevated levels of PTH resulting from the administration of cortisol were attributed to a transient lowering of serum calcium levels by way of the actions of cortisol to reduce intestinal absorption and renal tubular resorption of calcium. Au (3), however, has reported a direct stimulatory effect of cortisol on the secretion of PTH from rat parathyroid glands maintained as explants in culture, which suggests that cortisol may influence PTH secretion by mechanisms independent of changes in blood levels of calcium.

Growth hormone should be considered as a possible regulator of parathyroid gland activity. Rats given daily injections of bovine growth hormone developed enlargements of the parathyroid glands concomitant with increases in serum calcium and PTH levels (56). These observations may help to explain the tendency for some patients with acromegaly and excessive secretion of growth hormone to develop hypercalcemia.

Suppression of PTH levels in blood as a result of somatostatin administration has been reported in studies in vivo in rats and monkeys (49); other studies done in normal human subjects and patients with parathyroid adenomas failed to show any discernible effects of somatostatin in the secretion of PTH (22).

FORMS OF HORMONE SECRETED

Both in vivo and in vitro studies indicate that under certain circumstances the parathyroid gland secretes fragments of hormone along with the intact hormone (30, 48, 62). Most of the circulating immunoreactive hormone in peripheral blood consists of carboxy-terminal fragments of the hormone devoid of biological activity by virtue of the absence of the amino-terminal sequence in which biological activity resides (70). A substantial fraction of the circulating fragments arises as a result of cleavage of the intact, secreted hormone by enzymes located in the liver, kidney, bone, and possibly other organs (14, 21, 29, 42, 51, 59, 65, 66, 69, 70). In addition, however, hormonal fragments are produced in and released by the parathyroid gland itself (25, 30, 35, 48, 62). Prohormone does not appear to be secreted (46).

Analyses of the immunoreactive hormone released into parathyroid effluent blood in calves have shown that the relative amounts of fragment and intact hormone vary as a function of the rate of secretion as determined by the blood level of calcium (62). During hypocalcemia in which secretion rates of hormone are high, intact hormone predominated in the effluent blood—fragments constitute only a small portion of the total immunoreactive hormone. In contrast, during hypercalcemia suppression of hormone secretion, the fragment(s) made up the majority of the secreted immunoreactive material.

The physiologic significance of the fragment(s) released by the para-thyroid gland remains unknown. The evidence available indicates that the major fragment(s) detected are biologically inactive. Cathepsins have been discovered in extracts of parathyroid glands that cleave the hormone result-ing in the generation of a carboxyl-terminal fragment, but it is not known whether the activity of the cathepsin is regulated by calcium. Fischer et al (29) reported a calcium-regulated peptidase in porcine parathyroid glands. The enzyme was activated by chelating agents and inhibited by calcium; however, Mayer et al (62) found a greater relative proportion of fragments in effluent blood under conditions of hypercalcemia than under hypocal-cemia. It remains possible that the fragment(s) released from the gland may be a reflection of the calcium-regulated intracellular degradative pathway in the parathyroid gland (37). Whatever the physiologic role of this cleavage process, it appears that the enzymic activities are in some manner regulated by changes in extra-cellular calcium concentrations and/or changes in secretion rate and in this context may function in the regulation of the production of biologically active hormone by the gland.

Some evidence indicates that ProPTH may occasionally be synthesized and secreted by cancerous tissues. Synthesis and release of a prohormone-like substance has been described as a result of incubations in vitro of a renal cell carcinoma (34) and of a squamous-cell carcinoma of the esophagus (47).

REGULATION OF BIOSYNTHESIS

Studies of the control of the biosynthesis of parathyroid hormone now make it possible to draw some conclusions about the cellular mechanisms of control, though much information yet remains to be gathered. Figure 3 depicts the potential steps in the biosynthesis of PTH where regulatory influences might be expected to have an effect. As discussed earlier, several extracellular factors, principally calcium, control the secretion of para-thyroid hormone (Step 8, Figure 3). Ultimately, however, hormone secreted from the gland must be replenished by the synthesis of new hormone, a process that requires many steps and that could be controlled at any one or more of these steps. Studies in vitro of the effects of varying concentra-tions of calcium in the extracellular fluid (incubation media) on the rates of labeling of Pre-ProPTH, ProPTH, and PTH during pulse-chase incuba-tions with radioactive amino acids have shown no effects on the relative rates of conversion of Pre-ProPTH to ProPTH (Step 5, Figure 3) (37) or of ProPTH to PTH (Step 6, Figure 3) (37). Further, absolute rates of synthesis of Pre-ProPTH and of ProPTH change little over several hours; low calcium stimulates and high calcium suppresses synthesis of the prehor-mone and prohormone by 15–20% over a period of 4–5 hours (37). These observations suggest that no major regulatory effects are exerted at the level of translational events (Step 4, Figure 3) inasmuch as changes at this level would be expected to take place much more rapidly and to a much greater extent.

The effects of extracellular calcium on transcriptional and post-transcriptional events (Steps 2 and 3, Figure 3) are largely unknown. The small differences in rates of translation observed in response to differences in ECF calcium are consistent with regulation at the levels of transcription and/or post-transcriptional processing provided that rates of formation of Pre-ProPTH and of ProPTH directly reflect cytoplasmic levels of mRNA coding for Pre-ProPTH and that either the cytoplasmic half-life of the mRNA is relatively slow (i.e. $T_{1/2}$ of 12 hr or greater) and/or that nuclear pools of pre-mRNA to replenish cytoplasmic supplies of mRNA are large.

A predominant level of regulation may be that of DNA synthesis (Step 1, Figure 3). Chronic stimulation (hypocalcemia) of the parathyroid glands invariably leads to hyperplasia of the glands, a situation, for example, that is almost universally encountered in patients with chronic renal failure (4).

Regulation at the level of cell growth and division would also be in keeping with the overall physiologic functioning of the parathyroid gland. The pattern of secretion of parathyroid hormone is one of a relatively constant and steady release of hormone throughout the day. Evidence exists, however, for the presence of two additional mechanisms for regulat-

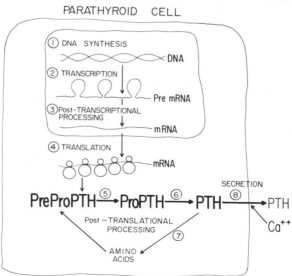

Figure 3 Diagram of parathyroid cell depicting hypothetical steps in the formation of parathyroid hormone that may be regulated.

ing the production of parathyroid hormone. Roth (67) has obtained evidence that the parathyroid gland contains hormone-producing cells (chief cells) in varying stages of activity and that the cells go through cycles of inactive to active with regard to hormone synthesis. Stimulation (hypocalcemia) of the parathyroid gland leads to a greater number of cells entering the active phase of hormone synthesis; suppression of glandular activity (hypercalcemia) results in the formation of a greater number of inactive cells.

Another regulatory mechanism utilized by the parathyroid gland is a degradative pathway involved in the destruction of some fraction of the hormone synthesized (Step 7, Figure 3). Changes in concentrations of calcium in the extracellular fluid appear to regulate intracellular stores of hormone through a pathway involving the turnover of the hormone (37). High concentrations of extracellular calcium stimulate, and low concentrations inhibit, intracellular degradation of hormone.

A key question, as yet unanswered, is how are extracellular stimuli coupled to intracellular events in the processes of hormone synthesis, transport, and secretion. In some manner signals must be transmitted within the cell that eventually lead to the synthesis of new hormone, be it via direct actions on DNA synthesis, RNA synthesis, protein synthesis, or any combination of these processes. Once the "coupling factors" that link extracellular stimuli with protein synthesis are identified it should be possible to begin to better understand at a molecular level the cellular mechanisms involved in the regulation of hormone synthesis and secretion.

Literature Cited

1. Abe, M., Sherwood, L. M. 1972. Regulation of parathyroid hormone secretion by adenyl cyclase. *Biochem. Biophys. Res. Commun.* 48:396–401
2. Anast, C. S., Winnacker, J. L., Forte, L. R., Burns, T. W. 1976. Impaired release of parathyroid hormone in magnesium deficiency. *J. Clin. Endocrinol. Metab.* 42:707–17
3. Au, W. Y. W. 1976. Cortisol stimulation of parathyroid hormone secretion. *Science* 193:1015–17
4. Avioli, L. V. 1978. Renal osteodystrophy. In *Metabolic Bone Disease*, ed. L. V. Avioli, S. M. Krane, 2:149–215. NY: Academic
5. Blobel, G., Dobberstein, B. 1975. Transfer of proteins across membranes. I. Presence of proteolytically processed and unprocessed nascent immunoglobulin light chains on membrane-bound ribosomes of murine myeloma. *J. Cell Biol.* 67:835–51
6. Blum, J. W., Fischer, J. A., Hunziker, W. H., Binswanger, U., Picotti, G. B., Da Prada, M., Guillebeau, A. 1978. Parathyroid hormone responses to catecholamines and to changes of extracellular calcium in cows. *J. Clin. Invest.* 61:1113–22
7. Brown, E. M., Gardner, D. G., Windeck, R. A., Aurbach, G. D. 1978. Relationship of intracellular 3',5'-adenosine monophosphate accumulation to parathyroid hormone release from dispersed bovine parathyroid cells. *Endocrinology* 103:2323–33
8. Brown, E. M., Gardner, D. G., Aurbach, G. D. 1980. Effects of the calcium ionophore A23187 on dispersed bovine parathyroid cells. *Endocrinology* 106:133–38
9. Brown, E. M., Gardner, D. G., Windeck, R. A., Aurbach, G. D. 1979. Cholera toxin stimulates 3',5'-adenosine monophosphate accumulation and

parathyroid hormone release from dispersed bovine parathyroid cells. *Endocrinology* 104:218–25

10. Brown, E. M., Hurwitz, S., Aurbach, G. D. 1977. Beta-adrenergic stimulation of cyclic AMP content and parathyroid hormone release from isolated bovine parathyroid cells. *Endocrinology* 100:1696–1702

11. Brown, E. M., Hurwitz, S., Aurbach, G. D. 1977. α-Adrenergic inhibition of adenosine 3',5'-monophosphate accumulation and parathyroid hormone release from dispersed bovine parathyroid cells. *Endocrinology* 103:893–99

12. Brown, E. M., Hurwitz, S., Woodard, C. J., Aurbach, G. D. 1977. Direct identification of beta-adrenergic receptors on isolated bovine parathyroid cells. *Endocrinology* 100:1703–9

13. Brumbough, P. F., Hughs, M. R., Haussler, M. R. 1975. Cytoplasmic and nuclear binding components for 1α,25-dihydroxy vitamin D_3 chick parathyroid gland. *Proc. Natl. Acad. Sci. USA* 72:4871–75

14. Canterbury, J. M., Bricker, L. A., Levey, G. S., Kozlovskis, P. L., Ruiz, E., Zull, J. E., Reiss, E. 1975. Metabolism of bovine parathyroid hormone: immunological and biological characteristics of fragments generated by liver perfusion. *J. Clin. Invest.* 55:1245–53

15. Canterbury, J. M., Lerman, S., Claflin, A. J., Henry, H., Norman, A., Reiss, E. 1978. Inhibition of parathyroid hormone secretion by 25-hydroxycholecalciferol and 24,25-dihydroxycholecalciferol in the dog. *J. Clin. Invest.* 61:1375–83

16. Care, A. D., Bates, R. F. L., Pickard, D. W., Peacock, M., Tomlinson, S., O'Riordan, J. L. H., Mawer, E. B., Taylor, C. M., DeLuca, H. F., Norman, A. W. 1976. The effects of vitamin D metabolites and their analyses on the secretion of parathyroid hormone. *Calcif. Tissue Res.* 21:142–46

17. Chase, L. R., Slatopolsky, E. 1974. Secretion and metabolic efficacy of parathyroid hormone in patients with severe hypomagnesemia. *J. Clin. Endocrinol. Metab.* 38:363–71

18. Chertow, B. S., Baylink, D. J., Wergedal, J. E., Su, M. H. H., Norman, A. W. 1975. Decrease in serum immunoreactive parathyroid hormone in rats and in parathyroid hormone secretion in vitro by 1,25-dihydroxycholecalciferol. *J. Clin. Invest.* 56:668–78

19. Cohn, D. V., MacGregor, R. R., Chu, L. L. H., Kimmel, J. R., Hamilton, J.

W. 1972. Calcemic fraction-A: biosynthetic peptide precursor of parathyroid hormone. *Proc. Natl. Acad. Sci. USA* 69:1521–25

20. Copp, D. H., Davidson, A. G. F. 1961. Direct humoral control of parathyroid function in the dog. 1961. *Proc. Soc. Exp. Biol. Med.* 107:342–44

21. D'Amour, P., Segre, G. V., Roth, S. I., Potts, J. T. Jr. 1979. Analysis of parathyroid hormone and its fragments in rat tissues: chemical identification and microscopical localization. *J. Clin. Invest.* 63:89–98

22. Deftos, L. J., Lorenzi, M., Bohanon, N., Tsalakian, E., Schneider, V., Gerich, J. E. 1976. Somatostatin does not suppress plasma parathyroid hormone. *J. Clin. Endocrinol. Metab.* 43:205–7

23. Deftos, L. J., Parthemore, J. G. 1974. Secretion of parathyroid hormone in patients with medullary thyroid carcinoma. *J. Clin. Invest.* 54:416–20

24. DeLuca, H. F., Schnoes, H. K. 1976. Metabolism and mechanism of action of vitamin D. *Ann. Rev. Biochem.* 45:631–66

25. Di Bella, F. P., Gilkinson, J. B., Flueck, J., Arnaud, C. D. 1978. Carboxyl-terminal fragments of human parathyroid tumors: unique new source of immunogens for the production of antisera potentially useful in the radio-immunoassay of parathyroid hormone in human serum. *J. Clin. Endocrinol. Metab.* 46:604–12

26. Dietel, M., Dorn, G., Montz, R., Altenahr, E. 1979. Influence of vitamin D_3, 1,25-dihydroxy vitamin D_3, and 24,25-dihydroxyvitamin D_3 on parathyroid hormone secretion, adenosine 3',5'-monophosphate release, and ultrastructure of parathyroid glands in organ culture. *Endocrinology* 105:237–45

27. Fischer, J. A., Blum, J. W., Binswanger, U. 1973. Acute parathyroid hormone response to epinephrine in vivo. *J. Clin. Invest.* 52:2434–40

28. Fischer, J. A., Oldham, S. B., Sizemore, G. W., Arnaud, C. D. 1971. Calcitonin stimulation of parathyroid hormone secretion in vivo. *Horm. Metab. Res.* 3:223–28

29. Fischer, J. A., Oldham, S. B., Sizemore, G. W., Arnaud, C. D. 1972. Calcium-regulated parathyroid hormone peptidase. *Proc. Natl. Acad. Sci. USA* 69:2341–45

30. Flueck, J. A., Di Bella, F. P., Edis, A. J., Kehrwald, J. M., Arnaud, C. D. 1977. Immunoheterogeneity of parathyroid hormone in venous effluent

serum from hyperfunctioning parathyroid glands. *J. Clin. Invest.* 60: 1367–75

31. Fucik, R. F., Kukreja, S. C., Hargis, G. K., Bowser, E. N., Henderson, W. J., Williams, G. A. 1975. Effect of glucocorticoids on function of the parathyroid glands in man. *J. Clin. Endocrinol. Metab.* 40:152–55

32. Gardner, D. G., Brown, E. M., Windeck, R., Aurbach, G. D. 1978. Prostaglandin E_2 stimulation of adenosine 3',5'-monophosphate accumulation and parathyroid hormone release in dispersed bovine parathyroid cells. *Endocrinology* 103:577–82

33. Gardner, D. G., Brown, E. M., Windeck, R., Aurbach, G. D. 1979. Prostaglandin F_{2a} inhibits 3',5'-adenosine monophosphate accumulation and parathyroid hormone release from dispersed bovine parathyroid cells. *Endocrinology* 104:1–7

34. Greenberg, P. B., Martin, T. J., Sutcliffe, H. S. 1973. Synthesis and release of parathyroid hormone by a renal carcinoma in cell culture. *Clin. Sci., Mol. Med.* 45:183–91

35. Habener, J. F. 1978. Responsiveness of neoplastic and hyperplastic parathyroid tissues to calcium in vitro. *J. Clin. Invest.* 62:436–50

36. Habener, J. F., Amherdt, M., Ravazzola, M., Orci, L. 1979. Parathyroid hormone biosynthesis: correlation of conversion of biosynthetic precursors with intracellular protein migration as determined by electron microscope autoradiography. *J. Cell Biol.* 80:715–31

37. Habener, J. F., Kemper, B., Potts, J. T. Jr. 1975. Calcium-dependent intracellular degradation of parathyroid hormone: a possible mechanism for the regulation of hormone stores. *Endocrinology* 97:431–41

38. Habener, J. F., Kronenberg, H. M. 1978. Parathyroid hormone biosynthesis: structure and function of biosynthetic precursors. *Fed. Proc.* 37: 2561–66

39. Habener, J. F., Maunus, R., Dee, P. C., Potts, J. T. Jr. 1980. Early events in the cellular formation of proparathyroid hormone. *J. Cell Biol.* 85:892–98

40. Habener, J. F., Potts, J. T. Jr. 1976. Relative effectiveness of magnesium and calcium on the secretion and release of parathyroid hormone. *Endocrinology* 98:197–202

41. Habener, J. F., Potts, J. T. Jr. 1978. Biosynthesis of parathyroid hormone. *N. Engl. J. Med.* 299:580–85; 635–44

42. Habener, J. F., Powell, D., Murray, T. M., Mayer, G. P., Potts, J. T. Jr. 1971. Parathyroid hormone secretion and metabolism *in vivo*. *Proc. Natl. Acad. Sci. USA* 68:2986–91

43. Habener, J. F., Rosenblatt, M., Kemper, B., Kronenberg, H. M., Rich, A., Potts, J. T. Jr. 1978. Pre-proparathyroid hormone: amino acid sequence, chemical synthesis, and some biological studies of the precursor region. *Proc. Natl. Acad. Sci. USA* 75:2616–20

44. Habener, J. F., Segre, G. V. 1979. Parathyroid hormone radioimmunoassay. [Editorial] *Ann. Int. Med.* 91:782–85

45. Habener, J. F., Stevens, T. D., Ravazzola, M., Orci, L., Potts, J. T. Jr. 1976. Effects of calcium ionophores on the synthesis and release of parathyroid hormone. *Endocrinology* 101:1524–37

46. Habener, J. F., Stevens, T. D., Tregear, G. W., Potts, J. T. Jr. 1976. Radioimmunoassay of human proparathyroid hormone: analysis of hormone content in tissue extracts and in plasma. *J. Clin. Endocrinol. Metab.* 42:520–30

47. Hamilton, J. W., Hartman, C. R., MacGregor, D. H., Cohn, D. V. 1977. Synthesis of parathyroid hormone-like peptides by a human squamous cell carcinoma. *J. Clin. Endocrinol. Metab.* 45: 1023–30

48. Hanley, D. A., Takatsuki, K., Sultan, J. M., Schneider, A. B., Sherwood, L. M. 1978. Direct release of parathyroid hormone fragments from functioning bovine parathyroid glands in vitro. *J. Clin. Invest.* 62:1247–54

49. Hargis, G. K., Williams, G. A., Reynolds, W. A., Chertow, B. S., Kukreja, S. C., Bowser, E. N., Henderson, W. J. 1978. Effect of somatostatin on parathyroid hormone and calcitonin secretion. *Endocrinology* 102:745–50

50. Henry, H. L., Norman, A. W. 1975. Studies on the mechanism of action of calciferol VII. Localization of 1,25-dihydroxy-vitamin D_3 in chick parathyroid glands. *Biochem. Biophys. Res. Commun.* 62:781–88

51. Hruska, K. A., Martin, K., Mennes, P., Greenwalt, A., Anderson, C., Klahr, S., Slatopolsky, E. 1977. Degradation of parathyroid hormone and fragment production by the isolated perfused dog kidney: the effect of glomerular filtration rate and perfusate Ca^{++} concentrations. *J. Clin. Invest.* 60:501–10

52. Hughes, M. R., Haussler, M. R. 1978. 1,25-Dihydroxyvitamin D_3 receptors in parathyroid glands: preliminary characterization of cytoplasmic and nuclear

binding components. *J. Biol. Chem.* 253:1065–73

53. Hurst, J. G., Wilson, P. R., Mayer, G. P. 1979. PTH secretory response during the administration of 1,25-dihydroxycholecalciferol (1,25–DHCC). *Endocrine Soc., 61st Ann. Meet.* No. 48. (Prog. Abstr.)

54. Kemper, B., Habener, J. F., Potts, J. T. Jr., Rich, A. 1972. Proparathyroid hormone: identification of a biosynthetic precursor to parathyroid hormone. *Proc. Natl. Acad. Sci. USA* 69:643–47

55. Kukreja, S. C., Hargis, G. K., Bowser, E. N., Henderson, W. J., Fisherman, E. W., Williams, G. A. 1975. Role of adrenergic stimuli in parathyroid hormone secretion in man. *J. Clin. Endocrinol. Metab.* 40:478 (Abstr.)

56. Lancer, S. R., Bowser, E. N., Hargis, G. K., Williams, G. A. 1976. The effect of growth hormone on parathyroid function in cats. *Endocrinology* 98:1289–93

57. MacGregor, R. R., Hamilton, J. W., Cohn, D. V. 1975. The by-pass of tissue hormone stores during the secretion of newly synthesized parathyroid hormone. *Endocrinology* 97:178–88

58. Martin, K. J., Freitag, J. J., Conrades, M. B., Hruska, K. A., Klahr, S., Slatopolsky, E. 1978. Selective uptake of the synthetic amino terminal fragment of bovine parathyroid hormone by isolated perfused bone. *J. Clin. Invest.* 62:256–61

59. Martin, K. J., Hruska, K. A., Freitag, J. J., Klahr, S., Slatopolsky, E. 1979. The peripheral metabolism of parathyroid hormone. *N. Engl. J. Med.* 301:1092–98

60. Mayer, G. P., Hurst, J. G. 1978. Sigmoidal relationship between parathyroid hormone secretion rate and plasma calcium concentration in calves. *Endocrinology* 102:1036–42

61. Mayer, G. P., Hurst, J. G., Barto, J. H., Keaton, J. A., Moore, M. P. 1979. Effect of epinephrine on parathyroid hormone secretion in calves. *Endocrinology* 104:1181–87

62. Mayer, G. P., Keaton, J. A., Hurst, J. G., Habener, J. F. 1979. Effects of plasma calcium concentration on the relative proportion of hormone and carboxyl fragments in parathyroid venous blood. *Endocrinology* 104:1778–84

63. Metz, S. A., Deftos, L. J., Baylink, D. J., Robertson, R. P. 1978. Neuroendocrine modulation of calcitonin and parathyroid hormone in man. *J. Clin. Endocrinol. Metab.* 47:151–59

64. Morrissey, J. J., Cohn, D. V. 1979. Regulation of secretion of parathormone and secretory protein I from separate intracellular pools by calcium, dibutyryl, cyclic AMP, and (1)-isoproteronol. *J. Cell Biol.* 82:93–102

65. Morrissey, J. J., Smardo, F. L., Cohn, D. V., Hamilton, J. W. 1979. Secretion of parathormone and parathormone fragment by dispersed porcine parathyroid cells. *Endocrine Soc. 61st Ann. Meet.* No. 39 (Prog. Abstr.)

66. Neuman, W. F., Neuman, M. W., Sammon, P. J., Simon, W., Lane, K. 1975. The metabolism of labeled parathyroid hormone. III: Studies in rats. *Calcif. Tissue Res.* 18:251–61

67. Roth, S. I., Raisz, L. G. 1966. The course and reversibility of the calcium effect on the ultrastructures of the rat parathyroid gland in organ culture. *Lab. Invest.* 15:1187–211

68. Rubin, R. P. 1970. The role of calcium in the release of neurotransmitter substances and hormones. *Pharmacol. Rev.* 22:389–428

69. Segre, G. V., Habener, J. F., Powell, D., Tregear, G. W., Potts, J. T. Jr. 1972. Parathyroid hormone in human plasma: immunochemical characterization and biological implications. *J. Clin. Invest.* 51:3163–72

70. Segre, G. V., Niall, H. D., Sauer, R. T., Potts, J. T. Jr. 1977. Edman degradation of radioiodinated parathyroid hormone: application to sequence analysis and hormone metabolism in vivo. *Biochemistry* 16:2417–27

71. Tregear, G. W., van Rietschoten, J., Greene, E., Keutmann, H. T., Niall, H. D., Reit, B., Parsons, J. A., Potts, J. T. Jr. 1973. Bovine parathyroid hormone: minimum chain length of synthetic peptide required for biological activity. *Endocrinology* 93:1349–53

72. Williams, G. A., Peterson, W. C., Bowser, E. N., Henderson, W. J., Hargis, G. K., Martinez, N. J. 1974. Interrelationship of parathyroid and adrenocortical function in calcium homeostasis in the rat. *Endocrinology* 95:707–12

Ann. Rev. Physiol. 1981. 43:225–238

HORMONAL CONTROL OF SKELETAL GROWTH

◆1307

Lawrence G. Raisz and Barbara E. Kream

Department of Medicine, Division of Endocrinology and Metabolism, University of Connecticut Health Center, Farmington, Connecticut 06032

Skeletal growth and development are under complex hormonal control. Thus it is not surprising that our current knowledge in this area is often contradictory and confused. One major source of confusion is that skeletal growth is regulated by many metabolic processes, and a particular hormone may affect several of the processes in different ways. Another source of confusion is that a variety of methods are used to assess skeletal growth and many have only limited application. This problem has been the subject of a recent text (96). This review emphasizes recent important findings concerning the influence of hormones on skeletal development. The earlier literature on this subject has been reviewed in detail (75).

SKELETAL GROWTH AND DEVELOPMENT

Let us summarize the features of bone biology important in skeletal development (74, 104). The mammalian skeleton serves two different and often incompatible functions (34–36). Structurally, the skeleton must be strong, light, mobile, and capable of orderly growth, response to stress, and repair. Metabolically, it must serve as an ion reservoir of calcium, phosphorus, magnesium, sodium, and carbonate. In bone and cartilage, hormones act in a coordinated manner to maintain a balance among these functions.

Skeletal growth is initiated by the formation of a cartilage template that is subsequently replaced by bone. Linear growth, particularly of the long bones, commences with the proliferation of epiphyseal cartilage cells and ceases with epiphyseal closure at puberty. Bone mass and the final pattern

225

0066-4278/81/0315-0225$01.00

of cortical and trabecular bone are determined by the coupled process of osteoclastic resorption and osteoblastic formation known as bone remodeling. Bone remodeling begins durings fetal development and continues throughout life even during periods of rapid skeletal growth. Until the third or fourth decade bone mass increases because bone formation exceeds bone resorption.

Three differentiated cell types, the chondrocyte, the osteoblast, and the osteoclast, are involved in skeletal development. The chondrocyte and the osteoblast are derived from the same mesenchymal precursors but develop quite differently. Cartilage grows by the orderly proliferation of chondrocytes, which synthesize a matrix of proteoglycan and Type II collagen. In addition, chondrocytes break down proteoglycans to initiate calcification of the cartilage in the hypertrophic zone. Resorption of calcified cartilage is carried out by chondroclasts, which are indistinguishable from bone osteoclasts.

Osteoblasts are derived from a population of rapidly dividing precursor cells, and once fully differentiated usually do not undergo further division. Osteoblasts are polygonal cells having an abundant rough endoplasmic reticulum and a highly developed Golgi apparatus. Bone formation commences with the proliferation of precursor cells and their differentiation into osteoblasts that secrete Type I collagen and other noncollagenous components of the bone matrix. Both chondrocytes and osteoblasts produce matrix vesicles that may have an important role in mineralization of the matrix. In bone, extracellular alterations in proteoglycan and collagen composition and structure precede mineralization. When osteoblasts complete their cycle of matrix synthesis they become osteocytes and show a decline in synthetic activity. However, these osteocytes remain connected to surface osteoblasts by cell processes.

The osteoclast, a unique multinucleated cell with a ruffled border and surrounding clear zone, resorbs bone and calcified cartilage. Osteoclasts are probably derived from a cell line different from the precursor of chondrocytes and osteoblasts, perhaps the monocyte-macrophage series. Even though osteoclasts and macrophages are similar, the conversion of one type into the other has not been demonstrated.

Most hormones that influence skeletal metabolism affect all three cell types and their precursors. However, whereas calcitonin acts only on osteoclasts, insulin and somatomedins affect only chondrocytes and osteoblasts. Many investigators suggest that the metabolic functions of the skeleton are not due to alterations in bone formation or resorption but are the result of mineral transport across a putative bone membrane consisting of osteocytes and osteoblasts (99). Although attractive, this hypothesis has little experimental support.

FACTORS INFLUENCING SKELETAL GROWTH

Hormones and factors that influence skeletal development can be classified as calcium regulating hormones, systemic hormones, and local factors that may or may not be hormones. We will use the term somatomedin to indicate a family of growth hormone dependent peptides, including insulin-like growth factor (IGF) and multiplication stimulating activity (MSA), that influence bone and cartilage growth. The effects of ions and the interactions of ions with hormones are important in bone growth but are outside the scope of this review.

Parathyroid Hormone

The effect of parathyroid hormone (PTH) on bone growth is controversial (6, 7). In vivo or in vitro, high concentrations of PTH inhibit osteoblastic collagen synthesis (25). However, chronic treatment with PTH increases osteoblastic activity and appositional growth rate (67, 100). This anabolic effect of PTH may be greater with the N-terminal 1-34 active fragment than with the intact 1-84 hormone (29). However, in our laboratory, 1-34 and 1-84 PTH were equipotent in decreasing collagen synthesis in fetal rat calvaria in vitro (79). Since PTH increases osteoclastic bone resorption, the anabolic effect of PTH may be indirect, reflecting the coupling of increased bone formation to increased bone resorption (44). PTH may also influence the skeleton by an effect on undifferentiated connective tissue cells (6, 65, 66). For example, excess PTH may cause proliferation of fibroblasts and a subsequent increase in woven bone. The effect of PTH on cartilage is unclear. In vitro, PTH has no effect on collagen synthesis in the cartilagenous ends of fetal long bones (73) but increases ornithine decarboxylase activity in rabbit chondrocytes (98) and impairs cartilage calcification (9).

The mechanism of action of PTH to decrease collagen synthesis in fetal bone has been studied in vitro. The effect of PTH is due largely to a decrease in synthesis and not an increase in the degradation of collagen (76). A decrease in collagen synthesis is evident 4–6 hr after exposure to PTH and can be correlated with morphologic changes in the osteoblasts (47). The activity of bone procollagen messenger RNA is also decreased by PTH and coincides with the decrease in collagen synthesis (52). In the rat calvarial model, PTH does not alter noncollagen protein synthesis but increases DNA synthesis, adenyl cyclase activity, and the cyclic AMP content of calvaria (64). Inhibition of cAMP phosphodiesterase with dibutyryl cAMP and isobutylmethylxanthine can mimic the effects of PTH (10, 25). Bone cells isolated from mouse calvaria by sequential enzymatic digestion respond to PTH by increasing their cAMP content and decreasing collagen synthesis (57). Finally, PTH increases cAMP and decreases collagen synthesis in a cell line derived from rat osteosarcoma that has many of the biochemical features characteristic of osteoblasts (B. Kream, R. Majeska, unpublished results).

Vitamin D

Vitamin D stimulates bone mineral mobilization to increase the supply of calcium and phosphate in the serum (23). It is also thought that vitamin D is essential in vivo for normal skeletal mineralization. For example, early in vitamin D deficiency, mineralization of new osteoid is impaired but chondrocytes and osteoblasts continue to synthesize their matrix at normal or even accelerated rates. However, in severe vitamin D deficiency, both mineralization and bone matrix synthesis are depressed (4) and the pattern of collagen cross-linking is altered (24). The decrease in matrix synthesis may not be due to lack of vitamin D but rather to the hypocalcemia subsequent to D deficiency since matrix synthesis and normal cross-linking can be restored when serum calcium is increased by dietary supplementation (24, 43). Thus, the trophic effect of vitamin D on skeletal growth could be explained by its ability to increase serum calcium and phosphate.

However, one would expect a direct effect of vitamin D on the skeleton since the active metabolite of vitamin D, 1,25-dihydroxyvitamin D, has a high affinity cytosolic receptor in bone (51). In vitro, 1,25-dihydroxyvitamin D directly stimulates osteoclastic bone resorption (83) and inhibits osteoblastic bone collagen synthesis (82). Other metabolites of vitamin D have similar effects but only at much higher concentrations since they probably have much less affinity for the 1,25-dihydroxyvitamin D receptor (78). These findings are difficult to reconcile with the direct anabolic effect of vitamin D on skeletal growth, which some investigators have hypothesized. It is possible that metabolites such as 25-hydroxyvitamin D or 24,25-dihydroxyvitamin D, which are present in high concentrations in the blood, are trophic hormones for skeletal development. In vivo, addition of one or both of these metabolites results in better management of vitamin D deficiency than can be obtained with 1,25-dihydroxyvitamin D alone (8). However, this effect may be pharmacokinetic rather than physiologic. In cartilage, 24,25-dihydroxyvitamin D may enhance matrix synthesis and cell replication (20).

One can consider the catabolic effect of 1,25-dihydroxyvitamin D on bone as teleologically appropriate and representing a special adaptation to calcium and phosphate deficiency. When serum calcium and phosphate are normal, the free level of 1,25-dihydroxyvitamin D in the serum is low and permits normal calcium and phosphate absorption in the intestine. When serum calcium and phosphate are low, the increased synthesis of 1,25-dihydroxyvitamin D would have a direct effect on bone to increase resorption and supply adequate calcium and phosphate for soft tissues and for mineralization of existing bone matrix. Therefore, during periods of decreased mineral supply, it would also be appropriate for 1,25-dihydroxyvitamin D to inhibit collagen synthesis so that the amount of additional new matrix to be mineralized would be limited.

Calcitonin

Calcitonin is an antihypercalcemic hormone that plays an important role in skeletal growth and development. Calcitonin inhibits osteoclastic bone resorption in vivo and in organ cultures of fetal bone. In vitro, no direct effect of calcitonin on osteoblastic collagen synthesis (25) or on mineralization (9) has been demonstrated. Calcitonin can prevent hypercalcemia and hypercalciuria during the absorption of calcium in rapidly growing animals by inhibiting bone resorption and by slowing intestinal absorption of calcium and phosphate (48). Thus, calcitonin deficiency could lead to inefficient utilization of dietary calcium. Calcitonin excess such as occurs in medullary carcinoma of the thyroid appears to have little effect on skeletal growth and remodeling. This may be attributable to the escape phenomenon —that is, the loss of hormone sensitivity after prolonged exposure to the hormone (106).

Growth Hormone

Growth hormone is an important regulator of skeletal growth. In vivo, growth hormone deficiency results in decreased cartilage cell proliferation and matrix synthesis, impaired osteoblastic function, and a subsequent decline in linear growth. Excess growth hormone produces an increase in linear growth before the epiphyses are closed and an increase in bone formation after closure (38, 39). Studies using bone densitometry and neutron activation analysis have suggested that this effect is limited to cortical bone and that trabecular bone volume may actually decrease, perhaps to compensate for increased cortical thickness (1). The effects of growth hormone on the skeleton are probably indirect and mediated through increased synthesis and secretion of somatomedins. However, biologically active growth hormone fragments may have a direct anabolic effect on cartilage (54).

Insulin

While it is clear that insulin alters skeletal growth, the mechanism and importance of this action remain to be established. In infants of diabetic mothers, the increase in somatic and skeletal growth has been attributed to hyperinsulinemia. Diabetes, particularly juvenile-onset diabetes mellitus, is associated with diminished bone mass (53, 60, 91). Insulin has important indirect effects on the skeleton. Insulin can stimulate somatomedin release from the liver as demonstrated by the accelerated skeletal growth of obese hypopituitary children (21, 22). In diabetic animals, somatomedin activity is decreased (70). Insulin may affect the formation of 1,25-dihydroxy-vitamin D since animals with streptozotocin-induced diabetes have low circulating 1,25-dihydroxyvitamin D (94), but no defect in intestinal absorption or vitamin D metabolism was detected in a population of juvenile-onset and maturity-onset diabetics. (42).

In vitro, insulin stimulates growth of bone and cartilage directly. In isolated bone cells, insulin increases amino acid uptake (31) and RNA synthesis (69). In cultures of fetal rat calvaria, $10^{-9}M$ insulin increases collagen synthesis with little effect on overall protein synthesis (10). High concentrations of insulin ($10^{-6}M$) increase both collagen and DNA synthesis but this effect may be due to the binding of insulin to somatomedin receptors (E. Canalis, unpublished observations). In cartilage, a high affinity insulin receptor has been identified (97), but insulin is probably less effective than somatomedins in stimulating cartilage growth.

Thyroid Hormone

Adequate thyroid hormone is necessary for normal bone development. In hypothyroidism, skeletal growth and maturation are impaired while in hyperthyroid children, linear growth is accelerated (62, 93). In adult hyperthyroidism, decreased bone mass is associated with increased osteoclastic activity and a high rate of bone turnover (61). In cartilage, thyroid hormone can enhance growth by increasing somatomedin production or sensitivity (71, 72, 103). The molecular mechanism by which thyroid hormone affects skeletal development is unclear. In bone organ culture, there is little evidence for an important effect of thyroid hormone on osteoblastic collagen synthesis. Thyroid hormone directly increases osteoclastic bone resorption in vitro, which could be responsible for enhanced bone turnover and remodeling (63).

Glucocorticoids

In many tissues including bone, glucocorticoids are the physiologic inhibitors of growth (26, 56). The effects of glucocorticoids vary with the species and age of the animal studied, and cyclic variations in bone growth may be related to changes in glucocorticoid secretion (107). In vitro, bones incubated for prolonged periods at physiologic concentrations of cortisol show decreased DNA, RNA and collagen as well as noncollagen protein synthesis (26). Glucocorticoids also decrease sulfate incorporation into cartilage (102). Morphologic studies indicate that the major mechanism for growth arrest is the inhibition of proliferation of precursor cells rather than the inhibition of preexisting osteoblasts (86). A similar effect may be responsible for the inhibition of bone resorption by glucocorticoids (84, 110). Glucocorticoids may also limit growth by inhibiting intestinal absorption of calcium (33).

In short-term bone organ culture, there is a paradoxical increase in collagen synthesis by glucocorticoids (26). This may represent a permissive effect since glucocorticoids enhance the stimulation of collagen synthesis by insulin, somatomedins (77), and a bone-derived growth factor (E. Canalis, W. Peck, L. Raisz, unpublished observation). Glucocorticoids may also affect the responsiveness of bone cells to calcium regulating hormones. For example, in vitro glucocorticoids enhance the change in adenyl cyclase activity (19, 32, 64) and hyaluronic acid synthesis (109) in response to PTH and the binding of 1,25-dihydroxyvitamin D to its receptors in isolated bone cells (59). However, there is no evidence that glucocorticoids enhance the sensitivity of bone to the resorptive effects of PTH or vitamin D in vitro. Interpretation of in vivo experiments is complicated by the fact that glucocorticoids produce secondary hyperparathyroidism, probably by impairing intestinal calcium absorption.

Sex Hormones

Estrogen, testosterone, and adrenal androgens are associated with accelerated linear growth and epiphyseal closure at puberty. In addition, these hormones have a role in the continued increase in bone mass that occurs after puberty (27). Hypogonadal individuals often have low bone mass, which can be reversed by sex hormone therapy (3). Bone growth appears to be more dependent on androgen than estrogen (90). Estrogen may actually decrease bone growth by inhibiting somatomedin production (108). At menopause, withdrawal of estrogen is associated with an accelerated loss of bone mass; this has been attributed to small increases in bone resorption and a decrease in intestinal calcium absorption (40, 41). However, kinetic measurements indicate that bone formation rates are either maintained or increased at menopause (41, 88). The fact that resorption increases more than formation may represent a defect in the osteoblastic response in coupled bone remodeling. However, despite the close association between estrogen deficiency and post-menopausal changes in mineral balance (28), the mechanism by which estrogens affect bone metabolism remains obscure. For example, the presence of estrogen receptors in bone has not been demonstrated (18). There is no convincing evidence of direct effects of estrogen or androgen on bone collagen synthesis or bone resorption (12, 17). An indirect mechanism such as an effect of estrogens on vitamin D metabolism has been suggested (30). The effects of androgens on bone metabolism may be mediated by an anabolic effect on muscle. Systemically and locally, increased muscle mass is associated with increased bone mass (46). High concentrations of progesterone have a glucocorticoid-like effect to inhibit collagen and noncollagen protein synthesis in vitro (12). Progestins, like estrogens, may prevent accelerated loss of bone mass in post-menopausal women (55).

Somatomedins

The somatomedins are a family of pituitary-dependent growth factors. Most somatomedins have been isolated from serum (71, 72). Two growth factors derived from serum have been chemically characterized and named insulin-like growth factors I and II (IGF-I and IGF-II) (111). IGF-I may be identical to somatomedin-C (105, 111). These factors are closely related to multiplication stimulating activity (MSA), which has been partially purified from the culture medium of a transformed rat liver cell line (87). The somatomedins stimulate cell proliferation as well as matrix synthesis in cartilage (49) and are important in fetal as well as postnatal growth (92). In fetal rat calvaria in vitro, partially purified preparations of somatomedin-C and MSA (11, 13) and a purified preparation of IGF-I (E. Canalis, unpublished observations) stimulate collagen and noncollagen protein synthesis and thymidine incorporation into DNA. In the presence of physiologic concentrations of glucocorticoids, collagen synthesis is further enhanced but noncollagen protein and DNA synthesis are unaltered (13).

Other growth factors such as fibroblast growth factor (FGF) (16) and epidermal growth factor (EGF) (14) increase the proliferation of bone cells but decrease collagen synthesis in vitro. Pituitary derived growth factors may also stimulate chondrocyte replication (58). In vitro, EGF also stimulates bone resorption by a mechanism that may involve prostaglandin synthesis (101).

Local Factors

Osteoclast activating factor (OAF), produced by normal and neoplastic lymphocytes, is a potent stimulator of bone resorption and an inhibitor of collagen synthesis (81). OAF has not been purified to homogeneity. However, it is likely that both of its effects can be attributed to the same molecule since the dose-response relations for resorption and formation remain the same through several stages of purification in our laboratory (G. Mundy, G. Eilon, L. Raisz, unpublished observations). Although OAF has been implicated as a cause of pathologic bone loss in inflammation and hematologic neoplasms, there is no evidence that it has a physiologic role.

Prostaglandins are potent stimulators of bone resorption (50). PGE_2, which may play a role in pathologic resorption, can also inhibit bone collagen synthesis, although only at concentrations much higher than those that stimulate resorption (80). Prostaglandins could also play a physiologic role in bone remodelling. Bone can produce a number of prostaglandins including prostacyclin (PGI_2) (85). Since PGI_2 can stimulate bone resorption and is synthesized by vascular epithelium it might be involved in the association between vascular invasion and resorption at the cartilage growth plate and in Haversian canals. Prostaglandins are also released by cultures of isolated bone cells in response to physical stress (95). This is associated with increased cAMP content and increased incorporation of thymidine into DNA. Thus stress might cause proliferation of osteoblast precursor cells by enhancing prostaglandin release.

There is also evidence for a growth factor synthesized by bone, termed bone-derived growth factor (BDGF) (15). Both organ and cell cultures of fetal rat calvaria produce BDGF, which stimulates collagen and noncollagen protein synthesis and the incorporation of thymidine into DNA in bone organ cultures (68). This factor resembles a somatomedin since it is a heat and acid stable macromolecule and its effect on collagen synthesis is enhanced by cortisol (E. Canalis, W. Peck, L. Raisz, unpublished observations). A similar activity has been demonstrated in the media from avian long bone cultures (45). It was suggested that this may represent the coupling factor that initiates new bone formation at sites of prior resorption (44).

SUMMARY

The endocrine control of skeletal growth involves not only calcium regulating hormones but also several systemic hormones and other factors. Many direct effects of these agents on skeletal growth have been demonstrated in vitro. While these direct effects may also predominate in vivo, and certainly are important in helping us understand how skeletal growth is controlled, it is likely that skeletal growth in vivo is determined by the complex interactions of a concert of hormones that play both permissive and regulatory roles.

Additionally the effect of hormones may be modified by local or intrinsic responses of the skeleton or by changes in ion concentration. Phosphate may have a hormone-like function in the skeleton since high serum concentrations are associated with increased growth and low serum concentrations with impaired growth and mineralization (2, 5, 7, 37, 89). Because of these interactions, in vivo and in vitro studies on hormonal control of skeletal growth are often contradictory. A careful distinction between indirect and direct effects will help to interpret the information now available and to devise better studies in the future.

Literature Cited

1. Aloia, J. F., Petrak, Z., Ellis, K., Cohn, S. H. 1976. Body composition and skeletal metabolism following pituitary irradiation in acromegaly. *Am. J. Med.* 61:59–63
2. Asher, M. A., Sledge, C. B., Glimcher, M. J. 1979. The effect of inorganic orthophosphate on the rates of collagen formation and degradation in bone and cartilage in tissue culture. *J. Clin. Endocrinol. Metab.* 38:376–89
3. Baran, D. T., Berfeld, M. A., Teitelbaum, S. L., Avioli, L. V. 1978. Effect of testosterone therapy on bone formation in an osteoporotic hypogonadal male. *Calcif. Tiss. Res.* 26:103–6
4. Baylink, D., Stauffer, M., Wergedal, J., Rich, C. 1970. Formation, mineralization and resorption of bone in vitamin D-deficient rats. *J. Clin. Inves.* 49:1122–34
5. Baylink, D., Wergedal, J., Stauffer, M. 1971. Formation, mineralization and resorption of bone in hypophosphatemic rats. *J. Clin. Invest.* 50:2519–30
6. Bingham, P. J., Brazell, I. A., Owen, M. 1969. The effect of parathyroid extract on cellular activity and plasma calcium levels in vivo. *J. Endocrinol.* 45:387–400
7. Bingham, P. J., Riasz, L. G. 1974. Bone growth in organ culture: Effects of phosphate and other nutrients on bone and cartilage. *Calcif. Tiss. Res.* 14:31–48
8. Bordier, P., Rasmussen, H., Marie, P., Miravet, L., Gueris, J., Ryckwaert, A. 1978. Vitamin D metabolites and bone mineralization in man. *J. Clin. Endocrinol. Metab.* 46:284–93
9. Burger, E. H. 1976. Effects of parathyroid extract and calcitonin on calcification of hypertrophic cartilage in vitro. *Proc. Kon. Ned. Acad. Wet. C* 79:427–37
10. Canalis, E. M., Dietrich, J. W., Maina, D. M., Raisz, L. G. 1977. Hormonal control of bone collagen synthesis in vitro—effects of insulin and glucagon. *Endocrinology* 100:668–74
11. Canalis, E. M., Hintz, R. L., Dietrich, J. W., Maina, D. M., Raisz, L. G. 1977. Effect of somatomedin and growth hormone on bone collagen synthesis in vitro. *Metabolism* 26:1079–87
12. Canalis, E. M., Raisz, L. G. 1978. Effect of sex steroids on bone collagen synthesis in vitro. *Calcif. Tiss. Res.* 25:105–10
13. Canalis, E. M., Raisz, L. G. 1979. Effect of multiplication stimulating activity on DNA and protein synthesis in cultured fetal rat calvaria. *Calcif. Tissue. Int.* 29:33–39
14. Canalis, E. M., Raisz, L. G. 1979. Effect of epidermal growth factor on bone formation in vitro. *Endocrinology* 104:862–69
15. Canalis, E. M., Raisz, L. G. 1979. Conditioned medium from cultured fetal rat calvaria stimulates bone formation in vitro. *Clin. Res.* 27:591A (Abstr.)
16. Canalis, E. M., Raisz, L. G. 1980. Effect of fibroblast growth factor on cultured fetal rat calvaria. *Metabolism* 29:108–14
17. Caputo, C. B., Meadows, D., Raisz, L. G. 1976. Failure of estrogens and androgens to inhibit bone resorption in tissue culture. *Endocrinology* 98:1065–68
18. Chen, T. L., Feldman, D. 1978. Distinction between alpha-fetoprotein and intracellular estrogen receptors: Evidence against the presence of estradiol receptors in rat bone. *Endocrinology* 102:236–44
19. Chen, T. L., Feldman, D. 1979. Glucocorticoid receptors and actions in subpopulations of cultured rat bone cells. Mechanism of dexamethasone potentiation of parathyroid hormone-stimulated cyclic AMP production. *J. Clin. Invest.* 63:750–58
20. Corvol, M. T., Dumontier, M. F., Garabedian, M., Rappaport, R. 1978. Vitamin D and cartilage. II. Biological activity of 25-hydroxycholecalciferol and 24,25- and 1,25-dihydroxycholecalciferol on cultured growth plate chondrocytes. *Endocrinology* 102:1269–74
21. Costin, G., Kogut, M. D., Phillips, L. S., Daughaday, W. H. 1976. Craniopharyngioma: The role of insulin in promoting postoperative growth. *J. Clin. Endocrinol. Metab.* 42:370–79
22. Daughaday, W. H., Phillips, L. S., Mueller, M. C. 1976. The effects of insulin and growth hormone on the release of somatomedin by the isolated rat liver. *Endocrinology* 98:1214–19
23. DeLuca, H. F. 1979. The vitamin D system in the regulation of calcium and phosphorus metabolism. *Nutr. Rev.* 37:161–70
24. Dickson, I. R., Eyre, D. R., Kodicek, E. 1979. Influence of plasma calcium and vitamin D on bone collagen. Effects of lysine hydroxylation and crosslink formation. *Biochim. Biophys. Acta* 588:169–73
25. Dietrich, J. W., Canalis, E. M., Maina, D. M., Raisz, L. G. 1976. Hormonal

control of bone collagen synthesis in vitro: Effects of parathyroid hormone and calcitonin. *Endocrinology* 98:943–49

26. Dietrich, J. W., Canalis, E. M., Maina, D. M., Raisz, L. G. 1979. Effects of glucocorticoids on fetal rat bone collagen synthesis in vitro. *Endocrinology* 104:715–21

27. Ducharme, J.-R., Forest, M. G., DePeretti, E., Sempe, M., Collu, R., Bertrand, J. 1976. Plasma adrenal and gonadal sex steroids in human pubertal development. *J. Clin. Endocrinol. Metab.* 42:468–76

28. Frumar, A. M., Meldrum, D. R., Geola, F., Shamonki, I. M., Tataryn, I. V., Deftos, L. J., Judd, H. L. 1980. Relationship of fasting urinary calcium to circulating estrogen and body weight in postmenopausal women. *J. Clin. Endocrinol. Metab.* 50:70–75

29. Gaillard, P. J., Wassenaar, A. M., Van-Wijhe-Wheeler, M. D. 1977. Effects of parathyroid hormone and a synthetic fragment (PTH I-34) on bone in vitro. *Proc. Kon. Ned. Akad. Wet. C* 80:267–80

30. Gallagher, J. C., Riggs, B. L., Eisman, J., Hamstra, A., Arnaud, S. B., DeLuca, H. F. 1979. Intestinal calcium absorption and serum vitamin D metabolites in normal subjects and osteoporotic patients effect of age and dietary calcium. *J. Clin. Invest.* 64:729–36

31. Hahn, T. J., Downing, S. J., Phang, J. M. 1969. Insulin effects on amino acid transport in bone. *Biochim. Biophys. Acta* 184:675–77

32. Hahn, T. J., Halstead, L. R. 1979. Cortisol enhancement of PTH-stimulated cAMP accumulation in cultured fetal rat long bone rudiments. *Calcif. Tiss. Int.* 29:173–75

33. Hahn, T. J., Halstead, L. R., Teitelbaum, S. L., Hahn, B. H. 1979. Altered mineral metabolism in glucocorticoid-induced osteopenia: Effect of 25-hydroxyvitamin D administration. *J. Clin. Invest.* 64:655–65

34. Harris, W. H., Heaney, R. P. 1969. Skeletal renewal and metabolic bone disease. *N. Engl. J. Med.* 280:193–201

35. Harris, W. H., Heaney, R. P. 1969. Skeletal renewal and metabolic bone disease. *N. Engl. J. Med.* 280:253–59

36. Harris, W. H., Heaney, R. P. 1969. Skeletal renewal and metabolic bone disease. *N. Engl. J. Med.* 280:303–11

37. Harris, W. H., Heaney, R. P., Davis, L. A., Weinberg, E. H., Coutts, R. D., Schiller, A. L. 1976. Stimulation of bone formation in vivo by phosphate supplementation. *Calcif. Tiss. Res.* 22:85–98

38. Harris, W. H., Heaney, R. P., Jowsey, J., Cockin, J., Akins, C., Graham, J., Weinberg, E. H. 1972. Growth hormone: The effect on skeletal renewal in the adult dog. I. Morphometric studies. *Calcif. Tiss. Res.* 10:1–13

39. Harris, W. H., Heaney, R. P., Jowsey, J., Cockin, J., Akins, C., Graham, J., Weinberg, E. H. 1972. Growth hormone: The effect on skeletal renewal in the adult dog. II. Mineral kinetic studies. *Calcif. Tiss. Res.* 10:14–22

40. Heaney, R. P., Recker, R. R., Saville, P. D. 1978. Menopausal changes in calcium balance performance. *J. Lab. Clin. Med.* 92:953–63

41. Heaney, R. P., Recker, R. R., Saville, P. D. 1978. Menopausal changes in bone remodeling. *J. Lab. Clin. Med.* 92:964–70

42. Heath, H., Lambert, P. W., Service, F. J., Arnaud, S. B. 1979. Calcium homeostasis in diabetes mellitus. *J. Clin. Endocrinol. Metab.* 49:462–66

43. Howard, G. A., Baylink, D. J. 1980. Matrix formation and osteoid maturation in vitamin D-deficient rats made normocalcemic by dietary means. *Mineral Electrolyte Metab.* 3:44–50

44. Howard, G. A., Bottemiller, B. L., Baylink, D. J. 1980. Evidence for the coupling of bone formation to bone resorption in vitro. *Metab. Bone Dis.* 2:131–35

45. Howard, G. A., Drivdahl, R., Baylink, D. J. 1980. Isolation of a bone formation stimulant from bone matrix. Presented at Am. Soc. Bone and Mineral Research, 2nd, Washington DC

46. Jones, H. H., Priest, J. D., Hayes, W. C., Tichenor, C. C., Nagel, D. A. 1977. Humeral hypertrophy in response to exercise. *J. Bone Joint Surg.* 59:204–8

47. Jones, S. J., Boyde, A. 1976. Experimental study of changes in osteoblastic shape induced by calcitonin and parathyroid extract in an organ culture system. *Cell Tiss. Res.* 169:449–65

48. Juan, D., Liptak, P., Gray, T. K. 1976. Absorption of inorganic phosphate in human jejunum and its inhibition by salmon calcitonin. *J. Clin. Endocrinol. Metab.* 43:517–22

49. Kato, Y., Nasu, N., Takase, T., Daikuhara, Y., Suzuki, F. 1980. A serum-free medium supplemented with multiplication stimulating activity (MSA) supports both proliferation and differentiation of chondrocytes in primary culture. *Exp. Cell Res.* 125:167–74

50. Klein, D. C., Raisz, L. G. 1970. Prostaglandins: Stimulation of bone resorption in tissue culture. *Endocrinology* 86:1436–40

51. Kream, B. E., Jose, M., Yamada, S., DeLuca, H. F. 1977. A specific high-affinity binding macromolecule for 1,25-dihydroxyvitamin D_3 in bone. *Science* 197:1086–88

52. Kream, B. E., Rowe, D. W., Gworek, S. C., Raisz, L. G. 1979. Insulin and parathyroid hormone alter collagen synthesis and procollagen messenger RNA levels in fetal rat bone in vitro. *Calcif. Tiss. Res.* 28:148 (Abstr.)

53. Levin, M. E., Boisseau, V. C., Avioli, L. V. 1976. Effects of diabetes mellitus on bone mass in juvenile and adult-onset diabetes. *N. Engl. J. Med.* 294:241–45

54. Liberti, J. P., Miller, M. S. 1978. Somatomedin-like effects of biologically active bovine growth hormone fragments. *Endocrinology* 103:29–34

55. Lindsay, R., Hart, D. M., Aitken, J. M., Purdie, D. 1978. Effect of ovarian sex steroids on bone mineral status in oophorectomized rat and in human. *Postgrad. Med. J.* 54:50–58

56. Loeb, J. N. 1976. Corticosteroids and growth. *N. Engl. J. Med.* 295:547

57. Luben, R. A., Wong, G. L., Cohn, D. V. 1976. Biochemical characterization with parathormone and calcitonin of isolated bone cells—provisional identification of osteoclasts and osteoblasts. *Endocrinology* 99:526–34

58. Malemud, C. J., Sokoloff, L. 1978. The effect of chondrocyte growth factor on membrane transport by articular chondrocytes in monolayer culture. *Connect. Tiss. Res.* 6:1–9

59. Manolagas, S. C., Anderson, D. C., Lumb, G. A. 1979. Glucocorticoids regulate the concentration of 1,25-dihydroxycholecalciferol receptors in bone. *Nature* 277:314–15

60. McNair, P., Madsbad, S., Christiansen, C., Christensen, M. S., Faber, O. K., Binder, C., Transbal, I. 1979. Bone Loss in diabetes: Effects of metabolic state. *Diabetologia* 17:283–86

61. Melsen, F., Mosekilde, L. 1977. Morphometric and dynamic studies of bone changes in hyperthyroidism. *Acta Pathol. Microbiol. Scand.* 85A:141–50

62. Mundy, G. R., Raisz, L. G. 1979. Thyrotoxicosis and calcium metabolisms. *Mineral Electrolyte Metab.* 2:285–92

63. Mundy, G. R., Shapiro, J. L., Bandelin, J. G., Canalis, E. M., Raisz, L. G. 1976. Direct stimulation of bone resorption by thyroid hormones. *J. Clin. Invest.* 58:529–34

64. Ng, B., Hekkelman, J. W., Heersche, J. N. M. 1979. Effect of cortisol on the adenosine 3'5'-monophosphate response to parathyroid hormone of bone in vitro. *Endocrinology* 104:1130–35

65. Parfitt, A. M. 1976. The actions of parathyroid hormone on bone: Relation to bone remodeling and turnover, calcium homeostasis, and metabolic bone disease. I; Mechanisms of calcium transfer between blood and bone and their cellular basis. *Metabolism* 25:809–44

66. Parfitt, A. M. 1976. The actions of parathyroid hormone on bone: Relation to bone remodeling and turnover, calcium homeostasis, and metabolic bone disease. III. PTH and osteoblasts, the relationship between bone turnover, bone loss and the state of the bones in primary hyperparathyroidism. *Metabolism* 25:1033–69

67. Parsons, J. A. 1976. Parathyroid physiology and the skeleton. In *Biochemistry and Physiology of Bone,* ed. G. H. Bourne, 4:159–225. NY: Academic. 580 pp.

68. Peck, W. A., Burks, J. K., Kohler, G. 1979. Selective enhancement of bone cell proliferation by a factor derived from cultured bone cells. *Calcif. Tiss. Int.* 28:150

69. Peck, W. A., Messinger, K. 1970. Nucleoside and ribonucleic acid metabolism in isolated bone cells. Effects of insulin and cortisol in vitro. *J. Biol. Chem.* 245:2722–29

70. Phillips, L. C., Belosky, D. C., Reichard, L. A. 1979. Nutrition and somatomedin V. Action and measurement of somatomedin inhibitors in serum from diabetic rats. *Endocrinology* 104: 1513–18

71. Phillips, L. S., Vassilopoulou-Sellin, R. 1980. Somatomedins. *N. Engl. J. Med.* 302:371–80

72. Phillips, L. S., Vassilopoulou-Sellin, R. 1980. Somatomedins. *N. Engl. J. Med.* 302:438–46

73. Raisz, L. G. 1970. Bone formation and resorption in tissue culture: Effect of agents implicated in renal osteodystrophy. *Arch. Intern. Med.* 126:887–90

74. Raisz, L. G. 1977. Bone metabolism and calcium regulation. In *Metabolic Bone Disease,* ed. L. V. Avioli, S. M. Krane, 1:1–48. NY: Academic. 447 pp.

75. Raisz, L. G., Bingham, P. J. 1972. Effect of hormones on bone development. *Ann. Rev. Pharmacol.* 12:337–52

76. Raisz, L. G., Canalis, E. M., Dietrich, J. W., Kream, B. E. 1978. Hormonal regulation of bone formation. *Recent Prog. Horm. Res.* 34:335–36
77. Raisz, L. G., Dietrich, J. W., Canalis, E. M. 1976. Factors influencing bone formation in organ culture. *Isr. J. Med. Sci.* 12:108–14
78. Raisz, L. G., Kream, B. E., Smith, M. D., Simmons, H. A. 1980. Comparison of the effects of vitamin D metabolites on collagen synthesis and resorption of fetal rat bone in organ culture. *Calcif. Tiss. Int.* 32:135–38
79. Raisz, L. G., Lorenzo, J., Gworek, S., Kream, B. E., Rosenblatt, M. 1979. Comparison of the effects of a potent synthetic analog of bovine parathyroid hormone with native bPTH (1–84) and synthetic bPTH (1–34) on bone resorption and collagen synthesis. *Calcif. Tiss. Int.* 29:215–18
80. Raisz, L. G., Koolemans-Beynen, A. R. 1974. Inhibition of bone collagen synthesis of prostaglandin E_2 in organ culture. *Prostaglandins* 8:377–85
81. Raisz, L. G., Luben, R. A., Mundy, G. R., Dietrich, J. W., Horton, J. E., Trummel, C. L. 1975. Effect of osteoclast activating factor from human leukocytes on bone metabolism. *J. Clin. Invest.* 56:408–13
82. Raisz, L. G., Maina, D. M., Gworek, S. C., Dietrich, J. W., Canalis, E. M. 1978. Hormonal control of bone collagen synthesis in vitro. Inhibitory effects of 1-hydroxylated vitamin D metabolites. *Endocrinology* 102:731–35
83. Raisz, L. G., Trummel, C. L., Holick, M. F., DeLuca, H. F. 1972. 1,25-dihydroxycholecalciferol: A potent stimulator of bone resorption in tissue culture. *Science* 175:768–69
84. Raisz, L. G., Trummel, C. L., Wener, J. A., Simmons, H. 1972. Effect of glucocorticoids on bone resorption in tissue culture. *Endocrinology* 90:961–67
85. Raisz, L. G., Vanderhoek, J. Y., Simmons, H. A., Kream, B. E., Nicolaou, K. C. 1979. Prostaglandin synthesis by fetal rat bone in vitro: Evidence for a role of prostacyclin. *Prostaglandins* 17:904–14
86. Rath, N. C., Reddi, A. H. 1979. Influence of adrenalectomy and dexamethasone on matrix-induced endochondral bone differentiation. *Endocrinology* 104:1698–1704
87. Rechler, M. M., Eisben, H. J., Higa, O. Z., Nissley, S. P., Moses, A. C., Schilling, E. E., Fennoy, I., Bruni, C. B., Phillips, L. S., Baird, K. L. 1979. Char-

acterization of a somatomedin (insulin-like growth factor) synthesized by fetal rat liver organ culture. *J. Biol. Chem.* 254:7942–950
88. Reeve, J., Hesp, R., Wooton, R. 1976. A new tracer method for the calculation of rates of bone formation and breakdown in osteoporosis and other generalized skeletal disorders. *Calcif. Tiss. Res.* 22:191–206
89. Rowe, J. C., Wood, D. H., Rowe, D. W., Raisz, L. G. 1979. Nutritional hypophosphatemic rickets in a premature infancy fed breastmilk. *N. Engl. J. Med.* 300:293–96
90. Rudman, D., Goldsmith, M., Kutner, M., Blackston, D. 1980. Effect of growth hormone and oxandrolone singly and together on growth rate in girls with X chromosome abnormalities. *J. Pediatr.* 96:132–35
91. Santiago, J. V., McAlister, W. H., Ratzan, S. K., Bussman, Y., Haymond, M. W., Shackelford, G., Weldon, V. V. 1977. Decreased cortical thickness and osteopenia in children with diabetes mellitus. *J. Clin. Endocrinol. Metab.* 45:845–48
92. Sara, V. R., Hall, K., Wetterberg, L. 1980. The role of somatomedins in fetal growth. Presented at Int. Congr. Endocrinol. 6th, Melbourne
93. Schlesinger, S., MacGillivray, M. H., Munschauer, R. W. 1973. Acceleration of growth and bone maturation in childhood thyrotoxicosis. *J. Pediatr.* 83:233–36
94. Schneider, L. E., Schedl, H. P., McGain, T., Haussler, M. R. 1977. Experimental diabetes reduces circulating 1,25-dihydroxyvitamin D in the rat. *Science* 196:1452–54
95. Somjen, D., Binderman, I., Berger, E., Harell, A. 1980. Bone remodeling induced by physical stress in prostaglandin E_2 mediated. *Biochim. Biophys. Acta* 627:91–100
96. Stern, P. H., Raisz, L. G. 1979. Organ culture of bone. In *Skeletal Research: an Experimental Approach,* ed. D. J. Simmons, A. S. Kunin, pp. 22–59. NY: Academic. 612 pp.
97. Stuart, C. A., Furlanetto, R. W., Lebovitz, H. E. 1979. Insulin receptor of embryonic chicken cartilage. *Endocrinology* 105:1293–1302
98. Suzuki, F. 1979. Induction by parathyroid hormone of ornithine decarboxylase in rabbit costal chondrocytes in culture. *J. Biochem.* 85:311–14
99. Talmage, R. V., Doppelt, S. H., Fondren, F. B. 1976. An interpretation of

acute changes in plasma ^{45}Ca following parathyroid hormone administration to thyroparathyroidectomized rats. *Calcif. Tiss. Res.* 22:117–28

100. Tam, C. S., Wilson, D. R., Harrison, J. E. 1980. Effect of parathyroid extract on bone apposition and the interaction between parathyroid hormone and vitamin D. *Mineral & Electrolyte Metab.* 3:74–80

101. Tashjian, A. H., Levine, L. 1978. Epidermal growth factor stimulates prostaglandin production and bone resorption in cultured mouse calvaria. *Biochem. Biophys. Res. Commun.* 85:966–75

102. Tessler, R. H., Salmon, W. D. Jr. 1975. Glucocorticoid inhibition of sulfate incorporation by cartilage of normal rats. *Endocrinology* 96:898–902

103. Thorngren, K.-G., Hansson, L. I. 1977. Stimulation of longitudinal bone growth by hypophyseal hormones in hypophysectomized rats. *Acta Endocrinol.* 84:485–96

104. Vaughan, J. 1975. *The Physiology of Bone*, pp. 1–27 Oxford: Clarendon Press. 306 pp.

105. Van Wyk, J. J., Svoboda, M. E., Underwood, L. E. 1980. Evidence from radioligand assays that somatomedin-C and insulin-like growth factor I are similar to each other and different from other somatomedins. *J. Clin. Endocrinol. Metab.* 50:206–8

106. Wener, J. A., Gorton, S. J., Raisz, L. G. 1972. Escape from inhibition of resorption in cultures of fetal bone treated with calcitonin and parathyroid hormone. *Endocrinology* 752–59

107. Whitson, S. W., Dawson, L. R., Jee, W. S. S. 1978. Tetracycline study of cyclic longitudinal bone growth in female rat. *Endocrinology* 103:2006–10

108. Wiedemann, E., Schwartz, E., Frantz, A. G. 1976. Acute and chronic estrogen effects upon serum somatomedin activity, growth hormone and prolactin in man. *J. Clin. Endocrinol. Metab.* 42:942–52

109. Wong, G. L. 1979. Basal activities and hormone responsiveness of osteoclast-like and osteoblast-like bone cells are regulated by glucocorticoids. *J. Biol. Chem.* 254:6337–40

110. Yasumura, S., Ellis, K. J., Fairchild, E., Brook, D., Cohn, S. H. 1976. Effect of graded doses of cortisol on total body calcium in rats. *Am. J. Physiol.* 231:1760–63

111. Zapf, J., Rinderknecht, E., Humbel, R. E., Froesch, E. R. 1978. Nonsuppressible insulin-like activity (NSILA) from human serum: Recent accomplishments and their physiologic implications. *Metabolism* 27:1803–28

Ann. Rev. Physiol. 1981. 43:239–50

RECEPTOR-MEDIATED ENDOCYTOSIS OF HORMONES IN CULTURED CELLS

♦1308

Ira H. Pastan and Mark C. Willingham

Laboratory of Molecular Biology, National Cancer Institute, N.I.H., Bethesda, Maryland 20205

Introduction

This review focuses on how cultured fibroblastic cells bind and internalize hormones and other molecules that bind to and enter cells via saturable highly specific receptors. Although fibroblasts have not been widely studied by endocrinologists, we believe these studies are relevant to cells and tissues of classical endocrinological interest. Cultured cells have several advantages over specialized endocrine cells or tissues. They can be obtained from single cell clones so that their behavior and appearance are uniform. For microscopic studies, very flat cells, such as fibroblasts grown in culture, are of great advantage because their intracellular organelles remain in one focal plane and can be observed continuously for one hour or longer.

Substances that bind to the surface of cultured cells rapidly undergo endocytosis. Various types of substances are handled quite differently. Hormones and other molecules that bind to a limited number of highly specific receptors enter the cell by a process termed receptor-mediated endocytosis (6, 15, 27, 36). Molecules that enter cultured cells via this pathway include insulin, epidermal growth factor (EGF), triiodothyronine (T_3), $\alpha_2$macroglobulin (α_2M), low density lipoprotein (LDL), lysosomal enzymes, and some toxins.

Endocytosis

The term endocytosis is used to describe how cells internalize molecules. What is not widely appreciated is that cells have at least three different mechanisms to internalize molecules (Figure 1). Macropinocytosis occurs when a ruffle falls back onto the cell surface trapping medium and injecting it into the cell interior. This process has been recorded on video tape by video intensification microscopy (VIM) (43). The newly formed *mac-*

ropinosomes, which range in size from 0.5–3 μm, are rapidly attacked by phase-dense lysosomes and torn into small pieces in a process termed "piranhalysis" (43). The small vesicles thus formed fuse with the lysosomes to which they are attached. *Micropinosomes* are structures about 800Å in diameter. They are derived from caveolae, small indentations in the cell surface, and are short-lived because they fuse with lysosomes within a few minutes of entry. A micropinosome fusing with a lysosome one minute after entry is shown in Figure 2A. Both macro- and micropinocytosis carry out nonconcentrative forms of endocytosis in which trapped fluid contents or materials adsorbed to the cell surface are internalized, transferred to lysosomes, and rapidly degraded. In fibroblasts, lectins such as concanavalin A (con A) and divalent antibodies to membrane proteins are internalized by micropinocytosis (Figure 2A,B). These multivalent ligands are cross-linked and form "patches" or aggregates on the outside of the plasma membrane. At high concentrations, con A covers the entire cell surface, including the surfaces of coated pits and caveolae (Figure 2B) (38, 40). At lower concentrations con A forms "patches." Similar patches are formed when antibodies to a histocompatability antigen (Figure 2D) or antibodies that cross-link dextran stearate (a lipid probe) (Figure 2C) are applied to a cell (J. Schlessinger, M. Willingham, P. Henkart, and I. Pastan, unpublished data). These "patches" do *not* form in the bristle-coated regions of the membrane. Their internalization mainly occurs through macro- or micropinocytosis. These types of endocytosis are nonspecific. Hormones and similar ligands are internalized in quite another manner.

Internalization of Hormones

Hormones are internalized by a concentrative mechanism that employs a set of specialized organelles. Initially the hormones bind to receptors

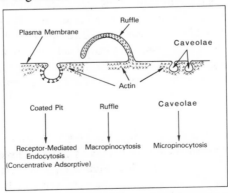

Figure 1 The morphologic structures involved in endocytic mechanisms on the surface of cultured cells.

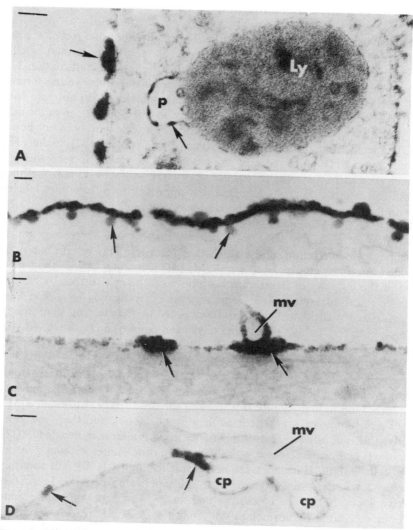

Figure 2 The binding and internalization of nonhormonal surface ligands in cultured fibro-blasts. Concanavalin A (con A), a plant lectin, binds to the entire plasma membrane and is internalized by micropinocytosis (40). In (A), a micropinosome (p) has entered the cell carrying peroxidase-labeled con A (arrows) and within one minute at 37°C has fused with a lysosome (Ly). Con A added to the cell at 4°C and then fixed, shows diffuse labeling of the cell surface (B) including surface micropinosomal invaginations (arrows). In (C), an artificial derivative of dextran coupled to a stearate moiety (which binds to the membrane as a lipid marker) and an antigenic DNP moiety, has been cross-linked by antibodies to DNP, and these patches (arrows) are unrelated to any specialized region of the membrane (mv = microvillus). In (D), an integral membrane protein, H2-D, has been cross-linked by specific antibodies. These surface patches of antibody (arrows) are absent in the region of coated pits (cp) (J. Schlessinger, P. Henkart, M. Willingham, and I. Pastan, unpublished data) (Mags: A = X108,000; B = X63,000; C = X55,000; D = X94,000; bars = 0.1 μ).

diffusely distributed on the cell surface; then the hormone-receptor complexes cluster in specialized structures in the membrane termed bristle-coated pits (Figure 1) (40). The bristle coat is the protein clathrin (22, 33). Next the ligands are transferred to a specialized intracellular vesicle termed a "receptosome" (42). Receptosomes, unlike pinosomes, do not fuse with lysosomes; instead, they carry their contents to the Golgi region of the cell.

Cells have specific high-affinity receptors for a wide variety of hormones (21); specific receptors also exist for some plasma proteins (32), toxins (31), and viruses (11). Until recently, the binding of hormones to receptors has been studied using isotopic methods (21). Here we focus on new methods and the insights they provide. One new approach uses hormones labeled with fluorescent compounds (rhodamine or fluorescein) (9, 13, 17, 23, 25, 26, 34, 35, 39). Binding of labeled hormones to living cells can be observed with an ultrasensitive television camera attached to a fluorescent microscope, a video monitor, and a video tape recorder. This system is termed video intensification microscopy (VIM) (41). Another new method measures the mobility of fluorescent hormones on the cell surface by fluorescence photo-bleaching (4). Hormones and other ligands have also been derivatized with a label that can be detected at the electron microscopic level; both ferritin and peroxidase have been employed (1, 19, 26, 40, 42). Finally, radioautography of ^{125}I-labeled molecules has been carried out (5, 7, 8, 14, 16).

Studies in our laboratory have focused on four molecules: $\alpha_2$macroglobulin, insulin, epidermal growth factor, and triiodothyronine. All four substances bind to high-affinity receptors on the cell surface. Although α_2M is not a hormone, cells handle it as they do hormones, and there are many advantages of using α_2M over hormones. α_2M is a large molecule (780,000 mol wt) and can be labeled with 20 or more rhodamines without affecting its cell binding. Hormones are much smaller and it is difficult to attach many fluorescent molecules to them without losing activity. Fibroblasts have about 200,000 receptors per cell for α_2M whereas they have many fewer receptors for hormones. Antibodies to α_2M are readily produced. These antibodies can locate α_2M in fixed cells both at the light and electron microscopic level. With small hormones the cell binding site and the antibody binding site may overlap and interfere with the detection of cell bound hormone (21). For these reasons, we have used α_2M as our prototype molecule. With minor exceptions detailed below, our results and those of others indicate that fibroblastic cells handle insulin, EGF, α_2M, triiodothryonine, and LDL in a similar manner.

Fluorescence Studies

When fibroblasts are incubated with rhodamine-labeled ligands such as α_2M, insulin, EGF, or T_3 at 1°C and viewed using VIM, a diffuse pattern of fluorescence is observed (Figure 3) (25, 27, 35), suggesting that the ligand is on the cell surface. At this stage it can be removed by trypsin (35).

If cells are then placed at 23°C for 10–15 min or at 37°C for 5 min, punctate accumulations of fluorescence are observed and the diffuse fluorescence disappears (27) because some of the ligand has been internalized in vesicles. Upon longer incubation at 37°C the surface fluorescence disappears entirely and punctate spots appear in the cytoplasm (25, 27, 32, 35). These spots are vesicles containing fluorescent ligand; these vesicles move about in the cytoplasm by saltatory motion (35, 41). These saltating vesicles are *not* lysosomes! Lysosomes are phase-dense structures and they do not contain fluorescence at this time (Figure 4). We have named these unique vesicles "receptosomes" to indicate that they contain materials that enter the cell by receptor-mediated endocytosis (42). By phase-contrast microscopy, receptosomes are neutral and difficult to distinguish from the cytoplasm of the cell. This is in contrast to phase-dense lysosomes or phase-lucent macropinosomes, which are easily seen (Figure 4). After 1–2 hr the ligands accumulate in the Golgi or GERL region (29, 42) close to the nucleus. No fluorescence has been detected within the nucleus (but even if small amounts of ligand were in the nucleus, they could not be detected). Certainly, the bulk of the ligand does not enter the nucleus. After 2–4 hr, the residual ligand is found in phase-dense lysosomes (Figure 4). With $\alpha_2 M$, which is highly fluorescent and less rapidly degraded than insulin or EGF, accumulation in lysosomes is easily detected. With the other ligands the fluorescent signal is very weak by this time.

We have made some rough estimates of the number of fluorescent molecules that can be detected by VIM. If the molecules are concentrated in a small vesicle, it takes about 50–100 rhodamines (or 3–5 rhodamine-labeled

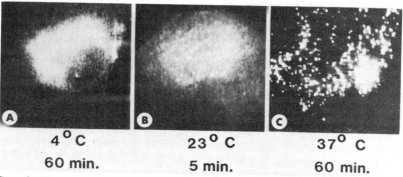

| 4°C | 23°C | 37°C |
| 60 min. | 5 min. | 60 min. |

Figure 3 Fluorescence images of cells incubated with rhodamine-labeled alpha₂-macroglobulin under various conditions. Cultured fibroblasts were incubated with rhodamine-labeled $\alpha_2 M$ under the conditions of time and temperature shown [reprinted with permission from (27)].

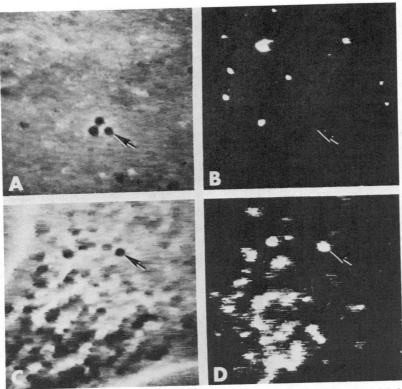

Figure 4   Fluorescence and phase-contrast images of cells incubated with rhodamine-labeled
alpha₂-macroglobulin at early and late times. Swiss 3T3 fibroblasts were incubated with
rhodamine-labeled α_2M and then viewed either a few minutes later (A,B) or 18 hr later (C,D)
by both phase-contrast and fluorescence microscopy. Note the absence of label in (B) in the
phase-dark lysosome (arrow) seen in (A), but the presence of label at later times in a lysosome
(D) seen as a phase-dark structure in (C) [reprinted by permission from (42)].

α_2M molecules) to be detected. However, when the fluorescent ligand is
diffusely distributed, many more molecules are required to give a detectable
signal (unpublished data).

Double Labeling Studies

To investigate whether ligands enter the cell in the same or different vesicles, cells were exposed simultaneously to rhodamine-insulin (or EGF or
T_3) and fluorescein-α_2M. In all cases, the fluorescently labeled vesicles contained both rhodamine (insulin) and fluorescein (α_2M), indicating that
ligands applied to a cell together entered the cell together (9, 25). However,
when the same or different ligands entered sequentially, they became se-
questered in different populations of vesicles (25).

Surface binding

To determine the initial site of ligand binding and, therefore, the distribution of unoccupied receptors, cells were fixed prior to the binding of α_2M or LDL and the location of these ligands determined by electron microscopy (40). With α_2M all of the α_2M receptors are diffusely distributed. However, with LDL the picture is different. Some LDL receptors appear to be diffusely distributed prior to LDL binding, whereas others are pre-clustered in coated pits (1, 2, 3). If cells are not fixed, but instead binding is performed at 1–4°C, then a significant amount of α_2M or LDL is found in coated pits after one hour (Figure 5a) (1, 40, 42). This indicates that clustering into coated pits occurs at 4°C.

To determine the mobility of receptor-ligand complexes, α_2M, insulin, EGF, or T_3, each labeled with rhodamine, were bound to cells for 15 min at 1°C, and then the cells were placed at 23°C. The mobility of the unclustered fluorescent receptor ligand complexes was measured (4, 34). These complexes diffuse in the membrane at about the same rate as other membrane proteins (3–9 $\times$ 10^{-10} cm^2 sec^{-1}) (34). We presume that the unoccupied receptors also move at this speed but do not accumulate or get trapped in coated pits. It seems likely that the ligand changes the receptor in some manner that causes the complex to accumulate in coated pits.

Internalization

Fluorescent studies show that after 5 min at 37°C, α_2M begins to enter the cell. To study this at the electron microscopic level α_2M was bound to cells at 1°C and then peroxidase-labeled antibody to α_2M was added and the temperature raised to 37°C (42). Samples were examined at various times by electron microscopy. By 5 min all the α_2M is within the cell in an uncoated vesicle of distinctive structure (Figure 5). This vesicle is a receptosome, and its characteristic features include an uncoated membrane with proteinaceous density attached to its inner surface, tubular protrusions, and a region of low density in the center of these vesicles. Receptosomes are approximately 2000–4000 Å in diameter (Figure 5B). Cytochemical labeling indicates that receptosomes are the endocytic derivatives of coated pits (42). Morphologic criteria distinguish them from other organelles.

A variety of intracellular vesicles have been demonstrated that roughly approximate the morphologic characteristics of receptosomes. These vesicles have been called multivesicular bodies (7, 16, 19), vacuoles (5, 12, 20, 37), acid phosphatase negative vesicles (5), or, in some cases, lysosomal elements (1, 3, 5, 7, 19). From our own studies, we have found that the receptosomal vesicles in cultured fibroblasts are, at least initially, acid phos-

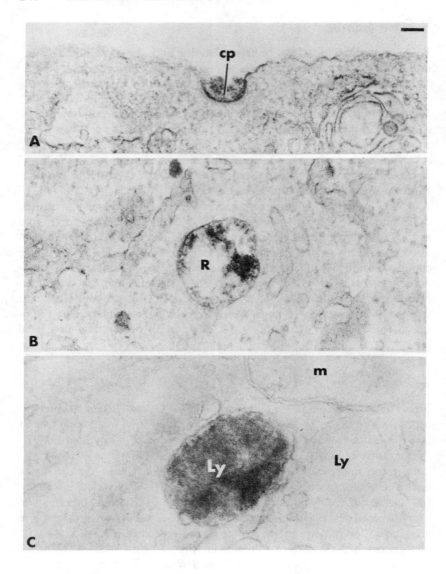

Figure 5   Electron microscopic cytochemical labeling of alpha$_2$-macroglobulin. Using peroxidase-labeled antibodies (40), α_2M was labeled at 4°C on the surface of a Swiss 3T3 fibroblast.
Note the clustering of α_2M in a coated pit (cp) in (A). After warming to 37°C for 15 min (B),
the labeled α_2M was internalized into an intracellular vesicle, the receptosome (R). By 60 min,
all of the labeled α_2M appeared in lysosomes (Ly) (C), although most of the lysosomes in the
cell (Ly, black letters) were unlabeled (m = mitochondrion) (Mags = X90,000; bar = 0.1).

phatase negative (unpublished data) and do not fuse with mature lysosomes (40, 42).

By determining the intracellular location of α_2M at various times after entry, we observe that the receptosomal vesicle increases in size over the initial 20 min after α_2M entry. This may occur by fusion with small tubular elements that are often closely associated with receptosomes. Images of receptosomes apparently fusing with tubular elements are often observed (42).

After about 30 min, α_2M begins to be found in small lysosomes in the region of the Golgi or GERL (29) (Figure 5C). In some manner, the receptosome has transferred its contents to these small, newly formed lysosomes (42, 44). For α_2M and hormones, this transfer may initiate degradation of the ligand. However, we believe it likely that the high-uptake forms of lysosomal enzymes (28) enter the cell via receptosomes and then are transferred to lysosomes by this same pathway without significant degradation. A diagram summarizing this pathway of internalization is shown in Figure 6.

It has been suggested that LDL and other ligands enter cells by a mechanism in which coated pits pinch off to form coated vesicles that subsequently lose their coats or transfer their contents directly to lysosomes (1, 2, 16). Our studies with α_2M do not support this model. Preliminary studies show that at 4°C all of these coated structures at the cell surface are in communication with the outside. Whether this is also the case at 37°C requires further study.

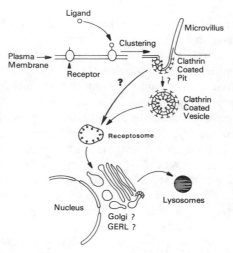

Figure 6 A diagrammatic summary of a proposed scheme of receptor-mediated endocytosis in cultured fibroblasts.

Degradation Rates and Cellular Entry

Studies with iodinated derivates of EGF, LDL, and insulin, and with rhodamine-labeled α_2M show that intracellular degradation of these molecules occurs. It is likely that degradation occurs in lysosomes (2, 6, 15, 19). Agents such as chloroquine that inhibit lysosomal function interfere with degradation. It is important to note that degradation does not begin directly upon cellular entry, but rather there is a lag period of 20–60 min before degradation ensues (2, 6, 15, 19). This lag period is consistent with the time it takes for ligands to traverse the receptosome system before entry into lysosomes.

Inhibition of Cellular Entry

Neufeld and coworkers (28) observed that the uptake of lysosomal enzymes was inhibited by some primary amines. We subsequently showed that methylamine, dansylcadaverine, and other amines inhibited the uptake of α_2M, insulin, and triiodothyronine. In the case of α_2M, electron microscopic studies showed that methylamine acted by preventing the clustering of the α_2M-receptor complex in coated pits (26). Our co-worker, Peter Davies, suggested that some step in the internalization process may require the intracellular enzyme transglutaminase to be active, because transglutaminase was a major cell enzyme known to be inhibited by various primary amines (13). Transglutaminase catalyzes the cross-linking of proteins by forming an isopeptide bond between a lysine residue of one protein and a glutamine residue of another.

To test this hypothesis, we studied the effect of a wide variety of inhibitors of transglutaminase on inhibiting the clustering and internalization of α_2M. These included various simple amines, short peptides containing lysine, analogs of glutamine, and affinity labels of transglutaminase (13). Since the cells employed were impermeable to many of the compounds tested, it was sometimes necessary to permeabilize the cells with DMSO to demonstrate the ability of these compounds to inhibit clustering and internalization of α_2M (13). The results of these studies are consistent with a role for transglutaminase in internalization, but its precise role is unclear. One possibility is that the interaction of receptor-ligand complexes in the coated pit activates intracellular transglutaminase and cross-links the receptor (presumed to be a trans-membrane protein) to some intracellular protein. This process could result in stabilization of the ligand-receptor complexes in coated pits.

Three inhibitors of transglutaminase that have been extensively used are methylamine, dansylcadaverine, and bacitracin. These substances are effective inhibitors of the internalization of α_2M, insulin (13, 26), and triiodothyronine (9). However, our results with EGF are somewhat different. We find that it requires a high concentration of dansylcadaverine (500 μM) to inhibit EGF internalization (18); further, bacitracin and methylamine are ineffective (19a). We previously reported that bacitracin and methylamine inhibit the internalization of a preparation of rhodamine-labeled EGF obtained from a commercial source (24, 26). H. Haigler (unpublished data) has now shown that this preparation of EGF is heavily contaminated with other peptides found in crude preparations of EGF. The nature of these peptides is under investigation. Radioautography has also been used to detect the binding and internalization of EGF and insulin. These studies showed that hormones bind to the plasma membrane and within a short time are internalized into intracellular vesicles, eventually being delivered to the lysosomal system (5, 7, 8, 14, 16).

Physiological Significance of Internalization

The ability of cells to rapidly concentrate and internalize ligands via coated pits enables cells to rapidly clear hormones from their surface. Thus, any direct surface-related actions (10) are limited in duration. If cells were to respond only to surface-bound hormone, its action would be rapidly terminated. On the other hand, if the hormone-receptor complexes remain intact within the receptosome, certain aspects of hormone action could continue, such as the generation of cyclic AMP in discrete intracellular locations. Melanocyte stimulating hormone (MSH), which activates the adenylate cyclase of melonoma cells, has been shown to enter melanoma cells using fluorescein-labeled MSH (39). It would be of interest to know if its action on adenylate cyclase continues after entry.

It seems unlikely that hormone destruction would be the primary goal of internalization. In some cases receptosomes may allow receptors to recycle to the surface. In other cases they may direct ligands or receptors to specialized intracellular sites prior to degradation. To date, we have not detected significant transfer of ligand into the nucleus, but such reactions could occur. Nuclear receptors for triiodothyronine have been widely studied (30), and there are reports of nuclear receptors for peptide hormones (14).

In this paper, we have focused our discussion on hormones, α_2M, LDL, and lysosomal enzymes. However, other substances enter fibroblasts by receptor-mediated endocytosis. These include toxins and viruses. There has been no clear identification of the structures involved in the internalization of toxins or lysosomal enzymes. Certain viruses, such as Semliki Forest virus, appear to cluster in coated pits prior to entry (20). Furthermore, viral particles are found early after infection in structures that resemble receptosomes (12, 20, 37).

Literature Cited

1. Anderson, R. G. W., Goldstein, J. L., Brown, M. S. 1976. *Proc. Natl. Acad. Sci. USA* 73:2434–38
2. Anderson, R. G. W., Goldstein, J. L., Brown, M. S. 1977. *Nature* 270:695–99
3. Anderson, R. G. W., Vasile, E., Mello, R. J., Brown, M. S., Goldstein, J. L. 1978. *Cell* 15:919–33
4. Axelrod, D., Koppel, D. E., Schlessinger, J., Elson, E. L., Webb, W. W. 1976. *Biophys. J.* 16:1055–69
5. Bergeron, J. J. M., Sikstrom, R., Hand, A. R., Posner, B. I. 1979. *J. Cell Biol.* 80:427–43
6. Brown, M. S., Goldstein, J. L. 1979. *Proc. Natl. Acad. Sci. USA* 76:3330–37
7. Carpentier, J. L., Gorden, P., Barazzone, P., Freychet, P., LeCam, A., Orci, L. 1979. *Proc. Natl. Acad. Sci. USA* 76:2803–7
8. Carpentier, J. L., Gorden, P., Freychet, P., LeCam, A., Orci, L. 1979. *J. Clin. Invest.* 63:1249–61
9. Cheng, S. Y., Maxfield, F. R., Robbins, J., Willingham, M. C., Pastan, I. 1980. *Proc. Natl. Acad. Sci. USA* 77:3425–29
10. Chinkers, M., McKanna, J. A., Cohen, S. 1979. *J. Cell Biol.* 83:260–65
11. Dales, S. 1973. *Bacteriol. Rev.* 37:103–35
12. Dales, S., Hanafusa, H. 1972. *Virology* 50:440–58
13. Davies, P. J. A., Davies, D. R., Levitzki, A., Maxfield, F. R., Milhaud, P., Willingham, M. C., Pastan, I. H. 1980. *Nature* 283:162–66
14. Goldfine, I. D., Smith, G. J., Wong, K. Y., Jones, A. L. 1977. *Proc. Natl. Acad. Sci. USA* 74:1368–72
15. Goldstein, J. L., Anderson, R. G. W., Brown, M. S. 1979. *Nature* 279:679–85
16. Gorden, P., Carpentier, J. L., Cohen, S., Orci, L. 1978. *Proc. Natl. Acad. Sci. USA* 75:5025–29
17. Haigler, H. T., Ash, J. F., Singer, S. J., Cohen, S. 1978. *Proc. Natl. Acad. Sci. USA* 75:3317–21
18. Haigler, H. T., Maxfield, F. R., Willingham, M. C., Pastan, I. 1980. *J. Biol. Chem.* 255:1239–41
19. Haigler, H. T., McKanna, J. A., Cohen, S. 1979. *J. Cell Biol.* 81:382–95
19a. Haigler, H. T., Willingham, M. C., Pastan, I. 1980. *Biochem. Biophys. Res. Commun.* 94:630–37
20. Helenius, A., Kartenbeck, J., Simons, K., Fries, E. 1980. *J. Cell Biol.* 84:404–20
21. Kahn, C. R. 1976. *J. Cell Biol.* 70:261–86
22. Keen, J. H., Willingham, M. C., Pastan, I. H. 1979. *Cell* 16:303–12

23. LeCam, A., Maxfield, F., Willingham, M., Pastan, I. 1979. *Biochem. Biophys. Res. Commun.* 88:873–81
24. Maxfield, F. R., Davies, P. J. A., Klempner, L., Willingham, M. C., Pastan, I. 1979. *Proc. Natl. Acad. Sci. USA* 76:5731–35
25. Maxfield, F. R., Schlessinger, J., Shechter, Y., Pastan, I., Willingham, M. C. 1978. *Cell* 14:805–10
26. Maxfield, F. R., Willingham, M. C., Davies, P. J. A., Pastan, I. 1979. *Nature* 277:661–63
27. Maxfield, F. R., Willingham, M. C., Schlessinger, J., Davies, P. J. A., Pastan, I. 1979. In *Hormones and Cell Culture, Cold Spring Harbor Conf. Cell Prolif.* 6:159–66. NY: Cold Spring Harbor Laboratory
28. Neufeld, E. F., Sando, G. N., Garvin, A. J., Rome, L. H. 1977. *J. Supramol. Struct.* 6:95–100
29. Novikoff, A. B., Novikoff, P. M. 1977. *Histochem. J.* 9:525–51
30. Oppenheimer, J. H. 1979. *Science* 203:971–79
31. Pappenheimer, A. M. 1977. *Ann. Rev. Biochem.* 46:69–94
32. Pastan, I., Willingham, M., Anderson, W., Gallo, M. 1977. *Cell* 12:609–17
33. Pearse, B. M. F. 1976. *Proc. Natl. Acad. Sci. USA* 73:1255–59
34. Schlessinger, J., Shechter, Y., Cuatrecasas, P., Willingham, M. C., Pastan, I. 1978. *Proc. Natl. Acad. Sci. USA* 75:5353–57
35. Schlessinger, J., Shechter, Y., Willingham, M. C., Pastan, I. 1978. *Proc. Natl. Acad. Sci. USA* 75:2659–63
36. Silverstein, S. C., Steinman, R. M., Cohn, Z. A. 1977. *Ann. Rev. Biochem.* 46:669–722
37. Simpson, R. W., Hauser, R. E., Dales, S. 1969. *Virology* 37:285–90
38. Storrie, B. 1979. *Exp. Cell Res.* 118:135–41
39. Varga, J. M., Moellmann, G., Fritsch, P., Grodawska, E., Lerner, A. B. 1976. *Proc. Natl. Acad. Sci. USA* 73:559–62
40. Willingham, M. C., Maxfield, F. R., Pastan, I. H. 1979. *J. Cell Biol.* 82:614–25
41. Willingham, M. C., Pastan, I. 1978. *Cell* 13:501–7
42. Willingham, M. C., Pastan, I. 1980. *Cell* 21:67–77
43. Willingham, M. C., Yamada, S. S. 1978. *J. Cell Biol.* 78:480–87
44. Willingham, M. C., Yamada, S. S., Pastan, I. 1978. *Proc. Natl. Acad. Sci. USA* 75:4359–63

Ann. Rev. Physiol. 1981. 43:251–63

EPIDERMAL AND NERVE GROWTH FACTORS IN MAMMALIAN DEVELOPMENT

❖1309

Denis Gospodarowicz

Cancer Research Institute and the Departments of Medicine and Ophthalmology, University of California Medical Center, San Francisco, California 94143

INTRODUCTION

Numerous growth factors active in cultured cells have been identified and purified in recent years. However, only in a few cases has their relevance to an in vivo situation been explored. Among the growth factors shown to have a profound effect in vivo are the epidermal growth factor (EGF), which stimulates the proliferation of the basal cell layer of various epithelia in vivo, and nerve growth factor (NGF), which has a dramatic effect on the development of the sympathetic adrenergic system. In this short review I concentrate on what is known of their biological effects in vivo and in vitro, as well as on the role they could play in mammalian development.

BIOLOGICAL EFFECT OF THE EPIDERMAL GROWTH FACTOR

In Tissue Culture

EGF has been shown to be a potent mitogen for a variety of cultured cells of ectodermal and mesodermal origin (1). Among the cells of ectodermal origin that respond to it are a variety of keratinocytes derived from skin, conjunctival, or pharyngeal tissue (2). In all cases, EGF markedly stimulates their proliferation and leads to enhanced keratinization and squame production (3). It also delays the ultimate senescence of the cells, thereby increasing their culture lifetime (4). Owing to these effects, culture of epidermal keratinocytes, particularly those of the human, has been greatly im-

251

0066-4278/81/0315-0251$01.00

proved (5). Single cultured cells can now generate in vitro stratified colonies that ultimately fuse and form an epithelium that is a reasonable approximation of the epidermis. Among the cells of mesodermal origin that respond to EGF in culture are granulosa cells, corneal endothelial cells, vascular smooth muscle, chondrocytes, and fibroblasts (6). This last cell type has been used extensively to study the extensive sequence of events that are part of the mitogenic response produced by EGF [for a recent review, see (1)].

In Vivo and in Organ Culture

The biological effect of EGF both in vivo and in organ culture is to promote the proliferation of the basal cell layer of various epithelia (7, 8), This can be observed in fetal, neonatal, and adult tissues (7). Early studies demonstrated that in vivo EGF can accelerate the opening of the eyelids and tooth eruption in the neonate (9, 10). This was later found to be the consequence of a more generalized biological effect, namely an enhancement of epidermal keratinization that affects the upper layers of the epidermis (11, 12), and results from an increased proliferative rate of the basal cell layer. The in vivo effect of EGF is not restricted to the epidermis of the eyelid but can affect other organs as well, such as the back skin. Nor is it restricted to the neonatal phase of life, since exposure to EGF in adults also results in increased keratinization, as well as in hyperplasia of the tail and the hind foot. The sensitivity of a given epidermal territory to EGF may change during the lifespan of the individual. It has been observed that, although the epidermis of the back skin is sensitive to EGF during the neonatal phase, it no longer responds in the adult (12). In order to respond to EGF, the basal epithelial cell layer must rest on a proper substrate. In vivo, this is provided by the dermis, while in organ culture it can be provided either by killed dermis or collagen (7).

Similar effects of EGF have been reported in the case of either the back skin or anterior shank skin from 9-day-old chick embryos maintained in organ culture (7). While the thickness of the epidermis in control cultures remained almost unchanged, a marked increase in the number of epidermal cell layers was seen by day 3 when the tissues were exposed to EGF. If the cultures were allowed to grow for 9 days, although feather development was observed in control cultures, in cultures exposed to EGF feather formation was inhibited and the subepidermal layer keratinized. Essentially similar results were obtained when the skin was derived from the anterior shank region of 11-day-old chick embryo, although in this case scale formation, rather than feather formation, was observed in control cultures (7).

Corneal epithelium, like skin epithelium, is extremely sensitive to the hyperplastic effect of EGF. In organ culture, both chick and human fetal corneas respond to EGF with a marked hyperplasia of epithelial cell layers

(11, 13). However, in accordance with the phenotypic expression of this tissue, the upper cell layers do not keratinize. Likewise, although the topical application of EGF in vivo to normal rabbit eye does not appear to affect the morphology of the corneal epithelium significantly, if one partially denudes the cornea of its epithelium, the topical application of EGF markedly stimulates the regeneration process, and a transitory hyperplasia of the epithelial layer can be observed once the denuded area is covered (13, 14).

EGF and Fetal Development

The ability of EGF to trigger epithelial cell proliferation in the neonate and adult animals has raised the possibility that EGF could be a fetal growth hormone responsible for the proliferation and development of specific epithelial territories in the embryo. This possibility has been tested in two different organs, the lung (15, 16) and the secondary palate (17, 18).

EGF AND THE EMBRYONIC LUNG DEVELOPMENT   Sundell et al (15) have shown that the constant infusion of EGF into fetal lambs for 3–5 days stimulates epithelial growth in many sites, including upper and lower airways. In addition, EGF appears to afford protection against the development of hyaline membrane disease when given in utero at 123–130 days of gestation. This suggests that cell differentiation is stimulated in addition to cell growth (16). Injection of EGF into 24-day rabbit fetuses also induces accelerated maturation of the lung (16). On sacrifice at day 27, there is greater distensibility and stability on deflation associated with the appearance of a complement of type II cells approaching that of the rabbit at term. It therefore seems that EGF is capable not only of promoting lung epithelial cell growth but differentiation as well in the fetal rabbit lung (16). It may therefore be an important hormone in the maturation of the lung and be capable of protecting the prematurely delivered fetus against the development of hyaline membrane disease (15, 16).

EGF AND THE DEVELOPMENT OF THE MAMMALIAN SECONDARY PALATE   The results of several studies suggest that the palate might be dependent upon EGF for some aspects of its growth and differentiation. In the mouse, the secondary palate first becomes morphologically distinct on the 12th day of gestation, at which time it exists as two low bilateral processes extending from the paired maxillary processes. Between the 14th and 15th days of gestation, the palatal processes reorient from a vertical position alongside the tongue to a horizontal position above the tongue and fuse with one another along their medial surfaces. This fusion brings about the separation of the oral and nasal cavities. The medial-epithelial lamina formed between apposing palatal processes disrupts during palatal fusion, and the mesenchymal tissues of the two processes become confluent (17, 18). By 17 days of gestation, the dorsal epithelium of the palate, which constitutes the floor of the nasal cavity, has differentiated into a pseudo-stratified ciliated columnar epithelium, and the ventral epithelium, which constitutes the roof of the oral cavity, has differentiated into a stratified squamous epithelium (19–21).

Both in vivo and in vitro studies have suggested that tissue interactions are important in the differentiation of the secondary palate. The occurrence of cell death within the medial-epithelial lamina between fusing palatal processes has been well documented (22–26). Cell death as a mechanism of morphogenesis has been shown to be one way to eliminate various transient tissues and organs during development (25–27). In the case of the palate, it appears that programmed cell death assists in the removal of the medial palatal epithelium. Organ culture techniques have demonstrated that cell death within the medial palatal epithelium does not depend upon the presence of the palatal mesenchyme, at least not during the 3 days that precede the fusion events (21, 25–28). Cell death occurs within the medial region of cultured palatal epithelium that has been isolated from its mesenchyme and occurs in accordance with the in vivo schedule. During the terminal stage of palate development, there is a transient increase in the endogenous level of cAMP in palatal tissue (29, 30). This increase either precedes or is concomitant with the sequence of biochemical events leading to the programmed death of the medial edge epithelial cell layer (31). These include cessation of DNA synthesis, appearance of a carbohydrate-rich surface coat that may be involved in the cell adhesion and subsequent fusion of the palatal shelves, and release of lysosomal enzymes (31).

Although it has yet to be established that cAMP and adenylate cyclase increases are directly involved in the events that induce terminal cell differentiation in the palate epithelium, glucocorticoid, in conjunction with EGF, could be involved in this increase. EGF can inhibit the degeneration of the medial edge palate epithelium and promote the hypertrophy and keratinization of these cells (17, 18, 32). The response to EGF can be prevented by the addition of dibutyryl cAMP (18). EGF can therefore act directly on the medial edge epithelial cells to prevent, through the keratinization process, the adhesion of the opposing palatal shelves. It has also been shown that cessation of DNA synthesis and cell death within the medial palatal epithelium can be inhibited in organ culture by the addition of EGF (17, 33). If EGF is administered after cells have lost their ability to make DNA, although it no longer stimulates cells to divide, it can nevertheless act as a survival agent and prevent cell death within this region. In contrast, if present in the culture medium before cells have lost their ability to make DNA, EGF will both induce hyperplasia and prevent cell death within the medial epithelium (17, 33). If EGF is added to organ culture of palatal shelves in their final stage of differentiation (day 13 or 14 of gestation in mice), while it can still affect the morphology of the isolated epithelium, it will not stimulate DNA synthesis or prevent cell death (34). Therefore, depending on the temporal sequence of epithelial cell differentiation in the palate, some aspects of palatal shelf growth and differentiation may depend on EGF. That this could be the case is suggested by recent demonstrations that palatal shelves can be successfully cultured in serum-free medium containing EGF as well as other growth factors and hormones (35). Removal of EGF from the medium results in a drastically reduced overall growth and in death of the palatal medial epithelial cells (35). At least in vitro, then, EGF may be important for the growth and differentiation of epithelial cells of the palate (35).

PRESENCE OF EGF RECEPTOR SITES AND EGF-LIKE SUBSTANCE IN THE FETUS   EGF receptor binding sites can be detected in mouse embryo as early as after 11–12 days of gestation (36). Autoradiographic studies have demonstrated their presence in the palatal shelves by 13 days of gestation (36). The appearance of an EGF-like substance as a function of the age of the embryo has been analyzed by both radioimmunoassay and radioreceptor assay. Although little or no EGF was found prior to day 11, a dramatic increase occurred on day 12 and continued to rise through day 14 (35). No corresponding increase occurred in the maternal serum during this time, although levels were considerably higher than those found in nonpregnant serum. This increase in EGF-like substance closely paralleled the increase in specific binding of iodine-labeled EGF to membrane of crude embryonic homogenates, which increased 10-fold from day 12 to 14 (36). The source and composition of the EGF present in the embryo are uncertain. Although the maternal level of EGF could contribute to the fetal level through transplacental transport, this is unlikely, because maternal and fetal EGF differ; the fetal form does not cross-react to the same extent as maternal EGF with anti-EGF antibodies, although both can cross-react to the same extent in the radioreceptor assay. This suggests that the fetal EGF could be distinct from adult EGF antigenically and, although related to it, may not be the same molecule (36).

Other Biological Effects of EGF That Could Affect Fetal and Neonatal Development

Although EGF is considered to be primarily a mitogen, it can affect the cells in many other ways, all of which could directly or indirectly affect their proliferation. For example, in cultured fibroblasts EGF increases the synthesis of fibronectin (37), a cell surface protein involved in cellular adhesion.

It also increases the synthesis of hyaluronic acid and of glycosaminoglycans (38), which are important components of the basal lamina and could play a permissive role in the control of cell proliferation. Fetal development may be influenced to some extent by hCG, while that of the neonate is influenced by growth hormone. It has been shown that EGF is able in choriocarcinoma cells to increase greatly the release and probably the synthesis of hCG (39). Likewise, addition of EGF to GH₃ cells, a pituitary cell line producing growth hormone and prolactin, leads to the cessation of growth hormone synthesis (40), while that of prolactin is greatly increased. In the human, EGF has been shown to be similar in structure to urogastrone (41–43). Like urogastrone, EGF elicits a gastric antisecretory response by blocking HCl release from the gastric mucosa (42, 43). If inhibition of acid secretion promotes fibroblastic proliferation and reepitheliazation of the mucosa, then human EGF or urogastrone could be of therapeutic value in the treatment of duodenal ulceration, not only because of its direct mitogenic effect on these two cell types, but also because it is an antisecretory agent.

BIOLOGICAL EFFECT OF NERVE GROWTH FACTOR

In Tissue Culture

In vitro, NGF is required by sympathetic adrenergic neurons if they are to survive and to differentiate properly. Three other types of neoplastic cells of neural crest origins, neuroblastoma (44), melanoma (45), and pheochromocytoma (46), have also been reported to bind ^{125}I-NGF, and in the case of pheochromocytoma cells neurite outgrowth is also induced by NGF. The ability of NGF to promote the survival of neurons for indefinite periods and to induce neurite outgrowth has made possible the study of the interaction and mechanism of action of NGF at the molecular level [for a recent review, see (47)].

NGF may be viewed as a trophic agent that acts as a pleiotypic activator of various anabolic and catabolic pathways (47). Among other effects, NGF causes: increases in uridine uptake and polysome formation; protein, RNA, and lipid synthesis; and glucose utilization (48–51). It also causes microtubule polymerization (52). In a limited way NGF can act as a mitogen (53). However, owing to the early differentiation of sympathetic neurons which coincides with a loss of their ability to proliferate, this effect has been difficult to demonstrate and is still in question.

NGF can also act as a trophic agent to attract growing axons in vitro (51, 52). It is likely that this reflects the ability of NGF to promote the assembly of microtubules, since this assembly will lead directly to the elongation of the nerve fiber. It also provides a molecular basis for the explanation of the neurotropism mediated by NGF both in vivo and in vitro, the tip of a growing sympathetic fiber elongating along a diffusion gradient of NGF (53).

In Vivo: NGF and the Development of the Sympathetic System

Of all growth factors currently known, NGF best qualifies as a fetal or a neonatal hormone. Its target organ, the sympathetic adrenergic system, develops and differentiates early in the life of the individual and in these early stages it is most sensitive to the trophic action of NGF. NGF is now thought to be the trophic factor upon which sympathetic neurons depend in vivo for their survival and proper differentiation (54).

Early findings on the growth of sympathetic nerve fibers in chick embryos bearing transplants of mouse sarcomas 180 or 37 indicated that NGF could have a chemotaxic effect on nerve fibers and demonstrated for the first time that chemical signals could play a role in the formation of neuronal circuits (55–57). The most convincing evidence for a trophic role of NGF on the sympathetic adrenergic systems has been derived from in vivo experiments in which one (*a*) tries to suppress its existence through the use of NGF antibodies or (*b*) tries to hypertrophy this system by locally increasing the concentration of NGF through its systemic injection.

As early as 1960 (58) it was demonstrated that injection into newborn mice of NGF antibodies results in the selective destruction in the paravertebral and prevertebral ganglions of the sympathetic nervous system. Dead and degenerating cells are seen in large numbers two to three days after the first injection, and by day 20 the ganglions are reduced to sclerotic nodules containing only a few remaining satellite cells and small neurons (59, 60). Such treated animals, although they appear to be in good health, show a number of aberrant physiological functions; they have provided a valuable model system for studying how the lack of sympathetic innervation interferes with a multiplicity of body functions (61).

Injection of NGF into newborn rodents results in a great increase in the size of their sympathetic ganglia, which can become 10–12 times larger than those of untreated littermates. This great increase in size is the result of hyperplastic and hypertrophic effects (57). The increase in mitotic activity caused by NGF in undifferentiated sympathetic cell precursors ceases around the middle of the second week after birth, at the same time as the sympathetic cells start to lose their proliferatic ability in untreated animals. The possibility that NGF at a given period of the development of the sympathetic system can be mitogenic has been examined in pulse labelling experiments performed in the first post-natal week in NGF-treated and control mice and rats (54). Autoradiographic studies performed in two-week-old mice and rats (a time when neuronal cells differ, by virtue of their larger size and certain specific morphological features, from satellite cells) showed a marked increase in heavily labeled nerve cells in the experimental ganglia (54). This gives convincing support to the hypothesis of a direct NGF effect on mitotic activity in sympathetic nerve cell precursors.

However, NGF seems to exert its hyperplastic effect on sympathetic ganglia primarily by promoting cell survival rather than cell proliferation (62, 63). Cell death is a normal occurrence in the nervous system; as age increases, populations of immature neurons, as well as neurons that do not establish contact with their peripheric target cells, are condemned to die. In the presence of NGF these will survive, thereby resulting in an increased size of the ganglia (64).

Simultaneous treatment of newborn rats with 6 hydroxydopamine [which destroys adrenergic nerve endings (65)] and NGF results in even greater hypertrophic and hyperplastic changes of the neuronal cell population than those caused by NGF alone. Under these conditions, in addition to an increase in size and number of nerve cells, the increase in volume of the superior ganglia of rats injected since birth with both agents can be 30 times that of control (66). This paradoxical volume increase is not only the result of the hypertrophic and hyperplastic effects called forth by NGF in nerve cells. It is due to a much greater extent to massive de novo production of axonal material, which accumulates inside the ganglion in the form of tangled masses of nerve fibers, and around the ganglion as a dense fibrillar capsule that encircles the nerve cell population and increases progressively in thickness (66).

NGF acts not only on immature, not yet fully differentiated sympathetic neurons but on fully differentiated ones as well. Systemic injection of NGF in young and adult mice leads to a marked increase in the density of the adrenergic plexuses that result from an increased collateral sprouting from the intact adrenergic neurons (67, 68). The neurotropic effect of NGF in vivo is also supported by experiments in which NGF was injected into the brain of newborn rat. This resulted in an outgrowth of sympathetic nerve fibers from sympathetic ganglia which invaded the neural tube through the spinal roots (62). Once inside the spinal cord, the nerve fiber could be traced as far as the brain (62). Discontinuation of the intracerebral injection results in the progressive disappearance of such nerve fibers, which suggests that these fibers neither belong nor find acceptance in the CNS, where they are ignored as intruders by intrinsic neuronal systems. The same fiber tracts persist indefinitely, however, if NGF is continuously supplied by the intracerebral or even the systemic route (54).

NGF not only has the ability to support the differentiation of the sympathetic adrenergic system, but in some cases it can also alter the pattern of differentiation of cells related to that system. Sympathetic neurons and adrenal chromaffin cells share a common origin from the neuroectoderm of stem cells (69). Although both cell types share and release catecholamine, their structure and function are markedly different. There are, however, a number of reasons to believe that chromaffin cells or their precursors could evolve into sympathetic neurons at an early stage of development. Unusually large numbers of sympathetic nerve fibers can be found among chromaffin cells in the adrenal medulla of neonate rats exposed to NGF for 21 days after delivery (70). In vitro, exposure of a cell line derived from a tumor of the adrenal medulla (pheochromocytoma) to NGF induces neurite outgrowth (71). Chromaffin cells dissociated from the adrenal medulla can also produce fiber outgrowth (72) and do exhibit the structural and biochemical features of sympathetic cells when exposed to NGF. Definitive proof that chromaffin cells could become sympathetic nerves was provided by injecting NGF into 10-day-old rat fetus until 10 days after birth (73). Such treatment produces massive transformation of the chromaffin cells present in the rat medulla into sympathetic nerve cells. NGF can therefore transform chromaffin cells that are not fully differentiated, as well as their precursors, into nerve cells indistinguishable by morphological criteria from sympathetic neurons (73). Likewise, when injection of NGF antiserum into 17-day-old fetuses is continued after birth it produces progressive and massive destruction of chromaffin cell precursors and of immature chromaffin cells (73). These observations lend further credence to the notion of a much broader role for NGF in the developing fetus than was previously thought.

Does NGF Play a Role in the Chemical Differentiation of Neurons?

Although the normal development of sympathetic adrenergic neurons in the intact animal depends to a great extent on the presence of NGF, this factor does not seem to play a role in the chemical differentiation of neurons. The factors that determine whether a given neuron in an autonomic pathway will become cholinergic or adrenergic were analyzed using in vitro culture of immature neurons derived from sympathetic ganglia of newborn rats (74), which have previously been shown to depend on NGF for survival and neurite outgrowth (75, 76). When the sympathetic neurons are cultured together with nonneuronal cells from the ganglion, striking differences in the chemical differentiation of the neurons are observed. Instead of expressing only adrenergic functions, as they do in the absence of the nonneuronal cells (76), the mixed cultures could manufacture and accumulate high levels of acetylcholine, indicating that many of the neurons have become cholinergic (77, 78).

Similar results were observed when media conditioned by nonneuronal cell cultures were added to pure culture of sympathetic neurons, indicating that treatment with conditioned medium is sufficient to induce cholinergic properties in sympathetic neurons and that the choice of transmitter is not the result of a direct contact between the sympathetic neurons and nonneuronal cells (78, 79). These results also demonstrate that the neurons that express adrenergic properties at the outset can still be remodelled with respect to neurotransmitter choice for a considerable period after birth and can become cholinergic under the influence of conditioned medium (78, 79). They also indicate that most neurons are adrenergic at the time they are put into culture but are susceptible to a "flip-flop" control mechanism that determines their ultimate choice of transmitter. The duration of the transition period during which dual function may be expressed is not known, but by four or five weeks after birth virtually all the neurons have differentiated into a state in which only one transmitter system is expressed to a significant degree. When the abilities of different tissues from newborn mice to induce chemical neuronal differentiation were compared, it was found that, although tissues such as skeletal muscle, heart, and liver are able to induce cholinergic differentiation, there are clear differences in their effectiveness (80). Cells originating from tissues that receive mainly cholinergic innervation (such as muscle) are the most potent cholinergic inducer, while cells from liver, which received mostly if not exclusively adrenergic innervation, are the least potent. Heart muscle, which received both kinds of innervation, is of intermediate potency (80). This suggests that during their development target cells can release chemical factors that influence the transmitter metabolism of the neuron that will innervate them.

Because NGF has the same potentiating effect on cholinergic as on adrenergic differentiation, NGF is permissive rather than instructive in transmitter production: It stimulates the growth and differentiation of immature sympathetic neurons along either the adrenergic path or the cholinergic one but does not influence which path is taken. In contrast to NGF, the cholinergic factor secreted by nonneuronal cells does not affect neuronal survival or growth but does instruct the neurons with respect to neurotransmitter choice (81).

The normal excitory impulses from the central neurons can prevent sympathetic neurons in the body from responding to cholinergic signals produced by nonneuronal cells. When mass neuronal cultures are depolarized either in the presence of conditioned medium or for 7–10 days before the addition of conditioned medium, the neurons remain primarily adrenergic (82). These changes occur without a significant alteration in the survival of neurons, suggesting that neurons that would have become cholinergic in response to conditioned medium now remain adrenergic (82). These observations raise the possibility that in the intact ganglia the majority of neurons are preserved in their prenatal adrenergic condition by electrical input from the spinal cord that begins during the first week after birth and that neurons in the ganglia that are destined to become cholinergic acquire their electrical input only after they have been influenced by nonneuronal cells. There is little doubt, therefore, that developing sympathetic neurons are plastic during the early phase of their differentiation with respect to the neurotransmitter they will produce. This conclusion is further supported by the elegant transplantation experiments of Le Douarin et al (83), who have demonstrated that the decision of immature neurons to become adrenergic or cholinergic can be altered if the cells are transplanted to new sites in the embryo. Precursor cell populations for both adrenergic and cholinergic neurons are originally present in the neural crest and at an early stage of development migrate ventrally (69, 84). Some cells stop in the dorsal structure of the trunk and give rise to adrenergic sympathetic neurons and to the adrenomedullary paraganglia, while others migrate more ventrally and colonize the splanchnopleural mesenchyme, giving rise to the cholinergic parasympathetic enteric ganglia (69, 84). The precursor cell population present in the neural crest caudad at the level of somites 1 to 5 normally gives rise to cholinergic neurons (85). If transplanted to a region of the neural crest between somites 18 to 24 where adrenergic neurons normally arise, it too will give rise to adrenergic neurons. Conversely, if the neural crest region between somites 18 to 24, which normally gives rise to adrenergic neurons, is transplanted to the anterior part of the neural crest, it will no longer give rise to adrenergic neurons but to cholinergic ones instead (85). Tissue containing neural crest cells located between somites 18 to 24 were also implanted in direct contact with chick embryo gut, thus eliminating the migratory pathway normally traversed (86). Under these conditions, the cells were able to populate intrinsic plexuses of the gut wall with nonadrenergic neurons (84). This demonstrated that cells that are normally progenitors of adrenergic neurons are capable of providing gut plexus neurons, which are demonstrably cholinergic, even when bypassing their normal migratory route through embryonic tissues.

CONCLUSION

Although numerous growth factors have been identified and purified in recent years, their role in vivo is still unclear. Only in the case of the nerve growth factor has a physiological function been demonstrated, and its role in supporting the development of the sympathetic adrenergic nervous system is no longer questioned. In the case of epidermal growth factor, all evidence gathered to date tends to prove that it could play an important role in the development of the neonate or in late fetal development. Whether other growth factors will be shown to play similar physiological roles in vivo can at present only be a matter of speculation.

Literature Cited

1. Carpenter, G., Cohen, S. 1979. *Ann. Rev. Biochem.* 48:193–216
2. Sun, T. T., Green, H. 1977. *Nature* 269:489–92
3. Green, H. 1977. *Cell* 11:405–16
4. Rheinwald, J. G., Green, H. 1977. *Nature* 265:421–24
5. Green, H., Kehinde, O., Thomas, J. 1979. *Proc. Natl. Acad. Sci. USA* 76:5665–68
6. Gospodarowicz, D., Greenburg, G., Bialecki, H., Zetter, B. 1978. *In Vitro* 14:85–118
7. Cohen, S. 1965. *Devel. Biol.* 12:394–407
8. Cohen, S., Taylor, J. M. 1974. *Recent Prog. Horm. Res.* 30:533–50
9. Cohen, S. 1959. *J. Biol. Chem.* 234:1129–37
10. Cohen, S. 1962. *J. Biol. Chem.* 237:1555–62
11. Cohen, S., Savage, C. R. Jr. 1974. *Recent Prog. Horm. Res.* 30:551–74
12. Cohen, S., Elliott, G. A. 1963. *J. Invest. Dermatol.* 40:1–5
13. Savage, C. R. Jr., Cohen, S. 1973. *Exp. Eye Res.* 15:361–72
14. Frati, L., Daniele, S., Delogu, A., Covelli, I. 1972. *Exp. Eye Res.* 14:135–49
15. Sundell, H., Serenius, F. S., Barthe, P., Friedman, Z., Kanarek, K. S., Escobedo, M. B., Orth, D. N., Stahlman, M. T. 1975. *Pediatr. Res.* 9:371–76
16. Catterton, W. Z., Escobedo, M. B., Sexson, W. R., Gray, M. E., Sundell, H. W., Stahlman, M. T. 1979. *Pediatr. Res.* 13:104–8
17. Hassell, J. R. 1975. *Develop. Biol.* 45:90–102
18. Hassell, J. R., Pratt, R. M. 1977. *Exp. Cell Res.* 106:155–62
19. Idoya-Vargas, V., Nasjleti, C. E., Azcurra, J. M. 1972. *J. Embryol. Exp. Morphol.* 27:413–30
20. Tyler, M. S. 1975. *Epithelial-mesenchymal interactions in the embryonic secondary palate of the mouse: an in vitro study.* PhD thesis. Univ. North Carolina, Chapel Hill
21. Tyler, M. S., Koch, W. E. 1975. *Anat. Rec.* 182:297–304
22. Farbman, A. I. 1968. *Devol. Biol.* 18:93–116
23. Shapiro, B. L., Sweney, L. 1969. *J. Dent. Res.* 48:652–660
24. Holmstedt, J. O. V., Han, S. S. 1973. *CBL Monogr.* 1:1–131
25. Smiley, C. R., Koch, W. E. 1972. *Anat. Rec.* 173:405–16
26. Glucksmann, A. 1951. *Biol. Rev. Cambridge Philos. Soc.* 26:59–86
27. Saunders, J. W. 1966. *Science* 154:604–12
28. Tyler, M. S., Koch, W. E. 1977. *J. Embryol. Exp. Morphol.* 38:19–48
29. Pratt, R. M., Martin, G. R. 1975. *Proc. Natl. Acad. Sci. USA* 72:874–77
30. Greene, R. M., Pratt, R. M. 1980. *J. Histochem. Cytochem.* In press
31. Greene, R. M., Pratt, R. M. 1976. *J. Embryol. Exp. Morphol.* 36:225–45
32. Pratt, R. M., Figueroa, A. A., Greene, R. M., Salomon, D. S. 1979. In *Abnormal Embryogenesis: Cellular and Molecular Aspects,* ed. T. V. N. Persaud; pp. 161–76. Lancaster: MTP Press
33. Pratt, R. M., Figueroa, A. A., Nexo, E., Hollenberg, M. D. 1978. *J. Cell Biol.* 79, 24a
34. Tyler, M. S., Pratt, R. M. 1980. *J. Embryol. Exp. Morphol.* In press
35. Pratt, R. M. 1980. In *Development in Mammals,* ed. M. Johnson. NY: Elsevier North Holland. In press
36. Nexo, E., Hollenberg, M. D., Figueroa, A., Pratt, R. M. 1980. *Proc. Natl. Acad. Sci. USA* 77:2782–85
37. Chen, L. B., Gudor, R. C., Sun, T. T., Chen, A. B., Mosesson, M. W. 1978. *Science* 197:776–78
38. Lembach, K. J. 1976. *J. Cell Physiol.* 89:277–88
39. Benveniste, R., Speeg, K. V., Carpenter, G., Cohen, S., Lindner, J., Rabinowitz, D. 1978. *J. Clin. Endocrinol. Metab.* 46:169–72
40. Johnson, L. K., Baxter, J., Vlodavsky, I., Gospodarowicz, D. 1980. *Proc. Natl. Acad. Sci. USA* 77:394–98
41. Cohen, S., Carpenter, G. 1975. *Proc. Natl. Acad. Sci.* 72:1317–21
42. Gregory, H. 1975. *Nature* 257:325–27
43. Gregory, H., Willshire, I. R. 1975. *Physiol. Chem.* 356:1765–74
44. Vigneti, M. 1974. *J. Exp. Med.* 140:437–51
45. Fabricant, R. N., DeLarco, J. E., Todaro, G. J. 1977. *Proc. Natl. Acad. Sci. USA* 74:565–69

46. Tischler, A. S., Greene, L. A. 1975. *Nature* 258:341–42
47. Greene, L. A., Shooter, E. M. 1980. *Ann. Rev. Neurosci.* 3:353–402
48. Partlow, L. M., Larrabee, M. G. 1971. *J. Neurochem.* 18:2101–18
49. Horii, Z. I., Varon, S. 1976. *Brain Res.* 124:121–33
50. Levi-Montalcini, R., Angeletti, P. U. 1968. *Physiol. Rev.* 48:534–69
51. Chamley, J. H., Dowel, J. J. 1975. *Cell Res.* 90:1–7
52. Chamley, J. H., Goller, J., Burnstock, G. 1973. *Develop. Biol.* 31:362–79
53. Charlwood, K. A., Lamont, D. M., Banks, B. E. C. 1972. In *Nerve Growth Factor and its Antiserum,* ed. E. Zaimis, J. Knight, pp. 102–7. London: Athlone Press
54. Levi-Montalcini, R. 1976. *Prog. Brain Res.* 45:235–58
55. Levi-Montalcini, R., Hamburger, V. 1951. *J. Exp. Zool.* 116:321–62
56. Levi-Montalcini, R., Hamburger, V. 1953. *J. Exp. Zool.* 123:233–88
57. Levi-Montalcini, R., Booker, B. 1960. *Proc. Natl. Acad. Sci. USA* 46:373–84
58. Levi-Montalcini, R., Booker, B. 1960. *Proc. Natl. Acad. Sci. USA* 46:384–91
59. Levi-Montalcini, R., Angeletti, P. U. 1966. *Pharmacol. Rev.* 18:619–28
60. Zaimis, E., Berk, L., Callingham, B. A. 1965. *Nature* 206:1220–22
61. Theonen, H. 1972. In *Catecholamines,* ed. H. Blaschko, E. Muscholl, pp. 813–44. NY: Springer
62. Levi-Montalcini, R., Angeletti, P. U. 1963. *Dev. Biol.* 7:653–59
63. Cohen, A. I., Nicol, E. C., Richter, W. 1964 .*Proc. Soc. Exp. Biol. Med.* 116:784–89
64. Hendry, I. A., Campbell, J. 1976. *J. Neurocytol.* 5:351–60
65. Angeletti, P. U., Levi-Montalcini, R. 1970. *Proc. Natl. Acad. Sci. USA* 65:114–21
66. Aloe, L., Mugnaini, E., Levi-Montalcini, R. 1975. *Arch. It. Biol.* 113:326–53
67. Bjerre, B., Bjorklund, A., Stenevi, U. 1973. *Brain Res.* 60:171–76
68. Bjerre, B., Bjorklund, A., Mobley, W., Rosengreen, E. 1975. *Brain Res.* 94:261–77
69. Le Douarin, N., Teillet, M. A. 1973. *C. R. Acad. Sci. Paris* 277
70. Angeletti, P. U., Levi-Montalcini, R., Kettler, R., Thoenen, H. 1972. *Brain Res.* 44:197–206
71. Greene, L. A., Tischler, A. S. 1976. *Proc. Natl. Acad. Sci. USA* 73:2424–28
72. Unsicker, K., Chamley, J. H. 1977. *Cell Tissue Res.* 177:247–68
73. Aloe, L., Levi-Montalcini, R. 1979. *Proc. Natl. Acad. Sci. USA* 76:1246–50
74. Yamauchi, A., Lever, J. D., Kemp, K. W. 1973. *J. Anat.* 114:271–84
75. Bray, D. 1970. *Proc. Natl. Acad. Sci. USA* 65:905–9
76. Mains, R. E., Patterson, P. H. 1973. *J. Cell Biol.* 59:329–40
77. Patterson, P. H., Chun, L. L. Y. 1974. *Proc. Natl. Acad. Sci. USA* 71:3607–11
78. Patterson, P. H., Reichardt, L. F., Chun, L. L. Y. 1975. *Cold Spring Harbor Symp. Quant. Biol.* 40:389–96
79. Patterson, P. H., Chun, L. L. Y., Reichardt, L. F. 1977. *Prog. Clin. Biol. Res. Cell. Neurobiol.* 15:95–104
80. Furshpan, E. J., MacLeish, P. R., O'League, P. H., Potter, D. D. 1976. *Proc. Natl. Acad. Sci. USA* 73:4225–29
81. Bunge, R. P., Johnson, M., Ross, C. D. 1978. *Science* 199:1409–16
82. Walicke, P. A., Campenot, R. B., Patterson, P. H. 1977. *Proc. Natl. Acad. Sci. USA* 74:5767–71
83. Le Douarin, N., Le Lièvre, C. 1978. In *Birth Defects,* ed. J. W. Littlefield, J. de Grouchy, pp. 141–53. Oxford: Excerpta Medica
84. Le Douarin, N. 1977. In *Cell Interactions in Differentiation,* ed. M. Karkinen-Jaaskelainen, L. Saxen, L. Weiss, pp. 171–78. London: Academic
85. Le Douarin, N., Renaud, D., Teillet, M. A., Le Douarin, G. H. 1975. *Proc. Natl. Acad. Sci. USA* 72:728–32
86. Smith, J., Cochard, P., Le Douarin, N. 1977. *Cell Diff.* 6:199–216

Ann. Rev. Physiol. 1981. 43:265–78

"ENDORPHINS" IN PITUITARY AND OTHER TISSUES

❖1310

Hiroo Imura and Yoshikatsu Nakai

Department of Medicine, Kyoto University Faculty of Medicine, Kyoto, Japan

Through studies on opiates and their receptors, the existence of endogenous opioid substances has been reported by several investigators. Hughes et al (28) identified two pentapeptides with opioid activity in the pig brain. They named these methionine-enkephalin (Met-enkephalin) and leucine-enkephalin (Leu-enkephalin). Since the amino acid sequence of Met-enkephalin corresponds to the 61–65 portion of β-lipotropin (β-LPH), a known pituitary peptide, several groups searched for opioid peptides in the pituitary and identified several β-LPH fragments with opioid activity beginning with the Met-enkephalin sequence (5, 44, 45). Among these, the most potent is β-endorphin, coinciding with the C-terminal 31 amino acids of β-LPH. More recently, some other peptides with the sequence of Leu-enkephalin or Met-enkephalin have been identified in either the pituitary or in the brain (16, 26, 33, 73). All these peptides have morphine-like activities and, therefore, are called "opioid peptides" or "endorphins." Although these terms have not yet been defined exactly, in this article "endorphins" designates structurally identified peptides that have morphinomimetic activity.

The isolation of these peptides has stimulated many biochemical, endocrinological, neurophysiological, and neuropharmacological studies. These have been surveyed often in reviews and monographs (2, 11, 48, 53, 79). This review focuses on the structure, biosynthesis, distribution, and regulation of the secretion of endorphins, with special emphasis on the peptides of pituitary origin.

STRUCTURE AND BIOSYNTHESIS OF ENDORPHINS

Endorphins so far known can be grouped into at least two categories (Figure 1). Group 1 is the family of peptides derived from β-LPH. Group 2 includes

0066-4278/81/0315-0265$01.00

Group I

β-endorphin (human)	H- Tyr-Gly-Gly-Phe-Met-Thr-Ser-Glu-Lys-Ser-Gln-Thr-Pro-Leu-Val-Thr-Leu-Phe-Lys-Asn-Ala-Ile-Ile-Lys-Asn-Ala-Tyr-Lys-Lys-Gly-Gln-OH
C-Fragment	Lys-Asn-Ala-Ile-Ile-Lys-Asn-Ala-Tyr-Lys-Lys-Gly-Gln-OH
δ-endorphin	H- Tyr-Gly-Gly-Phe-Met-Thr-Ser-·········· Asn-Ala-Tyr-OH
C'-Fragment	Thr-Ser-·········· Asn-Ala-Tyr-OH
γ-endorphin	H- Tyr-Gly-Gly-Phe-Met-Thr-Ser-·········· Val-Thr-Leu-OH
α-endorphin	H- Tyr-Gly-Gly-Phe-Met-Thr-Ser-·········· Val-Thr-OH
Acetylated β-endorphin	Ace- Tyr-Gly-Gly-Phe-Met-Thr-Ser-·········· Gly-Glu-OH
Acetylated δ-endorphin	Ace- Tyr-Gly-Gly-Phe-Met-Thr-Ser-·········· Asn-Ala-Tyr-OH
des-Tyr-γ-endorphin	H- Gly-Gly-Phe-Met-Thr-Ser-·········· Val-Thr-Leu-OH

Group II

Met-enkephalin	H- Tyr-Gly-Gly-Phe-Met	-OH
Pro-Met-enkephalin	H- Tyr-Gly-Gly-Phe-Met(o)-	Arg-OH
Adrenal heptapeptide	H- Tyr-Gly-Gly-Phe-Met-	Arg-Phe-OH
Adrenal tryptic peptide	H- Tyr-Gly-Gly-Phe-Met-	Lys-OH
Leu-enkephalin	H- Tyr-Gly-Gly-Phe-Leu	-OH
α-neo-endorphin	H- Tyr-Gly-Gly-Phe-Leu-	Arg-Lys-Arg-(Pro, Gly, Tyr$_2$, Lys$_2$, Arg)
dynorphin	H- Tyr-Gly-Gly-Phe-Leu-	Arg-Arg-Ile-Arg-Pro-Lys-Leu-Lys

Figure 1. Primary structures of endorphins. Group 1 peptides are considered to be derived from β-LPH. Group 2 includes enkephalins and their putative precursors. The sequence of first 8 and 13 amino acids has been determined in α-neo-endorphin and dynorphin, respectively.

enkephalins and recently discovered related peptides, which seem to have precursors other than β-LPH.

Group 1 Peptides

The primary structure of β-endorphin has been determined in several species including the human, pig, calf, sheep, camel, and salmon (34, 43). As shown in Figure 1, β-endorphin in mammals consists of 31 amino acids that correspond to the C-terminal portion of β-LPH, and a species difference is observed in only 3 residues. In salmon, however, two β-endorphins consisting of 29 amino acids and 30 amino acids, respectively, have been identified. Their primary structures are significantly different from those in mammals. Other β-LPH fragments with opioid activity, such as β-LPH 61–76 (α-endorphin), 61–77 (γ-endorphin), and 61–87 (δ-endorphin or C'-Fragment), have also been reported (17). Since a pulse-chase experiment with radioactive amino acid failed to demonstrate the production of peptides smaller than β-endorphin (51), the possibility of proteolytic cleavage during the process of extraction had been considered for smaller peptides. Very recently, however, Smyth and his associates (86) demonstrated by ion exchange column chromatography that the main opioid peptides in rat pituitaries are C'-Fragment or N-acetyl-C'-Fragment, and not β-endorphin or its N-acetyl-form. Removal of tetrapeptide from β-endorphin reduces morphinomimetic action, and acetylation of the N-terminus abolishes it. It appears, therefore, that pituitary endorphins have little opioid activity. In addition, production of γ- or α-endorphin and their destyrosinated forms are also suggested by high-pressure liquid chromatography (7). These results suggest the existence of heterogeneous molecular forms of endorphins, as shown in Figure 1.

The biosynthetic pathway of β-endorphin has recently been elucidated by several groups. The presence of a common precursor for ACTH and β-endorphin (or β-LPH) has been demonstrated by studying the hormone biosynthesis in mouse pituitary ACTH-producing tumor cells, AtT-20 (51), or by cell-free biosynthesis directed by messenger RNA obtained from the bovine pituitary (58) or AtT-20 cells (68). Nakanishi et al (57) have further determined the nucleotide sequence of complementary DNA for the ACTH-β-LPH precursor and have clarified the arrangement of ACTH and β-LPH on the precursor molecule. Figure 2 illustrates the biosynthetic pathway of ACTH, β-LPH, and β-endorphin. The translation product (preproACTH-β-LPH) of messenger RNA coding for the ACTH-β-LPH precursor has a molecular weight of approximately 30,000. After the N-terminal signal peptide is cleaved, the remaining portion is glycosylated, thus becoming proACTH-β-LPH. β-LPH, which resides in the C-terminal portion of the precursor molecule and is not a glycoprotein, is then cleaved,

268 IMURA & NAKAI

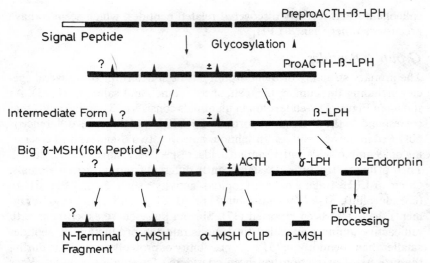

Figure 2. Biosynthetic pathway of ACTH, β-LPH, β-endorphin, and related peptides. The conversion of β-LPH to β-endorphin is limited in the anterior pituitary but almost complete in the intermediate lobe.

and the remaining portion is split further into ACTH of glycosylated or nonglycosylated form and the N-terminal portion (16 K peptide or big γ-MSH) (30). Then β-LPH is cleaved into γ-LPH (1–58) and β-endorphin (61–91). Further processing of β-endorphin could occur to give rise to various peptides mentioned above.

Group 2 Peptides

The amino acid sequences of Met- and Leu-enkephalin differ only at position 5 (Figure 1). The sequence of Met-enkephalin corresponds to the N-terminal 5 amino acids of β-endorphin. However, the precursor role of β-endorphin in Met-enkephalin biosynthesis seems unlikely because the Thr^6-Ser^7 sequence by which Met-enkephalin is attached to the remainder of β-endorphin appears to be a poor cleavage site and because Met-enkephalin and β-endorphin are distributed in different brain regions. In addition, hexa- or heptapeptides having the residues of Arg^6 (26), Lys^6 (73), or Arg^6-Phe^7 (73), adjacent to the C-terminus of Met-enkephalin, have been identified recently. All these results suggest that Met-enkephalin comes from a precursor or precursors other than β-endorphin.

As possible precursors of Leu-enkephalin, two peptides, α-neo-endorphin (33) and dynorphin (16), have been isolated from the pig hypothalamus and the pig pituitary, respectively. These peptides contain Leu-enkephalin in the N-terminal portion and have potent opioid activity, although the C-terminal portions differ considerably. The tryptic digestion of α-neo-endorphin gave rise to a hexapeptide, Arg^6-Leu-enkephalin, suggesting a possible precursor role. However, the importance of dynorphin itself as a putative neurotransmitter has been stressed (16), since it has potent morphinomimetic activity.

The biosynthetic pathway of Met- and Leu-enkephalin has not been clarified yet. Studies on the incorporation of radioactive amino acids (8, 72) and on peptides extracted from tissues (42), suggest the presence of precursors of high molecular weight forms. The question of whether Met- and Leu-enkephalin come from the same or different precursors is of interest. Although they coexist in the brain in different ratios in different species, a recent immunohistochemical study revealed that both peptides are present in separate neurons (39), suggesting the presence of different precursors for Met- and Leu-enkephalin. Very recently, two peptides of 3–5 kilodaltons were isolated from adrenal chromaffin granules, one of which contained two copies of Met-enkephalin sequence in its moiety. The other peptide contained both Met- and Leu-enkephalin sequences (35a). These are presumably precursors of the two forms of enkephalin, though the existence of other forms of precursors cannot be ruled out.

Besides the two groups of opioid peptides mentioned above, there seem to be other, still unidentified, peptides (27, 75). Leu^5-β-endorphin, a peptide identical to β-endorphin except for having Leu instead of Met at position 5, was claimed to exist in the hemodialysate of schizophrenic patients (65), but its existence could not be confirmed by later studies (41).

DISTRIBUTION OF ENDORPHINS

Group 1 Peptides

β-Endorphin is present both in the anterior and the intermediate lobes of the pituitary. It is produced in both lobes from the same common precursor, as demonstrated by the incorporation of labeled amino acids in vitro (12, 50, 69). Moreover, the identical messenger-RNA coding for the common precursor for ACTH and β-endorphin exists in both the anterior and intermediate lobes of the bovine pituitary (76). These results suggest that the biosynthetic pathway of β-endorphin is essentially the same in both lobes, though there is a significant difference in the processing of the precursor molecule. That is, the conversion of β-LPH to β-endorphin is limited in the anterior lobe and, therefore, the anterior lobe contains a large amount of β-LPH as compared with a small amount of β-endorphin (30, 47). In contrast, in the intermediate lobe, the conversion goes essentially to completion and the major product is β-endorphin (30, 50, 69). Immunohistochemical studies have shown that β-endorphin and ACTH exist in the same cells in the pituitary gland (63a, 84).

The presence of β-endorphin, β-LPH, and ACTH in the brain, especially in the hypothalamus, has been demonstrated by radioimmunoassay [for review see (36)]. In the hypothalamus, β-endorphin is predominant as compared with β-LPH (30, 37), suggesting an accelerated conversion of β-LPH to β-endorphin. Immunohistochemical studies have revealed the presence of β-endorphin, β-LPH, and ACTH within cell bodies of the arcuate nucleus and peri-arcuate region, and in fiber pathways in the hypothalamus, limbic system, mesencephalon, and telencephalon (4, 83). The site of production of these peptides is still controversial, and origins in both the pituitary and the central nervous system have been postulated (36). However, an in vitro study demonstrated that the ACTH-β-LPH precursor was synthesized in the bovine hypothalamus as in the pituitary (46).

Recent studies have revealed differences in endorphin moieties between the brain and pituitary in rats (86). The main peptide is β-endorphin in the hypothalamus, δ-endorphin in the hippocampus and midbrain, and δ-endorphin and its acetylated form in the anterior or neurointermediate lobe. All these peptides may show reactivity with anti-β-endorphin antisera. Therefore, radioimmunoassay or immunohistochemical techniques could not differentiate such heterogeneity.

β-Endorphin exists in human placenta (54, 63), where ACTH, β-LPH, and possibly the common precursor occur as well, suggesting the biosynthesis of these peptides in placental tissue similar to that in the pituitary. In fact, in vitro biosynthesis studies with labeled amino acids have demonstrated physiochemically similar precursor molecules in both human placentas and pituitaries, though posttranslational processing is different in these tissues (46a). In one study, however, β-endorphin of a slightly greater molecular weight was found in human placenta (25). Further research should clarify the heterogeneity and presence of acetylated forms of β-endorphin in human placenta. The presence of β-endorphin in human amniotic fluid was also demonstrated (15). Several reports showed that β-endorphin-like immunoreactivity also exists in the pancreas, gastrointestinal tract, and thyroid (6, 35), though its production in these tissues has not yet been confirmed. Ectopic ACTH-producing tumors elaborate not only ACTH and β-LPH, but also β-endorphin (3, 31). Study of in vitro biosynthesis has revealed that the biosynthetic pathway of ACTH and other peptides is essentially the same in tumors as in the pituitary (31).

The plasma level of β-endorphin is a matter of dispute, probably because of the difference in reactivity of antisera to heterogeneous β-endorphin moiety. At first, β-endorphin was reported to be virtually absent in humans (74). Later studies have reported basal levels of β-endorphin, distinct from

β-LPH, of 5.8 ± 1.1 pg ml^{-1} (61), 11.8–21.6 pg ml^{-1} (20), and 21 ± 7.3 pg ml^{-1} (82), when plasma was extracted and gel filtrated before assay. Somewhat higher values are reported when direct radioimmunoassay utilizing specific radioimmunoassay is employed (85). Much higher values are reported in animals that have an intermediate pituitary lobe (21).

β-Endorphin also exists in human cerebrospinal fluid (CSF), though its level varies considerably in different reports. In some studies, CSF β-endorphin levels were estimated, from the difference between C-terminal β-LPH immunoreactivity and N-terminal β-LPH immunoreactivity, to be 50–145 pmole l^{-1} (170–493 pg ml^{-1}) (32). More precise methods using gel chromatography (62) gave values of 17.9 ± 2.3 pg ml^{-1}. However, neither micro-size heterogeneity nor the existence of acetylated forms has yet been studied with regard to plasma and CSF β-endorphin and must await further clarification.

Group 2 Peptides

The distribution of Met- and Leu-enkephalin is somewhat different from that of β-endorphin. Although there had been controversy about the existence of enkephalins in the pituitary, recent studies with radioimmunoassay have revealed that both Met- and Leu-enkephalins are present in the intermediate and posterior lobes, and in the anterior lobe as well, though in very small amounts (13). Immunohistochemical staining has also shown their existence in the pituitary (77, 78). Regional distribution of enkephalins in the brain is different from, and more extensive than, that of β-endorphin (48, 53, 78, 83). That is, enkephalin-positive perikaryas are widely distributed in various parts of the central nervous system, suggesting the regional separation of enkephalin and β-endorphin neurons. Enkephalins are also present in the gastrointestinal tract, both in neuronal elements and endocrine cells (2). Enkephalin-like immunoreactivity has been found also in the adrenal medulla (49), human pheochromocytoma (49), the sympathetic ganglia, vagal nerve, retina (29), and pancreas [for review see (2, 53)].

Recent studies have shown that Met-enkephalin exists in human plasma at the concentration of 14–140 pg ml^{-1} (9), and in human cerebrospinal fluid at the concentration of 5–29 pg ml^{-1} (10). These values cannot be accounted for by the degradation of β-endorphin.

REGULATION OF BIOSYNTHESIS AND RELEASE OF ENDORPHINS

Group 1 Peptides

Secretion of β-endorphin from the pituitary gland has been studied extensively in man. Plasma β-endorphin levels are elevated in patients with

Addison's disease or Nelson's syndrome, and low in patients treated with steroids (55, 85). Administration of metyrapone, (an adrenal 11-β hydroxylase inhibitor), and insulin-induced hypoglycemia raise plasma β-endorphin levels, whereas steroid hormones lower them (30, 60, 61, 85). Since plasma β-endorphin is considered to come from the pituitary in humans, these results suggest that the β-endorphin release from the anterior pituitary is regulated in parallel with that of ACTH or β-LPH.

In animals having an intermediate lobe, the significance of plasma β-endorphin is complicated, since it reflects release from both the anterior and intermediate lobes of the pituitary. Nevertheless, stress or adrenalectomy has been reported to raise plasma β-endorphin, whereas steroid hormones lower it in rats (18, 21, 70). Studies in vitro with cultured anterior pituitary cells revealed that corticotropin releasing factor (CRF) and vasopressin enhanced the release of β-endorphin as well as ACTH, whereas dexamethasone blocked both basal and stimulated release of these hormones (81). The question of whether or not the release of ACTH and that of β-endorphin are dissociated under certain conditions is a matter of interest but is not clear at present.

The mechanism of action of various agents on the release and/or biosynthesis of β-endorphin has not been fully elucidated. A parallel change in ACTH content and mRNA activity specific for the ACTH-β-LPH precursor was observed in the rat pituitary following the administration of adrenal steroids (59). Further studies with AtT-20 cells revealed that steroids act directly on corticotropes rather than via the hypothalamus (56). These results indicate that the negative feedback mechanism of steroids occurs at least in part at the transcriptional level.

The control of β-endorphin release from the neurointermediate lobe is different from the control mechanism in the anterior lobe. Adrenal steroids, adrenalectomy, and CRF have little effect, if any, on β-endorphin release (67, 70, 80). However, dopamine or other dopaminergic agents block release of β-endorphin from the neurointermediate lobe (80). Chronic treatment with opiates is also reported to decrease the content of β-endorphin in the anterior and neurointermediate lobes (22).

Regulation of biosynthesis and release of β-endorphin in the brain have not been completely understood. β-Endorphin exists predominantly in the synaptosomal fraction of the rat brain (14). The peptide is released from hypothalamic fragments in vitro by potassium ions in the presence of calcium (64). These results suggest that β-endorphin is released in the brain from the synapse by membrane-depolarizing agents. This is further supported by the observations (1, 24) that β-endorphin in CSF increased markedly following the electrical stimulation of the central gray in humans.

The brain β-endorphin content is unaffected by adrenalectomy, steroid hormones, or stress (70). However, long-term treatment with opiates lowers brain β-endorphin (22).

Group 2 Peptides

Because of the difficulties in measuring a small amount of enkephalin, little is known about the regulation of its release from the pituitary. The content of enkephalin in the neurointermediate lobe was unchanged by adrenalectomy, steroid hormones, and stress (70). A cyclic change in Met-enkephalin content in the anterior pituitary with the estrous cycle was observed in rats (38). Chronic morphine treatment reduced the pituitary enkephalin (66).

In the brain, enkephalin exists in the synaptosomes and is released by membrane depolarizing agents, suggesting a possible neurotransmitter or neuromodulator role [for review see (2, 78)]. The brain enkephalin content is influenced by a variety of agents, such as morphine, neuroleptics, lithium, and electroconvulsive shocks [(23, 66); for review see (2)]. Although adrenalectomy or steroids have no effect, stress reduced enkephalin in the hypothalamus (70, 71).

ACTION OF ENDORPHINS

The physiological significance of β-endorphin and enkephalin released into blood is far from clear. Systemic administration of β-endorphin causes hypotension (40), and naloxone blocks endotoxin shock (19). Recent studies suggest, however, that the opiate receptors in the brain play an important role in the pathogenesis of spinal shock (19a). Further studies should clarify how endorphins in blood and in the brain are involved in the pathophysiology of various kinds of shock. β-Endorphin also stimulates adrenal steroidogenesis, skin darkening, and lipolysis at high doses [for review see (30)]. These may suggest a role of peripheral endorphins. Peripheral β-endorphin may not play a role in pain blockade, since only a large dose of β-endorphin given intravenously causes analgesia. Although pituitary endorphins do not seem to be main sources of brain endorphins, endorphins released from the pituitary may be retrogradely transported so that they can act on the hypothalamus.

Endorphins in the nervous tissue play an important role in pain blockade. They have effects on mood and behavior, and, therefore, may be related to some mental illnesses. Another possible action of endorphins is regulation of the hypothalamic function, such as regulation of body temperature, food intake, and endocrine functions [for review see (2, 11, 48, 52, 53, 78, 79)].

SUMMARY

The pituitary gland, brain, and various other tissues contain endorphins. These can be divided into at least two groups: peptides derived from β-LPH (Group 1), and enkephalins and related peptides (Group 2). In addition, there seem to be still unidentified peptides. Recent studies have revealed heterogeneity in endorphin moieties, such as different chain lengths and the presence of acetylated forms. Such heterogeneous peptides may have biologic activities different from those studied with synthetic β-endorphin or Met- and Leu-enkephalins. Further studies should clarify the exact nature of native endorphins present in various tissues and the actions of these native peptides. The interaction of endorphins with other putative neurotransmitters, as well as the nature and regulation of opioid receptors, must be studied to define all the features of the endorphin system.

Literature Cited

1. Akil, H., Richardson, D. E., Barchas, J. D., Li, C. H. 1978. Appearance of β-endorphin-like immunoreactivity in electrical stimulation. *Proc. Natl. Acad. Sci. USA* 75:5170–72
2. Beaumont, A., Hughes, J. 1979. Biology of opioid peptides. *Ann. Rev. Pharmacol. Toxicol.* 19:245–67
3. Bertagna, X. Y., Nicholson, W. E., Sorenson, G. D., Pettengill, O. S., Mount, C. D., Orth, D. N. 1978. Corticotropin, lipotropin, and β-endorphin production by a human non-pituitary tumor in culture: evidence for a common precursor. *Proc. Natl. Acad. Sci. USA* 75:5160–64
4. Bloom, F., Battenberg, E., Rossier, J., Ling, N., Guillemin, R. 1978. Neurons containing β-endorphin in rat brain exist separately from those containing enkephalin: Immunocytochemical studies. *Proc. Natl. Acad. Sci. USA* 75:1591–95
5. Bradbury, A. F., Smyth, D. G., Snell, C. R., Birdsall, N. J. M., Hulme, E. C. 1976. C fragment of lipotropin has a high affinity for brain opiate receptors. *Nature* 260:793–95
6. Bruni, J. F., Watkins, W. B., Yen, S. S. C. 1979. β-Endorphin in the human pancreas. *J. Clin. Endocrinol. Metab.* 49:649–51
7. Burbach, J. P. H., Loeber, J. G., Verhoef, J., Wiegant, V. M., de Kloet, E. R., de Wied, D. 1980. Selective conversion of β-endorphin into peptides related to γ- and α-endorphin. *Nature* 283:96–97
8. Childers, S. R., Snyder, S. H. 1979. Enkephalin synthesis in brain: Effect of cyclohexamide and identification of enkephalin precursor. In *Central Nervous System Effects of Hypothalamic Hormones and Other Peptides,* ed. R. Collu, A. Barbeau, J. R. Ducharme, J. G. Rochefort, pp. 253–60. NY: Raven Press. 435 pp.
9. Clement-Jones, V., Lowry, P. J., Rees, L. H., Besser, G. M. 1980. Met-enkephalin circulates in human plasma. *Nature* 263:295–97
10. Clement-Jones, V., McLoughlin, L., Lowry, P. J., Besser, G. M., Rees, L. H. 1979. Acupuncture in heroin addicts: changes in Met-enkephalin and β-endorphin in blood and cerebrospinal fluid. *Lancet* 2:380–82
11. Costa, E., Trabucchi, M. 1978. *The Endorphins.* NY: Raven Press. 379 pp.
12. Crine, P., Benjannet, S., Seidah, N. G., Lis, M., Chrétien, M. 1977. In vitro biosynthesis of β-endorphin, γ-lipotropin, and β-lipotropin by the pars intermedia of beef pituitary gland. *Proc. Natl. Acad. Sci. USA* 74:4276–80
13. Duka, T., Höllt, V., Przewlocki, R., Wesche, D. 1978. Distribution of methionine- and leucine-enkephalin within the rat pituitary gland measured by highly specific radioimmunoassay. *Biochem. Biophys. Res. Commun.* 85:1119–27
14. Fukata, J., Nakai, Y., Takahashi, K., Imura, H. 1980. Subcellular localization of β-endorphin-like immunoreactivity in the rat hypothalamus. *Brain Res.* 195(2):489–93
15. Gautray, J. P., Jolivet, A., Vielh, J. P., Guillemin, R. 1977. Presence of im-

munoassayable β-endorphin in human amniotic fluid: Elevation in cases of fetal distress. *Am. J. Obst. Gynecol.* 129:211–12

16. Goldstein, A., Tachibana, S., Lowney, L. I., Hunkapiller, M., Hood, L. 1979. Dynorphin-(1–13), an extraordinarily potent opioid peptide. *Proc. Natl. Acad. Sci. USA* 76:6666–70

17. Guillemin, R., Ling, N., Lazarus, L., Burgus, R., Minick, S., Bloom, F., Nicoll, R., Siggins, G., Segal, D. 1977. The endorphins, novel peptides of brain and hypophysial origin, with opiate-like activity: Biochemical and biologic studies. *Ann. NY Acad. Sci.* 297:131–57

18. Guillemin, R., Vargo, T., Rossier, J., Minick, S., Ling, N., Rivier, C., Vale, W., Bloom, F. 1977. β-Endorphin and adrenocorticotropin are secreted concomitantly by the pituitary gland. *Science* 197:1367–69

19. Holaday, J. W., Faden, A. I. 1978. Naloxone reversal of endotoxin hypotension suggests role of endorphins in shock. *Nature* 275:450–51

19a. Holaday, J. W., Faden, A. I. 1980. Naloxone acts at central opiate receptors to reverse hypotension, hypothermia and hypoventilation in spinal shock. *Brain Res.* 189:295–99

20. Höllt, V., Müller, O. A., Fahlbusch, R. 1979. β-Endorphin in human plasma: basal and pathologically elevated levels. *Life Sci.* 25:37–44

21. Höllt, V., Przewlocki, R., Herz, A. 1978. Radioimmunoassay of β-endorphin basal and stimulated levels in extracted rat plasma. *Naunyn-Schmiedeberg's Arch. Pharmacol.* 303:171–74

22. Höllt, V., Przewlocki, R., Herz, A. 1978. β-Endorphin-like immunoreactivity in plasma, pituitaries and hypothalamus of rats following treatment with opiates. *Life Sci.* 23:1057–66

23. Hong, J. S., Gillin, J. C., Yang, H.-Y., Costa, I. 1979. Repeated electroconvulsive shocks and the brain content of endorphins. *Brain Res.* 177:273–78

24. Hosobuchi, H., Rossier, J., Bloom, F. E., Guillemin, R. 1979. Stimulation of human periaqueductal gray for pain relief increases immunoreactive beta-endorphin in ventricular fluid. *Science* 203:279–81

25. Houck, J. C., Kimball, C., Chang, C., Pedigo, N. W., Yamamura, H. I. 1980. Placental β-endorphin-like peptides. *Science* 207:78–80

26. Huang, W.-Y., Chang, R. C. C., Kastin, A. J., Coy, D. H., Schally, A. V. 1979. Isolation and structure of pro-methio-

nine-enkephalin: Potential enkephalin precursor from porcine hypothalamus. *Proc. Natl. Acad. Sci. USA* 76:6177–80

27. Hughes, J. 1978. Enkephalin as neurotransmitters. In *Endorphins '78*, ed. L. Graf, M. Palkovitz, A. Z. Ronai, pp. 157–70. NY: Raven Press. 336 pp.

28. Hughes, J., Smith, T. W., Kosterlitz, H. W., Fothergill, L. A., Morgan, B. A., Morris, H. R. 1975. Identification of two related pentapeptides from the brain with potent opiate agonist activity. *Nature* 258:577–79

29. Humbert, J., Pradelles, P., Gros, C., Dray, F. 1979. Enkephalin-like products in embryonic chicken retina. *Neurosci. Lett.* 12:259–63

30. Imura, H. 1980. ACTH, β-endorphin and related peptides. *Proc. 6th Int. Congr. Endocrinol.*, pp. 58–65

31. Imura, H. 1980. Ectopic hormone production viewed as abnormalities in regulation of gene expression. *Adv. Cancer Res.* In press

32. Jeffcoate, W. J., Rees, L. H., McLoughlin, L., Ratter, S. J., Hope, J., Lowry, P. J., Besser, G. M. 1978. β-Endorphin in human cerebrospinal fluid. *Lancet* 1:119–21

33. Kangawa, K., Matsuo, H. 1979. α-Neoendorphin: A "big" Leu-enkephalin with potent opiate activity from porcine hypothalami. *Biochem. Biophys. Res. Commun.* 86:153–60

34. Kawauchi, H., Tsubokawa, M., Kanezawa, A., Kitagawa, H. 1980. Occurrence of two different endorphins in the salmon pituitary. *Biochem. Biophys. Res. Commun.* 92:1278–88

35. Kendall, J. W., Orwoll, E., Gaudette, D. 1980. Extrapituitary ACTH-β-endorphin in tissues of the APUD series. *Program, 6th Int. Congr. Endocrinol.* 528

35a. Kimura, S., Lewis, R. V., Stern, A. S., Rossier, J., Stein, S., Udenfriend, S. 1980. Probable precursors of [Leu]enkephalin and [Met]enkephalin in adrenal medulla: peptides of 3–5 kilodaltons. *Proc. Natl. Acad. Sci. USA* 77:1681–85

36. Krieger, D. T., Liotta, A. S. 1979. Pituitary hormones in brain. Where, how and why? *Science* 205:366–72

37. Krieger, D. T., Liotta, A., Suda, T., Palkovits, M., Brownstein, M. J. 1977. Presence of immunoassayable β-lipotropin in bovine brain and spinal cord: lack of concordance with ACTH concentrations. *Biochem. Biophys. Res. Commun.* 76:930–36

38. Kumar, M. S. A., Chen, C. L., Muther, T. F. 1979. Changes in the pituitary and hypothalamic content of methionine-enkephalin during the estrons cycle. *Life Sci.* 25:1687–96

39. Larsson, L.-I., Childers, S., Snyder, S. H. 1979. Met- and Leu-enkephalin immunoreactivity in separate neurons. *Nature* 282:407–10

40. Lemaire, I., Tseng, R., Lemaire, S. 1978. Systemic administration of beta-endorphin: potent hypotensive effect involving a serotonergic pathway. *Proc. Natl. Acad. Sci. USA* 75:6240–42

41. Lewis, R. V., Gerber, L. D., Stein, S., Stephen, R. L., Grosser, B. I., Velick, S. F., Udenfriend, S. 1979. On βh-Leu⁵-endorphin and schizophrenia. *Arch. Gen. Psychiatry* 36:237–39

42. Lewis, R. V., Stein, S., Gerber, L. D., Rubinstein, M., Udenfriend, S. 1978. High molecular weight opioid-containing proteins in striatum. *Proc. Natl. Acad. Sci. USA* 75:4021–23

43. Li, C. H. 1979. Chemistry of β-endorphin. *Adv. Biochem. Psychopharmacol.* 20:145–63

44. Li, C. H., Chung, D. 1976. Isolation and structure of an untriakontapeptide with opiate activity from camel pituitary glands. *Proc. Natl. Acad. Sci. USA* 73:1145–48

45. Ling, N., Burgus, R., Guillemin, R. 1976. Isolation, primary structure, and synthesis of α-endorphin and γ-endorphin, two peptides of hypothalamic-hypophysial origin with morphinomimetic activity. *Proc. Natl. Acad. Sci. USA* 73:3942–46

46. Liotta, A. S., Gildersleeve, D., Brownstein, M. J., Krieger, D. T. 1979. Biosynthesis in vitro of immunoreactive 31,000-dalton corticotropin/β-endorphin-like material by bovine hypothalamus. *Proc. Natl. Acad. Sci. USA* 76:1448–52

46a. Liotta, A. S., Krieger, D. T. 1980. *In vitro* biosynthesis and comparative posttranslational processing of immunoreactive precursor corticotropin/β-endorphin by human placenta and pituitary cells. *Endocrinology* 106:1504–11

47. Liotta, A. S., Suda, T., Krieger, D. T. 1978. β-Lipotropin is the major opioid-like peptide of human pituitary and rat pars distalis: lack of significant β-endorphin. *Proc. Natl. Acad. Sci. USA* 75:2950–54

48. Loh, H. H., Ross, D. H. 1979. *Neurochemical Mechanisms of Opiates and Endorphins.* NY: Raven Press. 526 pp.

49. Lundberg, J. M., Hamberger, B., Schultzberg, M., Hökfelt, T., Granberg, P. O., Efendic, S., Terenius, L., Goldstein, M., Luft, R. 1979. Enkephalin-and somatostatin-like immunoreactivities in human adrenal medulla and pheochromocytoma. *Proc. Natl. Acad. Sci. USA* 76:4079–83

50. Mains, R. E., Eipper, B. A. 1979. Synthesis and secretion of corticotropins, melanotropins, and endorphins by rat intermediate pituitary cells. *J. Biol. Chem.* 254:7885–94

51. Mains, R. E., Eipper, B. A., Ling, N. 1977. Common precursor to corticotropins and endorphins. *Proc. Natl. Acad. Sci. USA* 74:3014–18

52. Meites, J., Bruni, J. F., Van Vugt, D. A., Smith, A. F. 1979. Relation of endogenous opioid peptides and morphine to neuroendocrine functions. *Life Sci.* 24:1325–36

53. Miller, R. J., Cuatrecasas, P. 1978. Enkephalins and endorphins. *Vitam. Horm.* 36:297–382

54. Nakai, Y., Nakao, K., Oki, S., Imura, H. 1978. Presence of immunoreactive β-lipotropin and β-endorphin in human placenta. *Life Sci.* 25:2013–18

55. Nakai, Y., Nakao, K., Oki, S., Imura, H., Li, C. H. 1978. Presence of immunoreactive β-endorphin in plasma of patients with Nelson's syndrome and Addison's disease. *Life Sci.* 23:2293–98

56. Nakamura, M., Nakanishi, S., Sueoka, S., Imura, H., Numa, S. 1978. Effects of steroid hormones on the level of corticotropin messenger RNA activity in cultured mouse-pituitary-tumor cells. *Eur. J. Biochem.* 86:61–66

57. Nakanishi, S., Inoue, A., Kita, T., Nakamura, M., Chang, A. C. Y., Cohen, S. N., Numa, S. 1979. Nucleotide sequence of cloned cDNA for bovine corticotropin-β-lipotropin precursor. *Nature* 278:423–27

58. Nakanishi, S., Inoue, A., Taii, S., Numa, S. 1977. Cell-free translation product containing corticotropin and β-endorphin encoded by messenger RNA from anterior lobe and intermediate lobe of bovine pituitary. *FEBS Lett.* 84:105–9

59. Nakanishi, S., Kita, T., Taii, S., Imura, H., Numa, S. 1977. Glucocorticoid effect on the level of corticotropin messenger RNA activity in rat pituitary. *Proc. Natl. Acad. Sci. USA* 74:3283–86

60. Nakao, K., Nakai, Y., Jingami, H., Oki, S., Fukata, J., Imura, H. 1979. Substantial rise of plasma β-endorphin levels after insulin-induced hypoglycemia in

human subjects. *J. Clin. Endocrinol. Metab.* 49:838–41

61. Nakao, K., Nakai, Y., Oki, S., Horii, K., Imura, H. 1978. Presence of immunoreactive β-endorphin in normal human plasma. A concomitant release of β-endorphin with adrenocorticotropin after metyrapone administration. *J. Clin. Invest.* 62:1395–98

62. Nakao, K., Nakai, Y., Oki, S., Imura, H., Matsubara, S., Konishi, T., Nishitani, H. 1979. Immunoreactive β-endorphin in human cerebrospinal fluid. *J. Clin. Endocrinol. Metab.* 50:230–33

63. Odagiri, E., Sherrell, B. J., Mount, C. D., Nicholson, W. E., Orth, D. N. 1979. Human placental immunoreactive corticotropin, lipotropin, and β-endorphin: evidence for a common precursor. *Proc. Natl. Acad. Sci. USA* 76:2027–31

63a. Osamura, Y., Watanabe, K., Nakai, Y., Imura, H. 1980. Adrenocorticotropic hormone cells and immunoreactive β-endorphin cells in the human pituitary gland: normal and pathologic conditions studied by the peroxidase-labeled antibody method. *Am. J. Pathol.* 99:105–24

64. Osborne, H., Przewlocki, R., Höllt, V., Herz, A. 1979. Release of β-endorphin from rat hypothalamus in vitro. *Eur. J. Pharmacol.* 55:425–28

65. Palmour, R. M., Ervin, F. R., Wagemaker, H., Cadeø, R. 1979. Characterization of a peptide from serum of psychotic patients. See Ref. 79, pp. 581–93

66. Przewlocki, R., Höllt, V., Duka, T. W., Kleber, G., Gramsch, C. H., Haarmann, I., Herz, A. 1979. Long-term morphine treatment decreases endorphin levels in rat brain and pituitary. *Brain Res.* 174:357–61

67. Przewlocki, R., Höllt, V., Voigt, K. H., Herz, A. 1979. Modulation of in vitro release of β-endorphin from the separate lobes of the rat pituitary. *Life Sci.* 24:1601–8

68. Roberts, J. L., Herbert, E. 1977. Characterization of a common precursor to corticotropin and β-lipotropin: Cell-free synthesis of the precursor and identification of corticotropin peptides in the molecule. *Proc. Natl. Acad. Sci. USA* 74:4826–30

69. Roberts, J. L., Phillips, M., Rosa, P. A., Herbert, E. 1978. Steps involved in the processing of common precursor forms of adrenocorticotropin and endorphin in cultures of mouse pituitary cells. *Biochemistry* 17:3609–18

70. Rossier, J., French, E., Gros, C., Minick, S., Guillemin, R., Bloom, F. E. 1979. Adrenalectomy, dexamethasone or stress alters opioid peptides levels in rat anterior pituitary but not intermediate lobe or brain. *Life Sci.* 25:2105–12

71. Rossier, J., Guillemin, R., Bloom, F. 1978. Foot shock induced stress decreases Leu⁵-enkephalin immunoreactivity in rat hypothalamus. *Eur. J. Pharmacol.* 48:465–66

72. Sosa, R. P., McKnight, A. T., Hughes, J., Kosterlitz, W. H. 1977. Incorporation of labelled amino acids into enkephalins. *FEBS Lett.* 84:195–98

73. Stern, A. S., Lewis, R. V., Kimura, S., Rossier, J., Gerber, L. D., Brink, L., Stein, S., Udenfriend, S. 1979. Isolation of the opioid heptapeptide Met-enkephalin (Arg⁶, Phe⁷) from bovine adrenal medullary granules and striatum. *Proc. Natl. Acad. Sci. USA* 76:6680–83

74. Suda, T., Liotta, A. S., Krieger, D. T. 1978. β-Endorphin is not detectable in plasma from normal human subjects. *Science* 202:221–23

75. Swann, R. W., Li, C. H. 1980. Isolation and characterization of β-endorphin-like peptides from bovine brains. *Proc. Natl. Acad. Sci. USA* 77:230–33

76. Taii, S., Nakanishi, S., Numa, S. 1979. Distribution of the messenger RNA coding for the common precursor of corticotropin and β-lipotropin within the bovine pituitary. *Eur. J. Biochem.* 93:205–12

77. Tramu, G., Leonardelli, J. 1979. Immunohistochemical localization of enkephalin in median eminence and adenohypophysis. *Brain Res.* 168:457–71

78. Uhl, G. R., Childers, S. R., Snyder, S. H. 1978. Opioid peptides and the opiate receptor. *Front. Neuroendocrinol.* 5:289–328

79. Usdin, E., Bunney, W. E. Jr., Line, N. S. 1979. *Endorphins in Mental Health Research.* London: MacMillan Press. 618 pp.

80. Vale, W., Rivier, J., Guillemin, R., Rivier, C. 1979. Effects of purified CRF and other substances on the secretion of ACTH and β-endorphin-like immunoreactivities by cultured anterior or neuro-intermediate pituitary cells. See Ref. 8, pp. 163–76

81. Vale, W., Rivier, C., Yang, L., Minick, S., Guillemin, R. 1978. Effect of purified hypothalamic corticotropin-releasing factor and other substances on the secretion of adrenocorticotropin and

β-endorphin-like immunoreactivities *in vitro*. *Endocrinology* 103:1910–15

82. Wardlaw, S. L., Frantz, A. G. 1979. Measurement of β-endorphin in human plasma. *J. Clin. Endocrinol. Metab.* 48:176–80

83. Watson, S. J., Akil, H., Richard, C. W., Barchas, J. D. 1978. Evidence for two separate opiate peptide neuronal systems. *Nature* 275:226–28

84. Weber, E., Voigt, K. H., Martin, R. 1978. Concomitant storage of ACTH- and endorphin-like immunoreactivity in the secretory granules of anterior pituitary corticotrophs. *Brain Res.* 157:385–90

85. Wiedemann, E., Saito, T., Linfoot, J. A., Li, C. H. 1979. Specific radioimmunoassay of human β-endorphin in unextracted plasma. *J. Clin. Endocrinol. Metab.* 49:478–80

86. Zakarian, S., Smyth, P. 1979. Distribution of active and inactive forms of β-endorphins in rat pituitary and brain. *Proc. Natl. Acad. Sci. USA* 76:5972–76

COMPARATIVE AND INTEGRATIVE PHYSIOLOGY

Introduction, William R. Dawson, *Section Editor*

The four topics treated in this section initially appear quite diverse. However, three of them deal with problems of adjustment to particular environmental circumstances and the fourth concerns the general questions of how and why various types of physiological activity scale with body size. The reviews treating these topics summarize recent findings that, in some instances, necessitate modification of long-standing concepts. The greater reliance on data obtained from unrestrained subjects in the review on diving animals is a cogent example of this. This review and that on functional characteristics of parasites remind us of the importance of anaerobiosis in certain groups of animals and of the existence of functionally significant alternatives to anaerobic glycolysis in many of them. The review on thermal acclimation examines various manifestations of this phenomenon and details recent advances in analysis of its underlying mechanisms. A reminder of the importance of the physiological history of an animal in determining its functional capacities at any given period is implicit in this review.

Volume 43 marks the completion of the term of the present Section Editor. In this as in earlier volumes the section on Comparative and Integrative Physiology has attempted to develop two primary themes. The first of these is the resourcefulness of nature as revealed by a consideration of an array of physiological adaptations. The second theme has concerned the fact that choice of experimental animal is an important and frequently very useful variable in physiological analysis. Expansion of this choice can sometimes provide access to especially convenient experimental material as well as routinely enhance perspective concerning particular processes.

Ann. Rev. Physiol. 1981. 43:281–300
Copyright © 1981 by Annual Reviews Inc. All rights reserved

THE ROLE OF NERVOUS ❖1311
SYSTEMS IN TEMPERATURE
ADAPTATION OF POIKILOTHERMS

C. Ladd Prosser and D. O. Nelson[1]

Department of Physiology and Biophysics, University of Illinois,
Urbana, Illinois 61801

INTRODUCTION

Integration of the many observations on the role of nervous systems into a logical framework relating to temperature adaptation requires several definitions. Two categories of physiological adaptations are recognized. The first concerns internal state—e.g. body temperature, as a function of environmental temperature. Some animals are strict temperature conformers—poikilotherms. Other animals are temperature regulators—homeotherms. Still others are conformers in some organs and under some conditions and regulators of temperature of some body regions under specific conditions—heterotherms. The terms ectothermy and endothermy refer to use of environmental and metabolic heat, respectively, in body warming. The prefixes poikilo- and homeo- refer to internal state, ecto- and endo- refer to means of reaching and maintaining body temperatures. The maintenance of constancy of body temperature is an example of *homeostasis.*

The second category of physiological adaptation concerns either constancy or variability in activity, in energy production. Many poikilothermic animals compensate for body cooling or heating by changing their metabolism in such a way as to permit relatively constant activity over a wide range of body temperatures. Temperature regulators expend energy in maintaining body temperature over a range of environmental temperatures and thus are capable of relatively constant activity. Metabolic compensation of

[1]Present address: Department of Physiology, 314A Hamilton Hall, Ohio State University, Columbus, OH 43210

281

0066-4278/81/0315-0281$01.00

poikilotherms for body heating or cooling maintains constancy of activity; this is *homeokinesis*.

Adaptive responses that permit normal activity over an environmental range can occur only within limits imposed by the genotype. Within these limits, animals are capable of acclimation (in the laboratory) or acclimatization (in nature where many environmental factors change). The adaptations for constant activity are partly metabolic and partly behavioral (via the nervous system); they are *capacity adaptations*.

Beyond certain limits of environmental and/or body temperature, regulation of internal temperature and of activity fail. Various adaptations permit extension of tolerable limits—extremes of heat or cold. In general, the limits for normal function are narrower for integrated intact animals than for isolated tissues and cells; the limits for "survival" of enzymatic proteins or membrane phospholipids extend farther. At thermal extremes, nervous systems often fail before other systems and the resulting behavioral failures occur before protein inactivation. Adaptations that permit continued function at environmental extremes are called *resistance adaptations*.

CAPACITY ADAPTATIONS

Metabolism

Metabolic capacity adaptations in poikilotherms are best known for liver and muscle; little is known of compensatory changes of energy metabolism in nervous systems. Brain is highly aerobic in its metabolism, and showed marked thermal acclimation of several enzymes in green sunfish (*Lepomis cyanellus*). Pyruvate kinase activity of brain increased during cold acclimation whereas it decreased in muscle; succinate dehydrogenase (SDH) increased in both of these tissues. Activity of lactate DH increased slightly in brain, whereas its activity decreased in both muscle and liver (93). The brain evidently maintains a high energy production when acclimated at different temperatures.

It has been suggested that oxygen consumption of lateral muscle of eels may be under neural control. If the head (brain) alone was cooled for several days the V_{O_2} of isolated muscle was higher than it was if the brain was warmed (85). However, partial destruction of spinal cord did not prevent acclimation of oxidative enzymes in the lateral muscle (92). Also, acclimation of head and tail of trout (*Salmo gairdneri*) to low or high temperature, assessed by measurement of time to death of the fish at a high temperature, indicated localized responses within each region, probably in production of some toxic factor, and that the brain is not uniquely involved (33).

Some species show little or no metabolic capacity adaptation but do show resistance adaptations for extreme temperatures. This has been frequently noted for frogs (8), in which muscle and liver metabolism is unaltered by acclimation but neuromuscular transmission and functioning of the central nervous systems are sensitive to temperature acclimation.

Activity metabolism of fishes is maximal at mid-temperature. This temperature is often that of greatest locomotor activity—e.g. feeding (14), swimming speed (37). Other environmental factors, e.g. photoperiod and nutrients may counterbalance temperature in controlling locomotor activity, and acclimation may not only change metabolism but also facilitate neurally controlled behavior at particular temperatures. Locomotor activity, as controlled by the nervous system, probably determines the temperature for Vo_2max rather than being controlled by metabolism.

Behavior

THERMOREGULATION   Little recognized as a component of capacity adaptation is behavior that puts animals into thermal regimes facilitating metabolic compensation. Behavioral thermoregulation consists of coordinated activity that results in selection of an environment of "optimal" temperature. Many poikilotherms show active selection of a preferred temperature when placed in a thermal gradient and so regulate their body temperature (23, 82). Models of thermoregulation [summarized in (22a)] incorporate the set-point hypothesis. Interactions between regions of the nervous system for behavioral and physiological regulation in vertebrate ectotherms and endotherms, various environmental factors in addition to temperature, and autonomic regulatory functions are considered. The range of temperatures selected when the animals are first introduced into a gradient usually approximates that to which they have been acclimated and varies with acclimation (22, 74, 79), as shown for bullheads (*Ameiurus nebulosus*) and green sunfish (Table 1). In general, a higher temperature is selected after exposure to higher acclimation temperature (T_{acc}), but at extremes of the acclimation range preferred temperature may not change (52). However, the selected temperature decreases with increasing T_{acc} in rainbow trout (*Salmo gairdneri*) (38) and the cyprinodont *Lebistes reticulatus* (104), possibly because of nutritional correlates. When left in the gradient for some hours the fish from low acclimation and low selected temperatures tend to go toward higher temperatures. Table 1 shows that after 24 hr bullheads selected 30°C, irrespective of their previous acclimation. Neither the neural mechanism for change in preferred temperature with time in a gradient nor the time course of acclimation for preferred temperature is known.

The range of selected temperatures may be important in predator-prey relations, reproduction, migration, and optimal metabolic activity (76).

Table 1 Temperatures selected in a thermal gradient by bullheads (*Ameiurus nebulosus*) and green sunfish (*Lepomis cyanellus*) from different acclimation temperatures and after various times in the gradient

	T_{acc} (°C)	Selected temperatures at various times in gradient (°C)			
		0–1 hr	6 hr	10 hr	24 hr
Bullheads (22)	7	16	—	25	30
	15	21	—	25	30
	24	26	—	30	30
	32	31	—	—	30
Green sunfish (74)	5	8	12	—	—
	15	17	20	—	—
	25	26	29	—	—

Fish of each species, if left undisturbed for a long time in a thermal gradient will select a temperature called the final preferendum: the temperature at which T_{acc} and selected temperature are the same (36).

Neural control of temperature selection in fish is similar to temperature regulation in other vertebrates in that both peripheral and central receptors are used (43). Conditioning experiments indicate that several species of fish have considerable peripheral thermosensitivity (17). By means of brain lesions, the forebrain of fish was implicated in behavioral thermoregulation (95). Cooling or heating the anterior brainstem with thermodes changes thermoregulatory behavior (23). Lesions in the preoptic region of green sunfish and goldfish (*Carassius auratus*) disrupt behavioral selection and regulation of internal body temperature in a gradient (74). Distributions of lesioned animals in a gradient did not differ from that of controls when no thermal gradient was present. Temperature-sensitive neurons have been reported in the thalamus of brook trout (*Salvelinus fontinalis*) (41) and in the preoptic region of sunfish (73, 75). The proportions and relative sensitivities of warm and cold sensitive cells resemble those in endotherms. Some neurons are sensitive to both local and peripheral temperatures, suggesting that integration of thermal information takes place in the preoptic region. This correlates well with work showing that lesions (also heating and cooling with thermodes) of the preoptic region alter thermoregulatory behavior. Apparently the same region of the brain is used in poikilothermic vertebrates (mainly fish and reptiles) for behavioral thermoregulation as is used in homeotherms for metabolic and cardiovascular thermoregulation. Each type of regulation is useful in capacity adaptation to changes in environmental temperature.

Some animals bask in the sun on cold days or burrow or enter shade on hot days. Absorption of heat from solar radiation is important for terrestrial insects and reptiles and may be correlated with pigmentation. Insects are the most abundant and diverse group of terrestrial animals. They tend to be seasonal and thus cope with a limited environmental temperature range. Flight is highly energy-consuming and requires precise integration of the nervous system. Some insects control temperature of certain body regions, most importantly thoracic ganglia, during locomotor activity. For many insects, particularly large ones, thermoregulation is controlled by postural changes and by repeated contraction of wing muscles (30, 44, 55). Ectothermic insects bask (some butterflies) or remain inactive until air temperature reaches a critical point (cicadas). Endothermic insects (e.g. some butterflies, moths, bumblebees) use heat production during warm-up before flight (46, 47). Monarch butterflies were acclimated to 5° or to 23 °C, and warm-up contractions of the wing muscles were tested at 15°C. Ninety percent of the animals acclimated to 5°C showed shivering contractions, 40% of those acclimated at 23°C; in animals kept at the higher temperature warm-up commenced later (56). In nocturnal moths the muscles that move the wings contract in an uncoordinated fashion during warm-up. Flight is initiated at a thoracic temperature of 32.6°C or higher. The thorax warms at 4°C min^{-1} and body temperature reaches levels of 32°–36°C at ambient temperatures of 17°–29°C (1). Preflight warm-up increases O_2 consumption some 2.3 times, and fat is the principal fuel (44). The temperature of the nerve cord is more important than that of the muscles (44). Heating the nerve cord with a thermode in quiescent moths can stimulate the animal to fly without warm-up behavior. Behavioral regulation of temperature continues after connections between the head and thorax are severed, but interference with the connections within the thoracic ganglia disturbs the regulation (69). The desert moth, *Manduca* (48), does not initiate flight until the thorax temperature rises to 38°C, then to 42°C in flight; this T_b is maintained at ambient temperatures of from 17°–32°C. Heat produced in the thorax is transferred by the dorsal blood vessel to the abdomen. Flight stops owing to overheating if this vessel is occluded (47). Honeybees and termites use metabolic heat to maintain brood nest temperatures (32, 67). Populations (clusters) of honeybees can respond to decreases in ambient temperature with increased metabolism proportional to heat loss from the cluster. Increases in ambient temperature result in metabolic decrease and fanning (60). A hierarchy of thermal sensitivities exists in that complex behaviors occur over a narrower range of temperature than simple reflexes. In general, flight is blocked by cold before walking. Interactive or social behavior is more stenothermal than behavior of individuals (e.g. in cicadas, chorusing occurs at 31°–35°C, courtship 22°–36°C, flight 20°–37°C, walking 13°—40°C, feeding 10°–43°C) (46). The sensing neurons are unknown but can be localized to a particular ganglion in some insects (44).

CONDITIONING OF BEHAVIOR   Learning and memory formation also favor normal activity in the mid-range of temperature and can be altered by acclimation (9, 15, 83). Temperature has multiple effects on various processes in the nervous system, and the mechanism(s) by which temperature affects conditioning is not clear (9). Retention of conditioned responses can be blocked reversibly by temperatures beyond the normal physiological range (25, 34, 72, 90). Lowering of temperature decreased the rate of memory decay in conditioned goldfish whereas change to a higher temperature accelerated the process of information loss (91).

Interruption of opercular movements in breathing was conditioned to illumination in goldfish (83, 90). Conditioning did not occur below a minimum temperature, and the lower threshold for it varied with T_{acc}: At 30°C T_{acc} the minimum temperature for conditioning was 17–18°C; for 25°C, 12–13°C; for 15°C, 6–7°C. The conditioned responses were blocked by cooling and the blocking temperature varied linearly according to the temperature at which conditioning occurred, irrespective of T_{acc}. Temperature of cold block increased 5° for each 10° increase in conditioning temperature, as if the temperature of forgetting depended on the temperature of learning. Loss of conditionability at a low temperature could be detected within a few hours of acclimation at a high temperature, whereas gain of conditionability at a low temperature required 2–4 days of acclimation at a low temperature. These neural acclimatory changes take place faster than those for metabolic acclimation (83, 90).

Conditioned field potentials in the optic tectum were recorded in goldfish (84); the conditioned responses followed direct responses to visual stimulation by 105–110 msec. The conditioned evoked potentials were more sensitive to cooling than were the direct evoked responses (blocking temperature of 4–5°C vs >9°C). For each type of response the critical low temperature was several degrees lower during cooling, than during warming, i.e., there was a lag in recovery. The conditioned potential of the optic tectum was blocked by less cooling than was needed for the conditioned interruption of breathing behavior. This may indicate a simpler neural circuit for the respiratory conditioning than for the tectal conditioning.

Interaction between T_{acc} and intertrial interval has been noted in learning by goldfish (106). Fish acclimated to 5°, 10°, 20° and 25°C were conditioned at their T_{acc}, and fish acclimated to 13° and to 20°C were conditioned at 25° and 28°C, respectively. Fish acclimated to 5°C failed to acquire avoidance behavior; animals acclimated to 20°C learned at the same rate as fish acclimated to 29° and conditioned at 28°C. Animals acclimated to 13°C and conditioned at 25°C learned faster than fish acclimated to 20°C and conditioned at 20°C but more slowly than if conditioned at 28°C. The slowest learning rate was shown by fish acclimated to 10°C and conditioned at 10°C. Thus the temperature of conditioning affects the rate of information acquisition (15). The time course of acclimation for avoidance learning appears to be longer than for conditioned operator responses. The influence of long-term thermal acclimation on shock avoidance responses appeared after 34 days, and full conditionability, comparable to that of long-term warm-acclimated fish, was obtained 50 days after transfer (86). Significant compensation in the conditionability of fish occurs during the process of thermal acclimation. Such long-term effects may be the cause of discrepancies in results obtained from different training studies of fish (3).

Coordinated swimming was induced in green sunfish in a rotating device that measured maximum swimming speed at different temperatures. Thermal acclimation modified the temperature of maximum swimming speed and the temperatures below and above which no swimming could be induced (90): For T_{acc} of 30° cold block of swimming occurred at 15°, maximum swimming speed at 30–35°C, and heat block at 40°; for T_{acc} of 15° cold block was at 5°, maximum speed at 25°, and heat block at 30°C. Coordinated swimming is more thermolabile than spinal reflexes, as measured in goldfish (90). A T_{acc} of 35°C resulted in a spinal reflex cold block temperature of 10°C; a T_{acc} of 25°, a cold block temperature of 5°C; a 15°C T_{acc} a cold block temperature of 1°C. Thus complex behaviors such as conditioning surpass simple motor reflexes in sensitivity to cooling or heating.

RESISTANCE ADAPTATION

Behavior

Poikilothermic animals die after much less cooling or heating than is required for metabolic failure; the nervous system fails well before inactivation of key metabolic enzymes. Some animals show resistance adaptation without capacity adaptation, and the time course of acclimation for the two may be different. What fails in the nervous system and what changes acclimation brings about are poorly understood.

As fish are either heated or cooled (35), the first sign of stress is hyperactivity; they swim rapidly and with jerky motions and if touched may show looping movements. Slightly more heating or cooling produces motor incoordination and failure to swim straight ahead. With still more change in body temperature they lose righting ability; finally they show shallow breathing and enter a comatose state that may lead to death if thermal conditions do not improve. These behavioral deficits can also be induced by local cooling or heating of the brain (particularly of the cerebellum in the case of hyperactivity and loss of coordination) with a thermode (35). Similar sequences of behavior—hyperactivity, motor incoordination, disequilibrium, respiratory coma—have been observed in other animals—insects, crayfish, mammals—in hypo- or hyper-thermia. In fish the ultimate cause of death is probably not thermal denaturation but anoxia.

Electrical Activity in Central Nervous Systems

Electrical measurements of neural activity as affected by heat and cold suggest explanations of the sequence of behavior at thermal extremes and give evidence for a hierarchical neural organization.

Evoked potential responses of optic tectum of fish and of some reptiles decline on cooling and are blocked at temperatures well above those causing coma. In rainbow trout (*Salmo gairdneri*), responses to electrical stimulation of the retina increased in latency and duration on cooling from 10°C to 4°C, but these effects diminished during three weeks of cold acclimation. Fish transferred from 10°C to 16°C and acclimated at 16°C showed decreases in latency and duration of responses to retinal stimulation (59). In goldfish (*Carassius auratus*), two regions of synaptic negativity were observed in response to visual stimulation, one just below the tectal surface at synapses of pyramidal neurons and the other deeper in the layer of pyriform neurons. Evoked responses to visual stimulation in the deep layer had latencies 10–20 ms longer than those near the tectal surface. With T_{acc} of 15° and 25°C, blocking occurred at 4–5°C and 9–12°C (surface) and 5–8°C and 10–12.5°C (deep), respectively (84). Responses of single units in the facial lobes to tactile stimulation blocked at 6°C in 25°C-acclimated goldfish (78).

Electrical activity of Purkinje neurons in goldfish cerebellum correlated with behavioral deficits. Temperature of cold block in 25°C-acclimated fish covered nearly a 10°C range, much as did the lower thresholds for behavioral losses, which extended from 13°–15°C for inhibition (probably via Golgi cells) down to 5°C for antidromic responses. (35).

At high temperatures, histograms of interspike intervals of ongoing activity showed reduction of the peak on warming and random firing at coma temperatures. Some Purkinje cells fired in doublet patterns that changed reversibly to quadruplets on warming; finally spikes became random (35).

These results indicated: (*a*) Inhibitory synapses are more thermosensitive than excitatory ones. Behavioral hyperexcitability may result from removal of inhibition. (*b*) Disynaptic excitation may be more labile than monosynaptic. (*c*) Spike initiation blocks with less cooling than synaptic potentials. (*d*) Axon responses (antidromic) are more resistant than synaptic responses, and (*e*) Ongoing spontaneous activity may show pattern changes.

Synapses of lateral inhibition in the *Limulus* lateral eye are more thermosensitive (Q_{10} = 2.6) than excitatory responses (receptor potentials Q_{10} = 1.4, spike initiation Q_{10} = 1.6) (2).

Isolated nerve cords of cockroaches (*Periplaneta*) acclimated to 22° showed maximal frequency of ongoing activity at 22°C and at 31° for animals acclimated at 31°C (58). Isolated cockroach nerve cords of 20°C-acclimated animals had highest spontaneous activity at 18°C, and animals kept at 30°C had a maximum near 26°C (24). Temperatures for cold coma shifted downward with decreasing T_{acc}. Cockroach nerve cords (isolated or in vivo) showed ongoing activity at temperature below that for cold coma: Not all neural activity is blocked at coma temperatures. Intertidal snails (*Littorina littorea*) show heat coma at temperatures which can be altered by acclimation; ongoing activity in central ganglia stops at the coma temperature (42).

An Alaskan beetle, *Perostichus brevicornis,* can live in winter temperatures at which the hemolymph is frozen (6). Summer animals died if frozen at –6.6°C, winter ones froze at –10°C and died if cooled below –35°C. Extracellularly recorded action potentials of the trochanter nerve of the hind leg showed block of ongoing activity as follows: At T_{acc} (winter animals) of –20°C (frozen), 0°C (5 days), and +20°C (14 days), cold block occurred at –12°C, –8°C, and 0°C, respectively. Motoneurons fell into six groups, differing in blocking temperatures and in the thermal range over which they were active.

Multiple changes in synaptic properties occur over a functional range of temperature. In squid (*Loligo*) giant synapses the synaptic potentials (psp's) decline on cooling from 10°–12°C and fail to trigger spikes below 8°C, an effect not due to reduction in presynaptic impulses (99). The rise in Ca current is slowed by cold, and Ca entry may be insufficient for transmitter release (18).

Neuromuscular transmission may be used as a model for testing synaptic effects of temperature. Sensitivity to cold or heat decreases in the order: neuromuscular junction > muscle (direct stimulation) > nerve conduction. This was demonstrated for skates [*Raja erinacea* (5)], frog (*Rana pipiens*) sartorius and sternocutaneous (53, 80, 96, 100), crayfish (*Procambarus clarkii*) leg muscles (101), and rat diaphragm (51). The temperatures for cold and heat block can be altered by acclimation; for example, in frog sartorius, cold block for 10°C- and 25°C-acclimated frogs was at 1°C and 4°C, respectively (53).

Crayfish leg muscles receive fast and slow excitatory plus inhibitory innervation. Inhibitory junctions are more thermolabile than excitatory ones (101): For T_{acc} of 10°C, inhibitory junctions heat-blocked at 29.9° (3° lower than excitatory junctions), whereas for T_{acc} of 25°C the heat block of inhibition was at 34°C (4° lower than excitatory junctions). The greater sensitivity of inhibitory synapses to both cold and heat agrees with findings for cerebellum and *Limulus* eye (2).

Either postsynaptic membrane changes for Cl^- conductance are more labile than those for Na^+ conductance changes or liberation of inhibitory transmitters is more temperature labile than of excitatory endings. Limited biochemical evidence supports the transmitter hypothesis. Synaptosomal fractions containing GABA lose nearly 80% of transmitter after sudden cooling in contrast to only 20% lost from synaptosomes containing catecholamines (87).

Resting membrane potentials (RP) of frog muscle are relatively unaffected by temperature over a mid-range (53, 96). In crayfish leg muscles the RP became more negative on heating. However, in muscles treated with ouabain the gain in negativity was substantially reduced; hence the Na-K pump is stimulated by warming, especially above 28°C (101). The electrogenic pump contribution to RP appears to be greater in crayfish than in frog muscle.

Endplate potentials (EPPs), either as responses to motor nerve impulses or to iontophoresed transmitter (ACh in frog, glutamate in crayfish), show complex temperature relations. In frog sartorius and sternocutaneous muscles, the endplate responses show a maximum at 15–18°C, a minimum at 22–26°C, then a rapid increase in amplitude up to a critical temperature above which the responses drop rapidly at the blocking temperature (36°C frog, 35.5°C crayfish) (53, 101). Facilitation in frog muscle peaks at 14–16°C, near the acclimatization temperature (53). In closer muscles of walking legs of crayfish (*Astacus leptodactylus*), the temperatures of maximum amplitude of both fast and slow psp's shifted toward T_{acc}, and maximum facilitation also occurred at the T_{acc} (45). Similarly, dorsal root evoked potentials in cats with cooled spinal cords showed a maximum at 30°C (16). In rat diaphragm, the quantal content (m) and frequency of miniature endplate potentials (mepp's) were maximal at 20°C (51). The amplitude and duration of mepp's peak at 16–20°C in frog curarized sartorius (53). At temperatures above that of maximum synaptic potential a decline to a minimum usually occurs. In some muscles (crayfish) the epp's may show a plateau rather than a maximum in the mid-range and then decline in the range 20–30°C.

At temperatures above that at which the amplitude of the endplate potential was minimal (nerve-induced or iontophoresed transmitter-induced), the amplitude of spontaneous mepp's may decline further and reach zero. The rate of decline in amplitude of mepp's is usually less than the rate of fall in epp's (51, 101). At temperatures at which epp and mepp amplitude decline, the frequency of mepp's and the quantal content (m) values increase steeply. A maximum m value was reached for rat diaphram above 40°C (51). In frog sternocutaneous the frequency of mepp's continued to increase at temperatures well above those of epp block if Ca^{2+} was normal, but not in Ca^{2+}-free solution (4, 100).

In crayfish, values of m rose steeply and then fell abruptly (101, 102): At temperatures of 10°C, 30°C, and 36°C, m values were 3, 6.5, and 0, respectively. In curarized rat phrenic-diaphragm, m increased from 42.4 at 24° to 108.7 at 37° (50). Frequency of mepp's in rat diaphragm increased from 5° to a peak at 16°, then was minimal at 30° and increased steeply ($Q_{10} = 16.8$) to 39° (98).

Membrane resistance (R_m) declines on warming. In frog sartorius, R_m declined with a Q_{10} of 1.36 over the range 3°–25°C (26). In crayfish muscle the membrane resistance decreased steeply at low temperatures and less steeply at a higher range; a sharp break in slope occurred at 15–20°C. The slope was steeper for warm-acclimated than for cold-acclimated animals. In crayfish muscles the decline in epp's can be accounted for quantitatively by decline in membrane resistance and consequent shunting of the epp (101).

Different portions of the temperature range have been examined in different neuromuscular preparations. Figure 1 summarizes results; synaptic changes as temperature is raised are the following: (a) Endplate potentials increase on warming from a low temperature (3°–8°C) to a peak at an intermediate temperature (15–20°C in frog, fast muscle of crayfish) or show a plateau (18°–25°C in slow muscle of cold acclimated crayfish) (16°–20°C for mepp's in cat diaphragm). A similar increase in amplitude or a plateau occurs for responses to applied transmitter (Ach in frog, glutamate in crayfish). The peak is not altered by antiesterase (frog), hence the increase may be due either to enhanced transmitter-receptor binding (53) or to prolonged channel opening (57). (b) The decline in epp and in mepp amplitudes at slightly higher temperatures may be due to shunting associated with a fall in extrasynaptic resistance (26, 101). (c) The increase in frequency of mepp's and in m values with further heating is sensitive to calcium concentration (4, 51, 100) and probably is due to increased quantal content and increased probability of presynaptic liberation of transmitter (57, 68). (d) Block of transmission occurs abruptly, owing not so much to postsynaptic decline as to cessation of transmitter release (101).

Axon Conduction

Several studies deal with effects of temperature on action potentials in single giant fibers of earthworms (*Lumbricus*). Preparations from 13°C (T_{acc}) worms had higher conduction velocities over the 6°–32°C range than fibers from 23°C (T_{acc}) worms; the differences were greatest at 6°C (62). Spike duration at 6° and at 13°C was lower in fibers from cold-acclimated animals. Absolute refractory periods measured at intermediate temperatures were significantly shorter in nerve fibers from cold acclimated (13°C) animals. Giant fibers from cold-acclimated animals conducted impulses at low temperatures at nearly twice the velocity of fibers from warm-acclimated (23°C) worms (61). With intracellular recording (28), action potential dura-

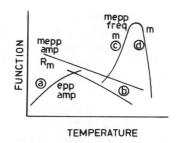

TEMPERATURE

Figure 1 Schematic representation of effects of temperature on different phases of postsynaptic responses as shown in various preparations. See text for key.

tion and input resistance were shown to be lower in axons from cold- (5°C) than from warm- (23°C) acclimated worms. Threshold and rates of rise and fall of action potentials were higher in the 5°C-acclimated preparations. When measured at 20°C the duration and rise and fall rates were significantly lower for cold acclimation. Ionic conductances apparently are altered in a compensatory manner by thermal acclimation. Not only input resistance but also axoplasmic resistance is reduced by cold acclimation (29).

In sciatic nerves of frogs, conduction velocity and heat and cold tolerance limits of nerves from frogs acclimated to 15°C were shifted to values 5°C higher than for nerves from 5°-acclimated frogs (31). Heat block occurred at 47.5°C and 38.9°C in nerves from frogs acclimated to 40° and 26°C, respectively. Conduction in nerves from cold-acclimated frogs was also more resistant to cold block (70). When isolated frog nerves were held at low temperatures for several hours, temperature for cold block was raised —i.e. an effect opposite to that with intact frogs (94).

In pedal nerves of the snail *Limnaea stagnalis* acclimated to 3°, 12°, or 21°C, temperature of lowest threshold (maximal excitability) was lowered by cold acclimation but absolute strengths of the required stimulus were increased (7).

Axon conduction is more thermo-stable and less susceptible to change by acclimation than is block of synaptic transmission. Conduction in peripheral nerves of catfish or in Purkinje axons of goldfish continues on cooling to temperatures 5–10° lower than for block of spinal reflexes or of cerebellar synapses (35, 90). These results should be compared with synaptic effects previously given.

Membrane Properties

Effects of temperature on certain muscle membranes were mentioned previously, specifically with warming a decrease in membrane resistance and little effect on the diffusion component, but a marked effect on the Na-pump component of resting potential. Effects of thermal acclimation on resting potential of the lateral giant neuron in the buccal ganglion of the freshwater snail *Helisoma trivolis* were examined in animals acclimated to 5° or to 25°C for at least 34 days (71). The component most sensitive to temperature and most capable of acclimation was the Na pump, as shown by effects of ouabain. Resting potentials (RP) of warm-acclimated snails increased more (from −44 to −58 mv after warming from 5° to 30°C) than did those from cold-acclimated snails (from −45 to −48 mv for the same range). RP's of ouabain-inhibited neurons were similar in cells from cold- and from warm-acclimated snails (25 mv at 5°C to 32 mv at 30°C). Thus the pump component is greater at high than at low temperatures, and pump acclimation tends to keep the RP of cold-acclimated cells more constant than that of warm cells. Short- and long-term effects of temperature on identified neurons in the snail *Helix aspersa* have been examined (105). The excitability and frequency of ongoing spikes in warm-acclimated animals were depressed by cooling from 20° to 5°C. Warming increased frequency of firing but, after acclimation at 20°C, the frequency at a given temperature decreased. Acclimation had no obvious effect on action potential duration, ion conductance, or Na-K pump activity. However, the ratios of permeability of other cations to that of potassium showed acclimatory change; this may reflect alteration in field strength of anionic sites.

A central neuron (F1) of the visceral ganglion was studied in snails (*Helix aspersa*) acclimated to 4°, 12°, 19°, or 30°C for at least 4 weeks (64, 65, 66). The hemolymph showed highest osmotic concentration in cold-acclimated snails; Na and K concentrations were highest in 4°C-acclimated animals. Concentrations of Ca and Mg showed little change during acclimation. Cells from 30°C- and 4°C-acclimated snails were more depolarized at intermediate test temperatures (20°C) than were cells from 19°C-acclimated animals. Input resistance, rates of potential change during an action potential, and frequency of spontaneous action potentials decreased in a linear fashion with increasing acclimation temperature in compensation for direct temperature effects. The insensitivity of electrical parameters of control neurons to hemolymph from acclimated individuals or corresponding saline concentrations suggest that thermal acclimation of neurons is not due to changes in composition of the hemolymph. It is more probable that warm acclimation results in increased resting conductance for Na and K.

Changes in Mg-ATPase and Na,K-ATPase of neuronal membranes have been suggested as important in thermal acclimation. Enzyme activities in homogenates of nerve cords from earthworms acclimated to 14° or to 25°C were measured over the range 1°–50°C. Temperature dependence of Mg-ATPase was similar in both acclimated groups but Na,K-ATPase activity from cold-acclimated animals was higher than that of nerve cords from warm-acclimated worms (61, 63). At high temperatures, crayfish and frog muscle cells become permeable to ions, and K^+ levels in hemolymph and blood may reach such high concentrations that neuromuscular and central nervous function are impaired (10, 11, 39, 40, 77). In crayfish (*Astacus leptodactylus*) the hemolymph K^+ increases on exposure to 32°C more slowly in warm- than in cold-acclimated animals. Heat inactivation of Mg-ATPase from muscle microsomes of crayfish occurred at a higher temperature and nearer the lethal level in warm- than in cold-acclimated crayfish.

Mg-ATPase might regulate passive permeability to ions. However, no change in fluidity or in phospholipid composition of microsomes was found in fish muscle with temperature acclimation (20). Also, in crayfish no depolarization of muscle cells occurred as they were warmed to as high as 40°C for 90 min, but muscle RP's hyperpolarized with warming. The LD_{50} at 40°C was 9 min; hence it was concluded that heat death is unlikely to result from K leaked from muscle (101, 102).

Thus warming increases Na,K-ATPase activity, this enzyme shows thermal compensation, and changes in passive ion permeability are small.

Synaptic Chemistry

Acclimatory changes in Na,K-ATPase of axons and striated muscle membranes were noted above. The observed effects could result from altered phospholipids in the membranes for it has been shown for many kinds of organisms that fatty acids formed at low temperatures are more unsaturated than those formed at high temperatures. More unsaturated fatty acids in membrane phospholipids may increase the Na,K-ATPase activity at a given temperature (81, 97).

Goldfish brain showed an increase in total lipid content and an increase in percentage of unsaturated fatty acids during cold acclimation (54). Increase or decrease in the amount of unsaturated lipids in cold or warm may maintain constancy of the fluid state of brain membranes at different temperatures. No significant changes occurred in total phospholipid, choline glycerophosphatide, ethanolamine glycerophosphatide, or serine glycophosphatide, but increase in unsaturation of the C-18 fraction of ethanolamine glycerophosphate took place with decreasing acclimation temperature (88). Large changes were noted with acclimation (30°C and 5°C) in neutral and polar plasmalogens (89); the proportion of glycerophosphatidyl ethanolamine increased at high temperature. Plasmalogens are particularly abundant in myelin (27).

Brain gangliosides also show changes in pattern with thermal acclimation (12, 13, 49). In brain of carp (*Cyprinus carpio*) and rainbow trout, acclimations at low temperatures resulted in a higher proportion of polysialogangliosides—i.e. more polar molecules. Low temperature reduces the stability of ganglioside-Ca^{2+} complexes, and this may be compensated by formation of more polar gangliosides. These are most abundant in gray matter.

Correlations have been observed among behavior, synaptic failure, synaptosome fatty acid composition, and fluidity in brains of goldfish acclimated to 5° and 25°C. These properties changed in parallel during the time of acclimation, faster after transfer from 5° to 25°C than in the reverse direction. Fluidity of synaptosomal membranes as estimated from fluorescence polarization decreased at high temperatures of measurement, but at a given temperature, fluidity was greater in 5°C- than in 25°C-acclimated brains. Synaptosomal fatty acids showed increased unsaturation in cold acclimation and decreased unsaturation in warm acclimation. Behavioral disturbances at high temperatures are related to synaptic block, and this correlates with fatty acid composition of membrane phospholipids and membrane fluidity (19, 20). Interspecific (genetic) differences parallel acclimation differences. Membrane fluidity decreased in the following order: Arctic sculpin (*Myoxocephalus verrucosus*) from 1°C, 5°C-acclimated sunfish, 25°C-acclimated sunfish, desert pupfish (*Cyprinodon nevadensis*) from 34°C, and rat 37°C (21). It appears that homeoviscous compensation of synaptic membranes is an important component of thermal adaptation.

CONCLUSIONS AND SUMMARY

Nervous systems are important in several aspects of temperature adaptation. Both direct responses and acclimatory adaptive changes play roles in capacity (constant energy over a range of body temperatures) and in resistance (tolerance of extreme temperatures) adaptations.

Neural tissue is highly aerobic and changes in enzyme activities may compensate for temperature changes. Other acclimatory alterations occur in membrane phospholipids (increased unsaturation in cold, changes in classes of phospholipids, changes in gangliosides) which may provide for constancy of membrane fluidity. Behavioral regulation of body temperature permits metabolic and locomotor activity to be relatively constant at various environment temperatures. Both ectothermic and endothermic mechanisms are used for this regulation and best examples are found in insects, fishes, and reptiles. Sensing mechanisms are not well known and shifts toward high selected temperatures after some hours in a thermal gradient are unexplained. Related capacity adaptations include conditioned responses; the limiting temperatures for conditioning, rate of learning, and retention of response patterns change with temperature of conditioning and of acclimation. Acclimation of simple behavioral responses may occur rapidly (within hours) whereas acclimation of rates of complex learning may require many days. The nature of changes during acclimation of behavior are virtually unknown but may represent a kind of neural plasticity.

At extremes of cold and heat, many animals respond by a sequence of behaviors—hyperexcitability, motor incoordination, loss of equilibrium, respiratory coma—that are reversible and occur with much less temperature change than is required for enzyme inactivation. Behavioral failures are hierarchical in decreasing sensitivity: complex learning, locomotion, simple reflexes, synaptic transmission and, at extremes of cold and heat, failure of axon conduction. Inhibitory synapses are more sensitive than excitatory ones. Effects of temperature on synapses (most observed for neuromuscular transmission) are multiple. Maximal postsynaptic potentials occur at an intermediate temperature. Postsynaptic membrane resistance decreases on warming and this may shunt synaptic potentials. Frequency of spontaneous miniature potentials, also quantal content, increase on warming, and Ca-dependent transmitter liberation fails at a critical temperature of synaptic block. Effects of temperature on membrane resting potential are greater for the electrogenic component due to the Na-K pump than for leak currents. With acclimation, the critical temperatures for synaptic block may change adaptively. Changes in phospholipids of synaptic membranes correlate with these compensatory changes, but alterations in postsynaptic receptors and in transmitter synthesis and release are poorly understood.

ACKNOWLEDGMENTS

This work was supported by NSF PCM 76-15861 to C.L.P. and HEW PHS GM 07143, a traineeship, to D.O.N.

Literature Cited

1. Adams, P. A., Heath, J. E. 1964. Temperature regulation in sphinx moth *Celerio*. *Nature* 201:20–21
2. Adolf, A. R. 1973. Thermal sensitivity of lateral inhibition in *Limulus* eye. *J. Gen. Physiol.* 62:392–406
3. Agranoff, B. W., Davis, R. E. 1968. The use of fishes in studies on memory formation. In *The Central Nervous System and Fish Behavior*, ed. D. Ingle, 3:193–201. Chicago: Univ. Chicago Press. 272 pp.
4. Barrett, E. F., Barrett, J. N., Boty, D., Chang, D. B., Mahaffey, D. 1978. Temperature sensitive aspects of evoked and spontaneous release at frog neuromuscular junction. *J. Physiol. London* 279:253–73
5. Battle, H. I. 1926. Lethal temperatures in relation to reflexes in skate. *Trans. R. Soc. Canad.* 20:127–43

6. Baust, J. G. 1972. Temperature-induced neural adaptations: motoneuron discharge in the Alaskan beetle *Pterostichus brevicornis* (Carabidae). *Comp. Biochem. Physiol. A* 41:205–13
7. Benthe, H. F. 1954. Über die Temperaturabhängigkeit neuromuskulärer Varänger. *Z. Vergl. Physiol.* 36:327–51
8. Bishop, L. G., Gordon, M. S. 1976. Thermal adaptation of metabolism in anuran amphibians. In *Molecular Mechanisms of Temperature*, ed. C. L. Prosser, 7:263–80. Washington DC: AAAS Publ. 84. 156 pp.
9. Borsook, D., Woolf, C. J., Vellet, A. D. 1978. Temperature acclimation and learning in fish. *Experientia* 34:70–71
10. Bowler, K. 1963. A study of the factors involved in acclimation to temperature and death at high temperatures in *Astacus pallipes*. II. Experiments at the

tissue level. *J. Cell. Comp. Physiol.* 62:113–46

11. Bowler, K., Gladwell, R. T., Duncan, C. J. 1973. Acclimation to temperature and death at high temperatures in the crayfish *Austropotamobius pallipes.* In *Freshwater Crayfish,* ed. S. Abrahamsson, 5:121–31. Lund: Student-litteratur. 361 pp.

12. Breer, H. 1975. Ganglioside pattern and thermal tolerance of fish species. *Life Sci.* 16:1459–64

13. Breer, H., Rahmann, H. 1976. Involvement of brain gangliosides in temperature adaptation of fish. *J. Therm. Biol.* 1:233–35

14. Brett, J. R. 1971. Energetic responses of salmon to temperature. *Am. Zool.* 11:99–113

15. Brezden, B. L., Fenwick, J. C., Moon, T. W. 1975. The effects of acclimation temperature and conditioning temperature on the learning rate of the goldfish, *Carassius auratus. Comp. Biochem. Physiol. A* 50:373–77

16. Brooks, C. M., Koizumi, K., Malcolm, J. L. 1955. Effects of changes in temperature on reactions of spinal cord. *J. Neurophysiol.* 18:205–16

17. Bull, H. O. 1936. Studies on conditioned responses in fishes. *J. Mar. Biol. Assoc.* 21:1–27

18. Charlton, M. P., Atwood, H. L. 1979. Synaptic transmission: temperature sensitivities of Ca entry in presynaptic terminals. *Brain Res.* 170:543–46

19. Cossins, A. R. 1977. Adaptation of biological membranes to temperature. *Biochim. Biophys. Acta* 470:395–411

20. Cossins, A. R., Friedlander, M. J., Prosser, C. L. 1977. Correlations between behavioral temperature adaptations of goldfish and the viscosity and fatty acid composition of their synaptic membranes. *J. Comp. Physiol.* 120:109–21

21. Cossins, A. R., Prosser, C. L. 1978. Evolutionary adaptation of membranes to temperature. *Proc. Natl. Acad. Sci. USA* 75:2040–43

22. Crawshaw, L. I. 1975. Attainment of the final thermal preferendum in brown bullheads acclimated to different temperatures. *Comp. Biochem. Physiol. A* 52:171–73

22a. Crawshaw, L. I. 1980. Temperature regulation in vertebrates. *Ann. Rev. Physiol.* 42:473–91

23. Crawshaw, L. I., Hammel, H. T. 1974. Behavioral regulation of internal temperature in brown bullhead. *Comp. Biochem. Physiol. A* 47:51–60

24. D'Ajello, V., Bettini, S., Grasso, A. 1967. Effect of temperature on the endogenous activity of *Periplaneta americana* L. nerve cord. *Riv. Parassitol.* 28:71–78

25. Davis, R. E., Bright, P. J., Agranoff, B. W. 1975. Effect of ECS and puromycin on memory of fish. *J. Comp. Physiol. Psychol.* 60:162–66

26. del Castillo, J., Machne, X. 1953. Effect of temperature on the passive electrical properties of the muscle fiber membrane. *J. Physiol. London* 120:431–34

27. Diedzic, W., Selivonchick, D. P., Roots, B. I. 1976. Alk-l-enyl ether-containing lipids of goldfish: brain and temperature acclimation. *Comp. Biochem. Physiol.* 53B:311-14

28. Dierolf, B. M., McDonald, H. S. 1969. Effects of temperature acclimation on electrical properties of earthworm giant axons. *Z. Vergl. Physiol.* 62:284-90

29. Dierolf, B. M., Brink, P. M. 1973. Effects of thermal acclimation on cable constants of the earthworm median giant axon. *Comp. Biochem. Physiol. A* 44:401–6

30. Dorsett, D. A. 1962. Preparation for flight by hawk moths. *J. Exp. Biol.* 39:579–88

31. Engelhardt, A. 1951. Die Temperaturabhängigkeit der Erregungsleitungs-geschwindigkeit in Kalt- und Warmblüternerven. *Z. Vergl. Physiol.* 33:125–28

32. Esch, H. Z. 1960. Temperature relations of honeybee. *Z. Vergl. Physiol.* 43:305–35

33. Fahmy, F. K. 1973. Effects of partial exposure to lethal temperature on heterogeneously acclimated fish. *Can. J. Zool.* 51:1249–55

34. French, J. W. 1942. The effect of temperature on the retention of a maze habit in fish. *J. Exp. Psychol.* 31:79–87

35. Friedlander, M. J., Kotchabhakdi, N., Prosser, C. L. 1976. Effects of cold and heat on behavior and cerebellar function in goldfish. *J. Comp. Physiol.* 112:19–45

36. Fry, F. E. J. 1947. Environmental effects on activity of fish. *Publ. Ontario Fish. Res. Lab.* 68:1–52

37. Fry, F. E. J., Hart, J. S. 1949. Swimming speed of goldfish at different temperatures. *J. Fish Res. Bd. Can.* 7:169–75

38. Garside, E. T., Tait, J. S. 1958. Preferred temperature of rainbow trout (*Salmo gairdneri*) and its unusual relationship to acclimation temperature. *Can. J. Zool.* 36:563–67

39. Gladwell, R. T. 1976. Heat death in the crayfish *Austropotamobius pollipes:* thermal inactivation of muscle membrane-bound ATPases in warm and cold adapted animals. *J. Therm. Biol.* 1:95–100

40. Gladwell, R. T., Bowler, K., Duncan, C. J. 1976. Heat death in the crayfish *Austropotamobius pollipes*—ion movements and their effects on excitable tissues during heat death. *J. Therm. Biol.* 1:79–94

41. Greer, G. L., Gardner, D. R. 1974. Characterization of responses from temperature-sensitive units in trout brain. *Comp. Biochem. Physiol. A* 48:189–203

42. Hamby, R. 1975. Heat effects on a marine snail. *Biol. Bull.* 149:331–47

43. Hammel, H. T., Crawshaw, L. I., Cabanac, H. P. 1973. The activation of behavioral responses in the regulation of body temperature in vertebrates. In *The Pharmacology of Thermoregulation,* ed. P. Lomax, E. Schonbaum, 2:33–45. NY: Basel. 367 pp.

44. Hanegan, J. L., Heath, J. E. 1970. Control of body temperature in moth *Hyalaphora. J. Exp. Biol.* 53:349–62

45. Harri, M., Florey, E. 1979. The effects of acclimation temperature on a neuromuscular system of the crayfish, *Astacus leptodactylus. J. Exp. Biol.* 78:281–94

46. Heath, J. E., Hanegan, J. L., Wilkin, P. J., Heath, M. S. 1971. Adaptation of the thermal responses of insects. *Am. Zool.* 11:147–58

47. Heinrich, B. 1970. Thoracic temperature in free flying moths. *Science* 168:580–82

48. Heinrich, B. 1971. Temperature regulation of sphinx moth *Manduca. J. Exp. Biol.* 54:141–52

49. Hilbig, R., Rahmann, H., Rosner, H. 1979. Brain gangliosides and temperature adaptation in eury- and stenothermic teleost fish (carp and rainbow trout). *J. Therm. Biol.* 4:29–34

50. Hoffman, W. W., Parsons, R.-L., Fergen, G. A. 1966. Effects of temperature and drugs on mammalian motor nerve terminals. *Am. J. Physiol.* 211:135–40

51. Hubbard, J. I., Jones, S. F., Landau, E. M. 1971. The effect of temperature change upon transmitter release, facilitation and posttetanic potentiation. *J. Physiol. London* 216:591–608

52. Javaid, M. Y., Anderson, J. M. 1967. Influence of starvation on selected temperature of some salmonids. *J. Fish. Res. Bd. Can.* 24:1515–19

53. Jensen, D. W. 1972. The effect of temperature on transmission at the neuromuscular junction of the sartorius muscle of *Rana pipiens. Comp. Biochem. Physiol. A* 41:685–95

54. Johnston, P. V., Roots, B. I. 1964. Brain lipid fatty acids and temperature acclimation. *Comp. Biochem. Physiol.* 2:303–9

55. Kammer, A. E. 1970. Thoracic temperature and flight in monarch butterfly. *Z. Vergl. Physiol.* 68:334–44

56. Kammer, A. E. 1971. Influence of acclimation temperature on the shivering behavior of the butterfly *Danaus plexippus* L. *Z. Vergl. Physiol.* 72:364–69

57. Katz, B., Miledi, R. 1965. The measurement of synaptic delay, and time course of acetylcholine release at the neuromuscular junction. *Proc. R. Soc. London Ser. B* 167:8–22

58. Kerkut, G. A., Taylor, B. J. R. 1958. The effect of temperature changes on the activity of poikilotherms. *Behavior* 13:259–79

59. Konishi, J., Hickman, C. P. 1964. Temperature acclimation in the central nervous system of rainbow trout (*Salmo gairdnerii*). *Comp. Biochem. Physiol.* 13:433–42

60. Kronenberg, F., Heller, H. C. 1980. Colonial thermoregulation in honey bees (*Apis mellifera*): influence of air temperature and brood presence. *J. Comp. Physiol.* In press

61. Lagerspetz, K. Y. H. 1974. Temperature acclimation and the nervous system. *Biol. Rev.* 49:477–514

62. Lagerspetz, K. Y. H., Talo, A. 1967. Temperature acclimation of the functional parameters of the giant nerve fibers in *Lumbricus terrestris* L. Conduction velocity and the duration of the rising and falling phase of action potential. *J. Exp. Biol.* 47:471–80

63. Lagerspetz, K. Y. H., Kohonen, J., Tirri, R. 1973. Temperature acclimation of the ATP-ase activity in the nerve cord of the earthworm, *Lumbricus terrestris* L. *Comp. Biochem. Physiol. B* 44:823–27

64. Langley, C. K. 1979. Thermal acclimation of a central neurone of *Helix aspersa.* I. Effects of temperature on ionic composition of the haemolymph. *J. Exp. Biol.* 78:181–86

65. Langley, C. K. 1979. Thermal acclimation of a central neurone of *Helix aspersa.* II. Electrophysiological recordings. *J. Exp. Biol.* 78:187–200

66. Langley, C. K. 1979. Thermal acclimation of a central neurone of *Helix as-*

persa. III. Ionic substitution and related studies. *J. Exp. Biol.* 78:201–12

67. Lensky, Y. 1964. Bee colony temperature extremes. *J. Insect Physiol.* 10:1–12

68. Li, C., Gouras, P. 1958. Effect of cooling on neuromuscular transmission in the frog. *Am. J. Physiol.* 192:464–70

69. McCrea, M., Heath, J. E. 1971. Dependence of flight on temperature regulation in the moth *Manduca. J. Exp. Biol.* 54:415–35

70. McDonald, H. S., Chiarmonte, G., Tornowski, L. E. 1967. Influence of temperature acclimation on conduction velocity in sciatic nerves of *Rana pipiens. Am. Zool.* 3:547–48

71. Merickel, M., Kater, S. B. 1974. Neuronal change: compensatory acclimation of the contribution of an electrogenic pump to the resting potential. *J. Comp. Physiol.* 94:195–206

72. Neale, J. H., Gray, I. 1971. Protein synthesis and retention of a conditioned response in rainbow trout as affected by temperature reduction. *Brain Res.* 26:159–68

73. Nelson, D. O. 1978. Temperature sensitive neurons in the preoptic region of sunfish. *Physiologist* 21:84

74. Nelson, D. O., Prosser, C. L. 1979. Effect of preoptic lesions on behavioral thermoregulation of green sunfish, *Lepomis cyanellus,* and of goldfish, *Carassius auratus. J. Comp. Physiol.* 129:193–97

75. Nelson, D. O., Prosser, C. L. 1979. Interval coding of temperature by preoptic neurons in sunfish. *Soc. Neurosci. Abstr.* 5:145

76. Norris, K. S. 1963. The functions of temperature in the ecology of the percoid fish. *Ecol. Mongr.* 33:23–62

77. Orr, P. R. 1955. Heat death: differential response of entire animal (*Rana pipiens*) and several organ systems. *Physiol. Zool.* 28:294–302

78. Peterson, R. H., Prosser, C. L. 1972. Cold block of central nervous responses in goldfish. *Comp. Biochem. Physiol. A* 42:1019–38

79. Pitt, T. K., Garside, E. T., Hepburn, R. L. 1956. Temperature selection of the carp. *Can. J. Zool.* 34:555–57

80. Precht, H. 1960. Über die Resistenzadaptation gegenüber extremen Temperaturen bei einigen Organfunktionen des grassfrosches (*Rana temporaria L.*). *Z. Wiss. Zool.* 164:335–53

81. Priestland, R. N., Whittam, R. 1972. The temperature dependence of activation by phosphatidylserine of the sodium pump adenosine triphosphatase. *J. Physiol. London* 220:353–61

82. Prosser, C. L. 1973. *Comparative Animal Physiology,* pp. 362–428. Philadelphia: Saunders. 951 pp.

83. Prosser, C. L., Farhi, E. 1965. Effects of temperature on conditioned reflexes and on nerve conduction in fish. *Z. Vergl. Physiol.* 50:91–101

84. Prosser, C. L., Nagai, T. 1968. Effects of low temperature on conditioning in goldfish. See Ref. 3, 9:171–80

85. Prosser, C. L., Precht, H., Jankowsky, H. D. 1965. Nervous control of metabolism during temperature acclimation of fish. *Naturwissenschaften* 52:168–69

86. Rahmann, H., Schmidt, W., Schmidt, B. 1980. Influence of long-term thermal acclimation on the conditionability of fish. *J. Therm. Biol.* 5:11–16

87. Racteri, M., Levy, G. 1973. Depletion of synaptosomal neurotransmitter pool by sudden cooling. *Nature* 243:180–82

88. Roots, B. I. 1968. Phospholipids of goldfish brain: the influence of environmental temperature. *Comp. Biochem. Physiol.* 25:457–66

89. Roots, B. I., Johnston, P. V. 1968. Plasmalogens of the nervous system and environmental temperature. *Comp. Biochem. Physiol.* 26:553–60

90. Roots, B. I., Prosser, C. L. 1962. Temperature acclimation and the nervous system in fish. *J. Exp. Biol.* 39:617–29

91. Rozin, P. 1968. The use of poikilothermy in the analysis of behavior. See Ref. 3, pp. 202–16

92. Scheil, H. G. 1970. Beiträge zur Temperatur-adaptation des Aales *Anguilla anguilla.* Einfluss der Adaptationtemperatur auf den denervierten Seitenmuskel. *Marine Biol.* 6:158–66

93. Shaklee, J. B., Christiansen, J. A., Sidell, B. D., Prosser, C. L., Whitt, G. S. 1977. Molecular aspects of temperature acclimation in fish: contributions of changes in enzyme activities and isozyme patterns to metabolic reorganization in the green sunfish. *J. Exp. Zool.* 201:1–20

94. Sjodin, R. A., Mullins, L. J. 1958. The action potential of frog nerve as affected by temperature narcosis and stimulation frequency. *J. Cell. Comp. Physiol.* 51:425–38

95. Sullivan, C. M., 1954. Temperature reception and responses in fish. *J. Fish. Res. Bd. Can.* 11:153–70

96. Takeuchi, N. 1958. The effect of temperature on the neuromuscular junction of the frog. *Jpn. J. Physiol.* 8:391–404

97. Tanaka, R., Teruya, A. 1974. Lipid dependence of activity-temperature relationship of (Na$^+$, K$^+$)-activated ATPase. *Biochim. Biophys. Acta* 323-584-91
98. Ward, D., Crowley, W. J., Johns, T. R. 1972. Effects of temperature at the neuromuscular junction. *Am. J. Physiol.* 222:216-19
99. Weight, F. F., Erulkar, S. D. 1976. Synaptic transmission and effects of temperature at squid giant synapses. *Nature* 261:720-22
100. White, R. L. 1976. The effects of high temperature and low calcium on neuromuscular transmission in the frog. *J. Thermobiol.* 1:227-36
101. White, R. L. 1978. *Effects of temperature on synaptic transmission in crayfish muscle.* PhD thesis. Univ. Illinois, Urbana
102. Deleted in proof
103. Deleted in proof
104. Zahn, M. 1962. Die Vorzugstemperaturen zweier Cypriniden und eines Cyprinodonten und die Adaptationstypen der Vorzugstemperatur bei Fischen. *Zool. Beitr.* 7:15-25
105. Zecevic, D., Levitan, H. 1980. Temperature acclimation effects on membrane physiology of identified neuron in land snail. *Am. J. Physiol.* 239:C47-58
106. Zerbolis, D. J. 1973. Temperature-dependent learning in goldfish: a multitrial active avoidance situation. *Behav. Biol.* 8:755-61

Ann. Rev. Physiol. 1981. 43:301–322

SCALING OF PHYSIOLOGICAL PROCESSES IN HOMEOTHERMIC ANIMALS

♦1312

William A. Calder III

Department of Ecology & Evolutionary Biology, University of Arizona, Tucson, Arizona 85721

INTRODUCTION

"The most obvious differences betweeen different animals are differences in size, but for some reason the zoologists have paid singularly little attention to them" (41). A half-century later, Haldane's criticism is still largely true for the basic biology curriculum, but in physiological publications one often encounters allometric equations of the form:

$$Y = aM^b, \qquad\qquad 1.$$

which expresses, empirically, some physiological or anatomical variable (Y), as a function of body mass (M in kg or m in g) raised to a fractional power b; a is a constant for a phylogenetic category in a defined set of environmental and physiological conditions. In the logarithmic form,

$$\log Y = \log a + b \log M, \qquad\qquad 2.$$

b is the slope of a straight-line plot and a is the Y-intercept.[1]

From a century's worth of exponential growth of raw data that could give "a sense of being engulfed by a flood tide . . . confused by complexity" (120), allometric equations provide an orderly reduction to formal statements from which patterns and parallels emerge. Ultimately we seek to identify the physical constraints and causes that explain the empirical exponents.

---

[1]Despite the mathematical simplicity of allometric equations 1 and 2, the exponent has been misinterpreted as a fraction of absolute mass rather than a fractional power of mass or a fraction of log mass (11, 15a, 35, 36, 84).

0066-4278/81/0315-0301$01.00

Perhaps convergent evolution offers insight into these physical constraints. Mammals and birds are descendants of very different reptilian stocks, and the first mammalian and avian fossils date from periods at least 40 million years apart (71). Independently, they attained an endogenous homeothermy, perhaps for different "reasons" of conservation of heat for nocturnal mammals and protection from solar overheating for diurnal birds (85). If the same quantitative relationships evolved independently after extensive adaptive radiation, we have at least circumstantial evidence of physical constraints upon natural selection.

This review explores the allometric similarities of these convergent homeotherms, comparing available information on the basic maintenance functions of energetics, respiration, circulation, and osmotic regulation of adult mammals and birds, identifying some gaps and contradictions worthy of further study, and speculating freely.

Bech et al (9) pointed out "the danger in developing allometric relations based on a small sample of partly indirect and estimated values." Their addition of 9 data points to the 6 originally used in an equation for tidal volume in birds (62) yielded an equation 25% higher (in Y-intercept or a value). However the original exponent 1.08 was very close to the refined 1.05, thereby expediting by 8 years (and at least 29 citations) the preliminary comparison of respiratory scaling in birds and mammals. Paucity of data will not inhibit the effort to describe patterns from what is available at the time of writing. Units have been converted from those used in original publications where necessary to facilitate comparison. While development and growth are outside the scope of this review, it is worth noting that one of the most extensive, exciting, and successful applications of allometry to date is the series of analyses of avian egg structure and function by Rahn, Ar, Paganelli and associates, recently reviewed elsewhere (4, 83).

For historical and logistical reasons an evaluation of the current status of allometry as a comparative approach to physiology centers on the scaling of metabolism to body size (reviewed in 7, 17, 89, 90). The metabolic rate represents the sum of all physiological processes, and these processes must all be geared to metabolic requirements. Therefore the Fick Principle and Stahl's technique of allometric cancellation (98–101) should be able to account, quantitatively, for the mass exchanges accomplished by respiration, circulation, and osmotic/renal physiology.

The maintenance of the internal environment depends upon delivery or removal of the right amounts (mass, m) to or from the right place (distance, or linear dimension, l) at the right time (t) and temperature (T). The rates at which an energy substrate and oxygen are required and carbon dioxide, amino groups, and heat (H) are liberated ($mt^{-1}, l^3 t^{-1}, \dot{H}$) are all dependent upon the size of the organism; in fact it appears that any process that includes external time as a dimension is size-dependent (67).

Yales (120) challenges: "Allometric analyses don't strike me as being as physical as they look . . . they don't give any details concerning the physical basis for the similarity, in the sense of constraints [or] laws." He urges use of similarity analysis in terms of the fundamental physical entities (m, l, t, T). Günther (38, 39) and Günther & Martinoya (40) have provided the most extensive synthesis of similarity and allometry. Günther obtained excellent statistical correlation ($r = 0.99$) between empirical and theoretical exponents (b) for 80 allometric equations. However, this was only possible when an empirical correction factor, Γ, was applied.

The Maxwell "dimension equation" (39) says that the dimensions of an entity Q are the product of the exponents:

$$[Q] = M^{\alpha} \, l^{\,\beta} t^{\gamma}. \hspace{3cm} 3.$$

Mass is proportional to volume, and volume in a geometric figure is proportional to l^3, so m^{α} can be replaced by $l^{3\alpha}$. Time periods of simple geometries are proportional to lengths, so l^{γ} can be substituted for t^{γ}. Thus the allometric exponent b can be viewed in linear dimensions as the composite of $3\alpha + \beta + \alpha$, or in terms of mass, b is $\frac{1}{3}(3\alpha + \beta + \gamma)$. To this theoretical exponent, Günther added the operational time exponent ($\Gamma \propto m^{-0.065}$) of Günther & Martinoya (40). The value -0.065 is the average of numerical differences between the empirical exponent $M^{0.734}$ for metabolism (15a) and the exponent for surface area $M^{0.667}$, also between theoretical ($M^{-0.333}$) and observed ($M^{-0.27}$) for mammalian heart rate. Economos (30) pointed out: "Günther's approach has only descriptive, not explanatory value because he acknowledged that rates are faster than predicted by a surface law, but he did not indicate the cause of this deviation." (See also 116.)

Underlying this manipulation of m, l, and t, the simplification to terms of l assumes a geometric similarity ($L \propto m^{\frac{1}{3}}$). However McMahon (72, 73) showed that a model of elastic similarity has theoretical exponents indistinguishable from the empirical exponents. If animals are scaled to preserve elastic similarity, including a size-independent safety factor for resisting buckling stresses, length and time would be proportional to $m^{\frac{1}{4}}$, not $m^{\frac{1}{3}}$. In this model, b in $y = aM^b$ is $\frac{1}{4}(4\alpha + \beta + \gamma)$. Thus for metabolic power, which has dimensions of $ml^2 t^{-3}$, with $l \propto m^{\frac{1}{4}}$, we get $\frac{1}{4}(4+2-3) = 3/4$; this is the Kleiber (58, 59) exponent, without any correction factor Γ. McMahon's model is therefore a major advance providing a better explanation for $b = 3/4$ than anything previous, but some reservations and alternative explanations have appeared recently (13, 30, 81). Further discussion of these explanations lies in the realm of biomechanics rather than the topic of this review, the physiology of metabolic supply.

METABOLISM

Phylogeny

Within a phylogenetic group of vertebrates [e.g. (*a*) avian order Passeriformes; (*b*) other avian orders pooled; mammalian infraclasses: (*c*) Metatheria (marsupials), and (*d*) Eutheria], the standard or basal metabolic rate scales approximately as $M^{3/4}$, whether the regression is for ectothermic or homeothermic animals (7).

These parallel metabolism/body mass regressions may be compared, as ratios of *a* constants, to the original Kleiber equation for eutherian mammals. When data from extant forms do not encompass sufficient size-range, comparisons may be made to Kleiber-equation predictions. The minimal metabolic power consumption of various groupings compares with eutherians as follows: passerine birds 163% (5,5a) to 183% (63), neognathid (nonpasserine carinate or flying) birds 112% (18), ratite birds (except kiwis) 83% (18), marsupials 66–68% (26, 69), kiwis 64% (18), monotremes 49% to 65% (37, 92). According to classic Darwinian assumptions natural selection should have minimized the energy cost of homeostasis within resting eutherian mammals and nonpasserine birds. How then can those mammals and birds erroneously labelled "primitive" maintain homeostasis with considerably less expensive standard metabolic levels than appear necessary for their "advanced" relatives, without sacrifice to alertness and dispatch? Because the metabolic factoral scope is relatively constant among homeotherms, so perhaps a higher basal expense could preserve a higher peak capacity (25).

Activity

Allometry has been powerfully and productively applied to the analysis of locomotion energetics. Since several excellent and extensive reviews have recently been concerned with this topic (3, 79), the present coverage focuses on the metabolic demands associated with, and capacities for, running and flying. The principal quantitative expressions have been concerned with the power requirements (input and output) of locomotion, and the energy cost of locomotion.

It appears that the power input requirements of high activity levels are affected by body size in approximately the same proportional fashion as is the resting metabolic power, supporting Dawson's notion of metabolic scope noted above. The ratio of predicted metabolic power (P_{T-G}) of running at the trot-gallop transition speed (speed$_{T-G}$) to resting power ($P_{std.}$) is:

$$P_{T-G}/P_{std.} = 22.6M^{0.82}/3.4M^{0.75} = 6.6M^{0.07} \qquad 4.$$

[recalculated from (103)]. The residual mass exponent 0.07 means that a 9-g pygmy mouse elevates metabolically by a factor of 4.8 to attain a speed$_{T-G}$ of 0.49 m sec^{-1} (7.7 times its body length sec^{-1}) and a 500-kg horse would expand to 9.9 times the standard rate to a speed$_{T-G}$ of 6.78 m sec^{-1} (3.4 body lengths sec^{-1}).

The maximum aerobic capacity ($\dot{V}_{O_2}$ in ml O$_2$ hr^{-1}) of running mammals scales in slightly closer parallel to standard metabolism than does power$_{T-G}$ (104):

$$P_{max} \propto \dot{V}_{O_2} max = 28.8m^{0.79} \text{ for wild species, } r = 0.93, \text{ or} \qquad 5.$$

$$\dot{V}_{O_2} max = 28.2m^{0.80} \text{ for all (19) spp., } r = 0.72. \qquad 5a.$$

A parallel equation has been derived for birds during flight (10):

$$\dot{H}_{fly} = 48.9M^{0.72} \qquad 6.$$

This equation pooled data from both passerine and nonpasserine birds, from hovering and forward flights of various durations. It predicts a flight metabolism 6.7 times standard for passerine birds and 11 times standard for others. An equation for power input at the speed for minimum cost of transport takes into account additional variables that are not themselves predictable from body mass, altitude (h) and wingspan (b) (110):

$$P_i = (0.00723h + 105.9)M^{1.382}b^{-1.236} \qquad 7.$$

This equation is a simplified approximation derived from a considerably more complex equation. However, neither is suited for simple allometric comparisons. Pooled data on maximal oxygen consumption in flying, swimming, and running animals are proportional to $M^{0.74}$ (10, 44, 82).

The minimum cost of transport is expressed by the ratio of metabolic rate (power input) to velocity, which has the dimensions (energy·time^{-1}) ÷ (distance·time^{-1}), reducing to energy cost per distance. In traditional comparative physiology, this relationship has usually been given in terms of g^{-1} or kg^{-1} body mass. The cost for flying locomotion (109) is:

$$kJ(kg \ km)^{-1} = 5.23M^{-0.229}. \qquad 8.$$

Earlier, it appeared that bipedal running was somewhat more expensive than quadripedal running (33). However, reanalysis of available data revealed that the bipedal running of birds and monkeys was not significantly more expensive than quadrupedal locomotion of lizards or mammals (77). Pooled running data for these animals are summarized in equation 9 ($n = 52$):

$$kJ \ (kg \ km)^{-1} = 11.0M^{-0.32}. \qquad 9.$$

Fedak & Seeherman (34) expanded the available data to 69 spp. of running lizards, birds, and mammals, summarized as:

$$kJ \ (kg \ km)^{-1} = 11.3M^{-0.28}. \qquad \qquad 10.$$

Biologically more meaningful than the preceding transport costs per unit body mass would be travel costs per animal:

$$\text{flying: } kJ \ km^{-1} = 5.23M^{0.77} \qquad \qquad 11.$$

$$\text{running: } kJ \ km^{-1} = 11.3M^{0.72} \qquad \qquad 11a.$$

Thus travel costs less than half as much for fliers as for runners.

A model for predicting total metabolic rate includes not only quadrupedal running and postural costs but thermoregulatory costs (118). However, the thermoregulatory costs were calculated from the allometry of resting thermoregulation (see below); certainly some, if not all of this supplemental heat production is unnecessary at the high level of waste heat production during locomotion. Despite the apparent thermoregulatory discrepancy and the use of a postural cost term that appears excessive (77), the model predicted total metabolic rates within 10–20% of those obtained experimentally.

Environmental

Most metabolic allometry has been derived from animals of temperate climates. Standard metabolic rates of birds increase 1% for each degree of increase in latitude from the equator to about 75°N (113).

Seasonal acclimatization of arctic mammals has been analyzed allometrically (21). The critical $T_b - T_{lc}$ is $1.7M^0$ times as great in winter as in summer, while h is reduced to $0.56M^{0.02}$ of the summer value.

The mean ratio of observed basal $\dot{V}O_2$ to the allometric prediction for 18 spp. of nocturnally active fossorial rodents was 0.86 (68). Most were from semi-arid to arid environments. Allometric analysis of the data is expressed as follows:

$$\text{Watts} = 2.87M^{0.74}, \ p < 0.0001. \qquad \qquad 12.$$

Pigeons of hot, arid climates have standard metabolic rates 71–81% of allometric predictions (24a).

Over the thermoneutral range of environmental temperatures, the standard metabolic rates ($\dot{H}_{smr} \propto M^{3⁄4}$) of adults are sufficient to maintain the appropriate body temperatures (T_b). Below the lower critical temperature (T_{lc}), the metabolic rate must be elevated in linear proportion to body-environment temperature difference, by shivering or non-shivering (endocrine-mediated) heat production. The critical temperature differences ($T_b - T_{lc}$) calculated separately for eutherian mammals, passerines, and other birds are proportional to $m^{0.23}$ or $m^{0.27}$ (7, 19). Normal resting T_b is generally size-independent ($\propto M^0$) within these phylogenetic groups, but

T_{lc} is inversely related to size. Therefore, lower environmental temperatures affect small homeotherms more than large ones (16, 78, 97, 107, 108).

Tracy (108) reasoned that "if there is a limit to the maximum heat production of a homeotherm then the lower limit to body size ... [is determined by] ambient temperature." He calculated hypothetical lower limits to body size for mammals assuming a maximum attainable metabolic rate for resting mammals of 0.065 W g^{-1}. At 24°C the minimum would be 3.5 g body mass; at 0°C, 8 g would be the lower limit.

Poczopko (80) pointed out the effect of curvature on insulation. The small radius of curvature of a smaller animal reduces insulative values (increasing heat transfer coefficients or conductance, h), even to the point that the lower conductivitiy of air on a naked neonate is apparently thermally preferable to the higher conductivity of hairs or feathers (6).

The interaction of allometries of basal metabolic rate and of critical temperature differences as functions of body size result in b exponents that decrease as a function of temperature (Table 1). Thus the metabolic rate at 0°C should be proportional to heat loss. A temperature of 0°C would be below thermoneutrality for eutherian mammals of $M < 6.9$ kg, for non-passerine birds of $M < 2.8$ kg, and passerine birds of $M < 0.7$ kg. The heat transfer coefficients of eutherian mammals and birds are proportional to $m^{0.50}$ and $m^{0.46}$, respectively (17, 45), so metabolic exponents should approximate these values (Table 1). The agreement is not perfect, but qualitatively reasonable (note that for the calculated $\dot{H}_m$ expressions, lines 4 and 5, the "comparison" is circular!).

Injection of noradrenaline into mammals produced a size-dependence of maximal $\dot{V}_{O_2}$ during nonshivering thermogenesis (NST) (43) that is size-dependent:

$$\log \text{NST-O}_2, \text{ ml (g hr)}^{-1} = 1.477 - 0.454 \log m. \qquad 13.$$

Converting units for comparison, we find a close parallel to what would be predicted from the allometry of heat transfer coefficients (Table 1).

While metabolic allometry below thermoneutrality has been analyzed fairly extensively, little attention has been directed to metabolic allometry during heat stress, which compounds effects of sweating or panting effort with the Q_{10}-effect of hyperthermia. Exposed to T_a from 30–45°C, birds increase their metabolism as follows (114):

$$\text{W(kg °C)}^{-1} = 0.12M^{-0.69}. \qquad 14.$$

This body mass function is similar to that ($M^{-0.61}$) for heat-transfer coefficients in T_a range 43.8°–46.5°C (19). If $T_a > T_b$, this increment in heat production plus the basal level would have to be dissipated by evaporation. Maximum evaporation rates of heat-stressed birds have been summarized.

Table 1 The effect of cold upon the allometry of resting metabolic rates

	Conditions	Metabolic rate (watts)[a]	Reference
Passeriform birds	0°C	$0.231m^{0.42}$	57
Other birds	0°C	$0.162m^{0.53}$	57
Eutherian mammals	0°C	$0.270m^{0.36}$	108
Eutherian mammals	0°C[b]	$0.211m^{0.50}$	45
Eutherian mammals, mostly rodents	0°C[b]	$0.198m^{0.51}$	42
Eutherian mammals	max. NST: NA inject.[c]	$0.167m^{0.55}$	43
Eutherian mammals, arctic	0°C	$0.394m^{0.40}$	117
Eutherian mammals, arctic	10°C	$0.260m^{0.39}$	117
Eutherian mammals, arctic	20°C	$0.090m^{0.56}$	117
Eutherian mammals, arctic	30°C	$0.061m^{0.62}$	117
Eutherian mammals	thermoneutrality	$0.020m^{0.76}$	7

[a] units converted from original reports
[b] not derived directly from metabolic rates, but calculated as $H_m = h(37° - 0°C)$
[c] Nonshivering thermogenesis, converted from $\dot{V}O_2$ following noradrenalin injection

$$\text{mg } H_2O \text{ min}^{-1} = 259M^{0.80} \qquad\qquad 15.$$

Thus the effects of temperature on metabolism are body-size dependent. Gravity affects mammals in size-dependent fashion as well. Economos (30, 31) suggests that the empirical $M^{3/4}$ vs geometric $M^{2/3}$ function for metabolic rate may be due to a disproportionate effect of gravity on larger mammals. He correlates:

$$\dot{H}_{basal}, \text{ kcal day}^{-1} = 12M_b^{0.89} + 58M_b^{0.67}. \qquad\qquad 16.$$

That complex allometric equation fits standard metabolic rate data as well as or better than the familiar Kleiber equation.

OXYGEN SUPPLY

The physiometry of cardiovascular and respiratory systems was reviewed recently (39). We can proceed to account allometrically for the oxygen requirements of steady-state metabolism. The evolutionary scaling guidelines seem to have been:

1. Conservation of body functions: Within the body-size range, the size of an organ or system cannot scale so disproportionately as to usurp other

functions. Therefore lung mass (mammals: $M^{1.06}$, birds: $M^{0.94}$), tidal volumes (V_T, mammals: $M^{1.04}$; birds: $M^{1.05}$), heart mass (mammals: $M^{0.98}$, birds $M^{0.94}$), and cardiac stroke volumes (V_s, mammals: $M^{1.06}$, birds: $M^{0.92}$) are approximately linear functions of body mass (17, 28, 39, 62, 65, 101). The entire viscera of mammals scales as $0.158M^{0.871}$, or 33% of a 3.5 g mammal and 5.4% of a 4000 kg body mass (76).

2. Synchrony of times: Cyclic periods are proportional to linear dimensions, or $M^{\frac{1}{3}}$ to $M^{\frac{1}{4}}$ (73, 98). Frequencies (f) are reciprocals of time, or $M^{-\frac{1}{3}}$ to $M^{-\frac{1}{4}}$.

3. Size independence: Pressures; flow velocities; and ratios of dead-space to tidal volume, oxygen uptake to tidal volume, and end systolic- to end-diastolic volumes all scale close to M^0 (28, 46, 49, 65, 101, 105).

4. Conservation of volume: When allometric expressions are substituted for terms in the Fick Principle, reasonable agreement of exponents is observed—e.g. for mammals (62, 101):

$$(f_r \propto M^{-0.26})\ (V_T \propto M^{1.04})\ (\Delta Fo_2 \propto M^0) = Vo_2,\ M^{0.78}\ \text{vs}\ M^{0.76} \quad \text{17a.}$$

$$(f_h \propto M^{-0.25})\ (V_s \propto M^{1.06})\ (\Delta Fo_2 \propto M^0) = Vo_2,\ M^{0.81}\ \text{vs}\ M^{0.76} \quad \text{17b.}$$

5. Elastic similarity: According to McMahon's (72, 73) model, the evolution of larger size would preserve proportionality between length (l) and diameter ($\frac{2}{3}d$) in supporting columns such as legs or torsos in order to resist buckling under self-loading when displaced from normal configuration: The weight of a column is proportional to its volume, or $l\cdot\pi(d/2)^2$:

$$m\cdot g = (\rho d^{\frac{2}{3}}\ \pi\ d^2/4) \propto d^{8/3} \quad \text{18.}$$

where g = gravitational acceleration, ρ = density. Thus:

$$d \propto m^{\frac{3}{8}} \quad \text{19.}$$

$$l \propto m^{\frac{1}{4}} \quad \text{20.}$$

Do the same proportionalities hold for the internal distributive systems? Diameters of aortae and tracheae have approximately the same ($M^{0.35}$ and $M^{0.39}$) scaling exponents as bone diameters and torso girth. There is a greater range in the higher exponents ($M^{0.3}-M^{0.4}$) for lengths of major blood vessels and tracheae compared to body linear dimensions (Table 2), providing the intriguing possibility of elastic similarity for external or support features and geometric similarity within. However, because heart and respiratory rates do not conform to internal geometric similarity, and skeletal mass data fit into the range predicted by geometrical similarity, $l \propto m^{\frac{1}{3}}$, the matter is still unresolved.

Table 2 Body mass proportionalities for dimensions of major vessels compared to the elastic similarity model

Structure	Length	Diameter	Reference
Theoretical	$M^{0.25}$	$M^{0.38}$	73
Limb bones	$M^{0.25}$	$M^{0.38}$	73
Cattle bodies	$M^{0.24}$	$M^{0.36}$	73
Mammal tracheae	$M^{0.40}$	$M^{0.39}$	46, pers. comm.
Bird tracheae	$M^{0.39}$	$M^{0.35}$	46
Mammal aortae	$M^{0.30}$	$M^{0.37}$	48
Mammal ascending aortae	$M^{0.28}$	$M^{0.36}$	50
Mammal inferior venae cavae	$M^{0.33}$	$M^{0.41}$	50
Mammal rt. renal artery	—	$M^{0.30}$	50
Mammal rt. iliac artery	—	$M^{0.31}$	50

Respiration

The allometry of respiration, summarized above, has been examined to the level of alveolar morphometry (reviewed in 28, 39, 62, 65, 91, 101). In mammals, alveolar surface area (S_a) has close linear correlation with resting oxygen uptake rate ($\dot{V}o_2$) (106). Lechner (64) examined the allometry of S_a and maximal oxygen consumption:

wild mammals, $S_a/\dot{V}o_2$ max $= 1.02m^{0.69}/3.36m^{0.66} = 0.30m^{0.03}$ 21a.

lab mammals, $S_a/\dot{V}o_2$ max $= 1.0m^{1.06}/2.67m^{0.71} = 0.38m^{0.35}$ 21b.

combined, $S_a/\dot{V}o_2$ max $= 1.01m^{0.89}/3.16m^{0.68} = 0.32m^{0.21}$ 21c.

Why the laboratory mammals should have such a disproportionality between S_a and $\dot{V}o_2$ is unclear. Similarly, one would expect lung diffusing capacity (D_{Lo_2}) to be proportional to $\dot{V}o_2$ or $M^{0.76}$ rather than (75):

D_{Lo_2}, ml(min·torr)$^{-1}$ 0.614$M^{0.985}$ 22.

The respiratory effort appears proportionately the same for both large and small mammals. The work (W) per ml of tidal volume ($\propto M^{1.04}$) is essentially size-independent (101). The pressures (P) required for ventilation [V_T/compliance $\propto M^{1.04}/M^{1.08}$, or W/$V_T \propto M^{1.08}/M^{1.04}$ (29, 101)] appear size-independent also. Dead-space (V_{ds}) is approximately a constant fraction of tidal volume or vital capacity ($\propto M^{0.96}/M^{1.04}$ or $M^{0.96}/M^{1.06}$), although calculations from tracheal diameters and lengths indicate tracheal $V_{ds} \propto M^{1.18}$, $M^{1.09}$ for mammals and birds, respectively (46, 105). The tracheae of birds are longer than those of mammals and have greater diameters, which would compensate for length in terms of resistance to air flow, but which would greatly increase dead-space. Breathing at lower f, deeper V_T, and slower airflows, the more compliant avian system tends to compensate partially for the proportionately large tracheal V_{ds}. The V_{ds} (including the mouth) of the chicken, measured by water-filling, was 23% of mean V_T determined before killing, and 1.5 times the allometric prediction for tracheal V_{ds} (60).

From this pattern of apparent tendency to preserve the V_{ds}/V_T ratio, it is interesting to consider some extreme "allometric deviants" with long necks. The flamingo (*Phoenicopterus ruber*) has a tracheal volume 2.1 times that predicted for a 2.21 kg bird. The V_T was 2.8 times that expected, more than compensating for the V_{ds}. The breathing rate was 0.71 of that predicted, giving a minute volume 62% above prediction, while O_2 extraction was 18% higher. The V_{O_2} was 1.91 times standard prediction, so that some of the V_T increase could have been a response to an elevated metabolic rate, rather than an overcompensation for V_{ds} (9).

The giraffe (*Giraffa camelopardalus*) has a 170-cm trachea (2.5 times that predicted for its 400-kg body mass) 3.8 cm in diameter (0.9 times that predicted), giving a dead space of 1.2 1 (1.38 times that predicted). In order to maintain typical resistance to inflow, diameter would have to increase in proportion to increases in length; instead, the decrease in cross-sectional area to 0.8 of that predicted causes a partial reduction in V_{ds}. V_T values (as twice the pneumotachographic flow from one nostril) were not greater, as would be necessary to preserve the V_{ds}/V_T ratio, but smaller. On the other hand, the respiratory rate was, however, only 0.8 of that predicted, suggesting that the V_T may have been underestimated (52).

Circulation

The allometry of the circulatory system has many quantitative parallels to the respiratory system (39, 101). In addition to those noted above, the blood volumes of mammals are, like respiratory vital capacities, approximately linearly proportional to body mass.

Available data for total blood volume of birds are too few and from too small a range in body mass for useful allometric analysis. Blood volume in mammals averages 6.6% of body mass, a value similar to that from 5 nonaquatic bird species, while 4 aquatic species had proportionately larger blood volumes (14).

Bird hearts are larger than those of equal-sized mammals ($8.6M^{0.94}$ vs $5.8M^{0.98}$), have lower resting heartbeat frequencies ($156M^{-0.23}$ vs $241M^{-0.25}$), and develop higher mean blood pressures ($kPa = 21M^{0.036}$ for birds vs $12M^{0.032}$ for mammals) (14, 39, 56). Although the regression for avian mean arterial pressure is not significant ($n = 11$, $r = 0.43$, $p > 0.10$) it appears size independent and consistently above mammalian arterial pressure.

Within a class, a larger animal's larger heart beats slower than a smaller heart. The difference in heart rates of birds and mammals does not appear to be due solely to differences in the ratio of heart mass (m_h) to body mass.

Mammals: $f_h = 379 m_\mathrm{h}^{-0.255}$ 23.

Birds: $f_h = 264 m_h^{-0.244}$ 24.

Further, the longer life spans of birds are not a mere result of conservation of heartbeats at a slower frequency, for in a lifetime $2.4M^{-0.01}$ times that of a mammal's, a bird's heart will beat 38% more times at resting level (66, 67). Furthermore, each contraction develops and withstands a significantly higher blood pressure, for reasons unclear.

A regression for cardiac output of 5 species of domestic birds that runs 75% higher than that for mammals should be regarded with reservation, for the heart frequencies were all very high, about 1.5–2 times values observed in unrestrained resting birds of the same species or values predicted from allometric relations. These are discrepancies not only in their own right but in their distortion of estimates of avian cardiac output, which hinders comparison with mammals. Since the cardiovascular physiology of birds has received less attention than that of mammals, we cannot compare the classes further now, except to note that the expansion factor for heart rates from resting to maximum values in activity is approximately the same for birds (2.56 ± 0.73 s.d., $n = 10$), eutherian mammals (2.13 ± 0.94 s.d., n = 6), and marsupial mammals (2.24 ± 0.35 s.d., n = 6). The eutherian and marsupial rates combine to yield:

max $f_h = 375M^{-0.19}$; $r = 0.967$; $p < 0.01$.   25.

This is $1.56M^{0.06}$ times resting f_h of eutherian mammals, and $3.54M^{0.08}$ times resting f_h of marsupials (8). Although a comparable avian regression is not significant ($p > 0.1$), the maximum f_h of birds appears to be about half that of mammals, similar to the proportions for resting rates.

There has been more progress in allometric analysis of cardiovascular function within the Eutheria. The systolic blood pressure (P_{sys}) is independent of body size, and equal to force developed by the left ventricle divided by the area of the ventricle walls:

$P_{sys} = $ Force/Area.   26.

The left ventricular volumes (end diastolic volume, V_{ed} and end systolic volumes, V_{es}) are linearly proportional to body mass (48):

V_{ed}, ml $= 1.76M^{1.02}$ 27.

V_{es}, ml $= 0.59M^{0.99}$ 28.

Thus, two thirds of the end diastolic volume is ejected by each contraction.

Laplace's law relates pressure (P), tension (T) and radius (r): For surfaces with major and minor radii of curvature,

$$P = T (1/R_1 + 1/R_2) \qquad\qquad 29.$$

This relationship has been examined in ventricles of mammals. Martin & Haines (70) assumed that tension, T, is proportional to wall-thickness, t: $T = kt$. The proportionality constant k and pressure P are assumed to be size-independent (M^0), so that we can restate (29) with a new constant $C = P/k$:

$$C = t (1/r_1 + 1/r_2). \qquad\qquad 30.$$

C was essentially the same for 7 species ranging from 310 g to 252 kg. From these data (70) the following allometric equations can be derived:

$$r_1 = 4.83M^{0.441}, P < 0.001 \qquad\qquad 31.$$

$$r_2 = 13.52M^{0.447}, P < 0.001 \qquad\qquad 32.$$

$$t = 2.50M^{0.455}, P < 0.001 \qquad\qquad 33.$$

Thus

$$t/r_1 \propto M^{0.455}/M^{0.441} = M^{0.01}, \text{ and} \qquad\qquad 34.$$

$$t/r_2 \propto M^{0.455}/M^{0.447} = M^{0.01}. \qquad\qquad 35.$$

Thus the mammalian right ventricle conforms to Laplace's law.

We might expect the surface area (A_v) of the ventricular walls to be:

$$A_v \propto V_{ed}^{2/3} \text{ or } (M^{1.02})^{2/3} \cong M^{0.67}. \qquad\qquad 36.$$

The force required

$$F = (P_{sys} \cdot A_v) \propto (M^0 \cdot M^{0.67}) \qquad\qquad 37.$$

and the force available should be proportional to cross-sectional area of the ventricular musculature $(A_{musc.})$ approximated as circumference $(2\pi r)$ times thickness (t):

$$F \propto (A_{musc.} = 2\pi rt). \qquad\qquad 38.$$

Thus

$$M^{0.67} \propto 2\pi rt. \qquad\qquad 39.$$

Substituting 31, 32, and 33 in 39 we find disagreement of exponents:

$$M^{0.67} \neq k2\pi M^{0.44} \cdot M^{0.45}$$

Particularly noteworthy in cardiovascular allometry are the contributions of J. P. Holt et al (47–51, 86):

work per stroke, $J = 5.8 \times 10^{-3} M^{1.15}$ 40.

total peripheral resistance, dyne·sec·cm^{-5} $= 4.87 \times 10^4 M^{-0.76}$ 41.

Further, one can calculate (47, 48):

mean aortic blood velocity, m min^{-1} $= 15.73 M^{0.07}$ 42.

Since pressure is size-independent, and cardiac output varies with $M^{0.78}$–$M^{0.81}$, according to Ohm's law we would expect total peripheral resistance to be approximately $\propto M^{-0.81}$, which it is (44, 101, 115). Work per stroke times heart frequency gives cardiac work rate (power), which appears to increase disproportionately to metabolic power:

$$5.8 \times 10^{-3} M^{1.15} \times 241 M^{-0.25} = 1.39 M^{0.90}$$ 43.

Resting breathing rates of mammals were correlated with a minimum ventilatory work rate (2, 24). Similarly, Milnor (74) and Noordergraaf et al (74a) hypothesized the natural selection for minimal cardiac work by a scaling of heart rate, f_h, to preserve a constant ratio of pulse wavelength λ to aortic length, l_{ao}. The pulse wave travels at a velocity c of about 6 m sec^{-1}, approximately size-independent like aortic blood velocity, $0.23 M^{0.05}$ but faster [calculated from (47, 48)]. This pulse wave is reflected throughout the arterial tree, causing a frequency dependent impedance to flow. The hydraulic power $\dot{W}$ is proportional to the impedance modulus, and is greatest at very low frequencies. In the 3 spp. studied, the impedance minimum occurred at $\lambda \cong 4 l_{ao}$. Since the characteristics of waves are related:

$$\lambda = c/f_h,$$ 44.

we would expect:

$$c/f_h = r\, l_{ao}.$$ 45.

However Milnor's data can be arranged:

$$c/f_h \cong 9.7\, l_{ao} M^{0.05},$$ 46.

where f_h sec^{-1} $= 4.70 M^{0.32}$. Therefore $\lambda = 1.28 M^{0.32}$ and $l_{ao} = 0.132 M^{0.27}$. From more extensive data (48,101): $f_h = 4.02 M^{-0.25}$; therefore $\lambda = 1.49 M^{0.25}$; l_{ao} (to bifurcation) $= 0.171 M^{0.30}$, which would reduce slightly the difference between optimal and actual λ:

$$\lambda = 8.7 M^{-0.05}$$ 47.

Milnor states the need for data on other species and conscious animals to evaluate this hypothesis.

However, Iberall (54) criticizes a lack of "attention to all existing reasonable hypotheses," such as a model proposed previously based on geometrical similarity of design elongated from a "compact animal" of surface area $= 6V^{2/3}$ to $12V^{2/3}$. If f_o is an undamped, standing wave frequency, related to l_{ao} as in the Milnor model through the Moens-Kortemeg velocity c (which is within the range of c stated by Milnor), it should be predicted as:

$$f_o = 74/(V^{1/3}-2)$$
48.

compared to the empirical:

$$f_h = 22.7V^{-1/4}$$
49.

A "corrected model":

$$f_o = 15.4V^{-0.2}$$
50.

comes closer to empirical predictions over a range in mass from $4-10^8$ g than an extrapolation from Milnor's f_h regression for the 3 species he tested. Some differences are not resolved at this writing. The Iberall model overlooks the fact that area of a "stretched" body varies not as $V^{2/3}$ or $W^{0.67}$ but as $M^{0.63}$, and that characteristic body lengths are proportional to $V^{1/4}$ or $M^{1/4}$ (72). On the other hand, the geometric constancy of l_{ao}/d_{ao}, assumed in the Iberall model, fits the observations listed in Table 2 above.

Inverse Small-Slope Advantages for Small Mammals

Stahl (99–102) developed size-independent dimensional constants and dimensionless variables by cancellation of power law formulae. These usually have small residual mass indexes (RMI), which in his analyses were not statistically distinct from M^0 in the range of $M^{-0.02}$ to $M^{0.08}$. Such small RMI's are therefore generally ignored in hopes of finding a neat allometric framework.

On the other hand, a consistent pattern of small negative exponents for single body mass functions favoring the support of high metabolic intensities in small mammals is seen for: capillary density $\propto M^{-0.14}$ [calculated from (94)], blood half saturation $Po_2 \propto M^{-0.054}$ (93), Bohr effect, $\Delta \log P_{50}/\Delta$ pH, $\propto M^{-0.06}$ (88); carbonic anhydrase concentration in red blood cells $\propto M^{-0.11}$ (61), and whole blood sugar concentration $\propto M^{-0.10}$ (111).

Environmental Allometry

Allometric predictions are often used as the basis for appreciating environmental adaptations of individual species. A detailed comparison provided separate allometries for montane and lowland birds (20):

$$\text{Heart mass,} \ \frac{\text{high altitude}}{\text{lowland}} = \frac{0.021m^{0.84}}{0.015m^{0.91}} = 1.4m^{-0.07} \qquad 51.$$

$$\text{Heart mass, passerine birds} = \frac{0.018m^{0.89}}{0.015m^{0.93}} = 1.2m^{-0.04} \qquad 52.$$

$$\text{Lung mass,} \ \frac{0.0132 \ m^{0.94}}{0.0068m^{1.06}} = 1.9m^{-0.12} \qquad 53.$$

$$\text{Lung mass, passerine birds} = \frac{0.011m^{1.0}}{0.007m^{1.07}} = 1.7m^{-0.07} \qquad 54.$$

RENAL AND OSMOTIC ALLOMETRY

Since the physiometry of renal function in mammals was reviewed by Günther (39)[2], several allometric equations and tabulations susceptible to allometric analysis have appeared, refining somewhat, but generally confirming the relationships pioneered by Adolph's (1) cornerstone of allometric physiology.

Mammalian renal structure and function appear to scale as follows:

1. Clearances, glomerular filtration rates ($\dot{V}_{gfr}$), renal blood flow ($\dot{V}_{rb}$), and nitrogen and sulfur outputs are roughly proportional to $M^{3/4}$ and therefore to metabolic and cardiac output rates (1, 32).

2. The ratio of $\dot{V}_{gfr}$ to renal plasma flow is $0.19M^{-0.02}$ (n = 10) to $0.25 M^{0.05}$ (n = 19 spp.) (32, 49).

3. The renal $\dot{V}_{rb}$ is $0.26M^{-0.02}$ of the cardiac output (32). The right renal artery has a diameter of $0.166M^{0.31}$ (51). Therefore the arterial cross-section is $0.022M^{0.62}$, and the velocity is $32.6 \ cm \ sec^{-1}M^{0.15}$.

4. The urine flow is $0.8\% M^{0.03}$ of the $\dot{V}_{gfr}$ (32). Thus the same proportion of filtrate is reabsorbed, regardless of body size.

5. Edwards (32) notes that there is no apparent allometry of renal concentrating ability, the main factor being environmental adaptation. However, there is an inverse correlation, similar to that for metabolic rate per g body mass, between maximum salinity of drinking fluid taken voluntarily (and presumably of processing ability) and body size in 4 spp. of desert birds (95). From (95), figure 1:

$$\text{max Osm.} = 3m^{-0.29} \qquad 55.$$

This tentative relationship within an environmental type seems worthy of further examination.

6. The number of nephrons and glomeruli is a multiple of $M^{0.62}$ (1, 49). Dividing $\dot{V}_{gfr}$ by this term gives the scaling of single nephron $\dot{V}_{gfr}$:

[2]While Günthers' Table 11 is headed "Body weight (w) in kg," four of the equations are expressed as functions of body mass in g; some of the equations are for one kidney, others for both kidneys.

$$\text{S N } \dot{V}_{gfr}, \text{ nl min}^{-1} = 28M^{0.10} \qquad \qquad 56.$$

Reported S N $\dot{V}_{gfr}$ values vary 2- to 3-fold with technique and other factors. Means for values tabulated for dogs and rats (119) plot as:

$$\text{S N } \dot{V}_{gfr} = 45M^{0.16} \qquad \qquad 57.$$

7. Individual glomerular volume varies with $M^{0.29}$, total volume of glomeruli varies with $M^{0.83}$ to $M^{0.91}$, as does glomerular capillary surface area (49).

8. Mean length of glomerular capillaries, linear velocity of their blood flow, blood flow rate per unit glomerular capillary surface area, and $\dot{V}_{gfr}$ per unit glomerular capillary area are constant in mammals, independent of body size (49).

Avian-Mammalian Comparisons

In birds, as for mammals, the $\dot{V}_{gfr}$ and $\dot{V}_{rb}$ are linearly proportional to $M^{3/4}$ and $\dot{H}_m$. Avian $\dot{V}_{gfr}$ (based on inulin clearance) is only $0.4M^{0.06}$ times that of mammals, perhaps reflecting the fact that antidiuresis is accomplished by reducing $\dot{V}_{gfr}$ via the reptilian-type nephrons (15, 32). However, the avian kidneys constitute a similar proportion of body mass, depending upon which equations are compared (Table 3). Birds with cephalic salt-secreting glands also have larger kidneys than other birds (53).

The Allometry of Water Balance

An attempt to account allometrically for mammalian and avian water budgets reveals gaps in our understanding of comparative fluid balance (Table 4; note especially the ? marks). Total water turnover seems to be in constant proportion to metabolic rate, as is the case for urine water loss in mammals, and probably for preformed and metabolic water intake. If so, drinking water would also have to scale as $M^{3/4}$; the available information

Table 3 Renal allometric comparison of mammals and birds

	Mammals	Reference	Birds	Reference	Mammal/ bird
kidney mass (g)	$7.52M^{0.85}$	1			$1.13M^{-0.06}$
	$6.85M^{1.00}$	39	$6.68M^{0.91}$	55	$1.03M^{0.09}$
bird spp. without salt glands:			$7.30M^{0.93}$	53	$.94M^{0.07}$
bird spp. with salt glands:			$11.27M^{0.88}$	53	$.61M^{0.12}$
Inulin clearance (ml/min.)	$5.36M^{0.72}$	32	$2.11M^{0.78}$	32	$2.5M^{-0.06}$

Table 4 The allometry of water balance

	Mammals	Birds	References
Intake			
Drinking, ml day^{-1}	$99M^{0.90}$	$11.4M^{0.19}$	22; calc. from 7a
Preformed, g day^{-1}	$?M^{0.75}$?	$?M^{0.75}$?	—
Metabolic,[a] g day^{-1}	$12.6M^{0.75}$	$14.1M^{0.72}$	7; 91[a]
Loss			
Evaporation, g day^{-1}	$38.8M^{0.88}$	$24.2M^{0.61}$	23
Evaporation, g day^{-1} bats	$40.7M^{0.67}$[b]		102
Feces	?	$\left.\right\}$? $60M^{0.72}$?[c]	
Urine, ml day^{-1}	$60.85M^{0.75}$		32
Total turnover, ml day^{-1}			
Eutheria	$123M^{0.80}$	$70.8M^{0.75}$	87; 112
Marsupialia	$90M^{0.80}$		27

[a] Metabolic water calculated, assuming R Q = 0.8, 0.578 g H_2O/l O_2 at 1.5 $\dot{H}_{m\text{-}std}$.
[b] Slope not significantly different from all mammals, evaporation rate 2.6 times that of other mammals at mid-point of body-mass range compared.
[c] Zebra finch, dehydrated: 60 ml (kg · day)$^{-1}$ (96).

does not support this conclusion, however. While the equations are statistically significant, the raw data may contain a significant artifact of "boredom polydipsia" in small caged birds. The accounted intake, not counting preformed water of mammals, exceeds the estimated total body water turnover.

There are more gaps and contradictions on the side of water loss. Without the allometry of fecal water loss, the evaporation and urine losses of mammals exceed the total turnover. Birds lose less water by evaporation than mammals, compared on an equal-size basis.

Until these unglamorous gaps are filled, the comparative regulatory physiology of terrestrial homeotherms remains poorly understood.

CONCLUSION

Mathematically simple, especially since electronic calculators appeared, allometric analysis is probably the most useful and powerful tool of comparative physiology. Although the approach is one of purely empirical description, expediting the digestion of raw data and synthesis of patterns allows us to prepare for the eventual explanation of physiological regulation and its evolution in terms of physical principles.

ACKNOWLEDGMENT

Supported in part by NSF grant DEB 79-03689. I thank David Hinds for reading the manuscript.

Literature Cited

1. Adolph, E. A. 1949. Quantitative relations in the physiological constitutions of mammals. *Science* 109:579–85
2. Agostini, E., Thimm, F. F., Fenn, W. O. 1959. Comparative features of the mechanics of breathing. *J. Appl. Physiol.* 14:679–83
3. Alexander, R.McN., Goldspink, G. 1977. *Mechanics and Energetics of Animal Locomotion.* London/NY: Wiley. 346 pp.
4. Ar, A., Rahn, M. 1978. Interdependence of gas conductance, incubation length, and weight of the avian egg. In *Respiratory Function in Birds, Adult and Embryonic,* ed. J. Piiper, pp. 227–36. Berlin: Springer. 310 pp.
5. Aschoff, J., Pohl, H. 1970a. Der Ruheumsatz von Vögeln als Function der Tageszeit und der Körpergrösse. *J. Ornithol.* 111:38–47
5a. Aschoff, J., Pohl, H. 1970b. Rhythmic variations in energy metabolism. *Fed. Proc.* 29:1541–52
6. Balmer, R. T., Strobusch, A. D. 1977. Critical size of newborn homeotherms. *J. Appl. Physiol.: Respir. Environ. Exer. Physiol.* 42:571–77
7. Bartholomew, G. A. 1977. Energy metabolism. In *Animal Physiology: Principles and Adaptations,* ed. M. S. Gordon, pp. 57–110. NY: MacMillan. 669 pp.
7a. Bartholomew, G., Cade, T. J. 1963. The water economy of land birds. *Auk* 80:504–39
8. Baudinette, R. V. 1978. Scaling of heart rate during locomotion. *J. Comp. Physiol.* 127:337–42
9. Bech, C., Johansen, K., Maloiy, G. M. O. 1976. Ventilation and expired gas composition in the flamingo *Phoenicopterus ruber,* during normal respiration and panting. *Physiol. Zool.* 52:313–26
10. Berger, M., Hart, J. S. 1974. Physiology and energetics of flight. In *Avian Biology,* ed. D. S. Farner, J. R. King, 4:415–77. NY/London: Academic.
11. Berger, M., Hart, J. S., Roy, O. Z. 1970. Respiration, oxygen consumption and heart rate in some birds during rest and flight. *Z. Vergl. Physiol.* 66:201–14
12. Bligh, J., Cloudsley-Thompson, J. L., MacDonald, A. G. 1976. *Environmental Physiology of Animals,* p. 421. NY: Wiley. 456 pp.
13. Blum, J. J. 1977. On the geometry of four dimensions and the relationship between metabolism and body mass. *J. Theor. Biol.* 64:599–601
14. Bond, C. F., Gilbert, P. W. 1958. Comparative study of blood volume in representative aquatic and non-aquatic birds. *Am. J. Physiol.* 194:519–21
15. Braun, E. J., Dantzler, W. M. 1972. Function of mammalian-type and reptilian-type nephrons in kidney of desert quail. *Am. J. Physiol.* 222:617–29
15a. Brody, S. 1945. *Bioenergetics and Growth.* NY: Reinhold. 1023 pp. (reprint 1964. NY: Hafner)
16. Brown, J. H., Calder, W. A. III, Kodric-Brown, A. 1978. Correlates and consequences of body-size in nectarfeeding birds. *Am. Zool.* 18:687–700
17. Calder, W. A. 1974. Consequences of body size for avian energetics. *Publ. Nuttall Ornithol. Club* 15:86–151
18. Calder, W. A., Dawson, T. J. 1978. Resting metabolic rates of ratite birds: The kiwis and the emu. *Comp. Biochem. Physiol.* 60A:479–81
19. Calder, W. A., King, J. R. 1974. Thermal and caloric relations of birds. See Ref. 10, 4:260–415
20. Carey, C., Morton, M. L. 1976. Aspects of circulatory physiology of montane and lowland birds. *Comp. Biochem. Physiol.* 54A:61–74
21. Casey, T. M., Withers, P. C., Casey, K. K. 1979. Metabolic and respiratory responses of arctic mammals to ambient temperature during the summer. *Comp. Biochem. Physiol.* 64A: 331–41
22. Chew, R. M. 1965. Water metabolism of mammals. In *Physiological Mammalogy,* ed. W. V. Mayer, R. G. Van Gelder, 2:43–178. NY/London: Academic. 326 pp.
23. Crawford, E. C., Lasiewski, R. C. 1968. Oxygen consumption and respiratory evaporation of the emu and rhea. *Condor* 70:333–39
24. Crosfill, M. L., Widdicombe, J. G. 1961. Physical characteristics of the chest and lungs and the work of breathing in different mammalian species. *J. Physiol. London* 158:1–14

24a. Dawson, W. R., Bennett, A. F. 1973. Roles of metabolic level and temperature regulation in the adjustment of western plumed pigeons (*Lophophaps ferruginea*) to desert conditions. *Comp. Biochem. Physiol.* 44A: 249–66

25. Dawson, T. J. 1973. "Primitive" mammals. In *Comparative Physiology of Thermoregulation, Special Aspects*, ed. G. C. Whittow, 3:1–46. NY: Academic

26. Dawson, T. J., Hulbert, A. J. 1970. Standard metabolism, body temperature, and surface areas of Australian marsupials. *Am. J. Physiol.* 218: 1233–38

27. Denny, M. J. S., Dawson, T. J. 1975. Comparative metabolism of tritiated water by macropodid marsupials. *Am. J. Physiol.* 228:1794–99

28. Dejours, P. 1975. *Principles of Comparative Respiratory Physiology*. Amsterdam: North Holland. pp. 163–75

29. Drorbaugh, J. E. 1960. Pulmonary function in different animals. *J. Appl. Physiol.* 15:1069–72

30. Economos, A. C. 1979. On structural theories of basal metabolic rate. *J. Theor. Biol.* 80:445–50

31. Economos, A. C. 1979. Gravity, metabolic rate and body size of mammals. *Physiologist* 22:S71–S72

32. Edwards, N. A. 1975. Scaling of renal functions in mammals. *Comp. Biochem. Physiol.* 52A:63–66

33. Fedak, M. A., Pinshow, K., Schmidt-Nielsen, K. 1974. Energy cost of bipedal running. *Am. J. Physiol.* 227:1038–44

34. Fedak, M. A., Seeherman, H. J. 1979. Reappraisal of energetics of locomotion shows identical cost in bipeds and quadrupeds including ostrich and horse. *Nature* 282:713–16

35. Gould, S. J. 1977. Our alloted lifetimes. *Nat. Hist.* 87(1):34–41

36. Gould, S. J. 1979. One standard lifespan. *New Sci.* 81:388–89

37. Grant, T. R., Dawson, T. J. 1978. Temperature regulation in the platypus, *Ornithorynchus anatinus:* production and loss of metabolic heat in air and water. *Physiol. Zool.* 51:315–32

38. Günther, B. 1972. Allometric ratios, invariant numbers and the theory of biological similarities. *Pflügers Arch.* 331: 283–93

39. Günther, B. 1975. On theories of biological similarity. In *Fortschritte der Experimentale und Theoretische Biophysik*, ed. W. Beier, 19:7–111. Leipzig: G. Thieme 111 pp.

40. Günther, B., Martinoya, C. 1968. Operational time and theory of biological similarities. *J. Theor. Biol.* 20:107–11

41. Haldane, J. B. S. 1928 (1958 reprint). On being the right size. In *A Treasury of Science*, ed. H. Shapley, S. Rapport, H. Wright, pp. 321–25. NY: Harper

42. Hart, J. S. 1971. Rodents. In *Comparative Physiology of Thermoregulation*, ed. G. C. Whittow, 2:1–149. NY/London: Academic. 410 pp.

43. Heldmaier, G. 1971. Zitterfreie Wärmebildung und Körpergrösse bei Saügetieren. *Z. Vergl. Physiol.* 73:222–48

44. Hemmingsen, A. M. 1960. Energy metabolism as related to body size and respiratory surfaces, and its evolution. *Rep. Steno Mem. Hosp. Nord. Insulin Lab.* 9:1–110

45. Herreid, C. F. II, Kessel, B. 1967. Thermal conductance in birds and mammals. *Comp. Biochem. Physiol.* 21: 405–14

46. Hinds, D. S., Calder, W. A. 1971. Tracheal dead space in the respiration of birds. *Evolution* 25:429–40

47. Holt, J. P., Rhode, E. A., Kines, H. 1968. Ventricular volumes and body weight in mammals. *Am. J. Physiol.* 215:704–15

48. Holt, W. W., Rhode, E. A., Holt, J. P. 1978. Geometric similarity in the vascular system. *Fed. Proc.* 37:823

49. Holt, J. P., Rhode, E. A. 1976. Similarity of renal glomerular hemodynamics in mammals. *Am. Heart J.* 92: 465–72

50. Holt, J. P., Rhode, E. A., Holt, W. W., Kines, H. Geometric similarity of aorta, venae cavae and certain of their branches in mammals. Unpublished

51. Holt, W. W., Rhode, E. A., Holt, J. P. Sr. 1980. Geometric similarity in the renal arterial system. *Fed. Proc.* 39:269

52. Hugh-Jones, P., Barter, C. E., Hime, J. M., Rusbridge, M. M. 1978. Dead space and tidal volume of the giraffe compared with some other mammals. *Resp. Physiol.* 35:53–58

53. Hughes, M. R. 1970. Relative kidney size in nonpasserine birds with functional salt glands. *Condor* 72:164–68

54. Iberall, A. S. 1979. Some comparative scale factors for mammals: comments on Milnor's paper concerning a feature of cardiovascular design. *Am. J. Physiol.* 237:R7–R9

55. Johnson, O. W. 1968. Some morpological features of avian kidneys. *Auk* 85: 216–28

56. Jones, D. R., Johansen, K. 1972. The blood vascular system of birds. See Ref. 10, 2:157–285

57. Kendeigh, S. C. 1969. Tolerance of cold and Bergmann's Rule. *Auk* 86:13–25

58. Kleiber, M. 1961. *The Fire of Life.* NY: Wiley. 454 pp.

59. Kleiber, M. 1975. Metabolic turnover rate: a physiological meaning of the metabolic rate per unit body weight. *J. Theor. Biol.* 53:199–204

60. Kuhlmann, W. D., Fedde, M. R. 1976. Upper respiratory dead space in the chicken: its fraction of the tidal volume. *Comp. Biochem. Physiol.* 54A:409–11

61. Larimer, J. L., Schmidt-Nielsen, K. 1960. A comparison of blood carbonic anhydrase of various mammals. *Comp. Biochem. Physiol.* 1:19

62. Lasiewski, R. C., Calder, W. A. 1971. A preliminary allometric analysis of respiratory variables in resting birds. *Respir. Physiol.* 11:152–66

63. Lasiewski, R. C., Dawson, W. R. 1967. A re-examination of the relation between standard metabolic rate and body weight in birds. *Condor* 69:13–23

64. Lechner, A. J. 1978. The scaling of maximal oxygen consumption and pulmonary dimensions in small mammals. *Respir. Physiol.* 34:29–44

65. Leith, D. E. 1976. Comparative mammalian respiratory mechanics. *Physiologist* 19:485–510

66. Lindstedt, S., Calder, W. A. 1976. Body size and longevity in birds. *Condor* 78:91–94

67. Lindstedt, S., Calder, W. A. 1981. Body size, physiological time and longevity of homeothermic animals. *Q. Rev. Biol.* In press

68. MacMillen, R. E., Lee, A. K. 1970. Energy metabolism and pulmocutaneous water loss of Australian hopping mice. *Comp. Biochem. Physiol.* 35:355–69

69. MacMillen, R. E., Nelson, J. E. 1969. Bioenergetics and body size in dasyurid marsupials. *Am. J. Physiol.* 217: 1246–51

70. Martin, R. R., Haines, H. 1970. Application of Laplace's law to mammalian hearts. *Comp. Biochem. Physiol.* 34: 959–62

71. McFarland, W. N., Pough, F. H., Cade, J. J., Heiser, J. B. 1979. *Vertebrate Life.* NY/London: MacMillan. 875 pp.

72. McMahon, T. A. 1973. Size and shape in biology. *Science* 179:1201–4

73. McMahon, T. A. 1975. Using body size to understand the structural design of animals: quadripedal locomotion. *J. Appl. Physiol.* 39:617–27

74. Milnor, W. R. 1979. Aortic wave length as a determinant of the relation between heart rate and body size in mammals. *Am. J. Physiol.* 237:R3–R6

74a. Noordergraaf, A., Li, J., Campbell, K. B. 1979. Mammalian hemodynamics: a new similarity principle. *J. Theor. Biol.* 79:485–89

75. O'Neil, J. J., Leith, D. E. 1980. Lung diffusing capacity scaled in mammals from 25 g to 500 kg. *Fed. Proc.* 39:972

76. Pace, N., Rahlmann, D. F., Smith, A. H. 1979. Scale effects in the musculoskeletal system, viscera and skin of small terrestrial mammals. *Physiologist* 22:S51–S52

77. Paladino, F. V., King, J. R. 1979. Energy cost of terrestrial locomotion: biped and quadruped runners compared. *Rev. Can. Biol.* 38:321–23

78. Pearson, O. P. 1948. Metabolism of small mammals, with remarks on the lower limit of mammalian size. *Science* 108:44

79. Pedley, T. J. 1977. *Scale Effects in Animal Locomotion.* London/NY: Academic. 545 pp.

80. Poczopko, P. 1971. Metabolic levels in adult homeotherms. *Acta Therol.* 16: 1–21

81. Prange, H. D. 1977. The scaling and mechanics of arthropod skeletons. In *Scale Effects in Animal Locomotion,* ed. T. J. Pedley, pp. 169–81. London/NY: Academic

82. Prothero, J. W. 1979. Maximal oxygen consumption in various animals and plants. *Comp. Biochem. Physiol.* 64A:463–66

83. Rahn, H., Ar, A., Paganelli, C. V. 1979. How bird eggs breathe. *Sci. Am.* 240:46–56

84. Ralph, C. L. 1978. *Introductory Animal Physiology,* p. 129. NY: McGraw-Hill. 586 pp.

85. Regal, P. J. 1975. The evolutionary origin of feathers. *Q. Rev. Biol.* 50:35–66

86. Rhode, E. A., Kines, H., Holt, J. P. 1970. Left ventricular volumes and heart and body weight in unanesthetized mammals. *Physiologist* 13:293

87. Richmond, C. R., Langham, W. M., Trujillo, T. T. 1962. Comparative metabolism of tritiated water by mammals. *J. Cell. Comp. Physiol.* 59:45–53

88. Riggs, A. 1960. The nature and significance of the Bohr effect in mammalian hemoglobins. *J. Gen. Physiol.* 43: 737–52

89. Schmidt-Nielsen, K. 1975. Scaling in biology: the consequences of size. *J. Exper. Zool.* 194:287–308

90. Schmidt-Nielsen, K. 1977. Problems of scaling: locomotion and physiological correlates. See Ref. 81, pp. 1–22

91. Schmidt-Nielsen, K. 1979. *Animal Physiology: Adaptation and Environment.* London: Cambridge Univ. Press. 560 pp. 2nd ed.

92. Schmidt-Nielsen, K., Dawson, T. J., Crawford, E. C. Jr. 1960. Temperature regulation in the echidna *Tachyglossus aculeatus. J. Cell. Physiol.* 67:63–72

93. Schmidt-Nielsen, K., Larimer, J. L. 1958. Oxygen dissociation curves of mammalian blood in relation to body size. *Am. J. Physiol.* 195:424–28

94. Schmidt-Nielsen, K., Pennycuik, P. 1961. Capillary density in mammals in relation to body size and oxygen consumption. *Am. J. Physiol.* 200:746–50

95. Skadhauge, E. 1975. Renal and cloacal transport of salt and water. *Symp. Zool. Soc. London* 35:97–106

96. Skadhauge, E., Bradshaw, S. D. 1974. Saline drinking and cloacal excretion of salt and water in the zebra finch. *Am. J. Physiol.* 227:1263–67

97. Spotila, J. R., Gates, D. M. 1975. Body size, insulation, and optimum body temperatures of homeotherms. In *Perspective in Biophysical Ecology,* ed. D. M. Gates. pp. 291–301. NY: Springer. 609 pp.

98. Stahl, W. R. 1962. Similarity and dimensional biology. *Science* 137:205–12

99. Stahl, W. R. 1963. Similarity analysis of physiological systems. *Perspect. Biol. Med.* 6:291–321

100. Stahl, W. R. 1963. The analysis of biological similarity. In *Advances in Biological and Medical Physics,* ed. J. H. Lawrence, J. W. Gofman, 9:355–464 NY: Academic. 481 pp.

101. Stahl, W. R. 1967. Scaling of respiratory variables in mammals. *J. Appl. Physiol.* 22:453–60

102. Studier, E. H. 1970. Evaporative water loss in bats. *Comp. Biochem. Physiol.* 35:935–43

103. Taylor, C. R. 1977. The energetics of terrestrial locomotion and body size in vertebrates. See Ref. 81, pp. 127–141

104. Taylor, C. R., Seeherman, H. S., Maloiy, G. M. O., Heglund, N. C., Kamau, J. M. Z. 1978. Scaling maximum aerobic capacity (Vo_2 max) to

body size in mammals. *Fed. Proc.* 37:473

105. Tenney, S. M., Bartlett, D. 1967. Comparative quantitative morphometry of the mammalian lung: trachea. *Respir. Physiol.* 3:130–35

106. Tenney, S. M., Remmers, J. E. 1963. Comparative quantitative morphology of the mammalian lung: diffusing area. *Nature* 197:54–56

107. Thompson, D'A. W. 1942. *On Growth and Form.* Cambridge: Cambridge Univ. Press. pp. 22–77

108. Tracy, C. R. 1977. Minimum size of mammalian homeotherms: role of the thermal environment. *Science* 198:1034–35

109. Tucker, V. A. 1970. Energetic cost of locomotion in animals. *Comp. Biochem. Physiol.* 34:841–46

110. Tucker, V. A. 1975. Flight energetics. *Symp. Zool. Soc. London* 35:49–63

111. Umminger, B. L. 1977. Relation of whole blood sugar concentration in vertebrates to standard metabolic rate. *Comp. Biochem. Physiol.* 56A:457–60

112. Walter, A., Hughes, M. R. 1978. Total body water volume and turnover rate in fresh water and sea water adapted glaucous-winged gulls, *Larus glaucescens. Comp. Biochem. Physiol.* 61A:233–37

113. Weathers, W. W. 1979. Climatic adaptation in avian standard metabolic rate. *Oecologia* 42:81–89

114. Weathers, W. W. 1980. Allometry of heat production by heat stressed birds. *Fed. Proc.* 39:1165

115. White, L., Haines, H., Adams, T. 1968. Cardiac output related to body weight in small mammals. *Comp. Biochem. Physiol.* 27:559–65

116. Wilkie, D. R. 1977. Metabolism and body size. See Ref. 81, pp. 23–36

117. Withers, P. C., Casey, T. M., Casey, K. K. 1979. Allometry of respiratory and haematological parameters of arctic mammals. *Comp. Biochem. Physiol.* 64A:343–50

118. Wunder, B. A. 1975. A model for estimating metabolic rate of active or resting mammals. *J. Theor. Biol.* 49:345–54

119. Wright, F. S., Giebisch, G. 1972. Glomerular filtration in single nephrons. *Kidney Int.* 1:201–9

120. Yale, F. E. 1979. Comparative physiology: Compared to what? *Am. J. Physiol.* 237:R1–R2

Ann. Rev. Physiol. 1981. 43:323–341

ENERGY METABOLISMS OF PARASITIC HELMINTHS: Adaptations to Parasitism

❖1313

Howard J. Saz[1]

Department of Biology, University of Notre Dame, Notre Dame, Indiana 46556

INTRODUCTION

Biochemical studies of parasitic helminths (worms) have led to a better understanding of numerous other animals both parasitic and free-living, including (*a*) those invertebrates that, like the parasites, have adapted to a microaerophilic environment in part of their life cycle (65), and (*b*) some fish, deep diving mammals, and possibly even ischemic mammalian heart muscle (16, 27, 35, 38).

A number of generalizations can now be made concerning biochemical adaptations to the parasitic mode of life: (*a*) Biochemical differences between the parasites and their hosts extend from the obvious differences in pathways and products of fermentation to subtle differences in enzyme structure and kinetics. (*b*) All helminths examined are capable of assimilating oxygen under appropriate conditions, but none can completely oxidize substrates to carbon dioxide and water. All accumulate organic end-products, indicating little or no terminal respiration. (*c*) Antibiotic therapy has not been successful for helminth infections because, unlike the case in bacterial, protozoan, or viral diseases, the adult parasite itself must be removed and continued infection is not dependent upon replication of the organism. Many anthelmintic agents appear to act by inhibiting either neuromuscular transmission or the machinery for energy metabolism in the parasite (48, 57, 67, 93).

[1]Recent studies from the laboratory of the author that are discussed in this review were supported in part by the N.I.H., U.S. Public Health Service grants AI-09483 and AI-10512.

323

0066-4278/81/0315-0323$01.00

Parasitic helminths may be divided into three arbitrary groups based upon their metabolic oxygen requirements. First, (a) some helminths, e.g. adult intestinal parasites such as the nematode *Ascaris lumbricoides* (101) and cestodes (tapeworms) *Hymenolepis diminuta* (13, 62, 83, 84), *H. nana* (86), and *Taenia crassiceps* (E. L. Schiller, personal communication), require no oxygen in their energy yielding pathways and appear to survive equally well in vitro either anaerobically or aerobically. The three tapeworms have been cultured anaerobically through all or part of their life cycle. Despite this, air has been reported to stimulate phosphorylation in *H. diminuta* (56, 103). (b) Some helminths are obligate aerobes, e.g. the adult stages of the filarial worm, *Litomosoides carinii,* which resides in the pleural cavity of some rodents (52, 98), the nematode of the rat intestine, *Nippostrongylus brasilensis* (61, 64, 101), and several of the larval stages of *Ascaris* (40, 71). Removal of oxygen results in a relatively rapid loss of motility in vitro and subsequent death. (c) The third group of parasites are primarily larval stages that require an aerobic metabolism for motility but not for survival. This dichotomy was first suggested for a larval stage of *Trichinella spiralis* (89, 97) but was questioned recently (17). However, the microfilariae of *L. carinii, Brugia pahangi,* and *Dipetalonema viteae* clearly fall into this category (58).

The physiological niche occupied by a parasite in its host does not determine the gas phase required by that parasite's energy metabolism. For example, the adult blood fluke, *Schistosoma mansoni,* is a homolactate fermenter (9, 85). Similarly, the adult filariids *D. viteae* and *B. pahangi,* obtained from hamster subcutaneous tissues and the peritoneal cavities of infected jirds, respectively, are both homolactate fermenters—i.e. the glucose carbons utilized can be accounted for quantitatively by the lactate recovered (98). This implies a strictly glycolytic or anaerobic pathway despite the availability of oxygen. Presumably, these organisms have adapted to a parasitic existence by losing their aerobic energy metabolisms in spite of the apparent availability of oxygen in their environments. The benefits of such an adaptation to the organism in a milieu of plenty might be argued, but the successful proliferation of these parasitic forms is undeniable.

In this necessarily eclectic review, I discuss some of what is known about the energy metabolisms of representative examples of each type of organism.

ANAEROBIC MITOCHONDRIAL ENERGY GENERATION IN ASCARIS

Studies with *Ascaris lumbricoides* var *suum* have uncovered an anaerobic energy-yielding pathway subsequently shown to be widely distributed in

Table 1 Some helminth and protozoan parasites that accumulate succinate or products derived from succinate

Nematodes	Cestodes	Trematodes	Protozoa	Acanthocephala
Ascaris lumbricoides	*Hymenolepis diminuta*	*Fasciola hepatica*	*Trypanosoma cruzi*	*Moniliformis dubius*
Heterakis gallinae	*Moniezia expansa*	*Paragonimus westermani*	*Trypanosoma lewisi*	
Trichuris vulpis	*Echinococcus granulosus* (cysts)	*Echinostoma liei*	*Trypanosoma congolensi*	
Trichinella spiralis (larvae)	*Taenia taeniaformis*		*Strigomonas oncopelti*	
Haemonchus contortus	*Spirometra mansonoides*			
Syphacia muris				
Dictyocaulus viviparus				

both parasitic and free-living invertebrates and in some vertebrates (34, 35, 83). This pathway requires CO_2 fixation, resulting in the accumulation of either succinate (a major fermentation product of *Ascaris*) or products derived from succinate (72). Shortly after elucidation of this pathway in the nematode *Ascaris*, essentially the same reaction scheme was demonstrated in the cestode, *Hymenolepis diminuta* (83). Reports followed of many other animal parasites that form succinate or products derived from succinate to a significant (though not necessarily major) extent (Table 1). Many of these also require CO_2 for optimal survival; the metabolisms of most, like that of *Ascaris*, require "fumarate reductase" [see (83) for references].

Overall Pathways of Formation of Succinate and Volatile Acids

Adult ascarids have adapted well to the low oxygen tensions of their habitat, the small intestine. The parasite can function anaerobically, and as early as 1901 it was realized that *Ascaris* survives in vitro for equal periods under oxygen or nitrogen atmospheres (100). Survival is increased further by the addition of carbon dioxide to the nitrogen. Unfortunately, like most helminth parasites, *Ascaris* cannot be cultured outside its host. The following compounds have been identified as products of the in vitro anaerobic as well as aerobic *Ascaris* carbohydrate fermentation: succinate, acetoin, acetate, propionate, butyrate, 2-methylbutyrate, n-valerate, cis-2-methylcrotonate (tiglate), and 2-methylvalerate (10, 12, 69, 75, 76, 77).

Use of ^{14}C labelled substrates, $^{32}P_i$ uptake studies, enzyme assay, and enzyme distribution techniques with *Ascaris* muscle and mitochondrial preparations has largely elucidated the pathways of succinate and volatile fatty acid formation. The overall pathway shown in Figure 1 is generally

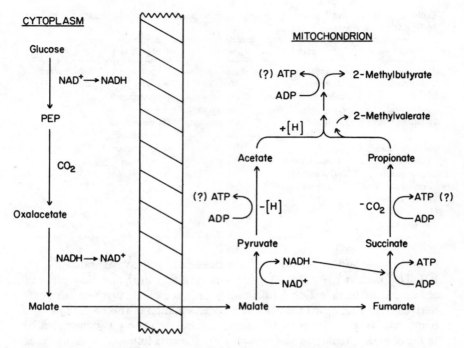

Figure 1 Pathway for the anaerobic dissimilation of carbohydrate in the nematode *Ascaris lumbricoides.*

accepted not only for *Ascaris* but also in part for many other parasitic and free-living invertebrates (34, 65, 72, 83). Saz & Vidrine (75) first presented evidence that succinate was formed by the "backward leg" of the tricarboxylic acid cycle.

According to present concepts, *Ascaris* muscle catabolizes glucose as far as phosphoenolpyruvate (PEP) *via* the glycolytic pathway. PEP serves as the point where the parasite and host metabolisms branch off on different pathways. Unlike the host tissues, the nematode muscle is not capable of forming significant quantities of cytoplasmic pyruvate, since the enzyme pyruvate kinase (PK) is only barely detectable (13, 15). Instead, CO_2 is fixed into the relatively high tissue levels of PEP to form oxalacetate (OAA), as catalyzed by PEP carboxykinase (71). A very active cytoplasmic malate dehydrogenase (MDH) then reduces OAA to malate with the glycolytically formed NADH, thereby regenerating cytoplasmic NAD^+ that can accept more electrons from the triose stage of glycolysis. Interestingly, the *Ascaris* PEP carboxykinase appears to act primarily in a direction opposite to that proposed for the enzyme in mammalian tissues, where it presumably acts in glyconeogenesis (92). Factors apparently responsible for this "backward" direction of the *Ascaris* enzyme are (65): (*a*) the *Ascaris* enzyme exhibits an apparent Michaelis constant (K_m) for PEP which is approximately one-seventh that obtained for OAA; (*b*) tissue concentrations of PEP are unusually high in *Ascaris* muscle as a consequence of the very low PK activity; (*c*) cytoplasmic MDH activity is high and the equilibrium lies in the direction of malate, which would tend to remove OAA rapidly. Recently, the PEP carboxykinase has been purified from the cestode *H. diminuta* and found to possess a considerably stronger affinity for PEP than the corresponding enzyme from rat liver (59).

Cytoplasmically formed malate then permeates the mitochondrial membrane and becomes the mitochondrial substrate, whereupon a dismutation reaction takes place. One mole of malate is oxidized to pyruvate and CO_2, catalyzed by the NAD^+-linked "malic" enzyme, thereby generating intramitochondrial reducing power in the form of NADH (25, 70). Intramitochondrial NADH serves to reduce another mole of malate via fumarate to succinate. This fumarate reductase reaction differs considerably from the succinate dehydrogenase of mammalian tissues. Unlike the host enzyme, it is pyridine nucleotide linked; under appropriate conditions can go to completion in the direction of succinate formation; and, most importantly, is coupled to an electron transport associated phosphorylation, presumably at the NADH-flavoprotein (site I) level (41, 45, 66, 87). In addition, the electron transport system couples with rhodoquinone rather than ubiquinone (63). To this point, the fumarate reductase reaction appeared to be the major source of mitochondrial ATP in *Ascaris* muscle metabolism. Recent findings (discussed below) however, suggest at least one and possibly other additional sites for ATP generation in *Ascaris* mitochondria.

Pyruvate and succinate formed in the mitochondrion (Figure 1) then serve as precursors for acetate and propionate, respectively, which in turn are precursors of the branched chain volatile acids 2-methylbutyrate, tiglate, and 2-methylvalerate [Figure 2; see also (77, 78)].

Ascaris mitochondria are remarkably different from mammalian mitochondria. The former function primarily anaerobically and were originally thought to be devoid of cytochrome *c* and cytochrome oxidase (11, 18). However, sensitive techniques have revealed low levels of cytochromes *b*, *c*, and oxidase, but the latter two activities are so low as to be of questionable physiological significance (19, 33). The facts that ascarids survive equally well under anaerobic or aerobic atmospheres and that $^{32}P_i$ incorporation into ATP by mitochondria oxidizing malate is essentially the same under air or nitrogen, with or without antimycin or cyanide, as well as other evidence may indicate that the cytochrome system plays little or no part in the adult muscle energy metabolism. The minor role played by the cyto-

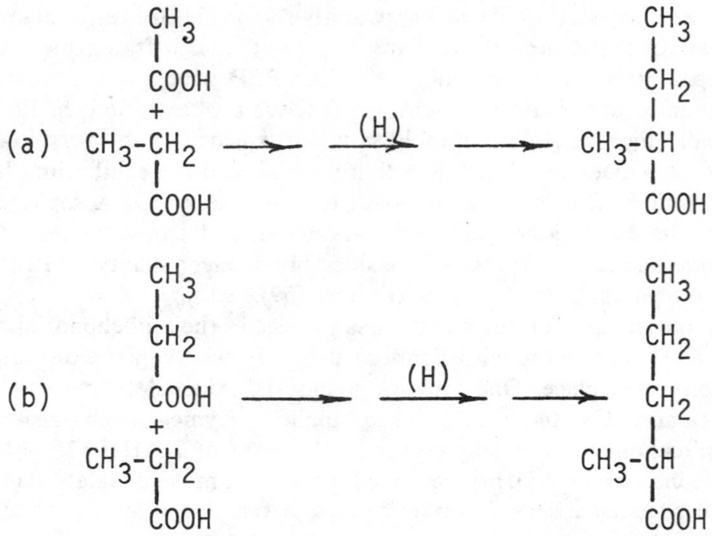

$$
\text{(a)} \quad
\begin{array}{c}
CH_3 \\
| \\
COOH \\
+ \\
CH_3-CH_2 \\
| \\
COOH
\end{array}
\quad \longrightarrow \quad \xrightarrow{\text{(H)}} \quad \longrightarrow \quad
\begin{array}{c}
CH_3 \\
| \\
CH_2 \\
| \\
CH_3-CH \\
| \\
COOH
\end{array}
$$

$$
\text{(b)} \quad
\begin{array}{c}
CH_3 \\
| \\
CH_2 \\
| \\
COOH \\
+ \\
CH_3-CH_2 \\
| \\
COOH
\end{array}
\quad \longrightarrow \quad \xrightarrow{\text{(H)}} \quad \longrightarrow \quad
\begin{array}{c}
CH_3 \\
| \\
CH_2 \\
| \\
CH_2 \\
| \\
CH_3-CH \\
| \\
COOH
\end{array}
$$

Figure 2 Condensation reactions in the formation of (*a*) 2-methylbutyrate and (*b*) 2-methyl-valerate by *Ascaris* muscle.

chrome system (sites II and III) in phosphorylation has also been indicated (42). Cheah (20) reported that succinate, alpha-glycerophosphate, and ascorbate plus N,N,N'-tetramethyl-p-phenylenediamine fostered presumed oxidative phosphorylation in *Ascaris* mitochondria. Unfortunately, these studies were indirect and conclusions were based upon the stimulation of oxygen uptake upon the addition of ADP. Phosphorylation per se was not measured. It is difficult, therefore, to evaluate fully the significance of these findings, particularly in light of (88). Employing Jerusalem artichoke, this study reported an NAD^+-linked, electron-transport-associated, substrate-induced oxygen uptake that was enhanced by the addition of ADP even though mitochondrial phosphorylation was uncoupled. These findings indicate that the stimulation of oxygen uptake by ADP may not be associated with phosphorylation. In addition, care must be taken in interpreting experiments concerning phosphorylation associated with the aerobic vs anaerobic utilization of succinate for several reasons. First, succinate can only be oxidized aerobically to malate and pyruvate, which, in turn, could be substrates for the anaerobic phosphorylation described above. Superficially, however, aerobic increase in phosphorylation might appear associated with the oxidation of succinate per se rather than with the reduction of malate formed from succinate. Second, recent findings indicate that acetyl CoA formed from pyruvate may regulate the decarboxylation of succinate to propionate, which appears to be associated with a substrate level phosphorylation [see below; (55)].

Hayashi et al (32) reported recently that in contrast with guinea-pig intestinal smooth muscle and rat diaphragm skeletal muscle, which were stimulated by oxygen, sustained contractile activities of *Ascaris suum* muscle were inhibited by oxygen. These observations, are consistent with earlier results (6) indicating that fatty acid transport across the *Ascaris* intestinal mucosa is most efficient in vitro under 95% $N:5\%$ CO_2. Oxygen inhibits this transport system. Relationships between aerobic and anaerobic metabolism in helminths are discussed from another point of view in (1).

Spectral evidence has been presented concerning the presence of a cytochrome of the *b* type, cytochrome *o*, in ascarids (21). This agrees with numerous earlier findings in many of the strictly anaerobic bacteria containing similar cytochromes. In the anaerobic bacteria, these cytochromes appear linked to anaerobic fumarate reductase activities. The bacteria include *Clostridium thermoaceticum, Cl. formicoaceticum* (29), *Vibrio succinogenes* (36), *Bacteroides sp.* (46, 60), and *Desulfovibrio gigas* (31).

Whether or not O_2 plays a physiological role in the energy metabolism of *Ascaris,* the anaerobic pathway appears dominant. However, O_2 may be required for other, possibly synthetic, reactions. It has been reported, for example, that the O_2-utilizing enzyme, proline hydroxylase, is needed for cuticle formation in *Ascaris* (14, 26). Interestingly, the *Ascaris* enzyme differs from others in being markedly inhibited by high concentrations of O_2. Similarly, *Schistosoma mansoni* requires O_2 only for the development of eggs, not for energy metabolism of the adult (85). The protozoan malaria parasite *Plasmodium falciparum* has finally been cultivated *in vitro* in red blood cells by decreasing the O_2 tension in the environment (37). Subsequent interesting studies have demonstrated that this protozoan parasite grows well at low O_2 tension but cannot grow under complete anoxia (82). From drug inhibition studies, it appears likely that O_2 is required for some process other than energy metabolism (81).

In the *Ascaris* mitochondrial metabolism (Figure 1) at least four possible sites exist where ATP might be generated. The first of these, the fumarate reductase, has been discussed. A second possible site would be associated with the decarboxylation of succinate to propionate; a third, with the anaerobic oxidative decarboxylation of pyruvate; and a fourth might be associated with the reduction of the double bond in the conversion of "tiglate" to 2-methylbutyrate.

Phosphorylation Associated with Succinate Decarboxylation to Propionate

In mammalian tissues, propionate is glycogenic as a consequence of its conversion to succinate, catalyzed by propionyl CoA carboxylase and methylmalonyl CoA mutase. This conversion requires the utilization of ATP. Reactions of the sequence, most of which were elucidated (39), may be illustrated thus:

(a) CO_2 + ATP + E (propionyl CoA carboxylase) $\rightleftharpoons$ "CO_2" $\sim$ E + ADP + P_i

(b) "CO_2" $\sim$ E + Propionyl CoA $\rightleftharpoons$ Methylmalonyl CoA + E

$$\text{(c) Methylmalonyl CoA} \xrightleftharpoons[]{\text{Mutase + Cofactor } B_{12}} \text{Succinyl CoA}$$

$$\text{(d) Succinyl CoA + Propionate} \xrightleftharpoons[]{\text{Transferase}} \text{Propionyl CoA + Succinate}$$

(e) Sum (a–d): CO_2 + ATP + Propionate $\rightleftharpoons$ Succinate + ADP + P_i

Under appropriate physiological conditions, all of these reactions could be reversible. That is, the decarboxylation of succinate might give rise to both propionate and ATP. The interconversion of succinate and propionate in *Ascaris* was reported in 1959 (75). In spite of the fact that it has long been established that numerous parasitic helminths, bacteria, and free living invertebrates form propionate as a major fermentation product, the possibility of obtaining energy from this conversion of succinate to propionate has not been examined until recently. This may be due to the fact that a propionyl CoA carboxylase purified from the bacterium *Veillonella gazogenes* (*Micrococcus lactilyticus*) was found not to couple with ADP (28). On the other hand, the purified mammalian enzyme requires the nucleotide for activity (39).

Tkachuck et al (90) expressed the possibility of ATP generation associated with propionate formation and examined part of this system in the cestode *Spirometra mansonoides*. Propionate and acetate were the major fermentation products of the adult cestode. In accordance with the above scheme, high activities of propionyl CoA carboxylase and methylmalonyl CoA mutase were assayed, and homogenates incorporated $^{32}P_i$ into ATP upon incubation with methylmalonyl CoA. Unfortunately, $^{32}P_i$ incorporation with succinate per se as substrate was not determined, nor was the system assayed for acyl CoA transferase activity. Therefore, reactions a–c were demonstrated, but reaction d and the overall phosphorylation remain to be examined.

Of particular interest are the recent reports (50, 51) involving purified acyl CoA carboxylases from the free-living nematode *Turbatrix aceti* and the cestode *Spirometra mansonoides,* respectively. In both cases, activity on propionyl CoA was considerably greater than that on acetyl or butyryl CoA.

Ascaris not only accumulates propionate but also utilizes it as a precursor for two of its major fermentation products, 2-methylbutyrate and 3-methylvalerate. It would profit this nematode, therefore, to accumulate ATP through succinate decarboxylation to propionate. Saz & Pietrzak (74) have presented evidence indicating that all of the above listed reactions, *a–e*, are catalyzed by *Ascaris* mitochondria. Mitochondrial preparations exhibit propionyl CoA carboxylase, methylmalonyl CoA mutase, and acyl CoA transferase activities. Inorganic $^{32}P_i$ is esterified during succinate decarboxylation with disrupted mitochondria and, in accord with the proposed reactions, both the decarboxylation and phosphate esterification are stimulated 6–8-fold by the addition of propionyl CoA. Most important, both stimulations are inhibited by avidin, a strong inhibitor of biotin-requiring enzymes such as propionyl CoA carboxylase. Some of these observations were reported earlier in preliminary form (55, 68).

The findings are consistent with the occurrence of a substrate level ATP generation coupled to the decarboxylation of succinate in *Ascaris* mitochondria. Unfortunately, the experiments required use of disrupted mitochondria owing to the low permeability of the coenzyme A derivatives. Thus ATP generation in these experiments may have arisen from a thiokinase reaction, but this appears unlikely in view of the strong inhibition by avidin.

Comparative studies with the liver fluke, *Fasciola hepatica,* indicate that ATP generation associated with succinate decarboxylation to propionate may not be unique to *Ascaris.* The adult stage of this trematode lives in a predominantly anaerobic environment, the bile duct, and ferments glucose to acetate plus propionate and smaller amounts of lactate. Conflicting reports indicate that *Fasciola* may (43) or may not (4, 94, 95) derive energy from succinate decarboxylation. S. M. Pietrzak & H. J. Saz (unpublished data) essentially have repeated with *Fasciola* mitochondria the experiments described above for *Ascaris.* All of the necessary enzyme activities were demonstrated, as well as both the avidin sensitive decarboxylation of succinate and the associated avidin sensitive incorporation of $^{32}P_i$. Thus, the nematode *Ascaris lumbricoides* var. *suum,* the trematode *Fasciola hepatica,* and possibly the cestode *Spirometra mansonoides* may well be utilizing succinate decarboxylation to generate energy.

Vitamin B_{12} cofactor is required in the above sequence of reactions. Schaefer et al (80) examined many helminth species for vitamin B_{12} content and concluded that only those containing significant levels of the vitamin accumulated propionate or its derivatives. Worms unable to assimilate vitamin B_{12} did not decarboxylate succinate. All of the "primitive" cestodes assayed contained high levels of the vitamin and also accumulated propionate, thereby correlating well with an evolutionary classification. Genetic deletions of the ability to bind and take up vitamin B_{12} correlated with an adaptive change in fermentation products from propionate to succinate or other acids. In *H. diminuta,* succinate but no propionate is formed. Within limits of assay, this cestode contains neither vitamin B_{12} (P. P. Weinstein, personal communication), propionyl CoA carboxylase, nor methylmalonyl CoA mutase, even when B_{12} coenzyme is added to the assay system (S. M. Pietrzak & H. J. Saz, unpublished data).

Branched-Chain Volatile Acid Formation

Ascaris was once thought to be unique in its synthesis of the 2-methyl branched-chain volatile acids. However, the important parasite of humans, *Paragonimus westermani,* and the saprophytic swamp worm *Alma emini* have now been reported to accumulate 2-methylbutyrate (22, 30). Low levels of this acid appear to accumulate in *Echinostoma liei* fermentations as well (79), and may be formed by other organisms, but detection would require gas chromatographic analysis. This or other acids with branched methyl groups at C_2 also have been described in humans, dogs, water fowl, and bacteria (23). In spite of their relatively wide distribution, the mechanism of synthesis of these branched-chain acids is not well understood. Buckner & Kollattukudy (7) reported that a purified fatty acid synthetase from the uropygial gland of the goose synthesized multi-branched chain acids from methylmalonyl CoA and normal straight chain acids from malonyl CoA. However, all attempts to demonstrate fatty acid synthetase activity in *Ascaris* have failed. This, together with the fact that *Ascaris,* like many other helminths, does not synthesize its own long-chain fatty acids de novo (5, 49), indicates a different pathway that does not involve the synthetase.

De Mata et al (23) partially purified and characterized two previously undescribed enzymes from *Ascaris* mitochondria: a propionyl CoA condensing enzyme and an NADH-linked methylacetoacetate ethyl ester reductase. Their findings were in accord with the synthesis of the branched acids from a condensation of either the carboxyl carbon of acetyl CoA with the number 2 carbon of propionyl CoA or two molecules of propionyl CoA followed by reduction of the condensation product to the saturated acid. In essence, this constitutes a modified reversal of the beta-oxidation sequence. Unfortunately, the last reaction of the proposed sequence, the reduction of the double bond of tiglyl CoA to 2-methyl-butyryl CoA, could not be demonstrated. This reaction resembles the *Ascaris* fumarate reductase reaction and could be coupled to an electron-transport-associated generation of ATP.

Disrupted *Ascaris* mitochondrial preparations have been obtained recently that form branched-chain fatty acids from incubations with acetyl CoA, propionyl CoA, and NADH (P. R. Komuniecki, R. Komuniecki, H. J. Saz, unpublished data). The mitochondrial soluble fraction catalyzes the sequence only as far as tiglate. Addition of the mitochondrial membrane fraction restores the ability of the preparation to form the more reduced

2-methylbutyrate. Both the soluble and membrane fractions of the mito-chondrion seem required for the reduction of tiglyl CoA in these prepara-tions. The apparent membrane association of the tiglyl CoA reductase also increases the possibility that electron-transport-associated ATP generation might be coupled to this reduction.

Recently, 3-keto-2-methylvalerate and 3-hydroxy-2-methylvalerate, both intermediates in the proposed pathway of 2-methylvalerate synthesis in *Ascaris* (77, 78), have been identified in the urine of children with propionic acidemia (47, 91). This severe genetic disease manifests itself in a defect in the activity of propionyl CoA carboxylase as a consequence of a mutant holoenzyme or of a deficiency in the utilization of biotin. Perhaps the presence of the above intermediates and of the ketone, 3-pentanone, which arises by urinary decarboxylation of 3-keto-2-methylvalerate, can be em-ployed diagnostically for this disorder (91). The high levels of propionyl CoA present in it may result in a condensation of two such units to form the C_6 compound, 3-keto-2-methylvalerate, which can then be reduced to the corresponding hydroxy compound, reactions similar to those reported in *Ascaris* (23, 77, 78).

Ascaris Pyruvate Dehydrogenase Complex

Ascaris fermentations accumulate varying quantities of acetate (77). The pyruvate dehydrogenase complex has been isolated and purified to near homogeneity (44), yielding a complex similar in size, shape, and most physical characteristics to its mammalian counterpart. It is dependent upon CoA, NAD^+, and pyruvate for activity and is competitively inhibited by acetyl CoA and NADH. Interesting differences between the host and para-site complexes were observed. Much lower $NAD^+/NADH$ ratios (higher NADH) are required to inhibit activity of the worm enzyme complex. This represents another adaptation of the parasite to its environment, since the free $NAD^+/NADH$ ratio in mammalian mitochondria is approximately 10, whereas that of *Ascaris* is in the range of 0.07–0.7 (3, 102). Within the range reported for the helminth mitochondrion, the *Ascaris* complex would be maximally regulated. Small changes in nucleotide concentration would lead to large changes in pyruvate dehydrogenation. Energy generation might be associated with this reaction, since both acetyl CoA and NADH are pro-duced anaerobically. How free acetate is formed from acetyl CoA is still not known, but acetyl CoA may have a positive regulatory effect upon branched chain fatty acid synthesis in disrupted *Ascaris* mitochondria (55).

HELMINTHS THAT REQUIRE O_2 FOR ENERGY GENERATION

Although many helminths, and particularly the larval stages, require O_2 for energy and survival, relatively little has been reported on details of their metabolisms. Some require O_2 but not for energy formation. For example, *Schistosoma mansoni* adults, homolactate fermenters, function and survive anaerobically as well as they do aerobically, but the development of their eggs presumably requires small amounts of O_2 for synthetic purposes, possibly for tanning (9, 85). *Ascaris* appears to require small quantities of O_2 for cuticle development (14), not for energy metabolism. All of the parasitic worms examined, however, accumulate fermentation products other than CO_2 and water. All of them, therefore, are obviously different biochemically from the mammalian host, and in adapting to a parasitic mode of life they appear to have sacrificed some or all of their terminal respiratory pathways. Even the aerobes have become less efficient in their energy metabolisms, also possibly less fastidious as a consequence of their more abbreviated metabolic pathways in an environment of plenty.

Most adult filarial parasites such as *Brugia pahangi, Dipetalonema viteae,* and *Dirofilaria uniformis* appear to be homolactate fermenters; the former two were shown to survive for equal periods of time aerobically or anaerobically (96, 98). However, the adult filariid *Litomosoides carinii* accumulates acetate plus CO_2 in addition to lactate, rapidly loses mobility, and dies if O_2 is not present (8, 98). Unfortunately, not all of the fermentation products of *L. carinii* have been identified. However, CO_2 arises almost exclusively from the 3 and 4 carbons of glucose. Pyruvate is decarboxylated, but essentially only the carboxyl carbon gives rise to respiratory CO_2 (52, 98). The evidence suggests, therefore, that O_2 may be required only for the single oxidation of pyruvate to acetate and CO_2. This single oxidation may provide additional energy for survival of the parasite.

Oxygen is required for initiation and maintenance of egg development in *Ascaris* (40). The egg is cleidoic—i.e. only water and gases permeate to the embryo. Employing developing *Ascaris* eggs, Passey & Fairbairn (54) reported the first substantiated demonstration of a conversion of lipid into carbohydrate. Subsequently, the development of the glyoxylate cycle enzymes was shown to occur at the appropriate time in the egg. Presumably, an aerobic component would be required for the physiological operation of the glyoxylate cycle. Kmetec et al (40) and subsequently Oya et al (53) showed that cytochrome oxidase activity was initially absent or very low. Upon contact with air the eggs start development, and a rapid elaboration of cytochrome oxidase activity is observed leading to very high levels that continue to increase throughout development. Barrett (2) recently reviewed some of the enzymology of *Ascaris* eggs.

The third or lung stage larvae of *Ascaris* also are obligate aerobes (73). Both anaerobiosis and cyanide inhibit motility. Cytochrome oxidase is present. Glycogen utilization is much more rapid when the larvae are incubated anaerobically, indicating a marked Pasteur effect. Incubation of the parasites with glucose labeled with ^{14}C in various carbons resulted in a preferential incorporation of isotope from the 3 and 4 carbons into respiratory CO_2, suggesting a decarboxylation of pyruvate formed from glucose to a C_2 compound plus CO_2. Relatively large quantities of acetate were isolated from these experiments and, as would be predicted, isotope was incorporated into acetate from the 1 and 6 carbons of glucose, but not from the 3 and 4 carbons. Therefore, as with *L. carinii,* most of the aerobic energy seems to arise from the oxidative decarboxylation of pyruvate to acetate.

HELMINTHS THAT REQUIRE O_2 FOR MOTILITY BUT NOT FOR SURVIVAL

Trichinella spiralis Larvae

In 1938 *Trichinella spiralis* larvae were found to become inactive when their respiration was inhibited either by cyanide or by a lack of O_2 (89). Even after a week of anaerobiosis, however, motility was restored upon the readmission of air. These authors proposed that anaerobic fermentative metabolism was sufficient to maintain the larvae alive but respiration was necessary for motility.

Von Brand et al (97) expanded the biochemical studies of *Trichinella* larvae. No significant differences were observed in the amounts of glycogen dissimilated either aerobically or anaerobically, while lipid disappearance was observed only under aerobic conditions. Carbohydrate fermentation to volatile fatty acid products evidently allowed the larvae to survive anaerobically but was insufficient to allow motility. Oxygen presumably was required for lipid oxidation, which provided the additional energy for motility. Unfortunately, these studies were carried out before the role of CO_2 fixation in some helminths was understood. The possibility remains, therefore, that had CO_2 been added to the pure N_2 atmosphere employed in the anaerobic experiments, an additional carbohydrate metabolism would have been obtained. Ward et al (99) reported the presence of an active PEP carboxykinase in *Trichinella* larvae.

Castro & Fairbairn (17) confirmed the findings of von Brand et al (97) that volatile acids (acetic, propionic, n-butyric, n-valeric, and n-caproic) were fermentation products of these larvae and that the rates of carbohydrate utilization and acid excretion were unaffected by the presence of O_2. In apparent conflict with the findings of von Brand et al, however, Castro & Fairbairn reported that total lipids did not decrease or change in constitution during aerobic or anaerobic incubation, implying that the *Trichinella* larvae had no lipid metabolism and could not use lipids for motility. The apparent inconsistency between the two may arise from differences in the relative motilities of the larval preparations; lipids would not be used if the larvae were not sufficiently motile. At any rate, there appears to be agreement that whatever the explanation, the larvae can survive anaerobically but require O_2 for motility.

Microfilariae of Brugia pahangi, Litomosoides carinii and Dipetalonema viteae

Rew & Saz (58) reported that these three species of microfilariids rapidly lost motility when O_2 was removed from their in vitro environment. Even after 7 days of anaerobiosis, however, the reintroduction of air resulted in a return to motility indistinguishable from that of worms maintained in aerobic control vessels. *B. pahangi* microfilariae could ferment glucose only as far as lactate when maintained anaerobically. This is reminiscent of the adult stage of the parasite, which is a homolactate fermenter regardless of the gas phase. However, when the microfilariids were incubated in air, the data obtained were consistent with dissimilation of a significant portion of the glucose via the one-step oxidative decarboxylation of pyruvate formed from glycolysis to acetate and CO_2. It is of interest also that addition of the drug levamisole to in vitro aerobic incubations immobilized the *B. pahangi* microfilariae. Concomitant with this aerobic immobilization metabolism shifted to a more nearly homolactate fermentation. The effects of levamisole on the metabolism may be secondary to the paralysis (58). Paralyzed worms presumably would require less energy and might shift their metabolism toward a more nearly homolactate fermentation.

All three species of microfilariae metabolically resemble the aerobic adult filariid *L. carinii* for they appear to utilize O_2 for energy derived from the oxidation of pyruvate, but only as far as acetate and CO_2. However, adult *L. carinii* cannot survive for extended periods without O_2, unlike the larval forms. Again, the microfilariids appear to have an aerobic requirement for motility but not for survival. Whether or not this adaptation of the larval parasites is related to the usual change in environments occurring at this period of the life cycle can only be speculated.

SUMMARY

Many metazoans, and particularly the parasitic forms, have adapted well to their environments. This is particularly obvious in organisms that reside in anoxic surroundings, such as the large lumen-dwelling intestinal parasites. However, anaerobic energy metabolisms are not confined to parasites in microaerophilic environments. Some that reside in highly aerobic surroundings (e.g. blood or lungs) also have lost much or all of their aerobic capabilities for energy generation. Adaptations toward anaerobiosis are many and varied: homolactate fermentation (schistosomes and filarial worms), heterolacate fermentations (*H. diminuta*), and succinate and heterosuccinate fermentations (*Ascaris*).

Even helminths that are obligate aerobes are not complete oxidizers. All accumulate aerobic fermentation products, indicating at best a limited terminal respiration. Some worms, particularly some of the larval stages, retain their ability to survive anaerobically but require the presence of oxygen for motility. Regardless of the type of oxygen requirement, all parasitic helminths examined are dramatically different from their mammalian hosts in regard to their energy metabolisms. Many similar adaptations have been shown to occur in nonparasitic organisms ranging from metazoans, through fish and mammals. There is much room for additional studies of these biochemical adaptations.

Literature Cited

1. Barrett, J. 1976. Bioenergetics in helminths. In *Biochemistry of Parasites and Host-Parasite Relationships,* ed. H. van den Bossche, pp. 67–80. Amsterdam: Elsevier/North-Holland Biomedical Press. 664 pp.
2. Barrett, J. 1976. Intermediary metabolism in *Ascaris* eggs. See Ref. 1, pp. 117–23
3. Barrett, J., Beis, I. 1973. The redox state of the free nicotin-amide-adenine dinucleotide couple in the cytoplasm and mitochondria of muscle tissue from *Ascaris lumbricoides* (Nematoda). *Comp. Biochem. Physiol.* 44a:331–40
4. Barrett, J., Coles, G. C., Simpkin, K. G. 1978. Pathways of acetate and propionate production in adult *Fasciola hepatica. Int. J. Parasitol.* 8:117–23
5. Beames, C. G. Jr., Harris, B. G., Hopper, F. A. 1967. The synthesis of fatty acids from acetate by intact tissue and muscle extract of *Ascaris lumbricoides suum. Comp. Biochem. Physiol.* 20:509–21
6. Beames, C. G. Jr., King, G. A. 1972. Factors influencing the movement of materials across the intestine of *Ascaris.* In *Comparative Biochemistry of Parasites,* ed. H. Van den Bossche, pp. 275–82. NY: Academic. 516 pp.
7. Buckner, J. S., Kolattukudy, P. E. 1976. Lipid biosynthesis in the sebaceous glands: Synthesis of multibranched fatty acids from methylmalonyl CoA in cell free preparations from the uropygial gland of the goose. *Biochemistry* 14:1774–82
8. Bueding, E. 1949. Studies on the metabolism of the filarial worm *Litomosoides carinii. J. Exp. Med.* 89:107–30
9. Bueding, E. 1950. Carbohydrate metabolism of *Schistosoma mansoni. J. Gen. Physiol.* 33:475–95
10. Bueding, E. 1953. Formation of tiglic and n-valeric acids by bacteria-free *Ascaris lumbricoides. J. Biol. Chem.* 202:505–12
11. Bueding, E., Charms, B. 1952. Cytochrome c, cytochrome oxidase and succinoxidase activities of helminths. *J. Biol. Chem.* 196:615–27
12. Bueding, E., Farrow, G. W. 1956. Identification of succinic acid as a constituent of the perienteric fluid of *Ascaris lumbricoides. Exp. Parasitol.* 5:345–49
13. Bueding, E., Saz, H. J. 1968. Pyruvate kinase and phosphoenolpyruvate carboxykinase activities of *Ascaris* muscle, *Hymenolepis diminuta* and *Schistosoma mansoni. Comp. Biochem. Physiol.* 24:511–18
14. Cain, G. D., Fairbairn, D. 1971. Protocollagen proline hydroxylase and collagen synthesis in developing eggs of *Ascaris lumbricoides. Comp. Biochem. Physiol.* 40B:165–79
15. Carter, C. E., Fairbairn, D. 1975. Multienzymic nature of pyruvate kinase during development of *Hymenolepis diminuta* (Cestoda). *J. Exp. Zool.* 194:439–48
16. Cascarano, J., Ades, I. Z., O'Connor, J. D. 1976. Hypoxia: A succinate-fumarate electron shuttle between peripheral cells and lung. *J. Exp. Zool.* 198:149–53
17. Castro, G. A., Fairbairn, D. 1969. Carbohydrates and lipids in *Trichinella spi-*

ralis larvae and their utilization *in vitro. J. Parasitol.* 55:51–58

18. Chance, B., Parsons, D. F. 1963. Cytochrome function in relation to inner membrane structure of mitochondria. *Science* 142:1176–80

19. Cheah, K. S. 1973. Purification and properties of *Ascaris* cytochrome b_{560}. *J. Biol. Chem.* 248:4101–5

20. Cheah, K. S. 1974. Oxidative phosphorylation in *Ascaris* muscle mitochondria. *Comp. Biochem. Physiol.* 47B:237–42

21. Cheah, K. S. 1976. *Ascaris lumbricoides* cytochrome b-560. See Ref. 1, pp. 145–50

22. Coles, G. C. 1970. Some biochemical adaptations of the swamp worm *Alma emini* to low oxygen levels in tropical swamps. *Comp. Biochem. Physiol.* 34:481–89

23. de Mata, Z. S., Saz, H. J., Pasto, D. J. 1977. 2-Methylacetoacetate reductase and possible propionyl CoA condensing enzyme activity in branched chain volatile fatty acid synthesis by *Ascaris lumbricoides. J. Biol. Chem.* 252:4215–24

24. Deleted in proof

25. Fodge, D. W., Gracy, R. W., Harris, B. G. 1972. Studies on enzymes from parasitic helminths. I. Purification and physical properties of malic enzyme from the muscle tissues of *Ascaris suum. Biochem. Biophys. Acta* 268:271–84

26. Fujimoto, D., Prockop, D. J. 1969. Protocollagen proline hydroxylase from *Ascaris lumbricoides. J. Biol. Chem.* 244:205–10

27. Gade, G., Wilps, H. 1975. Glycogen degradation and end products of anaerobic metabolism in the fresh water bivalve *Anodonta cygnea. J. Comp. Physiol.* 104:79–85

28. Galivan, J. H., Allen, S. H. G. 1968. Methylmalonyl CoA decarboxylase. Its role in succinate decarboxylation by *Micrococcus lactilyticus. J. Biol. Chem.* 243:1253–61

29. Gottwald, M., Andrusen, J. R., LeGall, J., Ljungdahl, L. G. 1975. Presence of cytochrome and menaquinone in *Clostridium formicoaceticum* and *Clostridium thermoaceticum. J. Bacteriol.* 122:325–28

30. Hamajima, F. 1967. Studies on metabolism of lung flukes genus *Paragonimus* III. Occurrence of organic acids in uterine eggs, larvae and adults. *Jpn. J. Parasiol.* 16:1–7

31. Hatchikian, E. C., LeGall, J. 1972. Evidence for the presence of a b-type cytochrome in the sulfate-reducing bacterium *Desulfovibrio gigas* and its role in the reduction of fumarate by molecular hydrogen. *Biochem. Biophys. Acta* 267:479–84

32. Hayashi, E., Hasuno, A., Shimizu, T., Terada, M. 1979. The influence of oxygen pressure on the survival time of *Ascaris lumbricoides* var. *suum.* (10). The effects of oxygen pressure and respiratory inhibitors on the contractile activities of *Ascaris* muscle. *Jpn. J. Parasitol.* 28:1–13

33. Hill, G. C., Perkowski, C. A., Mathewson, N. W. 1971. Purification and properties of cytochrome c_{550} from *Ascaris lumbricoides* var. *suum. Biochim. Biophys. Acta* 236:242–45

34. Hochachka, P. W., Mustafa, T. 1972. Invertebrate facultative anaerobiosis. *Science* 178:1056–60

35. Hochachka, P. W., Owen, T. G., Allen, J. F., Whittow, G. C. 1975. Multiple end products of anaerobiosis in diving vertebrates. *Comp. Biochem. Physiol.* 50B:17–22

36. Jacobs, N. J., Wolin, M. J. 1963. Electron transport system of *Vibrio succinogenes.* I. Enzymes and cytochromes of the electron transport system. *Biochim. Biophys. Acta* 69:18–28

37. Jensen, J. B., Trager, W. 1977. *Plasmodium falciparum* in culture: Use of outdated erythrocytes and description of the candle jar method. *J. Parasitol.* 63:883–86

38. Johnston, I. A. 1975. Anaerobic metabolism in the carp (*Carassius carassius* L.). *Comp. Biochem. Physiol.* 51B:235–41

39. Kaziro, Y., Ochoa, S. 1961. Mechanism of the propionyl carboxylase reaction. 1. Carboxylation and decarboxylation of the enzyme. *J. Biol. Chem.* 236:3131–36

40. Kmetec, E., Beaver, P., Bueding, E. 1963. Succinoxidase activities and cytochrome oxidase of extracts of *Ascaris* eggs. *Comp. Biochem. Physiol.* 9:115–20

41. Kmetec, E., Bueding, E. 1961. Succinic and reduced diphosphopyridine nucleotide oxidase systems of *Ascaris* muscle. *J. Biol. Chem.* 236:584–91

42. Köhler, P., Bachmann, R. 1978. The significance of oxygen in mitochondrial energy metabolism of *Ascaris suum.* 4th Int. Congr. Parasitol., Warsaw. p. 77

43. Köhler, P., Bryant, C., Behm, C. A. 1978. ATP synthesis in a succinate decarboxylase system from *Fasciola hepatica* mitochondria. *Int. J. Parasitol.* 8:399–404

44. Komuniecki, R., Komuniecki, P. R., Saz, H. J. 1979. Purification and properties of the *Ascaris* pyruvate dehydrogenase complex. *Biochim. Biophys. Acta* 571:1–11

45. Lee, I., Chance, B. 1968. Activation of malate-linked reductions of NAD and flavoproteins in *Ascaris* muscle mitochondria by phosphate. *Biochem. Biophys. Res. Commun.* 32:547–53

46. Macy, J. M., Ljungdahl, L. G., Gottschalk, G. 1978. Pathway of succinate and propionate formation in *Bacteroides fragilis. J. Bacteriol.* 134:84–91

47. Matsumoto, I., Shinka, T., Kuhara, T., Oura, T., Yamamoto, H., Hase, Y., Aoki, H., Isshiki, G., Tada, K. 1978. In *Recent Developments in Mass Spectrometry in Biochemistry and Medicine,* ed. A. Frigerio, 1:203–16. NY: Plenum

48. Metzger, H. 1970. Biochemie einiger parasitisch lebender Würmer und Protozoen, und die Wirkungsweise chemotherapeutisch wichtiger Stoffe. *Z. Parasitenk.* 34:271–95

49. Meyer, F., Meyer, H. 1972. Loss of fatty acid biosynthesis in flatworms. See Ref. 6, pp. 383–93

50. Meyer, H., Mueller, J., Meyer, F. 1978. Isolation of an acyl CoA carboxylase from the tapeworm *Spirometra mansonoides. Biochem. Biophys. Res. Commun.* 82:834–39

51. Meyer, H., Nevaldine, B., Meyer, F. 1978. Acyl CoA carboxylase of the free-living nematode *Turbatrix aceti.* 1. Its isolation and molecular characteristics. *Biochemistry* 17:1822–27

52. Middleton, K. R., Saz, H. J. 1979. Comparative utilization of pyruvate by *Brugia pahangi, Dipetalonema viteae* and *Litomosoides carinii. J. Parastiol.* 65:1–7

53. Oya, H., Costello, L. C., Smith, W. N. 1963. The comparative biochemistry of developing *Ascaris* eggs. II. Changes in cytochrome c oxidase activity during embryonation. *J. Cell. Comp. Physiol.* 62:287–94

54. Passey, R. F., Fairbairn, D. 1957. The conversion of fat to carbohydrate during embryonation of *Ascaris* eggs. *Can. J. Biochem. Physiol.* 35:511–25

55. Pietrzak, S. M., Saz, H. J., Dunbar, G. A. 1979. A possible role for acetyl CoA in succinate decarboxylation and the associated phosphorylation. Presented at Ann. Meet. Am. Soc. Parasitol., 54th, Minneapolis, p. 64 (Abstr.)

56. Rahaman, R., Meisner, H. 1973. Respiratory studies with mitochondria from the rat tapeworm *Hymenolepis diminuta. Int. J. Biochem.* 4:153–62

57. Rew, R. S. 1978. Mode of action of common anthelmintics. *J. Vet. Pharmacol. Therap.* 1:183–98

58. Rew, R. S., Saz, H. J. 1977. The carbohydrate metabolism of *Brugia pahangi* microfilariae. *J. Parasitol.* 63:123–29

59. Reynolds, C. H. 1980. Phosphoenolpyruvate carboxykinase from the rat and from the tapeworm *Hymenolepis diminuta.* Effects of inhibitors and transition metals on the carboxylation reaction. *Comp. Biochem. Physiol.* 65B: 481–87

60. Rizza, V., Sinclair, P. R., White, D. C., Cuorant, P. R. 1968. Electron transport of the protoheme requiring anaerobic *Bacteroides melaninogenicus. J. Bacteriol.* 96:665–71

61. Roberts, L. S., Fairbairn, D. 1965. Metabolic studies on adult *Nippostrongylus brasiliensis* (Nematoda: Trichostrongyloidea). *J. Parasitol.* 51:129–38

62. Roberts, L. S., Mong, F. N. 1969. Developmental physiology of cestodes. IV. *In vitro* development of *Hymenolepis diminuta* in presence and absence of oxygen. *Exp. Parasitol.* 26:166–74

63. Sato, M., Yamada, K., Ozawa, H. 1972. Rhodoquinone specificity in the reactivation of succinoxidase activity of acetone-extracted *Ascaris* mitochondria. *Biochem. Biophys. Res. Commun.* 46: 578–82

64. Saz, D. K., Bonner, T. P., Karlin, M., Saz, H. J. 1971. Biochemical observations on adult *Nippostrongylus brasiliensis. J. Parasitol.* 57:1159–62

65. Saz, H. J. 1971. Facultative anaerobiosis in the invertebrates: Pathways and control systems. *Am. Zool.* 11:125–35

66. Saz, H. J. 1972. Comparative biochemistry of carbohydrates in nematodes and cestodes. See Ref. 6, pp. 33–47

67. Saz, H. J., Bueding, E. 1966. Relationships between anthelmintic effects and biochemical and physiological mechanisms. *Pharmacol. Rev.* 18:871–94

68. Saz, H. J., Dunbar, G. A., Gardner, A. E. 1978. Propionate formation from succinate and possible ATP generation. Presented at Ann. Meet. Am. Soc. Parasitol., 53rd, Chicago, p. 60 (Abstr.)

69. Saz, H. J., Gerzon, K. 1962. Identification of α-methylvalerate as a product of *Ascaris lumbricoides* fermentation. *Exp. Parasitol.* 12:204–10

70. Saz, H. J., Hubbard, J. A. 1957. The oxidative decarboxylation of malate by

Ascaris lumbricoides. J. Biol. Chem. 225:921–33

71. Saz, H. J., Lescure, O. L. 1967. Glyconeogenesis, fructose-1,6-diphosphatase and phosphoenolpyruvate carboxykinase activities of *Ascaris lumbricoides* adult muscle and larvae. *Comp. Biochem. Physiol.* 22:15–28

72. Saz, H. J., Lescure, O. L. 1969. The functions of phosphoenolpyruvate carboxykinase and malic enzyme in the anerobic formation of succinate by *Ascaris lumbricoides. Comp. Biochem. Physiol.* 30:49–60

73. Saz, H. J., Lescure, O. L., Bueding, E. 1968. Biochemical observations of *Ascaris suum* lung-stage larvae. *J. Parasitol.* 54:457–61

74. Saz, H. J., Pietrzak, S. M. 1980. Phosphorylation associated with succinate decarboxylation to propionate in *Ascaris* mitochondria. *Arch. Biochem. Biophys.* 202:388–93

75. Saz, H. J., Vidrine, A. Jr. 1959. The mechanism of formation of succinate and propionate by *Ascaris lumbricoides* muscle. *J. Biol. Chem.* 234:2001–5

76. Saz, H. J., Vidrine, A. Jr., Hubbard, J. A. 1958. The formation of α-acetolactic acid and acetylmethylcarbinol by *Ascaris lumbricoides. Exp. Parasitol.* 7: 477–90

77. Saz, H. J., Weil, A. 1960. The mechanism of the formation of α-methylbutyrate from carbohydrate by *Ascaris lumbricoides* muscle. *J. Biol. Chem.* 235:914–18

78. Saz, H. J., Weil, A. 1962. Pathway of formation of α-methylvalerate by *Ascaris lumbricoides. J. Biol. Chem.* 237:2053–56

79. Schaefer, F. W. III, Saz, H. J., Weinstein, P. P., Dunbar, G. A. 1977. Aerobic and anaerobic fermentation of glucose by *Echinostoma liei. J. Parasitol.* 63:687–89

80. Schaefer, F. W. III, Weinstein, P. P., Coggins, J. R. 1978. Vitamin B_{12} as a marker for cestode evolution. Presented at Ann. Meet. Soc. Am. Parasitol., 53rd, Chicago, p. 52 (Abstr.)

81. Scheibel, L. W., Adler, A., Trager, W. 1979. Tetraethylthiuram disulfite (Antabuse) inhibits the human malaria parasite *Plasmodium falciparum. Proc. Natl. Acad. Sci. USA* 76:5303–7

82. Scheibel, L. W., Ashton, S. H., Trager, W. 1979. *Plasmodium falciparum:* Microaerophilic requirements in human red blood cells. *Exp. Parasitol.* 47: 410–18

83. Scheibel, L. W., Saz, H. J. 1966. The pathway for anaerobic carbohydrate dissimilation in *Hymenolepis diminuta. Comp. Biochem. Physiol.* 18:151–62

84. Schiller, E. L. 1965. A simplified method for the *in vitro* cultivation of the rat tapeworm *Hymenolepis diminuta. J. Parasitol.* 51: 516–18

85. Schiller, E. L., Bueding, ·E., Turner, V. M., Fisher, J. 1975. Aerobic and anaerobic carbohydrate metabolism and egg production of *Schistosoma mansoni in vitro. J. Parasitol.* 61:385–89

86. Seidel, J. S., Voge, M. 1975. Axenic development of cyticercoids of *Hymenolepis nana. J. Parasitol.* 61:861–64

87. Seidman, I., Entner, N. 1961. Oxidative enzymes and their role in phosphorylation in sarcosomes of adult *Ascaris lumbricoides. J. Biol. Chem.* 236:915–19

88. Sottibandhu, R., Palmer, H. M. 1975. The activation of non-phosphorylating electron transport by adenine nucleotides in Jerusalem artichoke (*Helianthus tuberosus*) mitochondria. *Biochem. J.* 152:637–45

89. Stannard, J. N., McCoy, O. R., Latchford, W. R. 1938. Studies on the metabolism of *Trichinella spiralis* larvae. *Am. J. Hyg.* 27:666–82

90. Tkachuck, R. D., Saz, H. J., Weinstein, P. P., Finnegan, K., Mueller, J. F. 1977. The presence and possible function of methylmalonyl CoA mutase and propionyl CoA carboxylase in *Spirometra mansonoides. J. Parasitol.* 63:769–74

91. Truscott, R. J. W., Pullin, C. J., Halpern, B., Hammond, J., Haan, E., Danks, D. M. 1979. The identification of 3-keto-2-methylvaleric acid and 3-hydroxy-2-methylvaleric acid in a patient with propionic acidemia. *Biomed. Mass Spectrom.* 6:294–301

92. Utter, M. F., Keech, D. B., Scrutton, M. C. 1964. In *Advances in Enzyme Regulation,* ed. G. Weber, 2:49–68. Oxford: Pergamon Press. 405 pp.

93. Van den Bossche, H. 1976. The molecular basis of anthelmintic action. See Ref. 1, pp. 553–72

94. Van Vugt, F., Kalaycioglu, L., Van den Bergh, S. G. 1976. ATP production in *Fasciola hepatica* mitochondrion. See Ref. 1, pp. 151–58

95. Van Vugt, F., Vander Meer, P., Van den Bergh, S. G. 1979. The formation of propionate and acetate as terminal processes in the energy metabolism of the adult liver fluke *Fasciola hepatica. Int. J. Biochem.* 10:11–18

96. Von Brand, T., Bowman, I. B. R., Weinstein, P. P., Sawyer, T. K. 1963.

Observations on the metabolism of *Dirofilaria uniformis. Exp. Parasitol.* 13:128–33

97. Von Brand, T., Weinstein, P. P., Mehlman, B., Weinbach, E. C. 1952. Observations on the metabolism of bacteria-free larvae of *Trichinella spiralis. Exp. Parasitol.* 1:245–55

98. Wang, E. J., Saz, H. J. 1974. Comparative biochemical studies of *Litomosoides carinii, Dipetalonema viteae,* and *Brugia pahangi* adults. *J. Parasitol.* 60:316–21

99. Ward, C. W., Castro, G. A., Fairbairn, D. 1969. Carbon dioxide fixation and phosphoenolpyruvate metabolism in *Trichinella spiralis* larvae. *J. Parasitol.* 55:67–71

100. Weinland, E. 1901. Über Kohlenhydratzersetzung ohne Sauerstoffaufnahme bei *Ascaris* einen tierischen Garungsprozess. *Z. Biol.* 42:55–90

101. Weinstein, P. P., Jones, M. F. 1956. The *in vitro* cultivation of *Nippostrongylus muris* to the adult stage. *J. Parasitol.* 42:215–36

102. Williamson, D. H., Lund, P., Krebs, H. A. 1967. The redox state of free nicotinamide-adenine dinucleotide in the cytoplasm and mitochondria of rat liver. *Biochem. J.* 103:514–27

103. Yorke, R. E., Turton, J. A. 1974. Effects of fasciolicidal and anti-cestode agents on the respiration of isolated *Hymenolepis diminuta* mitochondria. *Z. Parasitenk.* 45:1–9

Ann. Rev. Physiol. 1981. 43:343–356

PHYSIOLOGY OF DIVING IN MARINE MAMMALS

❖1314

G. L. Kooyman,[1] M. A. Castellini, and R. W. Davis

Physiological Research Laboratory, Scripps Institution of Oceanography, University of California, San Diego, La Jolla, California 93093

INTRODUCTION

The first comprehensive review of diving in vertebrates was published in 1870 by Paul Bert (2). It attempted to correlate the breathhold limits of aquatic birds and mammals with their blood volume. In 1939 another major review detailed the physiological adjustments to diving (26). Several surveys appeared in the mid-to-late 1960s (1, 12, 13, 21, 34). The following eclectic review emphasizes marine mammals and calls attention to the natural or unforced dive. Experimental procedures relevant to this subject both in the laboratory and in the field are discussed.

First we briefly review (*a*) the response to a forced breathhold, (*b*) the relationship of diving to tissue level biochemistry, (*c*) the energetics of extended breathholds with regard to O_2 deficit and debt, and (*d*) the physiology and behavior of natural dives.

GENERAL REVIEW

Marine mammals have considerable breathhold capacities. For example, harpooned sperm whales, *Physeter catodon,* have been reported to remain submerged for 90 min (26), and Weddell seals, *Leptonychotes weddelli,* have voluntarily dived for 73 min (37). The true seals, *Phocidae,* are generally thought to have a greater breathhold capacity than fur seals and sea lions, (*Otariidae*), or the small whales, *Delphinidae.* The latter two groups seldom

---

[1]The writing of this manuscript was supported by NIH Grant #HL 17731 and NSF Grant # DPP 23424.

dive longer than 5 min. Since most phocids are phlegmatic, and since their breathhold abilities are among the greatest, they have been the usual choice for investigations on diving.

Virtually all studies of breathhold responses in marine mammals have been conducted on a firmly restrained animal forced underwater in the laboratory. The investigator controls the length and the frequency of the experimental dives. Such a procedure has been effective in eliciting cardiovascular, neurological, and biochemical responses to asphyxia.

Oxygen Stores

If the oxygen store reflects a general breathhold capacity, it is not surprising that phocids might be the animal of choice for dive studies. Their oxygen capacity is much larger than that of sea lions or small whales. In seals, the O_2 store provided by the blood alone ranges from 30–40 ml per kg of body mass, whereas it is only 10–15 ml per kg body mass in humans and one species of porpoise; two other porpoise species were intermediate between humans and seals (38, 42a). However, if O_2 consumption remained the same as that measured during resting periods in air, and if aerobic metabolism were the only energy source, then even a seal's O_2 store would be far too small for the duration of breathholds observed in both natural dives and forced submersions.

Bradycardia, Cardiac Output, Blood Pressure, Vascular Redistribution

During a breathhold, complex vascular responses occur, the most obvious of which is a marked bradycardia. This slowing of heart varies with species; the most profound response occurs in the phocids, the least in the manatee (27). Similarly, cardiac output drops considerably during bradycardia as stroke volume remains nearly constant. In seals, cardiac output may drop to 10–20% of the pre-dive resting value (40, 48, 51). Despite this drop, central arterial blood pressure remains steady (30, 48). This indicates an increased resistance and a decreased distribution of blood within the vascular system. This redistribution of blood during the dive is the key to extended breathhold ability. It promotes the parsimonious use of the limited oxygen store because much less tissue is perfused during the breathhold and consumption of blood and lung oxygen drops greatly.

Experiments with flow transducers have shown that blood flow nearly stops in some tissues, such as the kidney (13). Labeled microsphere studies show this to be true of most peripheral organs (14, 51). This state has come to be known as the heart-lung-brain system of diving animals: Blood flow is directed to those vital organs that have a sustained energy requirement and low anaerobic capacity. It has been demonstrated recently that even coronary blood flow drops by about 90% during forced dives (5, 51), so that such a diving response is more like a lung-brain and large cardiac bypass system. Flow to the brain is maintained or slightly increased (14, 51).

As flow decreases, does the metabolic function of the organ decrease commensurately? Renal filtration ceases during forced dives (39), and kidney oxygen consumption is directly related to filtration rate; therefore, during the dive, the overall energy consumption rate of this organ is most likely reduced. The heart and other organs may also reduce function and metabolism during the dive.

The idea of a reduced metabolic rate during the dive was proposed as early as 1899 (42). In a study of diving birds and mammals, the O_2 deficit and debt of dives were seldom equal; when the subject was quiet during the dive the debt was usually less than the deficit (43).

During forced breathhold activity, core body temperature of seals declines even though their insulation increases owing to intense vasoconstriction (18, 45). This, too, must indicate a reduced metabolic rate during such dives.

Lactic Acid

A large increase in the concentration of lactic acid in the circulation is measurable shortly after the conclusion of prolonged breathhold dives (1, 40, 43). This indicates that some areas of the body have been starved of oxygen and have had to function anaerobically. The muscles appear to be the major source of this lactic acid. The only muscle biopsies of a diver, done long ago (44), show a strong relationship between muscle oxygen depletion and lactic acid accumulation. In young harbor seals, *Phoca vitulina,* muscle O_2 depletion during the forced dive occurred within 5 min. To quote Andersen (1), "Our best evidence indicates, as we have seen, that the large muscle masses are not circulated in a dive since they otherwise would take a heavy toll of the O_2 deposits"—namely the blood O_2 stores.

We have outlined above the implied consensus on how diving mammals function in the wild. If this is their usual *modus operandi,* then it would seem logical that these mammals have undergone obvious biochemical adaptations towards anaerobic metabolism. However, what if anaerobiosis is not the major energy resource of most dives: A greater flexibility in vascular redistribution should then occur; some organs may postpone and reduce function until at the surface. Such a mechanism would reduce the general energetic needs of the diving animal. The more flexible vascular response would then make it practical for some of the large blood O_2 stores to be shared not only by the heart, lung, and brain but also by other favored tissues or organs as the need arises during the animal's daily diving routine.

DIVING BIOCHEMISTRY

Potential Biochemical Modifications

Biochemical schemes involved in allowing extended breathholds, must provide energy during periods of low oxygen when standard oxidative pathways for the generation of ATP are inhibited. Three main possibilities have been studied: (*a*) an increase in activity of the glycolytic enzymes allowing an enhanced potential for the anaerobic generation of energy during the dive; (*b*) possible alternate pathways to standard mammalian glycolysis [a scheme studied only once or twice since these pathways in mammals were found to be insignificant (24)]; and (*c*) the ability for efficient recovery from anaerobic metabolism utilizing the lactic acid produced during the dive.

Muscle

Because laboratory diving studies had documented that the musculature of a marine mammal was cut off from blood flow, the first biochemical studies assayed the glycolytic enzymes in the epaxial muscles of the Pacific white-sided porpoise (*Lagenorhynchus obliquidens*) (49). In this study, lactate dehydrogenase activity (LDH is important for lactate metabolism and redox balance) was thought to be higher than the normal mammalian level. Pyruvate kinase was lower than normal, but regulated for more efficiency (PK is important in the control of the entire glycolytic pathway). Several other enzyme activities in the pathway also appeared elevated. These observations later led to the conclusion that marine mammal muscle was able to function better during periods of anaerobic metabolism than was muscle from terrestrial mammals (25). Separate studies also suggested that harp seal *(Pagophilus groenlandicus)* muscle was adapted for anaerobic metabolism during a dive because oxidative enzymes appeared to be low in activity. However, PK and LDH activities were not quantified in these muscle samples (16). More recently, muscle PK levels from harbor seal (*P. vitulina*) and Weddell seal (*L. weddelli*) were shown to be higher than that in sea lion (*Zalophus californianus*). Since PK was thought to correlate well with anaerobic capacity, this increase in activity was suggested as a basis for the greater diving times in the phocids (47). In 1977, normal mammalian LDH levels were found in muscle samples from a sea otter (*Enhydra lutris*), Pacific white-sided porpoise, and sea lion (41).

Owing to their varied experimental procedures, it is difficult from these studies to resolve controversies or draw general conclusions about enzyme activity levels in marine mammals. The initial porpoise data were based on one muscle sample from a single animal, and no terrestrial mammals were assayed. Other LDH and PK measurements used only the white rat or no terrestrial controls, and the assays were made at 25°C, hindering a realistic interpretation to metabolism at 37°C.

Table 1 contains values from a study in which consistent conditions were met for measuring tissue activity levels of LDH and PK from a range of terrestrial and marine mammals (8). The data suggest that (*a*) high LDH activity, either for the production or utilization of lactate, is not characteristic of marine mammal muscle, and (*b*) muscle PK activity is not low in marine mammals, nor does it parallel dive time, as suggested earlier. Using these criteria, marine mammal muscle does not seem especially adapted for increased glycolytic enzyme activity.

Peripheral Organs

The liver and kidney may also face hypoxic stress during a dive. Enzyme studies of these organs in marine mammals are scarce. Table 1 shows a slight, although not uniform, rise in enzyme activity for marine mammal liver and kidney. This information can be interpreted in several ways. On short aerobic dives, the liver and kidney may be slightly vasoconstricted to save energy and oxygen. The two organs may idle at reduced metabolic levels during such dives, and this low level increase in key anaerobic enzymes may be important for these periods. Also, seal kidneys can return

Table 1 Tissue enzyme activity levels (mean ± S.D.)[a]

	Heart	Brain	Liver	Kidney cortex	Kidney medulla	Muscle
LDH (pyruvate to lactate)						
Marine	813 ± 323	210 ± 29	538 ± 188	382 ± 133	322 ± 99	1,021 ± 203
Terrestrial	801 ± 102	214 ± 30	310 ± 182	312 ± 149	233 ± 93	1,086 ± 418
Rank	WS,D,B,HS	M,SO,WS,D	HS,M,WS,SL	WS,B,SL,HS	SO,B,WS,SA	WR,HS,WS,SA
LDH (lactate to pyruvate)						
Marine	189 ± 84	53 ± 9	155 ± 45	116 ± 49	84 ± 21	272 ± 60
Terrestrial	177 ± 28	53 ± 8	78 ± 46	69 ± 39	53 ± 19	315 ± 170
Rank	WS,B,HS,M	WS,M,SO,D	HS,M,WS,SO	WS,SL,HS,D	SO,B,SA,WS	WR,WS,HS,B
PK						
Marine	187 ± 98	150 ± 35	23 ± 7	47 ± 23	89 ± 48	697 ± 255
Terrestrial	225 ± 131	198 ± 45	32 ± 17	24 ± 12	66 ± 61	806 ± 374
Rank	WS,SO,M,D	M,D,WR,WS	M,D,SL,HS	HS,SL,WS,B	B,HS,SO,SL	SA,WR,WS,P

[a] Activities are expressed as international units (μmoles of substrate converted to product per minute) per gram wet mass tissue at 37°C, pH 6.8. All tissues are from adult animals. Muscle activities are pooled averages for all sites measured for each animal. Marine mammals: Weddell seal, *L. weddelli* (WS); harbor seal, *P. vitulina* (HS); sea otter, *E. lutris* (SO); sea lion, *Z. californianus* (SL); and porpoise, *Stenella attenuata* (SA). Land mammals: white mouse, *Mus musculus* (M); white rabbit, *Oryctolagus cunniculus* (WR); dog, *Canis familiaris* (D); domestic pig, *Sus scrofa* (P); and Beef, *Bos taurus* (B). Rank shows the highest four activities in decreasing order. Significant difference at 95% level (students t-test), shown by underlined values.

to normal function after a considerably longer anoxic exposure than can dog kidneys (17). Perhaps low metabolic rates during anoxia coupled to slightly enhanced anaerobic enzyme potential provide the necessary resistance to anoxia. Furthermore, the LDH activity for the removal of lactate suggests that these organs are well geared to handle any lactate that comes to them during or after a dive. Therefore, these organs may be adapted, for both an ability to function anaerobically and an efficient recovery from lactate loads.

Central Organs

Little biochemical information is available for marine mammal heart and brain. Simon et al reported that marine mammal heart tissue PK increased with diving ability (47). Also, LDH isozyme studies on seal and whale hearts depicted patterns and kinetics that seemed more characteristic of skeletal muscle than of heart (3, 4, 46). Hochachka & Murphy emphasize that these isozyme patterns imply a strong potential for both lactate production and utilization in the marine mammal heart (23, 40). PK and LDH activity comparisons between Weddell seal and ox heart further substantiate the proposition that anaerobic glycolysis potential in Weddell seal heart is greater than in terrestrial species (23, 40). However, owing to the lack of wide-ranging samples and controls, these findings may not be applicable to most marine mammals. Table 1 shows that overall enzyme activities for heart tissue are similar in marine and terrestrial mammals. Contrary to (47), PK activity appears normal in marine mammal heart tissue; among marine mammals, PK activity does not scale to diving ability, except that the Weddell has the highest value, as it does with LDH. Key enzymes for anaerobic metabolism are also claimed to be high in marine mammal brain tissue (23, 40, 47), but a more recent report notes that these enzymes appear constant in all terrestrial and marine species examined (8). The discrepancy may be explained by problems with sample size and terrestrial controls. For instance, the comparison of LDH activities between the Weddell seal and ox may be weak, for the latter appears low among terrestrial mammals (8, 23, 40). Attempts to show that LDH in the brain of whale and seal has important kinetic properties with regard to anaerobic function used no controls for the cetaceans and only showed a 10% difference between brains of hooded seal and sheep (4, 46). Thus no clear distinctions in brain glycolytic enzyme activity appear between most mammals, whether terrestrial or marine.

The elevated levels of PK and LDH in Weddell heart may reflect a system sharing the metabolic products available during the dive. The heart, lung, and brain of the Weddell seal may shuttle lactate produced by the heart, peripheral organs, or muscle to the lung, where some of it is converted to glucose and then metabolized by the brain (22, 23, 40). If such cycling of substrates occurs, the relationships of organ-specific enzyme activity to breathhold ability may be much more complex than the simple associations that have been visualized in the past.

Existing evidence does not support the hypothesis that major modifications of enzyme activity in marine mammal tissues significantly assist breathhold diving.

METABOLISM

Resting Steady-State Metabolism

The resting metabolism of many marine mammals is 1–3 times greater than that of terrestrial mammals of equivalent size (9, 28, 29, 36, 43). The respiratory quotient is usually about 0.75 because fat is the primary substrate for energy metabolism. The free fatty acid concentration in the blood of harbor seals (*Phoca vitulina*) is 2–3 times greater than that in humans or dogs but is comparable to that in many arctic carnivores (9, 15). Carbohydrate utilzation supports less than 10% of aerobic energy metabolism in harbor seals. However, the turnover rates of glucose and lactate fall within the normal mammalian range; glucose turnover is approximately 30 μmol min^{-1} kg$^{-0.75}$ and lactate turnover is 60 μmol min^{-1} kg$^{-0.75}$ (9, 10). More than 90% of the carbohydrate carbon is recycled, and that lost through oxidation is replaced by glucogenic amino acids and carbohydrate in the diet. The central nervous system metabolizes glucose preferentially and accounts for most of the glucose oxidized (32). Other organs and tissues have a predominantly fat-based metabolism. The anaerobic pathway provides <3% of the total energy used at rest (9).

Diving Metabolism

Breathholding disrupts steady-state aerobic metabolism. Diving marine mammals carry a limited supply of oxygen in their blood and tissues to support aerobic energy metabolism; this may be supplemented by anaerobiosis. The degree of steady-state disruption and the time necessary for complete recovery depend on the amount of anaerobic metabolism, which increases with the duration and level of activity during the dive.

The metabolic rate of diving marine mammals cannot be measured using indirect calorimetry (e.g. oxygen consumption). Consequently, many investigators have used the post-dive oxygen debt as an indicator of the diving metabolic rate. Oxygen debt is defined as the additional oxygen consumed during recovery in excess of the resting level. It is commonly divided into alactacid and lactacid components. The alactacid component replenishes blood and tissue oxygen and high energy phosphate compounds such as ATP and creatine phosphate in tissue. The lactacid component represents energy required to metabolize to glucose the lactic acid produced anaerobically during the dive. These hypothetical divisions have been difficult to distinguish, experimentally (6, 19, 20). Some studies showing that the oxygen debt is less than the estimated oxygen requirement to support a resting level of metabolism during the dive have suggested that metabolism was reduced. However, not all dives resulted in a small oxygen debt; often the excess intake equaled the calculated resting consumption for the period of the dive (9, 43, 45).

It is operationally difficult to separate accurately the oxygen debt from resting oxygen uptake. Calculation of the oxygen debt depends on the value used for resting metabolism. Small changes in resting oxygen consumption during recovery can result in significant errors in the oxygen debt calculated over a 30–60 min recovery period. Such changes are likely considering the disruption of steady-state metabolism and the added effects of stress and fatigue.

Since diving metabolism and the relative contributions of aerobic and anaerobic pathways cannot be determined simply from the post-dive oxygen debt, radioisotope turnover techniques have been used to determine anaerobic energy metabolism during restrained dives in harbor seals. Anaerobic activity during 10-min dives approximated 15% of resting metabolism, resulting in the production of 70 mmol lactate. Carbohydrate sources for anaerobiosis include both blood glucose and tissue glycogen (9). Aerobic metabolism during diving has not been determined. Oxygen stores in lung, blood, and tissue are theoretically sufficient to cover only 60% of the resting metabolic requirements for 10-min dives. It appears that metabolism during restrained dives is reduced at least 25% below the resting requirement. Substrate for the aerobic energy contribution may include not only carbohydrate, but also fat, which is the most abundant energy substrate. During recovery, most of the lactate produced during the dive is recycled, and less than 30% is oxidized (9).

Other indirect evidence exists for a reduction in metabolism below the resting level during restrained or voluntary dives involving little exertion. The core temperature of seals forcibly submerged (45) and diving voluntarily from an ice hole (37) decreased 2–3°C during or immediately after the dives. This drop, despite enhanced thermal insulation resulting from peripheral vasoconstriction, suggests a reduction in heat production. Furthermore, energy metabolism could be reduced by as much as 20% below the resting level as a result of decreased heart work and cessation of renal urine production (39). Energy savings may also result from a reduction in splanchnic organ and muscle metabolism because of reduced blood flow. Although anaerobic metabolism may supplement aerobic activity in these tissues, it may not completely restore metabolic rate to the resting level in air. Unfortunately, the metabolic activity of each organ during diving has not been determined.

PHYSIOLOGY OF THE NATURAL DIVE

Bradycardia

To better understand some of the cardiovascular responses to natural dives, heart rates during forced, trained, and free dives have been compared. Most of these studies have used semirestricted environments such as small pools. In such a situation, harbor seals made 2–3-min free dives. Variation in heart rate relative to dive duration suggested some associative learning with the dives (31). Harbor seals have also been trained to dive and surface upon command. Under such conditions, animals breathheld for slightly over 7 min and exhibited a less extreme bradycardia than during forced dives (11).

Under natural diving conditions with Weddell seals, heart rates for the initial phase of the dives were determined for dives ranging from a few minutes up to 50 min (35). Dive duration and heart rate correlated up to a dive duration of about 20–30 min. The most intense bradycardia occurred during the long dives. Similar results have been obtained with diving birds (7).

Thus circulation appears more open during free or unforced dives than during forced dives (or exceptionally long natural dives). Further evidence for this premise is available from the post-dive lactic acid concentrations in the blood.

Lactic Acid

The accumulation of lactic acid in muscle during the dive and its bolus-type release into the circulation after the dive have together been called "the hallmark" of diving in aquatic vertebrates (23, 50). In Weddell seals, however, no such event occurs for free dives lasting <20 min; the lactate concentrations after the dive are no different from resting values (Figure 1). In contrast, forced dives of 10–15 min produce peak lactic acid concentrations during recovery that are 10–20 times higher than control values (40). In natural dives exceeding 30 min, lactic acid profiles closely resemble those for laboratory dives (Figure 2). Circulation during short free dives appears to be more open than in forced dives, skeletal muscle apparently remaining aerobic.

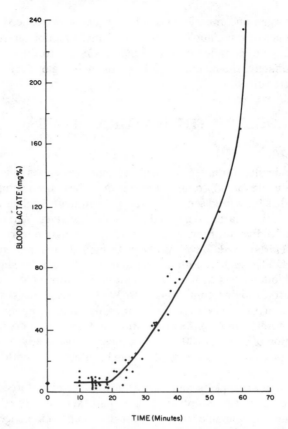

Figure 1   The peak arterial lactic acid concentrations obtained during recovery from a variety of dive durations in three different adult Weddell seals. The diamond at the abscissa zero is the average resting lactic acid concentration (n = 9) (37).

Body Temperature and Metabolism

During long free dives, body temperature drops despite exertion by the animal. This drop may be as much as 2°C in core temperature during a 50 min dive of a 450 kg seal. Although it may be argued that increased conduction due to the water flow past the animal enhances heat loss, it seems that such a drop is not possible unless metabolic rate is low (37). This seems to support further the idea that metabolic rate during diving, even in freely swimming Weddell seals, is not very great (36).

Dive Behavior

An aerobic diving schedule enables an animal to utilize more efficiently the time spent diving. After a 45-min anaerobic dive, a Weddell seal requires

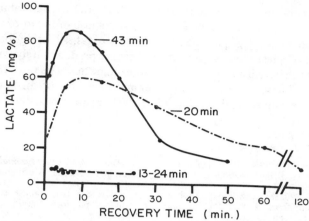

Figure 2 Arterial lactic acid concentration changes during recovery from a free dive of 43 min, pooled samples from three free dives of 13–24 min [modified from (37)] and a 20 min forced dive in Weddell seals [modified from (40)].

about 70 min to return to pre-dive lactic acid concentration and pH (37). Thus, out of a total of 115 min, only 39% is spent diving. If instead the seal makes six 15-min dives, each requiring only a 4 min recovery, almost 80% of the time is spent underwater. The normal feeding schedule of the Weddell seal follows this pattern of many short dives with short recoveries (37). Indeed, only 2% of the dives of Weddell seals exceed their proposed aerobic limit of 25 min (37). Such behavior may be universal in diving reptiles, birds, and mammals; recent evidence on diving patterns of fur seals lends support to this concept (G. L. Kooyman, unpublished observation). Because such variables as the blood O_2 store probably dictate the duration of feeding dives, fur seals make shorter dives than Weddell seals and likely remain aerobic during the dives.

SUMMARY

Natural dives are usually short and aerobic, involving swimming effort that is not energetically costly. Present evidence indicates few, if any, major biochemical enzyme adaptations that would promote an extended anaerobic capacity in marine mammals.

We have discussed the lack of evidence for unusual biochemical adaptations for anaerobiosis and the importance and characteristics of natural aerobic dives. What explanation can we offer for the known capability of some marine mammals, such as Weddell seals and sperm whales, to remain submerged for over an hour? Attributes that serve them well for shorter dives are important also for long dives, such as: (*a*) a large total oxygen store relative to body size, and (*b*) parsimonious use of blood oxygen due to the lowered energy requirements of various organs. During long dives, some organs deplete their oxygen stores, become predominately dependent on anaerobic metabolism, and build up large quantities of lactate. The result is a degree of fatigue that leaves the animal incapable of further intense diving activities for some time. Consequently, long anaerobic dives are quite rare in nature.

Literature Cited

1. Andersen, H. T. 1966. Physiological adaptations in diving vertebrates. *Physiol. Rev.* 46:212–43
2. Bert, P. 1870. De l'acte du plonger chez les mammifères et chez les oiseaux, trentieme leçon. In *Leçon sur la Physiologie Comparée de la Respiration.* Paris: Baillière et Fils. 588 pp.
3. Blix, A. S., Berg, T., Fyhn, H. J. 1970. Lactate dehydrogenase in a diving mammal, the common seal (*Phoca vitulina vitulina*). *Int. J. Biochem.* 1:292–94
4. Blix, A. S., From, S. H. 1971. Lactate dehydrogenase in diving animals—a comparative study with special reference to the eider (*Somateria mollissima*). *Comp. Biochem. Physiol. B* 40: 579–84
5. Blix, A. S., Kjekshus, J. K., Enge, I., Bergan, A. 1976. Myocardial blood flow in the diving seal. *Acta Physiol. Scand.* 96:277–80
6. Brooks, G. A., Brauner, K. E., Cassens, R. A. 1973. Glycogen synthesis and metabolism of lactic acid after exercise. *Am. J. Physiol.* 224:1162–66
7. Butler, P. J. 1979. The use of radio telemetry in the studies of diving and flying birds. In *Handbook on Biotelemetry and Radio Tracking,* ed. C. S. Amlaner, D. W. MacDonald, pp. 569–77. NY: Pergamon.
8. Castellini, M. 1980. *Enzyme biochemistry in the tissues of marine mammals.* PhD thesis. Univ. Calif., San Diego, La Jolla
9. Davis, R. W. 1980. *Diving energetics and intermediary metabolism in the harbor seal,* Phoca vitulina. PhD thesis. in prep. Univ Calif., San Diego, La Jolla
10. Davis, R. W., Kooyman, G. L. 1979. Diving energetics and intermediary metabolism in the harbor seal, *Phoca vitulina.* In *Abstracts from Presentations at the 3rd Biennial Conference of the Biology of Marine Mammals,* Oct. 7–11, 1979. Seattle, Washington
11. Elsner, R. E. 1965. Heart rate response in forced versus trained experimental dives in pinnipeds. *Hvalradets Skr.* 48: 24–29
12. Elsner, R. E. 1969. Cardiovascular adjustments to diving. In *The Biology of Marine Mammals,* ed. H. T. Andersen, pp. 117–45. NY: Academic. 511 pp.
13. Elsner, R. E., Franklin, D. L., Van Citters, R. L., Kenney, D. W. 1966. Cardiovascular defense against asphyxia. *Science* 153:941–49
14. Elsner, R. E., Blix, A. S., Kjekshus, J. 1978. Tissue perfusion and ischemia in diving seals. *Physiologist* 21:33
15. Ferguson, J. H., Falk, C. E. 1971. Free fatty acid levels in several species of arctic carnivores. *Comp. Biochem. Physiol.* 40B:309–12
16. George, J. C., Ronald, K. 1973. The harp seal, *Pagophilus groenlandicus.* XXV. Ultrastructure and metabolic adaptation of skeletal muscle. *Can. J. Zool.* 51:833–38
17. Halasz, N. A., Elsner, R., Garvie, R. S., Grotke, G. T. 1974. Renal recovery from ischemia: a comparative study of harbor seal and dog kidneys. *Am. J. Physiol.* 227:1331–35
18. Hammel, H. T., Elsner, R. W., Heller, H. C., Maggert, J. A., Bainton, C. R. 1977. Thermoregulatory responses to altering hypothalamic temperature in the harbor seal. *Am. J. Physiol.* 232: R18–26
19. Harris, P. 1969. Lactic acid and the phlogiston debt. *Cardiovas. Rev.* 3: 381–90
20. Harris, P., Bateman, M., Baley, T. J., Donald, K. W., Gloster, J., Whitehead, T. 1968. Observations on the course of the metabolic events accompanying mild exercise. *Q. J. Exp. Physiol.* 53: 43–64

21. Harrison, R. J., Kooyman, G. L. 1968. General physiology of the pinnipedia. In *The Behavior and Physiology of Pinnipeds*, pp. 211–96. NY: Appleton-Century-Crofts. 411 pp.

22. Hochachka, P. W., Liggins, G. C., Qvist, J., Schneider, R., Snider, M. Y., Wonders, T. R., Zapol, W. M. 1977. Pulmonary metabolism during diving: conditioning blood for the brain. *Science* 198:831–33

23. Hochachka, P. W., Murphy, B. 1979. Metabolic status during diving and recovery in marine mammals. In *International Review of Physiology, Environmental Physiology III, Vol. 20*, ed. D. Robertshaw, pp. 253–87. Baltimore: University Park Press

24. Hochachka, P. W., Owen, T. G., Allen, J. F., Whittow, G. C. 1975. Multiple end products of anaerobiosis in diving vertebrates. *Comp. Biochem. Physiol. B* 50:17–22

25. Hochachka, P. W., Storey, K. B. 1975. Metabolic consequences of diving in animals and man. *Science* 187:613–21

26. Irving, L. 1939. Respiration in diving mammals. *Physiol. Rev.* 19:112–34

27. Irving, L. 1964. Comparative anatomy and physiology of gas transport mechanisms. In *Handbook of Physiology Section III: Respiration*, ed. W. O. Fenn, H. Rahn, 1:177–212. Washington DC: Am. Physiol. Soc.

28. Irving, L., Hart, J. S. 1957. The metabolism and insulation of seals as bareskinned mammals in cold water. *Can. J. Zool.* 35:497–511

29. Irving, L., Scholander, P. F., Grinnell, S. W. 1941. The respiration of the porpoise, *Tursiops truncatus*. *J. Cell. Comp. Physiol.* 17:145–68

30. Irving, L., Scholander, P. F., Grinnell, A. D. 1942. The regulation of arterial blood pressure in the seal during diving. *Am. J. Physiol.* 135:557–66

31. Jones, D. R., Fisher, H. D., McTaggart, S., West, N. H. 1973. Heart rate during breathholding and diving in the unrestrained harbor seal (*Phoca vitulina*). *Can. J. Zool.* 51:671–80

32. Kety, S. S. 1957. The general metabolism of the brain *in vivo*. In *Metabolism of the Nervous System,* ed. D. Ridler, pp. 231–37. London: Academic

33. Deleted in proof

34. Kooyman, G. L., Andersen, H. T. 1969. Deep diving. In *The Biology of Marine Mammals*, ed. H. T. Andersen, pp. 65–94. NY: Academic. 511 pp.

35. Kooyman, G. L., Campbell, W. B. 1972. Heart rates in freely diving Weddell seals, *Leptonychotes weddelli*. *Comp. Biochem. Physiol. A* 43:31–36

36. Kooyman, G. L., Kerem, D. H., Campbell, W. B., Wright, J. J. 1973. Pulmonary gas exchange in freely diving Weddell seals, *Leptonychotes weddelli*. *Respir. Physiol.* 17:283–90

37. Kooyman, G. L., Wahrenbrock, E. A., Castellini, M. A., Davis, R. W., Sinnett, E. E. 1980. Aerobic and anaerobic metabolism during voluntary diving in Weddell seals: evidence of preferred pathways from blood chemistry and behavior. *J. Comp. Physiol.* 138:335–46

38. Lefant, C., Johansen, K., Torrance, S. D. 1970. Gas transport and oxygen storage capacity in some pinnipeds and the sea otter. *Respir. Physiol.* 9:277–86

39. Murdaugh, H. V., Schmidt-Nielsen, B., Wood, J. W., Mitchell, W. L. 1961. Cessation of renal function during diving in the trained seal (*Phoca vitulina*). *J. Cell Comp. Physiol.* 58:261–65

40. Murphy, B., Snider, M., Schneider, R., Zapol, W. M., Hochachka, P. W. 1980. Metabolic activities of the heart, lung and brain during diving and recovery in the Weddell seal. *J. Appl. Physiol.* 48:596–605

41. Pongannis, P. J., Pierce, R. W. 1978. Muscle metabolic profiles and fibertype composition in some marine mammals. *Comp. Biochem. Physiol. B* 59:99–102

42. Richet, C. 1899. De la résistance des canards a l'asphyxie. *J. Physiol. Pathol. Gen.* 1:641–50

42a. Ridgway, S. H., Johnston, D. G. 1966. Blood oxygen and ecology of porpoises of three genera. *Science* 151:456–58

43. Scholander, P. F. 1940. Experimental investigatory function in diving mammals and birds. *Hvalradets Skr.* 22:1–131

44. Scholander, P. F., Irving, L., Grinnell, S. W. 1942. Aerobic and anaerobic changes in seal muscles during diving. *J. Biol. Chem.* 142:431–40

45. Scholander, P. F., Irving, L., Grinnell, S. W. 1942. On the temperature and metabolism of the seal during diving. *J. Cell. Comp. Physiol.* 19:67–78

46. Shoubridge, E. A., Carscadden, J. E., Leggett, W. C. 1976. LDH isozyme patterns in cetaceans: evidence for a biochemical adaptation to diving. *Comp. Biochem. Physiol. B* 53:357–59

47. Simon, L. M., Robin, E. D., Elsner, R., Van Kessel, A. L. G. J., Theodore, J.

1974. A biochemical basis for difference in maximal diving time in aquatic mammals. *Comp. Biochem. Physiol. B* 47: 209–15

48. Sinnett, E. E., Kooyman, G. L., Wahrenbrock, E. A. 1978. Pulmonary circulation of the harbor seal. *J. Appl. Physiol. Respir. Environ. Exer. Physiol.* 45:718–27

49. Storey, K. B., Hochachka, P. W. 1974. Glycolytic enzymes in muscle of the pacific dolphin: role of pyruvate kinase in aerobic-anaerobic transitions during

diving. *Comp. Biochem. Physiol. B* 49: 119–28

50. Strauss, M. B., 1970. Physiological aspects of mammalian breathhold diving: a review. *Aerospace Med.* 41: 1362–81

51. Zapol, W. M., Liggins, G. C., Schneider, R. C., Qvist, J., Snider, M. T., Creasy, R. K., Hochachka, P. W. 1979. Regional blood flow during simulated diving in the conscious Weddell seal. *J. Appl. Physiol. Respir. Environ. Exer. Physiol.* 47:968–73

CARDIOVASCULAR PHYSIOLOGY

Introduction, Robert M. Berne, *Section Editor*

The main objectives in the section on Cardiovascular Physiology are to keep the reader abreast of current developments in the field and to balance consideration of the various components of this organ system. In the past two *Reviews,* electrophysiology of the heart, various aspects of cardiac contraction, the microcirculation, and neural control of the peripheral circulation have been covered. In the present volume, local regulation of the peripheral circulation and some aspects of cardiac function are reviewed.

The contractile state of vascular smooth muscle of the resistance vessels is the primary determinant of the distribution of peripheral blood flow. Thus the first chapter deals with reactivity of vascular smooth muscle under various physiological conditions, calcium as the final common pathway in responsiveness of the muscle, interaction of key ions in reactivity, the mechanics of vascular smooth muscle (length-tension and force-velocity relationships), and changes in the arterial and arteriolar walls that occur during prolonged increases in wall tension, as seen in hypertension. The second chapter is concerned with the circulatory changes that occur at birth. The discussion focuses on the action of circulating and local vasoactive substances, control of blood flow in the kidney, brain, and heart of the newborn, and the role of prostaglandins and other agents in closure of the ductus arteriosus. The remaining three chapters in the subsection on local control of the peripheral circulation consider the various mechanisms involved in the regulation of blood flow in cardiac and skeletal muscle, brain, and the splanchnic system.

The second subsection addresses certain aspects of cardiac function. The first chapter reviews energy metabolism, its control, and the effects of ischemia—a subject of considerable investigation in recent years. This is followed by a chapter on the origin and structure-function relationships of gap junctions in cardiac and noncardiac tissues and the factors that influence the permeability of these cell junctions. The next chapter reviews the recent findings on the neural regulation of the heart. Emphasis is placed on the mechanisms involved in vagal effects on cardiac rhythm and atrioventricular conduction, and the chapter is concluded with a brief discussion of the interaction of the sympathetic and parasympathetic nerves on the heart. The last chapter compares the cardiodynamics and the peripheral circulatory adjustments that occur under physiological states with those observed in congestive heart failure.

It is our expectation that over a period of about four years the most recent developments in the major areas of cardiovascular physiology will be reviewed.

Ann. Rev. Physiol. 1981. 43:359-70

VASCULAR SMOOTH MUSCLE ❖1315
REACTIVITY

Börje Johansson [1]

Department of Physiology and Biophysics, University of Lund, Lund, Sweden

Different vascular beds and in vitro preparations of different blood vessels vary significantly in specific responsiveness to catecholamines, angiotensin, etc (10, 68, 96). However, this review treats factors that may determine reactivity in any vascular smooth muscle or vascular bed. Vascular reactivity signifies the overall ability or propensity of the vessels to respond to vasoconstrictor (or vasodilator) stimuli (56). Reactivity can vary with the experimental situation; it is impaired under certain conditions (e.g. shock and trauma) and enhanced in other pathophysiological states (particularly in arterial hypertension). Changes in reactivity can originate in all possible links of the vascular stimulus-response relation (56), but this review concentrates on a few special topics.

The General Stimulus-Response Relation of the Vascular Smooth Muscle Cell

Contraction and relaxation in muscle are controlled through variations in cytoplasmic $[Ca^{2+}]$. Even if the supply of energy substrate (Mg ATP) to the contractile machine can be rate-limiting for force generation and shortening under particular circumstances, the calcium control of the actomyosin system is the final common path by which neurotransmitters, hormones, local physicochemical control factors, and vasoactive drugs normally exert their short-term influences on vascular tone. Studies in striated muscle with Ca sensitive dyes show that activation is indeed associated with increased

[1]The author's research is supported by grants from the Swedish Medical Council (28 – 14x) and from AB Hässle, Mölndal, Sweden. I gratefully acknowledge the help of colleagues all over the world who shared their observations with me by sending manuscripts, preprints, and reprints.

359

0066-4278/81/0315-0359$01.00

$[Ca^{2+}]_i$. This technique has also been applied recently to smooth muscle (26).

Comparative studies of the isolated contractile protein systems from skeletal muscle and vascular smooth muscle, indicated a marked similarity in their Ca sensitivity (27), but smooth muscle actomyosin appears not to be regulated via the troponin-tropomyosin system known from striated muscle. The mechanism of the Ca control in vertebrate smooth muscle is still controversial. A central role of an 80,000 dalton protein is advocated by some investigators (25), and a direct myosin-linked Ca sensitivity has been considered (70); but most authorities now seem to favor Ca control through a series of events involving, as the crucial step, phosphorylation of the 20,000 dalton myosin light chain (1, 20, 44, 71, 84). According to this concept, Ca ion, or a Ca^{2+}-calmodulin (15) complex, activates the enzyme myosin light-chain kinase, which executes the phosphorylation. A phosphatase acting on the myosin light chain is implicated in relaxation. This model offers a new possible site of action of cAMP in smooth muscle, as there is evidence that this nucleotide inhibits the myosin light-chain kinase (1, 20). Biochemical work on smooth muscle contractile proteins is complicated by the fact that several procedures, like washing and storage, can alter the Ca sensitivity of the system (71). A recent study on bovine arterial actomyosin indicated Ca regulation via both myosin and actin filaments (63).

The entire Ca concentration-response curve of the contractile machine can be shifted along the concentration axis by changes in pH (69). Metabolic factors like CO_2 and lactic acid, appreciated as possible mediators of functional hyperemia in vivo, may thus influence vascular tone by changing the intracellular milieu so that the entire Ca-response curve is displaced. It appears likely, however, that vasoactive agents generally do not operate through such variations in the "cytoplasmic climate" but by changing specifically the levels of $[Ca^{2+}]_i$.

The early steps in the excitation-contraction process, i.e. the mechanisms that mediate influx or release of Ca, can vary with vasoconstrictor substances (18, 19, 24, 42, 55, 60, 85, 95, 96), but in the end they should all focus on the Ca concentration-response relation of the contractile system. This final common path opens possibilities for unspecific interactions between vasoactive agents. For instance, a fully dilated blood vessel subjected to a threshold dose of vasoconstrictor "A" shows greater responsiveness to a modest dose of vasoconstrictor "B" than it does in the absence of "A." Similarly (or conversely), a vasodilator that brings a strongly constricted vessel back to the steep part of the general stimulus-response curve increases the reactivity of this vessel to any other constrictor or dilator. The literature on both isolated vessels and intact vascular beds abounds with reports on mere unspecific encounters of the various agents on the final common path.

We should not expect a simple relationship between the dose-response curve, measured experimentally in terms of vascular response as a function of drug concentration, and the Ca^{2+} control curve of the contractile proteins. The Ca activation at the regulatory sites is not necessarily proportionate to receptor occupancy, owing to the effect of the intermediate steps in excitation-contraction (e.-c.) coupling; the response of the actomyosin system is not reflected directly in our recording systems owing to the influence of passive elastic elements in the vascular wall and hemodynamic complexities in vivo (56).

Blood vessels with inherent myogenic tone, whether due to electrical spike discharge as in single-unit smooth muscle or to graded electrical or nonelectrical mechanisms in tonic muscle (24, 55, 60, 85), have a partially activated contractile system already in the absence of specific vasoexcitatory influences. Such vessels, as a result of their "false start" on the stimulus-response relation, often show greater reactivity than vessels without a basal tone.

Na-Ca Relations in the Vascular Smooth Muscle Cell

A central role of sodium in the pathogenesis of hypertension has long been considered, but the exact mechanism(s) through which Na^+ may affect smooth muscle has turned out to be most elusive. One reason for this is the complex distribution of sodium in the vascular wall. The large extracellular space, the amount of paracellular matrix and the extensive membrane area to which ions can be bound, the presence of damaged cells after dissection, the difficulties in standardizing blotting procedures, etc, make determinations of Na^+ distribution in vascular walls uncertain. $[Na^+]_i$ values depend on the tissue model upon which interpretation is based (58). The application of electron probe microanalysis to cryosections of vascular smooth muscle may provide direct information on different vessels and different states of reactivity, including normo- and hypertension (87). Indirect approaches so far indicate that normo- and hypertensive blood vessels handle Na and K differently. Essentially compatible comparisons between spontaneously hypertensive rats (SHR) and normotensive Wistar-Kyoto controls (WKY) have been reported using fluxes of radioactive ions (61, 62), electrophysiological techniques (51, 52), and various kinds of depletion and restoration procedures with Li^+, cold exposure, and ouabain (35, 36). These studies suggest that passive leakage of Na^+ and K^+ (and Cl^-) through the cell membranes of arterial smooth muscle is higher in SHR than in WKY. Active transport of Na^+ and K^+ compensates, at least in part, for the increased passive leakage and thus supports intracellular ion concentrations and membrane potential. However, evidence of impaired Na-K-ATPase activity (78) has been found in other forms of hypertension.

Abnormalities of ion transport in high blood pressure are not limited to vascular smooth muscle cells but occur also for instance in the red blood cells of SHR (80) and of humans with essential hypertension (99). A genetic factor determining membrane leakiness and/or membrane Na^+-K^+-ATPase activity has been considered. However, with respect to the changes in vascular smooth muscle, Campbell et al (14) propose, on the basis of transplantation experiments, that a trophic neural factor or a circulating hormone is involved.

The sodium ion does not seem to act directly on vascular actomyosin (75), but the changes in ion transport may influence reactivity through membrane excitability or e.-c. coupling. In his electrophysiological studies (51) Hermsmeyer observed an increased arterial responsiveness to norepinephrine in SHR and suggested that this was due to short-circuiting of the electrogenic pump when membrane permeability was increased by norepinephrine. Experiments with Ba^{2+} and tetraethylammonium, which reduce membrane conductance, supported this thesis (52, 53). Greater electrogenic ion pump activity in SHR than in WKY arterial muscle was indicated also by greater and more ouabain-sensitive relaxation in response to K^+ after exposure to low $[K^+]_o$ (98). Apart from possible effects on electrical membrane events, Na^+ may be related to Ca^{2+} and contraction through Na-Ca-exchange (8). If this mechanism is important for the extrusion of Ca from the smooth muscle cell, any decrease in the transmembrane gradient of Na_o^+/Na_i^+ would be associated with elevated sarcoplasmic Ca^{2+} and contraction. Contractile responses to changes in Na_o^+ suggested such a role of Na^+ (e.g. 7), but the implications of Na-Ca exchange for vascular reactivity in hypertension received special attention after Blaustein's (9) 1977 review. His model implies that even modest increases in Na_i^+ will limit Ca^{2+} extrusion and enhance vascular tone and reactivity. Factors that inhibit the Na^+-K^+-pump could produce contraction through this mechanism. With a coupling ratio of $Na:Ca > 2$ the exchange becomes electrogenic, and its effectiveness for outward Ca transport depends on membrane potential. In this way the Na-Ca exchange mechanism becomes part of the electromechanical coupling. Recent studies have provided evidence against an important role of Na-Ca exchange in vascular smooth muscle (23, 94). Contractile responses to ouabain and low K_o^+ do not prove the importance of Na-Ca exchange, as they may be mediated directly by membrane depolarization or indirectly by neural release of norepinephrine (11).

The sodium ion, not necessarily related to vascular reactivity through membrane excitability or Ca transport, may be involved in the structural changes of the vascular wall that lead to hyperreactivity (see below). Thus Na^+ was implicated in the arterial waterlogging in hypertension discussed by Tobian (91). More recently Friedman & Friedman (34, 36) and Jones (62) have considered Na^+ a factor in the stimulation of protein synthesis in hypertensive vascular smooth muscle, which leads to cell hypertrophy and increase of the paracellular matrix.

Mechanical Factors in Vascular Reactivity

Mechanical forces acting on the vascular wall, particularly the transmural pressure, influence reactivity in several ways. A fundamental mechanism of action is via the length–active-tension relation of the smooth muscle. In striated muscle this relationship is fairly well understood: The plateau and the descending limb can be attributed to the number of force-producing actomyosin cross-bridges, whereas the ascending limb reflects mechanical interference between myofilaments and/or reduced effectiveness of e.-c. coupling. Contractile force depends on length also in smooth muscle (e.g. 21, 50, 74, 88), but the mechanisms behind this dependence are more obscure. Changes in the length of smooth muscle preparations are associated with approximately proportionate and homogeneous changes in the length of the individual muscle fibres (22, 92). However, the relations between thin and thick myofilaments at different degrees of stretch are less clear. At short cell lengths the myofilaments assume an oblique or irregular orientation (28, 83), but at greater lengths they are roughly parallel to the long axis of the cell (3). A tendency to primitive sarcomeric arrangements has been described (3, 86), but there is disagreement as to the anchoring of the thin filaments to the dense bodies (83, 86).

A distinct plateau is not found in the length–active-tension relation of vertebrate smooth muscle. The apparent absence of a bare zone on the thick myofilaments (3, 83, 86) makes a plateau somewhat unlikely, and even if it existed at the "sarcomeric level" it could easily be obscured by cellular or ultrastructural inhomogeneity. However, a plateau with "sharp corners" was found in a mollusc smooth muscle, the ABRM (16).

The descending part of the length–active-tension relation at increasing lengths is of particular interest with respect to the possibility of a sliding filament contraction. Passive force increases steeply in smooth muscle at long lengths and makes measurements of active force unreliable. Investigators seem to agree that active force decreases beyond a given length (50, 74, 88), but the details of the descent are uncertain. Using a quick-release technique, Mulvany & Warshaw (73) followed the descending limb in preparations from small arteries for a considerable length; they extrapolated it to zero active force at $1.82 L_O$ (L_O = optimal length for force production). This figure is comparable to that of skeletal muscle.

In vivo the vascular transmural pressure sets the length of the contractile structures in the circular muscle. Conduit arteries and capacitance vessels have been examined with respect to responsiveness at graded transmural pressures (21, 76). Gore (43) studied precapillary microvessels in the frog mesentery to find out whether pressure and distensibility in the resistance section are balanced to provide optimal lengths for the smooth muscle cells. He found that optimal conditions prevailed in the arterioles but not in the terminal and larger arteries of the frog. By contrast, a recent analysis of microvascular mechanics in cat skeletal muscle (12) indicated that the passive elastic structures of the precapillary microvessels are not normally under distending stress; instead the smooth muscle appeared to exert a compressive force on passive elements in the walls. Thus these muscle fibres may be shortened to quite small cell lengths merely by their own myogenic activity. As judged from in vitro work on medium-sized (89) and small (B. R. Duling, personal communication) arteries, the smooth muscle has a remarkable ability to withstand large increases in transmural pressure at such degrees of shortening. This resistance to pressure distension may reflect an autoregulatory response (see below), but it also seems possible that the myofilament system may somehow "supercontract" at the short cell lengths—e.g. by formation of new cross-links between the obliquely or irregularly oriented filaments (cf above).

Myogenic vascular tone depends on the transmural pressure according to the classical Bayliss theory (4, 5, 13, 29) and to the more recent concept of a dynamic, rate-sensitive mechanism (45, 46, 59, 67). Experiments using the portal vein as a model of single unit vascular smooth muscle demonstrated how static and dynamic stretch and shortening operated through the electrical membrane mechanisms (59, 81). Stimulation of myogenic tone by pressure pulsations in vivo is most pronounced in the smallest precapillary microvessels and less important in proximal arterioles (45, 46). Dynamic forces acting on the vascular wall can also exert an opposite, inhibitory influence on smooth muscle tone as demonstrated by the effects of vibrations, which appear to act directly on the actomyosin system (65, 82). The transition from excitation by dynamic stretch to vibrational inhibition has not yet been clearly defined in terms of rates of vascular distension or frequency of oscillations (cf 65, 67, 77, 82).

The force-velocity relation is intimately associated with the chemomechanical transduction and the possible cross-bridge events in the contractile system. This justifies continued research interest in force-velocity characteristics (e.g. 49), but the implications for vascular reactivity are more remote and are not considered here.

Structural Adaptations and Vascular Responsiveness

Smooth muscle, like skeletal and cardiac muscle, hypertrophies when exposed to a sustained increase in load. The mechanisms behind this structural response have not been fully revealed, but very dramatic changes can occur. For instance, four days of experimental portal hypertension in the rat led to a two-fold increase in the cross-sectional area of the muscle layer of the portal vein (93). This increase was due to larger cross-sectional area of the individual cell, indicating that hypertrophy or swelling rather than hyperplasia accounts for the immediate structural adaptation.

Also experimental arterial hypertension of renal origin in which the blood pressure rises quite rapidly is associated with functional and morphological evidence of increased wall/lumen ratio in resistance vessels and arteries within 2–4 weeks (6, 66). Enhanced mitotic activity indicating hyperplasia was seen at this stage (6).

The ultrastructural changes in smooth muscle hypertrophy have been studied most extensively by Gabella (38–41) on guinea-pig ileum, subjected to experimental stenosis for 3–5 weeks. The enlarged smooth muscle cells were split into branches and the relative portion of the cell surface occupied by gap junctions (nexuses) was greatly increased. Both smooth and rough sarcoplasmic reticulum was markedly increased, whereas mitochondria took up a reduced percentage of cell volume compared to nonhypertrophied smooth-muscle fibers. The thin and thick myofilaments appeared normal, but owing to the increase in cell diameter there was a clear reduction in the number of myofilaments per unit sectional area. By contrast a conspicuous increase in the number of intermediate filaments was observed.

Morphometric studies of blood vessels in chronic, slowly developing hypertension have been done on the SHR and on the human essential form of high blood pressure (37, 72, 97). Small arterial vessels (lumen diameter around 150 μm) in the SHR at an age when the blood pressure elevation was well established showed a 31% increase in media volume per unit segment length (72). Hyperplasia was an important factor in this respect: There were an average of 4 layers of smooth muscle cells in these SHR vessels compared to 3 layers in control WKY rats. However, there was also a tendency toward increase in the cross-sectional area of the individual cells in SHR. The lumen diameter was reduced by 16% in the fully relaxed hypertensive vessel. Arterial wall and media hypertrophy was evident in SHR already at the early age of 6 weeks (97). Not only do the cellular elements of the arterial wall expand in hypertension but there is also an increase in collagenous and elastic material (17, 72, 97, 100). The relative importance of the structural proteins increases with time (100), perhaps partly as a consequence of degeneration of smooth muscle cells.

The structural vascular changes in hypertension seem restricted to vessels subjected to increased transmural pressure, and therefore the veins are essentially normal in arterial hypertension (see below). Also the smallest precapillary vessels do not appear to undergo medial hypertrophy (37, 54), probably owing to protection from pressure load by functional and structural autoregulation in the proximal vessels.

Functional consequences of vascular hypertrophy are pertinent to the problem of reactivity in hypertension. Acute forms of smooth-muscle hypertrophy are associated with reduced active force per unit cross-sectional area (41, 57), as if here the production of contractile material does not keep up with the increase in cell size. With more gradual increase in smooth muscle mass, as in SHR, the contractile force in large and small arteries changes in approximate proportion to muscle thickness (2, 72, 97); however, reduced contractility has also been reported (48). In many investigations the portal vein has represented vascular smooth muscle that has not been under the increased pressure load, and comparisons between SHR and normotensive controls have given variable results with respect to maximal active stress (2, 47, 64, 79, 90). It is important that comparative studies of contractility be carried out on appropriate strains of control animals, that measurements be made at maximal activation and at optimal muscle length (or vessel diameter), and that the subtracted passive force really represent full relaxation.

In vivo the structural adaptation with thickening of the media produces interesting changes in the reactivity of the intact resistance vessels. The increased wall/lumen ratio implies that the internal arteriolar diameter is restricted even at complete smooth muscle relaxation. This will have profound hemodynamic consequences since flow is related to the fourth power of the radius. Moreover, any given extent of shortening of the vascular smooth muscle will produce a greater lumen reduction and thereby a potentiated resistance response in a thick-walled vessel. Folkow and his associates have made extensive studies of the blood flow resistance in different vascular beds in hypertensive animals and patients (30–33). They have stressed the importance of the structural changes as a dominant mechanism of the increased peripheral resistance and the apparent vascular hyper-reactivity in high blood pressure. The factors that initiate the structural adaptation have been discussed extensively; a primary genetic predisposition to medial vascular hypertrophy must be weighed against a secondary load-induced growth of the smooth muscle resulting from pressure rises evoked by neurohormonal excitatory mechanisms (for reviews see 30, 32).

Literature Cited

1. Adelstein, R. S., Conti, M. A., Hathaway, D. R., Klee, C. B. 1978. Phosphorylation of smooth muscle myosin light chain kinase by the catalytic submit of adenosin 3':5'-monophosphate-dependent protein kinase. *J. Biol. Chem.* 253: 8347–50

2. Arner, A., Hellstrand, P. 1980. Energy turnover and mechanical properties of resting and contracting aortas and portal veins from normotensive and spontaneously hypertensive rats. *Circ. Res.* In press

3. Ashton, F. T., Somlyo, A. V., Somlyo, A. P. 1975. The contractile apparatus of vascular smooth muscle: intermediate high voltage stereo electron microscopy. *J. Mol. Biol.* 98:17–29

4. Baez, S., Laidlaw, Z., Orkin, L. R. 1974. Localization and measurement of microcirculatory responses to venous pressure elevation in the rat. *Blood Vessels* 11:260–76

5. Bayliss, W. M. 1902. On the local reactions of the arterial wall to changes in internal pressure. *J. Physiol. London.* 28:220–31

6. Bevan, R. D., van Martens, E., Bevan, J. A. 1976. Hyperplasia of vascular smooth muscle in experimental hypertension in the rabbit. *Circ. Res.* 38:(Suppl II.) 58–62

7. Biamino, G., Johansson, B. 1970. Effects of calcium and sodium on contracture tension in the smooth muscle of the rat portal vein. *Pflügers Arch.* 321:143–58

8. Blaustein, M. P. 1974. The interrelationship between sodium and calcium fluxes across cell membranes. *Rev. Physiol. Biochem. Pharmacol.* 70:33–82

9. Blaustein, M. P. 1977. Sodium ions, calcium ions, blood pressure regulation, and hypertension: a reassessment and a hypothesis. *Am. J. Physiol.* 232:C165–73

10. Bohr, D. F. 1965. Individualities among vascular smooth muscles. In *Electrolytes and Cardiovascular Diseases,* ed. E. Bajusz, pp. 342–55. Basel: Karger.

11. Bonaccorsi, A., Hermsmeyer, K., Smith, C. B., Bohr, D. F. 1977. Norepinephrine release in isolated arteries induced by K-free solution. *Am. J. Physiol.* 232:H140–45

12. Borgström, P., Grände, P.-O. 1979. Myogenic microvascular responses to change of transmural pressure. *Acta Physiol. Scand.* 106:411–23

13. Bouskela, E., Wiederhielm, C. A. 1979. Microvascular myogenic reaction in the wing of the intact unanesthetized bat. *Am. J. Physiol.* 237:H59–65

14. Campbell, G. R., Chamley-Campbell, J., Robinson, R., Hermsmeyer, K. 1980. Trophic interactions between nerve and vascular smooth muscle in transplants to an anterior eye chamber. In *Vascular Neuroeffector Mechanisms,* ed. J. A. Bevan, T. Godfriend, R. A. Maxwell, P. M. Vanhoutte, pp. 107–13. Raven. 401 pp.

15. Cheung, W. Y. 1980. Calmodulin plays a pivotal role in cellular regulation. *Science* 207:19–27

16. Cornelius, F., Lowy, J. 1978. Tension-length behaviour of a moluscan smooth muscle related to filament organisation. *Acta Physiol. Scand.* 102:167–80

17. Cox, R. H. 1979. Comparison of arterial wall mechanics in normotensive and spontanously hypertensive rats. *Am. J. Physiol.* 237:H159–67

18. Deth, R., Casteels, R. 1977. A study of releasable Ca fractions in smooth muscle cells of the rabbit aorta. *J. Gen. Physiol.* 69:401–16

19. Deth, R., van Breemen, C. 1974. Relative contributions of Ca^{2+} influx and cellular Ca^{2+} release during drug induced activation of the rabbit aorta. *Pflügers Arch.* 348:13–22

20. DiSalvo, J., Gruenstein, E., Silver, P. 1978. Ca^{2+} dependent phosphorylation of bovine aortic actomyosin. *Proc. Soc. Exp. Biol. Med.* 158:410–14

21. Dobrin, P. B. 1978. Mechanical properties of arteries. *Physiol. Rev.* 58:397–460

22. Driska, S. P., Murphy, R. A. 1978. Estimate of cellular force generation in an arterial smooth muscle with a high actin :myosin ratio. *Blood Vessels* 15:26–32

23. Droogmans, G., Casteels, R. 1979. Sodium and calcium interactions in vascular smooth muscle cells of the rabbit ear artery. *J. Gen. Physiol.* 74:57–70

24. Droogmans, G., Raeymaekers, L., Casteels, R. 1977. Electro- and pharmacomechanical coupling in the smooth muscle cells of the rabbit ear artery. *J. Gen. Physiol.* 70:129–48

25. Ebashi, S., Mikawa, T., Hirata, M., Toyo-oka, T., Nonomura, Y. 1977. Regulatory proteins of smooth muscle. In *Excitation-Contraction Coupling in Smooth Muscle,* ed. R. Casteels, T. Godfraind, J. C. Rüegg, pp. 325–34. Amsterdam, New York & Oxford: Elsevier/North Holland. 488 pp.

26. Fay, F. S., Shlevin, H. H., Granger, W. C. Jr., Taylor, S. R. 1979. Aequorin luminescence during activation of single isolated smooth muscle cells. *Nature* 280:506–8

27. Filo, R. S., Bohr, D. F., Rüegg, J. C. 1965. Glycerinated skeletal and smooth muscle: calcium and magnesium dependence. *Science* 147:1581–83

28. Fischer, B. A., Bagby R. M. 1977. Reorientation of myofilaments during contraction of a vertebrate smooth muscle. *Am. J. Physiol.* 232:C5–14

29. Folkow, B. 1964. Description of the myogenic hypothesis. *Circ. Res.* 15: (Suppl. I) 279–85

30. Folkow, B. 1978. Cardiovascular structural adaptation: its role in the initiation and maintenance of primary hypertension. *Clin. Sci. Mol. Med.* 55:3–22

31. Folkow, B., Grimby, G., Thulesius, O. 1958. Adaptive structural changes of the vascular walls in hypertension and their relation to the control of the peripheral resistance. *Acta Physiol. Scand.* 44:255–72

32. Folkow, B., Hallbäck, M., Lundgren, Y., Silvertsson, R., Weiss, L. 1973. Importance of adaptive changes in vascular design for establishment of primary hypertension studied in man and in spontaneously hypertensive rats. *Circ. Res.* 32–33: (Suppl. I) 2–16

33. Folkow, B., Hallbäck, M., Lundgren, Y., Weiss, L. 1970. Structurally based increase of flow resistance in spontaneously hypertensive rats. *Acta Physiol. Scand.* 79:373–78

34. Friedman, S. M. 1979. Sodium in blood vessels. *Blood Vessels* 16:2–16

35. Friedman, S. M. 1979. Evidence for enhanced Na transport in the tail artery of the spontaneously hypertensive rat. *Hypertension* 1:572–82

36. Friedman, S. M., Friedman, C. L. 1976. Cell permeability, sodium transport and hypertensive process in the rat. *Circ. Res.* 39:433–41

37. Furuyama, M. 1962. Histometrical investigations of arteries in reference to arterial hypertension. *Tohoku J. Exp. Med.* 76:388–414

38. Gabella, G. 1979. Hypertrophic smooth muscle I. Size and shape of cells, occurrence of mitoses. *Cell Tiss. Res.* 201:63–78

39. Gabella, G. 1979. Hypertrophic smooth muscle, II. Sarcoplasmic reticulum, caveolae and mitochondria. *Cell Tiss. Res.* 201:79–92

40. Gabella, G. 1979. Hypertrophic smooth muscle. III. Increase in number and size of gap junctions. *Cell Tiss. Res.* 201:263–76

41. Gabella, G. 1979. Hypertrophic smooth muscle. IV. Myofilaments, intermediate filaments and some mechanical properties. *Cell Tiss. Res.* 201:277–88

42. Golenhofen, K., Hermstein, N. 1975. Differentiation of calcium activation mechanisms in vascular smooth muscle by selective suppression with verapanil and D600. *Blood Vessels* 12:21–37

43. Gore, R. W. 1972. Wall stress: a determinant of regional differences in response of frog microvessels to norepinephrine. *Am. J. Physiol.* 222:82–91

44. Gorecka, A., Aksoy, M. O., Hartshorne, D. J. 1976. The effect of phosphorylation of gizzard myosin on actin activation. *Biochem. Biophys. Res. Commun.* 71:325–31

45. Grände, P.-O. 1979. Dynamic and static components in the myogenic control of vascular tone in cat skeletal muscle. *Acta Physiol. Scand.* 476 (Suppl.):1–46

46. Grände, P.-O., Borgström, P., Mellander, S. 1979. On the nature of basal vascular tone in cat skeletal muscle and its dependence on transmural pressure stimuli. *Acta Physiol. Scand.* 107:365–76

47. Greenberg, S., Palmer, E. C., Wilborn, W. M. 1978. Pressure-independent hypertrophy of veins and pulmonary arteries of spontaneously hypertensive rats. Characterization of function, structural and histochemical changes *Clin. Sci. Mol. Med.* 55:31–36

48. Hansen, T. R., Bohr, D. F. 1975. Hypertension, transmural pressure, and vascular smooth muscle response in rats. *Circ. Res.* 36:590–98

49. Hellstrand, P. 1979. Mechanical and metabolic properties related to contraction in smooth muscle. *Acta Physiol. Scand.* 464 (Suppl.):1–54

50. Herlihy, J. T., Murphy, R. A. 1973. Length-tension relationship of smooth muscle of the hog carotid artery. *Circ. Res.* 33:275–83

51. Hermsmeyer, K. 1976. Electrogenesis of increased norepinephrine sensitivity of arterial vascular muscle in hypertension. *Circ. Res.* 38:362–67

52. Hermsmeyer, K. 1977. Specificity of altered electrogenesis of membrane potential in hypertension. *Circ.* 40:(Suppl. I) 153–56

53. Hermsmeyer, K. 1980. Membrane electrical contribution to increased arterial reactivity in hypertension. See Ref. 14, pp. 365–67

54. Hertel, R., Henrich, H., Assman, R. 1978. Intravital measurement of arteriolar pressure and tangential wall stress in normotensive and spontaneously hypertensive rats (established hypertension). *Experientia* 34:865–67

55. Johansson, B. 1971. Electromechanical and mechanoelectrical coupling in vascular smooth muscle. *Angiologica* 8:129–43

56. Johansson, B. 1974. Determinants of vascular reactivity. *Fed. Proc.* 33:121–26

57. Johansson, B. 1976. Structural and functional changes in rat portal veins after experimental portal hypertension. *Acta Physiol. Scand.* 98:381–83

58. Johansson, B. 1978. Vascular smooth muscle biophysics. In *Microcirculation II*, ed. G. Kaley, B. M. Altura, pp. 83–117. Baltimore: University Park Press. 756 pp.

59. Johansson, B., Mellander, S. 1975. Static and dynamic components in the vascular myogenic response to passive changes in length as revealed by electrical and mechanical recordings from the rat portal vein. *Circ. Res.* 36:76–83

60. Johansson, B., Somlyo, A. P. 1980. Electrophysiology and excitation-contraction coupling. In *Handbook of Physiology. The Cardiovascular System II*, ed. D. F. Bohr, A. P. Somlyo, H. V. Sparks, pp. 301–33. Baltimore: Am. Physiol. Soc. 686 pp.

61. Jones, A. W. 1973. Altered ion transport in vascular smooth muscle from spontaneously hypertensive rats, influences of aldosterone, norepinephrine and angiotensin. *Circ. Res.* 33:563–72

62. Jones, A. W. 1976. Functional changes in vascular smooth muscle associated with experimental hypertension. See Ref. 14, pp. 182–89

63. Litten, R. Z. III, Solaro, R. J., Ford, G. D. 1979. Nature of the calcium regulatory system of bovine arterial actomyosin. *Blood Vessels* 16:26–34

64. Ljung, B., Mulvany, M. J., Stoltze, M., Kjellstedt, A. 1980. Contractile and morphological properties of the portal vein in spontaneously hypertensive and in Wistar-Kyoto rats. *Blood Vessels.* In press

65. Ljung, B., Sivertsson, R. 1980. The inhibitory response of vascular smooth muscle to vibrations. See Ref. 14, pp. 207–12

66. Lundgren, Y., Hallbäck, M., Weiss, L., Folkow, B. 1974. Rate and extent of adaptive cardiovascular changes in rats during experimental renal hypertension. *Acta Physiol. Scand.* 91:103–15

67. Mellander, S., Grände, P.-O., Borgström, P. 1980. Static and dynamic components in the myogenic vascular response. See Ref. 14, pp. 199–206

68. Mellander, S., Johansson, B. 1968. Control of resistance, exchange and capacitance function in the peripheral circulation. *Pharmacol. Rev.* 20:117–96

69. Mrwa, U., Achtig, I., Rüegg, J. C. 1974. Influences of calcium concentration and pH on the tension development and ATPase activity of the arterial actomyosin contractile system. *Blood Vessels* 11:277–86

70. Mrwa, U., Rüegg, J. C. 1975. Myosinlinked calcium regulation in vascular smooth muscle. *FEBS Lett.* 60:81–84

71. Mrwa, U., Troschka, M., Gross, C., Katzinski, L. 1980. Ca-sensitivity of pig carotid actomyosin ATPase in relation to phosphorylation of the regulatory light chain. *Eur. J. Biochem.* 103: 415–19

72. Mulvany, M. J., Hansen, P. K., Aalkjaer, C. 1978. Direct evidence that the greater contractility of resistance vessels in spontaneously hypertensive rats is associated with a narrowed lumen, a thickened media, and an increased number of smooth muscle cell layers. *Cir. Res.* 43:854–64

73. Mulvany, M. J., Warshaw, D. M. 1979. The active tension-length curve of vascular smooth muscle related to its cellular components. *J. Gen. Physiol.* 74:85–104

74. Murphy, R. A. 1976. Contractile system function in mammalian smooth muscle. *Blood Vessels* 13:1–23

75. Murphy, R. A., Bohr, D. F., Newman, D. L. 1969. Arterial actomyosin: Mg-, Ca-, and ATP-ion dependencies for ATPase activity. *Am. J. Physiol.* 217: 666–73

76. Öberg, B. 1967. The relationship between active constriction and passive recoil of the veins at various distending pressures. *Acta Physiol. Scand.* 71: 233–47

77. Ohhashi, T., Azuma, T., Sakaguchi, M. 1979. Effects of microvibration on activity of ureteral and portal smooth muscles. *Am. J. Physiol.* 236:C192–201

78. Overbeck, H. W., Pamnani, M. B., Akera, T., Brody, T. M., Haddy, F. 1976. Depressed function of a ouabain-sensitive sodium-potassium pump in blood vessels from renal hypertensive dogs. *Circulation Res.* 38: (Suppl. II) 48–52

79. Peiper, U., Klemt, P., Popov, R. 1979. The contractility of venous vascular smooth muscle in spontaneously hypertensive or renal hypertensive rats. *Basic Res. Cardiol.* 74:21–34

80. Postnov, Y., Orlov, S., Gulak, P., Shevchenko, A. 1976. Altered permeability of the erythrocyte membrane for sodium and potassium ions in spontaneously hypertensive rats. *Pflüger's Arch.* 365:257–63

81. Sigurdsson, S. B., Johansson, B., Mellander, S. 1977. Rate-dependent myogenic response of vascular smooth muscle during imposed changes in length and force. *Acta Physiol. Scand.* 99: 183–89

82. Sjöqvist, A., Ljung, B. 1980. Dissociation of electrical and mechanical activity caused by vibrations in the spontaneously active smooth muscle of the rat portal vein. *Acta Physiol. Scand.* In press

83. Small, J. V. 1977. The contractile and cytoskeletal elements of vertebrate smooth muscle. See Ref. 25, pp. 305–15

84. Small, J. V., Sobieszek, A. 1977. Caregulation of mammalian smooth muscle actomyosin via a kinase-phosphatase-dependent phosphorylation and dephosphorylation of the $20000-M_r$ light chain of myosin. *Eur. J. Biochem.* 76:521–30

85. Somlyo, A. V., Somlyo, A. P. 1968. Electromechanical and pharmacomechanical coupling in vascular smooth muscle. *J. Pharmacol. Exp. Ther.* 159:129–45

86. Somlyo, A. P., Somlyo, A. V. 1977. Ultrastructure of the contractile apparatus: controversies resolved and

questions remaining. See Ref. 25, pp. 317–22

87. Somlyo, A. P., Somlyo, A. V., Shuman, H. 1979. Electron probe analysis of vascular smooth muscle: composition of mitochondria, nuclei and cytoplasm. *J. Cell. Biol.* 80:316–35

88. Speden, R. N. 1960. The effect of initial strip length on the noradrenaline-induced isometric contraction of arterial strips. *J. Physiol. London* 154: 15–25

89. Speden, R. N. 1973. The maintenance of arterial constriction at different transmural pressures. *J. Physiol. London* 229:361–81

90. Sutter, M. C., Ljung, B. 1977. Contractility, muscle mass and agonist sensitivity of isolated portal veins from normo- and hypertensive rats. *Acta Physiol. Scand.* 99:484–95

91. Tobian, L. 1960. Interrelationship of electrolytes, juxtaglomerular cells and hypertension *Physiol. Rev.* 40:280–312

92. Uvelius, B. 1976. Isometric and isotonic length-tension relations and variations in cell length in longitudinal smooth muscle from rabbit urinary bladder. *Acta Physiol. Scand.* 97:1–12

93. Uvelius, B., Johansson, B., Gabella, G. 1980. Short term structural adaptation of smooth muscle in portal vein of rats with portal hypertension. *Blood Vessels* 17:166

94. van Breemen, C., Aaronson, P., Loutzenhiser, R. 1979. Sodium-calcium interactions in mammalian smooth muscle. *Pharmacol. Rev.* 30:167–208

95. van Breemen, C., Farinas, B. R., Gerba, P., McNaughton, E. D. 1972. Excitation-contraction coupling in rabbit aorta studied by the lanthanum method for measuring cellular calcium influx. *Circ. Res.* 30:44–54

96. Vanhoutte, P. M. 1977. Heterogeneity in vascular smooth muscle. See Ref. 58, pp. 181–309

97. Warshaw, D. M., Mulvany, M. J., Halpern, W. 1979. Mechanical and morphological properties of arterial resistance vessels in young and old spontaneously hypertensive rats. *Circ. Res.* 45:250–59

98. Webb, R. C., Bohr, D. F. 1979. Potassium relaxation of vascular smooth muscle from spontaneously hypertensive rats. *Blood Vessels* 16:71–79

99. Wessels, F., Zumkley, H., Losse, H. 1970. Untersuchungen zur Frage des Zusammenhanges zwischen Kationenpermeabilität der Erythrozyten und Hochdruckdisposition. *Z. Kreislaufforsch.* 59:415–26

100. Wolinsky, H. 1972. Long-term effects of hypertension on the rat aortic wall and their relation to concurrent ageing changes. *Circ. Res.* 30:301–9

Ann. Rev. Physiol. 1981. 43:371–83

FACTORS AFFECTING CHANGES IN THE NEONATAL SYSTEMIC CIRCULATION

❖1316

Michael A. Heymann, Harriet S. Iwamoto, and Abraham M. Rudolph

The Cardiovascular Research Institute and the Departments of Pediatrics, Obstetrics, Gynecology, and Reproductive Sciences, and Physiology, University of California, San Francisco, California 94143 .

INTRODUCTION

At birth many major changes must occur in the circulation. The function of gas exchange is transferred from the placenta to the lungs, the kidney assumes control of water and electrolyte balance, and nutrition is obtained through the gastrointestinal tract. Blood flow regulation now assumes greater importance than during fetal life, but little is known about the role of local or humoral factors in controlling the vascular beds of these organs.

CHANGES IN THE CIRCULATION AT BIRTH

General Changes

During fetal life, oxygenation is carried out in the placenta and oxygenated blood returns via the umbilical veins to the inferior vena cava, passing through either the ductus venosus or the hepatic microcirculation. Inferior vena caval return passes in part across the foramen ovale to the left atrium and then is ejected by the left ventricle into the ascending aorta. The remainder crosses the tricuspid valve into the right ventricle and with superior vena caval and coronary sinus blood is ejected into the main pulmonary trunk. Since the lungs do not serve a ventilatory function, most right ventricular blood bypasses the pulmonary microcirculation through the ductus arteriosus to the descending aorta allowing each ventricle to

371

0066-4278/81/0315-0371$01.00

contribute to systemic blood flow. The output of the two ventricles (combined ventricular output) is in parallel; this contrasts with the adult or infant circulation in which the ventricular outputs are in series.

The major hemodynamic changes at the time of birth are the rapid increase in pulmonary blood flow with the onset of pulmonary gas exchange, removal of the placental site of gas exchange, closure of the several sites of shunting within the heart and great vessels, and changes in cardiac output and its distribution.

In the close-to-term fetus, combined ventricular output is about 450 ml $min^{-1} kg^{-1}$ of fetal body weight. The right ventricle ejects approximately two thirds and the left ventricle ejects the remaining one third (34). Shortly after birth, resting cardiac output (i.e. the output of each ventricle) is about 400 ml $min^{-1} kg^{-1}$ of body weight (42, 46). Left ventricular output thus increases markedly, from about 150 to about 400 ml $min^{-1} kg^{-1}$ of body weight, and right ventricular output increases somewhat less. This marked increase of cardiac output in the newborn parallels quite closely the rise in oxygen consumption (46). Systemic arterial blood pressure increases immediately after birth and continues to rise for several weeks, concomitant with an increase in systemic vascular resistance. The organs involved in these changes of vascular resistance have not yet been clearly identified. The effects of these changes in afterload and cardiac output, particularly on the myocardium, are discussed below. Major changes in blood gases and oxygen delivery that may directly affect specific vascular beds are also discussed.

Changes in Organ Blood Flow

Changes in the circulation after birth would be delineated ideally by studying the same animal during fetal life and following delivery. No such sequential information is available, but data on organ blood flows are available in different groups of fetal and newborn animals of the same species —primarily sheep [(31, 61), our unpublished observations], but rhesus monkeys also have been examined (8). The most dramatic increase in blood flow is that to the lungs. In the fetus, pulmonary blood flow is approximately 30–40 ml $min^{-1} kg^{-1}$ of body weight, whereas, shortly after birth, this increases to about 400 ml $min^{-1} kg^{-1}$ of body weight. Our data (31, 61) on fetal and newborn sheep indicate an increase in myocardial, renal, and gastrointestinal blood flow (29, 30, 50%, respectively) with a fall in adrenal, cerebral, and carcass (skin, muscle, and bone) blood flows (53, 40, and 50% respectively). Similar observations were made in rhesus monkeys (8).

Both reflex and humoral factors may play a role in controlling these changes in organ blood flows and in distribution of cardiac output. Changes affected by humoral agents could be mediated by either local or remote production.

In the adult, local control of blood flow is closely related to oxygen availability and demand (65). Peripheral tissues regulate their blood flow locally, in order to maintain appropriate oxygen uptake; these tissue requirements thereby regulate cardiac output and its distribution. The mechanisms responsible for this autoregulation include intrinsic modulation of local vascular resistance and alterations in tissue oxygen extraction. Whether the fetus or newborn has, or requires, similar autoregulatory capacity is not known and requires study.

ROLE OF VASOACTIVE SUBSTANCES

Circulating Vasoactive Substances

Plasma concentrations of several vasoactive substances, e.g. angiotensin II and catecholamines, are elevated after birth (9, 11, 14, 24, 26, 28, 43, 48, 60). Whether this represents a stress response to labor and delivery or a specific mechanism involved in circulatory adaptation after birth is not yet known. These substances may influence the circulation coincidentally; their effects may not be essential for postnatal adaptation.

The fall in plasma concentration of vasoactive substances, such as prostaglandins (10, 16, 51, 52, 66) produced within the fetal-placental unit or actively catabolized in the pulmonary circulation, may also play a role in controlling circulatory changes after birth.

SYMPATHETICO-ADRENAL SYSTEM   In the newborn, plasma catecholamine concentrations are elevated, particularly in the first three hours after birth (28). Both norepinephrine and epinephrine concentrations increase, but norepinephrine consistently predominates. There is no difference in concentrations between infants delivered vaginally or by cesarean section, indicating that they are not elevated by stress of delivery alone. These catecholamines are involved in several physiologic adaptations, including maintenance of normal blood sugar concentrations, nonshivering thermogenesis, and free fatty acid metabolism (77). Whether they are involved in local regulation of systemic blood flow is not known. Studies in sheep (78) suggested that the autonomic nervous system does not play a significant role in the increase in systemic arterial blood pressure after birth. Complete ganglionic blockade before delivery of the lamb did not attenuate the normal postnatal rise in pressure. However, alpha adrenergic blockade in newborn lambs reduced systemic arterial blood pressure, whereas no effect was seen in adult sheep (79). The latter data suggest at least some sympathetic control of blood pressure in the newborn, but they cannot separate possible resting sympathetic activity from effects of circulating catecholamines.

Studies to define the relative roles of reflexes, resting neural activity, and humoral influences are required.

RENIN-ANGIOTENSIN-ALDOSTERONE SYSTEM (RAAS)   Elevations of plasma renin activity (PRA) and angiotensin II concentrations occur following normal vaginal delivery in lambs and humans (24, 48). Although hypoxemia does not affect renin release or angiotensin II production in the fetus (11), minor degrees of hemorrhage result in a marked increase in plasma angiotensin II concentration (12). Endogenous angiotensin II appears to play a role in controlling fetal vascular tone since competitive antagonism with saralasin causes a fall in systemic arterial blood pressure. Therefore angiotensin II may be important in maintaining arterial blood pressure (13) in the perinatal period, and the plasma concentrations may be elevated in response to an initial hypotensive stimulus. However, fetal animals survive delivery following bilateral nephrectomy (76).

Plasma aldosterone concentrations also are elevated in the newborn (9, 24, 60) by mechanisms unknown. Aldosterone half-life could be prolonged (9) owing to lack of maturation of the enzyme systems responsible for its catabolism and this might in part account for the elevated concentrations. It has also been suggested that concentrations are high to compensate for relative insensitivity to aldosterone of the newborn kidney (32, 60). Recently, the increased endogenous production of prostaglandins during labor and delivery, and increased sodium loss in the newborn, particularly in immature infants, have been implicated as causes for hyperfunction of the RAAS (68–71). Elevations in plasma concentrations of these substances may be due, at least in part, to the stress of labor, since infants after normal labor had higher circulating concentrations of angiotensin II (48) and aldosterone (9, 24) than those delivered by cesarean section. The importance of the high PRA, angiotensin II and aldosterone concentrations, and their interrelationships in local circulatory control in the newborn is unknown; however, a relationship may exist between the high concentrations and distal tubular sodium reabsorption, which is enhanced in the newborn (41). Despite the high baseline RAAS activity, acute challenge of newborn infants, either by volume depletion (25) or by the administration of furosemide (71), results in increased, locally produced prostaglandin-mediated RAAS activity, implying an active role of the RAAS in extracellular volume control.

Although the RAAS is active and PRA and angiotensin II and aldosterone concentrations are elevated, whether these are incidental or crucial to circulatory adaptation remains undetermined.

NEUROHYPOPHYSIS   Plasma arginine vasopressin (AVP) concentrations also are elevated in the newborn (45). As with the vasoactive substances already mentioned, stress in the fetus produces a marked increase in circulating plasma AVP concentrations. With AVP, the rise is induced both by hemorrhage and hypoxia as well as by other stressful situations, such as increased head pressure (27, 44, 45, 62, 63). The physiologic importance of the increased concentrations of AVP is unclear. Infusion of exogenous AVP in fetal lambs produces an increase in arterial blood pressure but only one of the specific changes in organ blood flow seen at birth, namely a fall in blood flow to the carcass (37). Perhaps of greater importance in controlling circulatory changes at birth is the interaction of AVP and catecholamines. Pressor responses to catecholamines are significantly enhanced by very small, subpressor concentrations of AVP (2).

THYROID   Within 24 hours after birth, serum thyroxine (T_4) and particularly triiodothyronine (T_3) concentrations rise to "chemical hyperthyroidal levels" in normal infants (1, 29). These increases are associated with a TSH surge and occur regardless of whether delivery is vaginal or by cesarean section (30). It is likely that, in concert with catecholamines, the iodothyronines are responsible for maintenance of body temperature by nonshivering thermogenesis as well as for fat mobilization and metabolism. Concomitant with these effects, oxygen consumption increases markedly. Paralleling this rise in oxygen consumption is a marked rise in cardiac output (46). Indirectly, therefore, postnatal changes in iodothyronine concentrations may affect local vascular beds.

PROSTAGLANDINS   In late pregnancy, fetal plasma prostaglandin concentrations are significantly higher than those in maternal plasma (15, 16, 23, 51). At delivery, whether vaginal or cesarean, umbilical cord blood plasma prostaglandin concentrations are also higher than those in maternal plasma (10, 51).

After birth, there is a rapid decrease in the concentration of both PGE and PGF in the arterial plasma of newborn lambs (15). This fall probably is due to both removal of the placental site of prostaglandin production (10, 52) and enhanced catabolism of circulating prostaglandins, subsequent to the marked increase in pulmonary blood flow (55). The high concentrations of PGE in fetal blood may play a part in maintenance of reduced vascular tone in the fetus. There is convincing evidence that PGE is responsible for maintaining the fetal ductus arteriosus in a dilated state (17, 21, 22). The marked fall in circulating concentrations of PGE after birth could lead to peripheral vasoconstriction, but this has not been examined in the newborn.

Prostaglandins and catecholamines interact to modulate vascular tone. Both PGE_1 and prostacyclin (PGI_2) reduce the vasoconstrictor effect of norepinephrine in the mesenteric and renal vascular beds (80, 81).

Role of Local Vasoactive Substances

Little information is available regarding local vascular or organ production or release of vasoactive substances in the fetus or newborn. Vascular synthesis of prostaglandins and prostacyclin has been studied mainly in umbilical vessels and in the ductus arteriosus (19, 56–58, 72–75). Intramural prostaglandin synthesis enables these locally produced substances to interact directly with other vasoactive substances such as the vasoconstrictors angiotensin II and catecholamines (49, 74) and thereby locally to modulate vascular tone, organ blood flow, and perhaps intraorgan blood flow distribution. Norepinephrine release from adrenergic nerve endings also is modulated by prostaglandins, and this too may affect local vascular tone (49).

CONTROL OF BLOOD FLOW TO SPECIFIC ORGANS

Renal Blood Flow

At birth the kidneys replace the placenta as the organ responsible for excretory and volume regulatory functions. During fetal life, renal blood flow is low, 1.7–1.9 ml min^{-1} g^{-1} tissue or about 4–5% of systemic blood flow (8, 61); immediately after birth, this increases to about 8–12% of cardiac output [(4, 6, 33); our unpublished observations]. Despite this initial increase when compared to the adult, renal blood flow in the newborn still is low and renal vascular resistance is high. There is then a slowly progressive fall in renal vascular resistance and rise in renal blood flow towards adult levels. In the growing piglet (up to 45 days after birth), cardiac index increases 7.2-fold, whereas the renal blood flow increases 18.2-fold (33). In the young lamb, cardiac index increases 4-fold, whereas renal blood flow increases 5- to 6-fold during the first 70 days (4). The increase in systemic arterial blood pressure and cardiac output during this period cannot account for the increase in renal blood flow because the neonate can autoregulate renal blood flow as early as 9 days of age (40). Using free-flow and stop-flow methods for measuring glomerular pressure, Spitzer & Edelmann (67) found that the pressure fall across the afferent arteriole decreased from 22 to 14 torr during the first 10 days of life in guinea pigs.

To assess whether there is a morphologic component to the fall in renal vascular resistance, Naeye measured the luminal diameter and medial muscle thickness in arteries of term human infants (53). He found dilation of the renal arteries from 1 month to 3 years of age, but little change during the immediate neonatal period. Why renal blood flow initially only increases to a certain degree and what factors are responsible for the subsequent progressive decrease in renal vascular resistance with advancing age are not clear.

A possible explanation for the initial increase in renal blood flow is a change in the intrarenal distribution of blood flow (54). Immediately upon clamping the umbilical cord, total renal blood flow does not change, but blood flow to the outer cortex increases relative to that in the inner cortex (5). In normally growing young lambs and puppies, blood flow to the outer cortex increases faster than the increase in cardiac output, but blood flow to the middle and inner cortex increases in proportion to the increase in cardiac output (4). In puppies, the increase in blood flow to the outer cortex relative to the inner cortex continues until 12–16 weeks after birth (38).

The mechanisms responsible for this redistribution of blood flow within the kidney are unclear, particularly since species differences exist. Prostaglandin catabolic enzymes are more active in the newborn than in the adult rat kidney (55), at a time when prostaglandin biosynthetic activity is unaltered. This leads to reduced prostaglandin concentrations in the kidney. Pace-Asciak (55) speculated that the reduced amounts of prostaglandins (which are vasoconstrictors, in this species) reaching the medullocortical region of the kidney therefore allows for increased blood flow to the outer cortex. Inhibition of prostaglandin synthesis by indomethacin produces a similar redistribution of flow, thereby supporting this hypothesis (3). In fetal lambs, renal blood increases (70) at a time when renal PGE_2 synthesis increases (55), suggesting that in this species PGE_2 is perhaps a renal vasodilator.

Siegler et al (66) speculated that a developmental imbalance between PGE and angiotensin II concentrations might be responsible. In adult animals, angiotensin II administration actively promotes renal vascular prostaglandin secretion which modulates the vasoconstrictor effect of the angiotensin II. In the newborn, compared with the adult, local PGE concentrations are low despite the high PRA and angiotensin II concentrations. The renal vasoconstrictor effect of angiotensin II then would be unopposed, leading to a relatively reduced renal blood flow. In addition, PGE modulates the vasoconstrictor effects of norepinephrine (49, 50) and this response too would be unopposed. The degree to which these interrelationships modulate vascular tone is variable between species (49), and the importance of these interrelationships in humans is unclear. Administration of furosemide to normal male infants produced an increase in RAAS activity associated with increased PGE and $PGF_{2\alpha}$ production and excretion in the urine (71), suggesting that the imbalance may be less pronounced in the human. Speculation that the elevated concentrations of renin and angiotensin II alone are responsible for the reduced renal blood flow also are not tenable since administration of competitive antagonists of angiotensin II did not alter renal blood flow (40).

Another possible explanation for the decrease in renal vascular resistance is a gradual decrease in the sensitivity of the renal vasculature to catecholamines (39). In puppies 45–56 days old, infusion of epinephrine decreased blood flow to the renal cortex and markedly increased the calculated vascular resistance. The decrease in blood flow to the outer cortex was more pronounced than the decrease in blood flow to the inner cortex. The equivalent dose of epinephrine had no effect on renal vascular resistance in adult dogs.

Cerebral Blood Flow

Local changes in arterial blood gases are probably responsible for the control of the cerebral circulation. Whether this is true for the changes occurring at birth is not yet known.

In the term fetal lamb, cerebral blood flow is about 132 ml min^{-1} $100g^{-1}$; this falls to about 79 ml min^{-1} $100g^{-1}$ in the newborn (our unpublished observations).

Cerebral blood flow per g of tissue in fetal rats is about twice that in the adult (7) and after birth adult levels are reached within about three hours. In these acute studies, changes in $PaCO_2$ were considered the main factor affecting the flow changes; however, changes in cerebral water content, PaO_2, and systemic arterial pressure also played a role. The relationship of $PaCO_2$ and cerebral blood flow was similar to that found in adults; as $PaCO_2$ was reduced, cerebral blood flow fell. The normal fall in $PaCO_2$ that occurs after birth could account for the observed decrease in cerebral blood flow (7). A similar direct relationship between cerebral blood flow and $PaCO_2$ exists in lambs (47, 59). Changes in PaO_2 also directly affect cerebral blood flow; flow, particularly to gray matter, increases when PaO_2 is reduced (47, 59). Epinephrine infusion had no consistent effect on flow despite a rise in systemic arterial blood pressure; norepinephrine, however, which produced an equivalent rise in pressure, did increase gray matter flow significantly (59). Differences in blood gases between the two groups of animals might have accounted for the different effects. Further evaluation of the role of catecholamines in controlling changes in the cerebral circulation is required.

Differences exist between newborn and adult rats in the ability to autoregulate the cerebral circulation (7). In infant rats, high perfusion rates were achieved at an arterial pressure of 25 mm Hg, far below the level required for autoregulation in the adult (50 mm Hg). Further studies are required to delineate pressure-flow relationships in the neonatal brain.

Myocardial Blood Flow

Left ventricular (LV) myocardial oxygen consumption increases significantly from the fetal to the newborn periods (382–577 μM min^{-1} 100g LV^{-1}) [(31); our unpublished observations]. This may be due to several factors. Myocardial work, as assessed by the rate-pressure product, is increased significantly; also, the increase in afterload and peripheral vascular resistance may lead to increased myocardial wall stress and, therefore, to an elevated myocardial oxygen consumption. In the adult, one of the most important factors regulating myocardial blood flow is the relationship of oxygen supply and demand. A fall in arterial oxygen content leads to a rise in blood flow. In the lamb, however, we have shown (unpublished observations) that after birth, in response to the increased oxygen requirements, LV myocardial blood flow increases (156–201 ml min^{-1} 100g LV^{-1}) despite an increase in arterial oxygen content. The mechanisms responsible for this are not yet established.

Ductus Arteriosus

The mechanisms responsible for constriction of the ductus arteriosus (DA) after birth have been the subject of intensive investigation. The role of an increased oxygen environment is well established (35). Such vasoconstricting agents as bradykinin (released from the lungs at birth), catecholamines, and acetylcholine have also been implicated (35).

Recent investigations into the role of prostaglandins have led to new concepts about the regulation of smooth muscle tone in the fetal DA and the possible mechanisms for closure after birth.

In both isolated preparations and tissue homogenates, the DA has been shown to have the fatty acid cyclooxygenase necessary to synthesize various prostaglandins in different concentrations (19, 56–58, 75). As in other major arteries, the dominant prostaglandin produced by the wall of the DA is prostacyclin (PGI_2), but PGE_2 is also produced (19, 56–58, 75). Both PGI_2 and PGE_2 relax the DA smooth muscle, but PGE_2 is considerably more potent on an equimolar basis (17, 20). These findings, coupled with the demonstration that pharmacologic inhibition of prostaglandin synthesis in fetal animals produces in vitro and in vivo constriction of the DA (22, 36, 64), indicate that patency of the fetal DA is not a passive state but rather a balance between constriction and relaxation with dilation sustained at least in part by locally produced prostaglandins. In addition, as described above, circulating plasma PGE concentrations are elevated in the fetus and, because the DA is far more sensitive to PGE than any other prostaglandin or prostaglandin metabolite, it is likely that the effects of locally produced agents are supplemented by the circulating PGE. The recent demonstration that the DA requires an oxygen tension greater than that present in the fetus in utero to produce effective amounts of PGE_2 (18) supports the importance of circulating PGE_2 in maintaining the fetal DA in a relaxed state.

After birth, the concentration of circulating plasma PGE falls dramatically as described above. This withdrawal of an active relaxant substance would allow the actions of vasoconstricting agents such as oxygen to act relatively unopposed, and active ductus arteriosus constriction would occur. The intricate interrelationships of oxygen and prostaglandins in postnatal closure of the DA are still not completely understood.

Literature Cited

1. Abuid, J., Stinson, D. A., Larsen, P. R. 1973. Serum triiodothyronine and thyroxine in the neonate and the acute increases in these hormones following delivery. *J. Clin. Invest.* 52:1195–99
2. Altura, B. M., Altura, B. T. 1977. Vascular smooth muscle and neurohypophyseal hormones. *Fed. Proc.* 36:1853–59
3. Anggard, E., Larsson, C. 1971. The sequence of the early steps in the metabolism of prostaglandin E_1. *Eur. J. Pharmacol.* 14:66–70
4. Aperia, A., Broberger, O., Herin, P. 1974. Maturational changes in glomerular perfusion rate and glomerular filtration rate in lambs. *Pediatr. Res.* 8:753–65
5. Aperia, A., Broberger, O., Herin, P., Joselsson, I. 1977. Renal hemodynamics in the perinatal period. A study in lambs. *Acta Physiol. Scand.* 99:261–69
6. Aschinberg, L. C., Goldsmith, D. I., Olbing, H., Spitzer, A., Edelmann, C. M. Jr., Blaufox, M. D. 1975. Neonatal changes in renal blood flow distribution in puppies. *Am. J. Physiol.* 228:1453–61
7. Barker, J. N. 1966. Fetal and neonatal cerebral blood flow. *Am. J. Physiol.* 210:897–902
8. Behrman, R. E., Lees, M. H. 1971. Organ blood flows of the fetal, newborn, and adult rhesus monkey. *Biol. Neonate* 18:330–40
9. Beitins, I. Z., Bayard, F., Levitsky, L., Ances, I. G., Kowarski, A., Migeon, C. J. 1972. Plasma aldosterone concentration at delivery and during the newborn period. *J. Clin. Invest.* 51:386–94
10. Bibby, J. G., Brunt, J. D., Hodgson, H., Mitchell, M. D., Anderson, A. B. M., Turnbull, A. C. 1979. Prostaglandins in umbilical plasma at elective caesarean section. *Br. J. Obstet. Gynaecol.* 86:282–84
11. Broughton-Pipkin, F., Kirkpatrick, S. M. L., Lumbers, E. R., Mott, J. C. 1974. Renin and angiotensin-like levels in foetal, new-born and adult sheep. *J. Physiol. London* 241:575–88
12. Broughton-Pipkin, F., Lumbers, E. R., Mott, J. C. 1974. Factors influencing plasma renin and angiotensin II in the conscious pregnant ewe and its foetus. *J. Physiol. London* 243:619–36
13. Broughton-Pipkin, F., Smales, O. R. C. 1975. Blood pressure and angiotensin II in the newborn. *Arch. Dis. Child.* 50:330
14. Broughton-Pipkin, F., Symonds, E. M. 1977. Factors affecting angiotensin II concentrations in the human infants at birth. *Clin. Sci. Mol. Med.* 52:449–56
15. Challis, J. R. G., Hart, I., Louis, T. M., Mitchell, M. D., Jenkin, G., Robinson, J. S., Thorburn, G. D. 1978. Prostaglandins in the sheep fetus: Implications for fetal function. In *Advances in Prostaglandin and Thromboxane Research*, ed. F. Coceani, P. M. Olley, 4:115–32. NY: Raven Press. 412 pp.
16. Challis, J. R. G., Osathanondh, R., Ryan, K. J., Tulchinsky, D. 1974. Maternal and fetal plasma prostaglandin levels at vaginal delivery and caesarean section. *Prostaglandins* 6:281–88
17. Clyman, R. I. 1980. Ontogeny of the ductus arteriosus response to prostaglandins and inhibitors of their synthesis. *Sem. Perinatol.* 4:115–24
18. Clyman, R. I., Mauray, F., Demers, L. M., Rudolph, A. M., Roman, C. 1980. Does oxygen regulate prostaglandin-induced relaxation in the lamb ductus arteriosus? *Prostaglandins* 19:489–98
19. Clyman, R. I., Mauray, F., Koerper, M. A., Wiemer, F., Heymann, M. A., Rudolph, A. M. 1978. Formation of prostacyclin (PGI_2) by the ductus arteriosus of fetal lambs at different stages of gestation. *Prostaglandins* 16:633–42
20. Clyman, R. I., Wong, L. B., Heymann, M. A., Rudolph, A. M. 1978. Responsiveness of the lamb ductus arteriosus to

prostaglandins and their metabolites. *Prostaglandins* 15:325–31

21. Coceani, F., Olley, P. M. 1980. Role of prostaglandins, prostacyclin, and thromboxanes in the control of prenatal patency and postnatal closure of the ductus arteriosus. *Sem. Perinatol.* 4: 109–13

22. Coceani, F., Olley, P. M., Bodach, E. 1975. Lamb ductus arteriosus: Effect of prostaglandin synthesis inhibitors on the muscle tone and the response to prostaglandin E_2. *Prostaglandins* 9: 299–308

23. Craft, I. L., Scrivener, R., Dewhurst, C. J. 1973. Prostaglandin $F_{2\text{-alpha}}$ levels in the maternal and fetal circulations in late pregnancy. *J. Obstet. Gynaecol. Brit. Commonwlth.* 80:616–18

24. Dillon, M. J., Gillin, M. A. E., Ryness, J. J., De Swiet, M. 1976. Plasma renin activity and aldosterone concentration in the human newborn. *Arch. Dis. Child.* 51:537–40

25. Dillon, M. J., Rajani, K. B., Shah, V., Ryness, J. M., Milner, R. D. G. 1978. Renin and aldosterone response in human newborns to acute change in blood volume. *Arch. Dis. Child.* 53:461–67

26. Drukker, A., Goldsmith, D. I., Spitzer, A., Edelmann, C. M. Jr., Blaufox, M. D. 1980. The renin angiotensin system in newborn dogs: Developmental patterns and response to acute saline loading. *Pediatr. Res.* 14:304–7

27. Drummond, W. H., Rudolph, A. M., Keil, L. C., Gluckman, P. D., Macdonald, A. A., Heymann, M. A. 1980. Arginine vasopressin and prolactin after hemorrhage in the fetal lamb. *Am. J. Physiol.* 238:E214–19

28. Eliot, R. J., Lam, R., Leake, R. D., Hobel, C. J., Fisher, D. A. 1980. Plasma catecholamine concentrations in infants at birth and during the first 48 hours of life. *J. Pediatr.* 96:311–15

29. Erenberg, A., Phelps, D. L., Lam, R., Fisher, D. A. 1974. Total and free thyroid hormone concentrations in the neonatal period. *Pediatrics* 53:211–16

30. Fisher, D. A., Odell, W. D. 1969. Acute release of thyrotropin in the newborn. *J. Clin. Invest.* 48:1670–77

31. Fisher, D. J., Heymann, M. A., Rudolph, A. M. 1980. Myocardial oxygen and carbohydrate consumption in fetal lambs in utero and in adult sheep. *Am. J. Physiol.* 238:H399–405

32. Greenberg, A. J., McNamara, H., McCrory, W. W. 1967. Renal tubular response to aldosterone in normal infants and children with adrenal disorders. *J. Clin. Endocrinol. Metab.* 27: 1197–1202

33. Gruskin, A. B., Edelmann, C. M. Jr., Yuan, S. 1970. Maturational changes in renal blood flow in piglets. *Pediatr. Res.* 4:7–13

34. Heymann, M. A., Creasy, R. K., Rudolph, A. M. 1973. Quantitation of blood flow patterns in the foetal lamb in utero. In *Foetal and Neonatal Physiology: Proceedings of the Sir Joseph Barcroft Centenary Symposium,* ed. K. S. Comline, K. W. Cross, G. S. Dawes, P. W. Nathanielsz, 129–35. Cambridge: Cambridge Univ. Press. 641 pp.

35. Heymann, M. A., Rudolph, A. M. 1975. Control of the ductus arteriosus. *Physiol. Rev.* 55:62–78

36. Heymann, M. A., Rudolph, A. M. 1976. Effects of acetylsalicylic acid on the ductus arteriosus and circulation in fetal lambs in utero. *Circ. Res.* 38: 418–22

37. Iwamoto, H. S., Rudolph, A. M., Keil, L. C., Heymann, M. A. 1979. Hemodynamic responses of the sheep fetus to vasopressin infusion. *Circ. Res.* 44: 430–36

38. Jose, P. A., Logan, A. G., Slotkoff, L. M., Lilienfield, L. S., Calcagno, P. L., Eisner, G. M. 1971. Intrarenal blood flow distribution in canine puppies. *Pediatr. Res.* 5:335–44

39. Jose, P. A., Slotkoff, L. M., Lilienfield, L. S., Calcagno, P. L., Eisner, G. M. 1974. Sensitivity of neonatal renal vasculature to epinephrine. *Am. J. Physiol.* 226:796–99

40. Jose, P. A., Slotkoff, L. M., Montgomery, S., Calcagno, P. L., Eisner, G. M. 1975. Autoregulation of renal blood flow in puppy. *Am. J. Physiol.* 229:983–88

41. Kleinman, L. I. 1975. Renal sodium reabsorption during saline loading and distal blockade in newborn dogs. *Am. J. Physiol.* 228:1403–8

42. Klopfenstein, H. S., Rudolph, A. M. 1978. Postnatal changes in the circulation and responses to volume loading in sheep. *Circ. Res.* 42:839–45

43. Kotchen, T. A., Strickland, A. L., Rice, M. S., Walters, D. R. 1972. A study of the renin-angiotensin system in newborn infants. *J. Pediatr.* 80:938–46

44. Leake, R. D., Weitzman, R. E., Effros, R. M., Siegel, S. R., Fisher, D. A. 1979. Maternal fetal osmolar homeostasis: Fetal posterior pituitary autonomy. *Pediatr. Res.* 13:841–44

45. Leake, R. D., Weitzman, R. E., Weinberg, J. A., Fisher, D. A. 1979. Control

of vasopressin secretion in the newborn lamb. *Pediatr. Res.* 13:257–60

46. Lister, G., Walter, T. K., Versmold, H. T., Dallman, P. R., Rudolph, A. M. 1979. Oxygen delivery in lambs: Cardiovascular and hematologic development. *Am. J. Physiol.* 237:H668–75

47. Lucas, W., Kirschbaum, T., Assali, N. S. 1966. Cephalic circulation and oxygen consumption before and after birth. *Am. J. Physiol.* 210:287–92

48. Lumbers, E. R., Reid, G. C. 1977. Effects of vaginal delivery and caesarean section on plasma renin activity and angiotensin II levels in human umbilical cord blood. *Biol. Neonate* 31:127–34

49. Malik, K. U., McGiff, J. C. 1975. Modulation by prostaglandins of adrenergic transmission in the isolated perfused rabbit and rat kidney. *Circ. Res.* 36:599–609

50. McGiff, J. C., Crowshaw, K., Terragno, N. A., Terragno, A. 1972. Differential effect of noradrenaline and renal nerve stimulation on vascular resistance in the dog kidney and the release of a prostaglandin E-like substance. *Clin. Sci.* 42:223–33

51. Mitchell, M. D., Brunt, J., Bibby, J., Flint, A. P. F., Anderson, A. B. M., Turnbull, A. C. 1978. Prostaglandins in the human umbilical circulation at birth. *Brit. J. Obstet. Gynaecol.* 85:114–18

52. Mitchell, M. D., Flint, A. P. F. 1978. Prostaglandin production by intrauterine tissues from periparturient sheep. Use of a superfusion technique. *J. Endocrinol.* 76:111–21

53. Naeye, R. L. 1966. Development of systemic and pulmonary arteries from birth to early childhood. *Biol. Neonate* 10:8–16

54. Olbing, H., Blaufox, M. D., Aschinberg, L. C., Silkalns, G. I., Bernstein, J., Spitzer, A., Edelmann, C. M. Jr. 1973. Postnatal changes in renal glomerular blood flow distribution in puppies. *J. Clin. Invest.* 52:2885–95

55. Pace-Asciak, C. R. 1978. Prostaglandin biosynthesis and catabolism in several organs of developing fetal and neonatal animals. See Ref. 15, pp. 45–59

56. Pace-Asciak, C. R., Rangaraj, G. 1977. The 6-ketoprostaglandin $F_{1-alpha}$ pathway in the lamb ductus arteriosus. *Biochim. Biophys. Acta* 486:583–85

57. Pace-Asciak, C. R., Rangaraj, G. 1978. Prostaglandin biosynthesis and catabolism in the lamb ductus arteriosus, aorta,

and pulmonary artery. *Biochim. Biophys. Acta* 529:13–20

58. Powell, W. S., Solomon, S. 1978. Biosynthesis of prostaglandins and thromboxanes in fetal tissues. See Ref. 15, pp. 61–74

59. Purves, M. J., James, I. M. 1969. Observations on the control of cerebral blood flow in the sheep fetus and newborn lamb. *Circ. Res.* 25:651–67

60. Raux-Eurin, M. C., Pham-Huu-Trung, M. T., Marrec, D., Girard, F. 1977. Plasma aldosterone concentrations during the neonatal period. *Pediatr. Res.* 11:182–85

61. Rudolph, A. M., Heymann, M. A. 1970. Circulatory changes during growth in the fetal lamb. *Circ. Res.* 26:289–99

62. Rurak, D. W. 1978. Plasma vasopressin levels during hypoxaemia and the cardiovascular effects of exogenous vasopressin in foetal and adult sheep. *J. Physiol. London* 277:341–57

63. Rurak, D. W. 1979. Plasma vasopressin levels during haemorrhage in mature and immature fetal sheep. *J. Develop. Physiol.* 1:91–101

64. Sharpe, G. L., Thalme, B., Larsson, S. K. 1974. Studies on closure of the ductus arteriosus. XI. Ductal closure in utero by a prostaglandin synthetase inhibitor. *Prostaglandins* 8:363–68

65. Shepherd, A. P., Granger, J. H., Smith, E. E., Guyton, A. C. 1973. Local control of tissue oxygen delivery and its contribution to the regulation of cardiac output. *Am. J. Physiol.* 225:747–55

66. Siegler, R. L., Walker, M. B., Crouch, R. H., Christenson, P., Jubiz, W. 1977. Plasma prostaglandin E concentrations from birth through childhood. *J. Pediatr.* 91:734–37

67. Spitzer, A., Edelmann, C. M. Jr. 1971. Maturational changes in pressure gradients for glomerular filtration. *Am. J. Physiol.* 221:1431–35

68. Sulyok, E., Nemeth, M., Tenyi, I., Csaba, I. F., Gyory, E., Ertl, T., Varga, F. 1979. Postnatal development of renin-angiotensin-aldosterone system (RAAS) in relation to electrolyte balance in premature infants. *Pediatr. Res.* 13:817–20

69. Sulyok, E., Nemeth, M., Tenyi, I., Csaba, I. F., Thurzo, V., Hadnagy, J. 1979. The possible role of prostaglandins in the hyperfunction of the renin-angiotensin-aldosterone system in the newborn. *Br. J. Obstet. Gynaecol.* 86:205–9

70. Sulyok, E., Nemeth, M., Tenyi, I., Csaba, I. F., Varga, F., Gyory, E., Thurzo, V. 1979. Relationship between maturity, electrolyte balance, and the function of the renin-angiotensin-aldosterone system in newborn infants. *Biol. Neonate* 35:60–65

71. Sulyok, E., Varga, F., Nemeth, M., Tenyi, I., Csaba, I. F., Ertl, T., Gyory, E. 1980. Furosemide-induced alterations in the electrolyte status, the function of renin-angiotensin-aldosterone system, and the urinary excretion of prostaglandins in newborn infants. *Pediatr. Res.* 14:765–68

72. Terragno, N. A., McGiff, J. C., Smigel, M. 1978. Patterns of prostaglandin: Production in the bovine fetal and maternal vasculature. *Prostaglandins* 16:847–54

73. Terragno, N. A., Terragno, A. 1979. Prostaglandin metabolism in the fetal and maternal vasculature. *Fed. Proc.* 38:75–77

74. Terragno, N. A., Terragno, A., McGiff, J. C. 1980. Role of prostaglandins in blood vessels. *Sem. Perinatol.* 4:85–90

75. Terragno, N. A., Terragno, A., McGiff, J. C., Rodriguez, D. J. 1977. Synthesis of prostaglandins by the ductus arteriosus of the bovine fetus. *Prostaglandins* 14:721–27

76. Thorburn, G. D. 1974. The role of the thyroid gland and the kidneys in fetal growth. *Ciba. Found. Symp. 27:* 185–200

77. van Duyne, C. M., Parker, H. R., Havel, R. J., Holm, L. W. 1960. Free fatty acid metabolism in fetal and newborn sheep. *Am. J. Physiol.* 199:987–90

78. Vaughn, D., Kirschbaum, T. H., Bersentes, T., Assali, N. S. 1967. Effects of autonomic blockade on pulmonary and systemic circulation before and after birth. *Am. J. Physiol.* 212:436–43

79. Woods, J. R. Jr., Dandavino, A., Murayama, K., Brinkman, C. R. III, Assali, N. S. 1977. Autonomic control of cardiovascular functions during neonatal development and in adult sheep. *Circ. Res.* 40:401–7

80. Yabek, S. M., Avner, B. P. 1979. Effects of prostaglandin E_1 and indomethacin on fetal and neonatal lamb mesenteric artery responses to norepinephrine. *Prostaglandins* 17:227–33

81. Yabek, S. M., Avner, B. P. 1980. Effects of prostacyclin (PGI_2) and indomethacin on neonatal lamb mesenteric and renal artery responses to electrical stimulation and norepinephrine. *Prostaglandins* 19:23–30

Ann. Rev. Physiol. 1981. 43:385–95

LOCAL FACTORS REGULATING CARDIAC AND SKELETAL MUSCLE BLOOD FLOW

♦1317

R. A. Olsson

Department of Internal Medicine, University of South Florida, Tampa, Florida 33612

INTRODUCTION

Peripheral blood flow regulation was reviewed comprehensively in this series only three years ago (79). Since then, important physiological and biochemical advances have increased our understanding of the fundamental mechanisms contributing to local flow regulation in cardiac and skeletal muscle. To present a coherent picture of the status of the various hypotheses advanced to explain flow regulation and to indicate what seem to be the directions of current research, this review refers not only to work cited in the previous review but also to preliminary reports just now appearing (April 1980). Several reviews and symposium proceedings complement the perspective developed here (3, 6, 7, 23, 28, 61, 72).

GENERAL CHARACTERISTICS OF MUSCLE VASCULAR BEDS

Both cardiac and skeletal muscle have relatively low basal flow rates and a large vasodilatory reserve to meet increases in workload. However, there are significant differences in the way these two tissues adjust to changes in work. The response of skeletal muscle involves reflex and metabolic vasodilation, changes in oxygen extraction, and an increase in the total number of perfused capillaries (recruitment). Further, anaerobic glycolysis effectively supports muscular energy needs. In contrast, cardiac muscle adjusts to changing workloads primarily by changing coronary flow. Basal coro-

385

0066-4278/81/0315-0385$01.00

nary resistance is high relative to the rate of oxygen usage, so that oxygen extraction is also high; increases in cardiac effort are met primarily by vasodilation. The anaerobic capacity of cardiac muscle can supply only a minor fraction of energy requirements, so oxygen consumption is closely related to cardiac effort. This high correlation of coronary vascular resistance with oxygen consumption rate underlies the various metabolic hypotheses advanced to explain myocardial blood flow regulation. Capillary recruitment and neural reflexes seem quantitatively less important in the coronary circulation than in skeletal muscle. Because of the heart's constant activity and its hemispherical geometry, which gives rise to anisotropic wall stresses, physical factors are prominent determinants of local flow regulation in cardiac muscle.

METABOLIC VASOREGULATION

Figure 1 is a generalized description of a control system for the metabolic regulation of muscle blood flow. The essential features of this system are an error signal, muscular effort, that modulates the release of the vasoregulatory metabolite. This metabolite interacts with a specific vascular receptor to vary local flow and, thereby, substrate delivery. This generalization views muscle activity rather than local Po_2 as the error signal, suggesting that cellular events rather than oxygen consumption (e.g. membrane depolarization) might directly effect metabolite production. For the purpose of this review, this schema provides useful criteria for judging the candidacy of the several metabolites currently implicated in vasoregulation: (*a*) The mechanism producing the metabolite must be identified, (*b*) how its production is coupled to muscle metabolism must be known, (*c*) the mechanism(s) dissipating the vasoregulatory metabolite must be identified, (*d*) the vascular smooth muscle target, be it a receptor in the pharmacological sense or some other cell component, must be known, (*e*) the vasoactivity of the metabolite must be commensurate with its physiological concentration in the vicinity of the resistance vessels, and (*f*) the process causing relaxation

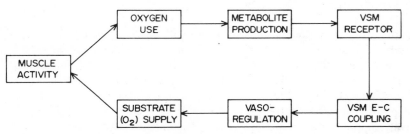

Figure 1   Elements in the system for local metabolic control of muscle blood flow.

of the resistance vessels must be identified. Although the support for some metabolites is stronger than for others, none as yet meets all the criteria.

Oxygen

The observation that hypoxia causes vasodilation underlies the hypothesis that oxygen directly controls vasomotion by limiting aerobic ATP production in vascular smooth muscle. This hypothesis envisions cytochrome aa_3 as the vascular "oxygen receptor" and the effect of lowered ATP as being exerted either on contractile protein function directly or indirectly by affecting excitation-contraction coupling at the level of membrane Ca^{2+} transport. Several lines of evidence collectively weaken this hypothesis. If oxygen lack acts directly on the resistance vessels, one would expect these myocytes to be more oxygen-sensitive than the striated muscle cells they serve. An oxygen consumption rate higher than that of the working muscle cells is one means of conferring this differential sensitivity. Available data from vessels of other organs suggest a basal oxygen usage of 0.5–0.6 nmole $O_2 \cdot g^{-1}$ dry weight $\cdot$ min^{-1} and an increase of four- to five-fold with the development of maximum isometric tension (35, 65). However, under near-basal conditions of cardiac work, myocardial oxygen consumption is equivalent to at least 15 nmole $O_2 \cdot g^{-1}$ dry weight $\cdot$ min^{-1}. This analysis predicts that the myocardium would already be appreciably hypoxic before Po_2 would fall sufficiently to alter coronary resistance. While respiratory chain function will not be affected until mitochondrial Po_2 reaches levels of ~0.05 mm Hg (17), the experimental evidence (68) that levels this low may exist in an "anoxic core" depend on a number of assumptions about oxygen diffusion and consumption that make this conclusion somewhat conditional. Further, the rate of glycolytic ATP production is high in vascular muscle, even under aerobic conditions (66), so that oxidative phosphorylation is not the rate-limiting step in ATP synthesis. Consistent with this, vascular strips maintain ATP levels (66) and active tension well at low Po_2 and do not begin to relax until Po_2 is ≤ 5mm Hg (26). Finally, specific inhibition of cytochrome aa_3 by cyanide can completely inhibit oxygen uptake but has less effect on active tension than lowering Po_2 (18, 19). This experiment has been interpreted as evidence for an oxygen receptor other than cytochrome aa_3, but this receptor has not been identified. Observations in intact animals also argue against a primary vasoregulatory role for local Po_2 and models of control systems that aim at maintaining a constant Po_2. A sustained fall in coronary venous Po_2 and O_2 content is well tolerated in responses such as exercise (40, 81), which certainly does not support a "Po_2-stat" model and shows that adjustments in oxygen extraction, while much more limited than those of skeletal muscle, do contribute to the heart's response to augmented workloads.

Carbon Dioxide

CO_2 is particularly attractive as a vasoregulator in "obligate aerobic" organs such as the heart, because CO_2 production is directly coupled to oxygen consumption and ATP production over the narrow range specified by the respiratory quotient. Case (14, 15) has systematically evaluated the coronary effects of Pco_2. Assuming that coronary venous Pco_2 is a valid index of tissue Pco_2 (16), he found that coronary resistance varies inversely with Pco_2, both in the direction of vasoconstriction and vasodilation. Similar effects of Pco_2 on coronary flow have been reported by others (69). These experiments were not designed to discriminate between the effects of Pco_2 and of pH. Evidence from experiments employing buffers to control pH are needed to better define the role of Pco_2. At this time the mechanism by which CO_2 (or H^+) initiates coronary vascular relaxation is unknown. Presumably the vasodilatory signal is dissipated by the washout of CO_2 into the coronary venous effluent.

Potassium

K^+ is released from muscle cells during cell membrane depolarization and reenters the cell during the recovery process. The possibility that K^+ is a vasoregulatory metabolite rests on this intimate relationship between muscular contraction and K^+ release. Following step increases in heart rate, the rise in interstitial $[K^+]$, estimated from coronary venous $[K^+]$ by correcting for transit effects, precedes the change in coronary vascular resistance (55). While this temporal relationship is consistent with a vasoregulatory effect, K^+ release often disappears even though vasodilation persists. Furthermore, intracoronary K^+ injections calculated to raise interstitial $[K^+]$ to the levels obtained during pacing caused less vasodilation, suggesting the participation of other vasodilatory metabolites. Other observations confirm that the coronary relaxing effects of K^+ are transitory in cardiac (13) and skeletal muscle (79), suggesting that K^+ may only contribute to the early phase of active hyperemia.

K^+ appears to play a similar contributory role in the hyperemic response to prolonged tetanus in skeletal muscle. Here, too, K^+ release precedes resistance changes, its vasodilatory effect is transitory, and changes in interstitial $[K^+]$ fail to account for the size of the resistance change (79). K^+ depletion by means of chronic deoxycorticosterone administration abolishes K^+ release and greatly attenuates the hyperemic responses of skeletal muscle to electrical stimulation (42). However, oxygen usage during tetanus is also greatly reduced, yet the ratio of the change in vascular resistance to that of oxygen usage is similar to that of normal muscles (31). Thus, one cannot decide from these depletion experiments whether K^+ release in normal muscles complements or is coincidental to vasodilation caused by

other metabolites. Muscle K^+ depletion produced by dietary K^+ deprivation alone (not by steroid administration) has no perceptible effect on the
hemodynamic responses to exercise in conscious dogs (49).

Ouabain reduces the vasodilatory effect of intracoronary K^+ injections
without altering oxygen usage, myocardial systolic compression, or autonomic neurotransmitter release (54). This evidence suggests that the electrogenic Na^+,K^+ transport system is the vascular K^+ receptor. Washout
into venous blood probably combines with net cellular uptake in regulating
interstitial $[K^+]$.

Adenosine

The current consensus holds that in heart muscle adenosine is produced by
the hydrolysis of 5'-AMP by 5'-nucleotidase, an ectoenzyme located in the
sarcolemma (73). Since the catalytic site of this enzyme is located on the
outer surface of the cell and its substrate is in the cell's interior, adenosine
production is vectorial, the result of movement of substrate across the
membrane by a hypothetical carrier, followed by hydrolysis (25). Total
5'-nucleotidase activity greatly exceeds adenosine production rates observed
in the beating heart, but the factors controlling activity have not been
identified (61). Two processes appear to regulate the concentration of
adenosine in the interstitial space: (*a*) carrier-mediated uptake by cardiocytes (59) and incorporation into the cardiac nucleotide pool (47), and
(*b*) degradation to inosine and hypoxanthine, which are then removed in
the coronary venous effluent (85). Adenosine appears to initiate coronary
relaxation via a specific receptor on the surface of the coronary myocyte (60,
76), but the steps subsequent to receptor occupancy are uncertain. Evidence
that coronary relaxation involves cyclic AMP (45, 82) suggests that the
adenosine receptor may be identical to the adenylate cyclase "R" receptor
(12, 48). Both receptors are located on the cell surface, have similar chemical specificity (48, 64), and activation is specifically inhibited by methylxanthines (38, 48). Because the adenosine kinase and adenosine deaminase
activities of heart muscle are high, the adenosine pool has been considered
essentially extracellular (61, 72). The earliest estimates of cardiac adenosine
content and the coronary vasoactivity of adenosine (58, 71) were consistent
with this model. However, newer work shows that the true values are 1–2
nmole adenosine $\cdot$ g^{-1} under "semibasal" conditions (63, 75). If all this
adenosine were distributed only in the interstitial space, the coronary circulation would be maximally dilated. To resolve this inconsistency Schrader
et al (75) revived the notion of an intracellular adenosine compartment (44)
and by radiolabelling the cardiac adenine nucleotide pool showed that the
cardiac adenosine pool consists of at least two compartments. Subsequent
work demonstrated the existence of "soluble" proteins in cardiac muscle

extracts that exhibit specific, high affinity adenosine binding (63). The likelihood of compartmentation complicates the interpretation of experiments relating total muscle adenosine content to coronary resistance.

Adenosine appears to participate in the regulation of coronary flow during myocardial reactive hyperemia (43, 62, 71). That methylxanthines block the coronary vasodilatory effect of adenosine but only partially block the reactive hyperemia response (38) challenges the adenosine hypothesis. It now appears that methylxanthine-insensitive factors such as myogenic relaxation (24, 77) and acidosis (51) contribute to the reactive hyperemia response normally, and it is possible that they account for most of the flow response under the influence of methylxanthines. The resolution of this challenge seems to lie in recognizing that adenosine is but one of several determinants of vascular resistance during reactive hyperemia.

The type of evidence supporting adenosine's vasoregulatory role in skeletal muscle is similar to that of heart. This muscle contains 5'-nucleotidase (73) but its distribution is different from that in heart. The greatest activity is found in the walls of blood vessels; activity in muscle cells decreases with distance from blood vessels. Further, substantial activity is found inside the myocytes, a peculiar distribution for an enzyme commonly used as a plasma membrane marker (20). Resting skeletal muscle contains adenosine, and the amount increases when the muscle is stimulated electrically while being perfused at a constant rate (5, 9, 10). Subsequent work demonstrates that adenosine levels do not change if flow is not restricted (67), so that ischemia appears to be an important factor in the adenosine release observed in constant-flow experiments.

Prostaglandins

These vasoactive substances are produced by the oxidation and cyclization of arachidonic acid, a highly unsaturated essential fatty acid that is a constituent of plasma membrance phospholipids. Arachidonic acid is liberated by phospholipase A_2, a plasma membrane enzyme that has an absolute requirement for Ca^{2+} (8). Prostaglandin synthesis is initiated by a cyclooxygenase that is irreversibly inactivated by aspirin (70) and reversibly inhibited by a variety of drugs including anti-inflammatory agents such as indomethacin (80). The prostaglandin biosynthetic pathway branches, giving rise to PGI_2, a powerful vasodilator and platelet aggregation inhibitor, or thromboxane A_2 (TXA_2), a powerful promotor of vasoconstriction and platelet aggregation. An unidentified switching mechanism may regulate the balance between PGI_2 and TXA_2 synthesis. The cardiovascular effects of the prostaglandins are species-specific (57), so that results cannot always be generalized. Bearing this caveat in mind support for a vasoregulatory role for prostaglandins comes first from observations that intracoronary administration of arachidonic acid causes indomethacin-sensitive coronary vasodilation. Ischemia stimulates the release of prostaglandins from heart muscle but the time course of release is not consistent with a vasoregulatory role (23). Isolated small ($\leq 100 \mu m$) coronary vessels have the capacity to synthesize PGI_2 and also TXA_2 (27), suggesting that prostaglandins exert their effects at the level of the microcirculation. Although vascular prostaglandin receptors have not been identified, the high potency of these substances strongly implies that such receptors exist, as in other cells (52). Recent observations indicate that the effects of PGI_2 may be mediated by cyclic AMP (1, 53). Other observations show that whereas the endothelial cells can convert arachidonic acid to either PGI_2 or TXA_2, vascular smooth muscle cells and cardiocytes synthesize only small amounts of PGI_2 (27, 36, 50). If the same pattern of cellular specificity applies to the blood vessels of cardiac and skeletal muscle, it is difficult to envision how prostaglandin synthesis in vascular endothelium would be coupled to striated muscle metabolism, for the signal initiating prostaglandin synthesis would have to penetrate through the entire vascular wall to reach the endothelium.

VASOREGULATION BY PHYSICAL FACTORS

The throttling effect of cardiac systole (74) creates a gradient of extravascular resistance that is highest in the subendocardium and diminshes toward the epicardium (2, 39, 41). This consensus stands mainly on the fact that it explains transmural coronary flow distribution at reduced levels of coronary perfusion pressure, for the insertion of pressure-sensing devices into myocardium alters local tissue pressure (11). That flow to the subendocardium is greater than to the superficial layers suggests a gradient of vascularity favoring the subendocardium (56) and/or a gradient of vascular tone that decreases from epicardium to endocardium (46). Studies of regional venous oxygen saturation employing reflectance spectrometry coupled with radiomicrosphere estimates of regional flow rate show directly that oxygen consumption rate is higher in the subendocardium (33, 83, 84). This supports the notion of a metabolically determined gradient of intrinsic vascular resistance, without diminishing the possible contribution of vascularity to the flow gradient. Systolic flow is distributed primarily to the subepicardium as a result of systolic wall stress (21, 32), so the transmural gradient of intrinsic vascular resistance is probably even steeper than the average endocardial/epicardial flow ratio indicates.

The coronary circulation seems to behave as a vascular waterfall; that is, coronary resistance is determined by "tissue" rather than venous pressure. Evidence favoring this model comes from the analysis of coronary pressure vs flow plots obtained in dogs whose coronary circulation was maximally dilated by means of adenosine (22) and from observations in conscious dogs that during prolonged diastole, coronary flow ceases at aortic pressures of about 40mm Hg (4). However, an important test of a waterfall mechanism, the demonstration that coronary resistance is independent of venous pressures below the "tissue" pressure, has apparently not been met. Further, the anatomical and/or physical factors constituting the waterfall resistance have not been identified.

MYOGENIC AND NEURAL FACTORS

Smooth muscle cells are thought to exhibit mechanoreceptor function that alters pacemaker activity and, consequently, active tone (28). It is now clear that in addition to this steady-state contribution to basal tone, the rate of muscle stretching directly determines the rate and magnitude of tension development (29, 30, 37, 78), a characteristic that may prove useful in experimentally separating myogenic from other effects in complex responses such as reactive hyperemia. The cellular mechanisms responsible for myogenic tone and particularly the identity of the "mechanoreceptor" are uncertain.

Recent work has identified an important adrenergic contribution to basal coronary tone. Regional "chemical sympathectomy" in conscious dogs by means of intracoronary infusions of 6-hydroxydopamine lead to a selective increase in flow to the affected area (34). The destruction of nerve terminals abolished the vasodilatory effects of β-adrenergic stimulation, so that the flow increase of 60% over unaffected regions is evidence for a significant α-adrenergic contribution to the high basal resistance characteristic of the coronary circulation.

Literature Cited

1. Alexander, R. W., Neer, E. J., Dugan, M. E., Atkinson, W. E., Gimbrone, M. A. Jr. 1980. Prostacyclin stimulation of adenylate cyclase in cultured vascular smooth muscle. *Fed. Proc.* 39:742
2. Armour, J. A., Randall, W. C. 1971. Canine left ventricular intramyocardial pressures. *Am. J. Physiol.* 220:1833–39
3. Baer, H. P., Drummond, G. I., eds. 1979. *Physiological and Regulatory Functions of Adenosine and Adenine Nucleotides.* NY: Raven Press. 438 pp.
4. Bellamy, R. F. 1978. Diastolic coronary artery pressure-flow relations in the dog. *Circ. Res.* 43:92–101
5. Belloni, F. L., Phair, R. D., Sparks, H. V. 1979. The role of adenosine in prolonged vasodilation following flow-restricted exercise in canine skeletal muscle. *Circ. Res.* 44:759–66
6. Belloni, F. L. 1979. Review: The Local control of coronary blood flow. *Cardiovasc. Res.* 13:63–85
7. Bevan, J. A., Godfraind, T., Maxwell, R. A., Vanhoutte, P. M., eds. 1980. *Vascular Neuroeffector Mechanisms.* NY: Raven Press. 401 pp.
8. Billah, M., Lapetina, E. G., Cuatrecasas, P. 1980. A platelet phospholipase A_2 releases arachidonate and generates lysoderivatives from endogenous phospholipids. *Fed. Proc.* 39:1039
9. Bockman, E. L., Berne, R. M., Rubio, R. 1975. Release of adenosine and lack of release of ATP from contracting skeletal muscle *Pflügers Arch.* 355:229–41

10. Bockman, E. L., Berne, R. M., Rubio, R. 1976. Adenosine and active hyperemia in skeletal muscle. *Am. J. Physiol.* 230:1531–37

11. Brandi, G., McGregor, M. 1969. Intramural pressure in the left ventricle of the dog. *Cardiovasc. Res.* 3:472–75

12. Braun, S., Levitzki, A. 1979. Adenosine receptor permanently coupled to turkey erythrocyte adenylate cyclase. *Biochemistry* 18:2134–38

13. Bunger, R., Haddy, F. J., Querengässer, A., Gerlach, E. 1976. Studies on potassium induced coronary dilation in the isolated guinea pig heart. *Pflügers Arch.* 363:27–31

14. Case, R. B., Greenberg, H. 1976. The response of canine coronary vascular resistance to local alterations in coronary arterial Pco_2. *Circ. Res.* 39:558–66

15. Case, R. B., Felix, A., Wachter, M., Kryakidis, G., Castellana, F. 1978. Relative effect of CO_2 on canine coronary vascular resistance. *Circ. Res.* 42:410–18

16. Case, R. B., Felix, A., Wachter, M. 1979. Measurement of myocardial Pco_2 with a microelectrode: Its relation to coronary sinus Pco_2. *Am. J. Physiol.* 236 (*Heart Circ. Physiol.* 5):H29–H34

17. Chance, B., Oshino, N., Sugano, T., Mayevsky, A. 1973. Basic principles of tissue oxygen determination from mitochondrial signals. *Adv. Exp. Med. Biol.* 37A:277–92

18. Coburn, R. F. 1977. Oxygen tension sensors in vascular smooth muscle. *Adv. Exp. Biol. Med.* 78:101–15

19. Coburn, R. F., Grubb, B., Aronson, R. D. 1979. Effect of cyanide on oxygen tension-dependent mechanical tension in rabbit aorta. *Circ. Res.* 44:368–78

20. De Pierre, J. W., Karnovsky, M. L. 1973. Plasma membranes of mammalian cells: A review of methods for their characterization and isolation. *J. Cell. Biol.* 56:275–303

21. Downey, J. M., Kirk, E. S. 1974. Distribution of the coronary blood flow across the canine heart wall during systole. *Circ. Res.* 34:251–57

22. Downey, J. M., Kirk, E. S. 1975. Inhibition of coronary blood flow by a vascular waterfall mechanism. *Circ. Res.* 36:753–60

23. Dusting, G. J., Moncada, S., Vane, J. R. 1979. Prostaglandins, their intermediates and precursors: Cardiovascular actions and regulatory roles in normal and abnormal circulatory systems. *Progr. Cardiovasc. Dis.* 21:405–30

24. Eikens, E., Wilcken, D. E. L. 1974. Reactive hyperemia in the dog heart: Effects of temporarily restricting arterial inflow and of coronary occlusions lasting one and two cardiac cycles. *Circ. Res.* 35:702–12

25. Frick, G. P., Lowenstein, J. M. 1978. Vectorial production of adenosine by 5'-nucleotidase in the perfused rat heart. *J. Biol. Chem.* 253:1240–44

26. Gellai, M., Norton, J. M., Detar, R. 1973. Evidence for direct control of coronary vascular tone by oxygen. *Circ. Res.* 32:279–89

27. Gerritsen, M. E., Printz, M. P. 1979. Isolation of metabolically active coronary microvessels: Characterization of prostaglandin endoperoxide metabolizing enzymes. *Circulation* 60(Suppl II):II-80

28. Golenhofen, K. 1978. Übersichten: Die myogene Basis der glattmuskulären Motorik. *Klin. Wschr.* 56:211–24

29. Grände, P.-O., Mellander, S. 1978. Characteristics of static and dynamic regulatory mechanisms in myogenic microvascular control. *Acta. Physiol. Scand.* 102:231–45

30. Grände, P.-O., Borgström, P., Mellander, S. 1979. On the nature of basal vascular tone in cat skeletal muscle and its dependence on transmural pressure stimuli. *Acta Physiol. Scand.* 107:365–76

31. Hazeyama, Y., Sparks, H. V. 1979. Exercise hyperemia in potassium-depleted dogs. *Am. J. Physiol.* 236 (*Heart Circ. Physiol.* 5):H480–86

32. Hess, D. S., Bache, R. J. 1976. Transmural distribution of myocardial blood flow during systole in the awake dog. *Circ. Res.* 38:5–15

33. Holtz, J., Grunewald, W. A., Manz, R., von Restorff, W., Bassenge, E. 1977. Intracapillary hemoglobin oxygen saturation and oxygen consumption in different layers of the left ventricular myocardium. *Pflügers Arch.* 370:253–58

34. Holtz, J., Mayer, E., Bassenge, E. 1977. Demonstration of alpha-adrenergic coronary control in different layers of canine myocardium by regional myocardial sympathectomy. *Pflügers Arch.* 372:187–94

35. Howard, R. O., Richardson, D. W., Smith, M. H., Patterson, J. L. 1965. Oxygen consumption of arterioles and venules as studied in the Cartesian diver. *Circ. Res.* 16:187–96

36. Ingerman, C. M., Aharony, D., Silver, M. J., Smith, J. B., Nissenbaum, M., Sedar, A. W., Macarak, E. 1980. Pros-

taglandin I_2 and Thromboxane A_2 can be produced by endothelial cells in culture. *Fed. Proc.* 39:391

37. Johansson, S., Mellander, S. 1975. Static and dynamic components in the vascular myogenic response to passive changes in length as revealed by electrical and mechanical recordings from the rat portal vein. *Circ. Res.* 36:76–83

38. Juhran, W., Voss, E. M., Dietmann, K., Schaumann, W. 1971. Pharmacological effects on coronary reactive hyperemia in conscious dogs. *Naunyn-Schmiedebergs Arch. Pharmakol.* 269: 32–47

39. Kelley, D. T., Pitt, B. 1973. Regional changes in intramyocardial pressure following myocardial ischemia. *Adv. Exp. Biol. Med.* 39:115–19

40. Khouri, E. M., Gregg, D. E., Rayford, C. R. 1965. Effect of exercise on cardiac output, left coronary flow and myocardial metabolism in the unanesthetized dog. *Circ. Res.* 17:427–37

41. Kirk, E. S., Honig, C. R. 1964. Experimental and theoretical analysis of myocardial tissue pressure. *Am. J. Physiol.* 207:261–67

42. Knochel, J. P., Schlein, E. M. 1972. On the mechanism of rhabdomyolysis in potassium depletion. *J. Clin. Invest.* 51:1750–58

43. Kroll, K., Schipperheyn, J. J., Hendriks, F. F. A., Laird, J. D. 1980. Role of adenosine in post-occlusion coronary vasodilation. *Am. J. Physiol. 238(Heart Circ. Physiol.* 7):H214–19

44. Kübler, W., Spieckermann, P. G., Bretschneider, H. J. 1970. Influence of dipyridamol (Persantin) on myocardial adenosine metabolism. *J. Molec. Cell. Cardiol* 1:23–38

45. Kukovetz, W. R., Pöch, G., Holzmann, S., Wurm, A., Rinner, I. 1978. Role of cyclic nucleotides in adenosine-mediated regulation of coronary flow. *Adv. Cyclic Nucleotide Res.* 9:397–409

46. L'Abbate, A., Marzilli, M., Ballestra, A. M., Camici, P. Trivella, M. G., Pelosi, G., Klassen, G. A. 1980. Opposite transmural gradients of coronary resistance and extravascular pressure in the working dog's heart. *Cardiovasc. Res.* 14:21–29

47. Liu, M. S., Feinberg, H. 1971. Incorporation of adenosine-8-^{14}C and inosine-8-^{14}C into rabbit heart adenine nucleotides. *Am. J. Physiol.* 220:1242–48

48. Londos, C., Wolff, J. 1977. Two distinct adenosine-sensitive sites on adenylate cyclase. *Proc. Natl. Acad. Sci. USA* 74:5482–86

49. Lowensohn, H. S., Patterson, R. E., Olsson, R. A. 1978. Exercise performance and hemodynamics during dietary potassium depletion in dogs. *Am. J. Physiol: Respir. Envir. Exer. Physiol.* 45:728–32

50. Marcus, A. J., Weksler, B. B., Jaffe, E. A. 1978. Enzymatic conversion of prostaglandin endoperoxide H_2 and arachidonic acid to prostacyclin by cultured human endothelial cells. *J. Biol. Chem.* 253:7138–41

51. Merrill, G. F., Haddy, F. J., Dabney, J. M. 1978. Adenosine, theophylline and perfusate pH in the isolated, perfused guinea pig heart. *Circ. Res.* 42:225–29

52. Miller, O. V., Gorman, R. R. 1979. Evidence for distinct prostaglandin I_2 and D_2 receptors in human platelets. *J. Pharmacol. Exp. Ther.* 210:134–40

53. Miller, O. V., Aiken, J. W., Hemker, D. P., Shebuski, R. J., Gorman, R. R. 1979. Prostacyclin stimulation of dog arterial cyclic AMP levels. *Prostaglandins* 18:915–25

54. Murray, P. A., Sparks, H. V. 1978. The mechanism of K^+-induced vasodilation of the coronary vascular bed of the dog. *Circ. Res.* 42:35–42

55. Murray, P. A., Belloni, F. L., Sparks, H. V. 1979. The role of potassium in the metabolic control of coronary vascular resistance of the dog. *Circ. Res.* 44: 767–80

56. Myers, W. W., Honig, C. R. 1964. Number and distribution of capillaries as determinants of myocardial oxygen tension. *Am. J. Physiol.* 207:653–60

57. Needleman, P., Kulkarni, P. P., Raz, A. 1977. Coronary tone modulation: formation and actions of prostaglandins, endoperoxides, and thromboxanes. *Science* 195:409–12

58. Olsson, R. A. 1970. Changes in content of purine nucleoside in canine myocardium during coronary occlusion. *Circ. Res.* 26:301–6

59. Olsson, R. A., Snow, J. A., Gentry, M. K., Frick, G. P. 1972. Adenosine uptake by canine heart. *Circ. Res.* 31: 767–78

60. Olsson, R. A., Davis, C. J., Khouri, E. M., Patterson, R. E. 1976. Evidence for an adenosine receptor on the surface of dog coronary myocytes. *Circ. Res.* 39: 93–98

61. Olsson, R. A., Patterson, R. E. 1976. Adenosine as a physiological regulator of coronary blood flow. *Progr. Molec. Subcell. Biol.* 4:227–48

62. Olsson, R. A., Snow, J. A., Gentry, M. K. 1978. Adenosine metabolism in ca-

nine myocardial reactive hyperemia. *Circ. Res.* 42:358–62

63. Olsson, R. A., Vomacka, R. B., Nixon, D. G. 1978. Adenosine-binding factors in cardiac muscle. *Fed. Proc.* 37:418

64. Olsson, R. A., Khouri, E. M., Bedynek, J. L. Jr., McLean, J. 1979. Coronary vasoactivity of adenosine in the conscious dog. *Circ. Res.* 45:468–78

65. Paul, R. J., Peterson, J. W., Caplan, S. R. 1973. Oxygen consumption rate in vascular smooth muscle: Relation to isometric tension. *Biochim. Biophys. Acta* 305:474–80

66. Paul, R. J. 1977. Comments on: Oxygen tension sensors in vascular smooth muscle. *Adv. Exp. Biol. Med.* 78:117–21

67. Phair, R. D., Sparks, H. V. 1979. Adenosine content of skeletal muscle during active hyperemia and ischemic contraction. *Am. J. Physiol.* 237(*Heart Circ. Physiol.* 6):H1–H9

68. Pittman, R. N., Duling, B. R. 1973. Oxygen sensitivity of vascular smooth muscle. I. In vitro studies. *Microvasc. Res.* 6:202–11

69. Raberger, G., Schütz, W., Kraup, O. 1975. Coronary reactive hyperaemia and coronary dilator action of adenosine during normal respiration and hypercapnic acidosis in the dog. *Clin. Exp. Pharmacol. Physiol.* 2:373–82

70. Roth, G. J., Majerus, P. W. 1975. The mechanism of the effect of aspirin on human platelets. I. Acetylation of a particulate fraction protein. *J. Clin. Invest.* 56:624–32

71. Rubio, R., Berne, R. M., Katori, M. 1969. Release of adenosine in reactive hyperemia of the dog heart. *Am. J. Physiol.* 216:56–62

72. Rubio, R., Berne, R. M. 1975. Regulation of coronary blood flow. *Progr. Cardiovasc. Dis.* 18:105–22

73. Rubio, R., Berne, R. M., Dobson, J. G. Jr. 1973. Sites of adenosine production in cardiac and skeletal muscle. *Am. J. Physiol.* 225:938–53

74. Sabiston, D. C. Jr., Gregg, D. E. 1957. Effect of cardiac contraction on coronary blood flow. *Circulation* 15:14–20

75. Schrader, J., Gerlach, E. 1976. Compartmentation of cardiac adenine nucleotides and formation of adenosine. *Pflügers Arch.* 367:129–35

76. Schrader, J., Nees, S., Gerlach, E. 1977. Evidence for a cell surface adenosine receptor on coronary myocytes and atrial muscle cells. *Pflügers Arch.* 369:251–57

77. Schwartz, G. G., McHale, P. A., Greenfield, J. C. Jr. 1980. Coronary vascular responses to a single fractional-diastolic coronary artery occlusion. *Fed. Proc.* 39:530

78. Sigurdsson, S. B., Johansson, B., Mellander, S. 1977. Rate-dependent myogenic responses of vascular smooth muscle during imposed changes in length and force. *Acta Physiol. Scand.* 99:183–89

79. Sparks, H. V. Jr., Belloni, F. L. 1978. The peripheral circulation: local regulation. *Ann. Rev. Physiol.* 40:67–92

80. Vane, J. R. 1978. Inhibitors of prostaglandin, prostacyclin and thromboxane synthesis. *Adv. Prostagl. Thrombox. Res.* 4:27–44

81. von Restorff, W., Holtz, J., Bassenge, E. 1977. Exercise induced augmentation of myocardial oxygen extraction in spite of normal coronary dilatory capacity in dogs. *Pflügers Arch.* 373:181–85

82. Walus, K. M., Silver, P. J., Jacobson, E. D., Di Salvo, J. 1980. Relaxation of coronary arteries by adenosine or its analogs is associated with activation of cAMP-dependent protein kinase. *Fed. Proc.* 39:581

83. Weiss, H. R., Neubauer, J. A., Lipp, J. A., Sinha, A. K. 1978. Quantitative determination of regional oxygen consumption in the dog heart. *Circ. Res.* 42:394–401

84. Weiss, H. R. 1979. Regional oxygen consumption and supply in the dog heart: Effect of atrial pacing. *Am. J. Physiol.* 236(*Heart Circ. Physiol.* 5):H231–37

85. Wiedmeier, V. T., Rubio, R., Berne, R. M. 1972. Incorporation and turnover of adenosine-U-^{14}C in perfused guinea pig myocardium. *Am. J. Physiol.* 223:51–54

Ann. Rev. Physiol. 1981. 43:397–407

REGULATION OF THE CEREBRAL CIRCULATION

❖1318

Hermes A. Kontos

Department of Medicine, Medical College of Virginia, Richmond, Virginia 23298

Because of space limitations this review considers selected aspects of the physiological regulation of the cerebral circulation.

NEUROGENIC REGULATION

This aspect of the regulation of the cerebral circulation has been under intensive investigation for the past several years. Many uncertainties have been clarified, but a satisfying answer to the important question of what role neurogenic influences play in the physiological regulation of cerebral blood flow (CBF) remains elusive. Since this subject has been reviewed repeatedly (7, 18, 46, 53), the present paper concentrates on the most recent evidence directly pertinent to the participation of vasomotor nerves in physiological adjustments of the cerebral circulation.

Adrenergic fibers originating in the ipsilateral superior cervical ganglion innervate both pial and intracerebral vessels (42). The effects of cerebral adrenergic nerves are substantially less pronounced than those seen in other vascular beds. In the cat stimulation of the cervical sympathetic nerves produced pial arteriolar vasoconstriction. The average response was modest, ranging from 7–12% (29, 69). Larger pial arteries responded more vigorously than smaller ones. In two studies (51, 69) from the same laboratory no significant response was detectable in the smaller (<100 μm in diameter) arterioles. The responses of CBF and cerebral vascular resistance (CVR) to electrical stimulation of the cerebral sympathetic nerves depend on the species studied. The most pronounced and consistent responses were obtained in monkeys (20) and rabbits (55); in the latter, the response was

397

0066-4278/81/0315-0397$01.00

largely transient owing to escape (55). Cats and dogs displayed lesser responses, or none at all (20). Unusually large decreases in CBF (80% of control), obtained in one study (4) using venous outflow measurements in dogs, were accompanied by increases in intracranial pressure, despite the marked decrease in blood flow, suggesting the occurrence of venoconstriction. Such venoconstriction, in the face of a surgically reduced venous drainage system, might have been a major determinant in the observed decreases in blood flow and may have little effect on flow under conditions of uncompromised venous outflow. The relatively weak responses of cerebral blood vessels to sympathetic nerve stimulation are clearly attributable to the very low responsiveness of their alpha-adrenergic receptors to norepinephrine (6). In the rabbit this behavior is related to the embryological development of the blood vessels (3). Evidently, the cerebral sympathetic nerves exert no resting neurogenic tone (20).

When the mean arterial blood pressure was raised to about 200 mm Hg, consistent vasoconstrictor responses were observed in cats, dogs, and monkeys in response to stimulation of the cerebral sympathetic nerves (20). Potentiation of the effects of sympathetic nerves at high pressures was most marked in cats, less pronounced in dogs, and virtually absent in the monkey (20). In the cat the change in responsiveness to sympathetic nerve stimulation at high arterial pressures may be explained by selectively greater effects of such stimulation on larger cerebral vessels (69). Since at high pressures these vessels make a greater contribution to total CVR than at normal pressures (26), a fixed percentile reduction in their caliber would result in greater decrease in blood flow at high than at normal pressures. These more pronounced effects of adrenergic nerves during arterial hypertension suggest that an important function of these nerves is to limit the increase in intravascular pressure in the capillaries and in the smaller cerebral arterioles and prevent disruption of the blood-brain barrier during arterial hypertension. The small cerebral arterioles are thin-walled (68) and have less vascular smooth muscle (41); hence, they are more vulnerable to damage from increased pressure.

The extent of the involvement of the cerebral sympathetic nerves in reflex regulation of CBF is controversial. The balance of the available evidence suggests that their participation is limited. Stimulation of the carotid baroreceptors (50), or of the arterial chemoreceptors (19), or denervation of these structures (1, 19, 50, 61) does not result in important alterations in resting CBF or CVR, or in the responsiveness of the cerebral vascular bed to CO_2, to changes in arterial blood pressure, or to arterial hypoxia. In contrast to these negative findings, carotid chemoreceptor stimulation in awake dogs caused cerebral vasoconstriction (62). Also, CO_2 inhalation in the cat caused reflex activation of the sympathetic nerves thereby exerting a slight vasoconstrictor effect exclusively on the larger pial arteries; this partially counteracted the local dilator effect of CO_2 (67). Similarly, the hyperemic effect of arterial hypercapnia in baboons was enhanced after cervical sympathectomy (24). During severe hypotension induced by bleeding, the associated increased sympathetic activity resulted in additional vasoconstriction of the cerebral vessels, thereby causing further reduction in CBF and a small additional increase in CVR (11). In the study of Ponte & Purves (45) carotid baroreceptor and chemoreceptor denervation eliminated the cerebral vasodilator response to hypoxia, depressed the vasodilator response to hypercapnia, and abolished autoregulation of CBF. This generalized depression of responses suggests strongly the operation of nonspecific influences.

Pial vessels, but not intracerebral vessels, are innervated by cholinergic fibers (12, 42). When these fibers are activated by transmural electrical stimulation of cerebral arteries from cats, they induce significant vasodilation (34). The cerebral arteries have cholinergic receptors (5, 34). Electrical stimulation of certain cranial nerves, such as the facial and the greater superficial petrosal nerve, induced modest increases in CBF, presumably owing to activation of cholinergic vasodilator fibers (5, 24). Little is known about the potential activation of these fibers under physiological circumstances, or about their contribution to the regulation of the cerebral circulation. It was suggested that they are responsible for cerebral vasodilation during hypoxia or during chemoreceptor stimulation (45). These findings, however, are contradicted by other more convincing evidence which shows that section of the 7th nerve, presumably the efferent pathway for these effects, does not interfere with autoregulation of CBF, or with responsiveness to CO_2 and to hypoxia, and causes no alteration in resting CBF (1, 21). In addition, the responses to hypoxia, hypercapnia, and to the changes in blood pressure were maintained after denervation of the chemoreceptors (1, 19, 61).

It was suggested that vasomotor fibers originating in the brain stem, mostly in the locus coeruleus, innervate brain vessels and thereby might regulate CBF (59). Stimulation or ablation of various areas of the brain stem produced significant effects on resting CBF, modified autoregulatory responses or responses to CO_2, and changed capillary permeability to water (2, 32, 38, 39, 48). At present, it appears that the evidence supporting central neurogenic vasomotor control is deficient in important respects, including the following: It is questionable that the adrenergic fibers originating in the brain stem truly innervate cerebral vessels. It is more likely that we are dealing with a close spatial association between these fibers and blood vessels without functional significance, since in many cases the nerve fibers are separated from vessels by a thick basement membrane (42). Also, the experiments in which stimulation or ablation of brain stem centers were shown to have significant effects on CBF do not provide convincing evidence that these changes were indeed produced as a result of changes in the activity of vasomotor fibers, because indirect effects, such as changes in blood pressure or in metabolic activity, may have been the major reason for the observed changes in flow, and in responsiveness (32, 38, 39) rather than direct vasomotor influences on these vessels. For these reasons, I believe that, at present, there is no adequate foundation to the belief that brain stem centers control CBF by direct action of vasomotor fibers on cerebral vessels.

Nerve endings resembling those of peptidergic fibers (42) containing vasoactive intestinal polypeptide (VIP) (33) have been shown in pial arteries. VIP is a potent relaxant of vascular smooth muscle, including cerebral vascular smooth muscle (33). Nothing is known about the possible role of these nerves in the regulation of the cerebral circulation.

CHEMICAL REGULATION

The effect of CO_2 on the cerebral circulation is one of the most pronounced and most easily demonstrable influences. Arterial hypercapnia dilates cerebral blood vessels (67), increases CBF, and lowers CVR (52). Arterial hypocapnia causes reverse changes in these variables (52, 67). Arterial hypercapnia dilates the smaller arterioles more than the larger ones, but the vasoconstrictor effect of hypocapnia is size-independent (67).

The main mechanism for the effect of CO_2 is a direct action on cerebral vascular smooth muscle, as demonstrated by the pronounced effects on pial arterioles of local changes in P_{CO_2} or pH (27, 63). The effect of CO_2 is dependent on changes in hydrogen ion concentration of the extracellular fluid in the vicinity of the cerebral blood vessels, whereas molecular CO_2 and the bicarbonate ion do not appear to have inherent vasoactivity, as shown by the fact that marked changes in CSF P_{CO_2} and bicarbonate ion concentration do not alter pial arteriolar caliber unless a change in pH is allowed to occur (25). The vasodilation induced by increased Pa_{CO_2} can be counteracted completely by a change in extravascular P_{CO_2} of the same magnitude but in opposite direction, showing that the local effect of CO_2 is sufficient to explain the alterations in vessel caliber produced by changes in Pa_{CO_2} (27). Several attempts have been made to explain the effect of CO_2 on cerebral vessels by a variety of actions at remote sites, such as brainstem centers (57) or the arterial chemoreceptors (45). Although these influences may modify the cerebral vascular effects of CO_2 under certain conditions, they are at best of secondary importance when compared to the local action, which is indisputably the major mechanism involved. The pial arteriolar dilation during hypercapnia is reduced by arterial hypotension (67), and the increase in CBF due to hypercapnia is heavily influenced by changes in blood pressure and cerebral metabolism (13, 16). It is likely that changes in these variables explain many of the alterations in responsiveness to CO_2 from various interventions. The increase in CBF during hypercapnia was severely reduced following administration of indomethacin, suggesting that prostaglandins may be involved as mediators (44). Several prostaglandins (PGI_2, PGE_2, PGG_2, and PGD_2) and their precursor arachidonic acid, dilate pial arterioles when applied topically (10, 66), and large cerebral vessels synthesize prostaglandins (14). However, the participation of prostaglandins in the response to CO_2 seems unlikely, because following administration of cyclooxygenase inhibitors that severely reduced the vasodilator effect of arachidonic acid on pial arterioles of cats, the responses to arterial hypercapnia, hypocapnia, and hypoxia were not altered (66).

Since the blood-brain barrier is freely permeable to CO_2, but impermeable to the bicarbonate ion, the effect of changes in Pa_{CO_2} would depend on the prevailing bicarbonate ion concentration in the CSF and in the extracellular fluid of the brain. Although the bicarbonate ion concentration in these locations changes little over short periods, substantial changes may occur during exposure to abnormal atmospheres over prolonged periods. Prolonged hypercapnia in rabbits caused an increase in the CSF concentration of bicarbonate ion and led to a depression of the vasodilator response to arterial hypercapnia (35). However, exposure to prolonged hypoxia resulted in decreased bicarbonate ion concentration in the CSF and led to augmentation of the vasodilator response to arterial hypercapnia (35). Similar changes in the sensitivity of CBF to CO_2 were found in rats exposed to 24 hr of hypercapnia or hypoxia (43). Changes of the same nature also occur on exposure to high altitude and explain the associated changes in CBF (56). The relative impermeability of the blood-brain barrier to the bicarbonate ion in the face of relatively free diffusion of CO_2 across this barrier explains why no changes in CBF occur with alterations in blood acidity in the absence of change in Pa_{CO_2} (15).

Arterial hypoxia dilates pial arterioles, increases CBF, and lowers CVR (28, 61). The same effect is found during carbon monoxide breathing (61). Local hypoxia, produced by application of CSF without oxygen on the brain surface, causes slight arteriolar vasodilation (28). The action of arterial hypoxia on cerebral arterioles is mediated by local mechanisms, since it can be counteracted completely by supplying sufficient oxygen via topical application of fluorocarbons that have a high oxygen carrying capacity (28).

METABOLIC REGULATION

A high level of resting metabolic rate and a heavy dependence on aerobic metabolism require that the brain have an uninterrupted high blood flow rate and a tight coupling between metabolism and blood flow. In this respect, the brain resembles tissues with similar characteristics, such as the heart and contracting skeletal muscle. There is a strong relationship between the level of functional activity and metabolic rate of the brain on the one hand, and regional CBF on the other. Physiological activation of specific areas of the cortex by various types of sensory stimulation, or in association with motor activity, led to increased blood flow to the activated areas (22); and such increased activity was associated with increased metabolism (58). Engaging in more complex mental activity causes more widespread increase in CBF, presumably because more extensive regions of the brain are activated (22). In a limited number of measurements of both CBF and metabolic rate, a close relationship between these two was confirmed (47). More generalized and more intense increases in brain metabolism induced by drugs that cause seizures are accompanied by pronounced arteriolar dilation (28, 30).

It is generally believed that the relationship between blood flow and metabolism is dependent on the production of vasodilator metabolites by the neural cells and that the abundance of these metabolites is dependent on blood flow. The number of candidates for mediating metabolic flow regulation is large. At present, adenosine, hydrogen ion, and potassium ion appear to be the most promising candidates. Adenosine is a strong dilator of pial vessels when applied in the perivascular space (64). Brain adenosine concentration increases under conditions of arterial hypoxia, ischemia, or increased metabolic activity of the brain (54). An increase in concentration of adenosine in the brain was detectable within 5 sec from the onset of ischemia (70). The increased adenosine production under these conditions may be the result of hypoxia of the neural cells, since increased supply of oxygen topically by superfusion with oxygenated fluorocarbons results in reduction of the vasodilation in response to seizures (28). Similarly, it has been shown that increased metabolic activity results in increased extracellular concentration of potassium ions (17), and it has been demonstrated that potassium dilates pial arterioles (31). During seizures, hydrogen ion concentration of brain extracellular fluid increases, particularly in the later stages (30).

AUTOREGULATION OF CEREBRAL BLOOD FLOW

Increases in arterial blood pressure induce net cerebral precapillary vessel constriction and increases in CVR (26, 37); conversely, decreases in arterial blood pressure induce net cerebral precapillary vessel dilation and result in decreases in CVR (26, 36). These compensatory responses tend to maintain CBF relatively constant over a wide range of arterial blood pressure and comprise the phenomenon of autoregulation of CBF. The range of blood pressure over which autoregulation is dominant and the exact relation between CBF and perfusion pressure in this range vary considerably with the conditions of the experiment. The dominant effect seems to be the state of the vascular bed at the time of testing. Generally, dilated vascular beds display a more limited range over which autoregulation is dominant and a steeper change in CBF with a given change in perfusion pressure (9, 40). The reverse is true with relatively constricted vascular beds. At very high arterial blood pressures, passive distention of some vessels exceeds the effects of active vasoconstriction, CBF rises markedly, and CVR falls (9, 36). At very low pressures, passive decrease in diameter of some vessels as a result of the decreased transmural pressure leads to decreases in CBF and may lead to increased CVR (36).

In cats with cranial windows, autoregulatory adjustments in vascular caliber when mean arterial blood pressure changed between 90 and 160 mm Hg were limited to the larger pial arterioles (26). The smaller vessels (<100 μm in diameter) dilated progressively at lower pressures, and their maximum dilation was greater than that of the larger arterioles. At very high pressures, the smaller arterioles dilated, while the larger vessels remained constricted (26). This would be expected to shift vascular resistance to the larger vessels. In other studies in cats (36, 37), using an open skull preparation in which the brain was covered with oil, changes in arterial blood pressure were associated with more pronounced autoregulatory adjustments in caliber in the smaller vessels than in the larger ones. These were greater than expected from the associated changes in blood flow.

The dominant view is that autoregulation is the result of local regulatory mechanisms. Vasomotor nerves may have secondary effects on autoregulation by changing the state of the vascular bed. They are not, however, required for the occurrence of autoregulation. Two basic mechanisms have been proposed to explain autoregulation in the brain: the myogenic mechanism, which holds that cerebral vessels are responsive to changes in transmural pressure; and the metabolic mechanism, whose basic premise is that changes in cerebral vascular caliber are the result of alterations in the concentration of vasodilator metabolites induced by alterations in blood flow secondary to the change in pressure.

The presently available evidence strongly favors the view that autoregulation of CBF is predominantly the result of the operation of a metabolic mechanism. Changes in blood pressure result quickly in autoregulatory changes in vascular caliber (26) or in CBF (60). It has been argued (60) that these changes are so fast that they are not consistent with expected delays from diffusion of metabolites. This argument loses considerable weight when one considers that the vascular adjustments secondary to recognized metabolic mechanisms, such as those seen secondary to increased metabolism associated with seizures, take place equally quickly (28). Since increased venous pressure causes reduced blood flow but increases in intravascular and in transmural pressure, one would expect net vasodilation if the metabolic mechanism is dominant and net vasoconstriction if the myogenic mechanism is dominant. In the baboon, increased venous pressure caused vasodilation of pial arterioles (49). In the dog, increases in venous pressure produced predominantly increases in CBF and decreases in CVR (23); in another study (8) in the same species, increases in venous pressure were associated with vasoconstriction in 3 animals and with slight vasodilation in 3 others, supporting the operation of a mixed mechanism involving both myogenic and metabolic factors with the former predominating. Direct evidence supporting a metabolic mechanism was obtained by showing that the vasodilation associated with arterial hypotension was markedly reduced or abolished by increased local supply of oxygen through superfusion with oxygenated fluorocarbons (28). This evidence supported the view that the vasodilation associated with hypotension was due to the induction of tissue hypoxia. The latter presumably acts by altering the production and, hence, the concentration of vasodilator substances. A prime candidate for such action is adenosine, whose concentration has been demonstrated to rise quickly during hypotension (70). Hydrogen ion does not seem to be involved, because pH does not change during hypotension (65) and because arterial hypocapnia does not alter the vasodilator response to hypotension (28). Similarly, the concentration of potassium ions does not change during hypotension (65).

ACKNOWLEDGMENT

The author's work is supported by grants HL-21851 and NS-12587 from the National Institutes of Health.

Literature Cited

1. Bates, D., Chir, B., Sundt, T. M. 1976. The relevance of peripheral baroreceptors and chemoreceptors to regulation of cerebral blood flow in the cat. *Circ. Res.* 38:488–93
2. Bates, D., Weinshilboum, R. M., Campbell, R. J., Sundt, T. M. Jr. 1977. The effect of lesions in the locus coeruleus on the physiological responses of the cerebral blood vessels in cats. *Brain Res.* 136:431–43
3. Bevan, J. A. 1979. Sites of transition between functional systemic and cerebral arteries of rabbits occur at embryological junctional sites. *Science* 204:635–37

4. D'Alecy, L. G., Feigl, E. O. 1972. Sympathetic control of cerebral blood flow in dogs. *Circ. Res.* 31:267–83
5. D'Alecy, L. G., Rose, C. J. 1977. Parasympathetic cholinergic control of cerebral blood flow in dogs. *Circ. Res.* 41:324–31
6. Duckles, S. P., Bevan, J. A. 1976. Pharmacological characterization of adrenergic receptors of a rabbit cerebral artery in vitro. *J. Pharmacol. Exp. Ther.* 197:371–78
7. Edvinsson, L., MacKenzie, E. T. 1977. Amine mechanisms in the cerebral circulation. *Pharmacol. Rev.* 28:275–348
8. Ekström-Jodal, B. 1970. Effect of increased venous pressure on cerebral

blood flow in dogs. *Acta Physiol. Scand. Suppl.* 350:51–61

9. Ekström-Jodal, B., Haggendal, E., Linder, L., Nilsson, N. J. 1977. The pressure-flow relations of the canine brain in acute mechanically induced arterial hypertension at different levels of cerebral blood flow. *Acta Anaesth. Scand.* 2:232–39

10. Ellis, E. F., Wei, E. P., Kontos, H. A. 1979. Vasodilation of cat cerebral arterioles by prostaglandins D_2, E_2, G_2 and I_2. *Am. J. Physiol.* 237:H381–85

11. Fitch, W., MacKenzie, E. T., Harper, A. M. 1975. Effects of decreasing arterial blood pressure on cerebral blood flow in the baboon. *Circ. Res.* 37:550–57

12. Florence, V. M., Bevan, J. A. 1979. Biochemical determinations of cholinergic innervation in cerebral arteries. *Circ. Res.* 45:217–18

13. Fujishima, M., Scheinberg, P., Buston, R., Reinmuth, O. M. 1971. The relation between cerebral oxygen consumption and cerebral vascular reactivity to carbon dioxide. *Stroke* 2:251–57

14. Hagen, A. A., White, R. P., Robertson, J. T. 1979. Synthesis of prostaglandins and thromboxane B_2 by cerebral arteries. *Stroke* 10:306–9

15. Harper, A. M., Bell, R. A. 1963. The effect of metabolic acidosis and alkalosis on the blood flow through the cerebral cortex. *J. Neurol. Neurosurg. Psychiat.* 26:341–44

16. Harper, A. M., Glass, H. E. 1965. Effect of alterations in the arterial carbon dioxide tension on the blood flow through the cerebral cortex at normal and low arterial blood pressures. *J. Neurol. Neurosurg. Psychiat.* 28:449–51

17. Heinemann, U., Lux, H. D., Gutnick, M. J. 1977. Extracellular free calcium and potassium during paroxysmal activity in the cerebral cortex of the rat. *Exp. Brain Res.* 27:237–43

18. Heistad, D. D., Marcus, M. L. 1978. Evidence that neural mechanisms do not have important effects in cerebral blood flow. *Circ. Res.* 42:295–302

19. Heistad, D. D., Marcus, M. L., Ehrhardt, J. C., Abboud, F. M. 1976. Effect of stimulation of carotid chemoreceptors on total and regional cerebral blood flow. *Circ. Res.* 38:20–25

20. Heistad, D. D., Marcus, M. L., Gross, P. M. 1978. Effects of sympathetic nerves on cerebral vessels in dog, cat, and monkey. *Am. J. Physiol.* 235:H544–52

21. Hoff, J. T., MacKenzie, E. T., Harper, A. M. 1977. Responses of the cerebral circulation to hypercapnia and hypoxia after 7th cranial nerve transection in baboons. *Circ. Res.* 40:258–62

22. Ingvar, D. H. 1976. Functional landscapes of the dominant hemisphere. *Brain Res.* 107:181–97

23. Jacobson, I., Harper, A. M., McDowall, D. G. 1963. Relationship between venous pressure and cortical blood flow. *Nature* 200:173–75

24. James, I. M., Miller, R. A., Purves, M. J. 1969. Observations on the extrinsic neural control of cerebral blood flow in the baboon. *Circ. Res.* 25:77–93

25. Kontos, H. A., Raper, A. J., Patterson, J. L. Jr. 1977. Analysis of vasoactivity of local pH, P_{CO_2} and bicarbonate on pial vessels. *Stroke* 8:358–60

26. Kontos, H. A., Wei, E. P., Navari, R. M., Levasseur, J. E., Rosenblum, W. I., Patterson, J. L. Jr. 1978. Responses of cerebral arteries and arterioles to acute hypotension and hypertension. *Am. J. Physiol.* 234:H371–83

27. Kontos, H. A., Wei, E. P., Raper, A. J., Patterson, J. L. Jr. 1977. Local mechanism of CO_2 action on cat pial arterioles. *Stroke* 8:226–29

28. Kontos, H. A., Wei, E. P., Raper, A. J., Rosenblum, W. I., Navari, R. M., Patterson, J. L. Jr. 1978. Role of tissue hypoxia in local regulation of cerebral microcirculation. *Am. J. Physiol.* 234:H582–91

29. Kuschinsky, W., Wahl, M. 1975. Alpha-receptor stimulation by endogenous and exogenous norepinephrine and blockade by phentolamine in pial arteries of cats. *Circ. Res.* 37:168–74

30. Kuschinsky, W., Wahl, M. 1979. Perivascular pH and pial arterial diameter during bicuculline induced seizures in cats. *Pflügers Arch.* 382:81–85

31. Kuschinsky, W., Wahl, M., Bosse, O., Thurau, K. 1972. Perivascular potassium and pH as determinants of local pial arterial diameter in cats. *Circ. Res.* 31:240–47

32. Langfitt, T. W., Kassell, N. F. 1968. Cerebral vasodilatation produced by brain-stem stimulation: neurogenic control vs. autoregulation. *Am. J. Physiol.* 215:90–97

33. Larsson, L. I., Edvinsson, L., Fahrenkrug, J., Hakanson, R., Owman, C., Schaffalitzky de Muckadell, O., Sundler, F. 1976. Immunohistochemical localization of a vasodilatory polypeptide (VIP) in cerebrovascular nerves. *Brain Res.* 113:400–4

34. Lee, T. J.-F., Hume, W. R., Su, C., Bevan, J. A. 1978. Neurogenic vasodilation of cat cerebral arteries. *Circ. Res.* 42:535–42

35. Levasseur, J. E., Wei, E. P., Kontos, H. A., Patterson, J. L. Jr. 1979. Responses of pial arterioles after prolonged hypercapnia and hypoxia in the awake rabbit. *J. Appl. Physiol.* 46:89–95

36. MacKenzie, E. T., Farrar, J. K., Fitch, W., Graham, D. I., Gregory, P. C., Harper, A. M. 1979. Effects of hemorrhagic hypotension on the cerebral circulation. I. Cerebral blood flow and pial arteriolar caliber. *Stroke* 10:711–18

37. MacKenzie, E. T., Strandgaard, S., Graham, D. I., Jones, J. V., Harper, A. M., Farrar, J. K. 1976. Effects of acutely induced hypertension in cats on pial arteriolar caliber, local cerebral blood flow, and the blood-brain barrier. *Circ. Res.* 39:33–41

38. Meyer, J. S., Teraura, T., Sakamoto, K., Kondo, A. 1971. Central neurogenic control of cerebral blood flow. *Neurology* 21:247–62

39. Mitchell, G., Mitchell, D., Rosendorff, C. 1978. Vasodilator mechanism of the intracerebral (non-sympathetic) adrenergic pathway. *Cardiovasc. Res.* 12:42–48

40. Morita, H., Nemoto, E. M., Bleyaert, A. L., Stezoski, W. 1977. Brain blood flow autoregulation and metabolism during halothane anesthesia in monkeys. *Am. J. Physiol.* 233:H670–76

41. Navari, R. M., Wei, E. P., Kontos, H. A., Patterson, J. L. Jr. 1979. Oxygen consumption of pial arteries. *Am. J. Physiol.* 5:H151–56

42. Owman, C., Edvinsson, L. 1977. Histochemical and pharmacological approach to the investigation of neurotransmitters, with particular regard to the cerebrovascular bed. In *Neurogenic Control of the Brain Circulation,* ed. C. Owman, L. Edvinsson, pp. 15–38. NY: Pergamon

43. Pannier, J. L., Leusen, I. 1972. Circulation to the brain of the rat during acute and prolonged respiratory changes in the acid-base balance. *Pflügers Arch.* 338:347–59

44. Pickard, J. D., MacKenzie, E. T. 1973. Inhibition of prostaglandin synthesis and the response of baboon cerebral circulation to carbon dioxide. *Nature New Biol.* 245:187–88

45. Ponte, J., Purves, M. J. 1973. The role of the carotid body chemoreceptors and carotid sinus baroreceptors in the control of cerebral blood vessels. *J. Physiol. London* 237:315–40

46. Purves, M. J. 1978. Do vasomotor nerves significantly regulate cerebral blood flow? *Circ. Res.* 43:485–93

47. Raichle, M. E., Grubb, R. L., Gado, M. H., Eichling, J. O., Ter-Pogossian, M. T. 1976. Correlation between regional cerebral blood flow and oxidative metabolism. *Arch. Neurol.* 33:523–26

48. Raichle, M. E., Hartman, B. K., Eichling, J. O., Sharpe, L. G. 1975. Central noradrenergic regulation of cerebral blood flow and vascular permeability. *Proc. Natl. Acad. Sci. USA* 72:3726–30

49. Raisis, J. E., Kindt, G. W., McGillicuddy, J. E., Giannotta, S. L. 1979. The effects of primary elevation of cerebral venous pressure on cerebral hemodynamics and intracranial pressure. *J. Surg. Res.* 26:101–7

50. Rapela, C. E., Green, H. D., Denison, A. B. Jr. 1967. Baroreceptor reflexes and autoregulation of cerebral blood flow in the dog. *Circ. Res.* 21:559–68

51. Raper, A. J., Kontos, H. A., Wei, E. P., Patterson, J. L. Jr. 1972. Unresponsiveness of pial precapillary vessels to catecholamines and sympathetic nerve stimulation. *Circ. Res.* 31:257–66

52. Reivich, M. 1964. Arterial P_{CO_2} and cerebral hemodynamics. *Am. J. Physiol.* 206:25–35

53. Rosenblum, W. I. 1971. Neurogenic control of cerebral circulation. *Stroke* 2:429–39

54. Rubio, R., Berne, R. M., Bockman, E. L., Curnish, R. R. 1975. Relationship between adenosine concentration and oxygen supply in rat brain. *Am. J. Physiol.* 228:1896–902

55. Sercombe, R., Lacombe, P., Aubineau, P., Mamo, H., Pinard, E., Reynier-Rebuffel, A. M., Seylaz, J. R. 1978. Is there an active mechanism limiting the influence of the sympathetic system on the cerebral vascular bed? Evidence for vasomotor escape from sympathetic stimulation in the rabbit. *Brain Res.* 164:81–102

56. Severinghaus, J. W., Chiodi, H., Eger, E. I., Brandstater, B., Hornbein, T. F. 1966. Cerebral blood flow in man at high altitude. Role of cerebrospinal fluid pH in normalization of flow in chronic hypocapnia. *Circ. Res.* 19:274–82

57. Shalit, M. N., Shimojyo, S., Reinmuth, O. M., Lockhart, W. S. Jr., Scheinberg, P. 1968. The mechanism of action of carbon dioxide in the regulation of cere-

bral blood flow. *Prog. Brain Res.* 30:103–6

58. Sokoloff, L. 1977. Relation between physiological function and energy metabolism in the central nervous system. *J. Neurochem.* 29:13–36

59. Swanson, L. W., Hartman, B. K. 1975. The central adrenergic system. An immunofluorescence study of the location of cell bodies and their efferent connections in the rat utilizing dopamine-b-hydroxylase as a marker. *J. Comp. Neurol.* 163:467–506

60. Symon, L., Held, K., Dorsch, N. W. 1971. On the myogenic nature of the autoregulatory mechanism in the cerebral circulation. *Eur. Neurol.* 6:11–18

61. Traystman, R. J., Fitzgerald, R. S., Loscutoff, S. C. 1978. Cerebral circulatory responses to arterial hypoxia in normal and chemodenervated dogs. *Circ. Res.* 42:649–57

62. Vatner, S. F., Priano, L. L., Rutherford, J. D., Manders, W. T. 1980. Sympathetic regulation of the cerebral circulation by the carotid chemoreceptor reflex. *Am. J. Physiol.* 238:H594–98

63. Wahl, M., Deetjen, P., Thurau, K., Ingraz, D. H., Lassen, N. A. 1970. Micropuncture evaluation of the importance of perivascular pH for the arterio-lar diameter on the brain surface. *Pflügers Arch.* 316:152–63

64. Wahl, M., Kuschinsky, W. 1976. The dilatatory action of adenosine on pial arteries of cats and its inhibition by theophylline. *Pflügers Arch.* 362:55–59

65. Wahl, M., Kuschinsky, W. 1979. Unimportance of perivascular H^+ and K^+ activities for the adjustment of pial arterial diameter during changes of arterial blood pressure in cats. *Pflügers Arch.* 382:203–8

66. Wei, E. P., Ellis, E. F., Kontos, H. A. 1980. Role of prostaglandins in pial arteriolar response to CO_2 and hypoxia. *Am. J. Physiol.* 238:H226–30

67. Wei, E. P., Kontos, H. A., Patterson, J. L. Jr. 1980. Dependence of pial arteriolar response to hypercapnia on vessel size. *Am. J. Physiol.* 238:H697–703

68. Wei, E. P., Navari, R. M., Kontos, H. A. 1979. Wall-to-lumen ratios of cat pial arterioles. *Fed. Proc.* 38:1194 (Abstr.)

69. Wei, E. P., Raper, A. J., Kontos, H. A., Patterson, J. L. Jr. 1975. Determinants of response of pial arteries to norepinephrine and sympathetic nerve stimulation. *Stroke* 6:654–58

70. Winn, H. R., Rubio, R. R., Berne, R. M. 1979. Brain adenosine production in the rat during 60 seconds of ischemia. *Circ. Res.* 45:486–92

Ann. Rev. Physiol. 1981. 43:409–418

THE SPLANCHNIC CIRCULATION: Intrinsic Regulation

❖1319

D. Neil Granger and Peter R. Kvietys

Department of Physiology, University of South Alabama, Mobile, Alabama 36688

INTRODUCTION

The gastrointestinal tract displays a wide variety of specialized functions that require highly organized vascular beds. Perfusion of the various organs of the GI tract sufficient to accommodate the differential demands of tissue function is essential. Thus local regulatory mechanisms have evolved that provide an intimate relationship between the circulation and tissue function. Here we present and discuss evidence for the existence of intrinsic mechanisms that control blood flow in the gastrointestinal tract and liver. Particular attention is given to the response of the vasculature to perfusion pressure reduction, venous pressure elevation, arterial and venous occlusions, arterial hypoxia, and enhanced functional activity. The reader is also referred to several excellent reviews of the gastrointestinal circulation (15, 26, 33, 34, 55, 60).

SMALL INTESTINE

Local vasoregulatory control systems exist in the small bowel. Autoregulation of blood flow does occur in the intestine; however, it is not the intense phenomenon seen in other organs (e.g. kidney, brain) since a reduction in perfusion pressure is usually accompanied by a reduction in blood flow, while resistance falls by a modest amount (change in resistance is one half the change in pressure) (29). The autoregulatory ability of the small intestine is unaffected by chronic denervation and sympatholytic agents (30), reduced by luminal distension (23), abolished by intra-arterial cyanide (30), and enhanced during absorption (45). Oxygen uptake by the small bowel remains virtually constant when perfusion pressure is lowered from 125 to

409

0066-4278/81/0315-0409$01.00

30 mm Hg (20). Intestinal oxygen extraction is normally less than 25% at a normal perfusion pressure and can increase to 80% when perfusion pressure is lowered to 30 mm Hg. Feedback control of diffusion parameters such as microvessel-to-cell diffusion distance and microvascular surface area (mediated through adjustments in precapillary sphincter tone) is considered to play an important role in maintaining a normal oxygen uptake by the small bowel (15). Autoregulation of intestinal O_2 uptake is also observed during arterial hypoxia (57) and luminal distension (46); however, the local mechanisms that maintain O_2 uptake via O_2 extraction are impaired by sympathetic stimulation (58) and various vasoactive agents (48) (assuming metabolism is unaffected).

The metabolic and myogenic hypotheses predict different responses to an increase in venous pressure—the myogenic predicts vasoconstriction and the metabolic, vasodilation. In the small intestine, venous pressure elevation results in an increased vascular resistance and a reduction in capillary density (16, 28, 56), findings consistent with the myogenic theory. The myogenic increase in vascular resistance in response to venous pressure elevation is either abolished or reversed (decreased vascular resistance) during absorption (20), arterial hypoxia (61), intra-arterial infusion of dinitrophenol (20), and by intentional under-perfusion (56). Blood flow distribution studies suggest that the constriction of arteriolar and precapillary sphincter smooth muscle during venous pressure elevation occurs predominately in the mucosa-submucosal layer of the intestine while the vasculature of the muscularis dilates (16).

The intestinal resistance and exchange vessel responses to arterial hypoxia are consistent with a metabolic mechanism—i.e. arteriolar and precapillary sphincter tone decreases. The increased blood flow and O_2 extraction during arterial hypoxia are sufficient to maintain intestinal O_2 uptake within 25% of control in spite of an arterial $Po_2 < 50$ mm Hg (57). Although the effects of arterial hypoxia appear to be mediated by low O_2, indirect effects on blood flow may result from changes in intestinal tonus and motility (15). The small intestine also exhibits a characteristic hyperemia after brief periods of arterial occlusion, the magnitude and duration of which are related to the duration of the occlusion (43, 47). Tissue Po_2 reduction and purine metabolite accumulation occur during arterial occlusions. Venous blood adenosine concentration increases four-fold at peak hyperemia (44), and theophylline, a competitive inhibitor of adenosine action, significantly reduces the hyperemic response (19). Blood flow distribution studies suggest that the hyperemic response to arterial occlusion occurs uniformly throughout the wall of the intestine for an occlusion period of 60 sec. A greater hyperemic response is observed in the muscularis layer for longer durations of occlusion, indicating a greater sensitivity of this region to arterial occlusion (47). Venous occlusion results in a reactive hyperemic response; however, the response is significantly smaller than that of arterial occlusions of equal duration (43). An increased O_2 demand is observed during venous occlusion, whereas a depression of O_2 uptake is noted during arterial occlusion (43). It is evident that both myogenic and metabolic mechanisms contribute to the intrinsic regulation of intestinal blood flow. Although the metabolic mechanism appears inadequate for precise regulation of intestinal blood flow under normal conditions, this mechanism is highly efficient in maintaining a constant supply of oxygen to parenchymal cells via modification of O_2 extraction. Metabolites that exhibit a demonstrable vasodilator effect on the intestinal vasculature and may elicit precapillary sphincter relaxation include adenosine, inosine, K^+, and osmolality (15, 18).

The functional hyperemia associated with food ingestion (noncephalic, postprandial) has been extensively analyzed in the small bowel. Blood flow increases by 30–130% in the small bowel after a meal (15). The hyperemic response is generally considered to be restricted to the segment(s) of small bowel exposed to chyme (7). Considerable disagreement exists regarding the transmural distribution of intestinal blood flow during absorption. Some investigators contend that the hyperemia occurs in all layers (mucosa-submucosa and muscularis-serosa) of the intestinal wall (1, 2), whereas others have shown that the hyperemia is restricted to the mucosal layer (7). The primary luminal stimulus of the postprandial hyperemic response appears to be the constituents of chyme (8). Although mucosal irritation, luminal pH, and osmolality have been proposed as stimuli, there is little evidence to support these mechanisms (15, 32). Of the numerous constituents of chyme, glucose and long-chain fatty acids (solubilized in bile) appear to be the likely stimulants of the hyperemic response (8, 11). Bile (when diluted to postprandial concentrations) does not produce a hyperemia in the upper small bowel, yet it greatly increases blood flow in the ileum (7, 12), which is the site of absorption of bile salts.

The mechanisms involved in eliciting postprandial intestinal hyperemia are not yet clearly defined, but may include: a nervous reflex, release of hormones, a metabolic control system, a myogenic control system, and changes in visceral smooth muscle tone (15). Of these, hormonal and metabolic factors appear most likely to be involved. Results from bioassay and cross-perfusion experiments suggest that humoral substances may be involved in the postprandial hyperemic response (11). The most likely humoral candidates are the gastrointestinal hormones, cholecystokinin (CCK), secretin, and gastrin. Of these, only CCK is capable of vasodilating the intestinal vasculature at concentrations that occur postprandially (6). Although CCK seems the most likely candidate for eliciting the hyperemic response in the upper small bowel where its tissue levels are high, it is less likely to be responsible for the hyperemic response in the lower small intestine where tissue levels of CCK are negligible (51). Other naturally occurring substances in the small bowel that are vasodilators and may be involved in the postprandial hyperemic response include serotonin and bradykinin.

The intestinal hyperemia and concomitant increase in oxygen consumption associated with food ingestion indicate metabolic involvement in the modulation of intestinal blood flow. Induction of intestinal absorption or secretion generally results in an increased oxygen consumption (17, 64). The increased metabolic demands during absorption and secretion are met by an increased blood flow and/or oxygen extraction. Increases in oxygen extraction result from an increased capillary density and blood-to-tissue Po_2 gradient (1, 64). The relative contribution of O_2 extraction and blood flow during periods of enhanced transport depends upon the stimulus (nutrient, secretagogue), and the preprandial levels of oxygen extraction and blood flow. The magnitude of the increase in O_2 uptake appears to be dependent on the solute(s) being transported and is directly related to absorption (or secretion) rate (17, 64). Experimental support for the involvement of metabolic factors in the functional hyperemia is also provided by the observations that the autoregulatory (blood flow) ability of transporting segments of small bowel is much greater than that of "fasted" segments (45). During transport, intestinal blood flow remains relatively constant although perfusion pressure is lowered from 125 to 40 mm Hg. Although intestinal O_2 uptake is as well regulated in both transporting and "fasted" preparations, the contribution of blood flow regulation becomes more important for maintaining intestinal O_2 uptake during transport (20). Blockade of adenosine with theophylline reduces the ability of the transporting small bowel to autoregulate blood flow to that level observed in the fasted state. Theophylline, however, does not block the postprandial hyperemic response (19).

Convincing evidence suggests the involvement of both hormonal (particularly cholecystokinin) and metabolic factors in eliciting the postprandial hyperemic response in the small bowel. Future studies should focus on experimental maneuvers allowing for separation of these factors.

STOMACH

Most studies on gastric hemodynamics have emphasized the relation between gastric secretion and blood flow. Little attention has been given the intrinsic control of gastric blood flow via conventional approaches—i.e.

pressure-flow autoregulation, reactive hyperemia, etc. Except for the colon, the stomach appears to be the poorest autoregulator of blood flow in the gastrointestinal tract. In sympathetically innervated preparations a 50% reduction in arterial pressure results in a 100% increase in gastric vascular resistance (27), indicating recoil of elastic elements or active contraction of the vasculature at low perfusion pressures. In sympathetically denervated preparations the gastric vasculature behaves as a passive system or dilates slightly (4, 38). The autoregulatory ability of the stomach is unaffected by bathing the mucosa with acid and intravenous atropine (4), yet it is abolished during perfusion with a dextran-Tyrode solution (38). Although gastric blood flow is poorly regulated when perfusion pressure is reduced, oxygen uptake is extremely well regulated (13). Oxygen extraction is normally less than 25% at control gastric blood flows. Reductions in blood flow (mechanical) of 50 and 75% do not result in a significant reduction in gastric oxygen uptake since oxygen extraction increases sufficiently to compensate for the reduced blood flow. An increased capillary density presumably accounts for part of the increased O_2 extraction at low perfusion pressures since intracellular P_{O_2} decreases by only 60% when blood flow is 25% of normal (13). Autoregulation of gastric O_2 uptake is not evident when blood flow is reduced by intra-arterial infusion of vasopressin.

Elevation of venous pressure results in a diminution of blood flow and an increased gastric vascular resistance (38), a reaction atrributable to myogenic control. The response of the gastric vasculature to venous pressure elevation is smaller than that observed in the small bowel, but the frequency of occurrence is comparable to that of other abdominal organs. The resistance response of the gastric vasculature to venous pressure elevation is abolished when the stomach is perfused with a dextran-Tyrode solution (38). Thus both myogenic and metabolic factors may be involved in the intrinsic regulation of gastric blood flow and oxygenation.

The relations among gastric acid secretion, blood flow, and O_2 consumption have been investigated (26). Considerable evidence strongly supports a direct relationship between gastric blood flow and acid secretion, observed when net secretion is induced by vagal stimulation, histamine, and pentagastrin (5, 40). The observation that many vasoconstrictor and vasodilator agents alter secretion and blood flow in a parallel fashion may not prove relevant to the functional hyperemic response. Unlike the case with acid secretion, there is little correlation between the secretion of pepsin and blood flow (50). The ultimate link between gastric acid secretion and blood flow is not yet known; however, histamine appears a likely candidate. Recent evidence suggests that the effects of histamine on blood flow are predominantly mediated through H_1 receptor activation, whereas H_2 receptors primarily control secretion. Thus cimetidine (an H_2 blocker) exerts little effect on gastric blood flow, yet inhibits acid secretion (10).

The relationship between gastric O_2 consumption and acid secretion has been studied during histamine, cimetidine, thiocyanate, and PGE_2 infusions (5, 31, 42). The available literature suggests that the increased O_2 demand during gastric secretion is met almost entirely by increases in blood flow, while O_2 extraction plays a more minor role. Early suggestions that O_2 extraction values are difficult to interpret due to A-V shunts (65) no longer apply, since arteriovenous anastomoses apparently do not exist in the gastric circulation (21). In spite of the close correlation between gastric O_2 consumption and acid secretion, little evidence supports the existence of a metabolic control system linking oxidative metabolism and blood flow.

LIVER

The circulation of the liver is coupled with the gastrointestinal tract in series through the portal vein and in parallel via the hepatic artery. Arterial flow is about one third of the total hepatic blood flow and supplies 50% of the O_2 consumed by the resting liver.

Autoregulation of blood flow has been described in the hepatic arterial system in sympathetically denervated preparations (24, 63); however, there is no evidence of autoregulation in sympathetically innervated preparations (54, 59). The intensity of hepatic arterial autoregulation (in sympathetically denervated preparations) equals that observed in the small intestine (the reduction in vascular resistance is one half the reduction in arterial pressure) at perfusion pressures below 100 mm Hg, yet it greatly exceeds that of the small bowel at perfusion pressures between 100–200 mm Hg (percentage changes in resistance and pressure are equal). Hepatic arterial autoregulation is reduced in intensity when portal inflow is diverted from the liver (24). Pressure-flow studies on the portal venous system generally indicate a passive vascular bed (3, 24, 54). Portal resistance either does not change or increases as portal pressure is decreased. Autoregulation of portal venous flow is often observed in preparations perfused with artificial perfusates of low hematocrit (9, 62). Hydrodynamic interactions between the hepatic artery and the portal vein have been established (14, 34); in general, a reduction in inflow and pressure in one circuit leads to a reduction in the inflow resistance of the other circuit. Although significant, the reciprocal relationship between portal and hepatic inflows is inadequate to compensate for compromised blood flow in one inflow circuit.

One variable that seems to be well regulated in the liver is oxygen uptake. Oxygen extraction is normally less than 40% at control blood flow and can increase to 95% during relative ischemia (39). The extreme efficiency of

O_2 extraction, which is otherwise only seen in the coronary circulation, is sufficient to allow for the maintenance of a constant O_2 uptake (within 10% of control) in spite of a reduction of hepatic blood flow in excess of 50% (39). Autoregulation of hepatic O_2 uptake is also observed when total liver blood flow is reduced by hepatic venous pressure elevation and sympathetic nerve stimulation (36). Oxygen uptake by the liver also remains unimpaired during moderate hemodilution (35). It appears that oxygen extraction by the liver is far more efficient than in most organs in the gastrointestinal tract, presumably owing to the small diffusion distances for O_2 transport between blood and parenchymal cells and the sensitivity of presinusoidal sphincters to either tissue Po_2 or metabolites.

Elevation of hepatic venous pressure increases hepatic arterial resistance (24), a reaction attributed to a myogenic control mechanism. The effects of increased venous pressure are most marked at portal pressures below 10 mm Hg. Reactive hyperemic responses by the hepatic artery are observed following brief periods of arterial occlusion. The magnitude and duration of the hyperemic response increase as the duration of arterial occlusion is increased. During shunting of portal venous flow, the postocclusion response of the hepatic artery is greatly attenuated or abolished (24).

Local mechanisms do appear to play an important role in regulating blood flow through the liver. The response of the hepatic circulation to venous outflow pressure elevation has prompted most investigators to put the accent on the myogenic control mechanisms whereas metabolic factors have been deemphasized (24, 34). Although the existance of a myogenic control mechanism cannot be refuted, a powerful metabolic control system also exists that allows for the maintenance of a relatively constant hepatic oxygen uptake over a wide range of liver blood flows. The latter observations are consistent with a metabolic model predicting that oxygen delivery to parenchymal cells, not blood flow per se, is the controlled variable. Metabolites that exhibit demonstrable vasodilator effects on the liver circulation and that may elicit presinusoidal sphincter relaxation include adenosine, K^+, osmolality, and H^+ (14, 37).

Little is known about the relationships among liver function, blood flow, and oxygen uptake. During digestion, total liver blood flow increases (25). The postprandial hyperemic response is primarily due to an increased portal venous outflow from the intestines. Comparable increases in liver blood flow (and oxygen uptake) are noted upon infusion of amino acids and glucose (22). Gastrointestinal hormones significantly increase hepatic arterial flow when infused locally to achieve levels observed after a meal (49, 53). The glycogenolytic hormones (glucagon and epinephrine) also increase total liver blood flow (52). Many choleretic agents alter hepatic blood flow (41, 49); however, quantitative relationships between biliary secretion, hepatic blood flow, and oxygen uptake have not been established. Bile acids can cause a decrease in portal venous flow, an increase in hepatic arterial flow, or exert no significant effect on either vascular circuit. Although it has been suggested that the enterohepatic circulation of bile salts might be involved in the control of liver blood flow (41), little evidence supports this possibility.

SUMMARY

Several mechanisms are involved in the intrinsic regulation of splanchnic blood flows. Of these, myogenic, metabolic, and hormonal factors appear particularly important. The relative contributions of these elements vary with the status of the tissue. Myogenic and metabolic mechanisms prevail during stress states such as arterial pressure reduction or venous pressure elevation, thereby regulating microvascular pressures and O_2 exchange. During periods of enhanced functional activity, hormonal and metabolic mechanisms appear to work in concert to assure adequate delivery of nutrients and O_2 to, and removal of metabolites and absorbed elements from, the active tissue.

Literature Cited

1. Bohlen, H. G. 1980. Intestinal tissue Po_2 and microvascular responses during glucose exposure. *Am. J. Physiol.* 238:H164–71
2. Bond, J. H., Prentiss, R. A., Levitt, M. D. 1979. The effects of feeding on blood flow to the stomach, small bowel and colon of the conscious dog. *J. Lab. Clin. Med.* 93:594–99
3. Brauer, R. W., Leong, G. F., McElroy, R. F., Holloway, R. J. 1956. Hemodynamics of the vascular tree of the isolated rat liver preparation. *Am. J. Physiol.* 186:537–42
4. Bruggeman, T., Wood, J. G., Davenport, H. W. 1979. Local control of blood flow in the dog's stomach: vasodilation caused by acid back-diffusion following topical application of salicylic acid. *Gastroenterology* 77:736–44
5. Cheung, L. Y., Moody, F. G., Larson, K., Lowry, S. F. 1978. Oxygen consumption during cimetidine and prostaglandin E_2 inhibition of acid secretion. *Am. J. Physiol.* 234:E445–50
6. Chou, C. C., Hsieh, C. P., Dabney, J. M. 1977. Comparison of vascular effects of gastrointestinal hormones on various organs. *Am. J. Physiol.* 232:H103–9
7. Chou, C. C., Hsieh, C. P., Yu, Y. M. 1976. Localization of mesenteric hype-

remia during digestion in dogs. *Am. J. Physiol.* 230:583–89
8. Chou, C. C., Kvietys, P. R., Post, J., Sit, S. P. 1978. Constituents of chyme responsible for postprandial intestinal hyperemia. *Am. J. Physiol.* 235:H677–82
9. Condon, R. E., Chapman, N. D., Nieus, L. M., Harkins, H. N. 1962. Hepatic arterial and portal venous pressure flow relationships in isolated perfused liver. *Am. J. Physiol.* 202:1090–94
10. Delaney, J. P., Michel, H. M., Bond, J. 1978. Cimetidine and gastric blood flow. *Surgery* 84:190–92
11. Fara, J. W., Rubinstein, E. H., Sonnenschein, R. R. 1972. Intestinal hormones in mesenteric vasodilation after intraduodenal agents. *Am. J. Physiol.* 223:1058–67
12. Gallavan, R. H., Chou, C. C., Kvietys, P. R., Sit, S. P. 1980. Distribution of blood flow during digestion in conscious dogs. *Am. J. Physiol. (Heart Circ. Physiol.)* 238:H220–25
13. Garg, D. K. 1979. Cellular oxygenation and metabolism during ischemia in gastric mucosa. *Texas Med.* 75:56–60
14. Gelman, S., Ernst, E. A. 1977. Role of pH and O_2 content of portal blood on

hepatic circulatory autoregulation. *Am. J. Physiol.* 233:E225–62

15. Granger, D. N., Richardson, P. D. I., Kvietys, P. R., Mortillaro, N. A. 1980. Intestinal blood flow. *Gastroenterology* 78:837–63

16. Granger, D. N., Richardson, P. D. I., Taylor, A. E. 1979. Volumetric assessment of the capillary filtration coefficient in the cat small intestine. *Pflügers Arch.* 381:25–33

17. Granger, D. N., Taylor, A. E. 1979. Intestinal secretagogues: effects on *in vivo* and *in vitro* oxygen consumption. *Fed. Proc.* 38:952

18. Granger, D. N., Valleau, J. D., Parker, R. E., Lane, R., Taylor, A. E. 1978. Effects of adenosine on vascular hemodynamics, oxygen delivery and capillary fluid exchange in the feline small intestine. *Am. J. Physiol.* 235:H707–19

19. Granger, H. J., Norris, C. P. 1980. Role of adenosine in local control of intestinal circulation. *Cir. Res.* 46:764–70

20. Granger, H. J., Norris, C. P. 1980. Intrinsic regulation of intestinal oxygenation in the anesthetized dog. *Am. J. Physiol.* 238:H836–43

21. Guth, P. H. 1976. Control of gastric blood flow. *Biblio. Anat.* 16:126–28

22. Hallberg, D., Soda, M. 1974. Effects of various parenteral nutritional solutions on hepatic blood flow in dogs. *Acta Chir. Scand.* 140:226–31

23. Hanson, K. M. 1973. Hemodynamic effects of distension of the dog small intestine. *Am. J. Physiol.* 225:456–60

24. Hanson, K. M., Johnson, P. C. 1966. Local control of hepatic arterial and total venous flow in the dog. *Am. J. Physiol.* 211:712–20

25. Hopkinson, B. R., Schenk, W. G. 1968. The electromagnetic measurement of liver blood flow and cardiac output in conscious dogs during feeding and exercise. *Surgery* 63:970–75

26. Jacobson, E. D. 1967. Secretion and blood flow in the gastrointestinal tract. In *Handbook of Physiology, Gastrointestinal Physiology,* Vol. II, Ch. 59, pp. 1043–62. Baltimore: Am. Physiol. Soc.

27. Jacobson, E. D., Scott, J. B., Frohlich, E. D. 1962. Hemodynamics of the stomach. I. Resistance-flow relationship in the gastric vascular bed. *Am. J. Dig. Dis.* 7:779–90

28. Johnson, P. C. 1959. Myogenic nature of increase in intestinal vascular resistance with venous pressure elevation. *Circ. Res.* 6:992–99

29. Johnson, P. C. 1960. Autoregulation of intestinal blood flow. *Am. J. Physiol.* 199:311–18

30. Johnson, P. C. 1964. Origin, localization and significance of autoregulation in the intestine. *Circ. Res.* 14–15: 225–33 (Suppl.)

31. Kowalewski, K., Kolodej, A. 1972. Relation between hydrogen ion secretion and oxygen consumption by ex vivo isolated canine stomach perfused with homologous blood. *Can. J. Physiol. Pharmacol.* 50:955–61

32. Kvietys, P. R., Pittman, R. P., Chou, C. C. 1976. Contribution of lumenal concentration of nutrients and osmolality to postprandial intestinal hyperemia in dogs. *Proc. Soc. Exp. Biol. Med.* 152: 659–63

33. Lanciault, G., Jacobson, E. D. 1976. The gastrointestinal circulation. *Gastroenterology* 71:851–73

34. Lautt, W. W. 1977. Hepatic vasculature: A conceptual review. *Gastroenterology* 73:1163–69

35. Lautt, W. W. 1977. Control of hepatic and intestinal blood flow: effect of isovolemic hemodilution on blood flow and oxygen uptake in the intact liver and intestines. *J. Physiol. London* 265: 313–26

36. Lautt, W. W. 1978. Hepatic presinusoidal sphincters affected by altered arterial pressure and flow, venous pressure and nerve stimulation. *Microvasc. Res.* 15:309–17

37. Lautt, W. W., McLaughlin, T. L., Brown, L. C. 1977. The effect of hypertonic infusions on hepatic blood flows and liver volume in the cat. *Can. Physiol. Pharmacol.* 55:1339–44

38. Lutz, J., Biester, J. 1971. Die Reaktion der Magengefabe auf venose und arterielle Druckreize und ihr vergleich mit Werten von Milz- und Intestinalstrombahn. *Pflügers Arch.* 330:230–42

39. Lutz, J., Schulze, H. G. 1978. Oxygen consumption and oxygen extraction of the feline liver under different types of induced hypoxia. In *Oxygen Transport to Tissue,* ed. I. A. Silver, Vol. 3. NY: Plenum

40. Main, I. H. M., Whittle, B. J. R. 1973. Gastric mucosal blood flow during pentagastrin- and histamine-stimulated acid secretion in the rat. *Brit. J. Pharmacol.* 49:534–42

41. Mitchell, G. G., Torrance, H. B. 1966. The effects of sodium dehydrocholate upon liver blood flow in man. *Brit. J. Surg.* 53:807–8

42. Moody, F. G. 1968. Oxygen consumption during thiocyanate inhibition of

gastric acid secretion in dogs. *Am. J. Physiol.* 215:127–31

43. Mortillaro, N. A., Granger, H. J. 1977. Reactive hyperemia and oxygen extraction in the feline small intestine. *Circ. Res.* 41:859–65

44. Mortillaro, N. A., Mustafa, S. J. 1978. Possible role of adenosine in the development of intestinal postocclusion reactive hyperemia. *Fed. Proc.* 37:874

45. Norris, C. P., Barnes, G. E., Smith, E. E., Granger, H. J. 1979. Autoregulation of superior mesenteric flow in fasted and fed dogs. *Am. J. Physiol.* 237:H174–77

46. Ohman, U. 1975. Studies on small intestinal obstruction. *Acta Chir. Scand.* 141:417–23

47. Parker, R. E., Granger, D. N. 1979. Effect of graded arterial occlusion on ileal blood flow distribution. *Proc. soc. Exp. Biol. Med.* 162:146–49

48. Pawlik, W., Shepherd, A. P., Jacobson, E. D. 1975. Effects of vasoactive agents on intestinal oxygen consumption and blood flow in dogs. *J. Clin. Invest.* 56:484–90

49. Post, J. A., Hanson, K. M. 1975. Hepatic vascular and biliary responses to infusion of gastrointestinal hormones and bile salts. *Digestion* 12:65–77

50. Reed, J. D., Sanders, D. J. 1971. Pepsin secretion, gastric motility and mucosal blood flow in the anesthetized cat. *J. Physiol. London* 216:159–68

51. Rehfeld, J. F., Larsson, L. I. 1979. The predominating molecular form of gastrin and cholecystokinin in the gut is a small peptide corresponding to their COOH-terminal tetrapeptide amide. *Acta Physiol. Scand.* 105:117–19

52. Richardson, P. D. I., Withrington, P. G. 1976. The vasodilator actions of isoprenaline, histamine, prostaglandin E_2, glucagon, and secretin on the hepatic arterial vascular beds of dogs. *Brit. J. Pharmacol.* 57:581–88

53. Richardson, P. D. I., Withrington, P. G. 1977. The effects of glucagon, secretin, pancreozymin and pentagastrin on the hepatic arterial vascular bed of the dog. *Brit. J. Pharmacol.* 59:147–56

54. Richardson, P. D. I., Withrington, P. G. 1978. Pressure flow relationships and effects of noradrenaline and isoprenaline on the hepatic arterial and portal venous vascular beds of the dog. *J. Physiol. London* 282:451–70

55. Roberts, K. B., Barrowman, J. A. 1979. Liver blood supply. In *The Liver and Biliary System in Infants and Children,* ed. R. K. Chandra, pp. 43–49. NY: Churchill-Livingstone.

56. Shepherd, A. P. 1977. Myogenic responses of intestinal resistance and exchange vessels. *Am. J. Physiol.* 233:H547–54

57. Shepherd, A. P. 1978. Intestinal O_2 consumption and 86 Rb extraction during arterial hypoxia. *Am. J. Physiol.* 234:248–51

58. Shepherd, A. P., Mailman, D., Burks, T. F., Granger, H. J. 1973. Effects of norepinephrine and sympathetic stimulation on extraction of oxygen and ^{86}Rb in perfused canine small bowel. *Circ. Res.* 33:166–74

59. Shoemaker, C. P. 1964. A study of hepatic hemodynamics in dog. *Circ. Res.* 15:216–33

60. Svanvik, J., Lundgren, O. 1977. Gastrointestinal circulation. *Int. Rev. Physiol. Gastrointest. Physiol. II* 12:1–34

61. Svanvik, J., Tyllstrom, J., Wallentin, I. 1968. The effects of hypercapnia and hypoxia on the distribution of capillary blood flow in the denervated intestinal vascular bed. *Acta Physiol. Scand.* 74:543–51

62. Tavoloni, N., Reed, J. S., Boyer, J. L. 1978. Hemodynamic effects on determinants of bile secretion in isolated rat liver. *Am. J. Physiol.* 234:E584–92

63. Torrance, H. B. 1961. The control of the hepatic arterial circulation. *J. Physiol. London* 158:39–49

64. Valleau, J. D., Granger, D. N., Taylor, A. E. 1979. Effect of solute coupled volume absorption on oxygen consumption in the cat ileum. *Am. J. Physiol.* 236:E198–203

65. Zeppa, H., LaRosa, J., Bilbro, R. H. 1968. Arterio-venous shunt mechanism in gastric secretion. *Am. J. Surg.* 115:185–90

Ann. Rev. Physiol. 1981. 43:419–30
Copyright © 1981 by Annual Reviews Inc. All rights reserved

CONTROL OF ENERGY ❖1320
METABOLISM OF HEART MUSCLE

Thomas C. Vary, Diane K. Reibel and James R. Neely

Department of Physiology, The Milton S. Hershey Medical Center,
The Pennsylvania State University, Hershey, Pennsylvania 17033

INTRODUCTION

Energy metabolism in cardiac muscle includes all processes involved in the production and utilization of ATP. However, this review emphasizes control of ATP production and focuses primarily on control of the pathways of fatty acid and carbohydrate oxidation. Reviews of various aspects of substrate utilization by heart muscle may be found in (36, 42, 43, 48, 60). Regulation of mitochondrial function was reviewed in (19, 23, 77). The present review concentrates on new data obtained in normal hearts and on the effects of ischemia on carbohydrate and lipid metabolism.

GENERAL FEATURES OF CONTROL OF ENERGY METABOLISM IN NORMAL HEARTS

ATP can be produced by three processes in cardiac muscle; oxidative phosphorylation (19, 77, 23), substrate level phosphorylation in glycolysis (42) and the citric acid cycle (77), and phosphorylation of ADP by creatine phosphokinase. By far the most important quantitatively is oxidative phosphorylation, which accounts for more than 90% of total ATP production over a wide range of rates of ATP use (26).

Feedback Control of Substrate Utilization

In normal tissue, the rate of oxidative phosphorylation and O_2 consumption is strictly coupled to the rate of ATP utilization (19, 77, 23). Several investigators have demonstrated a linear relationship between ventricular pressure development and myocardial oxygen consumption. The increase in O_2 consumption is accompanied by an increase in flux through the

419

0066-4278/81/0315-0419$01.00

electron transport chain resulting in a decreased mitochondrial NADH/NAD ratio (26). When O_2 consumption is increased, rates of oxidation of acetyl CoA via the citric acid cycle, β-oxidation of fatty acyl CoA, and flux through pyruvate dehydrogenase tend to increase owing to the lower NADH/NAD ratio (42, 43, 59, 77).

Fatty acid oxidation in normal hearts is also controlled by changes in the acetyl CoA/CoA ratio in the mitochondria and in the cytosol (42, 51, 50). High levels of acetyl CoA in the matrix reduce the level of free CoA available for β-oxidation (see Figure 1). The acetyl carnitine transferase and transport system is thought to play a key role in coupling the rates of fatty acid activation in the cytosol to rates of acetyl CoA oxidation in the mitochondria by adjusting the cytosolic acetyl CoA/CoA ratio in accordance with changes in the mitochondrial ratio (53, 75).

Acetyl CoA production from pyruvate oxidation is mediated by changes in mitochondrial matrix acetyl CoA/CoA and NADH/NAD ratios (59). Pyruvate dehydrogenase activity is regulated by both phosphorylation-dephosphorylation reactions and by allosteric control of the active form of the enzyme. Increased rates of oxidative phosphorylation tend to increase pyruvate dehydrogenase activity by lowering the NADH/NAD and acetyl CoA/CoA ratios. This mechanism appears to account for changes in pyruvate oxidation in isolated hearts (K. Kobayashi, J. R. Neely, unpublished observations).

The major source of pyruvate in cardiac muscle is production from glucose via glycolysis. Control of glycolysis occurs at glucose transport, phosphofructokinase, and glyceraldehyde-3-phosphate (42, 43). It is doubt-

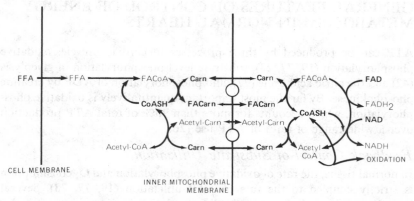

Figure 1 Pathway of fatty acid oxidation. FFA = Free fatty acids; FACoA = Long-chain acyl CoA; FACarn = Long-chain acyl carnitine; Carn = Free carnitine; CoASH = Free coenzyme A.

ful that the activity of pyruvate dehydrogenase ever controls the overall rate of glucose utilization. Coupling of glycolysis to mitochondrial oxidative rates is mediated by changes in the cytosolic energy charge, levels of citrate, and the NADH/NAD ratio. A decreased energy charge is important in acceleration of glycolysis in oxygen deficient tissue through stimulation of glucose transport and phosphofructokinase. It may also account for increased glucose utilization when cardiac work is raised in isolated hearts receiving glucose as the only exogenous substrate (45). Citrate inhibition of phosphofructokinase is important in restricting glycolysis in aerobic hearts when alternate substrates such as fatty acids are present (42, 43, 60).

Control of glycolysis is also mediated by the cytosolic redox state. NADH produced by glycolysis must be oxidized either by transport of reducing equivalents into the mitochondria via the malate-aspartate shuttle (23) or by lactate dehydrogenase conversion of pyruvate to lactate (26). When glycolysis is increased, production of NADH by glyceraldehyde-3-P dehydrogenase is also increased. Oxidation of this extra NADH by either the conversion of oxaloacetate to malate or pyruvate to lactate requires increased levels of NADH to accelerate these reactions. The level of NADH thus increases in proportion to glycolytic rate and eventually reaches a concentration inhibitory to glyceraldehyde-3-P dehydrogenase, whereupon no further increase in glycolytic rate can occur (26). In ischemic hearts where mitochondrial oxidation is reduced, failure to wash lactate out of the tissue results in high levels of NADH, which inhibits glycolysis even though the energy charge is low and glycolysis should be accelerated (38, 65, 66).

Control of Tissue Levels of Coenzyme A and Carnitine

Metabolism of fatty acids requires the presence of two cofactors, coenzyme A and carnitine (see Figure 1). CoA is required for activation of free fatty acids to the acyl CoA ester, which in turn serves as substrate for esterification of triglycerides and phospholipids and for the β-oxidation reactions. The long-chain acyl CoA ester is formed in the cytosol and cannot penetrate the inner mitochondrial membrane to the sites of β-oxidation. Carnitine is essential for the transport of the acyl unit into mitochondria (16, 54, 55). Carnitine: acyl CoA transferase I transfers the acyl unit from CoA to carnitine in the cytosol; the acyl carnitine is then transported into the matrix in exchange for free carnitine. Once inside the matrix, carnitine: acyl CoA transferase II transfers the acyl unit back to CoA (Figure 1). Normally, the total amount of CoA and carnitine in the tissue remains constant, but distribution among the various acyl esters and free cofactor can vary over a wide range (50, 57, 76). Although these cofactors are central in the metabolism of fatty acids, pyruvate, ketone bodies, certain amino acids, and other compounds, little is known about the control of their levels.

Coenzyme A is synthesized in the heart from pantothenic acid (63, 70). Hearts from diabetic (15) or fasting (64) animals have increased levels of total CoA as well as increased distribution of CoA into the acyl esters (58). In vivo studies with ^{14}C-pantothenic acid indicate that the rate of CoA synthesis is increased in both diabetic and fasted animals (64). The specific control of CoA synthesis is not understood. However, in vitro studies with perfused rat hearts have shown that pantothenic acid incorporation into CoA can be markedly altered depending on the type of energy substrate and the amount of insulin present (63). Inclusion of substrates that increase the acylation of CoA such as fatty acids, pyruvates, and ketone bodies inhibit ^{14}C-pantothenic acid conversion to CoA, suggesting that feedback control of synthesis by CoA or one of its acyl derivatives may exist. In addition, insulin is a powerful inhibitor of synthesis, and reduced levels of insulin in the diabetic or fasting animal may be an important factor determining the increased synthesis of CoA under these conditions.

Carnitine is synthesized by several tissues of the body, primarily liver, but not by heart muscle (18). Myocardial levels of carnitine are maintained by uptake from the blood. In rats, serum carnitine is approximately 50 μmolar, and cellular free carnitine ranges from 1–4 mmolar [(75); J. R. Neely, unpublished observation]. Thus transport of carnitine into the cells occurs against a concentration gradient. Kinetic data obtained on isolated cell preparations indicate that transport is a carrier-mediated process requiring metabolic energy (5, 39, 40). Tissue levels of total carnitine are low in newborn animals and reach adult levels within days to weeks (71); they decrease by 50% in aged rats (1) and are reduced in pathological conditions such as diabetes (15) and certain genetic carnitine deficiencies. It isn't clear whether changes in tissue carnitine reflect only changes in serum carnitine or whether control of transport regulates cellular levels under some of these conditions.

ENERGY METABOLISM IN ISCHEMIC HEARTS

Myocardial ischemia continues to be used in the literature to describe a wide variety of experimental conditions. By definition, ischemia means a deficiency of blood flow to a tissue. In the case of the heart, an ischemic state (as reflected by a decrease in the energy supply/demand ratio) may result (a) from coronary flow below that required to meet normal myocardial energy needs at body rest, or (b) when coronary arteries are partially occluded and will not permit the normal increase in coronary flow in response to increased cardiac work. In either case, a negative energy balance results, but the metabolic consequences may be quite different. Products of metabolism such as H^+, lactate, CO_2, and others would accumulate much more at subnormal coronary flow, and these compounds can inhibit metabolic processes.

A reduction in coronary flow results in several characteristic metabolic changes. Creatine phosphate levels decline by 80–90% within minutes, followed by a slower decrease in ATP and loss of total adenine nucleotides (7, 30, 44). An initial stimulation of glycogenolysis is followed by inhibition of glycolysis (66), and inhibition of β-oxidation of fatty acids (76) occurs. Long-chain acyl esters of CoA and carnitine and free fatty acids accumulate, reduce fatty acid uptake, and increase conversion to complex lipids.

Adenine Nucleotide Metabolism

Degradation of ATP occurs by the following pathway: ATP→ADP→AMP →adenosine→inosine→hypoxanthine. ATP is converted to ADP by numerous reactions and ADP is rephosphorylated primarily by oxidative phosphorylation. AMP is normally produced from synthetic reactions that hydrolyze pyrophosphate from ATP, and it is usually rephosphorylated to ADP by adenylate kinase in the cytosol and by the GTP requiring transphosphorylation reactions in mitochondria. Normally, AMP levels are low, and dephosphorylation to adenosine by 5'-nucleotidase occurs at a slow rate (67). Unlike the phosphorylated nucleotides, adenosine can penetrate the cell membrane, and loss of nucleotides by this route is normally balanced by de novo synthesis of adenosine (4, 25, 67). In oxygen deficient hearts, however, the loss of adenosine is accelerated, and a net decrease in the total adenine nucleotide pool occurs (21, 25, 62). The mechanism of nucleotide loss is unknown, but it may result from increased cytosolic levels of AMP (6). With decreased oxidative metabolism and reduced levels of ATP and GTP, rephosphorylation of AMP to ADP cannot occur. In the face of increased cytosolic AMP, the high activity and low K_m for AMP of 5'-nucleotidease could account for the increased adenosine production.

Reperfusion of ischemic hearts results in rapid resynthesis of creatine phosphate, but ATP levels remain depressed (62, 73). The lack of ATP resynthesis is due to loss of nucleosides and nucleotides as substrates for phosphorylation, and the depleted nucleotide pool cannot rapidly be replenished by de novo synthesis of nucleosides. It is estimated that only 0.4% of the nucleotide pool can be replaced per hour by de novo synthesis (80). Irreversible damage to myocardial cells may result when ATP levels are too low to support critical cellular functions such as contraction, cell ion and volume control, and substrate activation reactions (30, 61). Also, mitochondrial oxidative rates may be restricted by low matrix adenine nucleotides (28).

Carbohydrate Metabolism

Control of glycolysis has been reviewed extensively (42, 43, 47, 60). New developments in this area relate to control of maximum glycolytic rates in aerobic and ischemic hearts. Glycolysis is accelerated in aerobic hearts receiving glucose as the only substrate in proportion to cardiac work (26). Stimulation of glucose transport and phosphofructokinase account for the increased glycolytic flux (42). With activation of these normally rate-limiting steps, the slowest step in the pathway shifts to glyceraldehyde-3-P dehydrogenase (26), and the rate of this reaction probably determines the upper limit to which glycolysis can be stimulated. The maximum rate of this step depends on the rapidity of oxidation of cytosolic NADH by the malate-aspartate shuttle and by lactate production from pyruvate. As the rate of glycolysis increases, so does the rate of NADH production by glyceraldehyde-3-P dehydrogenase. Since tissue levels of oxaloacetate and pyruvate are normally low (23, 43, 60, 77), acceleration of NADH oxidation by malate and lactate dehydrogenases requires an increase in the cytosolic NADH (26). Thus levels of NADH rise in proportion to increased glycolysis, which causes a proportional increase in the activity of the malate-aspartate shuttle and pyruvate conversion to lactate. However, the progressive rise in cytosolic NADH eventually reaches a level where further increase in glyceraldehyde-3-P dehydrogenase is prevented owing to inhibition of the enzyme by NADH (38).

In ischemic tissue, the mitochondrial oxidation of NADH by the malate-aspartate shuttle is inoperative and only production of lactate allows glycolysis to proceed. Because of increased conversion of pyruvate to lactate and slow washout of lactate from the vascular spaces, cellular lactate accumulates to very high levels even at relatively low glycolytic rates (65, 66). This build-up of lactate causes a mass action effect on lactate dehydrogenase that results in an equal increase in cytosolic NADH. When NADH reaches inhibitory levels for glycolysis, the pathway becomes inhibited at glycolytic rates even lower than normal aerobic rates. This inhibition of anaerobic ATP production in ischemic tissue may accelerate onset of irreversible cellular damage.

Fatty Acid Metabolism

Ischemia results in lower rates of fatty acid oxidation to CO_2 and uptake by the tissue (76). Oxidation is inhibited at the level of β-oxidation probably owing to increased mitochondrial NADH and $FADH_2$. The slower rate of β-oxidation causes a build up of the intermediates, long-chain acyl CoA and acyl carnitine (Figure 1). Acyl CoA and acyl carnitine probably increase in both cytosolic and mitochondrial compartments because the equilibrium constants for the carnitine acyl CoA transferases are near 1 (42, 43). However, since 95% of the total CoA is mitochondrial, most of the increase in acyl CoA must occur in this organelle. On the other hand, 95% of the total carnitine is cytosolic, and most of the acyl carnitine must accumulate on the outside of the inner mitochondrial membrane (75). With the increase in cytosolic acyl carnitine, cytosolic acyl CoA would also increase. This rise in cytosolic acyl CoA would be expected to inhibit the acyl CoA synthases (11, 12, 51) resulting in higher tissue levels of free fatty acids; this would account for the observed decrease in fatty acid uptake.

Synthesis of triglycerides occurs in the cytosol using α-glycerolphosphate and acyl CoA as substrates, and triglyceride levels increase in ischemic hearts (42, 48, 76). The control of triglyceride homeostasis in heart muscle is poorly understood. Normally, a balance between synthesis and lipolysis is maintained and triglyceride levels remain fairly constant. However, a number of conditions upset this balance so that either net synthesis or lipolysis occurs. For example, isolated hearts show net lipolysis when perfused under conditions of substrate deprivation (10, 41, 46) at high levels of cardiac work with glucose the only exogenous substrate (9, 41), or when treated with catecholamines (7, 9, 29, 72). Triglyceride levels are increased when the supply of exogenous fatty acids and other substrates is elevated in isolated hearts (9, 20, 41) and under in vivo conditions such as diabetes (14). These observations suggest that triglyceride lipases are controlled by both hormonal and metabolic factors. Intercellular lipases, which appear to be under the control of catecholamines, have been identified (7, 10, 20, 29). The increase in triglycerides in the presence of excess substrate supply, diabetes, and in ischemic hearts, and the decrease with substrate deprivation or increased cardiac work may be mediated by changes in cytosolic levels of acyl CoA. The levels of acyl CoA are higher under conditions where net triglyceride synthesis occurs and are lower when net lipolysis occurs. Also, estimates of lipase activity in heart homogenates indicate that acyl CoA is a specific inhibitor of lipase activity (K. McDonough, J. R. Neely, unpublished observations).

Metabolic Products and Cellular Function in Ischemic Hearts

Simple oxygen deficiency does not in itself cause irreversible damage to the tissue. It results in decreased ATP production and, by an as yet unknown mechanism, an immediate decrease in contractility (17). Both the rate of ATP synthesis and contractility return to normal if oxygen supply is restored within several minutes. However, if the reduced supply of oxygen is continued, the tissue eventually becomes irreversibly damaged. The metabolic and structural alterations that occur during ischemia are numerous, and all of them probably contribute to a cascade of secondary alterations that result from reduced oxidative metabolism and that collectively cause irreversible damage. This cascade of events may start with the accumulation of metabolic products due to decreased oxidative metabolism and coronary flow. Of the many products that accumulate, the most notable are: inorganic phosphate, ADP, AMP, and the degradation products of adenine nucleotides. The rise in mitocondrial NADH inhibits β-oxidation of fatty acid causing the increase in acyl CoA and acyl carnitine. The magnitude of increase in these acyl esters is proportional to exogenous fatty acid concentration (76). Pyruvate oxidation to acetyl CoA and mitochondrial oxidation of cytosolic NADH are both curtailed. Consequently, cytosolic NADH increases and the pyruvate produced by glycolysis is converted to lactate that cannot be washed out of the tissue and thus accumulates. The H^+ that would normally be neutralized to H_2O by oxidative metabolism also increases. The combined effect of increased cytosolic NADH, lactate, and H^+ effectively shuts off ATP production by glycolysis. The increase in cytosolic AMP accelerates its dephosphorylation to adenosine, which is lost from the cell and probably accounts for the net decrease in adenine nucleotides and failure to restore ATP levels with reoxygenation. The decline in ATP is associated with and may account for irreversible loss of other cellular functions such as contractility, cell volume control, ion pumps, and synthetic reactions.

The rise in acyl CoA, acyl carnitine, and free fatty acids may have secondary effects that contribute to cell damage. These compounds are active detergents and bind extensively to cell membranes. Disruption of membrane structure and functions is a major event in ischemic damage. Plasma membranes become leaky to small molecules and enzymes. Mitochondrial membranes become distorted and broken; aggregates of electron opaque lipid material (probably broken membranes) appear (22). The appearance of these amorphous opacities is associated with the presence of exogenous fatty acid (13) and high tissue levels of acyl CoA and acyl carnitine (76). The presence of fatty acids also caused increased enzyme release from ischemic hearts (13). Hydrolysis of phospholipids by lipase action (52) may cause accumulation of lysophosphatidyl products, which are also detergents and which have effects on electrical and mechanical function of cardiac muscle (71). The combined effects of these detergents may cause conformational changes in membrane structure and, in severe cases, lysis of the membrane. Thus the insertion of these detergent molecules into the lipid membranes may account for much of the membrane damage that occurs during ischemia.

In addition to the detergent action, these products of ischemic heart metabolism may have numerous effects on specific enzymatic processes. From in vitro studies, acyl CoA inhibits adenine nucleotide transport in mitochondria (8), triglyceride lipase (K. McDonough, J. R. Neely, unpublished observation), and acyl CoA synthase activity (11, 12, 51). Acyl carnitine (78) and lysophosphatidyl choline (24) inhibit $Na^+K^+ATPase$. Acyl carnitine also inhibits oubain binding to sarcoplasma (3) and Ca^{2+} metabolism by sarcoplasmic reticulum (2). Free fatty acids also inhibit $Na^+K^+ATPase$ (32, 37) and Ca^{2+} efflux from sarcoplasmic reticulum (27). Whether or not these effects as demonstrated in vitro ever occur in ischemic tissue is not known, but this possibility should not be ignored. There is considerable evidence that excess fatty acid availability is detrimental to cardiac function under ischemic conditions (33, 34, 35, 48, 49, 56, 69, 79). The presence of excess fatty acids in hypoxic or ischemic hearts depresses cardiac function (6). Excess circulating fatty acids have been correlated with development of arrhythmias in ischemic heart patients (31). Pharmacological inhibition of acyl CoA formation and fatty acid oxidation greatly improved function of hypoxic hearts (56), suggesting that the effects of fatty acids are not mediated by the fatty acid per se or certainly not by the fatty acid alone. Thus, the associated rise in metabolites of fatty acids could contribute to the detrimental effects of high fatty acid concentration in ischemic tissue.

Literature Cited

1. Abu-Erreish, G. M., Neely, J. R., Whitmer, J. T., Whitman, V., Sanadi, D. R. 1977. Fatty acid oxidation by isolated perfused working hearts of aged rats. *Am. J. Physiol.* 232:E258–62

2. Adams, R. J., Cohen, D. W., Gupti, S., Johnson, J. D., Wallick, E. T., Wang, T., Schwartz, A. 1979. *In vitro* effects of palmitylcarnitine on cardiac plasma membrane Na,K-ATPase and sarcoplasmic reticulum Ca^{++}-ATPase and Ca transport. *J. Biol. Chem.* 254: 12404–10

3. Adams, R. J., Pitts, B. J. R., Woods, J. M., Gende, O. A., Wallick, E. T., Schwartz, A. 1979. Effects of palmitylcarnitine on ouabain binding to Na,K-ATPase. *J. Mol. Cell. Cardiol.* 11: 941–59

4. Berne, R. M. 1963. Cardiac nucleotides in hypoxia: Possible role in regulation of coronary blood flow. *Am. J. Physiol.* 204:317–22

5. Bohmer, T., Eiklid, K., Jonsen, J. 1977. Carnitine uptake into human heart in culture. *Biochim. Biophys. Acta* 465: 627–33

6. Burger, R., Lowenstein, J. M. 1967. Adenylate deaminase. *J. Biol. Chem.* 242:5281–88

7. Christian, D. R., Kilsheimer, G. S., Pettlett, G., Paradise, R., Ashmore, J. 1969.

Regulation of lipolysis in cardiac muscle: A system similar to hormone-sensitive lipase of adipose tissue. *Ad. Enz. Reg.* 7:71–82

8. Chua, B. H., Shrago, E. 1977. Reversible inhibition of adenine nucleotide translocation by long-chain acyl CoA esters in bovine heart mitochondria and inverted submitochondrial particles. *J. Biol. Chem.* 252:6711–14

9. Crass, M. F. III, McCaskell, E. S., Shipp, J. C., Murphy, V. K. 1971. Metabolism of endogenous lipids in cardiac muscle: Effects of pressure development. *Am. J. Physiol.* 220:428–35

10. Crass, M. F. III, Shipp, J. C., Pieper, G. M. 1975. Effects of catecholamines on myocardial endogenous substrates and contractility. *Am. J. Physiol.* 228: 618–27

11. DeJong, J. W., Hülsmann, W. C. 1970. A comparative study of palmitoly-CoA synthetase activity in rat liver, heart and gut mitochondrial and microsomal preparations. *Biochim. Biophys. Acta* 197:127–35

12. DeJong, W. C., Hülsmann, W. C. 1970. Effects of Nagarse, adenosine and hexokinase on palmitate activation and oxidation. *Biochim. Biophys. Acta* 210:499–501

13. DeLeiris, J., Feuvray, D. 1977. Ischemic-induced damage in working rat heart preparation: The effect of perfusate substrate composition upon subendocardial ultrastructure of ischemic left ventricular wall. *J. Mol. Cell. Cardiol.* 9:365–73

14. Denton, R., Randle, P. J. 1967. Concentration of glycerides and phospholipids in rat heart and gastrocnemius muscle: Effects of alloxan diabetes. *Biochem. J.* 104:416–22

15. Feuvray, D., Idell-Wenger, J. A., Neely, J. R. 1979. Effects of ischemia on rat myocardial function and metabolism in diabetes. *Circ. Res.* 44:322–29

16. Fritz, I. B. 1968. The metabolic consequences of the effects of carnitine on long-chain fatty acid oxidation. In *Cellular Compartmentation and Control of Fatty Acid Metabolism.* Oslo: Universitetsforlaget. pp. 39–63

17. Gudbjarnson, S., Mathes, P., Ravens, K. G. 1970. Functional compartmentation of ATP and creatine phosphate in heart muscle. *J. Mol. Cell. Cardiol.* 1:325–39

18. Haigler, H. T., Broquist, H. P. 1974. Carnitine synthesis in rat tissue slices. *Biochem. Biophys. Res. Commun.* 56:676–81

19. Hinkle, P. C., McCarty, R. E. 1978. How cells make ATP. *Sci. Am.* 238(3): 104–24

20. Hron, W. T., Menahan, L. A., Lech, J. J. 1978. Inhibition of hormonal stimulation of lipolysis in perfused rat heart by ketone bodies. *J. Mol. Cell. Cardiol.* 10:161–74

21. Imai, S., Riley, A. L., Berne, R. M. 1964. Effect of ischemia on adenine nucleotides in cardiac and skeletal muscle. *Circ. Res.* 15:443–50

22. Jennings, R. B., Ganote, C. E. 1976. Mitochondrial structure and function in acute myocardial ischemic injury. *Circ. Res.* 38:180–89

23. LaNoue, K. F., Schoolwerth, A. C. 1979. Metabolic transport in mitochondria. *Ann. Rev. Biochem.* 48:871–922

24. Karli, J. N., Karikas, G. A., Hatzipavlow, P. K., Levis, G. M., Moulopoulos, S. N. 1979. The inhibition of Na^+ and K^+ stimulated ATPase activity of rabbit and dog heart sarcolemma by lysophosphotidyl choline. *Life Sci.* 24:1869–76

25. Katori, M., Berne, R. M. 1966. Release of adenosine from anoxic hearts. Relationship to coronary flow. *Circ. Res.* 19:420–25

26. Kobayashi, K., Neely, J. R. 1979. Control of maximum rates of glycolysis in rat cardiac muscle. *Circ. Res.* 44:166–75

27. Katz, A. M., Nash-Adler, P., Micele, J., Messineo, F., Louis, C. F. 1979. Inhibition of Ca efflux from the sarcoplasmic reticulum by free fatty acids. *Circulation* 60:(Suppl. II) 12

28. Koch, C., LaNoue, K. F. 1977. Depletion of mitochondrial nucleotides due to cardiac ischemia. *Fed. Proc.* 36:432 (Abstr.)

29. Kreisberg, R. A. 1966. Effects of epinephrine on myocardial triglyceride and free fatty acid utilization. *Am. J. Physiol.* 210:385–89

30. Kubler, W., Spieckermann, P. G. 1971/72. Changes in glycolysis and in high energy phosphates during myocardial ischemia with intermittent coronary perfusion. *Cardiology* 56:100–7

31. Kurien, V. A., Oliver, M. F. 1970. Metabolic cause for arrhythmias during acute myocardial hypoxia. *Lancet* 1:813–15

32. Lamens, J. M. J., Hülsmann, W. C. 1977. Inhibition of $(Na^+–K^+)$-stimulated ATPase of heart by fatty acids. *J. Mol. Cell. Cardiol.* 9:343–46

33. Liedtke, A. J., Nellis, S., Neely, J. R. 1978. Effects of excess free fatty acids on mechanical and metabolic function in normal and ischemic myocardium in swine. *Circ. Res.* 43:652–61

34. Lochner, A., Kotzé, J. G. N., Benade, A. J. S., Gevers, W. 1978. Mitochondrial oxidative phosphorylation in low-flow hypoxia: Role of free fatty acid. *J. Mol. Cell. Cardiol.* 10:857–75

35. Lochner, A., Kotzé, J. C. N., Gevers, W., Benade, A. J. S. 1979. Substrate effects on mitochondrial function and tissue lipids in low-flow hypoxia of isolated perfused rat hearts. *Basic Res. Cardiol.* 74:303–12

36. Masoro, E. J. 1977. Lipid and lipid metabolism. 1977. *Ann Rev. Physiol.* 39:301–21

37. Miller, H. M., Woodhouse, S. P. 1977. Long-chain fatty acid inhibition of sodium plus potassium-activated adenosine triphosphatase from rat heart. *Aust. J. Exp. Biol. Med. Sci.* 55:741–52

38. Mochizuki, S., Neely, J. R. 1979. Control of glyceraldehyde-3-phosphate dehydrogenase in cardiac muscle. *J. Mol. Cell. Cardiol.* 11:221–36

39. Molstad, P., Bohmer, T., Eiklid, K. 1977. Specificity and characteristics of carnitine transport in human heart cells (CCL 27) in culture. *Biochim. Biophys. Acta* 471:296–304

40. Navin, T. R., Bahl, J. J., Bressler, R. 1978. Carrier mediated transport of carnitine in isolated rat myocytes. *Clin. Res.* 26:95A (Abstr.)

41. Neely, J. R., Bowman, R. H., Morgan, H. E. 1969. Effects of ventricular pressure development and palmitate in glucose transport. *Am. J. Physiol.* 216:804–11

42. Neely, J. R., Morgan, H. E. 1974. Relationship between carbohydrate and lipid metabolism and energy balance of the heart. *Ann. Rev. Physiol.* 36:413–59

43. Neely, J. R., Rovetto, M. J., Oram, J. F. 1972. Myocardial utilization of carbohydrate and lipid. *Prog. Cardiovasc. Dis.* 15(3):289–329

44. Neely, J. R., Rovetto, M. J., Whitmer, J. T., Morgan, H. E. 1973. Effects of ischemia on ventricular function and metabolism in isolated working rat heart. *Am. J. Physiol.* 225:651–58

45. Neely, J. R., Whitmer, K. M., Mochizuki, S. 1976. Effect of mechanical activity and hormones on myocardial glucose and fatty acid utilization. *Circ. Res.* 28:22–30

46. Olson, R. E., Hoeschen, R. J. 1967. Utilization of endogenous lipid by isolated perfused rat heart. *Biochem. J.* 103:796–801

47. Opie, L. H. 1968. Metabolism of the heart in health and disease. *Am. Heart J.* 76:685–98

48. Opie, L. H. 1979. Role of carnitine in fatty acid metabolism of normal and ischemic myocardium. *Am. Heart J.* 97:375–87

49. Opie, L. H., Tansey, M., Kennelly, B. M. 1977. Proposed metabolic vicious circle in patients with large myocardial infarcts and high plasma-free fatty acid concentrations. *Lancet* 2(8044):890–92

50. Oram, J. F., Bennetch, S. L., Neely, J. R. 1973. Regulation of fatty acid utilization in isolated perfused rat heart. *J. Biol. Chem.* 248:5299–309

51. Oram, J. F., Idell-Wenger, J. A., Neely, J. R. 1975. Regulation of long-chain fatty activation in heart muscle. *J. Biol. Chem.* 250:73–78

52. Owen, K., Pang, D. C., Weglicki, W. B. 1979. Production of lysophospholipids and free fatty acids by a sarcolemmal fraction from canine myocardium. *Biochem. Biophys. Res. Commun.* 89:368–73

53. Pande, S. V. 1973. Reversal by CoA of palmityl CoA inhibition of long-chain acyl-CoA synthase activity. *Biochim. Biophys. Acta* 306:15–20

54. Pande, S. V. 1975. A mitochondrial carnitine: acylcarnitine translocase system. *Proc. Natl. Acad. Sci. USA* 72:883–87

55. Pande, S. V., Parvin, R. 1976. Characterization of carnitine acylcarnitine translocase system of heart mitochondria. *J. Biol. Chem.* 251:6683–91

56. Pearce, F. J., Forster, J., DeLeeuw, G., Williamson, J. R., Tutwiller, G. F. 1979. Inhibition of fatty acid oxidation in normal and hypoxic perfused rat hearts by 2-tetradecylglycidic acid. *J. Mol. Cell. Cardiol.* 11:893–915

57. Pearson, D. J., Tubbs, P. K. 1967. Carnitine and derivatives in rat tissue. *Biochem. J.* 105:953–63

58. Randle, P. J., Garland, P. B., Hales, C. N., Newsholme, E. A., Denton, R. M., Pogson, C. I. 1966. Interactions of metabolism and physiological role of insulin. *Rec. Prog. Horm. Res.* 22:1–48

59. Randle, P. J., Sugden, P. H., Kerbey, A. L., Radcliffe, M., Hutson, N. J. 1978. Regulation of pyruvate oxidation and the conservation of glucose. *Biochem. Soc. Symp.* 43:47–67

60. Randle, P. J., Tubbs, P. K. 1979. Carbohydrate and fatty acid metabolism. In *Handbook of Physiology. The Cardiovascular System, Vol. I, The Heart*, ed. R. M. Berne, N. Sperelakis, pp. 805–844. Bethesda, MD: Am. Physiol. Soc.

61. Reibel, D. K., Rovetto, M. J. 1978. Myocardial ATP synthesis and mechanical function following oxygen deficiency. *Am. J. Physiol.* 234:H620–24

62. Reibel, D. K., Rovetto, M. J. 1979. Myocardial adenosine salvage rates and restoration of ATP content following ischemia. *Am. J. Physiol.* 237:H247–52

63. Reibel, D. K., Wyse, B. W., Berkich, D. A., Neely, J. R. 1980. The effect of energy substrates and hormones on pantothenic acid incorporation into coenzyme A in the isolated perfused rat heart. *Fed. Proc.* 39:1173 (Abstr.)

64. Reibel, D. K., Wyse, B. W., Berkich, D. A., Palko, W. M., Neely, J. R. 1981. The effect of fasting and diabetes on ^{14}C-pantothenic acid incorporation into coenzyme A in organs of the rat. Submitted for publication

65. Rovetto, M. J., Lamberton, W. F., Neely, J. R. 1975. Mechanism of glycolytic inhibition in ischemic rat hearts. *Circ. Res.* 37:742–51

66. Rovetto, M. J., Whitmer, J. T., Neely, J. R. 1973. Comparison of effects of anoxia and whole heart ischemia on carbohydrate utilization in isolated working rat hearts. *Circ. Res.* 32:699–711

67. Rubio, R., Berne, R. M. 1969. Release of adenosine by the normal myocardium in dogs and its relationship to the regulation of coronary resistance. *Circ. Res.* 25:407–15

68. Severson, D. L. 1979. Characterization of triglyceride lipase activities in rat hearts. *J. Mol. Cell. Cardiol.* 11:569–83

69. Shug, A. L., Shrago, E. 1973. Proposed mechanism for fatty acid effects on energy metabolism of the heart. *J. Lab. Clin. Med.* 81:214–19

70. Smith, C. M. 1978. The effect of metabolic state on incorporation of ^{14}C-panto-thenate into CoA in rat liver and heart. *J. Nutr.* 108:863–73

71. Sobel, B. E., Corr, P. B., Robison, A. K., Goldstein, A. A., Witkowski, F. X., Klein, M. S. 1978. Accumulation of lysophosphoglycerides with arrhythmogenic properties in ischemic myocardium. *J. Clin. Invest.* 62:546–53

72. Takenaka, K., Takeo, S. 1976. Effects of isoproterenol on myocardial lipid metabolism in rat hearts perfused with and without exogenous substrates. *J. Mol. Cell Cardiol.* 8:925–40

73. Vary, T. C., Angelakos, E. T., Schaffer, S. W. 1979. Relationship between adenine nucleotide metabolism and irreversible ischemic tissue damage in isolated perfused rat heart. *Circ. Res.* 45:218–25

74. Warshaw, J. B. 1969. Cellular energy metabolism during fetal development. *J. Cell Biol.* 41:651–57

75. Idell-Wenger, J. A., Grotyohann, L. W., Neely, J. R. 1978. Coenzyme A and carnitine distribution in normal and ischemic hearts. *J. Biol. Chem.* 253:4310–18

76. Whitmer, J. T., Idell-Wenger, J. A., Rovetto, M. J., Neely, J. R. 1978. Control of fatty acid metabolism in ischemic and hypoxic hearts. *J. Biol. Chem.* 253:4305–9

77. Williamson, J. R. 1979. Mitochondrial function in heart. *Ann. Rev. Physiol.* 41:485–506

78. Woods, J. M., Bush, B., Pitts, B. J. R., Schwartz, A. 1977. Inhibition of bovine heart Na,K-ATPase by palmitylcarnitine and palmityl CoA. *Biochem. Biophys. Res. Commun.* 74:677–84

79. Woolf, N., Steen, E., Rosen, D., Trickey, R., Long, P., Miller, A. L., Raoles, P. M. 1977. Effect of antilypolytic agents on isoprenaline-induced myocardial necrosis in the rat. *Br. J. Exp. Pathol.* 58:438–43

80. Zimmer, H. G., Trendelenburg, C., Kammermeier, H., Gerlach, E. 1973. *De novo* synthesis of myocardial adenine nucleotides in the rat. *Circ. Res.* 32:635–42

Ann. Rev. Physiol. 1981. 43:431–41
Copyright © 1981 by Annual Reviews Inc. All rights reserved

PERMEABLE JUNCTIONS
BETWEEN CARDIAC CELLS

♦1321

Ernest Page and Yosaburo Shibata

The Departments of Medicine and of Pharmacological and Physiological
Sciences, Pritzker School of Medicine, The University of Chicago, Chicago,
Illinois 60637

INTRODUCTION

In this review we assume that gap junctions are the physiological low-resistance pathways implicated in electrical coupling between cardiac cells in mammals. Alternative coupling mechanisms based on different assumptions have recently been reviewed (65) and are not considered here. We (*a*) argue that the understanding of gap junctional properties has been limited by constraints imposed on physiological experiments by the geometrical arrangement of cardiac cells; (*b*) summarize recent observations on gap junctions of noncardiac tissues, which provide essential background for the understanding of cardiac gap junctions; and (*c*) evaluate the present status of ultrastructural techniques for the study of gap junctional permeability and development.

The history of gap junctional physiology in cardiac tissues can be reconstructed from certain crucial observations: that injured heart muscle heals over (18) and that this healing requires the presence of Ca^{2+} ion and is sensitive to pH and temperature (13, 14); that cardiac tissues behave as if many cells in series and in parallel were connected by a low-resistance pathway for electric current (4, 33, 66, 74, 76, 79) and diffusion of small ions and molecules (32, 51, 71, 75, 77); that although heart muscle is electrophysiologically a syncytium, it is nevertheless made up of discrete cells (62); that gap junctions or nexuses are the loci of electrical coupling between heart muscle cells (4); that these loci are specialized membranes with a distinctive subunit structure (41, 54) resembling that of permeable junctions in many other mammalian tissues (5, 26, 37); that gap junctions

431

0066-4278/81/0315-0431$01.00

between dispersed, electrically separate embryonic heart muscle cells in culture can form and become functional within a few minutes after the cells come into adhesive contact with each other (11, 25) or with intervening non-cardiac cells (24); and that electrically coupled cardiac cells can be electrically decoupled by microinjecting Ca^{2+} or La^{2+} into the cytoplasm (15, 16) or by exposing the cells to ouabain (78) or dinitrophenol (17).

While it is clearly desirable to characterize the properties of cardiac gap junctions directly, the most useful experimental design, that of controlling the voltage across a single permeable junction, has so far proved unachievable in intact heart muscle with methods now available. In the following discussion we summarize recent observations on the properties of permeable junctions from other tissues that seem particularly relevant to the physiology of cardiac gap junctions.

GENERAL PROPERTIES OF PERMEABLE JUNCTIONS: RECENT OBSERVATIONS

Permeability of Gap Junctions

Permeability of gap junctions (63) has been estimated by studies of tracer permeation across the junctions, electrophysiological measurements, and experiments in which the presence or absence of coupling was inferred from secondary phenomena that require permeable gap junctions [e.g. the synchronization of cells beating with different intrinsic frequencies (11) or the establishment of "metabolic cooperation" (36, 70)].

TRANSJUNCTIONAL DIFFUSION OF TRACERS   The channels that cross the two lipid bilayers and the intervening interstitial space of gap junctions (39) are the largest (20) and most stable (38) known to exist in biological membranes and appear to be negatively charged. Channel dimensions and charge have been estimated with a series of linear molecular probes with an abaxial length of 1.4–1.6 nm and molecular weights ranging from 376 to 830 daltons (19, 20). Junctions from mammalian cell lines did not pass probes with a molecular weight > 850 daltons; moreover they sieved out to some extent probes with 3 negative charges and to a lesser extent those with two negative charges presumably because of negative fixed charge associated with channels. The upper size limits of the mammalian channel could not be precisely defined because the method did not distinguish between steric and polar constraints on the diffusion of molecular probes.

ELECTROPHYSIOLOGICAL MEASUREMENTS OF GAP JUNCTIONAL PERMEABILITY   Certain general properties of the junctional membrane as determined for the most part in noncardiac tissues (5) are of particular interest for the cellular physiology of cardiac tissues: (a) The junctional resistance is usually constant, the constancy being observed over different voltage ranges in different tissues. (*b*) Junctional resistivity is very low (5, 58) and the same order of magnitude ($\sim 1 \Omega$ cm^2) as that of heart muscle 33, 66, 75). Although rather imprecise, values of junctional resistivity can be combined with other data to calculate a single channel resistance of $\sim$ 10Ω(5). The low membrane resistivity results in a very low membrane time constant. (*c*). Capacity of gap junctions is low: ~ 0.5 μF cm^{-2} junction assumming a membrane capacity of 1 μF cm^{-2}. (*d*) Some gap junctions can rectify (5, 21).

REGULATION OF GAP JUNCTIONAL PERMEABILITY   At least four experimental variations can decrease the permeability of gap junctions and lead to partial or complete electrical decoupling: raising the cytoplasmic concentration of ionized calcium in the cytosol ([Ca^{2+}]) (58), lowering the pH of the cytosol (72), imposing a voltage gradient across the junction (67), and inhibiting oxidative or glycolytic metabolism, or both (19). There is as yet no consensus about whether lowering the pH of the cytosol or metabolic inhibition decreases junctional permeability by a direct interaction of protons with the permeable channel or by a secondary increase in [Ca^{2+}]$_{cyt}$ produced by acidification of the cytosol (19, 55, 57); or whether, under some conditions, raising [Ca^{2+}]$_{cyt}$, a procedure that can lower cytoplasmic pH (57), acts by protonation of junctional sites. A decrease in cytosolic pH is not necessary for junctional decoupling (57). Decoupling may be incomplete after exposure to metabolic inhibitors (19). Similarly, imposition of a trans-junctional voltage gradient leaves a residual voltage-insensitive conductance that persists at trans-junctional potential differences substantially exceeding 20 mV (67).

Experiments on single junctions show that when [Ca^{2+}]$_{cyt}$ is progressively raised from 10^{-7}M to 5 $\times$ 10^{-5}M, junctional permeability gradually diminishes (38). This graded permeability change of the whole junction represents the response of multiple channels operating in parallel. Measurements of single channel conductance indicate that microinjection of Ca^{2+} into electrically coupled cell pairs can decrease junctional conductance either in unitary (quantal) steps or in a clearly nonquantal manner, the decrease being reversible on lowering [Ca^{2+}]$_{cyt}$ (38). The quantal steps suggest channel closure when [Ca^{2+}]$_{cyt}$ reaches or exceeds a critical level, while the nonquantal steps suggest partial closure of channels, most probably by partial closure of individual channels (38).

A Ca^{2+}-sensitive gating process has been proposed for the changes in gap junctional permeability brought about by Ca^{2+} (5, 38, 48). Ca^{2+} does not itself block the channel, since molecular probes much larger than Ca^{2+} can readily pass. Among the ideas proposed are (*a*) a change in the bore of the channel due to a change in its charge configuration either by Ca^{2+}-binding to the channel protein or by a conformational change in the protein (40); (b) a conformational change in the channel protein resulting indirectly from Ca^{2+}-binding to the membrane lipid (38); (c) a gating mechanism in which Ca^{2+} acts at the cytoplasmic end of the channel via a change in a cytoplasmic contractile protein involved in channel closure (5), or via a cyclic nucleotide–mediated change (5); and, (d) obliteration of the channel by the binding of divalent cation to junctional proteins bearing two negative charges for each divalent cation binding site. The anionic site on the protein could also be blocked by two protons and weakly protected by K^+ ion against neutralization by divalent cations and protons (48).

Two mechanisms that prevent or minimize reductions in gap junctional permeability in response to physiological or abnormal fluctuations in $[Ca^{2+}]_{cyt}$ are sequestration of Ca^{2+} in the vicinity of the junctional channels (56) and specializations of cell geometry that, in combination with sequestering mechanisms, promote the maintenance of a low $[Ca^{2+}]_{cyt}$ (19).

Formation and Turnover of Gap Junctions

De novo formation of gap junctions occurs in vivo and is observed in cultured cells and cell aggregates in vitro, (5, 26, 37, 80). It is well-documented in monolayers and cell aggregates formed from enzymatically dispersed embryonic heart muscle cells (12, 26). In vitro, cells that were not previously coupled become so after the cells adhere to each other. The latent period between adhesion and electrical coupling is variable, but may be as short as 4 min or less. The formation of nascent channels in the junctions is detectable as quantal increments in cell-to-cell conductance, a process during which the junctional conductance rises by several orders of magnitude to a steady-state value (38). Inhibition of protein synthesis prevents the formation of functional gap junctions in aggregates of chick embryonic heart cells (25), but protein synthesis is not required during gap junctional formation in other in vitro systems (26). These diverse observations raise several intriguing questions. It is of interest to know from what natural peptide subunits the channel is assembled; where and when the peptides are synthesized and assembled; how they are transported to and inserted in the lipid bilayer of the plasma membrane; how two cells that are about to form a gap junction recognize this fact, align, join their respective hemichannels, and control when and to what extent the channels open; what forces and structures are implicated in the motions of the assembled channel proteins within the lipid bilayers; and where, how, and to what extent the assembled channel constituents are degraded, stored, or reutilized.

Much of what is known about gap junctional formation both in embryonic, growing, or regenerating tissues in situ and in cultured cells (5, 22, 26) is based on electron microscopy of thin-sectioned or freeze-fractured tissues. These techniques have revealed that gap junctions initially appear as small patches of membrane that enlarge in area. In membrane replicas of freeze-fractured junctions, membrane particles that presumably contain the channel protein are initially present singly, in linear arrays, in small clusters, or in clusters interrupted by particle-free "aisles" of lipid bilayer. Particle-free halos of lipid bilayer around the periphery of the junctions have been variously interpreted as "formation plaques," effects of interactions between cytoskeletal elements and junctional constituents, and preparative artifacts. Particles located in nearby nonjunctional membrane and resembling junctional particles in size and shape have been suggested as precursors of junctional particles, and junctional particles have been observed to become larger as development proceeds. The association of longer particles with the edges of forming gap junctions (1, 10) has been taken as evidence for initial sites of formation to which channels might attach if they were polarized to allow attachment at one side only (23). Single strands resulting from the breakup of occluding (tight) junctions have been interpreted as nucleation sites for gap junctional formation. In addition, cytoplasmic material at the cytoplasmic surface of gap junctions (6, 9, 10) has been taken as evidence that gap junctional protein may interact with cytoplasmic constituents to move channel proteins within the lipid bilayer, or to restrict such movements (5, 26).

Ultrastructural Correlates of Gap Junctional Permeability

Reviews of gap junctional structure in noncardiac tissues (5, 9, 22, 35, 68) and in cardiac tissues (41, 53, 64) should be consulted for details of the appearance of junctions in thin sections as well as of the subunit structure in lanthanum-stained thin sections (54) and in membrane replicas freeze-fractured either in the plane of the junction or in cross fracture. In addition, the literature on structural and biochemical characterization of gap junctions and of gap junctional proteins and lipids isolated from various tissues by biochemical fractionation is accessible in several recent experimental articles (7, 29, 30, 39, 73, 81). We confine ourselves here to a brief summary of ultrastructural evidence for the notion that gap junctions undergo electron microscopically detectable changes in ultrastructure during the transition from a normally permeable to a less permeable state.

Changes in gap junctional structure when the cells become electrically decoupled have been described by the laboratory of Peracchia (46-50). In a combined electrophysiological and ultrastructural study of crayfish gap junctions, the junctions were made less permeable either by returning them to Ca^{2+}-containing solutions after a prior exposure to Ca^{2+}- and Mg^{2+}-free solutions containing EDTA, or by dinitrophenol. Increased junctional resistance was associated with several changes in junctional structure: (a) a decrease in the overall width of the junction and in the width of the intercellular gap, revealed in thin sections; (b) an aggregation of the gap junctional particles with a resulting decrease in the mean center-to-center spacing between particles; (c) a change to a more orderly arrangement of the membrane particles to approximate a more nearly hexagonal array; and (d) possibly a decrease in particle diameter. Subsequent experiments on gap junctions of rat stomach or liver (46) showed that the effects produced by dinitrophenol or oxygen deprivation on these mammalian junctions were qualitatively similar to those in crayfish electrotonic synapses; the average center-to-center spacing of particles in the control (presumably permeable) junctions from the mammalian systems was, however, smaller ($\sim$ 10 nm). In addition, the structure of hepatocyte junctions decoupled by exposing them sequentially to EDTA and hypertonic sucrose-calcium solutions also became more ordered and closely packed. Peracchia interpreted these changes as "reflecting conformational rearrangements in the protein framework of the channels resulting in channel obliteration."

This interpretation is supported by the results of a study on isolated gap junctions obtained by fractionation of mouse liver, in which biochemical and electron microscopic observations were correlated with data from X-ray diffraction (7, 39). In the resulting model, gap junctions were built up of units called connexons. These units were arrayed hexagonally with a lattice constant (a measure of spacing between units) of $\sim$ 8.0–9.0 nm. Each connexon had a diameter of 6.0 nm and was made up of six protein subunits $\sim$ 8.0 nm long and 20 nm wide. The six subunits were arrayed to form an axial channel with a diameter of $\sim$ 2.0 nm. In the permeable state, connexons from each of the two cells making up the junction formed channels that extended from the cytoplasm of the cell, through the lipid bilayer, into the extracellular gap between plasma membranes. Within that gap, the two connexons from adjacent cells met to form a continuous axial channel. In the permeable configuration, the structure had considerable short-range disorder and flexibility. In the impermeable state, it became more ordered and less flexible. Two interconvertible forms of isolated gap junctions were also identified by optical diffraction and image analysis as applied to negatively stained junctions from rat livers (73, 81). This analysis suggested that the connexon is a cylindrical oligomer composed of six protein subunits tilted around the axis of the cylinder. In the second of its two forms, the central channel becomes constricted at the cytoplasmic end of the connexon by a radial inward movement of the subunits and a change in their inclination.

Peracchia subsequently compared the structural consequences of changes in $[Ca^{2+}]_{cyt}$ in situ with those produced in vitro in isolated gap junctions from epithelial cells from calf lens (47, 48, 50). He was able to show by freeze fracture that under in situ conditions, membrane replicas of junctions between lenticular epithelial cells had the configuration characteristic of the decoupled state; presumably, under the preparative conditions used, the cells had experienced a rise in $[Ca^{2+}]_{cyt}$. The particle pattern of junctions isolated from these cells was initially disordered but became more ordered and closely packed when $[Ca^{2+}]_{cyt}$ was increased from 3×10^{-7}-M to 5×10^{-7}M. Thus a minute fluctuation in $[Ca^{2+}]_{cyt}$ could bring about the structural transition. When $[Ca^{2+}]_{cyt}$ was kept low, an ordered (rhombic or orthogonal) particle packing could nevertheless be brought about by lowering the pH to or beyond 6.5, suggesting that Ca^{2+} and H^+ may cause cell decoupling independently (50).

Peracchia's conclusions were based on data from the pitted or extracellular fracture face of the membrane replica. The criteria for disordered particle distribution were qualitative, and the changes detected were large. Although most of Peracchia's material was fixed with glutaraldehyde, unfixed negatively stained junctions gave similar results (49). It is therefore improbable that the structural changes associated with decoupling were artifacts of glutaraldehyde fixation.

CARDIAC GAP JUNCTIONS

Morphometry of electron micrographs of thin sections indicates that gap junctions make up a minute percentage of total plasmalemmal area in adult left ventricular myocardial cells: 1.0% (.0047 μm^2 μm^{-3}) in rat ventricle (69), and 0.7% (0.0042 μm^2 μm^{-3}) in rabbit ventricle [calculated from (44, 59, 69)]. In ventricular myocardial cells, this area is distributed as numerous patches or maculae with a variably curved surface and a preferential but by no means exclusive localization to the plasmalemma near the longitudinal ends of the cells (41, 42, 43, 59, 64).

Quantification of Information in Membrane Replicas of Cardiac Gap Junctions

Particle density, center-to-center spacing between particles, particle distribution, particle size, and perhaps particle shape are related variables whose determination is useful for quantifying structural transitions related to permeability changes.

Two recent studies on rat and rabbit myocardial cells (2,3) report increased order and decreased interparticle spacing in junctions exposed to ischemia or high $[Ca^{2+}]$. "A more regular array of E-face pits" was also described in sheep cardiac Purkinje fibers (8). The fibers were electrically decoupled by loading them with Ca^{2+} while the activity of internal Ca^{2+} as well as the internal longitudinal resistance were measured. When internal Ca^{2+} activity rose to 8.0 μM from control values of < 0.1 μM, the distribution of P-face particle diameters changed from unimodal with a mean of 8.3 nm in the control to bimodal with a new second peak at 9.6 nm. Ca^{2+} - induced decoupling also reduced particle height and widened the extracellular gap at the nexus 1.6-fold.

In the authors' laboratory the structure of cardiac gap junctions has been examined by freeze fracture of three types of preparations: intact ventricular myocardial cells depleted of or loaded with Ca^{2+} by perfusion of rat hearts (45, 45a); sheep Purkinje fibers cut and exposed to solutions of defined $[Ca^{2+}]_{cyt}$ by Délèze's (13) method (60, 61); and gap junctions isolated from rabbit ventricles by biochemical fractionation (34). In each of these experimental preparations the gap junctional arrays of particles and pits at the lowest values of $[Ca^{2+}]_{cyt}$ showed substantial regularity and were never random or widely dispersed. Low $[Ca^{2+}]_{cyt}$ was achieved either by omission of $[Ca^{2+}]$ from the perfusate or by 5 mM EGTA in the absence of added Ca^{2+}. The presence of substantial regularity and the absence of either random or completely regular arrays in both E-face and P-face were established by rigorous statistical criteria on digitized E-face pit and P-face particle centers by Gilula, Karrison & Meier [see (22a) and appendix of (45a)]. They applied the criterion of Clark & Evans (7a) to the distribution of nearest neighbor distances between particle centers, with confidence intervals as described by Rogers (54a). It could thus be shown that, for arrays with particle diameters and densities comparable to those of cardiac gap junctions, particles that are randomly placed in the array will nevertheless appear to be regularly arrayed. This effect results from interactions between particles, based on the constraint that their diameters cannot overlap (22a). Owing to this constraint, the particle pattern of permeable cardiac gap junctions at low $[Ca^{2+}]_{cyt}$ will exhibit substantial regularity even though it may originate as a random array, as envisioned by Peracchia.

In intact rat heart muscle (45, 45a) and in cut cell preparations of sheep Purkinje fibers (60, 61) our laboratory has found three distinct changes at high $[Ca^{2+}]_{cyt}$: (*a*) *an increase in mean P-face particle diameter:* In Purkinje fiber gap junctions bathed in 10^{-3} M Ca^{2+} this increase of $\sim 10\%$ is complete within 1 min or less. The resultant unimodal distribution of particle diameters is shifted to the right, an effect which is not reversed by EGTA. (*b*) *A decrease in mean center-to-center spacing between P-face particles* with a narrowed dispersion around the mean. In cut Purkinje fibers bathed in 10^{-3} M $[Ca^{2+}]$ this change is detectable within 5 min or less. It progresses continuously for at least 30 min at which time the distance has decreased by $\sim 17\%$ (61). We have also observed an increase in P-face particle diameter when gap junctions isolated from rabbit ventricles are incubated in 10^{-3} M $[Ca^{2+}]$ at low ionic strength as described by Peracchia (47), but could detect no change in center-to-center spacing in these isolated junctions (52). (*c*) *A dispersal of gap junctional particles and pits:* This previously undescribed phenomenon, which is most unequivocally observable as the appearance of dispersed E-face pits outside the discrete junctional arrays, is absent at low and normal $[Ca^{2+}]_{cyt}$ (45, 45a, 60, 61). Dispersal has been detected within 3 min after start of Ca^{2+}-loading rat ventricular myocardial cells by perfusing rat hearts with high (8 mM) $[Ca^{2+}]$, low (38 mM) $[Na^+]$ solution, and within 0.5 min after exposing cut Purkinje fibers to 10^{-3} M $[Ca^{2+}]$. Since depolymerized connexons would not have been detectable by freeze fracture, the dispersed junctional components must be in the polymerized state.

In intact rat heart muscle cells depleted of Ca^{2+} by perfusion with low $[Ca^{2+}]$ solutions, as well as in cut Purkinje fibers exposed to $< 10^{-7}$M $[Ca^{2+}]$, the mean diameters of P-face gap junctional particles decreased significantly ($P < 0.001$) below control values (45a, 61). After exposure to the low $[Ca^{2+}]$ condition, the decreases were sufficiently large to be detectable by freeze fracture within 3 min in rat ventricle and within 5 min in Purkinje fibers. P-face diameter in cut Purkinje fibers decreased progressively with duration of incubation in $< 10^{-7}$ M $[Ca^{2+}]$, its value being 93.8% of control after 30 min. Thus P-face particle diameter, like junctional permeability, changes sensitively with $[Ca^{2+}]_{cyt}$. The form of the diameter vs $[Ca^{2+}]_{cyt}$ relationship over the physiological range of $[Ca^{2+}]_{cyt}$ must be more exactly established and correlated with studies of Ca^{2+} binding to isolated gap junctions (41a). Moreover, the presumed underlying conformational change in channel proteins requires investigation with structural techniques capable of better resolution than freeze fracture—e.g. optical, electron, and X-ray diffraction of isolated gap junctions with and without negative staining (7, 39). Our finding of a unimodal distribution of larger diameters at very high (10^{-3}M) $[Ca^{2+}]_{cyt}$, together with Dahl & Isenberg's observation of a bimodal distribution at 8×10^{-6} M $[Ca^{2+}]$, supports the notion that the Ca^{2+}-binding sites involved in the permeability-related conformational change are saturated at 10^{-3}M $[Ca^{2+}]$, but not at 8×10^{-6} M $[Ca^{2+}]$. Since 10^{-3}M $[Ca^{2+}]$ is a concentration like that in the interstitial space, the observed shift to a new unimodal distribution of gap junctional particle diameters correlates with the sealing that follows the entry of interstitial solutions into injured cardiac cells (13, 18).

Development of Junctional Ultrastructure

Electron microscopy of thin sections (31, 69) is a relatively insensitive tool for studying developmental changes in cardiac gap junctions. Freeze fracture (27, 28, 40, 59) provides more information, especially when quantitative analysis of the fracture faces is combined with morphometry of thin sections (59). In embryonic and neonatal myocardial cells from rabbit left ventricles, morphometry disclosed a nearly three-fold increase in gap junctional area per unit cell volume between the first and third days after birth. Measurements on freeze fractured hearts showed that the mean area of individual gap junctions doubled between the 9th and 5th days before birth, and doubled again between the first and third days after birth. Increase in junctional area was associated with the transient appearance of "aisle" configurations in large junctions, whose particle-free rows subsequently filled with particles. Aisle configurations were present in both glutaraldehyde-fixed and quick-frozen hearts. The appearance of junctional particles in initially particle-free aisles as development progresses suggests that junctional proteins are either inserted in the lipid bilayer of the aisles, or assembled there from precursor peptides already present in the membrane. Measurements of interparticle spacing supported the conclusion that large junctions develop by growth of preexisting small junctions, not by fusion of small junctions.

ACKNOWLEDGMENT

Supported by Grants Nos. H1 10503 and HL 20592, awarded by the National Heart, Lung and Blood Institute, US Public Health Service.

Literature Cited

1. Albertini, D. F., Anderson, E. 1975. *Anat. Rec.* 181:171–94
2. Ashraf, M., Halverson, C. 1978. *J. Mol. Cell Cardiol.* 10:263–69
3. Baldwin, K. M. 1979. *J. Cell Biol.* 82:66–75
4. Barr, L., Dewey, M. M., Berger, W. 1965. *J. Gen. Physiol.* 48:797–823
5. Bennett, M. V. L. 1977. In *Handbook of Physiology, Vol. I, Sect. I: The Nervous System,* ed. E. R. Kandel, pp. 357–416. Baltimore: Williams & Wilkins
6. Brightman, M. W., Reese, I. S. 1969. *J. Cell Biol.* 40:648–77
7. Caspar, D. L. D., Goodenough, D. A., Makowski, L., Phillips, W. C. 1977. *J. Cell Biol.* 74:605–28
7a. Clark, P. J., Evans, F. C. 1954. *Ecology* 35:445–53
8. Dahl, G., Isenberg, G. 1980. *J. Membr. Biol.* 53:63–75
9. Decker, R. S. 1976. *J. Cell Biol.* 69:669–84
10. Decker, R. S., Friend, D. S. 1974. *J. Cell Biol.* 62:32–47
11. De Haan, R. L., Hirakow, R. 1972. *Exp. Cell Res.* 70:214–20
12. De Haan, R. L., Sachs, H. B. 1972. *Curr. Top. Dev. Biol.* 7:193–228
13. Délèze, J. 1970. *J. Physiol. London* 208:547–62
14. De Mello, W. C. 1972. In *Electrical Phenomena of the Heart,* ed. W. C. De Mello, pp. 323–51. NY: Academic
15. De Mello, W. C. 1976. *J. Physiol. London* 263:171–97
16. De Mello, W. C. 1979a. *Cell Biol. Int. Rep.* 3:113–19
17. De Mello, W. C. 1979b. *Pflügers Arch.* 380:267–76
18. Engelmann, T. W. 1875. *Pflügers Arch.* 11:465–80
19. Flagg-Newton, J., Loewenstein, W. R. 1979. *J. Membr. Biol.* 50:65–100
20. Flagg-Newton, J., Simpson, I., Loewenstein, W. R. 1979. *Science* 205:404–7
21. Furshpan, E. J., Potter, D. D. 1959. *J. Physiol. London* 145:289–325
22. Gilula, N. B. 1977. In *International Cell Biology,* ed. B. R. Brinkley, K. R. Porter, pp. 61–69. NY: Rockefeller Univ. Press
22a. Gilula, Z., Karrison, T., Meier, P. 1980. *Tech. Rep. No. 116, Dept. Stat.* Univ. Chicago
23. Goodenough, D. A., Gilula, N. B. 1974. *J. Cell Biol.* 61:575–90
24. Goshima, K. 1970. *Exp. Cell Res.* 63:124–30
25. Griepp, E. B., Bernfield, M. R. 1978. *Exp. Cell Res.* 113:263–72
26. Griepp, E. B., Revel, J. P. 1977. In *Intercellular Communication,* ed. W. C. De Mello, pp. 1–32. NY: Plenum
27. Gros, D., Challice, C. E. 1976. *Experientia* 32:996–98
28. Gros, D., Mocquard, J. P., Challice, C. E., Schrevel, J. 1979. *J. Mol. Cell Cardiol.* 11:545–54
29. Henderson, D., Eibl, H., Weber, K. 1979. *J. Mol. Biol.* 132:193–218
30. Hertzberg, E. L., Gilula, N. B. 1979. *J. Biol. Chem.* 254:2138–47
31. Hirakow, R., Gotoh, T. 1976. In *Developmental and Physiological Correlates of Cardiac Muscle,* ed. M. Lieberman,

T. Sano, pp. 37–50. NY: Raven Press
32. Imanaga, I. 1974. *J. Membr. Biol.* 16:381–88
33. Jongsma, H. J., van Rijn, H. E. 1972. *J. Membr. Biol.* 9:341–60
34. Kensler, R. W., Goodenough, D. A. 1978. *Circulation* 58: Suppl. 2, p. 53
35. Larsen, W. J. 1977. *Tiss. Cell* 9:373–94
36. Lawrence, T. S., Beers, W. H., Gilula, N. B. 1978. *Nature* 272:501–6
37. Loewenstein, W. R. 1976. *Cold Spring Harbor Symp. Quant. Biol.* 40:49–63
38. Loewenstein, W. R., Kanno, Y., Socolar, S. J. 1978. *Fed. Proc.* 37:2645–50
39. Makowski, L., Caspar, D. L. D., Phillips, W. C., Goodenough, D. A. 1977. *J. Cell Biol.* 74:629–45
40. Mazet, F. 1977. *Dev. Biol.* 60:139–52
41. McNutt, N. S., Weinstein, R. S. 1970. *J. Cell Biol.* 47:666–68
41a. Nishiye, H., Mashima, H., Ishida, A. 1980. *Jpn. J. Physiol.* 30:131–36
42. Page, E. 1978. *Am. J. Physiol.* 4:C147–58
43. Page, E., McCallister, L. P. 1973. *J. Ultrastruc. Res.* 43:388–411
44. Page, E., Surdyk-Droske, M. 1979. *Circ. Res.* 45:260–66
45. Page, E., Upshaw-Earley, J. 1980. *J. Cell Biol.* 87:192a
45a. Page, E., Upshaw-Earley, J. 1981. *Fed. Proc.* 39:298
46. Peracchia, C. 1977. *J. Cell Biol.* 72:628–41
47. Peracchia, C. 1978. *Nature* 271:669–71
48. Peracchia, C., Bernardini, G., Peracchia, L. L. 1979. *J. Cell Biol.* 83:86a
49. Peracchia, C., Dulhunty, A. F. 1976. *J. Cell Biol.* 70:419–39
50. Peracchia, C., Peracchia, L. L. 1978. *J. Cell Biol.* 79:A217
51. Pollack, G. H. 1976. *J. Physiol. London* 255:275–98
52. Quertermous, T., Shibata, Y., Page, E. 1980. *J. Cell Biol.* 87:192a
53. Rayns, D. G., Simpson, F. O., Bertaud, W. S. 1968. *J. Cell Sci.* 3:467–74
54. Revel, J. P., Karnovsky, M. J. 1967. *J. Cell Biol.* 33:C7–12
54a. Rogers, A. 1974. *Statistical Analysis of Spatial Dispersion*, pp. 1–164. London: Pion Limited
55. Rose, B., Loewenstein, W. R. 1975. *Science* 190:1204–6
56. Rose, B., Loewenstein, W. R. 1976. *J. Membr. Biol.* 28:87–119
57. Rose, B., Rick, R. 1978. *J. Membr. Biol.* 44:377–415
58. Sheridan, J. D., Hammer-Wilson, M., Preus, D., Johnson, R. B. 1978. *J. Cell Biol.* 76:532–46
59. Shibata, Y., Nakata, K., Page, E. 1980. *J. Ultrastruct. Res.* 71:258–71
60. Shibata, Y., Page, E. 1980. *J. Cell Biol.* 87:192a
61. Shibata, Y., Page, E. 1981. *J. Ultrastruct. Res.* Submitted
62. Sjöstrand, F. S., Andersson, E. 1954. *Experientia* 9:369–71
63. Socolar, S. J., Loewenstein, W. R. 1979. *Methods Membr. Biol.* 10:123–79
64. Sommer, J., Johnson, E. A. 1979. In *Handbook of Physiology, The Cardiovascular System I*, ed. R. M. Berne, pp. 113–86. Baltimore: Williams & Wilkins
65. Sperelakis, N. 1979. *Ann. Rev. Physiol.* 41:441–57
66. Spira, A. W. 1971. *J. Ultrastruct. Res.* 34:409–25
67. Spray, D. C., Harris, A. L., Bennett, M. V. L. 1979. *Science* 204: 432–34
68. Staehelin, L. A. 1974. *Int. Rev. Cytol.* 39:191–283
69. Stewart, J., Page, E. 1978. *J. Ultrastruct. Res.* 65:119–34
70. Subak-Sharpe, H., Burk, R. R., Pitts, J. D. 1966. *Heredity* 21:342–43
71. Tsien, R. W., Weingart, R. 1976. *J. Physiol. London* 260:117–41
72. Turin, L., Warner, A. E. 1977. *Nature* 270:56–57
73. Unwin, P. N. T., Zampighi, G. 1980. *Nature* 283:545–49
74. Weidmann, S. 1952. *J. Physiol. London* 118:348–60
75. Weidmann, S. 1966. *J. Physiol. London* 187:323–42
76. Weidmann, S. 1970. *J. Physiol. London* 210:1041–54
77. Weingart, R. 1974. *J. Physiol. London* 240:741–62
78. Weingart, R. 1977. *J. Physiol. London* 264:341–65
79. Woodbury, J. W., Crill, W. B. 1961. In *Nervous Inhibition,* ed. E. Florey, pp. 124–35. Oxford: Pergamon
80. Yee, A. G., Revel, J. P. 1978. *J. Cell Biol.* 78:554–64
81. Zampighi, G., Unwin, P. N. T. 1979. *J. Mol. Biol.* 135:451–64

Ann. Rev. Physiol. 1981. 43:443–53
Copyright © 1981 by Annual Reviews Inc. All rights reserved

NEURAL REGULATION OF THE HEART BEAT

❖1322

Matthew N. Levy and Paul J. Martin

Department of Investigative Medicine, Mt. Sinai Hospital of Cleveland, and Case Western Reserve University, Cleveland, Ohio 44106

Sherry L. Stuesse

Neurobiology Program, Northeastern Ohio Universities College of Medicine, Rootstown, Ohio 44272

Neural Regulation of the Heart Beat

The mammalian heart receives innervation from the sympathetic and parasympathetic divisions of the autonomic nervous system. These nerves modulate such cardiac activities as sinoatrial and atrioventricular automaticity, conduction of the cardiac impulse, and the strength of atrial and ventricular contraction. There is a dense autonomic innervation of nodal and atrial structures in all mammals investigated. The ventricular myocardium is also well supplied with sympathetic fibers, but the parasympathetic supply is more sparsely distributed.

The presence of sympathetic nerve fibers in various regions of the heart has been determined histochemically and by direct assay of tissue norepinephrine content. In canine (38, 51) and guinea pig (38, 51, 56) hearts the concentration of norepinephrine in atrial tissue is two to four times higher than that found in ventricular tissue. There is little difference in concentrations of norepinephrine in the sinoatrial node and surrounding atrium (2, 56). The atrioventricular (AV) node and proximal conducting bundles also contain substantial amounts of norepinephrine (56). Within the AV node itself, the density of adrenergic terminations may be sparse (9, 51). However, electron microscopy studies of mouse AV node (66) indicate that the neural distribution within the AV node is uneven; some portions are richly supplied while others contain few nerve terminals. The effects of stellate

443

stimulation on AV nodal rhythm in the dog indicate that this region of the heart contains substantial sympathetic innervation (17).

The density of cardiac parasympathetic innervation has been determined by assaying the tissue acetylcholine content (5, 27) and by measuring the distribution of enzymes involved in acetylcholine metabolism, such as acetylcholine esterase (8, 26) and choline acetyltransferase (57). These studies have shown that the sinoatrial (SA) node contains the highest concentration of marker, and thus probably the greatest density of vagal innervation. In decreasing order, lower concentrations were found in the right atrium, left atrium, papillary muscles, right ventricular free wall, and left ventricular free wall.

The first clear-cut demonstration of a vagal depression of ventricular contractility was obtained in 1965 by DeGeest, Levy, and colleagues (11). In a canine isovolumetric left ventricular preparation, paced to beat at a constant rate, the effect of vagal stimulation on left ventricular pressure was monitored. Vagal stimulation frequencies as low as 1 Hz were sufficient to decrease the left ventricular pressure slightly; with more vigorous stimulation, the pressure diminished by about 30%. Such depressant effects on ventricular contractility were subsequently confirmed in a variety of other experimental preparations (19, 38). Recently, Kent et al (26) have shown that there is a much richer parasympathetic innervation of the ventricular specialized conducting system than of the ventricular myocardium. It was proposed that this innervation tends to raise the ventricular fibrillation threshold (26).

The diverse influences of the autonomic innervation of the heart are complex. We discuss three phenomena that have been studied intensively in recent years: the vagal control of sinoatrial rhythm, the interactions between heart rate changes and the direct autonomic influences on AV conduction, and the evidence for parasympathetic-sympathetic interactions in the heart.

Vagal Control of Sinoatrial Rhythm

In 1934, Brown & Eccles (3) studied the chronotropic responses to brief vagal stimuli. They found that the time course of the changes in cardiac cycle length consisted of two inhibitory phases, separated by a brief phase of relative or actual cardioacceleration. Their observations were subsequently confirmed by others (20, 21, 37, 59). A representative graph of cardiac cycle length as a function of the time from the vagal stimulus is shown in Figure 1. Recent work (21, 59) has provided considerable insight into the mechanism responsible for this complex chronotropic response.

Spear et al (59) measured transmembrane action potentials from cells in the sinus node region in isolated rabbit atrial preparations. They also used

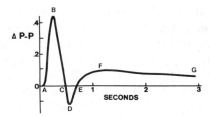

Figure 1   Time course of the changes in cardiac cycle length (P-P interval, in sec) produced by a single brief burst of vagal stimuli in an anesthetized dog [modified from (20)].

a potassium-sensitive electrode to assess the changes in extracellular K^+ activity in that same region. Intramural vagal fibers were stimulated by a brief train of electrical pulses. The chronotropic responses to such vagal stimuli were plotted in the form of a phase-response curve, similar to that shown in Figure 1.

The various phases of this response curve were ascribed to a number of different mechanisms (59). The first increase in the time between atrial depolarizations (P-P interval) appeared after a latent period of 170–250 msec. The initial portion of this response (the beginning portion of the upstroke, AB, of the primary phase of deceleration) was accounted for entirely by a slowing of sinoatrial conduction. The time interval between pacemaker cell depolarizations (i.e. the true cardiac cycle length) was not yet altered detectably; i.e. this initial response reflected a dromotropic, not a chronotropic, effect of the vagal stimulus. The remainder of the primary deceleration phase (ABC) did reflect a true lengthening of the intervals between pacemaker cell depolarizations. The prolongation of the cardiac cycle was achieved mainly by a hyperpolarization of the pacemaker cell (reflected by an increase in the maximum diastolic potential), but also by some reduction in the slope of diastolic depolarization. These changes were ascribed to a direct action of the neurally released acetycholine (ACh) on the membrane K^+ conductance. No changes in extracellular K^+ activity could be detected during this primary deceleration phase.

When a brief acceleratory phase (CDE, Figure 1) was present, it was associated with a reduction in the maximum diastolic potential of the sinus pacemaker cells. It was proposed that this change was associated with an increased Na^+ conductance of the pacemaker cell membrane (59). During the secondary phase of deceleration (EFG, Figure 1), the increase in cycle length was associated with a decreased slope of diastolic depolarization. The potassium-sensitive electrode disclosed a rise in extracellular K^+ activity that paralleled the course of the negative chronotropic response. Spear et al (59) postulated that this increased K^+ activity might be responsible for the diminished slope of diastolic depolarization.

Insight into several additional features of the phase-response curve were provided by the studies of Jalife & Moe (21). They confirmed the sequence of changes in transmembrane potential described by Spear et al—i.e. the cardiac deceleration that appears initially after a vagal stimulus is achieved by a hyperpolarization of the pacemaker cells, whereas the secondary phase of slowing is implemented by a diminished slope of diastolic depolarization. The latency for hyperpolarization (<150 msec) was invariably less than the latency for the chronotropic effect (>180 msec). Hence, there was a delay of at least 30 msec, and often of as much as 100 msec, between the onset of hyperpolarization and the beginning of the chronotropic response. When the vagal stimulus was given less than 200 msec in advance of the next expected pacemaker action potential, membrane hyperpolarization did not occur. The activation of the inward current responsible for the upstroke of the pacemaker action potential occurs about 100 msec before the upstroke itself (4). Jalife & Moe (21) concluded that the acetylcholine released late in the phase of diastolic depolarization cannot overcome this inward current, once it has been activated.

In intact animals, the activity in efferent cardiac vagal fibers tends to be clustered at certain portions of the cardiac cycle (23, 24, 29). Hence, the chronotropic response to repetitive efferent vagal activity has a marked phase-dependency (13, 36, 52), just as does that to a single, brief burst of activity. The phase-dependency imparts certain peculiar characteristics to repetitive bursts of vagal activity, the most prominent of which is a strong tendency for the vagal activity to entrain the pacemaker cells (13, 36, 52). As a consequence, there tends to be a "paradoxical response," such that the heart beat tends to speed up with increasing frequencies of vagal activity, despite the obvious negative chronotropic influence of the neurotransmitter (acetylcholine) released at the vagal terminals. Within limits, this tendency increases the greater the time delay between the individual action potentials within each burst of efferent vagal activity (39). Hence, there may be an augmented liberation of ACh per pulse of neural activity as the interpulse interval is increased.

The same type of phase-dependency to repetitive vagal stimulation was demonstrable in isolated rat atrium preparations (62). When each stimulus occurred about 300 msec after the beginning of atrial depolarization, the negative chronotropic response was maximal. If the time of stimulation was delayed by only a few more milliseconds, the negative chronotropic response was dramatically attenuated. Probably such stimuli, falling during the late phase of the cardiac cycle, occur at a time when the inward current responsible for the upstroke of the pacemaker cell action potential has already been activated (4). This may correspond to the late period of diastolic depolarization in the experiments of Jalife & Moe (21), wherein the neurally released ACh was unable to hyperpolarize the pacemaker cell membrane.

Atrioventricular Conduction

Cohn & Lewis, in their classic early work (7), were among the first to show that the vagus could slow AV conduction and induce various degrees of heart block. They recognized that the direct vagal influences on AV nodal conduction could be readily interpreted only if the heart was paced at a constant rate. Interpretation might still be difficult, however, because the pacing site and route of entry of excitation into the AV node can alter the resultant AV conduction (22, 28).

Pavlov (49) compared the simultaneous changes in heart period and AV conduction after 5 sec of vagal stimulation in anesthetized cats. The inhibition of AV conduction was most pronounced when the chronotropic effect was weak. When heart period was progressively increased with higher vagal stimulus levels, the prolongation of AV conduction reached a plateau. At still higher stimulus levels, the AV conduction time diminished as the heart period was further increased. Hence, the degree of vagal inhibition of AV conduction strongly depends upon the concomitant chronotropic response.

DeBeer et al (10) determined the transient effects of step changes in atrial rate on AV conduction in open-chest rabbits, and the effects of vagal stimulation on such induced changes in AV conduction. They found that the change in AV nodal conduction time in response to a step decrease in atrial rate could be described by a single exponential function of time. This vagally induced increase in the time constant was independent of the level of sympathetic activity. Furthermore, the changes in conduction time through atrial or ventricular tissue played no role; i.e. the exponential adaptation of AV conduction was purely an AV-nodal phenonenon. This adaptation possibly depended on the tendency for acetylcholine to shorten the nodal action potentials (49) by enhancing the outward potassium current during the plateau phase.

In our laboratory, the interaction of heart period and vagal activity on AV conduction was approached from a different perspective (46). We first determined the simultaneous effects of brief vagal stimuli and transient changes in heart period on AV conduction. Thus, the vagi were stimulated with the heart unpaced. The response at the AV node was the resultant of two oppositely directed forces; i.e. the transient increase in heart period acted to decrease the AV conduction time, whereas the acetylcholine released in the AV node acted to prolong AV conduction. Next, the heart was paced at a constant rate, and the identical vagal stimuli were again applied. Then the effects of vagal stimulation directly on AV conduction were determined. Finally, the SA node was crushed, and the identical sequence of changes in heart period that had previously been obtained with vagal stimulation were now imposed by atrial pacing, but in the absence of vagal stimulation. Thus the effects of the sequence of changes in heart period on AV conduction were assessed. Since the increased heart period and neurally released acetylcholine have oppositely directed effects on AV conduction, it was expected that the result of both influences together would be intermediate between the separate influences. This was not found. Paradoxically, during the second to fourth beats of the response, the decrease in AV conduction time evoked by the changes in heart period alone was less than that observed when the same sequence of heart period changes was induced by vagal stimulation. That is, the AV conduction time in the unpaced heart was actually shorter in the presence of vagal activity than in its absence. The sequence of atrial activation was found to be radically altered by the vagal stimulus, probably due to a shift in the pacemaker site. There are many atrial sites capable of subsidiary pacemaker function in the absence of SA nodal activity (16).

Our work focused on the transient effects of brief vagal stimuli. Pavlov (49) showed that there was also a considerable interaction between the effects of heart period and longer periods of vagal stimulation. DeBeer et al (10) examined the effects of step changes in heart period at different constant levels of vagal stimuli. The time required to reach a new AV conduction time increased markedly with vagal activity. Thus acetylcholine appears to buffer the effects of sudden changes of heart period on AV conduction time, and the heart-period–vagal-activity interaction may serve a protective function for AV conduction (10, 46, 49). When both influences are exerted simultaneously, which is the normal situation in an intact animal, AV conduction is not significantly impaired.

The vagus, however, can exert a considerable influence over AV junctional rhythms. Wallick et al. (70) showed that in the dog with an AV junctional rhythm, repetitive bursts of vagal activity produced responses that were similar to those in dogs with a normal sinus rhythm. For both SA and AV nodal rhythms: a) the impulses from the myriad of efferent vagal fibers must arrive almost synchronously, b) the released acetylcholine must be inactivated very rapidly, and c) the sensitivity of the pacemaker cells to acetylcholine must change rapidly at some critical time during the cardiac cycle. This time probably coincides with the beginning of the activation of the inward current that is responsible for the upstroke of the pacemaker action potential (4). Such detailed information is not presently available with respect to the sympathetic influences on AV junctional or Hisian pacemaker function.

The vagus does have an important role in the control of normal AV nodal conduction in anesthetized animals (43–45, 60) and in humans (1, 6, 18, 55).

In trained athletes, a significant prolongation of AV conduction was ascribed to their high vagal tone (6). Marcus et al (18) altered mean arterial pressure with drugs and recorded the His bundle electrogram. They concluded that baroreceptor activation has a marked influence on the AV node but not on infranodal structures. There was also a significant vagal–heart-period interaction, such that simultaneous heart period changes masked the direct neural effects on AV conduction; i.e. the interactions provided a protective effect for AV function. In a similar His bundle study in children with and without congenital heart disease, Sapire et al (55) concluded that vagal tone significantly prolongs the AV conduction time.

Sympathetic-Parasympathetic Interactions

When both divisions of the autonomic nervous system are stimulated simultaneously, the resultant cardiac effect is often different from the algebraic sum of the individual responses obtained by stimulating the nerves from the two divisions separately (33, 47, 63, 68, 69, 71). Rosenblueth & Simeone (53) demonstrated that tonic sympathetic stimulation greatly increased the absolute reduction in heart rate produced by vagal stimulation. Samaan (54) showed subsequently that the cardiac acceleration caused by stimulation of sympathetic nerves was markedly reduced if the vagal nerves were activated concurrently. This "accentuated antagonism" (33) between the two branches of the autonomic nervous system is operative in the control of numerous aspects of cardiac function. Such interactions have been reported with respect to the neural control of atrial (33) and ventricular (33, 34) contractility, automaticity of the sinoatrial (33, 53, 54) and atrioventricular (71) nodes, ventricular recovery properties (47), and cardiac vulnerability to ventricular fibrillation (69). Vatner and his colleagues (68) recently found that the ventricular inotropic response to infused sympathomimetic amines in conscious dogs was doubled in the presence of muscarinic blockade (68). They concluded that, in the resting state, the parasympathetic nervous system had little direct effect on ventricular contractility, but it exerted a pronounced indirect influence by antagonizing the β-adrenergic inotropic response.

The explanations for the antagonist effects of vagal stimulation on sympathetically induced responses have not been fully determined, but two major mechanisms have been suggested (15, 19, 33, 58). The first is a presynaptic mechanism, in which acetylcholine reduces the amount of norepinephrine released from sympathetic nerve terminals (33, 34, 61). The second is a postsynaptic mechanism, in which acetylcholine reduces the magnitude of the response to a given adrenergic stimulus (33, 34, 58). Evidence for both types of interactions has been adduced.

Löffelholz, Lindmar & Muscholl (40–42) proposed that peripheral sympathetic nerve fibers have presynaptic inhibitory muscarinic receptors. They found that in the rabbit heart, acetylcholine caused a reduction in the quantity of norepinephrine released in response to a given stimulus to the cardiac sympathetic nerves. Subsequent experiments have confirmed the existence of such muscarinic inhibition of norepinephrine release in the heart (30, 31, 35, 61). Levy & Blattberg (34) found that, in the intact dog during sustained cardiac sympathetic stimulation, concurrent vagal stimulation evoked a reduction in ventricular contractile force and in norepinephrine overflow into the coronary sinus blood. This vagally mediated inhibition was prevented by the administration of atropine. Similar observations were made by Lavallée and coworkers (31), who demonstrated that this vagal effect is substantial even at frequencies of vagal stimulation as low as 1 Hz.

The chronotropic effect of infused catecholamines can be antagonized by acetylcholine (19). This suggests that there may be a postsynaptic antagonism—i.e. at the receptor cell (33, 34). The positive inotropic and chronotropic effects of norepinephrine may be mediated through increases in cyclic adenosine 3'-5'-monophosphate (cAMP) in the myocardium (25, 58, 64, 65). It has been suggested that the negative inotropic effects of acetylcholine are mediated through cyclic guanosine 3'-5'-monophosphate (cGMP) (32). Furthermore, the antiadrenergic effects of acetylcholine may be mediated by an antagonism between the actions of the two nucleotides (72). Also, muscarinic agonists may curtail the amount of cAMP formed in response to β-adrenergic receptor stimulation (14, 64, 67, 72). These cholinergic agonists apparently inhibit the increase in adenylate cyclase activity elicited by catecholamine administration and thus decrease the formation of cAMP within the cell (72). However, the precise role of the nucleotides in cardiac function is still unclear (12, 48, 65). Several recent reviews discuss these mechanisms at length (14, 64, 67).

Literature Cited

1. Akhtar, M., Damato, A. N., Caracta, A. R., Batsford, W. P., Josephson, M. E., Lau, S. H. 1974. Electrophysiologic effects of atropine on atrioventricular conduction studied by His bundle electrogram. *Am. J. Cardiol.* 33:333–43
2. Angelakos, E. T., Fuxe, K., Toshiana, M. L. 1963. Chemical and histochemical evaluation of the distribution of catecholamines in the rabbit and guinea pig hearts. *Acta Physiol. Scand.* 59:184–92
3. Brown, G. L., Eccles, J. C. 1934. The action of a single vagal volley on the rhythm of the heart beat. *J. Physiol. London* 82:211–40
4. Brown, H. F., Giles, W., Noble, S. J. 1977. Membrane currents underlying activity in frog sinus venous. *J. Physiol. London* 271:783–816
5. Brown, O. M. 1976. Cat heart acetylcholine: structural proof and distribution. *Am. J. Physiol.* 231:781–85
6. Carlton, R. A., Graettinger, T. S., Bowyer, A. F. 1965. Parasympathetic influence on the atrial myocardium and atrioventricular node of man. *J. Lab. Clin. Med.* 66:413–22

7. Cohn, A. E., Lewis, T. 1913. The predominant influence of the left vagus nerve upon conduction between the auricles and ventricles of the dog. *J. Exp. Med.* 18:739–47

8. Cooper, T. 1965. Terminal innervation of the heart. In *Nervous Control of the Heart*, ed. W. C. Randall, pp. 130–53. Baltimore: Williams and Williams

9. Dahlstrom, A., Fuxe, K., Mya-Tu, M., Zetterstrom, B. E. M. 1965. Observations on adrenergic innervation of dog heart. *Am. J. Physiol.* 209:689–92

10. DeBeer, E. L., Boom, H. B. K., Naafs, B. 1977. The combined influence of the stimulus frequency of the vagal nerves and the atrial stimulus interval on the atrioventricular conduction time. *Cardiovas. Res.* 11:47–54

11. De Geest, H., Levy, M. N., Zieske, H., Lipman, R. I. 1965. Depression of ventricular contractility by stimulation of the vagus nerves. *Circ. Res.* 17:222–35

12. Diamond, J., TenEick, R., Trapani, A. J., 1977. Are increases in cyclic GMP levels responsible for the negative inotropic effects of acetylcholine in the heart. *Biochem. Biophys. Res. Commun.* 79:912–18

13. Dong, E. Jr., Reitz, B. A. 1970. Effect of timing of vagal stimulation on heart rate in the dog. *Circ. Res.* 27:635–46

14. Drummond, G. I., Severson, D. L. 1979. Cyclic nucleotides and cardiac function. *Circ. Res.* 44:145–53

15. Duchêne-Marullaz, P. 1973. Effets de l'innervation cholinergique sur le coeur de mammifère. Le tonus cardiomodérateur. *J. Physiol. Paris* 66:373–97

16. Euler, D. E., Jones, S. B., Gunnar, W. P., Loeb, J. M., Murdock, D. K., Randall, W. C. 1979. Cardiac arrhythmias in the conscious dog after excision of the sinoatrial node and crista terminalis. *Circulation* 59:468–75

17. Geis, W. P., Kaye, M. P., Randall, W. C. 1973. Major autonomic pathways to the atria and S-A and A-V nodes of the canine heart. *Am. J. Physiol.* 224:202–8

18. Gross, P. M., Heistad, D. D., Strait, M. R., Marcus, M. L., Brody, M. J. 1979. Cerebral vascular responses to physiological stimulation of sympathetic pathways in cats. *Circ. Res.* 44:288–94

19. Higgins, C. B., Vatner, S. F., Braunwald, E. 1973. Parasympathetic control of the heart. *Pharmacol. Rev.* 25:120–55

20. Iano, T. L., Levy, M. N., Lee, M. H. 1973. An acceleratory component of the parasympathetic control of heart rate. *Am. J. Physiol.* 224:997–1005

21. Jalife, J., Moe, G. K. 1979. Phasic effects of vagal stimulation on pacemaker activity of the isolated sinus node of the young cat. *Circ. Res.* 45:595–608

22. Janse, M. J. 1969. Influence of the direction of the atrial wave front on A-V nodal transmission in isolated hearts of rabbits. *Circ. Res.* 25:439–49

23. Jewett, D. L. 1964. Activity of single efferent fibers in the cervical vagus of the dog, with special reference to possible cardioinhibitory fibers. *J. Physiol. London* 175:321–57

24. Katona, P. G., Poitras, J. W., Barnett, G. O., Terry, B. S. 1970. Cardiac vagal efferent activity and heart period in the carotid sinus reflex. *Am. J. Physiol.* 218:1030–37

25. Keely, S. L., Corbin, J. D. 1977. Involvement of cAMP-dependent protein kinase in the regulation of heart contractile force. *Am. J. Physiol.* 233:H269–75

26. Kent, K. M., Epstein, S. E., Cooper, T., Jacobowitz, D. M. 1974. Cholinergic innervation of the canine and human ventricular conducting system. *Circulation* 50:948–55

27. Kilbinger, H. 1973. Gas chromatographic estimation of acetylcholine in the rabbit heart using a nitrogen selective detector. *J. Neurochem.* 21:421–29

28. Konishi, T., Matsuyama, E. 1976. Effect of changes in inputs to atrioventricular node on A-V conduction. *Jpn. Circ. J.* 40:1392–400

29. Kunze, D. L. 1972. Reflex discharge patterns of cardiac vagal efferent fibers. *J. Physiol. London* 222:1–15

30. Langley, A. E., Gardier, R. W. 1977. Effect of atropine and acetylcholine on nerve stimulated output of noradrenaline and dopamine-beta-hydroxylase from isolated rabbit and guinea pig hearts. *Naunyn Schmiedebergs Arch. Pharmakol.* 297:251–56

31. Lavallée, M., de Champlain, J., Nadeau, R. A., Yamaguchi, N. 1978. Muscarinic inhibition of endogenous myocardial catecholamine liberation in the dog. *Can. J. Physiol. Pharmacol.* 56:642–49

32. Lee, T. P., Kuo, J. F., Greengard, P. 1972. Role of muscarinic cholinergic receptors in regulation of guanosine 3':5'-cyclic monophosphate content in mammalian brain, heart muscle, and intestinal smooth muscle. *Proc. Natl. Acad. Sci., USA* 69:3287–91

33. Levy, M. N. 1971. Sympathetic-parasympathetic interactions in the heart. *Circ. Res.* 29:437–45

34. Levy, M. N. 1976. Parasympathetic control of the heart. In *Neural Regulation of the Heart,* ed. W. C. Randall, pp. 97–129. NY: Oxford

35. Levy, M. N., Blattberg, B. 1976. Effect of vagal stimulation on the overflow of norepinephrine into the coronary sinus during cardiac sympathetic nerve stimulation in the dog. *Circ. Res.* 38:81–85

36. Levy, M. N., Iano, T., Zieske, H. 1972. Effects of repetitive bursts of vagal activity on heart rate. *Circ. Res.* 30:186–95

37. Levy, M. N., Martin, P. J., Iano, T., Zieske, H. 1970. Effects of single vagal stimuli on heart rate and atrioventricular conduction. *Am. J. Physiol.* 218:1256–62

38. Levy, M. N., Martin, P. J. 1979. Neural control of the heart. In *Handbook of Physiology, Sect. 2: The Cardiovascular System,* ed. R. M. Berne, pp. 581–620. Washington DC: Am. Physiol. Soc.

39. Levy, M. N., Wexberg, S., Eckel, C., Zieske, H. 1978. The effect of changing interpulse intervals on the negative chronotropic response to repetitive bursts of vagal stimuli in the dog. *Circ. Res.* 43:570–76

40. Lindmar, R., Löffelholz, K., Muscholl, E. 1968. A muscarinic mechanism inhibiting the release of noradrenaline from peripheral adrenergic nerve fibers by nicotinic agents. *Brit. J. Pharmacol.* 32:280–94

41. Löffelholz, K., Muscholl, E. 1969. A muscarinic inhibition of the noradrenaline release evoked by postganglionic sympathetic nerve stimulation. *Naunyn-Schmiedebergs Arch. Pharmakol.* 265:1–15

42. Löffelholz, K., Muscholl, E. 1970. Inhibition by parasympathetic nerve stimulation of the release of the adrenergic transmitter. *Naunyn-Schmiedebergs Arch. Pharmakol.* 267:181–84

43. Martin, P. J. 1975. Dynamic vagal control of atrial-ventricular conduction: Theoretical and experimental studies. *Ann. Biomed. Eng.* 3:275–95

44. Martin, P. J. 1976. Depression of atrioventricular sensitivity in the dog by successive brief bursts of vagal stimulation. *Circ. Res.* 38:448–53

45. Martin, P. 1977. The influence of the parasympathetic nervous system on atrioventricular conduction. *Circ. Res.* 41:593–99

46. Martin, P. J. 1977. Paradoxical dynamic interaction of heart period and vagal activity on atrioventricular conduction in the dog. *Circ. Res.* 40:81–89

47. Martins, J. B., Zipes, D. P. 1980. Effects of sympathetic and vagal nerves on recovery properties of the endocardium and epicardium of the canine left ventricle. *Circ. Res.* 40:100–10

48. Mirro, M. J., Bailey, J. C., Watanabe, A. M. 1979. Dissociation between the electrophysiological properties and total tissue cyclic guanosine monophosphate content of guinea pig atria. *Circ. Res.* 45:225–33

49. Pavlov, V. 1975. Dependence of the atrioventricular conduction on the cardiac rate upon increased vagal activity. *Agressologie* 16:9–13

50. Deleted in proof

51. Randall, W. C., Armour, J. A. 1977. Gross and microscopic anatomy of the cardiac innervation. See Ref. 34, pp. 15–41

52. Reid, J. V. O. 1969. The cardiac pacemaker: effects of regularly spaced nervous input. *Am. Heart J.* 78:58–64

53. Rosenblueth, A., Simeone, F. A. 1934. The interrelations of vagal and accelerator effects on the cardiac rate. *Am. J. Physiol.* 110:42–55

54. Samaan, A. 1935. The antagonistic cardiac nerves and heart rate. *J. Physiol. London* 83:332–40

55. Sapire, D. W., Shah, J. J., Black, I. F. S. 1979. Prolonged atrioventricular conduction in young children and adolescents. *S. A. Med. J.* 55:669–73

56. Schmid, P. G., Dykstra, R. H., Mayer, H. E., Oda, R. P., Donnell, J. J. 1979. Evidence of nonuniform sympathetic neural activity to heart regions in guinea pigs. *Am. J. Physiol.* 237:H606–11

57. Schmid, P. G., Grief, B. G., Lund, D. D., Roskoski, R. Jr. 1978. Regional choline acetyltransferase in guinea pig heart. *Circ. Res.* 42:657–60

58. Schwegler, M., Jacob, R. 1976. Catecholamine antagonism of acetylcholine and dibutyrylguanosine 3',5'-monophosphate in the mammalian ventricular myocardium. In *Recent Advances in Studies on Cardiac Structure and Metabolism,* ed. P. Harris, R. J. Bing, A. Fleckenstein, pp. 391–99. Baltimore: University Park Press

59. Spear, J. F., Kronhaus, K. D., Moore, E. N., Kline, R. P. 1979. The effect of brief vagal stimulation on the isolated

rabbit sinus node. *Circ. Res.* 44:75–88

60. Spear, J. F., Moore, E. N. 1973. Influence of brief vagal and stellate nerve stimulation on pacemaker activity and conduction within the atrioventricular conduction system of the dog. *Circ. Res.* 32:27–41

61. Starke, K. 1977. Regulation of noradrenaline release by presynaptic receptor systems. *Rev. Physiol. Biochem. Pharmacol.* 77:1–124

62. Stuesse, S. L., Levy, M. N., Zieske, H. 1978. Phase-related sensitivity of the sinoatrial node to vagal stimuli in the isolated rat atrium. *Circ. Res.* 43: 217–24

63. Stuesse, S. L., Wallick, D. W., Levy, M. N. 1979. Autonomic control of right atrial contractile strength in the dog. *Am. J. Physiol.* 236:860–65

64. Stull, J. T., Mayer, S. E. 1979. Biochemical mechanisms of adrenergic and cholinergic regulation of myocardial contractility. See Ref. 38, pp. 741–74

65. Taniguchi, T., Fujiwara, M., Lee, J. J., Hikada, H. 1979. Effect of acetylcholine on the norepinephrine-induced positive chronotropy and increase in cyclic nucleotides of isolate rabbit sinatrial node. *Circ. Res.* 45:493–504

66. Thaemert, J. C. 1973. Fine structure of the atrioventricular node as viewed in serial sections. *Am. J. Anat.* 136:43–66

67. Tsien, R. W. 1977. Cyclic AMP and contractile activity in the heart. *Adv. Cyclic Nucleotide Res.* 8:363–420

68. Vatner, S. F., Rutherford, J. D., Ochs, H. R. 1979. Baroreflex and vagal mechanisms modulating left ventricular contractile responses to sympathomimetic amines in conscious dogs. *Circ. Res.* 44:195–207

69. Verrier, R. L., Lown, B. 1978. Sympathetic-parasympathetic interactions and ventricular electrical stability. In *Neural Mechanisms in Cardiac Arrhythmias*, ed. P. J. Schwartz, A. M. Brown, A. Milliani, A. Zanchetti, pp. 75–85. NY: Raven Press

70. Wallick, D. W., Levy, M. N., Felder, D. S., Zieske, H. 1979. Effects of repetitive bursts of vagal activity on atrioventricular junctional rate in dogs. *Am. J. Physiol.* 237:275–81

71. Wallick, D. W., Felder, D., Levy, M. N. 1978. Autonomic control of pacemaker activity in the atrioventricular junction of the dog. *Am. J. Physiol.* 235:H308–13

72. Watanabe, A. M., McConnaughey, M. M., Strawbridge, R. A., Fleming, J. W., Jones, L. R., Besch, H. R. Jr. 1978. Muscarinic cholinergic receptor modulation of beta-adrenergic receptor affinity for catecholamines. *J. Biol. Chem.* 253: 4833–36

Ann. Rev. Physiol. 1981. 43:455–76
Copyright © 1981 by Annual Reviews Inc. All rights reserved

CARDIOCIRCULATORY DYNAMICS IN THE NORMAL AND FAILING HEART[1]

❖1323

Robert Zelis, Stephen F. Flaim, A. James Liedtke, and Stephen H. Nellis

The Department of Medicine (Division of Cardiology) and The Department of Physiology, The Pennsylvania State University College of Medicine, The Milton S. Hershey Medical Center, Hershey, Pennsylvania 17033

INTRODUCTION

This review concerns chronic congestive heart failure (CHF), which exists when the heart is unable to pump an output sufficient for the needs of the regional circulations (4, 17). Cardiac compensatory mechanisms initially try to preserve cardiac output; ultimately peripheral circulatory mechanisms try to preserve systemic arterial pressure. We consider (*a*) how compensatory mechanisms relate to the normal processes regulating left ventricular pump function; (*b*) the regulation of the distribution of cardiac output and how it is altered with congestive heart failure; and (*c*) how a new group of drugs, the vasodilators, affects cardiac performance and regional blood flow in CHF.

DETERMINANTS OF LEFT VENTRICULAR PUMP FUNCTION

It is taught that cardiac output is the product of heart rate and stroke volume and that the three determinants of stroke volume are preload, afterload, and contractility. When the heart fails, stroke volume is inade-

[1]Supported in part by United States Public Health Service Grants HL 23836, 22917, grants from the American Heart Association, South Central Pennsylvania Chapter, the Sam Ostrow Cardiology Research Fund, and a gift from the Grand Pennsylvania Chapter Order of the Eastern Star.

455

0066-4278/81/0315-0455$01.00

quate and heart rate must rise. It is commonly stated that three mechanisms are utilized by the failing heart to enhance stroke volume: (*a*) ventricular dilation, whereby the Starling mechanism is used to raise the heart toward the apex of its depressed ventricular function curve (relating stroke volume to ventricular end diastolic pressure); (*b*) hypertrophy of ventricular muscle fibers to spread the increased workload over more contractile units; and (*c*) increased catecholamine stimulation to augment contractility. Let us examine these traditional concepts in more detail.

The Role of Diastolic Stretch and End Systolic Pressure in Determining Ventricular Performance

What is the Starling principle? In isolated cardiac muscle contracting isometrically, the peak tension developed becomes progressively greater as preload or end diastolic stretch is increased (6). In the isovolumically contracting left ventricle, peak developed pressure is similarly related to diastolic volume (Figure 1A) (14, 51). Increasing contracility by beta adrenergic receptor stimulation results in a shift of the relationship between isovolumic end diastolic volume and peak systolic pressure up and to the left (Figure 1D). With minor reservations, the isovolumic volume-pressure relationships reasonably reflect isometric length-tension relationships in isolated cardiac muscle (69, 76, 83). When heart muscle is allowed to shorten from different end diastolic pressures in the animal with an intact circulation and stroke volume is measured, the resultant ventricular function curve cannot be equated with the isometric length-tension curve (14, 51). In the ejecting heart, the extent to which cardiac muscle shortens (i.e. end systolic volume) is much more dependent upon end systolic pressure (ventricular afterload or aortic impedance) than end diastolic stretch. This is graphically presented in Figures 1B and 1C, which relate the systolic and diastolic changes in ventricular pressure and volume throughout the course of the cardiac cycle. This is known as the pressure-volume loop.

In Figures 1B and 1C, the normal cardiac cycle is depicted as the loop connecting points A,B,C,Y. (Point B accurately represents maximum volume just prior to aortic valve opening, but not pressure that has been distorted to accommodate volumetric relationships.) The extent of shortening, and hence the stroke volume (B-C), is determined by the systolic pressure at the end of ejection (point C). This point is equivalent to the peak systolic pressure that would be generated during an isolvolumic contraction at the same volume (point 6 in Figuare 1A). If preload and contractile state are held constant (point A in Figure 1B), the extent to which the ventricle shortens, the stroke volume, is totally dependent upon the pressure the ventricle "sees" at the end of ejection. With an increased end systolic pressure (point E in Figure 1B), stroke volume is reduced to D-E; with a

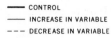

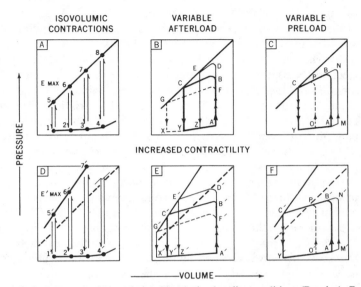

Figure 1   Ventricular pressure-volume relationships during baseline conditions (Panels A, B, C) and increased contractility (Panels D, E, F). Isovolumic contractions are depicted in Panels A and D. Ejecting beats are shown in Panels B, C, E, and F under conditions of variable afterload (Panels B and E) and variable preload (Panels C and F). The shapes of the systolic portions of the loops for the ejecting beats are deliberately distorted in order to illustrate more clearly the end systolic pressure-volume points. When these points are linearly connected, they resemble the line connecting the peak systolic pressures generated by the isovolumic ventricle contracting at different volumes (E_{max}). This slope is analogous to the length-tension relationship of isometrically contracting cardiac muscle. Thus, a shift up and to the left (E'_{max} in Panel D) represents an increase in contractility. [Relationships presented are similar to those described in (69) and (84).]

reduction in end systolic pressure (point G), stroke volume is augmented to F-G. The slope of the line G-C-E (Figure 1B) [called E_{max} by Sagawa (69)] is equivalent to the slope of 5-6-7 (Figure 1A), the isovolumic pressure-volume relationship. This slope is a function of myocardial contractility. Just as a shift in the isometric length-tension relationship up and to the left represents an augmented contractile state, so does a shift in E_{max}. In Figure 1D, this is represented by E'_{max}, the slope of 5'-6'-7'. It is important to note that this state of enhanced contractility, E'_{max}, can also be determined for ejecting beats by examining the end systolic pressure-volume relationships (E_{max}' = slope G'-C'-E') under conditions of variable afterload (23, 76). Hence, in the intact circulation, the logical application of the isometric cardiac muscle length-tension relationship is the E_{max} slope rather than the conventional stroke volume/end diastolic pressure curve (14, 51).

Pressure volume loops under conditions of variable preload are depicted in Figure 1C. Regardless of the preload (points O, A, and M), the extent of shortening is still determined by end systolic pressure (point C). The total stroke volume, however, is different. The additional volume entering the heart when filling volume is increased (A-M) is expelled during ventricular ejection (N-B); the increased total stroke volume (N-C) reflects this increment. Breathing, changing body position, and initiating upright exercise all change venous return and filling volume. The variations in venous return are all automatically handled by the normal heart by its ejection to a constant end systolic pressure, determined by aortic impedance (76).

Two additional points must be introduced briefly before considering the failing heart. First, in normals, variations in heart rate are much more important in producing major adjustments in cardiac output than variations in stroke volume (79). Second, diastolic compliance must always be considered in reviewing ventricular function curves (24, 47, 51, 59). Heart muscle is considerably stiffer than skeletal muscle. Consider the line Y-O-A-M in Figure 1C. If passively extended to larger volumes, it has been found to break sharply upward. Small increments in ventricular filling volume produce disproportionately large increments in ventricular filling pressure. This occurs in normal individuals lying supine when blood volume or plasma volume is expanded acutely by intravenous infusions (56). Thus the ventricular function curve must always demonstrate a flat plateau. The point at which the plateau begins is called the "apex" of the ventricular function curve. Normal supine humans and animals almost always operate at this point of near maximum and diastolic volume (56). Consider the normal loop (A-B-C-Y) (Figures 1B and 1C). Segment A-M of Figure 1C is small to reflect the very small changes in stroke volume (N-B) that result under extreme volume loading. When the normal individual stands, loop O-P-C-Y (Figure 1C) results, but the increase in venous return that occurs at the initiation of exercise brings the subject back to loop A-B-C-Y. Further increases in cardiac output during exercise are brought about by an increase in heart rate (major) and catecholamine stimulation of the myocardium (minor). The latter increases contractility (E_{max} to E'_{max}) and increases stroke volume, resulting in loop A'-B'-C'-Y' in Figure 1E. The final stroke volume that results is further influenced by aortic impedance (see below).

Ventricular Dilatation in Congestive Heart Failure

The most common causes of CHF include left ventricular pressure overload (systemic arterial hypertension or aortic valve stenosis), left ventricular volume overload (mitral or aortic valve incompetence), and overwork of the remaining normal myocardium after death or injury of significant portions of ventricular tissue due to ischemia (myocardial infarction or other causes —e.g. alcoholic cardiomyopathy, viral myocarditis). Clinically, it is widely taught that the patient with CHF is operating on a depressed ventricular function curve, shifted down and to the right. Stroke volume is low. Ventricular filling pressure is high. The failing ventricle is enlarged (dilated) and cardiac muscle cell mass is increased (hypertrophied). Although both dilation and hypertrophy can occur with all types of CHF, in general, pressure overload leads to a profound increase in cardiac mass with a great increase in wall thickness and little change in ventricular volume (25, 50, 60, 70). When chronic CHF results from volume overload or myocardial infarction, the hypertrophy process is less marked (10, 33, 49, 61, 68). Ventricular volume is greatly enlarged, but wall thickness increases minimally. The effects of ventricular dilation on the performance of the volume-overloaded heart is considered first, hypertrophy second.

It is widely accepted that the increase in ventricular volume accompanying CHF is an important compensatory mechanism to improve cardiac performance. In contrast to normal individuals, where ventricular filling pressure is optimal at 10–12 mmHg, in CHF, optimal cardiac performance occurs at 18–20 mmHg (56). Is this evidence to substantiate an increased use of the Starling mechanism, or does the higher filling pressure merely reflect a stiffer ventricle? Newman has presented data to suggest that the volume-overloaded heart appears to operate on a higher portion of the "length-tension curve" (49). He used a Walton-Brodie strain gauge sewn to the myocardium, taking care to ensure that resting length at the time of gauge attachment truly reflected basal normal length. However, his was an open-chest preparation, and it is well known that ventricular volume in an open-chest preparation is unphysiologically small (49). In these studies, the heart of the volume-overloaded animal may not have shrunk to the same extent as normal hearts when the chest was opened. In the awake, unanesthetized state, both normal and volume-overloaded animals appear to operate at maximum ventricular stretch at the apex of their ventricular function curve. Pinsky et al noted that during the creation of an acute aortocaval fistula, end diastolic dimensions acutely increased to their maximum and increased little after 12 weeks (61). Prior to shunt opening, when ventricular afterload was increased acutely by pressor drug administration, the increase in diastolic dimensions was much greater than occurred chronically after shunt opening.

One can also turn to histologic studies of sarcomere length and the relationship of the latter to cardiac performance to evaluate the functional significance of cardiac dilation in CHF secondary to volume overload.

Initially it was thought that the enhanced contractile performance of muscle that occurs with increasing diastolic stretch could be completely explained by a more optimal interaction between actin and myosin filaments at a sarcomere length of 2.2 μm (6). Contractile performance then decreased as the filaments were overstretched. Recent in vivo studies have indicated that there really is no "optimal" sarcomere length (63). The changes that occur in developed tension with stretch appear to be related to a variable extent of activation of sarcomeres by calcium ions (15, 29). With ventricular dilation and CHF accompanying chronic volume overload, end diastolic sarcomere length is not increased (69). Thus ventricular dilation in CHF appears to be the response by which the increased workload can be distributed over more contractile elements. In the dilated heart, much less shortening of the fibers is required to generate a given stroke volume than in a chamber of smaller dimensions. This is particularly important in the patient with mitral or aortic valve incompetence in whom there is a low forward cardiac output perfusing the regional vascular beds. *Total* stroke volume in such a patient is usually greatly increased except in very late stages of the disease. Much of that supranormal stroke volume is useless, since it is pumped back and forth across the low-impedance incompetent valve and never reaches the periphery. Thus normal fiber shortening in the dilated volume-overloaded ventricle will result in an increased stroke volume. However, the price paid for this mechanical advantage is an increased myocardial oxygen cost due to the increased wall tensions that must be sustained by the dilated ventricle (20). Thus, the Starling mechanism may be important in functional hypovolemic states (such as when exercise is initiated by an upright human), or during acute volume overload, or to match the output of each ventricle, but not during chronic adaptation to volume overload where the increase in muscle mass may be more important in distributing the workload.

Hypertrophy and Its Effect on Myocardial Contractility

Early studies of isolated muscle from the pressure-overloaded heart showed a gradation in the depression of systolic performance that was worse with increasing hypertrophy (4). Therefore it was concluded that myocardial hypertrophy resulted in decreased myocardial contractility. But does it? Subsequently it has been shown that, depending on the stimulus, hypertrophy can lead to a wide spectrum of physiologic and biochemical changes (85), reflecting enhanced (33, 44, 71), normal (70, 86) or depressed performance (5, 34, 39, 50). The ends of this hypertrophy spectrum have been called physiologic and pathologic, respectively (85).

Although in neonatal animals myocardial cell division occurs as a response to an increased workload (13) (a process more appropriately termed hyperplasia), in adults hypertrophy implies an increased cell volume. The stimulus initiating the hypertrophic process appears to be an increased stress; this has to be borne by cardiac fibers, which are required to increase their workload (78). Hypertrophy is greatest in the basal and subendocardial portions of the heart, where wall stress is greatest. The increased tension on the myocardial cells may produce local hypoxia or hypercapnia and/or be a stimulus for norepinephrine release. [Norepinephrine infused in subhypertensive doses can also produce left ventricular hypertrophy (32).] The exact sequence of events is uncertain; however, calcium and cyclic AMP appear to be involved in the initiating process (65). Performance of normal and hypertrophied hearts, as determined by the velocity of contraction, is related in part to the rate of ATP hydrolysis by myosin (12). Preferential synthesis of one or another of the myosin isoenzymes results in either enhanced (44) or decreased myosin ATPase activity (5, 34, 39). Although the rate of uptake and binding of calcium by the sarcoplasmic reticulum is reduced in CHF (73), a depressed velocity of contraction has been demonstrated in skinned fibers from hypertrophied hearts (39), suggesting that the depressed mechanical systolic performance of hypertrophy cannot be entirely explained by abnormalities in calcium flux. However, if the rate of calcium uptake by the sarcoplasmic reticulum during diastole were slower, it would lead to a slower rate of relaxation. Asynchronous synthesis of contractile proteins with misalignment of actin with myosin and/or increased production of collagen by connective tissue hyperplasia may also contribute to ventricular dysfunction (85). The production of collagen results in an increase in diastolic stiffness (24, 47, 61, 86) and perhaps also in an increased internal resistance to sarcomere shortening (47). Lastly, increased collagen may prevent the myocardium from returning to normal function after the hemodynamic burden is corrected by surgery (61). In brief, hypertrophy results in changes in a number of variables related to contractile performance and the end result is difficult to predict a priori.

In the foregoing discussion, we have called hypertrophy good or bad, depending upon the resultant change in ventricular contractile response. How is this defined? Sarnoff defined contractility in terms of the ventricular function curve relating stroke work to ventricular end diastolic filling pressure under conditions of constant afterload (14, 51, 56). The discussion of Figure 1 made it clear that the ventricular function curve is quite complex and very different from the simpler length-tension curve, from which changes in contractility can be inferred. The length-tension curve of isolated muscle from the pressure-overloaded ventricle is displaced down and to the right (5, 47). The greater the pressure overload, the more depressed is contractility. No such changes are seen with isolated muscle from the volume-overloaded ventricle (9). In an open-chest dog preparation in which in situ length-tension curves of intact left ventricle were evaluated, Newman has shown in the volume-overloaded ventricle without heart failure that contractile performance appears to be increased when expressed as force generation (49). When the force measurements were normalized for wall thickness, no impairment of contractile function was observed. When the volume-overloaded heart ultimately failed, a depressed contractile performance was demonstrated by both criteria. In similar studies of pressure-overload hypertrophy, he demonstrated a significant increase in total force generation, but contractile performance was depressed when normalized for the marked increase in wall thickness that occurred (50). Where E_{max} has been evaluated in humans from end systolic pressure and volume, the relationships were similar (23).

A decade ago, the characterization of contractility by evaluation of the inverse relationships of contractile element velocity (VCE) and force was widely studied in isolated tissue, animals, and in humans (4, 37). Maximum velocity (V_{max}) at zero load was thought to be a load-independent index of contractility. In experimental pathologic hypertrophy (pressure overload), a depressed mechanical V_{max} was correlated with a depression in myosin ATPase activity (4, 5, 39). Both variables increase with physiologic hypertrophy (e.g. thyroxine administration) but do not change with volume overload (9, 44). With regression of pathologic myocardial hypertrophy (pressure overload), V_{max} and myosin ATPase activity begin to return toward normal (5).

The supposition of load independence of V_{max} and related velocity parameters was criticized on both experimental and theoretical grounds (31, 57, 62). Mechanical V_{max} is related to biochemical myosin ATPase activity and sensitive to agents that alter calcium availability; thus it could not be preload-independent, since stretching cardiac muscle also increases the extent of calcium activation of contractile elements (15, 29). The isovolumic contractility indexes also fail to be helpful in the assessment and management of patients with heart disease (31, 57). One velocity measurement found useful in clinical and experimental studies is the fiber shortening rate (VCF) during ventricular ejection (67). It must be interpreted with respect to ventricular afterload, to which it is inversely related. In CHF, a reduction in mean VCF is seen only when hypertrophy (especially an increase in wall thickness) does not keep pace with the increased workload (25, 70). Thus even in pressure overload, hypertrophy does not necessarily result in depressed cardiac muscle function. In volume overload, an increased VCF has been noted and related to high levels of circulating catecholamines (33).

Clinically, the most commonly used index of global pump function is the ejection fraction (51, 83). This is the ratio of stroke volume to end diastolic volume, or the percent emptying of the left ventricle (normally 50–70%). This can be calculated from angiographic left ventricular volumes at the time of diagnostic left heart catheterization and measured noninvasively using radionuclide imaging techniques. Although it is of limited use as a physiologic tool, the ejection fraction correlates well with clinical prognosis, especially the results of certain types of cardiac surgery.

In summary, one might think of ventricular hypertrophy in terms of a spectrum. Abrupt pressure overload likely, but not inevitably, leads to depressed ventricular performance. Volume overload results in first hyper- and then hypofunction. Ventricular hypertrophy produced by intermittent volume overload (such as with athletic exercise conditioning) results in improved cardiac function (71). Thus by producing new sarcomeres the heart distributes an increased workload over more contractile units in order to normalize stress. Performance of these new contractile units depends on the pattern of contractile protein synthesis (especially myosin isoenzymes), as well as the cardiac architectural pattern assumed. Chamber volume, wall thickness, and connective tissue elements are major determinants of the latter.

AORTIC IMPEDANCE

We stated above that the extent of shortening of the ejecting ventricle (end systolic volume) was determined by end systolic pressure and that the latter was a function of aortic impedance (41). This term best describes the interface between the heart and circulation. Aortic impedance can be "simply" defined as the frequency-dependent relationship of pressure (P) to flow ($\dot{Q}$) (53). This is characterized by the amplitude or modulus ($Z = P \div \dot{Q}$) and phase angle ($\theta = p-\dot{Q}$), for each harmonic, when pressure and flow curves are reduced to a series of sine waves by Fourier analysis. Normally the phase angle is negative for the first few harmonics, indicating that the flow wave leads the pressure wave. The impedance modulus at the zero harmonic is the familiar systemic vascular resistance ($Z_0 =$ mean P $\div$ mean $\dot{Q}$, considering terminal downstream P to be zero). The major determinants of aortic impedance are the following: the viscoelastic properties of the large vessels ("stiffness" of the aorta), the peripheral vascular resistance (state of tone in the resistance vessels), the inertia of the blood, and the reflection of both pressure and flow waves back through the arterial tree from the periphery (41). To summarize, aortic impedance is the external or circulatory load against which the left ventricle must work in order to eject blood into the vascular system. The ventricle also has its own internal impedance

—i.e. the cardiac viscoelastic elements that resist fiber shortening. The latter is increased when connective tissue hyperplasia accompanies ventricular hypertrophy (47).

Total systemic vascular resistance is commonly calculated and is usually found to be considerably increased in patients with severe CHF. More recently, aortic impedance has been evaluted in humans utilizing a velocity catheter placed in the ascending aorta (58). In heart failure, phase angle changes were minimal; however, characteristic impedance, taken as the arithmetic mean of impedance moduli from 2–12 Hz, was found to be increased. The oscillations between maximum and minimum impedance moduli were also increased. These data suggest that the peripheral vessels in heart failure patients are stiffer than normal and there is greater reflection of both pressure and flow waves back from the periphery. Increased aortic stiffness is perhaps related to increased sodium content (see below) and increased alpha adrenergic receptor stimulation.

In summary, the characteristics of the arterial system in CHF are such that ejection of blood by the left ventricle is impeded. This adds to the burden of the failing heart. Vasodilators can reduce cardiac work by significantly reducing aortic impedance moduli. Although they also produce an unfavorable change in phase angle, making it less negative, the significance of this observation is uncertain (53). The effects of vasodilators on the heart and regional circulations vary with the specific drug and the type of peripheral circulatory abnormalities present in a given patient suffering from heart failure.

DISTRIBUTION OF THE CARDIAC OUTPUT IN HEART FAILURE

When cardiac output cannot be maintained by central or cardiac mechanisms (tachycardia, increased catecholamines, ventricular dilation, and hypertrophy) at a level appropriate for the demands of the body, systemic arterial pressure must be maintained. This is accomplished by a number of circulatory mechanisms designed to increase peripheral vascular resistance (90, 91). These can be grouped under three general headings: (a) increased neurogenic vasomotor tone; (b) increased humoral vasoconstrictors; (c) increased intrinsic vascular stiffness. Venous tone is also increased in CHF from neurohumoral and local factors [reviewed in (74, 87, 89, 90)].

Peripheral Vasoconstriction in Heart Failure
In mild or early heart failure, neurogenic vasomotor tone may be normal at rest. However, the sympathoadrenal response to exercise may be exaggerated (27, 91). The extent to which neurogenic and humoral vasoconstrictor

mechanisms become operative in heart failure is complex and depends on the integration of afferent stimuli from multiple peripheral receptors (1, 72). Different types of heart failure clearly evoke different responses. For example, aortic stenosis leads to a reduced stimulation of arterial baroreceptors (72). This results in increased neurogenic vasomotor tone despite the increased left ventricular wall tension that would tend to produce a depressor response from activation of cardiac afferent fibers (92). Conversely, when heart failure slowly develops from aortic valve incompetence, systolic hypertension and a wide pulse pressure lead to peripheral vasodilation. However, the sudden occurrence of severe aortic valve insufficiency leads to an intense neurogenically mediated vasoconstriction, presumably triggered by the precipitous fall in systemic arterial pressure and net systemic cardiac output (43). Other types of heart failure may preferentially activate release of humoral vasoconstrictors. For example, experimental pulmonary artery constriction increases circulating catecholamines (72).

In CHF, the renin-angiotensin-aldosterone system is activated frequently in a phasic pattern (82). At the onset of failure, blood pressure can be shown to be dependent upon circulating angiotensin II (82). The activity of this system may later be reduced as hypervolemia returns cardiac output to normal. Later it is again reactivated if cardiac function continues to decline. At that stage, angiotensin stimulates thirst through a central nervous system mechanism and leads to the release of antidiuretic hormone (ADH) (64). This contributes to hypervolemia, circulatory congestion, and edema formation. During the stage of fluid retention, vascular sodium content is increased (91). The vascular "stiffness" that results may contribute minimally to basal vascular tone but it plays an important role in limiting skeletal muscle metabolic vasodilation (91).

Both cardiac (94) and arterial baroreceptor (26) reflexes are attenuated in heart failure. Blunting of arterial baroreceptor reflexes may be related to increased vascular stiffness from a high sodium content; in the case of low pressure baroreceptors, atrial desensitization by excessive stretch, decreased atrial compliance, and degeneration of afferent nerve fibers may also play a role. Cardiac afferent nerve activity is inappropriately low; therefore, a reduction in ADH secretion that should normally reduce left atrial volume does not occur. Blunting of baroreceptor reflexes also partially explains the exaggerated sympathoadrenal response with exercise (1). Normally, arterial and cardiopulmonary receptors are activated during exercise, resulting in an attenuation of the efferent sympathetic nervous system response (81). This modulation does not occur in heart failure. An excessive sympathoadrenal response during exercise may also result from activation of somatic afferent fibers in skeletal muscle secondary to hypoxia from poor skeletal muscle perfusion (36).

Control of Blood Flow to the Regional Circulations

Because a considerable portion of the generalized vasoconstriction noted in chronic, well-established CHF is mediated by the sympathetic nervous system, regional vascular responses are predictable. Since the coronary and cerebral circulations rely primarily on local mechanisms to regulate blood flow, they receive preferential perfusion (88). Belloni has recently reviewed the role of a number of local coronary vascular control mechanisms that appear to be operative in mediating reactive hyperemia (adenosine, myogenic tone), hypoxic coronary vasodilation (adenosine, oxygen tension), active hyperemia or metabolic vasoregulation (potassium ion), and autoregulation (2). Vascular alpha adrenergic control of coronary blood flow can be demonstrated in humans, where it can be nullified by local metabolites (52), and in animals, where it can significantly attenuate metabolic vasodilation (42). Large coronary arteries react to alpha adrenergic stimulation (80) and neurogenic sympathetic tone may play a role in regulating blood flow through collateral channels to areas of the heart where intrinsic flow has been restricted (30). Spasm of both normal and atherosclerotic large coronary vessels (93) plays a major role in Prinzmetal's or variant angina; however, different mechanisms may be involved in different individuals (enhanced alpha adrenergic or cholinergic nerve activity, platelet aggregation and formation of thromboxane A2, increased receptor-operated calcium channel sensitivity). In most patients with CHF, however, it is likely that sympathetic adrenergic stimulation plays only a minor role in regulating coronary blood flow by virtue of a direct effect on vascular smooth muscle.

Blood flow through cerebral vessels also is controlled primarily by local metabolic factors (hydrogen or bicarbonate ions, prostaglandins, or adenosine) associated with increased neuronal activity (22). Here, too, minor control is exerted via alpha and beta adrenergic and cholinergic receptors, extrinsic sympathetic, and intrinsic nerves (54). This is not universally accepted, and D'Alecy has presented evidence to suggest that sympathetic nerves can override local mechanisms, even during hypercapnic vasodilation in dogs (11). In summary, in CHF, both coronary and cerebral blood flow can be relatively preserved by local mechanisms if arterial perfusion pressure is maintained.

As one might expect, those circulations most involved in the sympathetically mediated generalized vasoconstriction of chronic CHF are the cutaneous, splanchnic, and renal vascular beds (88). Although skin sensors play some role in regulating cutaneous blood flow, core temperature is considerably more important (66). Above a certain threshold, skin blood flow has been shown to be directly related to core temperature and roughly inversely related to splanchnic flow. The small reduction in skin blood flow accompanying exercise in normal individuals appears to be related to a transient small drop in body temperature when cooler blood from extremities is mobilized and returned to the central circulation rather than to a specific exercise-induced increase in sympathetic tones (66). However, with severe strenuous exercise, where blood flow to active skeletal muscles becomes the major fraction of the cardiac output, skin blood flow fails to rise normally despite an increase in core temperature (46). Following exercise, a marked cutaneous vasodilation is routinely observed (91). In CHF, even a small workload is extremely stressful. Therefore, CHF patients maintain a cutaneous vasoconstriction throughout exercise, and this continues into the post-exercise period (91).

Blood flow to the kidneys appears to be controlled by myogenic autoregulation, extrinsic sympathetic nerves, the renin-angiotensin system, and other vasoactive factors (88). At rest, normally very little sympathetic tone is present. Therefore, renal blood flow is near maximum. During exercise, renal vasoconstriction occurs (19, 40). This appears to be a myogenic response to the increase in systemic arterial pressure, rather than a catecholamine-mediated response (40). In heart failure, the sympathetic nerves to the kidneys play a major role in significantly reducing renal blood flow during exercise (40). With severe heart failure, flow is reduced at rest as well. Sodium retention and plasma volume expansion are favored by a number of mechanisms. Vasoconstriction leads to preferential redistribution of flow from cortical to juxtacortical glomeruli with long loops of Henle. Activation of the renin-angiotensin-aldosterone system occurs in the phasic pattern described earlier and probably results from stimulation of renal beta receptors, hypotension in the juxtaglomerular apparatus resulting from alpha adrenergically mediated vasoconstriction and reduction in sodium ion concentration in the distal tubule.

In chronic CHF, blood flow to the splanchnic circulation is moderately reduced at rest; however, during exercise in the rat, dog, and humans there is marked splanchnic vasoconstriction (27, 84). Recent data in a rat CHF model suggest that hepatic arterial flow is relatively preserved and that the reduction in splanchnic flow results primarily from intestinal vasoconstriction.

Skeletal Muscle Blood Flow During Exercise

By virtue of its mass and vasodilator potential during maximum exercise, skeletal muscle presents an enormous burden to circulatory homeostatic mechanisms. In normal individuals, cardiac output can increase five-fold and the percentage distribution to skeletal muscle can increase 30–80% (88). The problems that might be caused by the inability of the failing heart to increase cardiac output normally are extraordinary. Fortunately, two factors exist that either preserve nutritional flow to skeletal muscle or, failing that, preserve systemic arterial perfusion pressure (91). Respectively, these two factors are: (a) augmented alpha adrenergic receptor stimulation and (b) increased large vessel stiffness limiting maximum metabolic vasodilation.

Consider first the normal mechanism regulating skeletal muscle flow at rest and during exercise. Metabolic and myogenic autoregulation and tonic neurogenic sympathetic adrenergic nerve activity maintain resting skeletal muscle blood flow at a low level. Over a wide range of blood flow to resting skeletal muscle, oxygen consumption is unaltered. Honig has proposed three distinct mechanisms regulating blood flow to skeletal muscle during and after exercise (28). Immediately prior to and during the first half-minute of exercise, extrinsic nerves, presumably sympathetic cholinergic, actively increase skeletal muscle blood flow. Intrinsic nerves become active and reach a maximum between 30 and 40 seconds. Their activity ceases within moments after termination of exercise. These small intramural fibers, which become evident after extrinsic sympathetic denervation, may play a major role in maintaining maximal blood flow throughout exercise. The mechanism by which they are activated (perhaps linked to local metabolism) and their neurotransmitter (unresponsive to classic antagonists) are unknown. After a latency of a few minutes, metabolic factors (primarily adenosine and related purines) (77) contribute significantly to the vasodilation, and they are almost totally responsible for the post-exercise hyperemia.

The vasodilation that occurs during exercise of isolated skeletal muscle fibers in microcirculatory preparations has been shown to be a two-phase process (21). The early, transient phase may be neural, and the second, slower phase of dilation may be similar to the late metabolic phase of Honig. Capillary recruitment localized to the area of the active muscle fiber becomes maximal within 15 seconds. The regulatory site for capillary perfusion appears to be the terminal arteriole, which, when dilated, increases capillary perfusion pressure. No evidence for true precapillary sphincters was found (21), and it was suggested that the terminal arterioles should be considered the primary regulator of nutritional flow. Often overlooked is the fact that control of blood flow to skeletal muscle also resides at another site, the conductance vessels (small arteries and large arterioles) (91).

What might be the effect of limiting flow at either the nutritional or conductance-vessel level during exercise, and how does that help us understand the changes with CHF? We first explored the possible consequences of an exaggerated sympathoadrenal response in a canine exercising gracilis muscle preparation (Figure 2). During intra-arterial low-concentration

PARTITION OF BLOOD FLOW BETWEEN
INACTIVE(I) AND ACTIVE(A) SKELETAL MUSCLE FIBERS

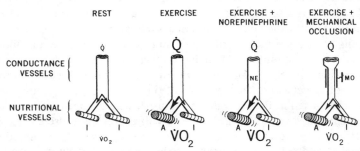

Figure 2   Schematic representation of blood flow ($\dot{Q}$) and oxygen consumption ($\dot{V} O_2$) in skeletal muscle at rest and during submaximal dynamic exercise. The size of $\dot{Q}$ and $\dot{V} O_2$ symbols represent relative magnitudes of these variables. Low concentration intra-arterial norepinephrine (NE) results in a reduction in total $\dot{Q}$ which is redistributed from inactive (I) to active (A) fibers at the nutritional vessel level, thus maintaining normal $\dot{V} O_2$. Restriction of total $\dot{Q}$ of a similar magnitude at the conductance vessel level by mechanical occlusion (MO) prevents normal autoregulation at distal sites and $\dot{V} O_2$ falls. High concentration of NE mimics MO and it is suggested that the high arterial sodium content associated with congestive heart failure produces similar changes. [Relationships are based on data from (18) and (48).]

norepinephrine infusion, we demonstrated that a favorable redistribution of blood flow from inactive to active skeletal muscle fibers occurs (7, 18, 48). Indirect evidence suggests that neuronally released norepinephrine might play a similar role (75). Bevan has shown that with small vessels, the neuroeffector junction between the adrenergic nerves and the vascular smooth muscle is tighter than that which occurs in larger vessels (3). Therefore, neuronally released norepinephrine would be expected to produce a more discrete effect in small vessels than in larger vessels, but that effect would be inhibited in the region of actively contracting skeletal muscle fibers if metabolites inhibited neuronal release of norepinephrine. Thus low- to moderate-level alpha receptor stimulation preserves or enhances nutritional flow and maintains oxygen consumption in the exercising muscle at normal levels despite reductions in total blood flow to the muscle. Such an intramuscular redistribution to preserve nutritional flow enhances metabolic autoregulation and may be a favorable effect that occurs early in CHF when the sympathetic nervous system is activated during exercise (91).

It has been known for some time that, in patients with chronic CHF, maximum metabolic vasodilation following release of temporary arterial occlusion (the reactive hyperemia response) is significantly attenuated; maximum blood flow, even during alpha blockade, is limited to half that seen in normal individuals (91). This "vascular stiffness" is probably related to an increased vascular sodium content (91) or extrinsic compression of blood vessels from subclinical edema (89). A similar limitation in metabolic vasodilation has also been noted during forearm dynamic (91) and static exercise (35) with the consequence that skeletal muscle oxygen consumption fails to rise normally. This could not be a consequence of moderate alpha adrenergic stimulation, which produced the opposite effect on oxygen consumption; therefore, we have suggested that this is best explained by stiffness of larger conductance vessels (91). This would be similar to the situation depicted at the far right in Figure 2, where we used a mechanical occluder in the dog to restrict blood flow to exercising muscle (48). Flow restriction at the level of the conductance vessels leads to an inability of distal autoregulatory mechanisms to redistribute flow from inactive to active muscle fibers. Therefore stiffness of the conductance vessels in heart failure may preserve systemic arterial perfusion pressure when heart failure patients exercise. However, this occurs at the expense of an adequate nutritional flow to exercising skeletal muscle. The resultant profound drop in skeletal muscle oxygen tension would be expected to stimulate somatic afferent receptors (36). This leads to a greatly exaggerated sympathoadrenal response, which is capable of further reducing oxygen supply to exercising skeletal muscle, since it was also shown that high concentrations of norepinephrine can also restrict flow at the conductance vessel level (18). The self-reinforcing nature of this cycle and the magnification of the deleterious effect on nutritional flow to exercising skeletal muscle are evident (91).

VASODILATOR THERAPY OF HEART FAILURE

At the present time, there is intense interest in a new category of drugs, the vasodilators, which can be used to treat CHF when standard therapy with digitalis and diuretics proves inadequate (8, 16, 38, 55, 90). The vasodilators are conventionally classified as (a) arteriolar dilators, which predominately increase stroke volume and relieve low output symptoms (phentolamine, hydralazine); (b) venodilators, which predominately reduce ventricular filling pressures and relieve congestive symptoms (nitroglycerin and other nitrates); and (c) the mixed vasodilators (nitroprusside, prazosin, trimazosin, and angiotensin-converting enzyme inhibitors). This classification is clinically useful but is far too simple to explain fully how these drugs interact with the complex regulatory systems activated in heart failure (reviewed in (90)]. As one example of this interaction, we present some of the data accumulated recently regarding nitroglycerin (45, 85). From these studies in humans and animal models of CHF, a clear picture of its actions can be assembled. During upright bicycle exercise, patients with CHF demonstrated a slightly greater cardiac output after the acute application of nitroglycerin ointment (45). This was accounted for primarily by an increase in heart rate, with minimal but favorable changes in stroke volume (increase) and left ventricular filling pressure (decrease). If the increased cardiac output had improved nutritional flow to skeletal muscle, one might have expected to see a higher systemic oxygen consumption, a reduction in lactate production, and a reduction in the catecholamine response. This was not observed. To determine to which circulations the increased cardiac output was delivered, we studied rats with chronic biventricular volume overload produced by aortocaval fistula at rest and during treadmill exercise while regional blood flow was measured by the radionuclide-tagged microsphere technique (84). These heart failure animals demonstrated an exaggerated vasoconstriction in the renal, intestinal and cutaneous circulations when exercised without nitroglycerin; however, during acute intravenous nitroglycerin infusion, blood flow was restored to these organs to near-normal levels. These observations help to explain why the chronic administration of nitroglycerin to CHF patients results in progressive improvement in exercise tolerance, whereas acute administration does not (8). It is suggested that nitrates help maintain a normal renal blood flow, potentiate diuretic drug effects, and reduce the stimulus for sodium and water retention. If a gradual reduction of vascular sodium content occurred with chronic drug administration, one might expect to see decreased vascular stiffness, an improved nutritional flow to exercising skeletal muscle, and lessening of fatigue. Despite the extensive clinical literature (8, 38, 55, 90), considerable work is still needed to unravel how and where vasodilator drugs act and in what type of situation specific drugs are indicated.

SUMMARY

Congestive heart failure is associated with ventricular hypertrophy and dilatation, increased circulating catecholamines, and peripheral vasoconstriction. The extent to which these changes occur, whether they are a favorable "compensatory mechanism" or contribute to cardiocirculatory dysfunction, depends on the cause and severity of the heart failure. The addition of new sarcomeres through ventricular hypertrophy distributes the excess workload of the failing ventricle over more contractile units. In ventricular pressure overload, hypertrophy primarily increases wall thickness and ventricular volume is not usually increased; the converse is true with ventricular volume overload. Hypertrophy can result in enhanced or depressed contractile performance, depending on the stimulus for hypertrophy and method by which contractility is evaluated. The "ventricular function curve," which relates stroke volume to ventricular filling pressure or volume, overestimates the role played by the "Starling principle" as a compensatory mechanism and underestimates how well contractile performance is preserved. The evaluation of end systolic pressure-volume relationships under conditions of variable afterload closely reflects the isometric length-tension relationship and is therefore a more accurate way to quantitate cardiac muscle performance. Pressure overload hypertrophy usually leads to a depression in contractility whereas volume overload may not.

An exaggerated sympathoadrenal response is another hallmark of severe heart failure that enhances contractility, helps initiate hypertrophy, and maintains arterial perfusion pressure. A generalized increase in peripheral vascular resistance occurs and is most prominent in those circulations most susceptible to neurohumoral control (renal, splanchnic, cutaneous). This favors perfusion of the cerebral and coronary circulations. Vasoconstriction is further enhanced by the activation of the renin-angiotensin-aldosterone system and secretion of ADH. This results in sodium retention and plasma volume expansion. In early mild heart failure, vasomotor tone may be normal at rest; however, the sympathoadrenal response to exercise may be intense. Moderate alpha receptor stimulation reduces skeletal muscle blood supply and favors the intramuscular redistribution of blood flow from inactive to active muscle fibers, thereby maintaining a normal oxygen consumption. During the later stages of heart failure, increased vascular stiffness due to increased sodium content and excessive norepinephrine appears to restrict nutritional blood flow to exercising muscle at the conductance-vessel level. Vasodilator drugs may reduce aortic impedance and improve cardiac output, may lower ventricular filling pressure, and relieve congestive symptoms, and may result in complex but favorable changes in the distribution of blood flow to the regional circulations.

ACKNOWLEDGMENTS

The authors gratefully acknowledge review of the manuscript by Dr. Evlin Kinney and the secretarial assistance of Judy Holzer.

Literature Cited

1. Abboud, F. M., Schmid, P. G. 1978. Circulatory adjustments to heart failure. See Ref. 17, 18:249–60
2. Belloni, F. L. 1979. The local control of coronary blood flow. *Cardiovasc. Res.* 13:63–85
3. Bevan, J. A. 1979. Some bases of differences in vascular response to sympathetic activity. Variations on a theme. *Circ. Res.* 45:161–71
4. Braunwald, E., Ross, J. Jr., Sonnenblick, E. H., eds. 1967. *Mechanisms of Contraction of the Normal and Failing Heart.* Boston, Mass: Little, Brown. 417 pp.
5. Carey, R. A., Bove, A. A., Coulson, R. L., Spann, J. F. 1978. Recovery of myosin ATPase after relief of pressure-overload hypertrophy and failure. *Am. J. Physiol.* 234:H711–17
6. Ciba Foundation Symposium 24. 1974. *The Physiological Basis of Starling's Law of the Heart.* Amsterdam: Assoc. Sci. Publ. 298 pp.
7. Coburn, R. F., Pendleton, M. 1979. Effects of norepinephrine on oxygenation of resting skeletal muscle. *Am. J. Physiol.* 236:H307–13
8. Cohn, J. N., Franciosa, J. A. 1977.

Vasodilator therapy of cardiac failure. *N. Engl. J. Med.* 297:27–31, 255–58

9. Cooper, G. IV, Puga, F. J., Zujko, K. J., Harrison, C. E., Coleman, H. N. III. 1973. Normal myocardial function and energetics in volume-overload hypertrophy in the cat. *Circ. Res.* 32:140–48

10. Crozatier, B., Ross, J. Jr., Franklin, D., Bloor, C. M., White, F. C., Tomoike, H., McKown, D. P. 1978. Myocardial infarction in the baboon: regional function and the collateral circulation. *Am. J. Physiol.* 235:H413–21

11. D'Alecy, L. G., Rose, C. J., Seller, S. A. 1979. Sympathetic modulation of hypercapnic cerebral vasodilation in dogs. *Circ. Res.* 45:771–85

12. Delcayre, C., Swynghedauw, B. 1975. A comparative study of heart myosin AT-Pase and light subunits from different species. *Pfluegers Arch.* 355:39–47

13. Dowell, R. T., McManus, R. E. III. 1978. Pressure-induced cardiac enlargement in neonatal and adult rats. Left ventricular functional characteristics and evidence of cardiac muscle cell proliferation in the neonate. *Circ. Res.* 42:303–10

14. Elzinga, G., Westerhof, N. 1979. How to quantify pump function of the heart. The value of variables derived from measurements on isolated muscle. *Circ. Res.* 44:304–8

15. Fabiato, A., Fabiato, F. 1975. Dependence of the contractile activation of skinned cardiac muscle cells on the sarcomere length. *Nature* 256:54–56

16. Faxon, D. P., Creager, M. A., Halperin, J. L., Gavras, H., Coffman, J. D., Ryan, T. J. 1980. Central and peripheral hemodynamic effect of angiotensin inhibition in patients with refractory congestive heart failure. *Circulation* 61:925–30

17. Fishman, A. P., ed. 1978. *Heart Failure.* Washington DC: Hemisphere. 356 pp.

18. Flaim, S. F., Crede, W., Beech, A., Nellis, S. H., Zelis, R. 1979. The effects of norepinephrine on active hyperemia in the canine gracilis muscle. *Circ. Res.* 44:660–66

19. Flaim, S. F., Minteer, W. J., Clark, D. P., Zelis, R. 1979. Cardiovascular response to acute aquatic and treadmill exercise in the untrained rat. *J. Appl. Physiol.–Respir. Environ. Exer. Physiol.* 46:302–8

20. Ford, L. E. 1980. Effect of afterload reduction on myocardial energetics. *Circ. Res.* 46:161–66

21. Gorczynski, R. J., Klitzman, B., Duling, B. R. 1978. Interrelations between

contracting striated muscle and precapillary microvessels. *Am. J. Physiol.* 235:H494–504

22. Gross, P. M., Marcus, M. L., Heistad, D. D. 1980. Regional distribution of cerebral blood flow during exercise in dogs. *J. Appl. Physiol.–Respir. Environ. Exer. Physiol.* 48:213–17

23. Grossman, W., Braunwald, E., Mann, T., McLaurin, L. P., Green, L. H. 1977. Contractile state of the left ventricle in man as evaluated from end-systolic pressure-volume relations. *Circulation* 56:845–52

24. Grossman, W., McLaurin, L. P., Stefadouros, M. A. 1974. Left ventricular stiffness associated with chronic pressure end volume overloads in man. *Circ. Res.* 35:793–800

25. Gunther, S., Grossman, W. 1979. Determinants of ventricular function in pressure-overload hypertrophy in man. *Circulation* 59:679–88

26. Higgins, C. B., Vatner, S. F., Eckberg, D. L., Braunwald, E. 1972. Alterations in the baroreceptor reflex in conscious dogs with heart failure. *J. Clin. Invest.* 51:715–24

27. Higgins, C. B., Vatner, S. F., Franklin, D., Braunwald, E. 1972. Effects of experimentally produced heart failure on the peripheral vascular response to severe exercise in conscious dogs. *Circ. Res.* 31:186–94

28. Honig, C. R. 1979. Contributions of nerves and metabolites to exercise vasodilation: a unifying hypothesis. *Am. J. Physiol.* 236:H705–19

29. Jewell, B. R. 1977. A re-examination of the influence of muscle length on myocardial performance. *Circ. Res.* 40:221–30

30. Jones, C. E., Scheel, K. W. 1980. Reduced coronary collateral resistances after chronic ventricular sympathectomy. *Am. J. Physiol.* 238:H196–201

31. Kreulen, T. H., Bove, A. A., McDonough, M. T., Sands, M. J., Spann, J. F. 1975. The evaluation of left ventricular function in man. A comparison of methods. *Circulation* 51:677–88

32. Laks, M. M. 1977. Norepinephrine, the producer of myocardial cellular hypertrophy and/or necrosis and/or fibrosis. *Am. Heart J.* 94:394–99

33. LeWinter, M. M., Engler, R. L., Karliner, J. S. 1980. Enhanced left ventricular shortening during chronic volume overload in conscious dogs. *Am. J. Physiol.* 238:H126–33

34. Lompre, A. M., Schwartz, K., d'Albis, A., Lacombe, G., Van Thiem, N.,

Swynghedauw, B. 1979. Myosin isoenzyme redistribution in chronic heart overload. *Nature* 282:105–7

35. Longhurst, J., Gifford, W., Zelis, R. 1976. Impaired forearm oxygen consumption during static exercise in patients with congestive heart failure. *Circulation* 54:477–80

36. Longhurst, J., Zelis, R. 1979. Cardiovascular responses to local hind-limb hypoxemia: relation to the exercise reflex. *Am. J. Physiol.* 237:H359–65

37. Mason, D. T., Spann, J. F. Jr., Zelis, R. 1970. Quantification of the contractile state of the intact human heart. Maximal velocity of contractile element shortening determined by the instantaneous relation between the rate of pressure rise and pressure in the left ventricle during isovolumic systole. *Am. J. Cardiol.* 26:248–57

38. Massie, B. M., Chatterjee, K., Parmley, W. W. 1979. Vasodilator therapy for acute and chronic heart failure. In *Progress in Cardiology,* ed. P. N. Yu, J. F. Goodwin, pp. 197–234. Philadelphia; Lea & Febiger. 349 pp.

39. Maughan, D., Low, E., Litten, R. III, Brayden, J., Alpert, N. 1979. Calcium-activated muscle from hypertrophied rabbit hearts. *Circ. Res.* 44:279–87

40. Millard, R. W., Higgins, C. B., Franklin, D., Vatner, S. F. 1972. Regulation of the renal circulation during severe exercise in normal dogs and dogs with experimental heart failure. *Circ. Res.* 31:881–88

41. Milnor, W. R. 1975. Arterial impedance as ventricular afterload. *Circ. Res.* 36:565–70

42. Mohrman, D. E., Feigl, E. O. 1978. Competition between sympathetic vasoconstriction and metabolic vasodilation in the canine coronary circulation. *Circ. Res.* 42:79–86

43. Morganroth, J., Perloff, J. K., Zeldis, S. M., Dunkman, W. B. 1977. Acute severe aortic regurgitation. Pathophysiology, clinical recognition, and management. *Ann. Intern. Med.* 87:223–32

44. Morkin, E. 1979. Stimulation of cardiac myosin adenosine triphosphatase in thyrotoxicosis. *Circ. Res.* 44:1–7

45. Moskowitz, R. M., Kinney, E. L., Zelis, R. 1979. Hemodynamic and metabolic responses to upright exercise in patients with congestive heart failure. *Chest* 76:640–46

46. Nadel, E. R., Cafarelli, E., Roberts, M. F., Wenger, C. B. 1979. Circulatory regulation during exercise in different ambient temperatures. *J. Appl. Physiol.–Respir. Environ. Exer. Physiol.* 46:430–37

47. Natarajan, G., Bove, A. A., Coulson, R. L., Carey, R. A., Spann, J. F. 1979. *Am. J. Physiol.* 237:H676–80

48. Nellis, S. H., Flaim, S. F., McCauley, K., Zelis, R. 1980. α-Stimulation protects exercise increment in skeletal muscle oxygen consumption. *Am. J. Physiol.* 238:H331–39

49. Newman, W. H. 1978. Volume overload heart failure: length-tension curves, and responses to β-agonists, Ca^{2+}, and glucagon. *Am. J. Physiol.* 235:H690–700

50. Newman, W. H., Webb, J. G. 1980. Adaptation of left ventricle to chronic pressure overload: response to inotropic drugs. *Am. J. Physiol.* 238:H134–43

51. Noble, M. I. M. 1978. The Frank-Starling curve. *Clin. Sci. Mol. Med.* 54:1–7

52. Orlick, A. E., Ricci, D. R., Alderman, E. L., Stinson, E. B., Harrison, D. C. 1978. Effects of alpha adrenegic blockade upon coronary hemodynamics. *J. Clin. Invest.* 62:459–67

53. O'Rourke, M. F., Taylor, M. G. 1966. Vascular impedance of the femoral bed. *Circ. Res.* 18:126–39

54. Owman, C., Edvinsson, L., eds. 1977. *Neurogenic Control of the Brain Circulation.* NY: Pergamon. 530 pp.

55. Packer, M., Meller, J. 1978. Oral vasodilator therapy for chronic heart failure: a plea for caution. *Am. J. Cardiol.* 42:686–89

56. Parker, J. O., Case, R. B. 1979. Normal left ventricular function. *Circulation* 60:4–12

57. Parmley, W. W., Diamond, G., Tomoda, H., Forrester, J. S., Swan, H. J. C. 1972. Clinical evaluation of left ventricular pressures in myocardial infarction. *Circulation* 45:358–66

58. Pepine, C. J., Nichols, W. W., Conti, C. R. 1978. Aortic input impedance in heart failure. *Circulation* 58:460–65

59. Peterson, K. L., Tsuji, J., Johnson, A., DiDonna, J., LeWinter, M. 1978. Diastolic left ventricular pressure-volume and stress-strain relations in patients with valvular aortic stenosis and left ventricular hypertrophy. *Circulation* 58:77–89

60. Pfeffer, J. M., Pfeffer, M. A., Fishbein, M. C., Frohlich, E. D. 1979. Cardiac function and morphology with aging in the spontaneously hypertensive rat. *Am. J. Physiol.* 237:H461–68

61. Pinsky, W. W., Lewis, R. M., Hartley, C. J., Entman, M. L. 1979. Permanent changes of ventricular contractility and

compliance in chronic volume overload. *Am. J. Physiol.* 237:H575–83

62. Pollack, G. H. 1970. Maximum velocity as an index of contractility in cardiac muscle, a critical evaluation. *Circ. Res.* 26:111–27

63. Pollack, G. H., Kreuger, J. W. 1976. Sarcomere dynamics in intact cardiac muscle. *Eur. J. Cardiol.* 4:53–65 (Suppl.)

64. Ramsay, D. J., Rolls, B. J., Wood, R. J. 1975. The relationship between elevated water intake and edema associated with congestive cardiac failure in the dog. *J. Physiol. London* 244:303–12

65. Rasmussen, H., Goodman, D. B. P. 1977. Relationship between calcium and cyclic nucleotides in cell activation. *Physiol. Rev.* 57:421–509

66. Roberts, M. F., Wenger, C. B. 1979. Control of skin blood flow during exercise: thermal and nonthermal factors. *J. Appl. Physiol.–Respir. Environ. Exer. Physiol.* 46:780–86

67. Ross, J. Jr. 1976. Afterload mismatch and preload reserve: A conceptual framework for the analysis of ventricular function. *Prog. Cardiovasc. Dis.* 18:255–64

68. Ross, J. Jr., Sonnenblick, E. H., Taylor, R. R., Spotnitz, H. M., Covell, J. W. 1971. Diastolic geometry and sarcomere lengths in the chronically dilated canine left ventricle. *Circ. Res.* 28:49–61

69. Sagawa, K. 1978. The ventricular pressure-volume diagram revisited. *Circ. Res.* 43:677–87

70. Sasayama, S., Ross, J. Jr., Franklin, D., Bloor, C. M., Bishop, S., Dilley, R. B. 1976. Adaptations of the left ventricle to chronic pressure overload. *Circ. Res.* 38:172–78

71. Scheuer, J., Bhan, A. K. 1979. Cardiac contractile proteins. Adenosine triphosphate activity and physiological function. *Circ. Res.* 45:1–12

72. Schmid, P. G., Mayer, H. E., Mark, A. L., Heistad, D. D., Abboud, F. M. 1977. Differences in the regulation of vascular resistance in guinea pigs with right and left heart failure. *Circ. Res.* 41:85–93

73. Schwartz, S., Sordahl, L. A., Entman, M. L., Allen, J. C., Reddy, Y. S., Goldstein, M. A., Luchi, R. J., Wyborny, L. E. 1973. Abnormal biochemistry in myocardial failure. *Am. J. Cardiol.* 32:407–22

74. Shepherd, J. T., Vanhoutte, P. M. 1975. *Veins and Their Control.* Philadelphia: Saunders. 269 pp.

75. Strandell, T., Shepherd, J. T. 1967. The effects in humans of increased sympathetic activity on the blood flow to active muscle. *Acta Med. Scand. Suppl.* 472:146–67

76. Suga, H., Kitabatake, A., Sagawa, K. 1979. End-systolic pressure determines stroke volume from fixed end-diastolic volume in the isolated canine left ventricle under a constant contractile state. *Circ. Res.* 44:238–49

77. Tominaga, S., Curnish, R. R., Belardinelli, L., Rubio, R., Berne, R. M. 1980. Adenosine release during early and sustained exercise of canine skeletal muscle. *Am. J. Physiol.* 238:H156–63

78. Vandenburgh, H., Kaufman, S. 1979. In vitro model for stretch-induced hypertrophy of skeletal muscle. *Science* 203:265–68

79. Vatner, S. F., Braunwald, E. 1975. Cardiovascular control mechanisms in the conscious state. *N. Engl. J. Med.* 293:970–76

80. Vatner, S. F., Pagani, M., Manders, W. T., Pasipoularides, A. D. 1980. Alpha adrenergic vasoconstriction and nitroglycerin vasodilation of large coronary arteries in the conscious dog. *J. Clin. Invest.* 65:5–14

81. Vatner, S. F., Rutherford, J. D. 1978. Control of the myocardial contractile state by carotid chemo- and baroreceptor and pulmonary inflation reflexes in conscious dogs. *J. Clin. Invest.* 61:1593–601

82. Watkins, L. Jr., Burton, J. A., Haber, E., Cant, J. R., Smith, F. W., Barger, A. C. 1976. The renin-angiotensin-aldosterone system in congestive heart failure in conscious dogs. *J. Clin. Invest.* 57:1606–17

83. Weber, K. T., Janicki, J. S. 1979. The heart as a muscle-pump system and the concept of heart failure. *Am. Heart J.* 98:371–84

84. Weitzel, R. L., Flaim, S. F., Zelis, R. 1979. Effects of nitroglycerin infusion on the hemodynamic response to exercise in rats in heart failure. *Clin. Res.* 27:442A (Abstr.)

85. Wikman-Coffelt, J., Parmley, W. W., Mason, D. T. 1979. The cardiac hypertrophy process. Analyses of factors determining pathological vs. physiological development. *Circ. Res.* 45:697–707

86. Williams, J. F., Potter, R. D. 1974. Normal contractile state of hypertrophied myocardium after pulmonary artery constriction in the cat. *J. Clin. Invest.* 54:1266–72

476   ZELIS ET AL

87. Zelis, R. 1974. The contribution of local factors to the elevated venous tone of congestive heart failure. *J. Clin. Invest.* 54:219–24

88. Zelis, R., ed. 1975. *The Peripheral Circulations.* NY: Grune & Stratton. 417 pp.

89. Zelis, R., Capone, R., Mansour, E., Field, J. M. 1978. The effects of short-term venous congestion on forearm venous volume and reactive hyperemia blood flow in human subjects. *Circulation* 57:1001–3

90. Zelis, R., Flaim, S. F., Moskowitz, R. M., Nellis, S. H. 1979. How much can we expect from vasodilator therapy in congestive heart failure? *Circulation* 59:1092–97

91. Zelis, R., Flaim, S. F., Nellis, S., Long-hurst, J., Moskowitz, R. 1978. Autonomic adjustments to congestive heart failure and their consequences. See Ref. 17, Ch. 17:237–47

92. Zelis, R., Lotysh, M., Brais, M., Peng, C., Hurley, E., Mason, D. T. 1977. Effects of isolated right and left ventricular stretch on regional arteriolar resistance. *Cardiovasc. Res.* 11:419–26

93. Zelis, R., Schroeder, J. S., eds. 1980. Symposium: Calcium, calcium antagonists, and cardiovascular disease. *Chest* 78 (Suppl.):121–247

94. Zucker, I. H., Earle, A. M., Gilmore, J. P. 1977. The mechanism of adaptation of left atrial stretch receptors in dogs with chronic congestive heart failure. *J. Clin. Invest.* 60:323–31

CELL AND MEMBRANE PHYSIOLOGY

Introduction, John Gergely, *Section Editor*

If one is to find one or two dominant themes in this section, communication and regulation are clearly in the forefront in five of these chapters. Gilula and his colleagues provide a clear overview of the problems of cell communication involving a specialized structure in which membrane-membrane interaction takes place. Membrane transport processes are at the heart of cell volume regulation as discussed by Kregenow et al. While the role of chemical transmitters at the nerve-muscle junction is well established, the subsequent steps, starting with membrane depolarization and eventually resulting in Ca^{2+} release from the sarcoplasmic reticulum, are not fully understood on the molecular level. Schneider's chapter explores a mechanism involving charge movements in coupling the events in the plasma membrane of muscle, and its extension the T-tubule system, to that of the sarcoplasmic reticulum. Hartshorne & Siemankowski discuss problems of smooth muscle control, reviewing the events taking place after Ca^{2+} is released from the sarcoplasmic reticulum into the cytoplasm. According to most authors in this area of research, phosphorylation of myosin is the most likely trigger of activation of the contractile apparatus of smooth muscle, although a more complicated process involving action on the thin filaments may yet have to be considered. The chapter by Jolesz & Sreter deals with complex processes controlling the unfolding of gene expression as muscle undergoes development or responds to changes in activity pattern. Nerve-muscle interactions play a key role although the relation of a possible specific chemical transmitter (trophic factor) to changes in activity is still not clear. Finally, Wray & Holmes deal with X-ray studies on muscle and provide an up-to-date picture of the molecular basis of structure and function in this important system whose regulation has been discussed in these chapters.

Ann. Rev. Physiol. 1981. 43:479–91
Copyright © 1981 by Annual Reviews Inc. All rights reserved

GAP JUNCTIONAL COMMUNICATION

❖1324

Elliot L. Hertzberg, Theodore S. Lawrence, and Norton B. Gilula

The Rockefeller University, New York, New York 10021

INTRODUCTION

The formation of low resistance pathways is one of the most common forms of cellular interaction. Since its discovery between neurons (40) this form of cell-to-cell communication has been documented widely in both excitable and nonexcitable cells. The presence of low resistance pathways between cells (ionic coupling) has been correlated with the capacity to transfer low molecular weight fluorescent dyes, as well as radiolabeled amino acids, nucleotides, and other small molecules. This ability to transfer small radiolabeled metabolites, assayed using autoradiography, has been termed metabolic coupling (46). It is now generally accepted that a specific membrane specialization, the gap junction, is most frequently associated with this form of cell-to-cell communication (46), although other junctional specializations may also provide a similar property.

The gap junction is present as a plaque-like element, variable in size and form in regions of contact between communicating cells. In thin-section electron microscopy, the gap junction is characterized by a septilaminar profile comprised of the two apposing plasma membranes separated by a 2–4 nm space or "gap" (88) that can be penetrated by extracellular dense tracers such as lanthanum and ruthenium red. With the freeze-fracture technique, gap junctions appear as specialized regions of the cell surface that contain a relatively high density of intramembrane particles in semi-regular or polygonal arrays (21, 39, 71). Isolated gap junctions that have been negatively stained exist as plaques containing a polygonal lattice of 8.5–9.0 nm subunits that correspond to the particles observed in freeze-fracture. These subunit arrays also correspond to those seen in *en face* views

479

0066-4278/81/0315-0479$01.00

of gap junctions between intact cells (88, 90). A 1.5–2.0 nm electron dense dot is observed in the central region of these subunits; this may represent the location of the gap junctional channel.

Cell-to-cell communication exists throughout the animal kingdom between contacting cells of all tissues, with the apparent exception of mature skeletal muscle, most neurons, and circulatory cells [for possible exceptions see (55, 77, 84)]. Studies utilizing cultured cells have shown that, in general, there is no specificity for establishing communication between cells derived from different vertebrate organisms and different tissues [(34, 56, 74); for possible exceptions see (36, 83)]. However, there is some specificity for establishing communication with cells from the arthropod phylum (34).

The concept that the gap junction provides a pathway for cell-to-cell communication is based primarily on correlations: (a) Gap junctions are almost invariably present between cells that are joined by low resistance pathways [for review see (8)]; (b) cells that form gap junctions communicate, while mutant cells incapable of forming gap junctions do not communicate (2, 46); and (c) disruption of gap junctions is necessary and sufficient for abolishing coupling whereas disruption of other types of cell contact is not (5, 33). At present, there is no general procedure for specifically inhibiting gap junction formation, and no assay for gap junctions other than ultrastructure. In addition, it has not been possible to develop a quantitative correlation between gap junction size and electrical coupling. These limitations have made it difficult to answer a number of important questions including: (a) Can communication take place in the absence of detectable junctional structure and, if so, is the same mechanism involved; in other words, can single particle associations between cells result in communication? (b) What steps are involved in junction synthesis and formation? (c) What are the biological roles of cell-to-cell communication in addition to providing a low resistance pathway for current flow in excitable tissues?

In this review, we discuss some of the recent progress in the area of cell-to-cell communication. No attempt has been made to cite all of the systems in which gap junctions have been demonstrated. That information and earlier studies have been summarized in other reviews (8, 9, 28, 35, 44, 66).

EXCITABLE CELLS

Communication between cells via a low resistance pathway was first documented as an electrical (electrotonic) synapse between invertebrate neurons (40) and in the mammalian myocardium (102). These cell-to-cell pathways were defined as low resistance compared to the nonjunctional membrane, so that current in the form of ions (Cl^-, K^+, Na^+) injected into one cell passed with little transmembrane leakage to the coupled neighboring cells. In the nervous system, the electrotonic junction permits more rapid synaptic transmission than a chemical synapse (8). In the mammalian myocardium, low resistance pathways provide the fundamental mechanism for synchronizing cells into a functional syncitium (100). The ability of intestinal smooth muscle to generate peristaltic waves is also dependent on the presence of low resistance pathways for impulse propagation, and the ability to form these pathways appears to be a general property of smooth muscle (4). In addition to these examples of highly differentiated cell types, electrical coupling has been described between cells of excitable epithelia in lower organisms such as hydromedusa (59); such networks may be evolutionary forerunners of neuronal transmission. Thus, the low resistance pathway occurs between a spectrum of excitable cells [for reviews see (8, 9)].

Recently two excitable cell systems have drawn increased attention: the vertebrate retina and the mammalian myometrium. While it has been known for some time that horizontal cells are electrically coupled (76), earlier models of the retina assumed that photoreceptors functioned as independent units. However, it has now become clear that electrical coupling exists between photoreceptors. Coupling has been demonstrated between cones of the same spectral sensitivity in turtles (7, 31) and between red rods of the toad retina (48). These findings are in basic agreement with ultrastructural studies which have shown gap junctions between adjacent photoreceptor processes (49, 86). The function of this coupling remains unclear; perhaps it represents a decrease in spatial resolution that provides an increase in sensitivity. Although the physiological data indicate that coupling occurs only between photoreceptors with similar spectral properties, gap junctions have been detected ultrastructurally between rods with different sensitivities, and between rods and cones. These observations may simply indicate that coupling does not always exist where junctional structure is found. It is also possible that junctions between photoreceptors modulate transiently from an uncoupled to a coupled state. If they function as static low resistance pathways in vivo, some additional mechanism would be required to recover information about color. In addition to an electrical role, low resistance pathways may mediate transfer of low molecular weight molecules between cells. This is of particular interest in photoreceptors, since cyclic GMP has been proposed as the mediator of light induced membrane permeability changes (19, 75).

It has been proposed that a modulation of gap junctional communication may be involved in parturition (43). During pregnancy, few, if any, gap junctions can be found between muscle cells of the uterus; junctions appear just prior to parturition (23, 43). In vitro studies indicate that estrogen may

stimulate junction formation (perhaps via prostaglandins) and that progesterone is inhibitory (42). It has been proposed that this increase is necessary
to mediate the synchronized uterine contractions of labor. The results of
physiological experiments, however, do not correlate readily with these
data, in that the myometrium remains well coupled throughout pregnancy,
with little change in the electrical space constant (61). This condition then
is the converse of that found in the retina. In the retina, gap junctions occur
between cells that do not appear to be functionally coupled, while in the
uterus, electrical coupling may exist in the absence of easily identifiable gap
junctions.

NONEXCITABLE CELLS

Although electrical synchrony may be critical for the function of excitable
tissues, gap junctional communication is found between cells in practically
all nonexcitable tissues as well. Since there is no apparent need for electrical
synchrony in such tissues, it has been suggested that cell-to-cell communication is involved in phenomena such as growth control, embryonic development and differentiation (66, 82, 101).

Since many hormonally responsive cell types communicate in vivo, it
seemed possible that such communication could allow the transmission of
hormonal stimulation from cell to cell. In order to investigate this possibility, two hormonally responsive cell types were cocultured: mouse myocardial cells and rat ovarian granulosa cells (62). Myocardial cells respond to
catecholamines (e.g. norepinephrine) with an increase in beat frequency and
action potential amplitude, and a decrease in action potential duration.
Granulosa cells, when stimulated by follicle stimulating hormone (FSH),
produce a protease, plasminogen activator, and undergo a morphological
change (63). All of these effects appear to be cyclic AMP mediated. When
the two cell types were cocultured, they established cell-to-cell communication. It was then possible to determine the effect of hormonal stimulation
of one cell type on the heterologous, contacting cells. Although myocardial
cells cultured alone are unaffected by FSH, addition of FSH to the cultures
mimicked the effect of norepinephrine. Conversely, stimulation of cocultures with physiological concentrations of norepinephrine in the presence
of a cyclic nucleotide phosphodiesterase inhibitor, methylisobutyl xanthine
(which has no effect on granulosa cells cultured alone), caused the granulosa
cells to respond as if exposed to FSH. This cross-stimulation probably
results from the cell-to-cell transfer of a communicator of hormonal stimulation.

An obvious candidate for the communicator molecule is cyclic AMP. Its
size (MW 329) is well within the limit of about 900 daltons for cell-to-cell
transfer (37). It has also been shown that radiolabeled cAMP can move

from cell to cell, presumably via gap junctions, when introduced into ventricular myocardium by the cut-end technique (96).

A similar coculture approach was used to examine the possibility that interferon can act like a hormone (14). Mouse myocardial cells, which are insensitive to human interferon, were cocultured with human amnion (WISH) cells, which are unaffected by norepinephrine but sensitive to human interferon. Exposure of cocultures of contacting cells to human interferon caused the myocardial cells to beat more rapidly; likewise norepinephrine exposure resulted in antiviral activity in WISH cells. While these results are suggestive, the presence of cell-to-cell communication has not been demonstrated in either this coculture system or in one used previously involving cocultures of L cells and WISH cells (13). In fact, communication almost certainly does not explain the results of the earlier study since: (a) L cells cannot communicate (2, 46); and (b) cell free supernatants from interferon-treated L cells could transfer viral resistance—i.e. there was no contact dependence (13).

The mammalian ovarian cumulus-oocyte complex represents an in vivo example of communication between heterologous cells. Prior to ovulation rat cumulus cells maintain gap junctional communication with the oocyte by processes that extend through the zona pellucida. Within the hours prior to ovulation, these connections are broken and ionic coupling is terminated (45). This occurs concomitantly with the resumption of oocyte maturation in preparation for fertilization. Recent in vitro evidence supports the theory that elevated levels of cAMP maintain the oocyte in its state of meiotic arrest (22). It was found that oocytes in isolated complexes can be kept immature by exposure to choleratoxin [a bacterial exotoxin capable of stimulating all known adenylate cyclases (10)] while oocytes stripped of their surrounding cumulus cells mature in the presence of choleratoxin (25). These and other data are consistent with the theory that the oocyte receives cAMP from the surrounding cumulus cells by gap junctional communication. A loss of this inhibitory influence, mediated by hormonally induced junctional disruption, may be a key step in regulating oocyte maturation.

Conversely, in the *Xenopus* ovary, it appears that junction formation, assayed by dye transfer between the oocyte and cumulus cells, is stimulated by hormonal treatment (18). The recent demonstration of gap junctions between Sertoli and germ cells in rat seminiferous tubules has raised the question of whether analogous phenomena occur in the testes (70).

Cell-to-cell communication may also play a physiological role in both the endocrine and exocrine pancreas. β cells (insulin containing) appear to be electrically coupled (73) and form gap junctions (72). The intracellular injection of glycolytic intermediates into cultured islet cells caused an increase in NAD(P)H fluorescence in the neighboring cell, indicating that some metabolite, perhaps the intermediate itself, is able to move from cell to cell (60). The electrical synchrony mediated by gap junctional communication may be important as well since electrical activity has been correlated with insulin release (73). In the exocrine pancreas, coupling between acinar cells is decreased by pharmacological doses of acetylcholine, which may alter junctional permeability through changes in intracellular pH or calcium (see below) (57).

The vertebrate lens is a nonexcitable tissue in which cell-to-cell communication may play an important role in cellular metabolism. Since the lens is avascular, the cortical and nuclear fiber cells have no direct access to nutrients. These could be supplied by active transport from the aqueous humor into the epithelial cells followed by intracellular passage via gap junctions to coupled fiber cells (15, 50). Electrophysiological and dye transfer experiments indicate that lens fiber cells are well coupled (85). These observations are consistent with the ultrastructural detection of extended regions of junctional contact between lens fiber cells (15).

DIFFERENTIATION

Gap junctional communication has often been proposed as a possible mechanism for the transmission of information between cells necessary for regulation of growth, development, and differentiation (66, 82, 101).

Several recent studies have focused on the appearance of gap junctions and cell-cell coupling in early embryonic stages of mammalian and amphibian systems. Studies in *Xenopus* (97), *Rana,* and *Ambystoma* (95) indicate that electrical coupling is present between adjacent blastomeres beginning at the 4 cell stage. In the mouse embryo, the appearance of gap junctions, electrical coupling, and the ability to transfer dye occur at the late 8 cell stage, at the onset of compaction (64). Prior to this stage, coupling between cells is limited to sister blastomeres; this was demonstrated to be a result of incomplete cytokinesis. At the subsequent blastocyst stage, ionic coupling and dye transfer exist throughout the inner cell mass (ICM) and trophoblast. However, with further development, dye transfer was not observed between the trophoblast and ICM although ionic coupling was still present. It is not known whether this is due to a decrease in the number of junctional channels or a reduction in individual channel size. In addition to the lack of detectable dye spread between trophoblast and ICM, compartmentalization of dye transfer within the ICM was also observed in the postimplantation embryo (65). Such compartmentalization is consistent with the polyclone theory in which the establishment of morphogenetic gradients and subsequent differentiation are dependent upon groups of cells, not single cells, generating required signals (41).

At later stages of embryogenesis, there is evidence that gap junctional communication is also developmentally regulated (11, 30, 32, 47, 51, 68).

In some systems, gap junctional communication is transiently altered or disrupted, while in others, the junctional interactions are completely terminated.

MODULATION OF GAP JUNCTIONAL COMMUNICATION

The potential for modulation of cell-to-cell communication exists at several stages. These include the synthesis of the polypeptide, its insertion into the plasma membrane, the formation of assembled plaques, the regulation of channel function, and the removal and degradation of junctions.

Formation

The formation of gap junctions has been investigated in several systems by using ultrastructural and physiological techniques [for review see (93)]. The formation process has been characterized by a series of assembly events that can be detected in freeze-fracture replicas (24, 58). In the regenerating liver, it has been found that gap junctional plaques abruptly disappear approximately 28 hr after partial hepatectomy, and reappear at 40 hr (103). In *Xenopus* cells, signal averaging techniques were used to greatly increase the ability to detect small voltage changes that were taken to represent the onset of coupling in recently apposed cells (67). These changes were quantal, which supports the concept that individual channels add to conductance in parallel.

Regulation

Studies on the regulation of gap junctional channel permeability have suggested that intracellular calcium levels and pH are involved. Using the *Chironomus* salivary glands and monitoring local intracellular calcium levels optically using aequorin luminescence, it was demonstrated that elevation of intracellular calcium levels by a variety of methods in the region of cell-cell contact resulted in a loss of electrical coupling (92). Partial decreases in coupling occurred as the estimated calcium concentration was increased from 0.1 μM to 50 μM, where uncoupling was obtained (92). These conclusions have been extended to vertebrate systems, including neuronal (6), cardiac (27), lymphoid (77), pancreatic acinar cells (81), and cells in culture (37, 94), although the intracellular calcium concentrations could not be monitored.

Other studies indicate that intracellular pH is a key regulator of cell-to-cell communication. With *Xenopus* embryos, it was found at the 32 cell stage that a lowering of the intracellular pH from about 7.4 to 6.8 (by incubation with elevated carbon dioxide) resulted in a rapid and reversible uncoupling of communication (97). Under these conditions, no substantial increase of the intracellular calcium level could be detected by the use of ion selective electrodes (89). Furthermore, treatments that caused an increase of intracellular calcium concentration led to a concomitant decrease of intracellular pH, indicating that calcium-induced uncoupling might be operating via a change in pH.

Lowered intracellular pH also appears to uncouple cardiac Purkinje fibers (29) and pancreatic acinar cells (57). In *Chironomus* salivary glands a decrease of intracellular pH invariably resulted in uncoupling, with a variable increase in intracellular calcium concentration (91). The variable nature of this calcium increase was attributed to a decrease in the sensitivity of aequorin as a function of pH. In addition, other conditions were found that caused uncoupling independent of pH. The ultimate resolution of this issue may await improvements in the technology for measurement of intracellular ionic activities, especially in the region of cell contact.

One important role for junctional modulation is in a tissue's response to injury. When one heart cell is injured, there is a transient, reversible decrease of the resting potential in the neighboring cells. The return to normal resting potential, termed resealing, does not occur in low calcium medium (26). Injury-induced uncoupling occurring during myocardial infarction may affect the EKG (38); this also takes place in nonexcitable cells (92).

Another possible mechanism for the regulation of junctional communication has been demonstrated in *Xenopus, Rana,* and *Ambystoma* embryos in which the establishment of a 30 mV potential difference between two cells of a coupled pair resulted in greater than a 95% decrease in gap junctional conductance and a loss of dye transfer (95). This uncoupling was rapidly and completely reversible. This mechanism of regulation may be of interest in light of the observation that different resting potentials are observed in different regions of developing embryos (12).

Several attempts have been made to correlate gap junctional structure with junctional conductance. In the crayfish septate lateral giant axon, intracellular calcium injections and other uncoupling treatments caused tighter, more regular particle packing within the gap junctional plaques compared to the coupled controls (80). Similar particle rearrangements in response to presumed uncoupling conditions such as anoxia or fixation have been observed in the myocardium (3), rat liver, and stomach by both conventional (78) and rapid freezing techniques (87). Whether these changes can be observed in noncrystallized gap junctions isolated from lens is controversial at present (50, 79).

BIOCHEMICAL AND STRUCTURAL ANALYSIS

Gap junctions have been successfully isolated from liver plasma membranes of rat (53), mouse (52), and calf (54). There is now general agreement that gap junctions from mammalian liver are comprised predominantly of a 27,000 dalton polypeptide. Lipid analysis indicates a composition similar to that of the plasma membranes from which they are derived (52, 53), although an enrichment for cholesterol has been demonstrated (52). No glycosylation has been detected (53). Lens fiber cells have also yielded material that is ultrastructurally similar to that of liver gap junctions and is characterized by a 25,000 dalton polypeptide (1, 15, 16, 50). It is likely that these two polypeptides are not related, based upon immunocytological (17, 99), immunochemical, and biochemical analysis (E. Hertzberg, M. Friedlander, D. J. Anderson, and N. B. Gilula, in preparation). It is therefore not clear what, if any, relationship might exist between the unique lens fiber junctions and the gap junctions present in other tissues.

Structural analysis of liver gap junctions has been carried out by optical diffraction of images of negatively stained samples and X-ray diffraction of pelleted gap junctions (20, 69, 98, 104). In one study (20, 69), a major variable feature observed was the lattice constant, which varied from 8–9 nm. The smaller lattice constant was associated with a partial collapse of the gap between apposing membranes. These observations were included in a model in which tighter particle packing and partial collapse of the gap occur with a narrowing of the gap junctional channel; this would be associated with a loss of channel conductance (20, 69).

In another study of gap junctions isolated from mouse liver, no significant variation in the lattice constant was detected. However, two forms were observed: One was obtained in the isolated (detergent treated) junction fraction (type A); the second was induced by prolonged dialysis (type B), presumably by removing traces of residual detergent. The B form is reversibly converted into the A form by addition of small amounts of detergent (98, 104). These observations were interpreted to indicate that the A form contains an open channel and that the B form is generated by a radial motion of the subunits at the cytoplasmic surface, resulting in closure of the channel. Although a mechanism dependent upon relative motion of protein subunits is attractive, it is difficult to extrapolate from these findings to an in vivo regulatory mechanism.

CONCLUSIONS

Progress continues to be made on understanding the role of gap junctional communication in various tissues. In excitable cells, the discovery of ionic coupling between certain photoreceptors has modified long-held concepts of retinal function, and the hormonal modulation of gap junctions in the myometrium suggests a role in parturition. In nonexcitable cells, gap junctional communication is probably involved in the mediation of hormonal responses and, very likely, in the cell-to-cell transmission of developmentally regulated signals. The mechanism for the regulation of junctional communication remains controversial, and its significance in physiological events other than cell injury or death remains obscure. It can be anticipated that the identification of the protein components of gap junctions will facilitate the development of the biochemical and immunological tools necessary to understand the communication process.

ACKNOWLEDGMENTS

We would like to thank Daniel Tranchina for helpful discussions and Madeleine Naylor for preparation of the manuscript. E.L.H. was supported by fellowships from the Helen Hay Whitney Foundation and the Cystic Fibrosis Foundation. This laboratory is supported by grants from the National Institutes of Health and the Rockefeller Foundation.

Literature Cited

1. Alcala, J., Lieska, N., Maisel, H. 1975. Protein composition of bovine lens cortical fiber cell membranes. *Exp. Eye Res.* 21:581–95
2. Azarnia, R., Larsen, W. J., Loewenstein, W. R. 1974. The membrane junctions in communicating and non-communicating cells, their hybrids and segregants. *Proc. Natl. Acad. Sci. USA* 71:880–84
3. Baldwin, K. M. 1979. Cardiac gap junction configuration after an uncoupling treatment as a function of time. *J. Cell Biol.* 82:66–75
4. Barr, L., Berger, W., Dewey, M. M. 1968. Electrical transmission at the nexus between smooth muscle cells. *J. Gen. Physiol.* 51:347–68
5. Barr, L., Dewey, M. M., Berger, W. 1965. Propagation of action potentials and the structure of the nexus in cardiac muscle. *J. Gen. Physiol.* 48:797–823
6. Baux, G., Simonneau, M., Tauc, L., Segundo, J. P. 1978. Uncoupling of electrotonic synapses by calcium. *Proc. Natl. Acad. Sci. USA* 75:4577–81
7. Baylor, D. A., Fuortes, M. G. F., O'Bryan, P. M. 1971. Receptive fields in cones in the retina of the turtle. *J. Physiol. London* 214:265–94
8. Bennett, M. V. L. 1977. Electrical transmission: a functional analysis and comparison with chemical transmission. In *Cellular Biology of Neurons, Vol. 1, Sect. 1, Handbook of Physiology, the Nervous System,* ed. E. Kandel, pp. 357–416. Baltimore: Williams and Wilkins
9. Bennett, M. V. L., Goodenough, D. A. 1978. Gap junctions, electrotonic coupling and intercellular communication. *Neuro. Res. Prog. Bull.* 16:373–486
10. Bennett, V., Cuatrecasas, P. 1977. Cholera toxin: Membrane gangliosides and activation of adenylate cyclase. In *The Specificity and Action of Animal, Bacterial and Plant Toxins,* ed. P. Cuatrecasas, pp. 3–66. London: Chapman and Hall. 345 pp.
11. Blackshaw, S. E., Warner, A. E. 1976. Low resistance junctions between mesoderm cells during development of trunk muscles. *J. Physiol. London* 255:209–30
12. Blackshaw, S. E., Warner, A. E. 1976. Alterations in resting membrane properties during neural plate states of development of the nervous system. *J. Physiol. London* 255:231–47
13. Blalock, J. E., Baron, S. 1977. Interferon induced transfer of viral resistance between animal cells. *Nature* 269:422–25
14. Blalock, J. E., Stanton, J. D. 1980. Common pathways of interferon and hormonal action. *Nature* 283:406–8
15. Bloemendal, H. 1977. The vertebrate eye lens. *Science* 197:127–38
16. Broekhuyse, R. M., Kuhlmann, E. D., Stols, A. L. H. 1976. Lens membranes II. Isolation and characterization of the main intrinsic polypeptide (MIP) of bovine lens fiber membranes. *Exp. Eye Res.* 23:365–71
17. Broekhuyse, R. M., Kuhlmann, E. D., Winkens, H. J. 1979. Lens membranes VII. MIP is an immunologically specific component of lens fiber membranes and

is identical with 26K band protein. *Exp. Eye Res.* 29:303–13

18. Browne, C. L., Wiley, H. S., Dumont, J. N. 1979. Oocyte-follicle cell gap junctions in *Xenopus laevis* and the effects of gonadotropin on their permeability. *Science* 203:182–83

19. Caretta, A., Cavaggioni, A., Sorbe, R. T. 1979. Cyclic GMP and the permeability of the disks of the frog photoreceptors. *J. Physiol. London* 295:171–78

20. Caspar, D. L. D., Goodenough, D. A., Makowski, L., Phillips, W. C. 1977. Gap junction structures. I. Correlated electron miroscopy and X-ray diffraction. *J. Cell Biol.* 74:605–28

21. Chalcroft, J. P., Bullivant, S. 1970. An interpretation of liver cell membrane and junction structure based on observations of freeze-fracture replicas of both sides of the fracture. *J. Cell Biol.* 47:49–60

22. Cho, W. K., Stern, S., Biggers, J. D. 1974. Inhibitory effects of dibutyryl cAMP on mouse oocyte maturation in vitro. *Exp. Zool.* 187:383–86

23. Dahl, G., Berger, N. 1978. Nexus formation in the myometrium during parturition and induced by estrogen. *Cell Biol. Int. Rep.* 2:381–87

24. Decker, R. S., Friend, D. S. 1974. Assembly of gap junctions during amphibian neurulation. *J. Cell Biol.* 62:32–47

25. Dekel, N., Beers, W. H. 1980. Development of the rat oocyte in vitro: inhibition and induction of maturation in the presence or absence of the cumulus oophorus. *Dev. Biol.* 75:247–54

26. Deleze, J. 1970. The recovery of resting potential and input resistance in sheep heart injured by knife or laser. *J. Physiol. London* 208:547–62

27. DeMello, W. C. 1975. Effect of intracellular injection of calcium and strontium on cell communication in heart. *J. Physiol. London* 250:231–45

28. DeMello, W. C., ed. 1977. *Intercellular Communication.* NY and London: Plenum Press. 255 pp.

29. DeMello, W. C. 1980. Influence of intracellular injection of H$^+$ on the electrical coupling in cardiac Purkinje fibers. *Cell Biol. Int. Rep.* 4:51–58

30. Dennis, M. J. 1975. Physiological properties of junctions between nerve and muscle developing during salamander limb regeneration. *J. Physiol. London* 244:683–702

31. Detwiler, P. B., Hodgkin, A. L. 1979. Electrical coupling between cones in

turtle retina. *J. Physiol. London* 291:75–100

32. Dixon, J. S., Cronly-Dillon, J. R. 1972. The fine structure of the developing retina in *Xenopus laevis. J. Embryol. Exp. Morphol.* 38:659–66

33. Dreifuss, J. J., Girardier, L., Forssmann, W. G. 1966. Etude de la propagation de l'excitation dans le ventricle de rat an moyen de solution hypertoniques. *Pflügers Arch.* 292:13–33

34. Epstein, M. L., Gilula, N. B. 1977. A study of communication specificity between cells in culture. *J. Cell Biol.* 75:769–87

35. Feldman, J., Gilula, N. B., Pitts, J. D. eds. 1978. *Intercellular Junctions and Synapses.* London: Chapman and Hall. 246 pp.

36. Fentiman, I., Taylor-Papdimitriou, J., Stoker, M. 1976. Selective contact-dependent cell communication. *Nature* 264:760–63

37. Flagg-Newton, J., Simpson, I., Loewenstein, W. R. 1979. Permeability of the cell-to-cell membrane channels in mammalian cell junction. *Science* 205:404–7

38. Fozzard, H. A., DasGupta, D. S. 1976. ST-segment potentials and mapping. *Circulation* 54:533–37

39. Friend, D. S., Gilula, N. B. 1972. Variations in tight and gap junctions in mammalian tissues. *J Cell Biol.* 53:758–76

40. Furshpan, E. J., Potter, D. D. 1959. Transmission at the giant motor synapses of the crayfish. *J. Physiol. London* 145:289–325

41. Garcia-Bellido, A. 1975. Genetic control of wing disc development in *Drosophila. Ciba Found.* Symp. 29:161–82

42. Garfield, R. E., Kannan, M. S., Daniel, E. E. 1980. Gap junction formation in myometrium: control by estrogens, progesterone, and prostaglandins. *Am. J. Physiol.* 238:C81–89

43. Garfield, R. E., Sims, S. M., Kannan, M. S., Daniel, E. E. 1978. Possible role of gap junctions in activation of myometrium during parturition. *Am J. Physiol.* 235:C168–79

44. Gilula, N. B. 1977. Gap junctions and cell communication. In *International Cell Biology 1976-1977,* ed. B. R. Brinkley, K. R. Porter, pp. 61–69. NY: Rockefeller Univ. Press. 694 pp.

45. Gilula, N. B., Epstein, M. L., Beers, W. H. 1978. Cell-to-cell communication and ovulation. A study of the cumulus-oocyte complex. *J. Cell Biol.* 78:58–75

46. Gilula, N. B., Reeves, O. R., Steinbach, A. 1972. Metabolic coupling, ionic cou-

pling and cell contacts. *Nature* 235:262–65

47. Ginzberg, R. D., Gilula, N. B. 1979. Modulation of cell junctions during differentiation of the chicken otocyst sensory epithelium. *Dev. Biol.* 68:110–29

48. Gold, G. 1979. Photoreceptor coupling in retina of the toad, *Bufo marinus.* II. Physiology. *J. Neurophysiol.* 42:311–28

49. Gold, G., Dowling, J. E. 1979. Photoreceptor coupling in the retina of the toad *Bufo marinus.* I. Anatomy. *J. Neurophysiol.* 42:292–310

50. Goodenough, D. A. 1979. Lens gap junctions: a structural hypothesis for nonregulated low-resistance intercellular pathways. *Invest. Ophthalmol.* 18:1104–22

51. Goodman, C. S., Spitzer, N. C. 1979. Embryonic development of identified neurones: differentiation from neuroblast to neurone. *Nature* 280:208–14

52. Henderson, D., Eibl, H., Weber, K. 1979. Structure and biochemistry of mouse hepatic gap junctions. *J. Mol. Biol.* 132:193–218

53. Hertzberg, E. L., Gilula, N. B. 1979. Isolation and characterization of gap junctions from rat liver. *J. Biol. Chem.* 254:2138–47

54. Hertzberg, E. L., Moganstern, R. A., Gilula, N. B. 1978. Isolation and characterization of gap junctions from rat, mouse and bovine liver. *J. Cell Biol.* 79:233a

55. Hülser, D. F., Peters, J. H. 1972. Contact cooperation in stimulated lymphocytes. *Exp. Cell Res.* 74:319–26

56. Hyde, A., Blondel, B., Matter, A., Cheneval, J. P., Filloux, B., Girardier, L. 1969. Homo- and heterocellular junctions in cell cultures: an electrophysiological and morphological study. *Prog. Brain Res.* 31:283–311

57. Iwatsuki, N., Peterson, O. H. 1979. Pancreatic acinar cells: the effect of carbon dioxide, ammonium chloride and acetylcholine on intercellular communication. *J. Physiol. London* 291:317–26

58. Johnson, R., Hammer, M., Sheridan, J., Revel, J.-P. 1974. Gap junction formation between reaggregated Novikoff hepatoma cells. *Proc. Natl. Acad. Sci. USA.* 71:4536–40

59. Josephson, R. K., Schwab, W. E. 1979. Electrical properties of an excitable epithelium. *J. Gen. Physiol.* 74:213–36

60. Kohen, E., Kohen, C., Thorell, B., Mintz, D., Rabinovitch, A. 1979. Intercellular communication in pancreatic islet monolayer cultures: a microfluorometric study. *Science* 204:862–65

61. Kuriyama, H., Suzuki, H. 1976. Changes in electrical properties of rat myometrium during gestation and following hormonal treatments. *J. Physiol. London* 260:315–33

62. Lawrence, T. S., Beers, W. H., Gilula, N. B. 1978. Transmission of hormonal stimulation by cell-to-cell communication. *Nature* 272:501–6

63. Lawrence, T. S., Ginzberg, R. D., Gilula, N. B., Beers, W. H. 1979. Hormonally induced cell shape changes in cultured rat ovarian granulosa cells. *J. Cell Biol.* 80:21–36

64. Lo, C. W., Gilula, N. B. 1979. Gap junctional communication in the preimplantation mouse embryo. *Cell* 18:399–409

65. Lo, C. W., Gilula, N. B. 1979. Gap junctional communication in the postimplantation mouse embryo. *Cell* 18:411–22

66. Loewenstein, W. R. 1979. Junctional intercellular communication and the control of growth. *Biochem. Biophys. Acta* 560:1–65

67. Loewenstein, W. R., Kanno, Y., Socolar, S. J. 1978. Quantum jumps of conductance during formation of membrane channels at cell-cell junction. *Nature* 274:133–36

68. LoPresti, V., Macagno, E. R., Levinthal, C. 1974. Structure and development of neuronal connections in isogenic organisms: transient gap junctions between growing optic axons and lamina neuroblasts. *Proc. Natl. Acad. Sci. USA* 71:1098–102

69. Makowski, L., Caspar, D. L. D., Phillips, W. C., Goodenough, D. A. 1977. Gap junction structures. II. Analysis of the X-ray diffraction data. *J. Cell Biol.* 74:629–45

70. McGinley, D. M., Posalaky, Z., Porvaznik, M., Russell, L. 1979. Gap junctions between Sertoli and germ cells of rat seminiferous tubules. *Tiss. Cell* 11:741–54

71. McNutt, M. S., Weinstein, R. S. 1970. The ultrastructure of the nexus. A correlated thin-section and freeze-cleaved study. *J. Cell Biol.* 47:666–87

72. Meda, P., Perrelet, A. Orci, L. 1979. Increase in gap junctions between pancreatic β-cells during stimulation of insulin secretion. *J. Cell Biol.* 82:441–48

73. Meissner, H. P. 1976. Electrophysiological evidence for coupling between β-cells of pancreatic islets. *Nature* 262:502–4

74. Michalke, W., Loewenstein, W. R. 1971. Communication between cells of different types. *Nature* 232:121–22

75. Miller, W. H., Nicol, G. D. 1979. Evidence that cyclic GMP regulates membrane potential in rod photoreceptors. *Nature* 280:64–66

76. Naka, K. I., Rushton, W. A. H. 1967. The generation and spread of S-potentials in fish (*Cyprinidae*). *J. Physiol. London* 192:436–61

77. Oliveira-Castro, G. M., Barcinski, M. A., Cukierman, S. 1973. Intercellular communication in stimulated human lymphocytes. *J. Immunol.* 111:1616–19

78. Peracchia, C. 1977. Gap Junctions. Structural changes after uncoupling procedures. *J. Cell Biol.* 72:628–41

79. Peracchia, C. 1978. Calcium effects on gap junction structure and coupling. *Nature* 271:669–71

80. Peracchia, C., Dulhunty, A. F. 1976. Low resistance junctions in crayfish. Structural changes with functional uncoupling. *J. Cell Biol.* 70:419–39

81. Peterson, O. H., Iwatsuki, N. 1978. The role of calcium in pancreatic acinar cell stimulus-secretion coupling: an electrophysiological approach. *Ann. N.Y. Acad. Sci.* 307:599–617

82. Pitts, J. D. 1978. Junctional communication and cellular growth control. In *Intercellular Junctions and Synapses,* ed. J. Feldman, N. B. Gilula, J. D. Pitts, pp. 61–80. London:Chapman and Hall. 246 pp.

83. Pitts, J. D., Burk, R. R. 1976. Specificity of junctional communication between animal cells. *Nature* 264:762–64

84. Porvaznik, M., MacVittie, T. J. 1979. Detection of gap junctions between the progeny of a canine macrophage colony-forming cell in vitro. *J. Cell Biol.* 82:555–64

85. Rae, J. L. 1979. The electrophysiology of the crystalline lens. In *Current Topics in Eye Research,* ed. J. A. Zadunaisky, H. Davson, 1:37–90. NY: Academic. 243 pp.

86. Raviola, E., Gilula, N. B. 1973. Gap junctions between photoreceptor cells in the vertebrate retina. *Proc. Natl. Acad. Sci. USA* 70:1677–81

87. Raviola, E., Goodenough, D. A., Raviola, G. 1978. The native structure of gap junctions rapidly frozen at 4°K. *J. Cell Biol.* 79:229a

88. Revel, J.-P., Karnovsky, M. 1967. Hexagonal array of subunits in intercellular junctions of the mouse heart and liver. *J. Cell Biol.* 33:c7–12

89. Rink, T. J., Tsien, R. W., Warner, A. E. 1980. Free calcium in *Xenopus* embryos measured with ion-selective microelectrodes. *Nature* 283:658–60

90. Robertson, J. D. 1963. The occurrence of a subunit pattern in the unit membranes of club endings in Mauthner cell synapses in goldfish brains. *J. Cell Biol.* 19:201–21

91. Rose, B., Rick, R. 1978. Intracellular pH, intracellular free Ca and junctional cell-cell coupling. *J. Membr. Biol.* 44:377–415

92. Rose, B., Simpson, I., Loewenstein, W. R. 1977. Calcium ion produces graded changes in permeability of membrane channels in cell junction. *Nature* 267:625–27

93. Sheridan, J. D. 1978. Junction formation and experimental modification. See Ref. 35, pp. 37–60

94. Simpson, S. J., Rose, B., Loewenstein, W. R. 1977. Size limit of molecules permeating the junctional membrane channel. *Science* 195:294–96

95. Spray, D. C., Harris, A. L., Bennett, M. V. L. 1979. Voltage dependence of junctional conductance in early amphibian embryos. *Science* 204:432–34

96. Tsien, R. W., Weingart, R. 1976. Inotropic effect of cyclic AMP in calf ventricular muscle studied by a cut-end method. *J. Physiol. London* 260:117–41

97. Turin, L., Warner, A. E. 1980. Intracellular pH in early *Xenopus* embryos: its effect on current flow between blastomeres. *J. Physiol. London* 300:489–504

98. Unwin, P. N. T., Zampighi, G. 1980. Structure of the junction between communicating cells. *Nature* 283:545–49

99. Waggoner, P. R., Maisel, H. 1978. Immunofluorescent study of a chick lens fiber cell membrane polypeptide. *Exp. Eye Res.* 27:151–57

100. Weidmann, S. 1952. The electrical constants of Purkinje fibers. *J. Physiol. London* 118:348–60

101. Wolpert, L. 1978. Gap junctions: channels for communication in development. See Ref. 35, pp. 83–94

102. Woodbury, J. W., Crill, W. E. 1961. On the problem of impulse conduction in the atrium. In *Nervous Inhibition,* ed. E. Florey, pp. 124–135. London: Pergamon

103. Yee, A. G., Revel, J.-P. 1978. Loss and reappearance of gap junctions in regenerating liver. *J. Cell Biol.* 78:554–64

104. Zampighi, G., Unwin, P. N. T. 1979. Two forms of isolated gap junctions. *J. Mol. Biol.* 135:451–64

Ann. Rev. Physiol. 1981. 43:493–505

OSMOREGULATORY SALT TRANSPORTING MECHANISMS: Control of Cell Volume in Anisotonic Media

❖1325

Floyd M. Kregenow

National Heart, Lung, and Blood Institute, National Institutes of Health, Bethesda, Maryland 20014

INTRODUCTION

A number of free-floating vertebrate cell types can regulate their volume in anisotonic media. These cells initially shrink or swell osmotically, but return toward their original volume with continued incubation. This adaptive response was first characterized in nucleated erythrocytes (11, 22–24, 33, 34). In duck erythrocytes corrective changes in cell size resulted from shifts in cell water brought about by changes in salt content (22–24).

The proposal was that these duck red cells contain a volume controlling mechanism (VCM) that senses cell size and transports salt (22–24). These early studies showed that the VCM utilizes ouabain-insensitive transport processes to move Na^+ and K^+ across the membrane in a controlled fashion. At that time, net Na^+ and K^+ movements taking place when the pump was blocked by ouabain were believed to represent transport through leak pathways. The leak was considered a fixed process separate from exchange diffusion systems and the pump. Since transport during the volume regulatory responses was dynamic and regulated, yet fit the above definition of the leak, the static nature of the leak had to be revised.

The study of osmoregulatory transport processes in duck erythrocytes and other cells has therefore led to a new understanding of the Na^+ and K^+ leak in nonexcitable cells. At least part of what was formerly defined as leak demonstrates a responsiveness and transport capacity that rivals the pump. In duck red cells these transport processes seem to couple cation (Na^+ and K^+) movement to anion (Cl^-) movement, while in salamander erythrocytes they can act as Na^+/H^+ antiporters. Blocked in some cases by

493

0066-4278/81/0315-0493$01.00

amiloride or furosemide, known inhibitors of epithelial transport, these transport processes have some of the characteristics of epithelial transport system(s).

This brief review focuses on the volume regulatory responses of nucleated erythrocytes from the duck and the salamander, *Amphiuma*. Relationships between these responses and those of other free-floating vertebrate cells are noted when appropriate. I emphasize recent research that deals with salt transport, cell volume control, and the regulation of cellular pH, and then present models that attempt to unify seemingly unrelated findings. The reader is referred to three more comprehensive reviews (17, 31, 42) on the control of cell volume and to a recent review (15) dealing with the responses of invertebrate cells to changes in external osmolarity.

The list of free-floating vertebrate cells capable of volume regulation in anisotonic media has grown; it includes mammalian erythrocytes (36, 40) as well as other types of cells (1, 8, 9, 18, 20, 43). Hoffmann's (17) excellent review summarizes the responses of most of these.

Not all these vertebrate cells respond in the same way to incubation in anisotonic solutions. First, some cell types can correct their volume when incubated in hypotonic media but not in hypertonic media (1, 8). It is unclear whether the inability to regulate volume in hypertonic media is a characteristic of these cells, or whether some of them could do so with modifications in the experimental conditions. Second, not all use salt to adjust cell volume as extensively as do duck erythrocytes; some use amino acids as well as salt (9, 11, 12, 19). During the hypotonic responses of flounder erythrocytes (11, 12) and Ehrlich ascites tumor cells (19), the transport of amino acids out of the cell accounts for part of the reduction in intracellular osmotic particles. Finally, although there is no convincing evidence that changes in metabolism modulate the volume regulatory responses of most of these cells, Davson, Parker & Hoffman, Solomon and associates, and Sha'afi and co-workers have demonstrated that the metabolic state can directly alter volume-induced transport in dog and cat erythrocytes [reviewed in (37)].

DUCK ERYTHROCYTES

Figure 1 is a schematic drawing of the responses of duck erythrocytes incubated in hypertonic media (Volume Regulatory Increase, VRI) or hypotonic media (Volume Regulatory Decrease, VRD).

Volume Regulatory Increase (VRI)

Duck erythrocytes shrink when first placed in hypertonic media (23). Osmotic shrinkage stimulates an otherwise quiescent ouabain-insensitive Na, K, and Cl transport system 10–20-fold. The activation step can be

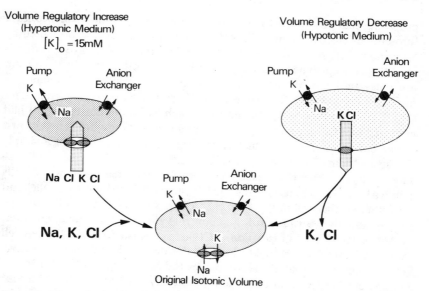

Figure 1   Schematic drawing of the Volume Regulatory Responses of duck erythrocytes

visualized as a gated response in which progressively more hypertonic solutions elicit still larger increases in transport if cells shrink below a threshold volume (23, 30).

Duck red cells can use this system to return to their original volume only if the external K concentration, $[K]_o$, is greater than 2. 5 mM. This effect of $[K]_o$ on enlargement plateaus at 15 mM. At a $[K]_o$ of 2.5 mM, cells neither gain nor lose electrolyte even though the transport process is operational (23, 26, 28).

If the $[K]_o$ exceeds 2.5 mM, cells accumulate Na^+, K^+, and Cl^- with continued incubation (23, 28). This additional salt increases cell water content and cell volume. Within certain limits the quantity of electrolyte accumulated depends upon how much the cell must enlarge. Na^+ enters the cell down its electrochemical gradient. K^+ enters against its electrochemical gradient and represents a form of active transport not directly related to the classical pump. The additional Cl^- distributes itself passively.

The cation pump, if not blocked by ouabain, exchanges newly acquired Na^+ for K^+ in an apparent one-to-one fashion. This does not affect the volume response, which depends only upon the total amount of new electrolyte (23, 24).

The VRI transport process has unusual properties. The bathing medium must contain all three transported electrolytes (Na^+, K^+, and Cl^-) for the system to function normally; removing one blocks transport (23, 24, 29). This requirement for all three ions has led to a co-transport hypothesis proposing that all three ions cross the membrane as a unit. Evidence for a furosemide-sensitive Na plus K co-transport system was first presented by Kregenow (24a; see 26–28). Schmidt & McManus (45–47) have also developed this concept. The experimental approach of both groups evolved from previous studies of ouabain-insensitive cation transport in human erythrocytes (16, 44, 51). The concept of Cl/cation co-transport came later (29). Earlier studies by Hoffmann in Ehrlich ascites tumor cells (18) had indicated that Cl transport might be rate-limiting for the cation movements.

The cation fluxes in the duck VRI response are not those of a simple diffusive system. For example at $[K]_o$ of 2.5 mM, rapid bidirectional Na^+ and K^+ fluxes resembling exchange diffusion continue indefinitely. Cells gain Na^+ and K^+ because raising the $[K]_o$ above 2.5 mM increases Na^+ and K^+ influx so that influx values exceed efflux values. As the cells enlarge, fluxes gradually return toward their control values. Cation fluxes, however, cannot be considered in isolation. ^{36}Cl fluxes, measured when the red cell anion exchanger has been blocked by the disulfonic stilbene derivative, SITS, demonstrate that Cl^- accompanies the Na^+ and K^+ (29). What was an apparent bidirectional movement of Na^+ and K^+ at a $[K]_o$ of 2.5 mM is in fact the bidirectional movement of NaCl and KCl. SITS treatment, by blocking rapid ^{36}Cl movement through the red cell anion exchanger (21), unmasks this previously unknown Cl^- pathway.

A hypothesis that partially explains how this transport process operates (28, 47) has two interrelated postulates based on thermodynamic concepts. First, energies within the Na^+ and K^+ electrochemical gradients interact; net movement through the transport system reponds to the sum of these two electrochemical potentials. Second, Na^+ entering the cell down its electrochemical gradient can drag K^+ into the cell against its gradient. Similarly, K^+ leaving the cell can drag Na^+ out of the cell against its gradient.

The hypothesis provides an explanation for the findings at a $[K]_o$ of 2. 5 mM (28). At 2.5 mM, the sum of the electrochemical potentials for Na^+ and K^+, $\Delta\mu Na$ and $\Delta\mu K$, is zero. Thus there is no net cation flux since there is no net force. Rapid bidirectional cation and anion fluxes can continue indefinitely since the system is at thermodynamic equilibrium. Raising the $[K]_o$ causes the sum of $\Delta\mu Na$ and $\Delta\mu K$ to become negative and provides a driving force for the uptake of cation, including the uphill movement of K.

The hypothesis successfully predicts the pattern of net cation movements when one alters the chemical gradient by varying the extracellular cation concentrations (28, 46) or changes the membrane potential as indicated by the chloride concentration ratio (47). The hypothesis does not explain how the transport system senses and responds to a thermodynamic parameter, the sum of two electrochemical potentials (28). It also does not explain why

Na^+ and K^+ transport rates differ and why the ratio of these two transport rates varies with changes in $[Na]_o$ and $[K]_o$ (28).

Catecholamines induce the same transport system and an almost identical enlargement process in cells in isotonic media (24, 26, 28, 41, 45–47). Norepinephrine, for instance, stimulates the response in much the same way that osmotic shrinkage does (24, 30, 41). However, the two responses differ subtly. The hormonal activation step is β-adrenergic and is mediated biochemically through the formation of cyclic AMP, whereas the formation of cAMP is not part of the hypertonicity-stimulated response (30, 41). The response to norepinephrine is also not volume regulatory in that salt uptake results in enlargement beyond the original isotonic control volume.

Furosemide, an epithelial transport inhibitor, blocks this transport process (30, 45), as do other substituted 3-amino-benzoic acid derivatives (35). The most potent compound yet tested (3-benzyl-amino-4-phenylthio-5-sulfamoylbenzoic acid) is half-maximally effective at an extracellular concentration of $4.6 \times 10^{-8}M$ (35).

It would be premature to equate this furosemide-inhibited transport system with furosemide-sensitive transport systems in other cells. See (14) for a list of cells. However, several similarities should be noted between salt transport in the duck VRI response and transport in "leaky" epithelia—e.g. rabbit gall bladder (10)—or furosemide-sensitive epithelia—e.g. frog cornea (10). These epithelial tissues exhibit coupled cation and Cl^- movements, and some demonstrate cAMP or catecholamine effects. Provided one stipulates the experimental conditions, these characteristics are also shared by furosemide-sensitive transport in avian erythrocytes.

Volume Regulatory Decrease (VRD)

Figure 1 shows that when duck red cells are enlarged, a ouabain-insensitive transport process is activated that controls the egress of KCl from the cell (22, 24). Water accompanies the salt, causing the cells to shrink and return to their original isotonic volume in 15–45 min (22, 24, 25). Several other cell types such as mouse leukemic cells (43), chicken lymphocytes (8), human lymphocytes (1), and Ehrlich ascites tumor cells (18) have analogous VRD responses involving a potassium loss. The swollen state triggers this response. In duck red cells the activation step, like its counterpart in the hypertonic response, has a threshold volume that must be exceeded before a gated response develops (22, 25). Within certain limits, the more enlarged the cell is initially, the more rapid is the rate of K^+ loss.

The controlled loss of KCl characterizes the duck red cell response (22, 24, 25). In contrast to the VRI response, Na^+ content and permeability do not change significantly during VRD (22, 24). The K^+ loss results from an increase in potassium efflux; the potassium efflux falls from a high value in the initial swollen state toward a normal value as cell volume is corrected (22, 24).

If analyzed separately from Cl^-, the K^+ movements behave as if transport is a simple diffusive process. The response is specific for K^+ and requires an outwardly directed K^+ electrochemical gradient (22, 24, 25, 27). In addition, K^+ fluxes with or without a K^+ gradient are those of a diffusive process. Despite apparent passive K^+ movements, this transport process requires Cl^- (or Br^-) (29). As in the VRI response, equivalent K^+ and Cl^- fluxes seem to be characteristic of the hypotonic response.

pH Changes

If one uses minimally buffered solutions, the medium becomes acidic during VRI and alkaline during VRD [(28); F. Kregenow, unpublished observations]. The pH changes are an integral part of each response and correlate with changes in both cation content and cell size. Although millimolar quantities of H^+ or OH^- are formed, the observed pH changes are small, due to the buffering capacity of the cells themselves. The anion exchange mechanism permits the effective interaction of extracellular H^+ or OH^- with the cellular buffering system via the Jacobs-Stewart cycle (15a).

The pH changes arise during VRI and VRD because a disparity develops between the number of cations (Na^+ and K^+) and the number of anions (Cl^-) that finally end up on the opposite side of the membrane. As cells undergo VRI, more Na^+ and K^+ is removed from the medium than Cl^-. As cells undergo VRD, more K^+ leaves the cell than Cl^-. The disparity comes about because chloride redistributes itself passively in accordance with the Donnan ratio which does not change much during either response. Part of the Cl^- apparently returns passively to its original side of the membrane after having initially crossed the membrane as neutral salt.

Thus, the route taken by Cl^- in duck red cells seems to be divided into two steps. In one step Cl^- enters or leaves the cell with an equivalent amount of cation in what is effectively an electroneutral translocation of salt. In step two, chloride, having crossed the membrane, redistributes itself through passive pathway(s) associated with the anion exchanger. This process produces the medium pH changes, as OH^- (or more probably HCO_3^-) exchanges for Cl^-.

SITS, by blocking these pathway(s) (21), should eliminate the pH changes as Cl^- becomes trapped inside or outside the cell. We find, in fact, that SITS-treated cells no longer acidify the medium as they enlarge (F. Kregenow, unpublished observations).

AMPHIUMA ERYTHROCYTES

The *Amphiuma* responses to hypertonic and hypotonic media resemble the duck red cell responses generally, but the former have important distinguishing features (48).

Perhaps the most striking difference between the *Amphiuma* and duck VRI responses is that *Amphiuma* erythrocytes remove only Na^+ from the media, not both Na^+ and K^+ (48). This net sodium uptake is downhill and follows the inwardly directed Na^+ electrochemical gradient. Extracellular K^+ and Cl^- are not essential to the Na^+ uptake, in contrast to the duck red cell response.

Amiloride, another epithelial transport inhibitor, blocks the *Amphiuma* response by preventing Na^+ uptake (48, 49). Amiloride's inhibitory effect suggested a similarity between the Na^+ transport mechanism induced in *Amphiuma* erythrocytes and amiloride sensitive transporter(s) in epithelia. The following features of the *Amphiuma* transport process (48, 49), which also are characteristic of amiloride-sensitive epithelia such as frog skin or toad bladder, support this hypothesis (6): (*a*) Amiloride has a K_I of 2 $\times$ $10^{-6}M$, and its inhibitory effect is readily reversible; (*b*) Na^+ uptake is a saturable function of extracellular Na^+ with a K_m of about 24 mM. (*c*) Li^+ substitutes for and competes with Na^+ in the uptake process. In addition, amiloride appears to act as a competitive inhibitor of Na^+ uptake (49) as it does in some epithelia (7).

Treating *Amphiuma* erythrocytes with SITS alters the VRI response in an interesting way (49). Like duck red cells, *Amphiuma* erythrocytes acidify a minimally buffered hypertonic solution as they enlarge. Medium acidification is again a direct consequence of cell enlargement. In contrast to the case in duck cells, SITS treatment increases medium acidification in *Amphiuma* red cells. The ratio between H^+ ion secreted and Na^+ taken up is approximately one to one after SITS treatment. Both H secretion and Na^+ uptake are a hyperbolic function of the extracellular Na concentration.

Thus, SITS treatment seems to unmask the coupled exchange of Na^+ and H^+ (or co-transport of Na^+ and OH^-). By blocking passive Cl^- transport, SITS apparently prevents OH^- and Cl^- from distributing passively as the cell interior becomes more alkaline.

Three findings support this interpretation (49). First, even though SITS-treated cells gain 30 millimoles of Na^+, they fail to show any change in Cl^- influx or efflux and gain no Cl^-. Second, although SITS-treated cells enlarge, they swell less than untreated cells, having apparently failed to amass osmotically active anions such as Cl^- or HCO_3^-. Finally, pH measurements on frozen-thawed cells demonstrate that the cell's interior becomes alkaline.

Direct and indirect measurements of membrane potential (PD) also support the concept of coupled Na^+/H^+ (or Na^+/OH^-) transport in *Amphiuma* red cells and the coupled Na^+/Cl^- and K^+/Cl^- transport in duck red cells. Since no charge is displaced during this kind of coupled transport, one would not expect the PD to change. As either duck or *Amphiuma* red cells regulate volume, various estimates of the PD [(2, 22–24, 27, 48); and unpublished microelectrode measurements on *Amphiuma* red cells by both P. Cala and F. Kregenow] indicate that despite the rather large cation movements, the PD is changed by only a few millivolts, if at all.

The following picture emerges (3, 49). The *Amphiuma* red cell membrane contains separate cation and anion exchange pathways normally operating in parallel. Na^+ enters the cell through the cation pathway in a coupled process involving H^+ or OH^-. Cl^- seems to enter the cell through the anion exchange pathway. Blocking this pathway with SITS traps OH^- inside the cell and Cl^- outside. Thus the route taken by Cl^- during VRI differs in *Amphiuma* and duck erythrocytes. In the duck response Cl^- entry is coupled to that of cations, while in *Amphiuma* erythrocytes Cl^- enters passively through a SITS-sensitive pathway.

Osmotically enlarged *Amphiuma* erythrocytes shrink toward their original volume by losing K^+ and Cl^- (48). In this regard they resemble duck erythrocytes. However, as in the flounder red cell VRD response (2), the *Amphiuma* response demonstrates a small Na^+ uptake. This Na^+, once inside the cells, is immediately extruded by a stimulated pump. When ouabain is present, the gain in Na^+ requires that more K^+ leave the ouabain-treated cells compared to untreated cells, so that both lose the same amount of cation.

SPECULATIVE MODELS

Figure 2 presents speculative models that make use of specialized antiporters to explain some of the findings discussed above. The models also use the basic tenets of the chemiosmotic hypothesis (4, 32). Models using symporters instead of antiporters would also explain the findings since the flow of OH^- in one direction is equivalent to the flow of H_2O and a proton in the opposite direction.

Model A depicts an antiport mechanism that can explain the Na^+ and H^+ movement during the VRI response of *Amphiuma* erythrocytes. The antiporter is described by a loop; the upper arm provides a pathway for Na^+ and the lower arm furnishes a pathway for H^+. The resultant coupling between the inward movement of Na^+ and the outward movement of H^+ renders the cell alkaline and acidifies the medium. It also causes cell volume and cellular Na^+ content and concentration to increase. Thus, the Na^+

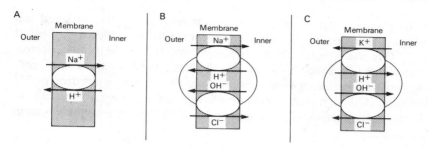

Figure 2   Models for the osmoregulatory transport processes

gradient decreases, but an inwardly directed H^+ gradient develops with a resultant transfer of energy.

The VRI transport mechanism that brings about the inward movement of $Na^+ + K^+ + Cl^-$ in duck red cells can be separated conceptually into two distinct cation/Cl^- transporters. One transports NaCl, the other KCl. Model B depicts the NaCl transporter. This model obligatorily couples an anion antiporter specific for Cl^- and OH^- to a Na^+/H^+ antiporter such as that described in Model A. This postulated anion antiporter resembles the major red cell anion exchanger except that it is SITS-sensitive, obligatorily coupled to the Na^+/H^+ antiporter, and specific for Cl^- and OH^-. This coupling process results in NaCl co-transport. Energy in the Na^+ gradient can then be transferred to the Cl^- gradient, allowing Cl^- to accumulate against its electrochemical gradient. Model B is presently indistinguishable experimentally from a carrier model like the one proposed for "leaky" and furosemide-sensitive epithelia (10).

A scheme similar to the one formulated for model B also explains the KCl transporter, provided the upper loop functions as an antiporter exchanging K^+ for H^+. Figure 2 shows a model with these characteristics that attempts to explain the efflux of KCl during the VRD response.

Observations in *Amphiuma* erythrocytes suggesting that energy within a cation gradient can be transferred to a pH gradient raise the possibility that the energy in a cation gradient may be converted into a usable form. For, according to the chemiosmotic hypothesis of Mitchell (32), a pH gradient is one of the two energy forms the cell can use to transduce energy across a membrane. Thus the chemiosmotic hypothesis may apply to portions of the erythrocyte membrane (20a) during the volume regulatory responses. This notion is supported by the fact that the chemiosmotic hypothesis also requires that the membrane contain antiporters and symporters. More specifically, it is possible that the protomotive force of the chemiosmotic hypothesis and the elusive thermodynamic parameter ($\Delta\mu$ Na + $\Delta\mu$K) sensed by duck cells during VRI are identical.

To complete the model for ion movements during the duck red cell response to hypertonicity, NaCl movements must be coupled with those of KCl. One can invoke the chemiosmotic hypothesis; the proton electrochemical gradient would then couple the NaCl and KCl movements, provided these movements were translated into changes in the electrical or PH gradient. Although such energy conversion and coupling are possible in theory, in the absence of additional evidence, this idea must simply remain a possibility.

CONCLUSION

The erythrocyte responses described above and analogous responses of other cells have rekindled interest in the cation leak of nonexcitable cells. Previous erythrocyte leak definitions assume that Na^+ and K^+ permeate the membrane independently and use routes separate from the pump and exchange diffusion pathways.

During the VRI response of duck red cells, the leak, as defined in net terms, and components of the Na^+ and K^+ fluxes that would previously have been classified as exchange diffusion, change in parallel. This may indicate that both are responding to the same stimulus, so that subtracting an exchange diffusion component when defining the leak with tracers may not be appropriate. A tracer cation movement resembling exchange diffusion might simply signify the presence of energy coupling.

Knowledge of these volume regulatory responses therefore brings about the need for a new conceptualization of the "leak." Na^+ and K^+ transport studies during the VRI and VRD responses of duck and *Amphiuma* erythrocytes suggest that the leak routes taken by cations are not independent. The findings indicate that these routes may interlink under some conditions and are coupled to routes for Cl^- or H^+ (or OH^-). At least part of what has been considered leak then is a complex, versatile mechanism that may be able to transfer and store the cell's energy. According to the models presented above, this is accomplished by increasing or decreasing transport and by controlling the use of coupling mechanisms.

To prevent colloid osmotic swelling, animal cells must maintain a constant cation content (31). The prevailing view proposes that a cation steady state results from the parallel activity of pumps and leaks (50). The pump, by removing cations against their electrochemical gradients, just balances the downhill entry of cations through the leak. The fact that cells can regulate their volume with the pump blocked during VRI and VRD demonstrates that the pump-leak hypothesis, as usually formulated, does not apply to all examples of volume regulation (31). At the same time, the basic relationship implied by the pump-leak concept is necessary on simple thermodynamic grounds to explain the steady-state volume and cation concentration of most animal cells.

The transport scheme used to explain Na and K transport by duck red cells placed in hypertonic media indicates that energy in one cation gradient, if linked, can counter the downhill net movement of another cation. This new proposal suggests that the Na^+ and K^+ "leak," while exhibiting rapid cation movements resembling exchange diffusion, is capable of rendering the duck erythrocyte "effectively" cation impermeable when the $[K]_o$ is slightly greater than 2.5 mM. However, in order for this new version of the "leak" to achieve "effective" cation impermeability, the pump must have previously displaced Na^+ and K^+ from their equilibrium conditions.

Dog and cat erythrocytes maintain a steady-state Na and K content and concentration in isotonic media yet lack the usual ouabain-inhibitable cation pump (37). Although recent studies on dog erythrocytes (5, 38) have tended to cloud an earlier Na/Ca co-transport hypothesis for volume-induced transport in these cells (39), dog and cat erythrocytes remain promising experimental systems for the study of volume regulation. Perhaps a linkage between divalent and monovalent cation gradients, like the linkage proposed for the Na^+ and K^+ gradients in duck red cells, permits dog and cat red cells to maintain a monovalent cation steady state in isotonic media. This would require that a divalent cation pump maintain a continuous disequilibrium for divalent cations.

Several studies in human erythrocytes (13, 50) have demonstrated tracer or net cation fluxes that satisfy the requirements for a diffusive process. These findings indicate that the erythrocyte membrane may also contain unregulated passive channels as suggested by the original pump-leak hypothesis. Usually, however, these studies have used nonphysiological conditions to define the leak—either replacing or removing Na or Cl from the medium or adding one or more pharmacological agents. A second possibility, then, is that the leak, when studied in this way, represents an experimentally induced entity. A third more likely possibility is that the membrane contains both "unregulated" fixed leaks as well as the "regulated" kind observed in the volume regulatory responses. A fourth possibility is that the two kinds may be different forms of the same entity. Appraisal of these possibilities is made difficult by an absence of techniques that assess diffusive pathways without potentially altering their characteristics.

In summary, the response of some nonexcitable vertebrate cells to incubation in anisotonic media reveals that ouabain-insensitive transport mechanisms are versatile and precisely controlled. These mechanisms have a wide distribution and may be similar to transport systems in epithelia. Recent studies indicate that a relationship may exist between the control of cell volume and the control of cell pH.

Literature Cited

1. Ben-Sasson, S., Shaviv, R., Bentwich, Z., Slavin, S., Doljanski, F. 1975. Osmotic behavior of normal and leukemic lymphocytes. *Blood* 46(6):891–99
2. Cala, P. M. 1977. Volume regulation by flounder red blood cells in anisotonic media. *J. Gen. Physiol.* 69:537–52
3. Cala, P. M. 1980. Volume Regulation by *Amphiuma* red blood cells: the nature of the ion flux pathways. *Fed. Proc.* 39(3):379
4. Caplan, S. R. 1971. Transport phenomena in natural and synthetic membranes. In *Membrane Processes in Industry and Biomedicine,* ed. M. Bier, pp. 1–21. NY/London: Plenum
5. Castranova, V., Hoffman, J. F. 1979. Heterogeneity in dog red blood cells: Sodium and postassium transport. *J. Gen. Physiol.* 73:61–71
6. Cuthbert, A. W., Fanelli, G. M., Scriabine, A., eds. 1978. *Amiloride and Epithelial Sodium Transport,* pp. 1–179. Baltimore & Munich: Urban & Schwarzenberg, Inc.
7. Cuthbert, A. W., Shum, W. R. 1974. Binding of amiloride to sodium channels in frog skin. *Mol. Pharmacol.* 10:880–91
8. Doljanski, F., Ben-Sasson, S., Reich, M., Grover, N. B. 1974. Dynamic osmotic behavior of chick blood lymphocytes. *J. Cell Physiol.* 84:215–24
9. Forster, R. P., Goldstein, L. 1976. Intracellular osmoregulatory role of amino acids and urea in marine elasmobranchs. *Am. J. Physiol.* 230(4):925–31
10. Frizzell, R. A., Field, M., Schultz, S. G. 1979. Sodium-coupled chloride transport by epithelial tissues. *Am. J. Physiol.* 236(1):F1–8
11. Fugelli, K. 1967. Regulation of cell flounder (*Pleuronectes flesus*) erythrocytes accompanying a decrease in plasma osmolality. *Comp. Biochem. Physiol.* 22:253–61
12. Fugelli, K., Reierson, L. O. 1978. Volume regulation in flounder erythrocytes —The effects of osmolality on taurine influx. In *Alfred Benzon Symposium XI: Osmotic and Volume Regulation,* ed. C. B. Jorgensen, E. Skadhauge, pp. 418–32. Copenhagen: Munksgaard
13. Funder, J., Wieth, J. O. 1967. Effects of some monovalent anions on fluxes of Na and K and on glucose metabolism of ouabain treated human red cells. *Acta Physiol. Scand.* 71:168–85
14. Gargus, J. J., Slayman, C. W. 1980. Mechanism and role of furosemide-sensitive K transport in L cells: a genetic

approach. *J. Membrane Biol.* 52:245–56
15. Gilles, R. 1978. Intracellular organic osmotic effectors In *Mechanisms of Osmoregulation: Maintenance of Cell Volume,* ed. R. Gilles, P. B, 3:112–54. Chichester, NY: Wiley
15a. Hladky, S. B., Rink, T. J. 1977. pH equilibration across the red cell membrane. See Ref. 27, pp. 115–35
16. Hoffman, J. F., Kregenow, F. M. 1966. The characterization of new energy dependent cation transport processes in red blood cells. *Ann. NY Acad. Sci.* 137:566–76
17. Hoffmann, E. K. 1977. Control of cell volume. In *Transport of Ions and Water in Animals,* ed. B. L. Gupta, R. B. Moreton, J. L. Oschman, B. J. Wall, pp. 285–332. London: Academic
18. Hoffmann, E. K. 1978. Regulation of cell volume by selective changes in the leak permeabilities of Ehrlich ascites tumor cells. See Ref. 12, pp. 397–417
19. Hoffmann, E. K., Hendil, R. B. 1976. The role of amino acids and taurine in isosmotic intracellular regulation in Ehrlich ascites mouse tumor cells. *J. Comp. Physiol. B* 108:279–86
20. Katz, U. 1978. Ionic and volume regulation in selected tissues of the euryhaline toad *Bufo viridis.* See Ref. 12, pp. 457–64
20a. Kell, D. B. 1979. On the functional current pathway of electron transport phosphorylation. *Biochem. Biophys. Acta* 549:55–99
21. Knauf, P. A., Rothstein, A. 1971. Chemical modification of membranes. I. Effect of sulphydryl and amino reactive reagents on anion and cation permeability of the human red blood cell. *J. Gen. Physiol.* 58:190–210
22. Kregenow, F. M. 1971. The response of duck erythrocytes to non-hemolytic hypotonic media. *J. Gen. Physiol.* 58:372–95
23. Kregenow, F. M. 1971. The response of duck erythrocytes to hypertonic media. *J. Gen. Physiol.* 58:396–412
24. Kregenow, F. M. 1973. The response of duck erythrocytes to norepinephrine and an elevated extracellular potassium. *J. Gen. Physiol.* 61:509–27
24a. Kregenow, F. M. 1973. A furosemide-sensitive Na plus K co-transport system in duck erythrocytes. Presented at the 2nd. Ann. Meet. Red Blood Cell Club, Yale Univ., New Haven, Connecticut
25. Kregenow, F. M. 1974. Functional separation of the Na-K exchange pump

from the volume controlling mechanism in enlarged duck red cells. *J. Gen. Physiol.* 64:393–412

26. Kregenow, F. M. 1976. Cell volume control. In *Water Relations in Membrane Transport in Plants and Animals,* ed. A. M. Jungries, T. K. Hodges, A. Kleinzeller, S. G. Schultz, pp. 291–302. NY/London: Academic

27. Kregenow, F. M. 1977. Transport in avian red cells. In *Membrane Transport in Red Cells,* ed. C. Ellory, V. L. Lew, pp. 383–426. NY/London: Academic

28. Kregenow, F. M. 1978. An assessment of the co-transport hypothesis as it applies to the norepinephrine and hypertonic responses. See Ref. 12, pp. 379–91

29. Kregenow, F. M., Caryk, T. 1979. Co-transport of cations and Cl during the volume regulatory responses of duck erythrocytes. *Physiologist* 22(4):73 (Abstr.)

30. Kregenow, F. M., Robbie, D. E., Orloff, J. 1976. Effect of norepinephrine and hypertonicity on K influx and cyclic AMP in duck erythrocytes. *Am. J. Physiol.* 231:306–12

31. Macknight, A. D. C., Leaf, A. 1977. Regulation of cellular volume. *Physiol. Rev.* 57:510–73

32. Mitchell, P. 1966. Chemiosmotic coupling in oxidative and photosynthetic phosphorylation. *Biol. Rev.* 41(3):445–502

33. Ørskov, S. L. 1954. The potassium absorption by pigeon blood cells. A considerable potassium absorption by pigeon and hen blood cells is observed when a hypertonic sodium chloride solution is added. *Acta Physiol. Scand.* 31:221–29

34. Ørskov, S. L. 1956. Experiments on the influence of adrenaline and noradrenaline on the potassium absorption of red blood cells from pigeons and frogs. *Acta Physiol. Scand.* 37:229–306

35. Palfrey, H. C., Feit, P. W., Greengard, P. 1980. cAMP-stimulated cation co-transport in avian erythrocytes: inhibition by "loop" diuretics. *Am. J. Physiol.* 238(3):C139–48

36. Parker, J. C. 1973. Dog red blood cells: Adjustment of salt and water content *in vivo. J. Gen. Physiol.* 62:147–56

37. Parker, J. C. 1977. Solute and water transport in dog and cat red blood cells. See Ref. 27, pp. 427–65

38. Parker, J. C. 1979. Active and passive Ca movements in dog red cells and re-sealed ghosts. *Am. J. Physiol.* 237(1):C10–16

39. Parker, J. C., Gitelman, H. J., Glosson, P. S., Leonard, D. L. 1975. Role of calcium in volume regulation by dog red blood cells. *J. Gen. Physiol.* 65:84–96

40. Poznansky, M., Solomon, A. K. 1972. Regulation of human red cell volume by linked cation fluxes. *J. Membr. Biol.* 10:259–66

41. Riddick, D. H., Kregenow, F. M., Orloff, J. 1971. Effect of norepinephrine and dibutyryl cyclic adenosine monophosphate on cation transport in duck erythrocytes. *J. Gen. Physiol.* 57:752–66

42. Rorive, G., Gilles, R. 1979. Intracellular organic effector. See Ref. 15, Part B, 13, pp. 83–109

43. Roti Roti, L. W., Rothstein, A. 1973. Adaption of mouse leukemic cells (L5178Y) to anisotonic media. I. Cell volume regulation. *Exp. Cell Res.* 79:295–310

44. Sachs, J. R. 1971. Ouabain-insensitive sodium movements in human red blood cell. *J. Gen. Physiol.* 57:259–82

45. Schmidt, W. F., McManus, T. J. 1977. Ouabain-insensitive salt and water movements in duck red cells. I. Kinetics of cation transport under hypertonic conditions. *J. Gen. Physiol.* 70:59–70

46. Schmidt, W. F., McManus, T. J. 1977. Ouabain-insensitive salt and water movements in duck red cells. II. Norepinephrine stimulation of sodium plus potassium co-transport. *J. Gen. Physiol.* 70:81–97

47. Schmidt, W. F., McManus, T. J. 1977. Ouabain-insensitive salt and water movements in duck red cells. III. The role of chloride in the volume response. *J. Gen. Physiol.* 70:99–121

48. Siebens, A. W., Kregenow, F. M. 1978. Volume regulatory responses of salamander red cells incubated in anisotonic media-effect of amiloride. *Physiologist* 21(4):110 (Abstr.)

49. Siebens, A. W., Kregenow, F. M. 1980. Analysis of amiloride-sensitive volume regulation in *Amphiuma* red cells. *Fed. Proc.* 39(3):379 (Abstr.)

50. Tosteson, D. C., Hoffman, J. F. 1960. Regulation of cell volume by active cation transport in high and low potassium sheep red cells. *J. Gen. Physiol.* 44:169–94

51. Wiley, J. S., Cooper, R. A. 1974. A furosemide sensitive co-transport of sodium plus potassium in human red cell. *J. Clin. Invest.* 53:745–55

Ann. Rev. Physiol. 1981. 43:507–17

MEMBRANE CHARGE   ❖1326
MOVEMENT AND
DEPOLARIZATION-CONTRACTION
COUPLING

M. F. Schneider

Department of Physiology, University of Rochester School of Medicine
and Dentistry, Rochester, New York 14642

INTRODUCTION

Electrical depolarization of the transverse (T) tubule membrane of a skeletal muscle fiber initiates a release of Ca^{2+} from the sarcoplasmic reticulum (SR) into the myofilament space. The released Ca^{2+} binds to thin filament troponin sites, thereby allowing thick filament cross bridges to interact with the thin filament for tension development and/or shortening. Under physiological conditions T-tubule depolarization is achieved by an action potential propagating along the fiber and into the T-system (26, 45). Mechanical activation can however be produced and indeed more closely studied experimentally using fiber depolarization in the absence of the ionic conductance changes underlying the action potential (4, 34). This review is devoted to the initial potential-sensitive step following T-tubule depolarization in the depolarization-contraction coupling process. Other aspects are treated in several recent reviews (22, 42, 45).

A basic mechanism for sensing and responding to a change in membrane potential was suggested by Hodgkin & Huxley (35), who postulated the existence of charged or dipolar molecules that changed position or orientation within the membrane as a result of changes in the membrane electric field. Subsequently charge displacements currents, I_Q, attributed to the movement of intramembrane charges were identified first in muscle (49) and then, almost simultaneously, in nerve (14) by combining signal averaging with blockage and subtraction of the relatively larger ionic and linear

507

0066-4278/81/0315-0507$01.00

capacitative currents. The nerve charge movement appears to be involved in gating Na channels (11, 15) whereas the muscle charge movement, which is roughly two orders of magnitude slower than that in nerve, was tentatively associated with depolarization-contraction coupling (24, 49).

The characteristics and possible functional roles of muscle charge movement have been reviewed recently (1, 11). Many of the subsequent findings, which will be stressed here, have been made using the cut muscle fiber preparation introduced by Hille & Campbell (33) for studying Na channels and modified by Kovács and Schneider (41) so as to preserve depolarization-contraction coupling.

CHARGE MOVEMENT IN MUSCLE

Charge movements have now been recorded both from intact muscle fibers using the three microelectrode technique (5) and from cut fibers using single (41), double (39), and triple (33) vaseline gap voltage clamps. All studies have been carried out on frog fibers, generally at about 0–5°C. To avoid fiber damage during microelectrode measurements of charge movement in intact fibers maintained close to the physiological resting potential, contraction was either eliminated using hypertonic bathing solutions (2, 23, 49, 52) or tetracaine (10, 13, 31, 38) or was avoided by keeping pulses below threshold for contraction (13, 50). In contrast, single gap measurements have been obtained from physiologically polarized cut fibers using pulses producing vigorous contractions (36, 37). Cut fibers also provide the possibility of eliminating contraction with internal EGTA (36, 53).

Charge Measurements

All authors agree that ON and OFF charge movements, Q_{ON} and Q_{OFF}, are approximately equal for pulses from holding potentials near -100 mV to as far as about 0 mV. For pulses to positive potentials Q_{OFF} has generally been observed to exceed Q_{ON} (2, 13, 23), and both have been thought to be contaminated by K^+ current (23). Recent observations indicate that a Ca^{2+} current tail may also contribute to Q_{OFF} following pulses to positive potentials. External application of the calcium channel blocker Co^{2+} to cut fibers having K^+-currents already blocked by both internal Cs^+ and external TEA^+ decreased Q_{OFF} following pulses to positive potentials, making $Q_{ON} = Q_{OFF}$, and eliminated the otherwise observed increase of Q_{OFF} with increasing ON duration at positive potentials (36).

The two-state Boltzmann model (23, 49) provides a convenient basis for characterizing and comparing various determinations of the steady Q versus V relationship, even though the model is unrealistically simple in that it cannot account for observed I_Q time courses (below). A comparison (36) of the various Q versus V results reported for fully polarized intact fibers in hypertonic (2, 23, 49, 52) and isotonic (10, 50) solutions indicates that hypertonicity may shift the midpoint voltage $\bar{V}$ by about 20 mV to more negative potentials and steepen the voltage dependence of Q without altering the maximum charge, Q_{max}. The cut fiber results are comparable to those from intact fibers in isotonic solution (36). Tetracaine was originally reported to have minimal effect on Q versus V (10, 13), but subsequent studies indicate that it may suppress at least some component of Q (below).

The "Bump" Component

I_Q does not follow a simple exponential time course during depolarizing pulses to between about −50 and −30 mV (7, 11, 12, 36, 37). Within this range a late shoulder or bump in I_Q appears abruptly and changes kinetics markedly with small changes in potential (7, 8, 36, 37). Using contracting cut fibers, Horowicz & Schneider (37) have observed that the bump component first appears at about the rheobase voltage for contraction and that during larger pulses it begins at or slightly before the pulse duration required for producing just-detectable contraction. These findings indicate that the bump may be an accompaniment of Ca release or elevated myoplasmic Ca rather than part of the mechanism for activating SR Ca release. Such an interpretation would be consistent with the observations that the bump is selectively depressed both by tetracaine [(37a); C. S. Hui, personal communication] and by dantroline (C. S. Hui, personal communication), another agent that blocks Ca release (28, 32), and that the bump component is decreased relatively more than the overall Q during steady partial depolarizations that depress contraction (37; see also 8).

The bump component probably constitutes a small fraction of the overall Q for large pulses so large pulse measurements would have to be extremely precise in order to establish whether it fulfills the ON OFF equality criterion for a charge movement. It may however constitute an appreciable fraction of Q measured with small pulses in the appropriate range (7, 8), so small pulse measurements may prove to be more helpful in this regard.

Adrian & Peres (7) presented a model having two components of I_Q, one proportional to the time derivative of the Hodgkin-Huxley (35) variable for muscle delayed rectifier K$^+$ current (5) and a second proportional to the time derivative of the fourth power of the same variable. The second component, which was supposed to account for the I_Q bumps, would be generated during the actual opening of the K$^+$ channels (7). This would not be inconsistent with the bumps' starting at or slightly before pulse durations t_{th} required for threshold contractions (37) since delayed rectification begins slightly before t_{th} in the voltage range of the bump (4). Because of the unreasonably large amount of charge that would be associated with each

K channel (11), Adrian & Peres (8) subsequently abandoned their suggestion that a major portion of charge movement is associated with gating and
opening K channels.

Horowicz & Schneider (37) generalized the Adrian & Peres (7) two-
component model for I_Q using powers n from 2 to 6 for the second component, but were unable to reproduce the bump. The model with $n = 3$ most
closely approximated the observed I_Q time courses but gave theoretical
records that passed below the bump, which such an analysis showed to
constitute about 4–8% of Q_{ON} unaccounted for by the model (37).

An Alternative Mechanism for Charge Movement

Measured charge movements are generally attributed to the redistribution
of charges or dipoles within the membrane. A nonlinear capacitative current could, however, also arise from a membrane with linear capacitance
in series with a nonlinear conductance. The T and SR membrane systems
of skeletal muscle might provide a morphological basis for such an effect.
Chandler et al (23) examined several models involving voltage and time
dependent T-SR coupling conductances but were unable to reproduce the
observed ON OFF equality, voltage dependence, and time course of charge
movement. Mathias et al (43) have recently reconsidered such models with
the modification that the SR terminal cisternae be electrically isolated from
the SR longitudinal tubules. The predictions of their model regarding fiber
electrical and morphological properties invite experimental verification.

GATING CHARGE FOR IONIC CHANNELS

Muscle fibers should have charge movements for gating Na and K channels
as well as for depolarization-contraction coupling. Both calculations (12)
and relatively high time resolution measurements (54) indicate that the
amount of charge moved by Na gating current may be less than 10% of the
Q_{max} determined in routine lower time resolution measurements. The observations that Na gating current in frog axon is about 80% immobilized
in a few ms at positive potentials (46) whereas $Q_{ON} = Q_{OFF}$ in frog muscle
for 50–100 ms pulses to positive potentials providing that all ionic conductances are indeed blocked (36) indicate that Na gating current probably
constitutes a minimal fraction of the charge routinely determined in muscle.
Both the theoretically and experimentally based arguments for expecting
negligible Q contribution from K channel gating current have been recently
reviewed (11). A subsequent observation consistent with this view is that
in the presence of tetracaine delayed K current can be activated from a
holding potential of –20 mV with minimal preceding charge movement (9).

VOLTAGE SENSOR FOR DEPOLARIZATION-CONTRACTION COUPLING

From the various studies considered in the following sections no findings have as yet emerged that are clearly inconsistent with charge movement's acting as voltage sensor for depolarization-contraction coupling.

Contractile Repriming

One reason for associating charge movement with depolarization-contraction coupling is that both Q (24) and contraction (34) decline during prolonged depolarization and are restored ("reprimed") by repolarization. The time constants of 10's of seconds for charge disappearance and reappearance (24) may be generally consistent with the durations (21) and repriming times (20) reported for K contractures under similar conditions.

Adrian et al (6) determined the repriming times at a fixed potential that were required to restore just-detectable contraction during long post-repriming pulses to various potentials. The data were used to predict the relative Q versus V relationship based on the assumptions (a) that the relative Q versus V is independent of the extent of repriming and (b) that the amount of charge Q_{th} that must move to produce a just-detectable contraction during a long pulse is constant, independent of the extent of repriming. Their predictions were generally consistent with reported direct Q measurements on fully polarized fibers in isotonic solution. Insofar as steady partial depolarization is equivalent to partial repriming, recent observations (37) support assumption a and show b to be a good approximation since partial depolarization only slightly decreases Q_{th}. Adrian et al (6) managed to obtain both contractile repriming and direct subthreshold charge measurements in one fiber and found the predicted and measured relative Q versus V to be in good agreement.

Charge Repriming

Several recent studies (9, 47, 48) have reexamined the repriming of charge movement during repolarization of depolarized fibers. Reprimed I_Q was defined as the difference between currents for two pulses between identical potentials, one applied after and the other before a period of repolarization (9). Adrian and Rakowski (9) did not detect saturation of reprimed Q at positive potentials, which may be attributable to ionic current contamination (above). Rakowski found reprimed charge to vary linearly with V (47) but subsequently reported that changes in microelectrode impalement leak conductances were probably the origin of the apparent change in linear capacitance (48). In vaseline gap measurements without microelectrodes partial depolarization that reversibly reduced Q to 60% of control left linear capacitance unaffected (37), clearly demonstrating that charge movement can be depressed and restored independently of changes in linear capacitance.

Charge Moved at Contraction Thresholds

Horowicz & Schneider (37) measured charge movement and pulse durations, t_{th}, required to produce microscopically just-detectable contraction and calculated threshold charge Q_{th} as Q moved during t_{th}. In fully polarized fibers Q_{th} was constant both for pulses to different potentials ($100 \leq t_{th} \leq 9$ ms) and also for a given pulse, with or without prepulses, that alone produced no contraction. Both t_{th} and rheobase thus appear to be determined by the pulse durations and amplitude required to move a set amount of charge.

A constant Q_{th} determining contraction threshold necessitates a reinterpretation of previous models for threshold. Hodgkin & Horowicz (34) supposed that an unidentified "activator" is "released" during depolarization and that contraction begins when the activator reaches a threshold level. Adrian et al (4) developed this approach, used it to account for strength-duration curves for contraction threshold, and suggested that the activator might be Ca^{2+}. The activator was subsequently equated with charge movement (1), consistent with the experimentally demonstrated constancy of Q_{th} (37). The change in activator identification from Ca^{2+} to Q has the interesting consequence of removing the implication that rheobase be a state of constant myoplasmic free Ca^{2+} produced by balanced Ca^{2+} release and uptake.

Horowicz & Schneider (37) further observed that under steady partial depolarization Q_{th} was still about the same for pulses to different potentials but was somewhat less than under full polarization. Partial depolarizations that decreased Q to $60 \pm 8\%$ of its value at full depolarization decreased Q_{th} to $86 \pm 11\%$ [mean $\pm$ SD from 10 bracketed runs (37)]. Both Q versus V and the effects of partial depolarization on Q and Q_{th} were accommodated by a model with two Q components, component A due to intramembrane charges moving across a single energy barrier and component B instantaneously proportional to an integer power of the fraction of A charges that had crossed the barrier [(37) and above]. In the model components A and B are uniformly depressed by steady depolarization, and contraction threshold corresponds to a set amount of component B charge. The observed I_Q time courses were largely but not completely accounted for by the model (above).

Charge Movement and Calcium Transients

In order to compare depolarization-contraction coupling steps somewhat closer together than charge movement and contraction, Kovács et al (39,

51) monitored charge movement and myoplasmic free Ca transients. The optimal comparison would be between charge movement and SR Ca permeability, P_{Ca}. Unfortunately, the P_{Ca} time course has as yet not been deduced from the Ca transient. However, if the Ca transient were generated by Ca redistribution between three intracellular compartments, it could at least be used to determine the transition time required for P_{Ca} to reach its steady level during a step depolarization (39). This transition time has been found to correspond with or occur slightly later than the time taken for charge movement to be completed during the step (39), as expected if Q were to control P_{Ca}.

Another temporal relationship between charge movement and the Ca transient has been established using 100 ms test pulses with or without immediately preceding prepulses that alone cause no Ca signal (51). Such prepulses shift the test pulse Ca transient to earlier in time without changing its time course (51). They also shift the latter portion of the I_Q recorded for the test pulse alone toward the start of the test pulse with minimal change in its time course, apparently by selectively mobilizing the charge that moves first when the test pulse is applied alone (37). For a given prepulse–test pulse combination the time shifts of Ca and Q were identical (51), again as expected if Q were to control P_{Ca}.

Effects of External pH and Calcium

Shlevin (52) has determined Q versus V in intact fibers bathed in hypertonic solutions of varying pH and Ca concentration. Changing external pH from 7.2 to 9.0 or 5.5 simply shifted Q versus V along the V axis, as expected for surface charge titration. The shifts of V were generally consistent with shifts of contraction threshold reported by Dörrscheidt-Käfer (29) for similar pH changes. Elevation of external Ca from 2.5 to 25, 50, or 100 mM not only shifted V to more positive potentials but also decreased the steepness of Q versus V without apparent effect on Q_{max} (52). Elevated external Ca also raises contraction thresholds (25), but the basis for the Ca effect on the Q versus V steepness and its significance for depolarization-contraction coupling remain to be determined.

Slow Fibers

Gilly & Hui (30, 31) have compared various properties of frog slow and twitch fibers. Strength-duration curves for threshold contractions and time constants for the rapid component of decay of subthreshold activation were similar for the two fiber types (30). The Q/Q_{max} versus V relationships and the I_Q kinetics were also similar for the two types with contraction eliminated by tetracaine (31). Charge movement could thus serve as voltage sensor for both slow and twitch fibers, with the slower contraction and relaxation of slow fibers due to slower shortening velocities and calcium uptake (27) rather than to differences in voltage sensor kinetics.

Stretch

It has recently been reported that much of charge movement is abolished in fibers stretched well beyond slack length (3). This would be inconsistent with charge movement's serving as voltage sensor for depolarization-contraction coupling since Ca^{2+} transients are present in stretched fibers (17, 19, 39, 44). Hui & Gilly (38) reinvestigated this question and found no effect of sarcomere length (2.5–3.5 μm) on Q versus V for fibers in isotonic solution with movement eliminated by tetracaine when Q was expressed relative to the linear capacitance measured at the same sarcomere length.

T-SR TRANSMISSION

If charge movement is the voltage sensor for depolarization-contraction coupling, the question arises as to how a molecular movement in the T-tubule membrane might modulate P_{Ca} in the adjacent SR membrane. One proposed mechanism involved a mechanical link connecting each charged group in the T-tubule to a plug blocking one SR Ca channel, with charge movement pulling the plug and unblocking the channel (24). The similarity of numbers of charged groups detected electrically and of "feet" between T-tubules and SR determined by electron microscopy provided the basis for assigning one T-SR link to each charged group (49). It was subsequently determined that the voltage dependence of several optical signals that may be associated with changes of SR membrane potential (16, 53) or of myoplasmic Ca^{2+} (17, 18) is considerably steeper than Q versus V. Furthermore, an appreciable fraction of Q_{max} is moved at contraction thresholds (37) and at the rheobase potential for Ca^{2+} transients (39), and the various optical signals exhibit relatively long latencies at potentials slightly beyond rheobase (16, 17, 39, 40, 51, 53). Depending on the nature and importance of subsequent steps and parallel processes, such observations might require T-SR transmission to be more complex than each charged group controlling one channel. Two possible alternatives might involve several T-tubule charged groups controlling each SR channel (53) or 1 to 1 control combined with another process that almost completely counteracts the effect of the increased P_{Ca} for small charge movements but that saturates steeply as Q approaches Q_{th}. The T-SR messenger might be mechanical or chemical in either case. The further possibility of a voltage-dependent T-SR coupling conductance (above) introduces another class of mechanisms. In view of the multiple possibilities it appears that additional types of data will be required to establish the nature of T-SR transmission.

ACKNOWLEDGMENT

I am grateful to Drs. C. Bergman and P. Ascher for their hospitality during my stay at the Laboratoire de Neurobiologie, École Normale Supérieure, Paris, France, where this review was written, and to Dr. P. Horowicz for many stimulating discussions on this subject over the last few years. M.F.S. was supported by RCDA grant K04-NS0078 from the USPHS.

Literature Cited

1. Adrian, R. H. 1978. Charge movement in the membrane of striated muscle. *Ann. Rev. Biophys. Bioeng.* 7: 85–112
2. Adrian, R. H., Almers, W. 1976. Charge movement in the membrane of striated muscle. *J. Physiol. London* 254:339–60
3. Adrian, R. H., Caputo, C., Huang, C. L.-H. 1978. Effect of stretch on intramembrane charge movement in striated muscle. *J. Physiol. London* 284:151P
4. Adrian, R. H., Chandler, W. K., Hodgkin, A. L. 1969. The kinetics of mechanical activation in frog muscle. *J. Physiol. London* 204:207–30
5. Adrian, R. H., Chandler, W. K., Hodgkin, A. L. 1970. Voltage clamp experiments in striated muscle fibres. *J. Physiol. London* 208:607–44
6. Adrian, R. H., Chandler, W. K., Rakowski, R. F. 1976. Charge movement and mechanical repriming in striated muscle. *J. Physiol. London* 254:361–88
7. Adrian, R. H., Peres, A. R. 1977. A gating signal for the potassium channel? *Nature* 267:800–4
8. Adrian, R. H., Peres, A. 1979. Charge movement and membrane capacity in frog muscle. *J. Physiol. London* 289: 83–97
9. Adrian, R. H., Rakowski, R. F. 1978. Reactivation of membrane charge movement and delayed potassium conductance in skeletal muscle fibres. *J. Physiol. London* 278:533–57
10. Almers, W. 1976. Differential effects of tetracaine on delayed potassium channels and displacement currents in frog skeletal muscle. *J. Physiol. London* 262:613–37
11. Almers, W. 1978. Gating currents and charge movements in excitable membranes. *Rev. Physiol. Biochem. Pharmacol.* 82:96–190
12. Almers, W., Adrian, R. H., Levinson, S. R. 1975. Some dielectric properties of muscle membrane and their possible importance for excitation-contraction coupling. *Ann. NY Acad. Sci.* 264: 278–92
13. Almers, W., Best, P. M. 1976. Effects of tetracaine on displacement currents and contraction of frog skeletal muscle. *J. Physiol. London* 262:583–611
14. Armstrong, C. M., Bezanilla, F. 1973. Currents related to the movement of the gating particles of the sodium channels. *Nature* 242:459–61
15. Armstrong, C. M., Bezanilla, F. 1974. Charge movement associated with the opening and closing of the activation gates of the Na channels. *J. Gen. Physiol.* 63:533–52
16. Baylor, S. M., Chandler, W. K. 1978. Optical indications of excitation-contraction coupling in striated muscle. In *Biophysical Aspects of Cardiac Muscle,* ed. M. Morad, pp. 207–88. NY: Academic.
17. Baylor, S. M., Chandler, W. K., Marshall, M. W. 1979. Arsenazo III signals in singly dissected frog twitch fibres. *J. Physiol. London* 287:23P
18. Baylor, S. M., Chandler, W. K., Marshall, M. W. 1979. Temporal comparison of different optical signals associated with E-C coupling in frog muscle. *Biophys. J.* 25:119a
19. Blinks, J. R., Rüdel, R., Taylor, S. R. 1978. Calcium transients in isolated amphibian skeletal muscle fibres: detection with aequorin. *J. Physiol. London* 277:291–323
20. Caputo, C. 1972. The effect of low temperature on the excitation-contraction coupling phenomena of frog single muscle fibres. *J. Physiol. London* 223: 461–82
21. Caputo, C. 1972. The time course of potassium contractures in single muscle fibres. *J. Physiol. London* 223:483–505
22. Caputo, C. 1978. Excitation and contraction processes in muscle. *Ann. Rev. Biophys. Bioeng.* 7:63–83

23. Chandler, W. K., Rakowski, R. F., Schneider, M. F. 1976. A nonlinear voltage dependent charge movement in frog skeletal muscle. *J. Physiol. London* 254:245–83

24. Chandler, W. K., Rakowski, R. F., Schneider, M. F. 1976. Effects of glycerol treatment and maintained depolarization on charge movement in skeletal muscle. *J. Physiol. London* 254:285–316

25. Costantin, L. L. 1968. The effect of calcium on contraction and conductance thresholds in frog skeletal muscle. *J. Physiol. London* 195:119–32

26. Costantin, L. L. 1970. The role of sodium current in the radial spread of contraction in frog muscle fibers. *J. Gen. Physiol.* 55:703–15

27. Costantin, L. L., Podolsky, R. J., Tice, L. W. 1967. Calcium activation of frog slow muscle fibres. *J. Physiol. London* 188:261–71

28. Desmedt, J. E., Hainaut, K. 1977. Inhibition of the intracellular release of calcium by dantroline in barnacle giant muscle fibres. *J. Physiol. London* 265:565–85

29. Dörrscheidt-Käfer, M. 1976. The action of Ca^{2+}, Mg^{2+} and H^+ on the contraction threshold of frog skeletal muscle: evidence for surface charges controlling electromechanical coupling. *Pflügers Arch.* 362:33–41

30. Gilly, W. F., Hui, C. S. 1977. Contractile activation of slow and twitch muscle fibres of the frog. *Nature* 266:186–88

31. Gilly, W. F., Hui, C. S. 1980. Voltage-dependent charge movement in frog slow muscle fibres. *J. Physiol. London* 301:175–90

32. Hainaut, K., Desmedt, J. E. 1974. Effect of dantroline sodium on calcium movements in single muscle fibres. *Nature* 252:728–30

33. Hille, B., Campbell, D. T. 1976. An improved vaseline gap voltage clamp for skeletal muscle fibers. *J. Gen. Physiol.* 67:265–93

34. Hodgkin, A. L., Horowicz, P. 1960. Potassium contractures in single muscle fibres. *J. Physiol. London* 153:386–403

35. Hodgkin, A. L., Huxley, A. F. 1952. A quantitative description of membrane current and its application to conduction and excitation in nerve. *J. Physiol. London* 117:500–44

36. Horowicz, P., Schneider, M. F. 1981. Membrane charge movement in contracting and non-contracting skeletal muscle fibres. *J. Physiol. London* In press

37. Horowicz, P., Schneider, M. F. 1981. Membrane charge moved at contraction thresholds in skeletal muscle fibres. *J. Physiol. London* In press

37a. Huang, C. L.-H. 1980. Charge movement components in skeletal muscle. *J. Physiol. London* 305:31–32P

38. Hui, C. S., Gilly, W. 1979. Mechanical activation and voltage-dependent charge movement in stretched muscle fibres. *Nature* 281:223–25

39. Kovács, L., Ríos, E., Schneider, M. F. 1979. Calcium transients and intramembrane charge movement in skeletal muscle fibres. *Nature* 279:391–96

40. Kovács, L., Schneider, M. F. 1977. Increased optical transparency associated with excitation-contraction coupling in voltage-clamped cut skeletal muscle fibres. *Nature* 265:555–60

41. Kovács, L., Schneider, M. F. 1978. Contractile activation by voltage clamp depolarization of cut skeletal muscle fibres. *J. Physiol. London* 277:483–506

42. Lüttgau, M. C., Moisescu, G. D. 1978. Ion movements in skeletal muscle in relation to the activation of contraction. In *Physiology of Membrane Disorders,* ed. T. E. Andreoli, J. F. Hoffman, D. F. Fanestil, pp. 493–515. NY: Plenum

43. Mathias, R. T., Levis, R. A., Eisenberg, R. S. 1980. Electrical models of excitation-contraction coupling and charge movement in skeletal muscle. *J. Gen. Physiol.* 76:1–31

44. Miledi, R., Parker, I., Schalow, G. 1977. Measurement of calcium transients in frog muscle by the use of arsenazo III *Proc. R. Soc. London Ser. B* 198:201–10

45. Nakajima, S., Bastian, J. 1976. Membrane properties of the transverse tubular system in amphibian muscle. In *Electrobiology of Nerve, Synapse and Muscle,* ed. D. P. Purpura, M. V. L. Bennett, E. R. Kandel, pp. 243–68. NY: Raven

46. Nonner, W., Rojas, E., Stämpfli, R. 1978. Asymmetrical displacement currents in the membrane of frog myelinated nerve: Early time course and effects of membrane potential. *Pflügers Arch.* 375:75–85

47. Rakowski, R. F. 1978. Reprimed charge movement in skeletal muscle fibres. *J. Physiol. London* 281:339–58

48. Rakowski, R. F. 1981. Inactivation and recovery of membrane charge movement in skeletal muscle. In *The Regula-*

tion of Muscle Contraction: Excitation-Contraction Coupling, ed. A. D. Grinnell, M. A. B. Brazier. NY: Academic. In press

49. Schneider, M. F., Chandler, W. K. 1973. Voltage dependent charge movement in skeletal muscle: a possible step in excitation-contraction coupling. *Nature* 242:244–46

50. Schneider, M. F., Chandler, W. K. 1976. Effects of membrane potential on the capacitance of skeletal muscle fibres. *J. Gen. Physiol.* 67:125–63

51. Schneider, M. F., Ríos, E., Kovács, L. 1981. Calcium transients and intramembrane charge movement in skel-etal muscle. In *The Regulation of Muscle Contraction: Excitation-Contraction Coupling,* ed. A. D. Grinnell, M. A. B. Brazier. NY: Academic. In press

52. Shlevin, H. H. 1979. Effects of external calcium concentration and pH on charge movement in frog skeletal muscle. *J. Physiol.* 288:129–58

53. Vergara, J., Bezanilla, F., Salzberg, B. M. 1978. Nile blue fluorescence signals from cut single muscle fibers under voltage or current clamp conditions. *J. Gen. Physiol.* 72:775–800

54. Vergara, J., Cahalan, M. 1978. Charge movements in a cut skeletal muscle fiber. *Biophys. J.* 21:167A

Ann. Rev. Physiol. 1981. 43:519–30

REGULATION OF SMOOTH MUSCLE ACTOMYOSIN

❖1327

David J. Hartshorne and Raymond F. Siemankowski

Muscle Biology Group, Departments of Biochemistry and Nutrition and Food Science, University of Arizona, Tucson, Arizona 85721

INTRODUCTION

It is generally assumed that length changes in smooth muscle occur as a result of a relative sliding of the thick and thin filaments. The orientation of the filaments within the cell and the mode of assembly of the thick filament are not established (70) but the available evidence is consistent with a cross-bridge-actin interaction as the site of tension development. The components of the thick and thin filaments of striated and smooth muscles, although possessing tissue specific features, show gross molecular similarities and many equivalent biochemical properties (27). Thus it appears that the contractile mechanism in smooth muscle can be described by the classical skeletal muscle model, although the rate of contraction is usually slower. However, in one area a fundamental difference exists between smooth and striated muscles—i.e. in the regulatory mechanism that controls the interaction of the myosin cross bridges with actin.

BASIC REQUIREMENTS FOR REGULATION

The early studies on the regulatory mechanism followed the discovery of troponin in skeletal muscle and were concerned with whether or not a mechanism involving a troponin-like component exists in smooth muscle. Some evidence in favor of this possibility was reported (12, 20), but the contemporary feeling is that a skeletal muscle–like troponin is not present in smooth muscle. In support of this opinion it was shown that thin filaments and crude actin preparations from chicken gizzard did not contain troponin-like subunits (19, 26, 68). The next surge of interest also followed an historical precedent, namely that regulation in various invertebrates was linked to Ca^{2+}-binding by myosin light chains (39). Bremel tested this possibility with chicken gizzard actomyosin (9) and found that the regulation by Ca^{2+} was indeed myosin-linked. Myosin-linked regulation has subsequently been detected in several smooth muscles (see 27). This was a key discovery and yet initially it raised a puzzling situation. It has been known for many years that as smooth muscle myosin was purified the activation of Mg^{2+}-ATPase activity by actin was reduced (7, 19, 74). In the simplest myosin-linked system, i.e. that of the invertebrates, pure myosin and pure actin constitute an active and regulated complex. Thus it became apparent that components in addition to actin and myosin were required for the activation of the ATPase activity of smooth muscle actomyosin. Nevertheless the system retains its classification as myosin-linked since these additional components are thought to exert their influence via a modification of the myosin molecule. This situation is quite distinct from that found in skeletal muscle where pure myosin and actin form an active, but unregulated, complex and the function of the regulatory proteins (troponin and tropomyosin) is to inhibit the Mg^{2+}-ATPase activity in the absence of Ca^{2+}. In the smooth muscle system pure myosin and actin form an inactive complex and the function of the regulatory components is to activate Mg^{2+}-ATPase activity but only in the presence of Ca^{2+}. That activation constitutes the fundamental requirement for the regulatory mechanism in smooth muscle is generally accepted. The nature of the activation and whether or not the system is myosin-linked forms the basis of the current controversies. Two mechanisms have been proposed for the activating or regulatory system: that activation is achieved by the phosphorylation of the myosin molecule, or that a different system termed leiotonin is involved in the regulatory process.

At this point it should be emphasized that although the initial requirement for regulation in smooth muscle calls for an activation of an inactive state it does not preclude the possibility of a secondary regulatory mechanism that could moderate the activated complex. Some evidence consistent with a dual regulatory mechanism in vascular smooth muscle has recently been reported (44).

REGULATION VIA THE STATE
OF MYOSIN PHOSPHORYLATION

In 1975 it was shown that the phosphorylation of chicken gizzard myosin was associated with an increase in its actin-activated ATPase activity (10, 67), suggesting that the actin-myosin interaction might be regulated via phosphorylation of the myosin molecule. These observations were confirmed (3, 24, 35, 36, 66, 69) and extended to show the phosphorylation of myosin from several smooth muscles (14, 18, 23, 34, 64). A number of conclusions were drawn from these studies forming the basis for the phosphorylation theory of regulation in smooth muscle. (*a*) A maximum of 2 moles of phosphate are incorporated per mole of myosin, and the sites of phosphorylation are the two 20,000 dalton light chains of myosin[1] (14, 23, 24, 66, 67); (*b*) phosphorylation is achieved by a myosin light chain kinase (MLCK) that is active in the presence of Ca^{2+} at concentrations similar to those required to activate the Mg^{2+}-ATPase activity of actomyosin (3, 18, 66, 67); (*c*) the event of phosphorylation allows the activation by actin of the myosin Mg^{2+}-ATPase activity (14, 35, 66, 69), thus fulfilling the requirement for an activator; and (*d*) in the absence of Ca^{2+} the MLCK is not active and a second enzyme, a myosin light chain phosphatase (MLCP), dephosphorylates the light chains and returns the myosin to its inactive state. A simple scheme can be used to summarize these data as follows: The Ca^{2+}-dependent phosphorylation of myosin initiates contraction, and continued cross bridge cycling will occur as long as Ca^{2+} is present. In the relaxation phase the level of intracellular Ca^{2+} is reduced, MLCK activity ceases, and this results in the dephosphorylation of myosin by the MLCP and the return of myosin to its inactive state.

Properties of the Myosin Light Chain Kinase

The MLCK from chicken gizzard is composed of two distinct subunits (16). Each has been purified and the M_r's were estimated to be 105,000 and 17,000. Subsequently the smaller subunit was identified as calmodulin (17) a Ca^{2+}-binding protein implicated in the regulation of several enzymic processes (15). Neither component has any MLCK activity alone (16), but together they effect both a phosphorylation of myosin and an activation of Mg^{2+}-ATPase activity of gizzard actomyosin. Calmodulins from several sources can substitute for chicken gizzard calmodulin in the MLCK (17). The subunit structure of the smooth muscle MLCK was confirmed by Adelstein et al (2) with the turkey gizzard enzyme, in which the larger subunit had a M_r of 125,000. The MLCKs from skeletal and cardiac muscle are also dependent on calmodulin (53, 72, 73, 75), though the molecular weight of the larger subunit is 80,000 (53, 76) for the skeletal and 85,000 (73) for the cardiac enzymes.

With MLCK isolated from chicken gizzard maximum activity is obtained at equimolar stoichiometry of the two subunits; the K_m for ATP is 60–70 μM (28), indicating a slightly higher affinity for ATP than with the

---

[1]Myosin is composed of two large subunits (heavy chains) of M_r about 200,000, and 4 smaller subunits (light chains) in an $\alpha_2\beta_2$ arrangement. To an extent the light chain composition is characteristic of the cell type from which the myosin is isolated (27). The molecular weights of the smooth muscle myosin light chains are about 20,000 and 17,000.

striated muscle enzymes (59, 73, 76); the V_{max} (using isolated myosin light chains as substrate) ranges between 5 and 15 μmol of P_i transferred per min per mg of kinase at 25°C (28, 49); the pH dependence shows a broad optimum between pH 7 and 8 (49), which is distinct from the acidic pH optimum reported for the skeletal muscle MLCK (59); from Arrhenius plots the Q_{10} is estimated to be approximately 2 (49); MLCK required Mg^{2+} or Mn^{2+}-ATP as the phosphate donor (28) but a requirement for divalent cation in excess of ATP is not observed; ITP (58), Ca^{2+}-ATP, and ATP in the absence of divalent cations did not support phosphorylation (28); the kinase activity is reduced upon modification of sulfhydryl groups, the sulfhydryl reactivity is slightly accelerated in the presence of calmodulin and Ca^{2+} (28); MLCK activity is not inhibited by IDP, AMP, cyclic AMP, cyclic GMP, and adenosine (at concentrations up to 100 μM), though a variable inhibition is observed with ADP (28).

It was calculated that the cross bridge cycling rate in arterial muscle at 37°C is about 1 sec^{-1} (50). The V_{max} for the MLCK is in the order of 15 sec^{-1}. Thus it would appear that the initiation of the contractile process (i.e. as a result of the phosphorylation of myosin) is faster than the subsequent cross-bridge cycling rate. This conclusion, however, should be regarded as tentative since the concentration of the MLCK in the muscle cell is not known and the in vivo rates of myosin phosphorylation and ATP hydrolysis by actomyosin are not firmly established. For example, preliminary experiments indicate that the phosphorylation of myosin is slower than the phosphorylation of isolated light chains (49). Also pertinent to this discussion is the finding of Adelstein et al (2) that the larger MLCK subunit is phosphorylated by the cAMP-dependent kinase, resulting in an inhibition of kinase activity. Thus it was suggested (2) that cAMP might play a direct role in regulating contractile activity in smooth muscle via the phosphorylation of the MLCK. Some support for this suggestion comes from reports that smooth muscle actomyosin preparations that contained the cAMP-dependent kinase showed an inhibition of Mg^{2+}-ATPase activity (52, 63) and of myosin phosphorylation (63) on the addition of cAMP.

Calmodulin has physical properties similar to troponin C (15). Both are acidic proteins, bind Ca^{2+}, and have similar molecular weights: 16,700 for calmodulin and about 18,200 for troponin C. These similarities led to a report that a troponin C–like protein was present in smooth muscle (30) and the suggestion that this might reflect the presence of an actin-linked regulatory system. It has since been established that the protein isolated was in fact calmodulin (25, 29) and that troponin C is not present in smooth muscle at significant levels. This finding does not eliminate the possibility of a thin-filament-based regulatory system in smooth muscle, but in view of the many functions of calmodulin its presence per se does not necessarily indicate actin-linked regulation.

Effect of Phosphorylation on the Properties of Myosin

Phosphorylation of myosin is accompanied by the activation of ATPase activity by actin, as observed with actomyosin (3, 64, 66), myofibrils (66), and with partially purified components (14, 16, 24, 34, 35). A linear relationship between the extent of myosin phosphorylation and the Mg^{2+}-ATPase activity of gizzard actomyosin and myofibrils was observed (66), and at complete phosphorylation a specific ATPase activity of close to 300 nmoles min^{-1} mg^{-1} myosin was obtained. Using purified MLCK and partially purified myosin from chicken gizzard and actin and tropomyosin from skeletal muscle a specific activity of about 60 nmol min^{-1} mg^{-1} myosin was obtained for the fully phosphorylated myosin (16). An approximate correlation between the extent of actin-activated ATPase activity and myosin phosphorylation was also apparent from this study. However it should be emphasized that a correlation between myosin phosphorylation and actin-activation of ATPase activity has yet to be demonstrated using components of established homogeneity. The effect of phosphorylation of smooth muscle myosin on the other ATPase activities is not dramatic, though some effects have been observed for the Mg^{2+}-ATPase activity in the absence of actin (71). Other effects of phosphorylation have been reported. It was found that filaments of phosphorylated myosin were more resistant to dissociation by Mg^{2+}-ATP than filaments formed from dephosphorylated myosin (71). Phosphorylation of light chains from skeletal muscle myosin was claimed to alter the light chain conformation and Ca^{2+}-binding properties (4), though other investigators reported no effect of phosphorylation on Ca^{2+}-binding by cardiac (33, 41) and skeletal myosins (33).

The activation by actin of ATPase activity concomitant with myosin phosphorylation is not restricted to smooth muscle systems and was observed originally with platelet myosin (1) and subsequently with several nonmuscle myosins. Skeletal and cardiac muscle myosins are also phosphorylated by a similar system (6), though actin-activation is not markedly altered as a result of phosphorylation (48).

Initially it was thought that the use of proteolytic fragments of myosin might be useful in probing the effects of phosphorylation as related to light chain function. Heavy meromyosin subfragment 1 produced by papain digestion lacks the 20,000 light chain (38) but retains an actin-activated ATPase activity that is usually Ca^{2+}-insensitive (43, 51, 60, 68). These results suggest that the 20,000 light chain is inhibitory in the dephosphorylated state and that inhibition is relieved either by removing the light chain or by phosphorylation. Digestion with α-chymotrypsin (57, 60) or trypsin (54) also resulted in the disappearance of the 20,000 light chain; however, this was concomitant with the loss of actin activation. In these cases proteolysis of the 20,000 light chain produced a 17,000 fragment that was retained by the myosin (54, 57) and that might influence the ATPase activity of the myosin. A further complication with the interpretation of all of the proteolysis experiments is the possibility of heavy chain cleavage and the effect that this might have on the ATPase characteristics. More direct methods of probing light chain function have not been successful; for example, it is not possible to selectively remove the 20,000 light chain, and light chain exchange studies have resulted only in the hybridization of the 17,000 light chain (55).

Heavy meromyosin retains some of the properties of the parent molecule including the requirement of phosphorylation for actin-activated ATPase activity (57, 60). This is a reflection of the presence of the 20,000 light chain, which is largely preserved during the initial stages of proteolysis but is progressively lost on prolonged digestion (60).

It is known that myosins from a variety of sources bind Ca^{2+} (5, 11, 33, 68), and an earlier point of discussion was whether or not this property was involved in the regulatory mechanism of smooth muscle. The two basic hypotheses were that (a) phosphorylation alone is adequate for regulation (35, 65, 66), or (b) Ca^{2+} binding by myosin forms an additional component of the regulatory mechanism (14). One approach toward a choice between the two possibilities was to use adenosine 5'-0-(3-thiotriphosphate), ATPγ S, which serves as a thiophosphate donor for the MLCK, but the transferred thiophosphate is resistant to hydrolysis by the MLCP. The net result is that myosin becomes trapped in the thiophosphorylated state. Following preincubation of gizzard myosin with ATPγS it was observed that as the extent of thiophosphorylation increased the actin-activated ATPase activity in the absence of Ca^{2+} increased until at saturating levels of thiophosphorylation Ca^{2+}-sensitivity was lost (62). These results argue strongly against a dominant inhibitory role of the Ca^{2+}-free light chain and also provide good evidence in support of the phosphorylation theory of regulation.

It has also been found that sulfhydryl modification of gizzard myosin apparently mimics the effect of light chain phosphorylation (61). This effect is not yet understood but should prove useful in future studies.

Myosin Light Chain Phosphatase

This enzyme has not been characterized from smooth muscle sources, though this has been achieved for the skeletal muscle MLCP that was shown to be a single component of M_r 70,000 dalton (48). Phosphatase activity, however, has been detected in several smooth muscle preparations (14, 35, 56, 62). Onishi et al (56) found that a partially purified MLCP preparation caused an inhibition of superprecipitation and ATPase activity of previously phosphorylated actomyosin. This, coupled with the finding (62) that the decrease in ATPase rate on the addition of EGTA followed a similar time dependence to the disappearance of the phosphorylated light chains, suggests that a dephosphorylation process is an essential component of relaxation.

Phosphatase rates in most actomyosin preparations are low—e.g. ~ 1 nmol P_i liberated min^{-1} mg^{-1} actomyosin (62). The V_{max} of the purified skeletal muscle MLCP is reported to be 1–2 μmol min^{-1} mg^{-1} (48). Neither the MLCP from skeletal nor from smooth muscles requires Ca^{2+} for activity (48, 62). This property is obligatory if the MLCP is to play a role in relaxation. Currently there is no evidence from studies in vitro that would support any mechanism for the regulation of MLCP activity.

Evidence in Favor of the Phosphorylation Theory

The initial suggestion (67) that phosphorylation of myosin is a prerequisite for the activation of Mg^{2+}-ATPase by actin is still accepted as strong support for this theory. However a precise causal relationship between phosphorylation of myosin and ATPase activation still remains to be established. The major practical difficulty involves obtaining homogeneous myosin preparations. In studies with intact smooth muscle it was found that contraction is accompanied by the phosphorylation of myosin (8, 37), and this correlation was also obtained using various types of skinned fibers (32, 40). These observations are consistent with the phosphorylation theory but are not conclusive since it is possible that Ca^{2+} activation of the contractile process and the phosphorylation of myosin occur fortuitously at similar Ca^{2+} levels. Some of the ambiguity was removed by the use of ATPγS. It was shown that preincubation of skinned fiber preparations with ATPγS abolished the Ca^{2+}-sensitivity of contractile activity (13, 32). Thus the ATPγS experiments eliminate the possibility that two unrelated processes were being activated at the same Ca^{2+} concentration and provide a direct link between phosphorylation and contraction. Another approach has been the use of various phenothiazine derivatives. These compounds were shown to be bound specifically by calmodulin (42) and to inhibit the calmodulin-dependent processes, including the MLCK (31). When applied to strips of skinned intestinal and arterial muscle the phenothiazines inhibit tension development in the presence of Ca^{2+} and prevent the thiophosphorylation of myosin in the presence of ATPγS (40). Thus substantial evidence in favor of a role for phosphorylation in the regulatory process has been accumulated from a variety of disciplines, and while it is probably true that no single experimental finding is in itself conclusive, the cumulative evidence strongly supports such a role. It cannot be claimed that phosphorylation is the only component required for activation, but it probably can be stated that a phosphorylation-dephosphorylation process is at least an integral component of the regulatory mechanism in smooth muscle.

THE LEIOTONIN SYSTEM

The major controversy concerning the regulatory mechanism of smooth muscle is whether regulation operates via the phosphorylation of myosin or through another system termed leiotonin by Ebashi and his colleagues. Both mechanisms are similar in that they activate the Mg^{2+}-ATPase activity of smooth muscle actomyosin in the presence of Ca^{2+}, but they differ in many other respects. The major distinction is that the activation effected by leiotonin does not involve the phosphorylation of myosin (46). A further point of difference is that leiotonin is thought to be actin-linked. Evidence to support the thin filament location of leiotonin was obtained by Mikawa (45), who showed that thin filaments from smooth muscle could be cross-linked by glutaraldehyde in the presence and absence of Ca^{2+} and fixed in either an active or inhibited state, respectively. Full regulation was obtained at a molar stoichiometry of less than 1 leiotonin to 100 actins (21). Although tropomyosin is required by the leiotonin system the mechanism of action of leiotonin is unlikely to be analogous to that of skeletal troponin where a higher stoichiometry is required (1 troponin for each tropomyosin molecule). In contrast to the phosphorylation system leiotonin shows a preference for smooth muscle actin and tropomyosin (22). Leiotonin has been resolved into two components (47): leiotonin A of M_r 80,000, and leiotonin C of M_r 18,000. The latter is an acidic Ca^{2+}-binding protein similar to, but not identical with, calmodulin. The two proteins, however, can be used interchangeably with leiotonin A to sensitize smooth muscle actomyosin to Ca^{2+} (47). The mechanism of action of leiotonin must be established before the merits of the two conflicting theories can be fully evaluated.

CONCLUSIONS

The basic mechanism of regulation in smooth muscle involves the activation of a dormant or inactive state in the presence of Ca^{2+}. Controversy is centered on the nature of the activator. The most popular theory is that activation occurs as a consequence of myosin phosphorylation and that the level of phosphorylation determines the contractile activity of the muscle. The alternate theory is that regulation does not involve the phosphorylation of myosin but is due to a system called leiotonin, which operates via the thin filaments. Obviously one of the priorities for the future will be to evaluate the roles of each system and to determine whether each is exclusive of the other or whether the two systems constitute a dual and cooperative control mechanism. Considerable evidence indicates that the phosphorylation of myosin is at least a part of the control mechanism, and a dual control system is difficult to rationalize since the leiotonin system does not require phosphorylation. It should be of high priority for adherents of the phosphorylation scheme to correlate different levels of phosphorylation with the degrees of actin-activated ATPase activity using components of established homogeneity. Also, more detailed information is clearly required before the role of the MLCP in the regulatory process can be evaluated. In intact muscle, features such as the high holding economy of smooth muscle should be correlated with biochemical data. A knowledge of the kinetic parameters associated with different phases of the cross bridge cycle would be valuable in this regard.

ACKNOWLEDGMENT

D. J. Hartshorne is supported by grant HL 23615 from the National Institutes of Health.

Literature Cited

1. Adelstein, R. S., Conti, M. A. 1975. Phosphorylation of platelet myosin increases actin-activated myosin ATPase activity. *Nature* 256:597–98
2. Adelstein, R. S., Conti, M. A., Hathaway, D. R., Klee, C. B. 1978. Phosphorylation of smooth muscle myosin light chain kinase by the catalytic subunit of adenosine 3':5'-monophosphate-dependent protein kinase. *J. Biol. Chem.* 253:8347–50
3. Aksoy, M. O., Williams, D., Sharkey, E. M., Hartshorne, D. J. 1976. A relationship between Ca^{2+} sensitivity and phosphorylation of gizzard actomyosin. *Biochem. Biophys. Res. Commun.* 69:35–41
4. Alexis, M. N., Gratzer, W. B. 1978. Interaction of skeletal myosin light chains with calcium ions. *Biochemistry* 17:2319–25
5. Bagshaw, C. R., Kendrick-Jones, J. 1979. Characterization of homologous divalent metal ion binding sites of vertebrate and molluscan myosins using electron paramagnetic resonance spectroscopy. *J. Mol. Biol.* 130:317–36
6. Bárány, M., Bárány, K. 1980. Phosphorylation of the myofibrillar proteins. *Ann. Rev. Physiol.* 42:275–92
7. Bárány, M., Bárány, K., Gaetjens, E., Bailin, G. 1966. Chicken gizzard myosin. *Arch. Biochem. Biophys.* 113:205–21
8. Barron, J. T., Bárány, M., Bárány, K. 1979. Phosphorylation of the 20,000-dalton light chain of myosin of intact arterial smooth muscle in rest and in contraction. *J. Biol. Chem.* 254: 4954–56
9. Bremel, R. D. 1974. Myosin linked calcium regulation in vertebrate smooth muscle. *Nature* 252:405–7
10. Bremel, R. D., Sobieszek, A., Small, J. V. 1977. Regulation of actin-myosin interaction in vertebrate smooth muscle. In *The Biochemistry of Smooth Muscle*, ed. N. L. Stephens, pp. 533–49. Baltimore: University Park
11. Bremel, R. D., Weber, A. 1975. Calcium binding to rabbit skeletal myosin under physiological conditions. *Biochim. Biophys. Acta* 373:366–74
12. Carsten, M. E. 1971. Uterine smooth muscle: troponin. *Arch. Biochem. Biophys.* 147:353–57
13. Cassidy, P. S., Hoar, P. E., Kerrick, W. G. L. 1979. Irreversible thiophosphorylation and activation of tension in functionally skinned rabbit ileum strips by [^{35}S] ATPγS. *J. Biol. Chem.* 254: 11148–53
14. Chacko, S., Conti, M. A., Adelstein, R. S. 1977. Effect of phosphorylation of smooth muscle myosin on actin activa-

tion and Ca^{2+} regulation. *Proc. Natl. Acad. Sci. USA* 74:129–33

15. Cheung, W. Y. 1980. Calmodulin plays a pivotal role in cellular regulation. *Science* 207:19–27

16. Dabrowska, R., Aromatorio, D., Sherry, J. M. F., Hartshorne, D. J. 1977. Composition of the myosin light chain kinase from chicken gizzard. *Biochem. Biophys. Res. Commun.* 78: 1263–72

17. Dabrowska, R., Sherry, J. M. F., Aromatorio, D. K., Hartshorne, D. J. 1978. Modulator protein as a component of the myosin light chain kinase from chicken gizzard. *Biochemistry* 17:253–58

18. DiSalvo, J., Gruenstein, E., Silver, P. 1978. Ca^{2+} dependent phosphorylation of bovine aortic actomyosin. *Proc. Soc. Exp. Biol. Med.* 158:410–14

19. Driska, S., Hartshorne, D. J. 1975. The contractile proteins of smooth muscle. Properties and components of a Ca^{2+}-sensitive actomyosin from chicken gizzard. *Arch. Biochem. Biophys.* 167:203–12

20. Ebashi, S., Iwakura, H., Nakajima, H., Nakamura, R., Ooi, Y. 1966. New structural proteins from dog heart and chicken gizzard. *Biochem. Z.* 345: 201–11

21. Ebashi, S., Mikawa, T., Hirata, M., Toyooka, T., Nonomura, Y. 1977. Regulatory proteins of smooth muscle. In *Excitation-Contraction Coupling in Smooth Muscle,* ed. R. Casteels, T. Godfraind, J. C. Rüegg, pp. 325–34. Amsterdam: Elsevier/North Holland

22. Ebashi, S., Toyooka, T., Nonomura, Y. 1975. Gizzard troponin. *J. Biochem. Tokyo* 78:859–61

23. Frearson, N., Focant, B. W. W., Perry, S. V. 1976. Phosphorylation of a light chain component of myosin from smooth muscle. *FEBS Lett.* 63:27–32

24. Gorecka, A., Aksoy, M. O., Hartshorne, D. J. 1976. The effect of phosphorylation of gizzard myosin on actin activation. *Biochem. Biophys. Res. Commun.* 71:325–31

25. Grand, R. J. A., Perry, S. V., Weeks, R. A. 1979. Troponin C-like proteins (calmodulins) from mammalian smooth muscle and other tissues. *Biochem. J.* 177:521–29

26. Hartshorne, D. J., Abrams, L., Aksoy, M. O., Dabrowska, R., Driska, S., Sharkey, E. M. 1977. Molecular basis for the regulation of smooth muscle actomyosin. See Ref. 10, pp. 513–32

27. Hartshorne, D. J., Gorecka, A. 1980. The biochemistry of the contractile proteins of smooth muscle. In *Handbook of Physiology, Section 2, The Cardiovascular System. Vol. II. Vascular Smooth Muscle,* ed. D. F. Bohr, A. P. Somlyo, H. V. Sparks, pp. 93–120. Bethesda, Md: Am. Physiol. Soc.

28. Hartshorne, D. J., Siemankowski, R. F., Aksoy, M. O. 1980. Ca regulation in smooth muscle and phosphorylation: some properties of the myosin light chain kinase. In *Regulatory Mechanisms of Muscle Contraction,* ed. S. Ebashi, K. Maruyama, M. Endo, pp. 287–301. Tokyo: Japan. Sci. Soc. Press. Berlin: Springer-Verlag

29. Head, J. F., Mader, S., Kaminer, B. 1977. Troponin-C-like modulator protein from vertebrate smooth muscle. In *Calcium Binding Proteins and Calcium Function,* ed. R. H. Wasserman, R. A. Corradino, E. Carafoli, R. H. Kretsinger, D. H. MacLennan, F. L. Siegel, pp. 275–77. Amsterdam: Elsevier North-Holland

30. Head, J. F., Weeks, R. A., Perry, S. V. 1977. Affinity-chromatographic isolation and some properties of troponin C from different muscle types. *Biochem. J.* 161:465–71

31. Hidaka, H., Naka, M., Yamaki, T. 1979. Effect of novel specific myosin light chain kinase inhibitors on Ca^{2+}-activated Mg^2-ATPase of chicken gizzard actomyosin. *Biochem. Biophys. Res. Commun.* 90:694–99

32. Hoar, P. E., Kerrick, W. G. L., Cassidy, P. S. 1979. Chicken gizzard: relation between clacium-activated phosphorylation and contraction. *Science* 204:503–6

33. Holroyde, M. J., Potter, J. D., Solaro, R. J. 1978. The calcium binding properties of phosphorylated and unphosphorylated cardiac and skeletal myosins. *J. Biol. Chem.* 254:6478–82

34. Huszar, G., Bailey, P. 1979. Relationship between actin-myosin interaction and myosin light chain phosphorylation in human placental smooth muscle. *Am. J. Obstet. Gynecol.* 135:718–26

35. Ikebe, M., Aiba, T., Onishi, H., Watanabe, S. 1978. Calcium sensitivity of contractile proteins from chicken gizzard muscle. *J. Biochem. Tokyo* 83:1643–55

36. Ikebe, M., Onishi, H., Watanabe, S. 1977. Phosphorylation and dephosphorylation of a light chain of the chicken gizzard myosin molecule. *J. Biochem. Tokyo* 82:299–302

37. Janis, R. A., Gualteri, R. T. 1978. Contraction of intact smooth muscle is associated with the phosphorylation of a 20,000 dalton protein. *The Physiologist* 21:59

38. Kendrick-Jones, J. 1973. The subunit structure of gizzard myosin. *Philos. Trans. R. Soc. London Ser. B* 265: 183–89

39. Kendrick-Jones, J., Szentkiralyi, E. M., Szent-Györgyi, A. G. 1972. Myosin-linked regulatory systems: The role of the light chains *Cold Spring Harbor Symp. Quant. Biol.* 37:47–53

40. Kerrick, W. G. L., Hoar, P. E., Cassidy, P. S. 1980. Ca^{2+}-activated tension: The role of myosin light chain phosphorylation. *Fed. Proc.* 39:1558–63

41. Kuwayama, H., Yagi, K. 1979. Ca^{2+} binding of pig cardiac myosin subfragment-1 and g_2 light chain. *J. Biochem. Tokyo* 85:1245–55

42. Levin, R. M., Weiss, B. 1977. Binding of trifluoperazine to the calcium-dependent activator of cyclic nucleotide phosphodiesterase. *Mol. Pharmacol.* 13:690–97

43. Marston, S. B., Taylor, E. W. 1978. Mechanism of myosin and actomyosin ATPase in chicken gizzard smooth muscle. *FEBS Lett.* 86:167–70

44. Marston, S. B., Trevett, R. M., Walters, M. 1980. Calcium ion-regulated thin filaments from vascular smooth muscle. *Biochem. J.* 185:355–65

45. Mikawa, T. 1979. 'Freezing' of the calcium-regulated structures of gizzard thin filaments by glutaraldehyde. *J. Biochem. Tokyo* 85:879–81

46. Mikawa, T., Nonomura, Y., Ebashi, S. 1977. Does phosphorylation of myosin light chain have direct relation to regulation in smooth muscle? *J. Biochem. Tokyo* 82:1789–91

47. Mikawa, T., Nonomura, Y., Hirata, M., Ebashi, S., Kakiuchi, S. 1978. Involvement of an acidic protein in regulation of smooth muscle contraction by the tropomyosin-leiotonin system. *J. Biochem. Tokyo* 84:1633–36

48. Morgan, M., Perry, S. V., Ottaway, J. 1976. Myosin light-chain phosphatase. *Biochem. J.* 157:687–97

49. Mrwa, U., Hartshorne, D. J. 1980. Phosphorylation of smooth muscle myosin and myosin light chains. *Fed. Proc.* 39:1564–68

50. Mrwa, U., Paul, R. J., Kreye, V. A. W., Rüegg, J. C. 1975. The contractile mechanism of vascular smooth muscle. *INSERM* 50:319–26

51. Mrwa, U., Rüegg, J. C. 1977. The role of the regulatory light chain in pig carotid smooth muscle ATPase. See Ref. 21, pp. 353–57

52. Mrwa, U., Troschka, M., Rüegg, J. C. 1979. Cyclic AMP-dependent inhibition of smooth muscle actomyosin. *FEBS Lett.* 107:371–74

53. Nairn, A. C., Perry, S. V. 1979. Calmodulin and myosin light-chain kinase of rabbit fast skeletal muscle. *Biochem. J.* 179:89–97

54. Okamoto, Y., Sekine, T. 1978. Effects of tryptic digestion of the enzymatic activities of chicken gizzard myosin. *J. Biochem. Tokyo* 83:1375–79

55. Okamoto, Y., Sekine, T. 1980. Involvement of 17K dalton light chain of smooth muscle myosin in substrate-induced conformational change. *J. Biochem. Tokyo* 87:167–78

56. Onishi, H., Iijima, S., Anzai, H., Watanabe, S. 1979. The possible role of myosin light-chain phosphatase in relaxation of chicken gizzard muscle. *J. Biochem. Tokyo* 86:1283–90

57. Onishi, H., Watanabe, S. 1979. Chicken gizzard heavy meromyosin that retains the two light-chain components, including a phosphorylatable one. *J. Biochem. Tokyo* 85:457–72

58. Onishi, H., Watanabe, S. 1979. Calcium regulation in chicken gizzard muscle and inosine triphosphate-induced superprecipitation of skeletal acto-gizzard myosin. *J. Biochem. Tokyo* 86: 569–73

59. Pires, E. M. V., Perry, S. V. 1977. Purification and properties of myosin light-chain kinase from fast skeletal muscle. *Biochem. J.* 167:137–46

60. Seidel, J. C. 1978. Chymotryptic heavy meromyosin from gizzard myosin: a proteolytic fragment with the regulatory properties of the intact myosin. *Biochem. Biophys. Res. Commun.* 85:107–13

61. Seidel, J. C. 1979. Activation by actin of ATPase activity of chemically modified gizzard myosin without phosphorylation. *Biochem. Biophys. Res. Commun.* 89:958–64

62. Sherry, J. M. F., Gorecka, A., Aksoy, M. O., Dabrowska, R., Hartshorne, D. J. 1978. Roles of calcium and phosphorylation in the regulation of the activity of gizzard myosin. *Biochemistry* 17:4411–18

63. Silver, P. J., DiSalvo, J. 1979. Adenosine 3':5'-monophosphate-mediated inhibition of myosin light chain phospho-

rylation in bovine aortic actomyosin. *J. Biol. Chem.* 254:9951–54

64. Small, J. V., Sobieszek, A. 1977. Ca-regulation of mammalian smooth muscle actomyosin via a kinase-phosphatase-dependent phosphorylation and dephosphorylation of the 20,000 – M_r light chain of myosin. *Eur. J. Biochem.* 76:521–30

65. Small, J. V., Sobieszek, A. 1977. Myosin phosphorylation and Ca-regulation in vertebrate smooth muscle. See Ref. 21, pp. 385–93

66. Sobieszek, A. 1977. Ca-linked phosphorylation of a light chain of vertebrate smooth-muscle myosin. *Eur. J. Biochem.* 73:477–83

67. Sobieszek, A. 1977. Vertebrate smooth muscle myosin. Enzymatic and structural properties. See Ref. 10, pp. 413–43

68. Sobieszek, A., Small, J. V. 1976. Myosin-linked calcium regulation in vertebrate smooth muscle. *J. Mol. Biol.* 102:75–92

69. Sobieszek, A., Small, J. V. 1977. Regulation of the actin-myosin interaction in vertebrate smooth muscle: activation via a myosin light-chain kinase and the effect of tropomyosin. *J. Mol. Biol.* 112:559–76

70. Somlyo, A. V. 1980. Ultrastructure of vascular smooth muscle. See Ref. 27, pp. 33–67

71. Suzuki, H., Onishi, H., Takahashi, K., Watanabe, S. 1978. Structure and function of chicken gizzard myosin. *J. Biochem. Tokyo* 84:1529–42

72. Waisman, D. M., Singh, T. J., Wang, J. H. 1978. The modulator-dependent protein kinase. A multifunctional protein kinase activatable by the Ca^{2+}-dependent modulator protein of the cyclic nucleotide system. *J. Biol. Chem.* 253:3387–90

73. Walsh, M. P., Vallet, B., Autric, F., Demaille, J. G. 1979. Purification and characterization of bovine cardiac calmodulin-dependent myosin light chain kinase. *J. Biol. Chem.* 254:12136–44

74. Yamaguchi, M., Miyazawa, Y., Sekine, T. 1970. Preparation and properties of smooth muscle myosin from horse esophagus. *Biochim. Biophys. Acta* 216:411–21

75. Yazawa, M., Kuwayama, H., Yagi, K. 1978. Modulator protein as a Ca^{2+}-dependent activator of rabbit skeletal myosin light-chain kinase. Purification and characterization. *J. Biochem. Tokyo* 84:1253–58

76. Yazawa, M., Yagi, K. 1978. Purification of modulator-deficient myosin light-chain kinase by modulator protein-Sepharose affinity chromatography. *J. Biochem. Tokyo* 84:1259–65

NOTE ADDED IN PROOF   Recently two phosphatases, termed I and II, have been isolated from turkey gizzard. Both enzymes dephosphorylate the myosin light chains but only phosphatase I dephosphorylates the phosphorylated myosin light chain kinase. Phosphatase I is composed of 3 subunits of molecular weights 60,000, 55,000, and 38,000. Phosphatase II is a single polypeptide chain of M_r 43,000 (Pato, M. D., Adelstein, R. S. 1980. Dephosphorylation of the 20,000-dalton light chain of myosin by two different phosphatases from smooth muscle. *J. Biol. Chem.* 255:6525–38)

Ann. Rev. Physiol. 1981. 43:531–52
Copyright © 1981 by Annual Reviews Inc. All rights reserved

DEVELOPMENT, INNERVATION,   ❖1328
AND ACTIVITY-PATTERN INDUCED
CHANGES IN SKELETAL MUSCLE[1]

F. Jolesz and F. A. Sreter

Department of Muscle Research, Boston Biomedical Research Institute;
Department of Neurology, Massachusetts General Hospital; and Department
of Neurology, Harvard Medical School, Boston, Massachusetts 02114

INTRODUCTION

During the past two decades impressive evidence has shown that muscle,
while preserving its specific tissue characteristics, can respond in a plastic
manner to a variety of stimuli. This plasticity results in changes of the
phenotype reflecting altered gene expression. This limited review deals with
some recent work bearing on alterations and transformations (*a*) occurring
in mammalian twitch muscles in the course of normal development and
(*b*) induced experimentally by changes in functional demands, innervation,
and activity pattern. These problems are discussed in the light of biochemical and physiological differences among muscle fibers. We first briefly review some key structural, physiological, and biochemical features of the
various types of muscle. We emphasize the structural and physiological
differences among motoneurones and the delicate match between the
motoneuron and the muscle fibers it innervates, resulting in a homogeneous
motor unit.

Polymorphic Forms of Myofibrillar Proteins

The time course of force generation by the contractile proteins and relaxation governed by the Ca^{2+} uptake of sarcoplasmic reticulum is very different

[1]The preparation of this manuscript was supported by grants from NIH (AG02103, HL5949),
NSF (PCM77–04289, PCM77–12173), and the Muscular Dystrophy Association. The authors
wish to thank Drs. J. Gergely and E. Henneman for their valuable advice in preparing this
manuscript. Address for reprint requests: Boston Biomedical Research Institute, 20 Staniford
St., Boston, MA 02114

531

0066-4278/81/0315-0531$01.00

in fast- and slow-twitch muscles (28). The difference correlates with the higher activity of myosin or actomyosin ATPase (6, 8, 56, 167) and the higher rate of Ca^{2+} uptake (156) in fast-twitch as compared with slow-twitch muscles.

Almost every protein of the contractile-regulatory system is polymorphic; the distribution of forms can be shown by a variety of methods. Differences exist between fast- and slow-muscle myosins with respect to ATPase activity (56, 167), stability at alkaline and acid pH (167), susceptibility to proteolytic digestion (5, 121), N^r-methylhistidine content and amino acid sequence (86), one- or two-dimensional electrophoretic pattern (32, 81, 180), and immunological specificity (53, 54). A myosin molecule consists of two heavy chains, and each heavy chain is associated with two light chains. The light chain pattern revealed by gel electrophoresis depends on whether the myosin is isolated from fast- or slow-twitch muscle (166). A myosin molecule may contain pairs of identical (homodimer) or different (heterodimer) light chains (33, 79, 103). The distribution of homo- and heterodimeric fast myosin isoenzymes is heterogeneous among single fibers (1963).

The regulatory proteins (the three subunits of the troponin complex and tropomyosin) of the thin filament that are involved in the Ca^{2+}-control of the interaction of actin and myosin (38, 133) also differ depending on the fiber type (35). Judged by such criteria as amino acid composition, electrophoretic mobility, and antigenicity, the proteins of the troponin complex are polymorphic in fast- and slow-twitch muscles, and the subunits of tropomyosin are present in different ratios (35, 133, 139). It has been suggested that the proteins and enzymes of sarcoplasmic reticulum also exist in polymorphic form (73), but immunological studies have so far revealed only quantitative differences (89).

Heterogeneity of Muscle Fibers and Motor Units

In a section of muscle, fibers can be detected by histochemical enzyme reactions (37). Differences in staining for oxidative, glycolytic (168), and myosin ATPase activity under various conditions (13, 65, 109, 182) have led to the recognition of various fiber types (8, 15, 40).

The use of ATPase reaction for fiber typing is based on biochemical findings of differences in the acid and alkali stability of ATPase activity between fast- and slow-type myosin or actomyosin (167). ATPase activity of type 1 (slow) fibers is inactivated after alkaline-preincubation and reflects the activity of slow-type myosin, which is relatively stable at acid pH; type 2 (fast) fibers remain active after alkaline-preincubation but exhibit lower activity than type 1 fibers at acid pH (37, 65). Typing by histochemical ATPase reaction agrees well with that by immunocytochemical methods using anti-fast or anti-slow myosin antibodies (12, 52, 54, 107, 143) and also agrees with gel-electrophoretic patterns of myosin light chains in histochemically identified single fibers (127, 130, 163, 179).

The activity of myosin or actomyosin ATPase is closely related to the intrinsic speed of shortening measured in the whole muscle under isotonic conditions (6, 7, 28). Different muscles and muscle fibers of the same histochemical type exhibit a wide range of isotonic shortening velocities (28, 29, 90). The isometric contraction time of muscles and motor units probably not only reflects the type of activity of myosin detected by histochemical or biochemical methods but also depends on other factors such as release and uptake of Ca^{2+} by the sarcoplasmic reticulum and Ca^{2+} binding to the regulatory proteins (28, 38, 105). Therefore, some motor units containing type 1 fibers may have shorter isometric contraction times than motor units with type 2 fibers, and motor units of a histochemically homogeneous muscle exhibit a wider range of contraction times (3, 23, 24). Isometric measurements are also influenced by the length of the muscle and the interstitial connective tissue and fat content (compliance). Thus in the case of different experimental and pathological conditions the atrophied muscle may exhibit marked changes in isometric contractile characteristics caused by increased connective tissue content (18, 28).

Based on histochemical differences in staining intensity between oxidative or glycolytic enzymes and myosin ATPase after acid preincubation at slightly different pH's (2A and 2B), subdivision of fast-twitch muscle fibers is possible (13, 37, 147, 152). However, actual enzyme activity among histochemically identified fast-oxidative and fast-glycolytic single fibers covers a very broad and almost continuous range (155). Furthermore, although there is generally a strong correlation between the glycolytic character of 2B fibers and the oxidative character of 2A fibers, there are muscles and conditions under which this apparent correlation breaks down (152, 163, 182).

Recent results based on immunological methods using different anti-fast "alkali" light chain antibodies or on the pyrophosphate-gel electrophoretic pattern suggest differences in the fast myosin isoenzyme distribution between 2A and 2B fibers (54, 163). However, there is no fundamental difference in the mechanism of ATP hydrolysis by the two isoenzymes at higher ionic strength (175), and the isotonic-contractile characteristic does not correlate with the electrophoretically determined distribution of alkali light chains in isolated single fibers (90). Therefore, differences in the isometric contraction time of motor units composed of 2A and 2B fibers (23) remain unexplained.

Repetitive stimulation of a motor axon or a single motoneuron depletes the glycogen in all muscle fibers belonging to the motor unit (23, 24, 41).

Use of this method has shown that muscle fibers of a given motor unit are scattered over the whole muscle. Serial sections stained for oxidative and glycolytic enzymes or for myosin ATPase show that within each motor unit all the fibers have the same histochemical profile and belong to the same type or subtype (23). Muscle fibers belonging to the same motor units are ultrastructurally and physiologically homogeneous (15, 20, 105).

Motor units as well as their muscle fibers are classified by multiple criteria that reflect the physiological and metabolic properties of muscle fibers innervated by the same motoneuron. Fibers and motor units may exhibit a continuous spectrum with respect to many properties such as isometric contraction time (23, 28), fatiguability (41, 126), and oxidative or glycolytic enzymatic activity (8); with respect to other properties two or more discrete sets are distinguishable. This distinction may be quantitative, when two distributions with well-separated maxima are found [Z-line thickness, potentiation of twitch contraction (23, 28, 52, 126)], or qualitative, as is the case for isomorphic proteins or isoenzymes (53).

In some muscle fibers, most likely the so-called 2C fibers or "promiscuous" fibers (178), immunocytochemical studies indicate the coexistence of the slow and fast types of myosin (12, 54, 107) and troponin-I (35). These fibers do not fit in any motor unit classification and most likely represent a rare, undifferentiated form (13). It was suggested, based on the SDS-gel electrophoretic pattern of isolated single fibers, that in an individual normal adult muscle fiber either fast or slow myosin light chains are present (90, 127, 130, 179). More recently it has been shown that some fibers seem to contain both the slow and fast types of light chains in various ratios (161).

Neural Control of Muscle Function

The specialization and organization of muscle fibers belonging to a motor unit correlate strongly with the morphological and electrophysiological properties of the motoneuron (15, 20, 25, 39, 75). The threshold or excitability of a motoneuron is inversely related to its size; it follows that as the size of a motoneuron increases, its susceptibility to discharge decreases (74, 76, 77). This "size principle" dictates the order of recruitment (74, 75). Slight tension is produced by the selective mobilization of varying numbers of slow motor units innervated by smaller motoneurons with a higher susceptibility to discharge. With an increased demand for tension, fast motor units are progressively activated by larger motoneurons with lower excitability. The order of recruitment is the same when motoneurons are subjected to various combinations of excitation and inhibition by different inputs, and a relatively fixed order of recruitment may be deduced from electromyographic studies of the pattern of motor unit activation during voluntary movement (118, 154, 176). The modulation of tension output is possible not only by recruiting more motor units but also by regulating the firing rate of the motoneurons. Motoneurons innervating slow muscle fibers are recruited more frequently and discharge for prolonged periods, but their firing rate is lower and the frequency range is narrower than those of fast motoneurons (61). In a slow-twitch muscle the predominant mechanism for increasing the strength of contraction is the recruitment of more motor units, whereas in fast-twitch muscles it is the increase in the firing rate (15, 25, 61, 74, 118).

Certain properties of motoneurons (axonal conduction velocity, input resistance, critical firing level) vary with the size, resulting in a gradation in the physiological appearance of motor units rather than discrete types (20, 25, 26, 72). Size-independent differences may be due to the intrinsic properties of motoneurons (membrane time constants, accommodation, duration of afterhyperpolarization) (20, 25). Motoneurons have a prominent hyperpolarizing afterpotential (AHP) that is a size-independent determinant of the discharge frequency (25, 84). The duration of AHP of slow motoneurons limits the firing frequency to a lower and more stable rate than that of fast motoneurons. However, the activity pattern of motoneurons depends not only on their intrinsic properties, but also on activation and inhibition by different synaptic inputs. The differences in activity pattern may be due to the different density or efficacy of synaptic endings and to the different arborization of afferent fibers going to motoneurons (25, 72, 106).

The activity patterns of slow and fast motoneurons must be matched by the physiological and metabolic properties of the muscle fibers of the corresponding motor units; any serious mismatching between muscle and motorneuron properties (i.e. contraction time vs axonal conduction velocity, fusion frequency of muscle vs discharge frequency of motoneuron) would result in functional inefficiency (39).

The evidence suggests that the mutual influence between nerve and muscle is mediated in part by the impulse activity of the efferent and afferent nerves and in part by mechanisms independent of the impulses. To account for impulse activity–independent influences of nerve on muscle the existence of trophic substances delivered to the muscle by axonal transport has been suggested (69). After denervation there is a direct relationship among (a) the length of the distal nerve stump, (b) the decrease of resting membrane potential, and (c) development of extrajunctional acetylcholine sensitivity of muscles (64, 69). The elimination of nerve impulses by hibernation, spinal transection, or nerve conduction blockade produces inactivity of the muscle; however, the changes in resting membrane potential and extrajunctional sensitivity are not equivalent to those produced by denervation (31, 64). The blocking of axonal transport by colchicine and vinblastine does not affect impulse conduction but induces depolarization and extrajunctional acteylcholine sensitivity (64). These experimental data support the possibility of neurotrophic regulation of muscle; however, the hypothetical trophic substances have not been identified or exactly defined.

Some experiments suggest a close retrograde trophic interaction between a muscle and its motoneuron, which is present even after dorsal root section. The duration of AHP decreases after axotomy in a slow motoneuron (98). There is a similar change in nonaxotomized intact motoneurons if other motoneurons in the same pool have lost functional contact with their fibers after partial denervation or incomplete reinnervation of the muscle (84, 99). The decreased duration of AHP in slow motoneurons induced by inactivity of the muscle (immobilization, conduction blockage, or spinal transaction) is reversed by chronic stimulation (31, 49, 50). It was suggested on the basis of these experiments that motoneuron properties depend in part upon factors associated with the activity of the muscle and that a hypothetical signal from the muscle is retrogradely carried by motor axons (31, 50).

Development of Skeletal Muscle and Differentiation of Fiber Types

That the time course of the contraction and relaxation of embryonic muscles is very similar to that of adult slow-twitch muscles (17, 28, 36, 132) has led to the suggestion that fast fibers develop from an embryonic slow-type muscle (15). However, the question whether myosin synthesized in the fetal stage or in tissue culture is identical with either adult type has not been definitely settled. There is good agreement on the identity of the embryonic light chains with the light chains of the fast type (81, 139–142) except that in an early stage of development and in cultured muscle the so-called LC_3 light chain is present in a greatly reduced amount (93, 158, 160). It should be stressed that the similar electrophoretic mobility of embryonic and adult light chains does not in itself mean they are identical. On the basis of the staining pattern of light meromyosin paracrystals and the absence of N^τ-methylhistidine it appears that the embryonic heavy chains are different from those in adult fast myosin under nondissociating conditions (85, 158). This view gains further support from the results of electrophoresis and two-dimensional peptide mapping (81, 180). Recent work using anti-heavy-chain antibodies failed to detect antigenic differences (141).

In the embryonic or in the early postnatal stages all fibers react with both anti-fast and anti-slow myosin, and clonal lines or mass cultures synthesize all fast and slow light chains; the rate of synthesis of fast-myosin light chains is significantly higher (55, 93, 115, 124). In the early embryonic stage all fibers exhibit the same distribution of tropomyosin subunits; β subunits predominate at this stage of development in all fibers (35, 139, 140). In clonal line cultures both subunits are synthesized, but the α/β ratio is about 1 (51).

Since monozygotic twins have a similar fiber type distribution, while nonidentical twins may show differing histochemical profiles, a genetic determination of type distribution appears evident (95). Inherited fiber-type disproportion syndromes also reflect the role of genetic factors (13). It seems that this genetic control is exerted through the nervous system because differentiation into distinct fiber types is not achieved in tissue cultures (2). When embryonic or newborn muscles are denervated, the differentiation of muscle fibers and the synthesis of slow-type myosin light chains are inhibited (92, 142, 151).

The histochemical differentiation of muscle fibers and the development of the adult motor unit pattern parallel the time course of motoneuron differentiation (71, 96). An increase in the size of motoneurons resulting in changes in their size-dependent electrophysiological properties, an increase in duration of AHP in slow motoneurons, redistribution of synaptic endings, differentiation of activity pattern (49, 83, 148), and the loss of polyneural innervation (125) are all characteristics of their development. The postnatal increase in the duration of AHP of slow motoneurons parallels the increase in the number of slow-type fibers in slow-twitch muscle (49, 83, 96). Cordotomy (49, 142), immobilization (50, 112), and increased work load (110) modify the normal development of muscle fiber types (92) and motor units; and these changes in activity influence the duration of the AHP.

Thus an anatomical and functional connection between the muscle and its motoneurons is necessary for the differentiation of both muscle fibers and motoneurons. Postnatal development into completely differentiated slow motoneurons and slow-twitch muscles depends on the activity of the motor units.

It seems that muscle fibers and motoneurons acquire fast properties provided the low-frequency activation pattern is absent. The progressive increase in contraction velocity accompanying development of both muscle types does not correlate with the developmental changes of motoneurons (49, 71). The relatively high myosin ATPase activity of the alkali-stable embryonic myosin detected biochemically or histochemically (66, 158, 160) is surprising in view of the slow contractility. The slow contraction and relaxation of immature fibers are most likely due to the differences between embryonic and adult fast myosin, the incomplete activation of contractile elements, and the immaturity of the internal membrane systems (132). An increase in contractility parallels the increasing actomyosin ATPase and Ca^{2+} transport activity of muscle fibers during embryonic and early postnatal stages (36, 114).

The role of hormones in determining or modifying the phenotype characteristic of muscle fibers has received considerably less attention than that of neural factors. While effects on heart muscle have been known for some time, the effects of long-term hypo- and hyperthyroidism on skeletal muscle have only recently been demonstrated (47, 88). Thyroxin treatment in the rat speeds up the isometric twitch contraction and relaxation in soleus muscle. There is a simultaneous increase in the percentage of type 2 fibers, myosin ATPase activity, and the rate of Ca^{2+} uptake of sarcoplasmic reticulum. The isotonic shortening velocity and activity of actomyosin ATPase, however, do not change significantly (47).

Adaptation of Skeletal Muscle to Functional Demands

The muscle itself is a highly adaptive tissue and quickly reacts to changes in functional demand with hypertrophy or atrophy and with modulation of energy metabolism and fatiguability. The plasticity of muscle is restricted by the adaptability and plasticity of the motoneurons and their synaptic organization (20, 21, 25). During voluntary activity the supraspinal inputs can only slightly modify the stereotype of the recruitment order and modulate the frequency and activity pattern of motoneuron discharges in a limited physiological range.

EXERCISE   The adaptive response of muscle to training reflects the intensity, duration, and temporal pattern of activity (21). During voluntary movements the motor units are recruited in a relatively stable (stereotype) sequence, and slow- or fast-twitch motor units participate in different movements in various combinations. However, during certain types of movement not only are motor units recruited more frequently, but the stereotyped order of recruitment is also modified. In the case of rapid, forceful movements there is either synchronous activation of all motor unit types, or preferential activation of fast motor units, with consequent inhibition of slow motoneurons (63, 154, 176).

The more frequent activation of all fast motor units increases the metabolic capacity and fatigue resistance of fast-twitch fibers; therefore the differences between fast-twitch motor units with respect to their oxidative enzymatic activity and fatiguability are less distinguishable (9, 134). After endurance training the oxidative enzymatic activity and mitochondrial content of fast-twitch fibers increase and the changes in energy metabolism are reflected in the histochemical profile; the percentage of the fast-oxidative fiber is higher in trained muscles (9, 28, 147). Exercise-induced changes in the distribution of subtypes, distinguished by the pH sensitivity of myosin ATPase staining reaction, were found in biopsies from athletes showing a conversion of type 2B to 2A (147).

Contractile characteristics as well as myosin ATPase activity are unchanged after relatively short endurance training (10), but more prolonged endurance training (46) or intensive weight-lifting exercise (60) does induce small changes in isometric contraction time and actomyosin ATPase activity. However, the isometric contraction times of the exercised muscles in a well-trained weight lifter were the same as in sedentary subjects (15). In young, developing animals limited transformation of slow- to fast-twitch fibers induced by endurance exercise is possible (170). In adult animals and humans there is no convincing histochemical or biochemical evidence for transformation (15, 21, 147); however, higher proportions of "promiscuous" 2C fibers in the muscles of intensely endurance-trained athletes have been regarded as indicating an ongoing fiber-type transformation (12).

COMPENSATORY HYPERTROPHY   If the work load on a muscle is suddenly increased by tenotomy or denervation of its synergistic muscles, its weight increases, as does the tetanic force exerted by slow and fast fatigue-resistant motor units (70, 110, 177). The hypertrophy is caused by an increase in protein synthesis, an increased number of fibers per cross-sectional area, larger fiber diameters, and an increased proliferation of satellite cells into the growing fibers (57, 149).

The isometric contraction time increases during compensatory hypertrophy. This finding is explained by a decrease in the overlap of the filaments induced by the lengthening of the muscles undergoing compensatory hypertrophy (70). The decrease of myosin ATPase activity and the higher percentage of type 1 fibers (68, 70, 87) are most likely due to the splitting of preexisting slow fibers and to new fiber formation. Newly formed fibers under the influence of increased activity would differentiate into slow-twitch fibers.

According to unconfirmed reports, after denervation of its antagonistic muscles the isotonic speed of shortening and the activity of myosin ATPase increase in rat soleus with a parallel increase of type 2 fibers (30, 67).

IMMOBILIZATION   Immobilization of muscles in lengthened (increased passive stretch), shortened (reduced passive stretch), or mid-position as well as prolonged inactivity not only limits active movement but also reduces the electromyographic activity of muscle without changing its frequency range (34, 45). Inactivity of slow-twitch muscles decreases the duration of AHP of innervating slow motoneurons. This change is independent of the presence or absence of a stretch reflex, but does depend on the degree of atrophy, which is higher if the muscle is immobilized in a shortened position (50). Immobilization in a lengthened position reduces the rate of protein breakdown while the synthesis of new muscle proteins, as well as the number of sarcomeres, increases (58). Similar changes in stretched denervated muscles indicate that increased passive stretch regulates the growth and hypertrophy of muscles independently of innervation (59).

After prolonged immobilization there is a slight preferential atrophy of type 1 and type 2A fibers, and the tension output of fast fatigue-resistant motor units decreases (92, 111). Long-term inactivity stimulates connective tissue formation and causes degenerative changes. Therefore, the observed decrease of isometric contraction time in slow-twitch muscle (45, 112) is most likely due to factors other than fiber type transformation, because there is no marked change in the histochemical profile and motor unit distribution of immobilized muscles (22, 92, 111).

TENOTOMY   Despite the decrease in the electromyographic activity the frequency pattern of tenotomized muscle is unchanged (122, 173, 174). The tenotomized muscle atrophies severely, and the fat and connective tissue content progressively increases with concomitant degenerative changes (11, 116). There are variable results concerning the decrease of isometric contraction times in tenotomized slow-twitch muscles and motor units (3, 18, 122, 146, 173). The severe atrophy and dramatic decrease in twitch and tetanic tension raise doubts about isometric measurements (18). Histochemical and biochemical data do not support the idea of transformation of slow-twitch fibers to fast-twitch ones. There is no significant change in the histochemical profile, Ca-uptake or light chain pattern of tenotomized rabbit soleus muscle (113, 161).

It has been suggested that the slowest contracting motor units disappear after tenotomy, causing preferential atrophy of slow-twitch fibers (18). This seems unlikely: A detailed study of motor units of tenotomized muscle suggests a uniform decrease of isometric contraction times and tension output among different motor units (3).

Spinal transection prevents atrophy and degenerative changes in tenotomized slow-twitch muscle, while chronic electrical stimulation induces these changes (116, 146, 173). It was concluded that, in the absence of passive stretch, unloaded muscle contractions induced by residual reflex activity or artificial stimulation increase the rate of atrophy (116). Regeneration of the tendon and contractions against adhesions reduce atrophy, and the tension of the muscle may become normal.

Changes in Motoneuron-Muscle Interaction

CORDOTOMY   After spinal transection and dorsal rhizotomy motoneurons are completely "silent" without supraspinal and segmental input (16). This model was adapted to simulate complete disuse without damaging the anatomical integrity and possible trophic effect of the motoneurons (31, 42, 49).

In paraplegic patients and animals there is a progressive increase in type 2 fibers, and in predominantly slow-twitch muscles the fast myosin light chain content increases (62, 80, 92, 142, 161). There is no evidence that these changes are due to preferential atrophy of type 1 fibers or to the transformation from type 1 to type 2. It has been suggested that the preexisting muscle fibers are progressively lost and newly formed fibers take over (48).

The isometric contraction time of the slow-twitch muscles becomes shorter, while the contraction time of fast-twitch muscles is unchanged in cordotomized animals (16, 31, 42, 49). It was concluded that the contractile properties of the fast-twitch muscles are independent of the discharge of the fast motoneurons, while the normally existing differences in contraction time between fast- and slow-twitch muscles and the longer duration of AHP of slow motoneurons are achieved by the particular discharge pattern of slow motoneurons (49).

DENERVATION AND REINNERVATION   The effects of denervation on the intrinsic properties of skeletal muscle have been variously attributed to inactivity, lack of the postulated neurotrophic substances, and the products of nerve degeneration (64, 69, 171, 172, 174). Denervated muscle is not a normal tissue merely lacking neural influences but rather a pathological one that has progressively lost its integrity; and the observed structural-functional alterations are mainly due to degenerative processes (69, 172).

The time course of the increase in isometric contraction time after denervation differs in slow-twitch and fast-twitch muscles (101, 169), but in each type of muscle the increase accompanies the progress of atrophy (92, 123, 172). The isotonic shortening velocity decreases equally in both muscle types (101). Changes in membrane function are related to the prolongation of isometric contraction time because the duration and conduction of the action potential and the coupling of excitation-contraction are slower in denervated muscles (101, 171). The initial rate of Ca^{2+} uptake by sarcoplasmic reticulum decreases in denervated muscles (156). Histochemically, preferential atrophy of type 2 fibers followed by atrophy of type 1 fibers is the typical feature of denervation (92, 123). Although the formation of myotubes appears to be characteristic of denervated muscle there is no increase in total fiber population, because degeneration occurs at a higher rate (150).

Self-reinnervation almost completely restores the normal distribution of motor units, which is determined by the unchanged motoneuron pool, and there are no major changes in the contractile behaviour of whole muscle following reinnervation (4, 97). However, growing motor axons reinnervate the muscle fibers in an anatomical arrangement different from that existing before denervation; and the majority of the muscle fibers are reinnervated by new motoneurons (84, 97, 99, 181). The anatomical reorganization of motor units leads to the rematching of the properties of individual fibers with those of the new motoneuron. In a heterogeneous muscle this process involves transformation of some muscle fibers. The normal histochemical profile of muscle is restored after self-reinnervation, but the original scattered distribution of fiber types and subtypes is changed by the appearance of groups of histochemically similar muscle fibers. This fiber-type grouping is due to the very localized sprouting of preterminal collaterals of regenerating axons that innervate neighboring denervated muscle fibers (91, 181) independent of their original type. This so-called "internal cross-reinnervation" is one of the clearest examples of fiber-type transformation.

CROSS-REINNERVATION   In experiments in which motor nerves to fast-twitch and slow-twitch muscles have been interchanged, the new innervation results in the formation of fully organized motor units, and the contractile properties of the reinnervated muscle fibers are determined by the reinnervating motoneuron (16, 19). Control experiments with self-reinnervation established that the changes are not due merely to denervation and subsequent reinnervation, but also to newly acquired innervation (19).

After cross-reinnervation the isometric contractile characteristics of muscles and motor units exhibit a clear shift toward the behavior of the opposite type, but only the measurement of isotonic contractile characteristics (intrinsic speed of shortening, force : velocity curves) gives evidence for an almost complete physiological transformation (27, 28, 104, 162).

Cross-reinnervation reverses the histochemical profile of muscles with respect to oxidative and glycolytic activity and myosin APTase staining intensity (135, 137). After cross-reinnervation the correlation between myosin ATPase activity and isometric contraction time or isotonic speed of shortening is maintained, although the ATPase activity is not completely transformed (7, 117, 162). The light chain pattern of cross-reinnervated muscles shows a mixture of slow and fast myosin isoenzymes indicative of transformation which, however, remains incomplete even after long periods (80, 117, 145, 162). Among the regulatory proteins, troponin-I is almost completely converted after cross-reinnervation, but the ratio of the tropomyosin subunits was unchanged (1). The rates of Ca^{2+} uptake and ATPase activity of the isolated, fragmented sarcoplasmic reticulum are affected by cross-reinnervation, but again the transformation is incomplete (162).

The partially transformed cross-reinnervated muscles may contain individual fibers in which both types of myosin coexist (28, 135). Alternatively, the incompleteness of the transformation may result from the denervated muscle fibers' more easily accepting reinnervating motor axons corresponding to their type from a heterogeneous motoneuron pool (78).

While the axonal conduction velocities are changed (although only slightly) after cross-reinnervation, the physiological properties and reflex activities of motoneurons remain unchanged (99,100). This indicates that while the motoneurons exert an effect on muscle, there is none in the reverse direction. It has been suggested that presumptive trophic factors play a role in determining the properties of slow and fast muscle fibers (16, 19). However, the effect of an implanted, but synaptically not connected, nerve on the contractile and histochemical characteristics of a muscle innervated by an opposite type motoneuron is not confirmed (30, 44, 67) and the primary role of the activity pattern is emphasized (19, 145).

CHRONIC ARTIFICIAL STIMULATION   Continuous electrical stimulation of the motor nerve of a fast-twitch muscle at low frequency (10 Hz) produces a marked increase in the isometric contraction time (131, 146). The changes in isometric twitch characteristics become significant after two weeks of stimulation, and after twenty weeks the stimulated transformed muscle contracts even more slowly than the contralateral control slow-twitch muscle (145). The isotonic contractile characteristics change later, suggesting different time courses of transformation for myosin and for regulatory proteins and sarcoplasmic reticulum (19). Muscles fatigue much less after chronic stimulation, and the early changes in fatiguability parallel a rapid increase in capillary density, active blood flow, and oxidative enzymatic activity (14, 82).

Histochemical studies show an early increase in oxidative enzyme activity with a subsequent reduction in the activity of glycolytic enzymes followed by a gradual decrease in the ratio of type 2 fibers. After eight weeks the stimulated muscle is almost completely made up of type 1 fibers (136, 143). There is no sign of preferential atrophy or collateral sprouting of nerves, but the average fiber diameter decreases and atrophy is characteristic in the early stages of stimulation (14, 119). Electron microscopic findings show an early and complete transformation of Z-line thickness, mitochondrial content, and structure (144).

The myosin ATPase activity of stimulated fast-twitch muscles declines progressively to the level of slow-twitch muscle (145, 164). The increased alkali-lability of myosin (164), the appearance and accumulation of slow myosin light chains (165), the changed striation pattern of negatively stained paracrystals of light meromyosin (145), and the disappearance of N^r-methylhistidine amino acid residues (159) all indicate a fast-to-slow transformation. The simultaneous presence of slow and fast myosin isoenzymes within the single fiber, detected electrophoretically and with the immunofluorescence technique, is transient, and there is no dual antibody reaction in fibers 8 weeks after stimulation (129, 143). Myosin extracted from muscles stimulated for 20 weeks consists of only slow-type myosin (128, 143, 145). The distribution of tropomyosin subunit isoenzymes changes to that characteristic of slow-twitch muscles, and their transformation is completed earlier than the complete reversal of the myosin light chain pattern (138). Changes in the function of sarcoplasmic reticulum apparently precede the alterations in myosin (73, 145, 164). During the first few days of stimulation there is a change in the electrophoretic polypeptide and phosphoprotein pattern of the isolated, fragmented sarcoplasmic reticulum with a concomitant decrease in ATPase activity (73). The membrane potential and intracellular K^+ and Na^+ content of the fibers change only during stimulation in the direction of the values characteristic of those of slow-twitch muscles, and the cessation of stimulation restores the original values within a few hours (157). The activity pattern has to be continuously imposed because cessation of stimulation for longer periods, which is atypical of postural muscles, does not lead to complete transformation (128, 131). Continuous stimulation for 7 weeks for a daily 7–8 hr period results in a transformation of 2B fibers to 2A parallel with changes in fast myosin isoenzyme distribution in nondissociating gel electrophoresis (163).

Cross-reinnervated slow-twitch muscle does not undergo transformation if the reinnervating fast motor axons are stimulated with a continuous low-frequency activity pattern (145). Thus low-frequency stimulation of the nerve affects the signal transmitted by the crossed nerve, which would by itself transform the slow muscle into a fast one.

Experiments involving stimulation of a "fast" nerve with a low frequency suggests prima facie that (a) there is no need to involve a specific nerve (trophic) effect and (b) the activity pattern of the muscle itself—imposed by whatever means—is the cause of transformation. On the other hand, the retrograde effect of chronic stimulation may alter the properties of the motoneuron, and these changes could induce the transformation of the muscle by trophic signals (E. Henneman, personal communication).

Stimulation of innervated slow-twitch muscles with brief trains at a higher frequency (100 Hz) causes no marked change in the activity of oxidative enzymes and capillary density, but there is a decrease in the isometric contraction time and a marked reduction of twitch tension (14, 153). Denervation eliminates the activity pattern of slow motoneurons, and the stimulation of denervated slow-twitch muscle can prevent the denervation-induced changes in membrane properties including an increased acetylcholine sensitivity (102, 174). A slow-type artificial stimulation pattern maintains the isometric contractile characteristics of denervated slow-twitch muscle, while phasic-type stimulation changes the isometric characteristics and histochemical profile toward the characteristics of an innervated fast-twitch muscle (43, 102). Four weeks after electrode implantation and high-frequency phasic stimulation, the denervated slow-twitch muscle contains almost exclusively fast-type myosin, as shown by histochemical ATPase staining or by the electrophoretic pattern in nondissociating gels (161). However, electrode implantation without any stimulation and the wrapping of the muscle with aluminum foil results in an almost complete replacement of the original slow fibers by fast ones (161). That these findings can be explained by new fiber formation rather than transformation is indicated by the presence of fibers with a small diameter, high myosin ATPase activity, and centrally positioned nuclei. Newly formed fibers in chemically (marcaine) or mechanically injured regenerating muscle exhibit high myosin ATPase activity, synthesize fast-type light chains, and react with fast myosin antibody (94).

Chronic phasic-type stimulation of paralyzed muscles of patients suffering from upper motoneuron lesions leads to clinical improvement; interestingly, the population of type 1 fibers increases (120).

There is no evidence that the fast activity pattern plays a significant role in determining fast-twitch muscle properties. The activity pattern of motoneurons in the physiological range is quantitatively different and does not explain satisfactorily the qualitative differences between slow- and fast-twitch muscles. Elucidation of the detailed mechanism by which motoneurons switch on and switch off the genes responsible for the synthesis of polymorphic forms of myofibrillar proteins requires further work.

CONCLUSION

Considerable evidence has accumulated indicating that imposed changes are more readily achieved in a direction of what might be termed fast-to-slow transformation; also, although many details are still obscure, in the course of normal development the final critical process producing the diversity found in the adult is a change from a fast-type muscle into a slow one.

The almost inextricable interrelationship between the innervating motoneuron and the muscle is a strong feature of both natural developmental and experimentally induced transformations. The final phases of muscle development appear to be related to the invasion of the muscle by the nerve. The fine tuning of muscle toward adult properties appears to be determined by a similar maturation in the motoneuron.

Literature Cited

1. Amphlett, G. W., Perry, S. V., Syska, H., Brown, M., Vrbova, G. 1975. Cross innervation and the regulatory protein system of rabbit soleus muscle. *Nature* 257:602–4
2. Askanas, V., Shafiq, S. A., Milhorat, A. T. 1972. Histochemistry of cultured aneural chick muscle. Morphological maturation without differentiation of fiber types. *Exp. Neurol.* 37:218–30
3. Bagust, J. 1979. The effects of tenotomy upon the contraction characteristics of motor units in rabbit soleus muscle. *J. Physiol. London* 290:1–10
4. Bagust, J., Lewis, D. M. 1974. Isometric contractions of motor units in self-reinnervated fast and slow twitch muscles of the cat. *J. Physiol. London* 237:91–102
5. Bálint, M., Sreter, F. A., Gergely, J. 1975. Fragmentation of myosin by papain—Studies on myosin from adult fast and slow skeletal and cardiac and embryonic muscle. *Arch. Biochem. Biophys.* 168:557–66
6. Bárány, M. 1967. ATPase activity of myosin correlated with speed of muscle shortening. *J. Gen. Physiol.* (Suppl.) 50:197–218
7. Bárány, M., Close, R. I. 1971. The transformation of myosin in cross-innervated rat muscles. *J. Physiol. London* 213:455–74
8. Barnard, R. J., Edgerton, V. R., Furukawa, T., Peter, J. B. 1971. Histochemical, biochemical and contractile properties of red, white and intermediate fibers. *Am. J. Physiol.* 220:410–14
9. Barnard, R. J., Edgerton, V. R., Peter, J. B. 1970. Effect of exercise on skeletal muscle. I. Biochemical and histochemical properties. *J. Appl. Physiol.* 28:762–66
10. Barnard, R. J., Edgerton, V. R., Peter, J. B. 1970. Effect of exercise on skeletal muscle II. Contractile properties. *J. Appl. Physiol.* 28:767–70
11. Bergman, R. A., Afifi, A. K. 1969. The structure of the rabbit soleus muscle and the structural alterations resulting from tenotomy. *Johns Hopkins Med. J.* 124:119–31
12. Billeter, R., Weber, M., Lutz, M., Howard, M., Eppenberger, H. M., Jenny, E. Myosin types in human skeletal muscle fibers. Unpublished
13. Brooke, M. H., Kaiser, K. K. 1974. The use and abuse of muscle histochemistry. *Ann. N.Y. Acad. Sci.* 228:121–43
14. Brown, M. D., Cotter, M. A., Hudlicka, O. Vrbova, G. 1976. The effects of different pattern of muscle activity on capillary density, mechanical, properties and structure of slow and fast rabbit muscles. *Pflügers Arch.* 361:241–50
15. Buchtal, F., Schmalbruch, H. 1980. Motor unit of mammalian muscle. *Physiol. Rev.* 60:91–142
16. Buller, A. J., Eccles, J. C., Eccles, R. M. 1960. Interactions between motoneurons and muscles in respect to the characteristic speeds of their responses. *J. Physiol. London* 150:417–39
17. Buller, A. J., Lewis, D. M. 1965. Further observations on the differentiation of skeletal muscles in the kitten hind limb. *J. Physiol. London* 176:335–70
18. Buller, A. J., Lewis, D. M. 1965. Some observations on the effects of tenotomy in the rabbit. *J. Physiol. London* 178:326–42
19. Buller, A. J., Pope, R. 1977. Plasticity in mammalian skeletal muscle. *Philos. Trans. R. Soc. Ser. B.* 278:295–305
20. Burke, R. E. 1973. On the central nervous system control of fast and slow twitch motor units. In *New Developments in Electromyography and Clinical Neurophysiology,* ed. J. E. Desmedt, 3:69–94. Basel: Karger
21. Burke, R. E., Edgerton, V. R. 1975. Motor unit properties and selective involvement in movement. In *Exercise and Sport Sciences Reviews,* ed. J. H. Wilmore, J. F. Keogh, 3:31–81. NY:Academic
22. Burke, R. E., Kanda, K., Mayer, R. F. 1975. The effect of chronic immobilization on defined types of motor units in cat medial gastrocnemius. *Neurosci. Abstr.* 1:763
23. Burke, R. E., Levine, D. N., Tsairis, P., Zajac, F. E. 1973. Physiological types and histochemical profiles in motor units of the cat gastrocnemius. *J. Physiol. London* 234:723–48
24. Burke, R. E., Levine, D. N., Salcman, M., Tsairis, P. 1974. Motor units in cat soleus muscle: Physiological, histochemical and morphological characteristics. *J. Physiol. London* 238:503–14
25. Burke, R. E., Rudomin, P. 1977. Spinal neurons and synapses. In *The Nervous System: The Cellular Biology of Neurons, Vol. 1, Handbook of Physiology,* ed. E. R. Kandel, pp. 877–944. Washington: Am. Physiol. Soc.
26. Clamann, H. P., Henneman, E. 1976. Electrical measurement of axon diameter and its use in relating motoneuron size to critical firing level. *J. Neurophysiol.* 39:844–51

27. Close, R. 1969. Dynamic properties of fast and slow skeletal muscles of the rat after nerve cross-union. *J. Physiol. London* 204:331–46

28. Close, R. I. 1972. Dynamic properties of mammalian skeletal muscles. *Physiol. Rev.* 52:129–97

29. Close, R. I. 1974. Specialization among fast twitch muscles. In *Exploratory Concepts in Muscular Dystrophy*, ed. A. T. Milhorat, 2:309–16. Amsterdam: Excerpta Medica (Int. Congr. Ser. 333)

30. Crockett, I. L., Edgerton, V. R. 1974. Responses of normally innervated soleus muscle to supplementary nerve implantation. *Expl. Neurol.* 43:207–15

31. Czeh, G., Gallego, R., Kudo, N., Kuno, M. 1978. Evidence for the maintenance of motoneuron properties by muscle activity. *J. Physiol. London* 281:239–52

32. d'Albis, A., Pantaloni, C., Bechet, J.-J. 1979. Structural relationship of myosin isoenzymes. *FEBS Lett.* 106:81–84

33. d'Albis, A., Pantaloni, C., Bechet, J.-J. 1979. An electrophoretic study of native isoenzymes and their subunit content. *Eur. J. Biochem.* 99:261–72

34. Davis, C. J. F., Montgomery, A. 1977. The effect of prolonged inactivity upon the contraction characteristics of fast and slow mammalian twitch muscles. *J. Physiol. London* 270:581–94

35. Dhoot, G. K., Perry, S. V. 1979. Distribution of polymorphic forms of troponin components and tropomyosin in skeletal muscle. *Nature* 278:714–18

36. Drachman, D. B., Johnston, D. M. 1973. Development of mammalian fast muscle: dynamic and biochemical properties correlated. *J. Physiol. London* 234:29–42

37. Dubowitz, V., Brooke, M. H. 1973. *Muscle Biopsy: A Modern Approach.* London: W. B. Saunders

38. Ebashi, S., Nonomura, Y., Mikawa, T., Hirata, M., Saida, K. 1979. Regulatory mechanism of muscle contraction. In *Cell Motility: Molecules and Organization*, ed. S. Hatano, H. Ishikawa, H. Sato, pp. 225–37. Tokyo: Univ. Tokyo Press

39. Eccles, J. C. 1963. Specificity of neural influence on speed of muscle contraction. In *The Effect of Use and Disuse on Neuromuscular Function*, ed. E. Gutmann, P. Hnik. Prague: Czech. Acad. Sci.

40. Edjtehadi, G. D., Lewis, D. M. 1979. Histochemical reactions of fibres in a fast twitch muscle of the cat. *J. Physiol. London* 287:439–53

41. Edstrom, L., Kugelberg, E. 1968. Histochemical composition, distribution of fibres and fatiguability of single motor units. *J. Neurol. Neurosurg. Psychiat.* 31:424–33

42. Deleted in proof

43. Engebretsen, L., Lomo, T., Westgaard, R. H. 1980. Effects of electrical stimulation on denervated muscle. See Ref. 80. In press

44. Fex, S., Sonesson, B. 1970. Histochemical observations after implantation of fast nerve into an innervated mammalian slow skeletal muscle. *Acta Anat.* 77:1–10

45. Fischbach, G. D., Robbins, N. 1969. Changes in contractile properties of disused soleus muscle. *J. Physiol. London* 201:305–20

46. Fitts, R. H., Holloszy, J. D. 1977. Contractile properties of rat soleus muscle: effects of training and fatigue. *Am. J. Physiol.* 233:C86–91

47. Fitts, R. H., Winder, W. W., Brooke, M. H., Kaiser, K. K., Holloszy, J. O. 1980. Contractile, biochemical and histochemical properties of thyrotoxic rat soleus muscle. *Am. J. Physiol.* 238:C15–20

48. Fugl-Meyer, A. R., Sjostrom, M., Anquist, K. A., Grimby, G. 1978. Can changes in muscle fiber structure influence reflex category. In *4th Int. Congr. Neuromusc. Dis. Montreal* (Abstr.)

49. Gallego, R., Huizar, P., Kudo, N., Kuno, M. 1978. Disparity of motoneurone and muscle differentiation following spinal transection in the kitten. *J. Physiol. London* 281:253–65

50. Gallego, R., Kuno, M., Nunez, R., Snider, W. D. 1979. Dependence of motoneurone properties on the length of immobilized muscle. *J. Physiol. London* 291:179–89

51. Garrels, J. I. 1979. Changes in protein synthesis during myogenesis in a clonal cell line. *Devel. Biol.* 73:134–52

52. Gauthier, G. F. 1979. Ultrastructural identification of muscle fiber types by immunocytochemistry. *J. Cell. Biol.* 82:391–400

53. Gauthier, G. F., Lowey, S. 1977. Polymorphism of myosin among skeletal muscle fiber types. *J. Cell. Biol.* 74:760–79

54. Gauthier, G. F., Lowey, S. 1979. Distribution of myosin isoenzymes among skeletal muscle fiber types. *J. Cell. Biol.* 81:10–25

55. Gauthier, G. F., Lowey, S., Hobbs, A. W. 1978. Fast and slow myosin in developing muscle fibers. *Nature* 274:25–29

56. Gergely, J., Pragay, D., Scholz, A. F., Seidel, J. C., Sreter, F. A., Thompson, M. M. 1965. Comparative studies on white and red muscle. In *Molecular Biology of Muscle Contraction*, ed. H. Kumagai, S. Ebashi, pp. 145–59. Amsterdam: Elsevier

57. Goldberg, A. L., Etlinger, J. D., Goldspink, D. F., Jablencki, C. 1975. Mechanism of work induced hypertrophy of skeletal muscle. *Med. Sci. Sport* 7: 248–61

58. Goldspink, D. F. 1977. The influence of immobilization and stretch on protein turnover of rat skeletal muscle. *J. Physiol. London* 264:267–82

59. Goldspink, D. F. 1978. The influence of passive stretch on the growth and protein turnover of the denervated extensor digitorum longus muscle. *Biochem. J.* 174:595–602

60. Gonyea, W. J., Bonde-Petersen, F. 1978. Alterations in muscle contractile proteins and fiber composition after weight-lifting exercise in cats. *Expl. Neurol.* 59:75–84

61. Granit, R. 1972. *Mechanisms Regulating the Discharge of Motoneurones.* Liverpool: Liverpool Univ. Press

62. Grimby, L., Broberg, C., Krotkiewska, T., Krotkiewski, M. 1976. Muscle fiber composition in patients with traumatic cord lesions. *Scand. J. Rehabil. Med.* 8:37–42

63. Grimby, L., Hannerz, J. 1977. Firing rate and recruitment order of toe extensor motor units in different modes of voluntary contraction. *J. Physiol. London* 264:865–79

64. Guth, L., Albuquerque, E. X. 1979. The neurotrophic regulation of resting membrane potential and extrajunctional acetylcholine sensitivity in mammalian skeletal muscle. In *Muscle Regeneration*, ed. A. Mauro, pp. 405–17. NY: Raven Press

65. Guth, L., Samaha, F. J. 1969. Qualitative differences between actomyosin ATPase of slow and fast mammalian muscle. *Exp. Neurol.* 25:138–52

66. Guth, L., Samaha, F. J. 1972. Erroneous interpretations which may result from application of the "myofibrillar ATPase" histochemical procedure to developing muscle. *Exp. Neurol.* 34:465–75

67. Guth, L., Wells, J. B. 1972. Physiological and histochemical properties of the soleus muscle after denervation of its antagonists. *Exp. Neurol.* 36:463–71

68. Guth, L., Yellin, H. 1971. The dynamic nature of the so-called "fiber types" of mammalian skeletal muscle. *Exp. Neurol.* 31:277–300

69. Gutmann, E. 1976. Neurotrophic relations. *Ann. Rev. Physiol.* 38:177–216

70. Gutmann, E., Schiaffino, S., Hanzlikovà, V. 1971. Mechanism of compensatory hypertrophy in skeletal muscle of the rat, *Exp. Neurol.* 31:451–64

71. Hammerberg, C., Kellerth, J. O. 1975. The postnatal development of some twitch and fatigue properties of single motor units in the ankle muscles of the kitten. *Acta Physiol. Scand.* 95:243–57

72. Harris, D. A., Henneman, E. 1979. Different species of α motoneurons in the same pool: further evidence of effects of inhibition on their firing rates. *J. Neurophysiol.* 42:927–35

73. Heilmann, C., Pette, D. 1979. Molecular transformations in sarcoplasmic reticulum of fast-twitch muscle by electro-stimulation. *Eur. J. Biochem.* 93:437–46

74. Henneman, E., Clamann, H. P., Gilles, J. D., Skinner, R. D. 1974. Rank order of motoneurones within a pool: law of combination. *J. Neurophysiol.* 37:1338–49

75. Henneman, E., Olson, C. B. 1965. Relations between structure and function in the design of skeletal muscles. *J. Neurophysiol.* 28:581–98

76. Henneman, E., Somjen, G., Carpenter, D. O. 1965. Functional significance of cell size in spinal motoneurons. *J. Neurophysiol.* 28:560–80

77. Henneman, E., Somjen, G., Carpenter, D. O. 1965. Excitability and inhibitibility of motoneurons of different sizes. *J. Neurophysiol.* 28:599–620

78. Hoh, J. F. Y. 1975. Selective and nonselective reinnervation of fast-twitch and slow-twitch rat skeletal muscle. *J. Physiol. London* 251:791–801

79. Hoh, J. F. Y. 1978. Light chain distribution of chicken skeletal muscle myosin isoenzymes. *FEBS Lett.* 90: 297–300

80. Hoh, J. F. Y., Kwan, B. T. S., Dunlop, C., Kim, B. H. 1980. The effects of nerve cross-union and cordotomy on the myosin isoenzymes in fast-twitch and slow-twitch muscles of the rat. In *Plasticity of Muscle*, ed. D. Pette. W. DeGruyter: Berlin. In press

81. Hoh, J. F. Y., Yeoh, G. P. S. 1979. Rabbit skeletal myosin isoenzymes from fetal fast-twitch and slow-twitch muscles. *Nature* 280:321–22

82. Hudlická, O., Brown, M. D., Cotter, M., Smith, M., Vrbova, G. 1977. The effect of long-term stimulation of fast

muscles on their blood flow, metabolism and ability to withstand fatigue. *Pflügers Arch.* 369:141–49

83. Huizar, P., Kuno, M., Miyata, Y. 1975. Differentiation of motoneurones and skeletal muscles in the kitten. *J. Physiol. London* 252:465–79

84. Huizar, P., Kuno, M., Kudo, M., Miyata, Y. 1977. Reaction of intact spinal motoneurones to partial denervation of the muscle. *J. Physiol. London* 265:175–92

85. Huszar, G. 1972. Developmental changes of the primary structure and histidine methylation in rabbit skeletal muscle myosin. *Nature New Biol.* 240:260–63

86. Huszar, G., Elzinga, M. 1971. Amino acid sequence around the single 3-methylhistidine residue in rabbit skeletal muscle myosin. *Biochemistry* 10:229–36

87. Ianuzzo, C. D., Chen, V. 1979. Metabolic character of hypertrophied rat muscle. *J. Appl. Physiol.* 46:738–42

88. Ianuzzo, D., Patel, P., Chen, V., O'-Brien, P., Williams, C. 1977. Thyroidal trophic influences on skeletal muscle. *Nature* 270:74–76

89. Jorgensen, A. O., Kalnins, V., McLennan, D. H. 1979. Localization of sarcoplasmic reticulum proteins in rat skeletal muscle by immunofluorescence. *J. Cell. Biol.* 80:372–84

90. Julian, F. J., Moss, R. L., Waller, G. S. 1980. Mechanical properties and myosin light chain composition of skinned muscle fibers from adult and new-born rabbits. *J. Physiol. London.* In press

91. Karpati, G., Engel, W. K. 1968. "Type grouping" in skeletal muscles after experimental reinnervation. *Neurology* 18:447–55

92. Karpati, G., Engel, W. K. 1968. Correlative histochemical study of skeletal muscle after suprasegmental denervation, peripheral nerve section and skeletal fixation. *Neurology* 18:681–92

93. Keller, L. R., Emerson, C. P. 1980. Synthesis of adult myosin light chains by embryonic muscle cultures. *Proc. Natl. Acad. Sci. USA* 77:1020–24

94. Kelly, A. M., Rubinstein, N. 1980. Pattern of myosin synthesis in regenerating muscle. In *Plasticity of Muscle*, ed. D. Pette. Berlin: W. DeGruyter. In press

95. Komi, P. V., Viitasalo, J. H. T., Havu, M., Thorstensson, A., Sjöden, B., Karlsson, J. 1977. Skeletal muscle fibers and muscle enzyme activities in monozy-gous and dizygous twins of both sexes. *Acta Physiol. Scand.* 100:385–92

96. Kugelberg, E. 1976. Adaptive transformation of cat soleus motor units during growth. Histochemistry and contraction speed. *J. Neurol. Sci.* 27:269–89

97. Kugelberg, E., Edstrom, L., Abbruzzese, M. 1970. Mapping of motor units in experimentally reinnervated rat muscle. *J. Neurol. Neurosurg. Psychiat.* 33:319–29

98. Kuno, M., Miyata, Y., Munoz-Martinez, E. J. 1974. Differential reaction of fast and slow motoneurones to axotomy. *J. Physiol. London* 240:725–40

99. Kuno, M., Miyata, Y., Munoz-Martinez, E. J. 1974. Properties of fast and slow α motoneurones following motor reinnervation. *J. Physiol. London* 242:273–88

100. Lewis, D. M., Bagust, J., Webb, S., Westerman, R. A., Finol, H. 1977. Axon conduction velocity modified by reinnervation of mammalian muscle. *Nature* 270:745–46

101. Lewis, D. M., Kean, C. J. C., McGarrick, J. D. 1974. Dynamic properties of slow and fast muscles and their trophic regulation. *Ann. N.Y. Acad. Sci.* 228:105–20

102. Lomo, T., Westgaard, R. H., Dahl, H. A. 1974. Contractile properties of muscle: control by pattern of muscle activity in the rat. *Proc. R. Soc. Ser. B 87:* 99–103

103. Lowey, S., Benfield, P. A., Silberstein, L., Lang, L. M. 1979. Distribution of light chains in fast skeletal myosin. *Nature* 282:522–24

104. Luff, A. R. 1975. Dynamic properties of fast and slow skeletal muscles in the cat and rat following cross reinnervation. *J. Physiol. London* 248:83–96

105. Luff, A. R., Atwood, H. L. 1972. Membrane properties and contraction of single muscle fibers in the mouse. *Am. J. Physiol.* 222:1435–40

106. Lüscher, H.-R., Ruenzel, P., Henneman, E. 1979. How the size of motoneurones determines their susceptibility to discharge. *Nature* 282:859–61

107. Lutz, H., Weber, H., Billeter, R., Jenny, E. 1979. Fast and slow myosin within single skeletal muscle fibers of adult rabbits. *Nature* 281:142–44

108. Mabuchi, K., Sreter, F. A. 1978. Use of cryostat sections for measurement of Ca^{2+} uptake by sarcoplasmic reticulum. *Analyt. Biochem.* 86:733–42

109. Mabuchi, K., Sreter, F. A. 1980. Actomyosin ATPase II. Fiber typing by

histochemical ATPase reaction. *Muscle and Nerve* 3:233–39

110. Mackova, E., Hnik, P. 1972. Time course of compensatory hypertrophy of slow and fast rat muscles in relation to age. *Physiol. Bohemoslov.* 21:9–17

111. Maier, A., Crockett, J. C., Simpson, D. R., Saubert, C. W., Edgerton, V. R. 1976. Properties of immobilized guinea pig hindlimb muscles. *Am. J. Physiol.* 231:1520–26

112. Mann, W. S., Salafsky, B. 1970. Enzymic and physiological studies of normal and disused developing fast and slow cat muscles. *J. Physiol. London* 208:33–47

113. Margreth, A., Carraro, V., Salviati, G. 1977. Effects of denervation on protein synthesis and on properties of myosin of fast and slow muscles. In *Pathogenesis of Human Muscular Dystrophies*, ed. L. P. Rowland, pp. 161–67. Amsterdam: Excerpta Medica (*Int. Congr. Ser.* 404)

114. Martonosi, A., Roufa, D., Boland, R., Reyes, E., Tillack, T. W. 1977. Development of sarcoplasmic reticulum in cultured chicken muscle. *J. Biol. Chem.* 252:318–32

115. Masaki, T., Yoshizaki, C. 1974. Differentiation of myosin in chick embryos. *J. Biochem. Tokyo* 76:123–31

116. McMinn, R. M. H., Vrbova, G. 1964. Motoneurone activity as a cause of degeneration in the soleus muscle of the rabbit. *Q. J. Exp. Physiol.* 52:411–15

117. Mommaerts, W. F. H. M., Seraydarian, K., Suh, M., Kean, C. J. C., Buller, A. J. 1977. Conversion of some biochemical properties of mammalian skeletal muscles following cross-reinnervation. *Exp. Neurol.* 55:637–53

118. Monster, A. W., Chan, H. 1977. Isometric force production by motor units of extensor digitorum communis muscle in man. *J. Neurophysiol.* 40:1432–43

119. Morris, C. J., Salmons, S. 1975. The innervation pattern of fast muscle fibres subjected to long-term stimulation. *J. Anat.* 120:412–15

120. Munsat, T. L., McNeal, D., Waters, R. 1976. Effects of nerve stimulation on human muscle. *Arch. Neurol.* 33:608–17

121. Nakamura, A., Sreter, F. A., Gergely, J. 1971. Comparative studies of light meromyosin paracrystals derived from red, white and cardiac muscle myosin. *J. Cell. Biol.* 49:883–98

122. Nelson, P. G. 1969. Functional consequences of tenotomy in hind limb muscles of the cat. *J. Physiol. London* 201:321–33

123. Niederle, B., Mayr, R. 1978. Course of denervation atrophy in type I and type II fibres of rat extensor digitorum longus muscle. *Anat. Embryol.* 153:9–21

124. Obinata, T., Masaki, T., Takano, H. 1980. Types of myosin light chains present during the development of fast skeletal muscle in chick embryo. *J. Biochem. Tokyo* 87:81–86

125. O'Brien, R. A. D., Ostberg, A. J. C., Vrbova, G. 1978. Observations on the elimination of polyneuronal innervation in developing mammalian skeletal muscle. *J. Physiol. London* 282:571–82

126. Olson, C. B., Swett, C. P. 1971. Effect of prior activity on properties of different types of motor units. *J. Neurophysiol.* 34:1–16

127. Pette, D., Henriksson, J., Emmerich, M. 1979. Myofibrillar protein patterns of single fibres from human muscle. *FEBS Lett.* 103:152–55

128. Pette, D., Müller, W., Leisner, E., Vrbova, G. 1976. Time dependent effects on contractile properties, fibre population, myosin light chains and enzymes of energy metabolism in intermittently and continuously stimulated fast twitch muscles of the rabbit. *Pflügers Arch.* 364:103–12

129. Pette, D., Schnez, V. 1977. Coexistence of fast and slow type myosin light chains in single muscle fibres during transformation as induced by long term stimulation. *FEBS Lett.* 83:128–30

130. Pette, D., Schnez, V. 1977. Myosin light chain pattern of individual fast and slow-twitch fibers of rabbit muscles. *Histochemistry* 54:97–107

131. Pette, D., Smith, M. E., Staudte, H. W., Vrbova, G. 1973. Effects of long-term electrical stimulation on some contractile and metabolic characteristics of fast rabbit muscle. *Pflügers Arch.* 338:257–72

132. Pette, D., Vrbova, G., Whalen, R. C. 1979. Independent development of contractile properties and myosin light chains in embryonic chick fast and slow muscle. *Pflügers Arch.* 378:251–57

133. Potter, J. D., Gergely, J. 1974. Troponin, tropomyosin and actin interactions in the Ca^{2+} regulation of muscle contraction. *Biochemistry* 13:2697–703

134. Reinking, R. M., Stephens, J. A., Stuart, D. G. 1975. The motor units of cat medial gastrocnemius: problem of their categorization on the basis of mechanical properties. *Exp. Brain Res.* 23:301–13

135. Robbins, N., Karpati, G., Engel, W. K. 1969. Histochemical and contractile

properties in the cross-innervated guinea pig soleus muscle. *Arch. Neurol.* 20:318–29

136. Romanul, F. C. A., Sreter, F. A., Salmons, S., Gergely, J. 1974. The effect of changed pattern of activity on histochemical characteristics of muscle fibers. See Ref. 29, 2:344–48

137. Romanul, F. C. A. van der Meulen, J. P. 1967. Slow and fast muscle after cross-innervation. *Arch. Neurol.* 17:387–401

138. Roy, R. K., Mabuchi, K., Sarkar, S., Mis, C., Sreter, F. A. 1979. Changes in tropomyosin subunit pattern in chronic electrically stimulated rabbit fast muscle. *Biochem. Biophys. Res. Commun.* 89:181–87

139. Roy, R. K., Sreter, F. A., Sarkar, S. 1979. Changes in tropomyosin subunits and myosin light chains during development of chicken and rabbit striated muscles. *Devl. Biol.* 69:15–30

140. Roy, R. K., Sreter, F. A., Sarkar, S. 1979. Evidence for an intrinsic developmental program in avian and mammalian skeletal muscle. In *Motility in Cell Function,* ed. F. A. Pepe, J. W. Sanger, V. T. Nachmias, pp. 371–75. NY: Academic

141. Rubinstein, N. A., Holtzer, H. 1979. Fast and slow muscles in tissue culture synthesize only fast myosin. *Nature* 280:323–25

142. Rubinstein, N. A., Kelly, A. M. 1978. Myogenic and neurogenic contributions to the development of fast and slow twitch muscles in rat. *Devel. Biol.* 62:473–85

143. Rubinstein, N. A., Mabuchi, K., Pepe, F., Salmons, S., Gergely, J., Sreter, F. A. 1978. Use of type-specific antimyosins to demonstrate the transformation of individual fibers in chronically stimulated rabbit fast muscles. *J. Cell. Biol.* 179:252–61

144. Salmons, S., Gale, D. R., Sreter, F. A. 1978. Ultrastructural aspects of the transformation of muscle fiber type by long term stimulation: changes in Z discs and mitochondria. *J. Anat.* 127:17–31

145. Salmons, S., Sreter, F. A. 1976. Significance of impulse activity in the transformation of skeletal muscle type. *Nature* 263:30–34

146. Salmons, S., Vrbova, G. 1969. The influence of activity on some contractile characteristics of mammalian fast and slow muscles. *J. Physiol. London* 201:535–49

147. Saltin, B., Henriksson, J., Nygaaard, E., Andersen, P., Jansson, E. 1977. Fiber types and metabolic potentials of skeletal muscles in sedentary man and endurance runners. *Ann. N.Y. Acad. Sci.* 301:3–29

148. Sato, N., Mizuno, N., Konishi, Z. 1977. Postnatal differentiation of cell body volumes of spinal motoneurons innervating slow-twitch and fast-twitch muscles. *J. Comp. Neurol.* 175:27–36

149. Schiaffino, S., Bormioli, P., Aloisi, M. 1979. Fiber branching and formation of new fibers during compensatory muscle hypertrophy. In *Muscle Regeneration,* ed. A. Mauro, pp. 177–89. NY: Raven Press

150. Schultz, E. 1978. Changes in the satellite cells of growing muscle following denervation. *Anat. Rec.* 190:299–312

151. Shafiq, S. A., Asiedu, S., Milhorat, A. T. 1972. Effect of neonatal neurectomy on differentiation of fiber types in rat skeletal muscle. *Exp. Neurol.* 35:529–40

152. Sjogaard, G., Houston, M., Nygaaard-Jensen, E., Saltin, B. 1978. Human skeletal muscle: subgrouping of fast-twitch fibers. *Acta Physiol. Scand.* 102:40A–41A

153. Smith, D. M. 1978. Miniature stimulator for chronic animals. *Pflügers Arch.* 376:93–95

154. Smith, J. L., Edgerton, V. R., Betts, B., Collatos, T. C. 1977. EMG of slow and fast ankle extensors of cat during posture, locomotion and jumping. *J. Neurophysiol.* 40:503–13

155. Spamer, C., Pette, D. 1977. Activity patterns of phosphofructokinase, glyceraldehyde-phosphate dehydrogenase, lactate dehydrogenase, and malate dehydrogenase in micro-dissected fast and slow fibers from rabbit psoas and soleus muscle. *Histochemistry* 52:201–17

156. Sreter, F. A. 1970. Effect of denervation on fragmented sarcoplasmic reticulum of white and red muscle. *Exp. Neurol.* 29:52–64

157. Sreter, F. A. 1980. Transformation of fast-twitch and slow-twitch muscles by chronic stimulation. In *Plasticity of Muscle,* ed. D. Pette. Berlin: W. De-Gruyter.

158. Sreter, F. A., Balint, M., Gergely, J. 1975. Structural and functional changes of myosin during development. Comparison with adult fast, slow and cardiac myosin. *Devel. Biol.* 46:317–25

159. Sreter, F. A., Elzinga, M., Mabuchi, K., Salmons, S., Luff, A. R. 1975. The

N^τ-methylhistidine content of myosin in stimulated and cross-reinnervated skeletal muscles of the rabbit. *FEBS Lett.* 57:107–11

160. Sreter, F. A., Holtzer, S., Gergely, J., Holtzer, H. 1972. Some properties of embryonic myosin. *J. Cell Biol.* 55:586–94

161. Sreter, F. A., Jolesz, F., Pinter, K., Mabuchi, K., Gergely, J. 1980. Effect of various forms of hypo- and inactivity on slow muscle. In *28th Int. Congr. Physiol. Sci. Satellite Symp. on Muscle, Szeged.* Budapest: Akademiai Kiadó. In press

162. Sreter, F. A., Luff, A. R., Gergely, J. 1975. Effects of cross-reinnervation on physiological parameters and on properties of myosin and sarcoplasmic reticulum of fast and slow muscles of the rabbit. *J. Gen. Physiol.* 66:811–21

163. Sreter, F. A., Mabuchi, K., Pinter, K., Szvetko, D., Jolesz, F. 1980. Comparative studies of human and rabbit single fibers. In *28th Intl. Congr. Physiol. Sci. Satellite Symp. on Muscle, Szeged.* Budapest: Akademiai Kiadó. In press

164. Sreter, F. A., Romanul, F. C. A., Salmons, S., Gergely, J. 1974. The effect of changed activity pattern on some biochemical characteristics of muscle. See Ref. 29, pp. 338–43

165. Sreter, F. A., Salmons, S., Romanul, F. C. A., Gergely, J. 1973. Synthesis by fast muscle of myosin light chains characteristic of slow muscle in response to long-term stimulation. *Nature New Biol.* 241:17–19

166. Sreter, F. A., Sarkar, S., Gergely, J. 1972. Myosin light chains of slow twitch (red) muscle. *Nature New Biol.* 239:124–25

167. Sreter, F. A., Seidel, J. C., Gergely, J. 1966. Studies on myosin from red and white muscles of rabbit. I. Adenosine triphosphatase activity. *J. Biol. Chem.* 241:5772–76

168. Stein, J. M., Padykula, H. A. 1962. Histochemical classification of individual skeletal muscle fibers of the rat. *Am. J. Anat.* 110:103–24

169. Syrovy, I., Gutmann, E., Melichna, J. 1972. The effect of denervation on contraction and myosin properties of fast and slow rabbit and cat muscles. *Physiol. Bohem.* 21:353–59

170. Syrovy, I., Gutmann, E., Melichna, J. 1972. Effect of exercise on skeletal muscle myosin ATPase activity. *Physiol. Bohemoslov.* 21:633–38

171. Thesleff, S. 1974. Physiological effects of denervation of muscle. *Ann. N.Y. Acad. Sci.* 228:89–104

172. Tomanek, R. J., Lund, D. D. 1973. Degeneration of different types of skeletal muscle fibers. I. Denervation. *J. Anat.* 116:395–407

173. Vrbova, G. 1963. The effect of motoneurone activity on the speed of contraction of striated muscle. *J. Physiol. London* 169:513–26

174. Vrbova, G., Gordon, T., Jones, R. 1978. *Nerve-Muscle Interaction.* London: Chapman and Hall. pp. 136–39

175. Wagner, P. D., Slater, C. S., Pope, B., Weeds, A. G. 1979. Studies on the actin activation of myosin subfragment-1 isoenzymes and the role of myosin light chain. *Eur. J. Biochem.* 99:385–94

176. Walmsley, B., Hodgson, J. A., Burke, R. E. 1978. The forces produced by medial gastrocnemius and soleus muscles during locomotion in freely moving cats. *J. Neurophysiol.* 41:1203–16

177. Walsh, J. V,., Burke, R. E., Rymer, W. Z., Tsairis, P. 1978. Effect of compensatory hypertrophy studies in individual motor units in medial gastrocnemius of the cat. *J. Neurophysiol.* 41:496–508

178. Weeds, A. 1978. Myosin: polymorphism and promiscuity. *Nature* 274:417–18

179. Weeds, A. G., Hall, R., Spurway, N. C. S. 1974. Characterization of myosin light chains from histochemically identified fibres of rabbit psoas muscle. *FEBS Lett.* 49:320–24

180. Whalen, R. G., Schwartz, K., Bouveret, P., Sell, S. M., Gros, F. 1979. Contractile protein isoenzymes in muscle development: Identification of an embryonic form of myosin heavy chain. *Proc. Natl. Acad. Sci. USA* 76:5197–20

181. Yellin, H. 1967. Neural regulation of enzymes in muscle fibers of red and white muscle. *Exp. Neurol.* 19:92–103

182. Yellin, H., Guth, L. 1970. The histochemical classification of muscle fibers. *Exp. Neurol.* 26:424–32

Ann. Rev. Physiol. 1981. 43:553–65
Copyright © 1981 by Annual Reviews Inc. All rights reserved

X-RAY DIFFRACTION STUDIES OF MUSCLE

♦1329

J. S. Wray and K. C. Holmes

Max-Planck-Institut für Medizinische Forschung, 6900 Heidelberg, West Germany

X-ray diffraction, whose traditional and most successful application is in crystallography, has in recent years been applied to studying the remarkable geometrical order of the contractile proteins of muscle. We summarize here some recent achievements in this field, emphasizing conclusions of biological interest and indicating areas of uncertainty. We omit technical arguments and refer the reader to the systematic account by Squire (41). The especially clear physiological implications of X-ray studies of heart muscle are reviewed in (22a).

STRUCTURE OF THE MYOSIN FILAMENTS IN RELAXED MUSCLE

X-ray diffraction allows periodicities in structures to be measured accurately. When a frog muscle is stretched, the spacings of the principal reflections in its X-ray pattern do not change. This fact was a key influence in suggesting that muscle contracts by sliding of the myofilaments past each other rather than by their shortening, and led to the classic X-ray study of filament structure by Huxley & Brown (17) on living frog muscles (both relaxed and contracting) and muscles in rigor.

The contributions of the thick and thin filaments to the X-ray pattern from living muscle were distinguished and described (17). Huxley had previously suggested, from electron microscopy of negatively stained filaments, that the thick filaments were formed from the rod segments of the myosin molecules, anchoring the globular heads of each (namely two subfragment 1, or S1, particles) to positions at the surface. The thick filament diffraction from relaxed muscles was recognized as due largely to this

553

arrangement of the heads, and was very detailed, showing that in this state the heads form an orderly array. This surface lattice was described in helical terms, with a separation of 143 Å between successive levels of bridges and an exact repeat of 429 Å. However, certain additional reflections, some of them strong, indicated that the bridges are perturbed in a systematic way from this idealized picture; moreover, the diffraction contained contributions from additional components of the thick filaments, later identified as C-protein (38). The X-ray pattern was essentially independent of sarcomere length and thus of filament overlap: the cross bridge arrangement therefore does not depend on the presence of surrounding actin filaments. (It may well be influenced by the ordering of the thick filaments into a lattice: The structure of isolated thick filaments has not yet been directly observed by X-ray diffraction.) The interpretation of bridge conformation was not considered in detail. It was assumed that the eight heads of four myosin molecules are disposed in two diametrically opposed groups in each 143 Å level.

Insect flight muscles exhibit a filament lattice as beautifully ordered as that of vertebrate skeletal muscles, though differing in the positions of the thin filaments. X-ray results showed that cross bridges are arranged along the thick filaments with a spacing (145 Å) almost equalling that in frog muscle, but have a different helical repeat (27, 37). The intensities of this pattern are much lower than in that from living frog muscle, indicating reduced order in the arrangement of relaxed cross bridges, and no sign of a comparable systematic perturbation of the surface lattice was found. Miller & Tregear (27) attempted to explain this second type of relaxed pattern quantitatively and to deduce the conformation of relaxed bridges, but their conclusions require revision in the light of more recent work (41). Study of other invertebrate muscles indicated further diversity of thick filament structure. Thus decapod crustaceans, whose fast muscles are similar in structure to insect flight muscles, show remarkable polymorphism: Characteristic differences in the helical repeat of the myosin filaments occur not only between fast and slow fibers but even between individual fast fibers (47). Relaxed thick filaments of the striated adductor muscles of scallops show a characteristic and highly ordered surface lattice which, like that in vertebrate filaments, shows a systematic perturbation (28, 50). X-ray patterns from *Limulus,* an arthropod, indicate no such perturbation, but a striking resemblance to frog muscle in many other aspects of thick filament structure, including surface lattice geometry and bridge conformation. These data from *Limulus* gave the first evidence that relaxed bridges have a specific tilted conformation (50). The lability of the order in resting cross bridges of *Limulus* was shown by an order/disorder transition governed by ionic strength, apparently in the physiological range (49). It is not clear whether or how the arrangement or orderliness of the relaxed cross bridge array is significant in the physiology of individual muscle types. The large amount of detail available from the known relaxed patterns has not yet been interpreted in terms of the shape and orientation of the myosin heads and the spatial relationships between the two heads of each molecule. Such information is urgently needed as a prerequisite for understanding the physical state of unattached bridges, their relation to the backbone structure, and the movements they make in contraction.

Concepts of the underlying structure of the filament backbone, and of how filaments in different muscles are interrelated, have developed independently of the above observations on cross bridges. The backbone structure diffracts X-rays only weakly, and has not hitherto been clearly resolved by electron microscopy. The relation between cross bridge arrangements and backbone structures was discussed in general terms in a provocative study by Squire (40). He suggested how all thick filaments might essentially represent variations of a single packing arrangement for the myosin rods. Many details of this arrangement could be specified from knowledge of how myosin aggregates to form paracrystals, but decisive tests of the model seemed to be lacking. Recently the fast muscles of crustaceans have been found to give especially clear X-ray patterns in which, mainly for technical reasons, diffraction from the filament backbone could be identified for the first time. This diffraction directly suggested that in crustacean thick filaments the rod segments of the molecules are twisted into intermediate subfilaments arranged in a ring to form the apparently tubular backbone. The same description seemed to apply also to insect filaments (as expected from their similar electron microscopic appearance), and appeared to exclude Squire's general model (40) at least for these cases. Corresponding data may be harder to obtain for other muscles but will be required both in order to show whether such subfilament models have a wider applicability and to suggest the underlying design principles. The only common feature of thick filament structure in muscles studied hitherto is the 145 Å axial spacing of bridges, and the significance of this spacing is unknown.

Invertebrate muscles have thus been invaluable in exploring thick filament structure. The filaments of vertebrates are more complex, as indicated by their unusually intricate relaxed pattern (17) and reflecting the presence of proteins other than myosin distributed along their length (4). Certain aspects of this more specialized structure may perhaps be understood in terms of a transformation of the subfilament structure found in the above-mentioned invertebrates (see 47), but confirmation of this will require much fuller interpretation of the available X-ray data. It would be interesting to know whether all vertebrate myosin filaments resemble those of the frog. For example, rabbit psoas muscles have generally been studied after glycerination; they then give very poor diffraction from myosin, and this preparation may be a poor model of living vertebrate muscle (11). [X-ray diffraction after chemical skinning (51) has now proved promising with frog muscles (21a).] X-ray patterns from mammalian heart muscle, although again much weaker, indicate many basic structural features in common with frog skeletal muscle (23). The question remains whether specializations exist at the level of filament structure in individual vertebrate muscles and, if not, how a single filament design can serve the requirements of different vertebrate fiber types.

THIN FILAMENT STRUCTURE

The basic architecture of actin filaments in muscle has become rather well known, because the X-ray patterns from all striated muscles include layer lines long recognized as corresponding to the simple double-helical arrangement of globular actin subunits. The main focus of recent interest has been the organization of the associated regulatory proteins and possible structural changes underlying the 'steric blocking model' of thin filament regulation. This model was originally prompted by X-ray evidence from several different muscle types that the diffraction from the thin filament changes between relaxed and contracting states (15, 46). Model calculations for filaments in the relaxed state (represented by actin and tropomyosin, but neglecting troponin) compared with filaments during contraction (actin, tropomyosin, and attached bridges) showed that a radial and azimuthal shift of tropomyosin in the actin groove could well explain the observations (10, 15, 32). A similar change is observed between relaxation and rigor in frog muscle; and only at non-overlap lengths does it appear to depend on the presence of calcium ions, so that the triggering effect of calcium and the activation induced by rigor complexes appear to result in the same structural state (as far as is resolved by X-ray diffraction) (10). Whether the structural change is relevant to regulation in muscle in the way envisaged by the steric blocking model is obscured by the recent suggestion that tropomyosin might not in fact lie in a position where binding of myosin heads is sterically prevented (39). Further evaluation of these data should show whether the steric blocking model can be appropriately modified or must be abandoned. Rapidly advancing crystallographic studies of tropomyosin with and without associated troponin complexes are now showing that the functioning of tropomyosin may not be adequately understood by picturing it as a rigid rod (33).

The pitch of the actin helix is still uncertain in many instances, since it is difficult even by X-ray diffraction to measure the relevant layer line spacings sufficiently accurately. [This pitch is of great interest in the light of evidence from studies of actin paracrystals that it can vary with concentration of calcium ions (7).] In relaxed and contracting vertebrate skeletal muscles, the half-pitch (distance between cross-over points of the double helix) is in the range 360–370 Å (17), and though a small increase may occur in rigor the value does not seem to reach that of 385 Å found in the sharp pattern from rigor insect muscle (27). A recent study of certain crab muscles (21) suggested a half-pitch of 366 Å in the relaxed state compared to 383 Å in rigor, but this evidence for a pitch-change may be misleading because a layer line of spacing 360 Å from the myosin filaments could have been present in the region where the actin layer line was measured. The 385 Å half-pitch has special significance in that troponin complexes spaced the same distance apart are then confined to certain azimuths on the thin filament; X-ray patterns from fast lobster muscles showed this structure in both relaxed and rigor states especially clearly (51). At least in lobster and crab muscles (21, 51), X-ray studies confirmed the expectation (see 6) that the troponin complexes associated with the two actin strands are aligned transversely as closely as possible. In lobster muscles the first structural evidence was found for a conformational change in troponin induced by calcium ions, occurring even though the filaments were permanently "switched on" by rigor attachments (51). The possibly elongated shape of the troponin complex has not yet been resolved nor has its orientation relative to the thin filament been established.

STRUCTURES INVOLVED IN ACTIN-MYOSIN INTERACTION

Although the existence of cross bridges between thick and thin filaments was suggested by H. E. Huxley's work on longitudinal sections of vertebrate muscle, the idea that a change in their conformation could underlie the generation of force (14, 35) was first prompted by observations of glycerinated insect muscle. Addition of ATP to the rigor muscle caused a structural change, both electron microscopy and X-ray diffraction suggesting that myosin projections are tilted in rigor but perpendicular in relaxed muscle (37). The concept of a contractile cycle presupposes a coupling of biochemical states to structural states of attached bridges (see ref. 42). Rigor is one readily accessible attached state, even though a nonphysiological one, and it is still being debated exactly how bridges attach in rigor and whether they ever take up any other conformation.

The diffraction given in the rigor state by insect muscles (13, 27) and by the closely related crustacean muscles (21, 30, 51) is entirely different from that from relaxed muscle. The form of these layer lines depends in a complex way on how the bridges attach and how they are distributed on the thin filaments (in insect muscle there are insufficient S1 subunits to occupy all the actin monomers). Model calculations show that part of the pattern depends strongly on the shape of the cross bridges attached to the actin monomers. This part is well explained by attachment of myosin heads having the dimensions and tilted conformation found by electron microscopy (29) of reconstituted thin filaments fully decorated with S1 (using rabbit proteins). Therefore myosin heads held at the surface of the myosin filament are also free to bind in a specific conformation to actin, and the enhancement of the actin helix diffraction is in fact the most direct evidence that myosin heads can and do attach to the thin filaments in muscle. Unfortunately, analysis of the mode of attachment is limited by the complexity of the incompletely occupied structure. The layer lines indicate that bridges attach at target areas spaced at intervals of 385 Å on both sides of the actin filaments. This may mean either that cross bridges can reach only a certain azimuthal range on each filament, or that the troponin complexes hinder attachment elsewhere (51). The X-ray diffraction results confirm the electron microscopy of Reedy (36) on insect muscle, and it must be emphasized that no corresponding analysis for vertebrate muscle has yet been achieved. An attractive but still unconfirmed suggestion (31), both refining the description of target area attachment and suggesting its origin, is that the two rods of density observed by electron microscopy linking thick and thin filaments in each target area represent respectively a 'left-handed' and a 'right-handed' myosin head from different molecules. This view embodies the idea that the heads of each molecule are widely splayed apart and bind to different actin filaments in the rigor state of insect muscle. The rigor X-ray pattern has not yet been interpreted at sufficient resolution to test this relatively refined model.

Because the diffraction from rigor insect muscle is so detailed, it was natural to seek evidence for modified configurations of attached cross bridges. The nucleotide AMPPNP, which is not hydrolyzed by actomyosin, offers the most encouraging approach so far. It binds strongly and competitively to the ATP-binding site; it produces a large and reversible change in the rigor pattern of the insect muscle; and it has a mechanical effect, lowering the tension of the slightly stretched muscle and thus presumably affecting the structure or arrangement of attached bridges (22). The AMPPNP X-ray pattern is not yet interpreted. One view (43) is that it indicates reversion of attached bridges to a more nearly perpendicular conformation intermediate between a perpendicular unattached state and a tilted rigor conformation. Since even the rigor pattern is still understood only in a general way, it may be premature to conclude that the difference between the AMPPNP and rigor patterns corresponds to such a conformational change in actomyosin. Further studies of other muscles will show whether the observed effects of AMPPNP are general. X-ray patterns from insect muscle in the presence of the hydrolyzable nucleotides ATP (γ-S) and α,β-methylene ATP resemble the pattern in ATP (8). Since in the steady state these analogs are bound in the uncleaved form, while ATP is bound as the products of its hydrolysis, any change in the structure of detached heads when hydrolysis occurs appears not to be resolved by X-ray diffraction of insect muscle. There is still little evidence as to whether unattached heads change conformation when neither nucleotide nor hydrolysis products are bound: Although the cross-bridge array of living frog muscle at non-overlap lengths becomes disordered when put into rigor (11), this effect could result from pH or other incidental changes within the muscle.

ACTIVATED MUSCLE

A natural approach to understanding structural changes in contraction is to record the X-ray pattern in this state. Attempts to do this face the difficulty that contraction is not easily maintained for the time required for data collection [though synchrotron radiation has recently revolutionized this area (3, 44)]. It is also far from self-evident that the states that are of special interest in the contractile cycle occur with sufficient duration to be visible at all by this method. Earlier film measurements on frog muscle (17) showed that the relaxed pattern is greatly weakened in contraction, and thus that cross bridges do move substantially, but the nature and timing of these movements remained unknown. In particular it was impossible to show whether or how cross bridges attach to actin filaments, though since the rigor X-ray pattern did not appear in contraction, at most only a small fraction of the heads can be attached at any one time. The film results also showed that the spacing of the meridional reflection at 143 Å from relaxed muscle increases to 145 Å on activation (17). Such an effect occurs also in rigor (11), and its origin is unknown (no such change occurs in invertebrate muscles that have been studied). The suggestion that the myosin filaments untwist and thus lengthen slightly (11) remains unconfirmed, since the structure of the backbone of these filaments is not yet open to direct observation by X-ray diffraction.

Initiation of Bridge Attachment

Calcium ions are believed to trigger bridge attachment in all striated muscles but act, according to muscle type, either on the thick or on the thin filaments or on both. Neither mode of operation has been adequately described in structural terms. Whether or not tropomyosin moves so as to block cross bridge attachment sterically in thin-filament regulation, the structural change by which the proteins of the troponin complex promote this movement is unknown, and may remain so until crystallography of the regulatory proteins (26, 33) is further advanced. Myosin-linked regulation is especially interesting because of its possible direct relation to cross bridge mechanisms. It appears to be the only mode of regulation in molluscan muscles, and scallop myosin has proved an ideal model system. Removal of one regulatory light chain from the molecule renders the activity of both heads independent of calcium (19), suggesting cooperative regulation of the two heads and thus that the regulatory light chains are located near the junction between them. Clear confirmation of this comes from electron microscopy of actin decorated with S1 from which the regulatory light chain has been removed; the structure of the S1 appeared to be modified in the region furthest from its attachment to actin (5). X-ray diffraction of the deregulated intact scallop muscle shows a comparably dramatic change, not yet interpreted in terms of the pattern of actin-myosin association in rigor (45). X-ray observations of the state of unattached myosin heads after light-chain removal or calcium activation, in comparison with the unusual and highly ordered structure in relaxed muscle (28, 50), would suggest more directly the structural basis of this mode of regulation but has not yet been technically feasible. The type of myosin regulation existing alone in molluscs is probably not unique to them, and observations of corresponding modified structural states elsewhere would be informative. Key questions are whether thick- and thin-filament regulation operate over the same range of Ca^{2+} concentration in intact muscle fibers, and what is the significance of dual as compared with single regulation. X-ray experiments with muscles stretched to non-overlap lengths in principle allow calcium activation of both thick and thin filaments to be observed simultaneously without mutual interference. Vertebrate skeletal muscle is unusual in its apparent lack of myosin-linked regulation. Although according to an earlier report a change in the layer lines of the X-ray pattern of frog muscle was observable on stimulating at non-overlap lengths (15), more recent experiments find no such change (18, 53). There is thus no clear evidence that the rapid release of cross bridges from their ordered positions in the relaxed muscle reflects a direct action of calcium ions. The strongest X-ray reflections from striated muscle are those innermost on the equator, which arise not from the structure of thick or thin filaments alone but from their regular packing to form a lattice. These reflections change dramatically in intensity when the muscle is contracting or is put into rigor, in a way that can be interpreted in terms of redistribution of cross-bridge density away from the thick towards the thin filaments (12). The time-course with which these intensities change at the beginning and end of contraction has recently been studied in frog muscle and, in either twitch or tetanus, presumably reflects both the time-course of deregulation and the kinetics of subsequent bridge attachment. The intensities of low-angle reflections on the equator of the X-ray pattern, and thus even the large-scale distribution of density between thick and thin filaments, change as early as 15–20 msec after stimulation, preceding tension development by 10–15 msec (see 16). If, as seems likely, the structural change detected corresponds to attachment, this result shows that attachment is rapid enough that some other slower transition *after* attachment must limit the rate of rise of tension. Equivalent observations of twitches (16, 25) reveal a similar delay of tension after structural change, with intensities ·at peak tension not very different from those in tetanus. The return to resting intensities begins simultaneously with the fall of tension, and proceeds in parallel with it, but may be finally completed only much later (after 0.7–1.1 sec) (52). The X-ray pattern away from the equator is much weaker, and measurements of the time course of changes in it during twitches have only very recently become possible (18). The several off-meridional layer lines from the myosin filaments reflect the fact that relaxed cross bridges are positioned along particular helical tracks, and the observed changes in their intensities occur in striking parallel with the change of tension. This observation constitutes the most direct evidence yet that it is specifically the density ordered on the myosin filaments in relaxed muscle (namely the cross bridges) that moves when tension is being generated. The same small delay between movement and tension may occur but has not yet been observed. The 143 Å meridional reflection shows a more complex behavior, sometimes even increasing in intensity during contraction; such behavior is not entirely surprising, because of the sensitivity of this reflection to small changes in cross bridge conformation and in the degree of order in the filament lattice (16).

Contractile State

The previous dynamic measurements achieved their purpose without requiring detailed modelling to relate the X-ray effect to a structural change. We finally mention certain X-ray studies that are especially subject to difficulties of interpretation, namely those aiming to describe movements occurring during actin-myosin interaction in relation to models of cross bridge action. A notable early attempt using insect flight muscle (see 2) was designed to correlate the movements of bridges in the oscillating muscle with its mechanical output. These experiments suffered from insufficiently intense signal, however, and would yield important new information if repeated using the greater intensity of synchrotron radiation. A comparable study of rhythmic contraction in mammalian heart muscle has also proved technically feasible (22a, 24).

The most satisfactory results to date have been obtained with frog skeletal muscle, where the intensities of the two strong innermost equatorial reflections have been compared in isotonic and isometric contractions (other parts of the pattern are too weak to be recorded in such experiments so far). The ratio of these intensities lies between that characteristic of relaxed and that of rigor muscle; but it is not strongly dependent on speed of shortening, and even when the force is small and the shortening rapid it moves only slightly closer to the relaxed ratio (1, 16, 34). The difficulty in interpreting this result arises because equatorial intensities are sensitive to many types of change in mass distribution, and do not necessarily provide a linear measure of the extent of movement from one specific distribution towards another (20). Since we do not know the specific distribution characteristic of relaxed or of rigor muscle or of any contracting state, we cannot yet relate the equatorial intensity ratio to the extent of movement of activated bridges. An experimental approach to eliminating these uncertainties has been taken by Podolsky. Using skinned fibers, where calcium level can be directly controlled, mechanical studies show that calcium affects the number of bridges but not their intrinsic kinetic properties (9). On living fibers, caffeine can be used to control the level of force (again presumably through calcium level), and the intensity change in the equatorial X-ray pattern between relaxation and contraction is then graded in proportion to tension (54). Combining these observations, it is reasonable to conclude that the intensity change is indeed roughly linearly dependent on the number of tension-generating bridges. That the intensity ratio in isotonic contraction does not revert towards the relaxed ratio in proportion to the reduced force must then mean that the nature of attached bridges, rather than just the number of them, is affected by the rapid movement of the filaments. This conclusion requires verification; however, it has recently been suggested that in contractions where both length and force can vary, the intensity ratio is not influenced by shortening per se (1a).

CONCLUSION

The last-mentioned dynamic measurements, and still more rapid measurements of X-ray changes following application of step changes of length, are now approaching a time-resolution where they provide a structural counterpart of mechanical tests of muscle models. Interpretation of these X-ray results is seriously hampered by ignorance of many aspects of static structure. Thus, in modelling diffraction from the cross bridge array in contraction, we cannot yet specify the number or precise arrangement of the myosin heads at each level along the filament or what range of movement they must make to attach to actin. Regarding thin filament structure, it is unknown how far bridge attachment should manifest itself as enhanced diffraction from actin if the bridges can adopt more than a single conformation. The search for evidence that bridges can indeed attach in more than one state is not far advanced, and one should perhaps bear in mind that the relevant structural change still being sought by X-ray studies may not be merely a change in tilt of a rigid myosin head but, for example, a change in subunit shape or slew, or the shortening of some part of the molecule, such as subfragment 2, comprising relatively little mass.

Aside from the specific purpose of allowing dynamic studies to be fully interpreted, further knowledge of filament structure in the environment of the living fiber has another purpose: The physical state of muscle proteins and their relative geometries must have large effects on the kinetics of their interactions. Thus, for example, the behavior of myosin heads as observed in free solution must be modified by close association with the myosin filament backbone, by cooperative interactions with each other, and by the large interparticle forces within organized arrays of filaments. A more specific instance where knowledge of filament geometry is crucial is provided by insect flight muscle. Here the very regular filament array may incorporate a geometrical adaptation by which the effective concentration of cross bridges available for attachment depends on the sarcomere length, thereby contributing to the pronounced stretch-activation needed for the functioning of this muscle (48). While the curiosity of many about the mechanism of contraction will be satisfied only when X-ray crystallography resolves the atomic structure of the contractile proteins and their conformational changes, others will recognize the unique contribution of less exhaustive X-ray observations in revealing the architecture of intact muscles.

Literature Cited

1. Amemiya, Y., Sugi, H., Hashizume, H. 1979. X-ray diffraction studies on the dynamic properties of cross-bridges in skeletal muscle. In *Cross-bridge Mechanism in Muscle Contraction,* ed. H. Sugi, G. H. Pollack, pp. 425–40. Tokyo: Univ. Tokyo Press. 665 pp.

1a. Amemiya, Y., Tameyasu, T., Tanaka, H., Hashizume, H., Sugi, H. 1980. Time-resolved X-ray diffraction from frog skeletal muscle during shortening against an inertial load and a quick release. *Proc. Jpn. Acad.* 56B:235–40

2. Armitage, P. M., Tregear, R. T., Miller, A. 1975. Effect of activation by calcium on the X-ray diffraction pattern from insect flight muscle. *J. Mol. Biol.* 92:39–53

3. Barrington Leigh, J., Rosenbaum, G. 1976. Synchroton X-ray sources: a new tool in biological structural and kinetic analysis. *Ann. Rev. Biophys. Bioeng.* 5:239–70

4. Craig, R., Offer, G. 1976. The location of C-protein in rabbit skeletal muscle. *Proc. R. Soc. London Ser. B* 192:451–61

5. Craig, R., Szent-Györgyi, A., Beese, L., Flicker, P., Vibert, P. J., Cohen, C. 1980. Electron microscopy of thin filaments decorated with a Ca^{++}-regulated myosin. *J. Mol. Biol.* 140:35–55

6. Ebashi, S. 1980. Regulation of muscle contraction. *Proc. R. Soc. London Ser. B* 207:259–86 (correction in 208:483)

7. Gillis, J. M., O'Brien, E. J. 1975. The effect of calcium ions on the structure of reconstituted muscle thin filaments. *J. Mol. Biol.* 99:445–59

8. Goody, R. S., Holmes, K. C., Mannherz, H. G., Barrington Leigh, J., Rosenbaum, G. 1975. Cross-bridge conformation as revealed by X-ray diffraction studies of insect flight muscles with

ATP analogues. *Biophys. J.* 15:687–705
9. Gulati, J., Podolsky, R. J. 1978. Contraction transients of skinned muscle fibers: effects of calcium and ionic strength. *J. Gen. Physiol.* 72:701–15
10. Haselgrove, J. C. 1972. X-ray evidence for a conformational change in the actin-containing filaments of vertebrate striated muscle. *Cold Spring Harbor Symp. Quant. Biol.* 37:341–52
11. Haselgrove, J. C. 1975. X-ray evidence for conformational changes in the myosin filaments of vertebrate striated muscle. *J. Mol. Biol.* 92:113–43
12. Haselgrove, J. C., Huxley, H. E. 1973. X-ray evidence for radial cross-bridge movement and for the sliding filament model in actively contracting skeletal muscle. *J. Mol. Biol.* 77:549–68
13. Holmes, K. C., Tregear, R. T., Barrington Leigh, J. 1980. Interpretation of the low angle X-ray diffraction from insect flight muscle in rigor. *Proc. R. London Ser. B* 207:13–33
14. Huxley, H. E. 1969. The mechanism of muscular contraction. *Science* 164:1356–66
15. Huxley, H. E. 1972. Structural changes in the actin- and myosin-containing filaments during contraction. *Cold Spring Harbor Symp. Quant. Biol.* 37:361–76
16. Huxley, H. E. 1979. Time resolved X-ray diffraction studies on muscle. See Ref. 1, pp. 391–405
17. Huxley, H. E., Brown, W. 1967. The low-angle X-ray diagram of vertebrate striated muscle and its behaviour during contraction and rigor. *J. Mol. Biol.* 30:383–434
18. Huxley, H. E., Faruqi, A. R., Bordas, J., Koch, M. H. J., Milch, J. R. 1980. The use of synchrotron radiation in time-resolved X-ray diffraction studies of myosin layer-line reflections during muscle contraction. *Nature* 284:140–43
19. Kendrick-Jones, J., Szentkiralyi, E. M., Szent-Györgyi, A. G. 1976. Regulatory light chains in myosins. *J. Mol. Biol.* 104:747–75
20. Lymn, R. W. 1975. Equatorial X-ray reflections and cross arm movement in skeletal muscle. *Nature* 258:770–72
21. Maéda, Y., Matsubara, I., Yagi, N. 1979. Structural changes in thin filaments of crab striated muscle. *J. Mol. Biol.* 127:191–201
21a. Magid, A., Reedy, M. K. 1980. X-ray diffraction observations of chemically skinned frog skeletal muscle processed by an improved method. *Biophys. J.* 30:27–40

22. Marston, S. B., Rodger, C. D., Tregear, R. T. 1976. Changes in muscle cross-bridges when β,γ-imido-ATP binds to myosin. *J. Mol. Biol.* 104:263–76
22a. Matsubara, I. 1980. X-ray diffraction studies of the heart. *Ann. Rev. Biophys. Bioeng.* 9:81–105
23. Matsubara, I., Millman, B. M. 1974. X-ray diffraction patterns from mammalian heart muscle. *J. Mol. Biol.* 82:527–36
24. Matsubara, I., Suga, H., Yagi, N. 1977. An X-ray diffraction study of the cross-circulated canine heart. *J. Physiol. London* 270:311–20
25. Matsubara, I., Yagi, N. 1978. A time-resolved X-ray diffraction study of muscle during twitch. *J. Physiol. London* 278:297–307
26. Mercola, D., Bullard, B., Priest, J. 1975. Crystallization of troponin C. *Nature* 254:634–35
27. Miller, A., Tregear, R. T. 1972. Structure of insect fibrillar flight muscle in the presence and absence of ATP. *J. Mol. Biol.* 70:85–104
28. Millman, B. M., Bennett, P. M. 1976. Structure of the cross-striated adductor muscle of the scallop. *J. Mol. Biol.* 103:439–67
29. Moore, P. B., Huxley, H. E., DeRosier, D. J. 1970. Three-dimensional reconstruction of F-actin, thin filaments and decorated thin filaments. *J. Mol. Biol.* 50:279–95
30. Namba, K., Wakabayashi, K., Mitsui, T. 1980. X-ray structure analysis of the thin filament of crab striated muscle in the rigor state. *J. Mol. Biol.* 138:1–26
31. Offer, G., Elliott, A. 1978. Can a myosin molecule bind to two actin filaments? *Nature* 271:325–29
32. Parry, D. A. D., Squire, J. M. 1973. Structural role of tropomyosin in muscle regulation: analysis of the X-ray diffraction patterns from relaxed and contracting muscles. *J. Mol. Biol.* 75:33–55
33. Phillips, G. N., Lattman, E. E., Cummins, P., Lee, K. Y., Cohen, C. 1979. Crystal structure and molecular interactions of tropomyosin. *Nature* 278:413–17
34. Podolsky, R. J., St. Onge, R., Yu, L., Lymn, R. W. 1976. X-ray diffraction of actively shortening muscle. *Proc. Natl. Acad. Sci. USA* 73:813–17
35. Pringle, J. W. S. 1967. The contractile mechanism of insect fibrillar muscle. *Progr. Biophys. Mol. Biol.* 17:1–60
36. Reedy, M. K. 1968. Ultrastructure of insect flight muscle. *J. Mol. Biol.* 31:155–76

37. Reedy, M. K., Holmes, K. C., Tregear, R. T. 1965. Induced changes in orientation of the crossbridges of glycerinated insect flight muscle. *Nature* 207: 1276–80

38. Rome, E. 1972. Structural studies by X-ray diffraction of striated muscle permeated with certain ions and proteins. *Cold Spring Harbor Symp. Quant. Biol.* 37:331–39

39. Seymour, J., O'Brien, E. J. 1980. The position of tropomyosin in muscle thin filaments. *Nature* 283:680–82

40. Squire, J. M. 1973. General model of myosin filament structure. III. Molecular packing arrangements in myosin filaments. *J. Mol. Biol.* 77:291–323

41. Squire, J. M. 1975. Muscle filament structure and muscle contraction. *Ann. Rev. Biophys. Bioeng.* 4:137–63

42. Tregear, R. T., Marston, S. B. 1979. The crossbridge theory. *Ann. Rev. Physiol.* 41:723–36

43. Tregear, R. T., Milch, J. R., Goody, R. S., Holmes, K. C., Rodger, C. D. 1979. The use of some novel X-ray diffraction techniques to study the effect of nucleotides on cross-bridges in insect flight muscle. See Ref. 1, pp. 407–21

44. Vazina, A. A., Gerasimov, V. S., Zheleznaya, L. A., Matyushin, A. M., Son'kin, B. Y., Srebnitskaya, L. K., Shelestov, V. M., Frank, G. M., Avakyan, T. M., Alikhanyan, A. I. 1975. Experience with the use of synchrotron radiation for X-ray diffraction study of biopolymers. *Biophysics* 20:813–20

45. Vibert, P., Szent-Györgyi, A. G., Craig, R., Wray, J., Cohen, C. 1978. Changes in crossbridge attachment in a myosin-regulated muscle. *Nature* 273:64–66

46. Vibert, P. J., Haselgrove, J. C., Lowy, J., Poulsen, F. R. 1972. Structural changes in actin-containing filaments of muscle. *J. Mol. Biol.* 71:757–67

47. Wray, J. S. 1979. Structure of the backbone in myosin filaments of muscle. *Nature* 277:37–40

48. Wray, J. S. 1979. Filament geometry and the activation of insect flight muscle. *Nature* 280:325–26

49. Wray, J. S., Vibert, P. J., Cohen, C. 1974. Cross-bridge arrangements in *Limulus* muscle. *J. Mol. Biol.* 88: 343–48

50. Wray, J. S., Vibert, P. J., Cohen, C. 1975. Diversity of cross-bridge configurations in invertebrate muscles. *Nature* 257:561–64

51. Wray, J. S., Vibert, P. J., Cohen, C. 1978. Actin filaments in muscle: pattern of myosin and tropomyosin/troponin attachments. *J. Mol. Biol.* 124:501–21

52. Yagi, N., Ito, M. H., Nakajima, H., Izumi, T., Matsubara, I. 1977. Return of myosin heads to thick filaments after muscle contraction. *Science* 197:685–87

53. Yagi, N., Matsubara, I. 1980. Myosin heads do not move on activation in highly stretched vertebrate striated muscle. *Science* 207:307–8

54. Yu, L. C., Hartt, J. E., Podolsky, R. J. 1979. Equatorial X-ray intensities and isometric force levels in frog sartorius muscle. *J. Mol. Biol.* 132:53–67

RENAL AND ELECTROLYTE PHYSIOLOGY

Introduction, Thomas E. Andreoli,
Section Editor

The theme of this year's section for Renal Physiology is the interaction of hormones with the kidney. It is now evident that the kidney serves, in many respects, as an endocrine organ. The articles in this section deal with some of the major hormonal interactions either within the kidney or between hormones and the kidney.

In the first article, F. Morel and colleagues discuss the way in which hormone-dependent adenyl cyclases modify the activity of intracellular second messenger cyclic adenosine monophosphate (cAMP) in various segments of the nephron. This kind of analysis obviously provides a model for how hormonal receptors will be assayed in various regions of the nephron in what ultimately will be a wide variety of circumstances. Z. S. Agus and S. Goldfarb then discuss one particular adenyl cyclase response: the effects of PTH, calcitonin, and cyclic nucleotides in modifying transport processes in various segments of the nephron.

A. Nasjletti and K. U. Malik describe the complex interactions of intra-renal kallikrein-kinin systems with renal prostaglandins; these observations, which have led to the explosion of an entirely new field in the past decade, strongly support the view that the renal kallikrein-kinin and prostaglandin systems are tightly coupled. In future years these complex interrelations will probably be shown to govern a number of homeostatic mechanisms.

J. S. Handler and J. Orloff review the detailed effects of vasopressin on various segments of the nephron; some of the interactions of vasopressin with the prostaglandin systems; and interactions of the hormone in cultured cells that have ADH-sensitive adenyl cyclase systems.

P. Insel and M. D. Snavely summarize data on adrenergic receptors within the kidney, and explore in detail the particular effects of various adrenergic agents on tubular function as well as on renal hemodynamics.

Finally, D. D. Fanestil and C. S. Park discuss the complexities of steroid hormone binding to high-affinity steroid-specific receptor proteins in the cytoplasm of various target cells within the kidney; the particular role of RNA, proteins, and lipid synthesis in modulating the steroid receptor effect; and the current status of information about the intracellular mechanism of action of steroid hormones on renal tubular cells.

Ann. Rev. Physiol. 1981. 43:569–81
Copyright © 1981 by Annual Reviews Inc. All rights reserved

DISTRIBUTION OF HORMONE-   ♦1330
DEPENDENT ADENYLATE
CYCLASE IN THE NEPHRON AND
ITS PHYSIOLOGICAL SIGNIFICANCE

F. Morel, M. Imbert-Teboul, and D. Chabardès

Laboratoire de Physiologie Cellulaire, Collège de France, Paris 75231, France

INTRODUCTION

Since 1975, microtechniques have become available (28, 37, 51) that allow hormone-dependent adenylate cyclase (AC) to be measured in isolated, single pieces of kidney tubule. The pattern of AC activation by various hormones along the successive nephron portions was first investigated with this method in the rabbit (5–7, 29, 36), then in the mouse (8, 16), rat (38) and human (9) kidney. Each hormone tested was observed to stimulate AC activity in several well-delineated nephron portions. Thus, for example, parathyroid hormone (PTH) was active not only in proximal tubules, as expected, but also in distal nephron segments (5, 36); similarly, arginine-vasopressin (AVP) was active in collecting tubules and also in portions of the loop's ascending limb (29, 30). These observations were recently confirmed in other laboratories (13, 26, 42, 52). Where established, dose-response curves indicated high sensitivity of the enzyme to the active hormones, suggesting that the observed distributions of responsiveness might be of physiological relevance.

In this short review, we correlate these enzymatic data regarding hormone action-sites with recent reports about the biological effects induced by hormones in microperfused nephron segments. Evidence indicating that biological responses were cAMP-mediated will be given where available. Permeability and transport properties of the different nephron portions

569

0066-4268/81/0315-0569$01.00

were extensively investigated in the rabbit by single tubule microperfusion techniques. These properties were recently reviewed by Grantham et al (19), and are only recalled here briefly.

The physiological effects elicited by a given hormone may be expected to vary from one responsive segment to another, since, like permeability and transport properties, cAMP-induced changes in cell functioning are assumed to exhibit high cell-type specificity. Recent physiological data substantiate this assumption. Various agents—e.g. calcium ions, prostaglandins, α-adrenergic agonists, or steroid hormones—are known to modulate cell responsiveness. This kind of interaction was analyzed by Strewler & Orloff (47) for the vasopressin action in collecting tubules and the PTH action in proximal tubules. Despite its importance, it is not considered here.

PROXIMAL TUBULE (PARS CONVOLUTA, PCT, AND PARS RECTA, PR)

Up to now, adenylate cyclase of proximal tubules was observed to be highly responsive to one hormone only, namely PTH. This holds for rabbit (5), rat, mouse (16), and human (9) kidneys. Therefore we focus on experimental evidence indicating that the well-known effects of PTH on proximal tubules [inhibition of phosphate and fluid (Jv) reabsorption] are mediated by cyclic AMP. The following biochemical results deserve mention: PTH-dependent adenylate cyclase is located in basolateral cell membranes (46); addition of PTH to suspensions of cortical tubules (mainly PCT) induced a rapid increase in cAMP cell content (21); in appropriate cell broken preparations, cAMP increased cAMP-dependent protein kinase activity and induced autophosphorylation of protein components more efficiently in brush border than in basolateral membrane fractions (34), suggesting that some physiological function located at the apical cell border might be regulated by PTH via cAMP. Finally, in brush border vesicles prepared from either PTH-treated or control T-PTX rats, the Na-dependent phosphate entry diminished in PTH-treated compared to control animals, whereas the Na-dependent glucose entry and the passive component of phosphate entry were similar in both groups of rats (15). This observation might account for the in vivo inhibition of phosphate transport by PTH, since proximal phosphate reabsorption is a Na-dependent process (see 12). The permeability changes through which PTH regulates fluid reabsorption are not yet established. But this effect on Jv is also mediated by cAMP on the basis of the following evidence: Inhibition of fluid reabsorption (Jv) by PTH in rat PCT was obtained only when the hormone was microperfused on the peritubular side (3), where adenylate cyclase is located; maximal and half-maximal inhibitions of Jv corresponded to PTH concentrations of about 10^{-6} and 3 $\times 10^{-9}$M, respectively (3); these values are similar to those measured for AC activation by PTH in isolated single proximal tubules (5); low cAMP and dibutyryl cAMP (dbcAMP) concentrations, applied on either the luminal or peritubular sides, mimicked the effects of PTH on Jv (3). When perfused intravenously into T-PTX rats, cAMP (about 10^{-6}M in systemic blood plasma) inhibited fluid and phosphate reabsorptions, as measured in free-flow micropuncture experiments (35). It should be stressed here that exogenous cAMP or cAMP derivatives are only active in the range of 10^{-4} to 10^{-3} M in tubular segments other than proximal tubules, due to a much lower cell-membrane permeability to nucleotides than in PCT.

Phosphate handling by proximal tubules was recently reviewed by Dennis et al (12). It should be recalled that, besides PTH, many factors—such as the pH and calcium concentration—also modulate phosphate transport by proximal tubules. Moreover, in rats the phosphate transport capacity was observed to be definitely higher in the early than in the late proximal convolutions (12); PTH, however, inhibited phosphate reabsorption mainly in late PCT (54). Heterogeneity along proximal tubules as regards PTH effects was also observed in vitro in rabbit microperfused tubules; thus, PTH inhibited fluid reabsorption mainly in PCT, whereas it inhibited phosphate transport in PR only (11). This observation might account for the rather poor phosphaturic action of PTH in the rabbit, as compared to its natriuric action (17).

Adrenergic receptors of the α type are likely to be present in proximal tubules, since: (*a*) Addition of norepinephrine (5 $\times 10^{-7}$M) to a suspension of rat cortical tubules reduced by about 50% the cAMP accumulation induced by PTH (21); this effect was suppressed in the presence of an α-blocker (phentolamine) but persisted in the presence of a phosphodiesterase inhibitor (21), suggesting that α-agonists regulated PTH-induced cAMP generation rather than cAMP inactivation. Such inhibition of PTH-dependent adenylate cyclase activity might involve some intermediate step (a change in the Ca^{2+} cell concentration for example), since it is difficult to obtain in cell broken systems (unpublished data of the authors). (*b*) More recently, norepinephrine (10^{-6}M), when microperfused in vivo in peritubular capillaries of the rat kidney surface, increased proximal fluid reabsorption from 2.8 to 3.8 nl mm^{-1} min^{-1}; this effect was blocked by phentolamine (40). It would be of interest to test whether, under the same experimental conditions, norepinephrine also stimulates phosphate transport, since it has not been established whether α-agonists increased Jv (contrary to PTH) by decreasing the cAMP cell concentration and/or by other mechanisms. (*c*) Unilateral denervation is known to be associated with polyuria and natriuresis of proximal origin. As recently reviewed by Gottschalk (18), these effects of denervation are likely to result mainly from α-adrenergic tone suppression in proximal tubules. Interestingly, unilateral denervation not only reduced salt and water reabsorption in proximal tubules, but also Tm values for the transport of phosphate, glucose, amino acids and organic acids in the denervated compared to the intact kidney. The corresponding literature is detailed in (18).

THIN LIMB OF THE LOOP OF HENLE

Adenylate cyclase activities were relatively low and comparable in the descending (TDL) and ascending (TAL) portions of the rabbit thin limb regarding both basal and fluoride values (30). This is accounted for by the small diameter and low protein content per mm of this tubular portion (29). In rat and rabbit TDL, no clearcut stimulation of AC could be obtained with any of the hormones we have so far tested, including PGE (10^{-6}M) (unpublished results of the authors). Quite recently, however, Torikai & Kurokawa (53) reported AC stimulation in isolated rat TDL with 3×10^{-6} to 3×10^{-5} M of PGE_2 (these authors also obtained a small PGE_2 effect on AC in collecting tubules; in the other nephron segments, including TAL, no effect was observed).

In contrast, the enzyme present in TAL was stimulated 10–15-fold by vasopressin (10^{-6}M) in rabbit (30) and rat (39). Imai & Kokko investigated the effects of vasopressin on the permeability to water (Pd) in microperfused rabbit thin limbs by measuring tritiated water efflux. No effect of AVP on Pd was obtained in TDL (Imai, personal communication) whereas, in TAL a statistically significant increase in the Pd value was observed in the presence of AVP (27). These authors did not attribute physiological relevance to this effect. It would be of interest, however, to investigate the effects of vasopressin on TAL further, for example by measuring L_p, P_{Na}, and P_{urea}.

THICK ASCENDING LIMB

It is necessary to distinguish between the medullary (MAL) and cortical (CAL) portions of thick ascending limbs (straight distal tubules), since these two portions (*a*) are surrounded by extracellular environments of different ionic concentrations, (*b*) are formed by cells with a somewhat different morphological ultrastructure (1, 33), and (*c*) contain adenylate cyclase exhibiting different hormonal requirements, as summarized in a semi-quantitative way in Table 1 for four animal species.

As reviewed by Grantham et al (19), microperfused MAL and CAL tubules are known to exhibit lumen-positive PD and to reabsorb salt (NaCl)

Table 1   Hormone-sensitive adenylate cyclase in thick ascending limbs

Species	Nephron portion	PTH[a]	SCT	AVP	Gluc	Iso	References
Rabbit	MAL	0	+++	(++)[b]	+	0	5, 6, 7, 29, 30
	CAL	++	+	+	NT	0	
Rat[c]	MAL	0	++	++++	++++	0	2, 31, 38
	CAL	++++	++++	++	+++	++	
Mouse	MAL	0	0	+++	NT	0	8, 16
	CAL	++++	+	++	NT	+	
Human	MAL	++	++	0	NT	NT	9
	CAL	++	++	0	NT	NT	

[a] Abbreviations used: PTH, 1–34 synthetic fragment of bovine parathyroid hormone (1–10 U ml^{-1}); SCT, synthetic salmon calcitonin (10–100 ng ml^{-1}); AVP, arginine-vasopressin (10^{-6}M); Gluc, porcine glucagon; Iso, Isoproterenol (10^{-6}M); MAL and CAL, medullary and cortical portions, respectively, of the thick ascending limb of Henle's loop. Adenylate cyclase activities are given semi-quantitatively: 0, no statistically significant effect; +, ++, +++, and ++++, responses below 100, between 100 and 300, between 300 and 500, and over 500 femtomoles mm^{-1} 30 min^{-1}, respectively. NT, not tested.

[b] The AVP-induced response in rabbit MAL was highly variable depending on the animals, for yet unknown reasons.

[c] Detailed results of the authors regarding PTH, SCT, and Iso actions in the rat are in preparation.

with the chloride net efflux proceeding against the electrochemical potential difference. Tubular walls are poorly permeable to water and also to phosphate ions (41). Finally, both MAL and CAL were observed to reabsorb calcium, but there is some controversy regarding the active or passive origin of calcium net transport along these two nephron portions, as recently reviewed by Suki (48).

Evidence demonstrating hormonal actions on isolated microperfused MAL and CAL tubules is rapidly accumulating.

Vasopressin

As we expected (29, 31), AVP did not affect permeability to water in rat and mouse MAL (42). In contrast, AVP was observed by Hall (22) to enhance reversibly the lumen-positive PD in microperfused mouse MAL. More recently, Hall & Varney demonstrated (23) that this effect of AVP resulted from an increase in the active component of chloride transport, since the Cl$^-$ efflux increased from 29 to 73 peq cm^{-1}sec^{-1} and the net Cl$^-$ transport, from 20 to 58 peq cm^{-1} sec^{-1} in response to vasopressin (23). Sasaki & Imai (42) confirmed these observations and showed that AVP increases PD in mouse MAL in a concentration range (5 × 10^{-11} to 5 × 10^{-9} M) similar to that reported to stimulate adenylate cyclase in rat MAL (31). In addition, 10^{-4}M of a cAMP derivative mimicked the effect of AVP in perfused mouse MAL (42). AVP also increased PD in microperfused MAL from rats, provided an hyperosmotic bathing solution was used (42). No effect of ADH on PD has so far been reported in rabbit MAL (42). However it should be recalled at this point that cyclase responsiveness to AVP is rather poor in rabbit compared to mouse and rat MAL (see Table 1).

Parathyroid Hormone

Concordant evidence is now available from in vitro rabbit tubule microperfusion experiments that PTH (0.1–1 U/ml) stimulated calcium transport in CAL (4, 26, 44, 50) but not in MAL (50), in agreement with the presence of PTH-sensitive AC in rabbit CAL and its absence in MAL (Table 1). It is worth mentioning that at first Shareghi & Stoner (45) observed no effect of PTH on Ca^{2+} transport in rabbit CAL [in contrast to connecting tubule (CNT)] by using 0.01–0.02 U/ml, whereas Shareghi & Agus later obtained an increase in calcium transport in CAL by using 1 U/ml (44). The 0.01–0.02 U/ml PTH concentration stimulated adenylate cyclase in rabbit PCT, but was below threshold in CAL (5). The PTH effects on calcium transport in CAL are mimicked by cAMP or cAMP derivatives (4, 26, 44). There is, therefore, good evidence that PTH stimulates Ca^{2+} transport in rabbit CAL via cyclase activation and cAMP generation. It was recently observed that, in addition to Ca^{2+} transport, PTH and dbcAMP also stimulate Mg^{2+} net transport in microperfused rabbit CAL (44).

Calcitonin

Contrarily to PTH, salmon calcitonin (SCT) activates adenylate cyclase strongly in MAL and poorly in CAL (see Table 1, rabbit) (7). Quite recently, Suki & Rouse (49) analyzed the effects of calcitonin on calcium transport in perfused rabbit thick limbs. As could be anticipated from the cyclase data, SCT reversibly stimulated calcium net outflux in MAL but produced no effect in CAL (49).

To sum up, available data demonstrate that the medullary and cortical portions of the rabbit thick ascending limb differ not only in cyclase responsiveness, but also in biological responsiveness to different hormones. However, one major question raised by examination of Table 1 cannot be answered yet. When several hormones activate adenylate cyclase in a nephron portion with a relatively homogeneous cell composition (as in MAL or CAL), do they all produce the same, or different biological effects? This question should be investigated in microperfused rat MAL [since this nephron portion of the rat kidney has been successfully perfused in vitro (42)] by comparing the biological effects elicited by AVP, calcitonin, and glucagon, respectively, under similar experimental conditions. Note that in rat

CAL, PTH and calcitonin effects on adenylate cyclase activity (39) and on cell cAMP accumulation (52) were observed to be nonadditive, suggesting that the two hormones stimulated the same pool of enzyme.

DISTAL CONVOLUTED TUBULE (DCT)

Some clarification regarding cell heterogeneity of DCT is needed before discussing the regulation of physiological functions via cAMP in this nephron portion. Moreover, the data concerning the rabbit and the rat will be presented separately, since marked species differences were noted with respect to hormone-dependent AC distribution along distal tubules.

Rabbit

Systematic enzyme (AC responses to hormones) (36) and ultrastructural (33) studies demonstrated that, in the rabbit, the so-called distal convoluted tubule may include up to four well-delineated, successive portions between the *macula densa* and the first branching with another tubule: (*a*) The initial DCT portion corresponds—morphologically and functionally—to the CAL terminal part extending beyond *macula densa* over a short and variable distance; (*b*) the second portion (DCT_b) has a "bright" appearance, contains essentially a single, specific cell type, and represents the genuine distal convolution; (*c*) the next portion has a "granular" appearance (DCT_g). In the rabbit kideny, most DCT (except those of very superficial nephrons) end as DCT_g and are branched with a particular portion of the cortical collecting system—the arcades—of a similar granular appearance (CCT_g). As discussed previously (25, 33, 36), DCT_g and CCT_g form a single nephron segment, the connecting tubule (CNT), since they share the same two or three intermingled cell types (granular, gray, and dark cells) and the same AC responsiveness to hormones. (*d*) Finally, in very superficial distal tubules, there is a last portion of a "light" appearance (DCT_l) similar to that of the true cortical collecting tubule (CCT_l) to which DCT_l are always branched. The DCT_l belongs to the cortical collecting tubules (CCT). DCT_l and CCT_l mainly consist of light cells with fewer intercalated or dark cells. Moreover, DCT_l and CCT_l contain cyclase with similar hormone requirements.

There is still little information concerning the permeability and transport properties of the rabbit distal convoluted tubule (DCT_b). In vitro microperfusion experiments (20, 25) revealed lumen-negative PD (about 30–40 mV) and low permeability to water in DCT_b. This negative PD value did not alter by in vivo DOCA treatment, or application of vasopressin (20, 25) or isoproterenol (25) to the tubules. Osmotic permeability to water was not increased by vasopressin in this nephron portion (20). These negative observations fit with the lack of cyclase responsiveness to AVP and isoproterenol in isolated rabbit DCT_b (36). In fact, rabbit DCT_b contained cyclase sensitive to calcitonin only (7). The biological effects induced by calcitonin in isolated DCT_b remain to be investigated.

The rabbit connnecting tubule (CNT) was shown to contain adenylate cyclase highly responsive to PTH (36) and to isoproterenol (6, 36), and poorly responsive to vasopressin (36). PTH and isoproterenol effects on AC were fully additive (6, 39), suggesting that each of the two hormones might have stimulated the enzyme contained in a different cell type (39). Physiological data indicate that vasopressin did not raise osmotic permeability to water in perfused rabbit CNT, although a limited drop in negative PD was noted in response to high AVP concentrations (25). On the other hand, isoproterenol (25) induced a marked and reversible decrease in PD which was dose-dependent in the same concentration range (10^{-8} to 10^{-5}M) as for adenylate cyclase activation (6). Finally, PTH was also reported by Shareghi et al (45) to produce effects in perfused rabbit CNT, but these effects were different from those elicited by isoproterenol. PTH induced a reversible increase in net calcium transport without any measurable change in negative PD (45). This effect of PTH on calcium in perfused rabbit CNT was confirmed by Imai (26), who showed, in addition, that PTH stimulated the efflux component of Ca^{2+} transport. Therefore, the physiological results also suggest that isoproterenol and PTH stimulated separate cell types in rabbit CNT since the two hormones produced different biological effects. Application of dbcAMP (10^{-3}M) to isolated rabbit CNT was observed by Imai (26) to mimick the PTH effect on calcium. Unfortunately this author did not mention if, in these experiments, dbcAMP also reduced the lumen-negative PD by mimicking the isoproterenol effect. In any case, further studies are needed in order to establish the permeability changes that account for the effect of isoproterenol on PD in rabbit CNT.

Rat

The well-delineated segmentation of DCT into successive portions with different morphological and enzyme properties which is observed in the rabbit is no longer present in the rat and mouse distal convoluted tubules. In these species, the connecting tubules (CNT) do not form arcades (CCT_g) containing AVP-insensitive adenylate cyclase. Most distal tubules in fact include a "light" (DCT_l) terminal portion of a variable length; it belongs to the collecting tubule, judging by its morphology, its ADH-dependent increase in osmotic permeability to water (rat, 55), and the presence of AC highly responsive to AVP [mouse (8) and man (9)]. The distal convolution itself no longer exhibits a sharp transition between its "bright" and "granular" moieties. In the rat, both portions are heterogeneous at the cell level and contain at least 4 cell types, distributed in variable proportions along their full length. In accordance with these morphological observations, the AC responses to calcitonin, isoproterenol, and PTH were not segregated as in the rabbit—but were all present (although quantitatively variable) in both DCT_b and DCT_g from the mouse (8, 16) and rat (unpublished results of the authors) kidneys.

Few physiological results are available regarding direct hormonal effects induced via cAMP in rat DCT. Costanzo & Windhager (10) performed in vivo microperfusions of distal tubules in T-PTX rats injected or not with PTH. They noted that PTH increased distal calcium reabsorption without changing sodium reabsorption. When a cAMP derivative (10^{-4}M) was added to the luminal perfusate in T-PTX control rats, calcium transport again increased in the perfused distal tubules, but, in addition, the distal Na^+ transport was also stimulated (10). These data suggest that, in rat DCT, one cell type was responsible for the PTH-dependent Ca^{2+} transport process, and another cell type—regulated by a different hormone via cAMP —was responsible for the Na^+ transport process. High doses of exogenous cAMP would stimulate both cell types and activate the two transport processes. It is worth mentioning that rat DCT contains adenylate cyclase sensitive to PTH and several other hormones as well (38).

COLLECTING TUBULE

The cortical (CCT) and medullary (MCT) collecting tubules contain mainly light cells, and also dark, intercalated cells in proportion decreasing towards the medulla. Adenylate cyclase sensitivity to various hormones in these two portions of tubule from four animal species is given in Table 2.

Vasopressin

As shown by the table, AVP stimulated this enzyme to a considerable and comparable extent in the two collecting portions from all species, suggesting that light cells contain AVP-sensitive AC. Isolated collecting tubules were shown to contain phosphodiesterase activity (32) and cAMP-dependent protein kinase activity (14), and to respond to vasopressin addition by an increase in cAMP generation from endogenous ATP (13). It is well established, on the other hand, that AVP increases diffusion and osmotic permeability to water in microperfused rabbit collecting tubules, an effect accounting for the antidiuretic action of this hormone in the mammalian kidney. Evidence demonstrating the role of cAMP as the mediator of AVP-induced permeability changes in collecting tubule cells is detailed in (19) and (47). As discussed in (19), studies using perfused rabbit collecting tubules also revealed a vasopressin-induced transient increase of active

Table 2   Hormone-sensitive adenylate cyclase in collecting tubules

Species	Nephron portion	PTH	SCT	AVP	Gluc	Iso	References
Rabbit	CCT[a]	0	0	++++	0	++	5, 6, 7, 29
	MCT	0	0	++++	0	+	
Rat	CCT	(+)	+++	++++	++	++	2, 31, 38
	MCT	0	0	++++	++	0	
Mouse	CCT	0	+	++++	NT	++	8, 16
	MCT	0	0	++++	NT	0	
Human	CCT	0	(+)	++++	NT	NT	9
	MCT	NT	0	++++	NT	NT	

[a] Abbreviations used: CCT and MCT, cortical and medullary portions of the collecting tubule. Hormone abbreviations and concentrations as in legend to Table 1. Adenylate cyclase activities are given semi-quantitatively as in Table 1. (+) indicates a reproducible but quantitatively very limited effect of the hormone.

sodium transport and of negative PD in CCT. High lumen-negative PD values were only obtained in CCT isolated from rabbits receiving a low sodium diet or from DOCA-treated rabbits. Moreover, it was recently observed in microperfused CCT from adrenalectomized rabbits (43) that corticosteroids exert in vitro a "permissive" effect on the hydroosmotic response to AVP similar to that previously described in toad bladder cells (see 47). The data suggest that this permissive effect could correspond to a corticosteroid-induced decrease in phosphodiesterase activity (43); PGE also might be involved, since they are known to blunt the CCT response to AVP (see 19).

Isoproterenol

Rabbit (6), rat, and mouse (8) CCT contain AC sensitive to β agonists. As depicted in Table 2, the AC responses to isoproterenol in CCT were lower than those to vasopressin; they were nearly absent in MCT. This pattern of response roughly correlates with dark cell distribution, suggesting that dark rather than light cells might contain AC sensitive to β agonists. This hypothesis is also supported by the observation that isoproterenol reduced negative PD without changing permeability to water in perfused rabbit CCT (25). Quite recently (24), isoproterenol was reported to decrease PD and to enhance chloride reabsorption (stimulation of Cl^- efflux) in perfused rabbit CCT; Na^+ fluxes were not affected; the effect of isoproterenol on Cl^- flux was blocked by acetazolamide (24). Thus, in rabbit CCT, isoproterenol induced biological effects that were clearly different from those induced by vasopressin. It would be of interest to investigate whether the marked depolarization induced by isoproterenol in CNT (25) also involved changes in chloride fluxes.

Parathyroid Hormone

Neither CCT nor MCT contained PTH-dependent adenylate cyclase in rabbit, mouse, or man (Table 2). In accordance with this lack of AC responsiveness, PTH was reported to induce no effect on either phosphate (11) or calcium (26) effluxes in perfused rabbit CCT.

CONCLUSION AND SUMMARY

In addition to the well established action of PTH in proximal tubules and of AVP in collecting tubules, polypeptide hormones were recently shown to regulate transport properties in other tubular portions. Although still scarce, such physiological studies using isolated perfused tubules demonstrated hormonal effects in those nephron segments observed to contain responsive adenylate cyclase and not in the others. Moreover, the same effects were elicited by applying exogenous cAMP or cAMP derivatives. There is, therefore, good evidence that hormone-dependent adenylate cyclase is involved in the cell mechanisms through which many hormones regulate tubular functions. The effects obtained varied depending on the segment of tubule used. It is not yet established whether the nature of the hormonal effect induced via cAMP is entirely specified by the responding cell types or is also specified by the hormone itself. Further studies are needed to clarify this important problem, as well as many other as yet unsolved questions. There is obviously much more to learn about the hormonal regulation of tubular cell functions by using appropriate biochemical and physiological micromethods.

Literature Cited

1. Allen, T., Tisher, C. C. 1976. Morphology of the ascending thick limb of Henle. *Kidney Int.* 9:8–22
2. Bailly, C., Imbert-Teboul, M., Chabardès, D., Hus-Citharel, A., Montégut, M., Clique, A., Morel, F. 1980. A new target site for glucagon: the distal nephron of the rat kidney. *Proc. Natl. Acad. Sci. USA* 77:3422–24
3. Baumann, K., Chan, Y. L., Bode, F., Papavassiliou, F. 1977. Effect of parathyroid hormone and cyclic adenosine 3',5'-monophosphate on isotonic fluid reabsorption: polarity of proximal tubular cells. *Kidney Int.* 11:77–85
4. Bourdeau, J. E., Burg, M. B. 1980. Effect of PTH on calcium transport across the cortical thick ascending limb of Henle's loop. *Am. J. Physiol.* 239:F121–26
5. Chabardès, D., Imbert, M., Clique, A., Montégut, M., Morel, F. 1975. PTH

sensitive adenyl cyclase activity in different segments of the rabbit nephron. *Pflügers Arch.* 354:229–39
6. Chabardès, D., Imbert-Teboul, M., Montégut, M., Clique, A., Morel, F. 1975. Catecholamine sensitive adenylate cyclase activity in different segments of the rabbit nephron. *Pflügers Arch.* 361:9–15
7. Chabardès, D., Imbert-Teboul, M., Montégut, M., Clique, A., Morel, F. 1976. Distribution of calcitonin-sensitive adenylate cyclase along the rabbit kidney tubule. *Proc. Natl. Acad. Sci. USA* 73:3608–12
8. Chabardès, D., Imbert-Teboul, M., Gagnan-Brunette, M., Morel, F. 1978. Different hormonal target sites along the mouse and rabbit nephrons. In *Biochemical Nephrology*, ed. W. G. Guder, U. Schmidt, pp. 447–54. Bern: Hans Huber. 484 pp.

9. Chabardès, D., Gagnan-Brunette, M., Imbert-Teboul, M., Gontcharevskaia, O., Montégut, M., Clique, A., Morel, F. 1980. Adenylate cyclase responsiveness to hormones in various portions of the human nephron. *J. Clin. Invest.* 65:439–48

10. Costanzo, L. S., Windhager, E. E. 1978. Effect of parathyroid hormone (PTH) and cyclic AMP on calcium (Ca)-sodium (Na) transport in the distal tubule. *Kidney Int.* 14:638 (Abstr.)

11. Dennis, V. W., Bello-Reuss, E., Robinson, R. R. 1977. Response of phosphate transport to parathyroid hormone in segments of rabbit nephron. *Am. J. Physiol.* 233:F29–38

12. Dennis, V. W., Stead, W. W., Myers, J. L. 1979. Renal handling of phosphate and calcium. *Ann. Rev. Physiol.* 41:257–71

13. Edwards, R. M., Jackson, B. A., Dousa, T. P. 1979. Differential effect of vasopressin (VP) on adenylate cyclase activity and on cyclic AMP levels in medullary thick ascending limb of Henle's loop (MAL) in rat and mouse. *Kidney Int.* 16:812 (Abstr.)

14. Edwards, R. M., Jackson, B. A., Dousa, T. P. 1980. Protein kinase activity in isolated tubules of rat renal medulla. *Am. J. Physiol.* 238:F269–78

15. Evers, C., Murer, H., Kinne, R. 1978. Effect of parathyrin on the transport properties of isolated renal brush-border vesicles. *Biochem. J.* 172:49–56

16. Gagnan-Brunette, M., Chabardès, D., Imbert-Teboul, M., Clique, A., Montégut, M., Morel, F. 1979. Hormone sensitive adenylate cyclase along the nephron of hypophosphatemic mice. *Kidney Int.* 15:357–69

17. Gilbert, P. J., Schlondorff, D., Trizna, W., Fine, L. G. 1978. Absence of PTH-induced phosphaturia with normal adenylate cyclase stimulation in the rabbit. *Proc. VIIth. Int. Congr. Nephrol., Montreal, June 1978*, E11 (Abstr.)

18. Gottschalk, C. W. 1979. Renal nerves and sodium excretion. *Ann. Rev. Physiol.* 41:229–40

19. Grantham, J. J., Irish, J. M. III, Hall, D. A. 1978. Studies of isolated renal tubules in vitro. *Ann. Rev. Physiol.* 40:249–77

20. Gross, J. B., Imai, M., Kokko, J. P. 1975. A functional comparison of the cortical collecting tubule and the distal convoluted tubule. *J. Clin. Invest.* 55:1284–94

21. Guder, W. G., Rupprecht, A. 1975. Antagonism between parathyroid hormone and norepinephrine on cyclic adenosine-3':5'-monophosphate (cAMP) levels in isolated tubules from rat kidney cortex. *Pflügers Arch.* 354:177–86

22. Hall, D. A. 1979. Possible role of vasopressin in regulating solute transport in mouse medullary thick ascending limbs of Henle's loop. *Clin. Res.* 27:A416 (Abstr.)

23. Hall, D. A., Varney, D. 1979. Effect of vasopressin on electrical potential difference and chloride transport in mouse medullary thick ascending limb of Henle's loop. *J. Clin. Invest.* 66:792–802 16:821 (Abstr.)

24. Iino, Y., Brenner, B. M. 1979. Stimulation of chloride transport by isoproterenol (Iso) in isolated rabbit cortical collecting tubule (CCT). *Kidney Int.* 16:821 (Abstr.)

25. Imai, M. 1979. The connecting tubule: a functional subdivision of the rabbit distal nephron segments. *Kidney Int.* 15:346–56

26. Imai, M. 1979. Effect of parathyroid hormone and N^6,O^2-dibutyryl cyclic AMP on Ca^{2+} transport across the rabbit distal nephron segments perfused in vitro. *1st Asian Pacific Congr. Nephrol., Tokyo, Oct. 1979*, p. 18 (Abstr.)

27. Imai, M., Kokko, J. P. 1974. Sodium chloride, urea and water transport in the thin ascending limb of Henle: generation of osmotic gradients by passive diffusion of solutes. *J. Clin. Invest.* 53:393–402

28. Imbert, M., Chabardès, D., Montégut, M., Clique, A., Morel, F. 1975. Adenylate cyclase activity along the rabbit nephron as measured in single isolated segments. *Pflügers Arch.* 354:213–28

29. Imbert, M., Chabardès, D., Montégut, M., Clique, A., Morel, F. 1975. Vasopressin dependent adenylate cyclase in single segments of rabbit kidney tubule. *Pflügers Arch.* 357:173–86

30. Imbert, M., Chabardès, D., Montégut, M., Clique, A., Morel, F. 1975. Présence d'une adenyl-cyclase stimulée par la vasopressine dans la branche ascendante des anses des néphrons du rein de lapin. *C.R. Acad. Sci. Paris* 280:2129–32

31. Imbert-Teboul, M., Chabardès, D., Montégut, M., Morel, F. 1978. Vasopressin dependent adenylate cyclase activities in the rat kidney medulla: evidence for two separate sites of action. *Endocrinology* 102:1254–61

32. Jackson, B. A., Edwards, R. M., Dousa, T. P. with technical assistance of Heublin, D. M., Braun, J. L. 1980. Measure-

ments of cyclic AMP and cyclic GMP phosphodiesterase activity in isolated tubular segments. *Kidney Int.* 18:512–18

33. Kaissling, B., Kriz, W. 1979. Structural analysis of the rabbit kidney. *Adv. Anat. Embryol. Cell Biol.* 56:1–123

34. Kinne, R., Shlatz, L. J., Kinne-Saffran, E., Schwartz, I. L. 1975. Distribution of membrane-bound cyclic AMP-dependent protein kinase in plasma membranes of cells of the kidney cortex. *J. Membr. Biol.* 24:145–59

35. Kuntziger, H., Amiel, C., Roinel, N., Morel, F. 1974. Effects of parathyroidectomy and cyclic AMP on renal transport of phosphate, calcium and magnesium. *Am. J. Physiol.* 227:905–11

36. Morel, F., Chabardès, D., Imbert, M. 1976. Functional segmentation of the rabbit distal tubule by microdetermination of hormone-dependent adenylate cyclase activity. *Kidney Int.* 9:264–77

37. Morel, F., Chabardès, D., Imbert-Teboul, M. 1976. Methodology for enzymatic studies of isolated tubular segments: adenylate cyclase. In *Methodes in Pharmacology, Vol. 4, B: Renal Pharmacology,* ed. M. Martinez-Maldonado, pp. 297–323. NY: Plenum

38. Morel, F., Chabardès, D., Imbert-Teboul, M., 1978. Heterogeneity of hormonal control in the distal nephron. *Proc. 7th Int. Congr. Nephrol., Montreal,* pp. 209–16. Basel: Karger

39. Morel, F., Chabardès, D., Imbert-Teboul, M. 1980. Distribution of adenylate cyclase activity in the nephron. *Curr. Top. Membr. Transp.* 13:415–26

40. Pastoriza, E. 1979. Effect of alpha-adrenergic stimulation and blockade in the proximal convoluted tubule (PCT) of the rat. *Kidney Int.* 16:831 (Abstr.)

41. Rocha, A. S., Magaldi, J. B., Kokko, J. P. 1977. Calcium and phosphate transport in isolated segments of rabbit Henle's loop. *J. Clin. Invest.* 59:975–83

42. Sasaki, S., Imai, M. 1980. Effects of vasopressin on water and NaCl transport across the in vitro perfused medullary thick ascending limb of Henle's loop of mouse, rat and rabbit kidneys. *Pflügers Arch.* 383:215–21

43. Schwartz, M. J., Kokko, J. P. 1980. The urinary concentration defect of adrenal insufficiency: the permissive role of adrenal steroids on the hydroosmotic response across the rabbit cortical collecting tubule. *J. Clin. Invest.* 66:234–42

44. Shareghi, G. R., Agus, Z. S. 1979. PTH sensitive magnesium transport in the rabbit cortical thick ascending limb of Henle (CTAL). *Kidney Int.* 16:837 (Abstr.)

45. Shareghi, G. R., Stoner, L. C. 1978. Calcium transport across segments of the rabbit distal nephron in vitro. *Am. J. Physiol.* 235:F367–75

46. Shlatz, L. J., Schwartz, I. L., Kinne-Saffran, E., Kinne, R. 1975. Distribution of parathyroid hormone-stimulated adenylate cyclase in plasma membranes of cells of kidney cortex. *J. Membr. Biol.* 24:131–44

47. Strewler, G. J., Orloff, J. 1977. Role of cyclic nucleotides in the transport of water and electrolytes. *Adv. Cyclic Nucleotide Res.* 8:311–60

48. Suki, W. N. 1979. Calcium transport in the nephron. *Am. J. Physiol.* 237:F1–6

49. Suki, W. N., Rouse, D. 1980. Heterogeneity of calcium transport in the medullary and cortical thick ascending limb of Henle. Effect of calcitonin. *Clin. Res.* 536A (Abstr.)

50. Suki, W. N., Rouse, D., Ng, R. C. K., Kokko, J. P. 1980. Calcium transport in the thick ascending limb of Henle. Heterogeneity of function in the medullary and cortical segments. *J. Clin. Invest.* 66:1004–9

51. Torikai, S., Imai, M. 1979. A simple method to determine adenylate cyclase activity in isolated single nephron segments by radioimmunoassay for succinyl adenosin 3'5'-cyclic monophosphate. *Tohoku J. Exp. Med.* 129:91–99

52. Torikai, S., Klein, K. L., Kurokawa, K. 1979. Effects of parathyroid hormone (PTH), calcitonin (CT) and vasopressin (VP) on adenylate cyclase (AC)—AMP (cAMP) systems in cortical thick ascending limb of Henle's loop (CTAL) of rats. *Kidney Int.* 16:841 (Abstr.)

53. Torikai, S., Kurokawa, K. 1979. Distribution of prostaglandin E_2 (PGE$_2$)-sensitive adenylate cyclase (AC) along the rat nephron. *Kidney Int.* 16:841 (Abstr.)

54. Ullrich, K. J., Rumrich, G., Klöss, S. 1977. Phosphate transport in the proximal convolution of the rat kidney. I. Tubular heterogeneity, effect of parathyroid hormone in acute and chronic parathyroidectomized animals and effect of phosphate diet. *Pflügers Arch.* 372:269–74

55. Woodhall, P. B., Tisher, C. C. 1973. Response of the distal tubule and cortical collecting duct to vasopressin in the rat. *J. Clin. Invest.* 52:3095–108

Ann. Rev. Physiol. 1981. 43:583–95
Copyright © 1981 by Annual Reviews Inc. All rights reserved

PTH, CALCITONIN, CYCLIC NUCLEOTIDES AND THE KIDNEY

Zalman S. Agus, Alan Wasserstein, and Stanley Goldfarb

Renal-Electrolyte Section, Department of Medicine, University of Pennsylvania School of Medicine, Philadelphia, Pennsylvania 19104

PARATHYROID HORMONE

Cellular Basis for PTH Action

Evidence for the mediation of the renal effects of parathyroid hormone (PTH) by intracellular cyclic AMP is derived from a series of observations. Recent studies have shown that cAMP originating from the kidney (nephrogenous cAMP) is almost entirely accounted for by PTH-stimulated production of the nucleotide (10), with most of the net addition to the urine occurring by the end of the accessible superficial proximal convoluted tubule (40). Virtually all of the physiologic actions of PTH on renal tubular function have been reproduced in clearance and micropuncture studies with either cAMP or dibutyryl cAMP administration (see below). These studies are not conclusive proofs. Many cyclic nucleotide analogs that resist hydrolysis initially are subsequently catabolized by phosphodiesterases to 5'-nucleotides and adenosine analogs. Adenosine in particular may have potent pharmacologic effects independent of cAMP and can alter adenylate cyclase activity.

PTH RECEPTORS   Many investigations have attempted to characterize the PTH–adenyl cyclase system with respect to the PTH-receptor component (19, 53, 54, 67, 68). While species differences and technical differences in the preparation of radiolabelled hormone analogs have caused discrepancies among various reports, several general features are apparent. The binding of PTH to receptors is a cell-surface phenomenon and seems to have physiologic significance: Specific binding occurs only with biologically active PTH or PTH fragments and analogs (53), or with synthetic PTH antagonists. Biologically inactive PTH fragments and other peptide hor-

0066-4278/81/0315-0583$01.00

mones such as insulin, calcitonin, glucagon, and ACTH do not bind significantly (68). Also, equilibrium displacement studies suggest that the PTH receptor is a single high-affinity binding site (Km 7–10 nM) and is present in large concentration (4–6 pmol/mg of membrane protein) (53). However, the physiologic regulation of PTH-receptor interactions has not been adequately studied.

ADENYL CYCLASE ACTIVITY   Recent studies of PTH- sensitive changes in adenylate cyclase activity have emphasized the anatomical localization of this enzyme system both within the cells of the proximal tubule and along the various nephron segments.

Intracellular localization and activation   PTH was initially shown to stimulate cAMP production primarily in a plasma membrane fraction derived from cortical rather than medullary tissue (48). More recent studies utilizing techniques capable of differentiating brush-border and basolateral cell membranes have refined these observations. Free-flow electrophoresis of membranes from rat kidney (64) showed that the activity of PTH-specific adenylate cyclase paralleled that of Na$^+$-K$^+$-activated ATPase, an enzyme located in contraluminal but not in luminal membranes. Utilizing more sophisticated separation techniques, Liang & Sacktor analyzed the response of luminal brush-border and contraluminal basal-lateral segments of the plasma membrane (41). Adenylate cyclase stimulated by PTH was found in the same distribution as Na$^+$-K$^+$ ATPase, but the brush-border membrane activity for these enzymes was one half the basolateral activity. These data suggest that cellular polarity for PTH action exists and may have functional significance, as described below. However, some controversy exists regarding the physiologic significance of in vitro studies of PTH-induced adenylate cyclase activation. Kugai et al (39) have noted that the dosages of PTH required to stimulate adenylate cyclase in either intact renal tubules or in broken cell preparations is approximately 5.5 $\times$ 10^{-8}M bPTH(1–34), while the maintenance of normal serum calcium levels in test systems is achieved by a circulating level of PTH two orders of magnitude lower. These data are preliminary and as yet unconfirmed, but they suggest the caution required in the extrapolation of in vitro data of the PTH-adenylate cyclase system to other settings.

Recent studies indicate that the adenylate cyclase enzyme system contains at least two sites, in addition to the receptor site, in which ligands interact with and alter enzyme activity: (*a*) a nucelotide regulatory site that binds preferentially to guanosine-5' triphosphate (GTP) or high concentrations of ATP, and (*b*) a catalytic site that reacts with Mg^{2+}-ATP (59). Hormones serve as regulators of the enzyme, as their binding and actions at the receptor sites facilitate activation of adenylate cyclase by GTP at the regulatory site. In addition to guanine nucleotides, recent studies have implicated intracellular calcium levels (8, 38, 79) and/or calcium-dependent regulator proteins (calmodulin) (78) as modulators of intracellular cAMP levels.

Tubular localization of adenylate cyclase activity   The intrarenal sites of PTH-sensitive adenylate cyclase activity have been detailed recently. By enzymatic analysis of anatomic subsections of isolated, collagenase-treated rabbit tubules, various hormone-dependent adenyl cyclase systems were localized (13, 14, 29, 52). These studies have significantly influenced recent research in renal tubular function. PTH-stimulated cAMP production was found in several portions of the nephron including the proximal convoluted tubule, pars recta, cortical thick ascending limb, and granular segments of the distal nephron; but no response was detected in the cortical or medullary collecting tubule, medullary thick ascending limb, or either thin limb of Henle's loop (14, 29, 52). Subsequent detailed studies of the distal nephron demonstrated several cell types as determined by visual appearance (52). The "bright" and "light" segments of the distal convoluted tubule were found to possess little if any PTH-sensitive adenylate cyclase activity while the "granular" epithelium characteristic of the arcade configuration of subsurface cortical collecting tubules (connecting tubule) as well as late segments of the distal convoluted tubule were highly responsive to PTH.

Striking differences exist for adenylate cyclase sensitivity to PTH in various nephron segments. Half-maximal stimulation was achieved with 50 mU/ml (10^{-8}M) PTH in both proximal convoluted tubule and pars recta, though the absolute peak response in the proximal convoluted tubule was twice that of the pars recta. In cortical thick ascending limb, half-maximal stimulation was only achieved with 350 mU/ml (14). Several possible explanations underlie these differences. First, the assay of adenylate cyclase in distal nephrons required disruption of cellular permeability by hypoosmotic shock in order to allow radiolabelled substrate (α-^{32}P ATP) to enter the cytosol. Whether this procedure alters cell response to PTH has not been determined, but no such effect of cell disruptions was found in the proximal tubule (29). Second, this difference may have functional significance since only high dosage of PTH (1U/ml) has been found to influence calcium transport in the cortical thick ascending limb (62) while lower doses (30mU/ml), effective in granular segments, are without effect (63). Finally, the caveat regarding interpretation of PTH-stimulated cAMP production [(39) and cited above] may apply in this setting. These problems notwithstanding, the correlation between PTH-stimulated cAMP production, particularly in the distal nephron, and studies of PTH-sensitive transport as determined in micropuncture and isolated perfused tubule studies is quite clear, as discussed below.

PTH receptors and PTH-stimulated adenylate cyclase have been identified in glomeruli, as well, by two independent techniques (19, 67). These receptors exist at relatively high concentration (1.12 pmole receptor protein/mg tissue) and PTH stimulation of adenylate cyclase occurs at a Km of 1.7×10^{-7}M PTH, both values compatible with data from studies of plasma membranes of renal cortical tubular cells.

Effects of PTH on Specific Nephron Segments

In clearance studies in humans, synthetic bPTH (1–34) infusions increase the renal excretion of phosphate, bicarbonate, sodium, and potassium and reduce the excretion of calcium and magnesium (16a). These observations confirm many earlier experiments. The infusion of cAMP mimics the phosphaturic effect of PTH, but it has been difficult to demonstrate an effect of cAMP on magnesium and calcium transport (1, 40). The latter effect has recently been reported, however, in a clearance study of the Golden Hamster (12), a species particularly sensitive to the anticalciuric effects of PTH.

PROXIMAL CONVOLUTED TUBULE   Initial studies suggested that PTH and cAMP acted to inhibit the reabsorption of fluid, sodium, calcium and phosphate in the proximal tubule of the dog (1) and rat (46). More recently, in situ microperfusion and shrinking droplet studies were utilized to study the polarity of the proximal renal tubular epithelium with respect to PTH and cAMP action by measuring changes in fluid reabsorption under the influence of each agent (3). PTH infusion in a dose of 3×10^{-9}M in the peritubular capillary plexus reduced fluid absorption by approximately 30% while intraluminal PTH led to a 4% change. Conversely, cAMP and dibutyryl cAMP, but not a series of guanyl nucleotides or ATP, led to inhibition of fluid absorption only when applied on the luminal surface in doses of 10^{-10}M.

There are several potential mechanisms whereby PTH could lead to an alteration in proximal tubular fluid reabsorption. First, there could be a specific effect to reduce sodium (fluid) permeability at the luminal membrane. Evers et al (20) studied the effects of in vitro and in vivo PTH and cAMP administration on the transport of sodium, phosphate, and glucose in brush-border membrane vesicles in the rat. In vivo administration of PTH or dibutyryl cAMP led to a dose-dependent decrease in the Na^+-dependent phosphate uptake by the brush-border membrane vesicles while there was no effect on the uptake of D-glucose, sodium, or mannitol. Both dibutyryl cAMP and PTH were ineffective when added in vitro to brush-border membrane vesicles. These data suggest that PTH does not act to alter intrinsic membrane permeability to sodium, at least in a persistent fashion. However, Taylor & Windhager (74) have recently proposed that increased cytosolic calcium levels lead to a reduction in luminal membrane permeability, and PTH has been shown to lead to a rise in cytosolic calcium in kidney epithelial cells grown in culture (8). Thus, acute changes in luminal membrane sodium permeability may occur in vivo.

A second mechanism of action of PTH on fluid absorption could involve changes in transtubular sodium permeability at the tight junctions between proximal tubular cells. Utilizing intratubular injections of radiolabelled inulin and mannitol, Lorentz showed that PTH infusion (47) or cAMP and dibutyryl cAMP infusions (46) led to an increased efflux of mannitol but not inulin, a result consistent with the suggestion that PTH alters tubular permeability. Pastoriza-Munoz et al were unable to reproduce these findings in micropuncture studies (55); but Jacobson (31), in a careful study utilizing the isolated perfused rabbit tubule preparation, showed that an analog of cAMP, 8-[P-chloro-phenylthio] cyclic 3'5' adenosine monophosphate, albeit in high concentration, increased bath-to-lumen sucrose permeability and reduced trans-epithelial potential difference, findings consistent with the data of Lorentz.

A third mechanism by which PTH could alter sodium reabsorption in the proximal tubule is by inhibition of Na^+-H^+ exchange and a reduction in bicarbonate reabsorption. At least in proximal convoluted tubules derived from the superficial cortex of the rabbit, the presence of a high luminal chloride concentration, a consequence of prior bicarbonate reabsorption, can drive volume reabsorption (32). Inhibition of Na^+-H^+ exchange would reduce preferential bicarbonate reabsorption and thereby reduce chloride concentration later in the tubule. Dennis et al (24) found that reduction in fluid absorption by PTH required the presence of bicarbonate in the tubular perfusate. It should be noted, however, that removal of bicarbonate per se from the perfusate leads to a fall in fluid absorption (17, 18), and a further inhibitory effect in such circumstances may be difficult to show. Even large doses of PTH inhibited bicarbonate and fluid reabsorption proportionally, so that proximal tubular bicarbonate concentration did not increase (28). Micropuncture studies (57) also found no disproportionate effect of PTH to elevate bicarbonate concentration in proximal tubular fluid. It thus appears that PTH-induced inhibition of bicarbonate reabsorption is not due to a primary inhibition of Na^+-H^+ exchange, since alterations in proximal tubular chloride or bicarbonate concentrations do not occur.

Taken together, the data support the view that PTH action to reduce fluid and sodium reabsorption in the proximal convoluted tubule is probably the result of altered permeability and enhanced backflux through intercellular tight junctions. However, the proximal tubule is heterogeneous with respect to fluid and phosphate (50, 75) absorption: The earliest segments more avidly reabsorb phosphate, but the later segments reabsorb fluid at a faster rate. Most of the studies outlined above fail to consider this issue; differing data could be obtained with various segments of the proximal tubule.

The mechanism of the phosphaturic effect of PTH has been extensively studied with regard to the proximal convoluted tubule. The earliest micropuncture studies of PTH action demonstrated inhibition of proximal tubular phosphate as well as sodium, fluid, and calcium transport (1). A number of subsequent micropuncture and microperfusion studies have confirmed this effect (2, 25, 55, 75). It is unclear why studies in the isolated perfused rabbit proximal convoluted tubule have failed to show inhibition of phosphate absorption by PTH in this segment (17). Initial micropuncture studies suggested that phosphate transport was closely linked to that of sodium and that the effect of PTH was to reduce sodium reabsorption with a secondary effect on phosphate reabsorption. Several observations argue against this. First, in maximally volume-expanded dogs, PTH leads to further inhibition of proximal tubular phosphate reabsorption without influencing net sodium reabsorption (77). Second, studies in brush-border membrane vesicles suggest that phosphate uptake is inhibited while sodium uptake is not influenced by in vivo PTH treatment (20). While a close dependence of phosphate uptake on sodium transport in the proximal tubule is well established (18, 69), apparently PTH does not act to reduce phosphate transport by specifically inhibiting sodium uptake. The data from studies of brush-border membrane vesicles cited above point to some alteration in components of the cell membrane induced by PTH (20). One candidate recently proposed as a membrane protein that alters phosphate uptake is alkaline phosphatase (34). However, there is no apparent effect of PTH on proximal tubular brush-border alkaline phosphatase activity (20).

Since there is no compelling evidence that PTH alkalinizes the proximal convoluted tubule fluid, the hypothesis that changes in luminal pH may be the mechanism of PTH-induced inhibition of proximal tubular phosphate reabsorption (2, 4, 76) is unlikely. Moreover, dibasic phosphate may actually be preferentially reabsorbed in the proximal tubule (4, 76). Careful studies of PTH using physiologically relevant dosages found no effect of PTH on carbonic anhydrase (21), and the infusion of PTH superimposed on maximal doses of acetazolamide leads to a rise in phosphate excretion but to no further changes in bicarbonaturia (35).

PARS RECTA   Effects of PTH beyond the proximal convoluted tubule had been inferred from micropuncture studies, and a large phosphate reabsorptive capacity beyond the accessible late superficial proximal tubule was demonstrated in the acutely parathyroidectomized dog (5). Studies in the rat showed a large, PTH-inhibitable component of phosphate transport between late proximal and early distal tubules (55). Studies utilizing isolated tubule perfusion then directly demonstrated a phosphate reabsorptive system in the pars recta (17). Phosphate transport in the pars recta occurs at a rate approximately one sixth that of the pars convoluta and is clearly inhibited by PTH (17). Morever, this PTH effect is accompanied by a small inhibition of fluid absorption in the presence of a high bicarbonate perfusate but may be completely dissociated from fluid transport during low bicarbonate, high chloride perfusion (17).

The effect of PTH on bicarbonate transport in the pars recta has also been examined. In contrast to its effects in the convoluted tubule, PTH leads to a rise in luminal bicarbonate concentration whether tubules are perfused with bicarbonate at equilibrium conditions (51) or when perfused with high bicarbonate perfusate at faster rates (28, 51). In fact, the effect of PTH in this nephron segment may account for the rise in urinary bicarbonate produced by PTH infusion. While recent studies suggest a calcium transport system in the pars recta (60), no information is yet available on the effects of PTH.

LOOP OF HENLE   Morel et al found no evidence of PTH-sensitive adenylate cyclase activity in the thin limbs of Henle's loop (14, 29), and in vitro perfusion of these nephron segments failed to reveal any net transport of calcium (58, 60) or phosphate (58). The thick ascending limb of Henle's loop contains PTH-sensitive adenylate cyclase activity (14, 29) but is far less sensitive to the hormone than more proximal segments, as noted above. While phosphate absorption does not occur along the thick ascending limb of Henle's loop (58) calcium and magnesium are transported in this segment, and absorption is stimulated by high (9, 62) but not low levels of PTH in vitro (63). In addition, both dibutyryl and 8-Br-cyclic AMP mimic the effects of PTH on this segment (9). Suki & Rouse have suggested that PTH-induced stimulation of calcium transport varies from medullary to cortical portions of the thick ascending limb (71). They noted approximately similar rates of net flux for calcium in the two segments, but PTH-stimulated calcium transport only occured in the cortical segment. These data correlate well with the finding (14) of a three-fold, statistically nonsignificant rise in cAMP production following PTH in the medullary thick ascending limb but a 15-fold rise in the cortical segments. The mechanism of these effects is unclear since the relative roles of active and passive calcium transport in this segment are controversial (70).

DISTAL NEPHRON SEGMENTS   Micropuncture studies have suggested the presence of PTH-sensitive calcium transport in the terminal portions of the nephrons (25). Recent in situ microperfusion studies directly demonstrated a greater than two-fold increase in calcium transport in the distal convoluted tubule with intravenous PTH infusion or intratubular 8-P[chloro-phenyl-thio]-cyclic AMP perfusion (16). Distal convoluted tubules containing granular epithelium and cortical collecting tubule containing granular but not light epithelium demonstrated both calcium transport and PTH-stimulated calcium transport (63). The granular epithelium was the only type found to contain PTH-sensitive adenylate cyclase (52). These data suggest that the granular segment of the distal convoluted tubule and the cortical collecting tubule is the important site of PTH action on calcium transport.

The effects of PTH on phosphate transport in the distal nephron have not been well studied. In fact, controversy persists regarding the importance of distal nephron phosphate transport vs heterogenity of function between superficial and deep nephron in modulating final urinary phosphate excretion (36). However, recent micropuncture studies in which both early and late segments of the distal convoluted tubule were punctured show unequivocal evidence of reabsorption that is inhibited by PTH (55). Whether these data represent an action in the granular epithelium has not been determined. Studies of phosphate transport in the light segment of the cortical collecting tubule have revealed a small phosphate reabsorptive system seemingly driven by purely passive forces and unaffected by PTH (61).

The last segments of the nephrons, the medullary and papillary collecting tubule system, have been evaluated in only a few studies primarily because of technical difficulties. Attempts at microinjection or microperfusion have generally revealed no evidence of transport beyond the late accessible distal nephron (23), though one microinjection study in parathyroidectomized rats did reveal a small loss of phosphate tracer reflecting efflux from tubular fluid (56). The use of a more sensitive free flow method such as retrograde microcatheterization of the inner medullary collecting duct has revealed no evidence of reabsorption of phosphate in this segment in intact rats but a small reabsorption equal to 1.3% of the filtered load in parathyroidectomized animals (6). These data combined with the absence of PTH-sensitive adenylate cyclase (52) suggest that this portion of the collecting duct system is not an important site of PTH effect.

GLOMERULUS   Glomerular receptors for PTH have been identified (19, 30, 67). Early studies of PTH action revealed a renal vasodilation and rise in glomerular filtration rate following administration of crude extracts. More recent studies, however, using highly purified PTH preparations, have generally failed to show an effect of PTH on glomerular filtration rate (1, 42, 65). Ichikawa et al (27) studied the determinants of glomerular ultrafiltration in the Munich-Wistar rat during plasma volume expansion. They found an increase in ultrafiltration coefficient (K_f) with acute thyroparathyroidectomy, and PTH infusion lowered both single-nephron and whole-kidney GFR primarily because of a decrease in K_f back to the level seen in intact animals. In addition, the effect of acute hypercalcemia to reduce glomerular filtration rate and K_f is only seen if PTH levels are maintained in the physiologic range (26). It is possible therefore that under the conditions of volume expansion or hypercalcemia, PTH does play a specific role in reducing effective filtration by reducing K_f. However, as noted above, no clear evidence exists for a role of PTH in glomerular function under other conditions.

CALCITONIN (CT)

Cellular Aspects of Calcitonin Action

Specific membrane receptors for CT (45, 49) and CT-sensitive adenylate cyclase have been demonstrated in plasma membranes isolated from renal cortex. The coupling between binding of the hormone and adenylate cyclase stimulation has been established by three lines of evidence: similar ranges of hormonal concentration for binding and enzyme stimulation, elimination of hormone binding and enzyme stimulation by treatment with a detergent (48), and reduction in CT stimulation by experimental immunologic renal disease (43).

The tubular localization of CT activity in cAMP production along the nephron has been studied in the rabbit (15), mouse (11), and human (13). Important differences have been observed. In the rabbit, CT stimulates cAMP production in the medullary ascending limb of Henle's loop, the bright segment of the distal convoluted tubule, and, to a lesser extent in the cortical thick ascending limb (15). These effects occur at near-physiologic concentrations of CT (0.07–0.1 nM). In humans, an additional site of sensitivity was found in the proximal tubule. Also, the cortical and medullary collecting tubules were found to demonstrate small degrees of CT-stimulated cAMP production (13). In the mouse, sensitivity was found in the proximal convoluted tubule, the cortical but not medullary thick ascending limbs, and the cortical collecting tubule light segment but not medullary collecting tubules (11). Thus extropolation from one species to another regarding any specific action of calcitonin on renal transport function may be hazardous.

The regulation of renal receptors for CT has been examined in a limited number of conditions. First, CT receptor sites in rat kidney membranes are increased in number, but not affinity, when animals are parathyroidectomized seven days prior to study (66). This response may have physiologic significance since adenylate cyclase stimulation by CT was also greater in this setting (66) and differences in renal physiologic response to CT have been suggested in intact vs parathyroidectomized rats. Guanyl nucleotides at any given rate of CT receptor occupancy may increase the rate of cAMP generation (44). In this respect certain similarities between the CT and PTH receptors are apparent (59).

Renal Effects of CT

The physiologic significance of CT action on the kidney is unclear. Few studies have dissected out the relative roles of changes in plasma composition and filtered load induced by CT from specific changes in tubular handling of a given species. For example, early studies in thyroidectomized, parathyroid intact rats (22) revealed transient post-prandial hypercalcemia that could account for changes in renal calcium excretion noted in balance studies. Similar results have recently been reported in thyroidectomized patients (24) in whom post-prandial elevations in serum calcium occur and are prevented by CT infusion. Also, in rats, post-prandial increases in urinary calcium excretion were noted despite no detectable elevations in serum calcium (73); however, sampling at 2 and 5 hr after feeding may have failed to detect a small elevation. Acute infusion of calcitonin has both increased and decreased urinary calcium excretion (33, 37). Preliminary studies in rabbit tubules suggest enhanced calcium transport in the medullary portion of the thick ascending limb of Henle's loop (72). More definitive studies are required before CT can be considered to play a role in regulation of urinary calcium excretion.

Careful clearance studies have shown that CT infusion into intact and parathyroidectomized experimental animals produces a variable natriuresis and a phosphaturia (33, 37) despite a progressive fall in serum phosphate levels and filtered load. This phosphaturic effect occurs in the absence of a rise in urinary cAMP excretion (7). Whether this denotes an effect of the hormone independent of the adenyl-cyclase system or merely demonstrates that excretion of cAMP and cellular activation of adenyl cyclase are dissociable phenomena is unclear.

Literature Cited

1. Agus, Z. S., Puschett, J. B., Senesky, D., Goldberg, M. 1971. Mode of action of parathyroid hormone and cyclic adenosine 3'5' monophosphate on renal tubular phosphate reabsorption in the dog. *J. Clin. Invest.* 50:617–26
2. Bank, N., Aynedjian, H. S., Weinstein, S. W. 1975. A microperfusion study of phosphate reabsorption by the rat proximal renal tubule. Effect of parathyroid hormone. *J. Clin. Invest.* 54:1040–48
3. Baumann, K., Chan, Y. L., Bode, F., Papavassiliou, F. 1977. Effect of parathyroid hormone and cyclic adenosine 3'5' monophosphate on isotonic fluid reabsorption. Polarity of proximal tubular cells. *Kidney Int.* 11:77–85
4. Baumann, K., Rumrich, G., Papavassiliou, F., Kloss, S. 1975. pH dependence of phosphate reabsorption in the proximal tubule of rat kidney. *Pfluegers Arch.* 360:183–87
5. Beck, L. A., Goldberg, M. 1973. Effects of acetazolamide and parathyroidectomy on renal transport of sodium, calcium and phosphate. *Am. J. Physiol.* 224:1136–42
6. Bengele, H. H., Lechene, C. P., Alexander, E. A. 1979. Phosphate transport along the inner medullary collecting duct of the rat. *Am. J. Physiol.* 237:F48–54
7. Bijvoet, O. L. M., Vander Sluys Veer, J., deVrie, H. R., van Koppen, A. T. J. 1971. Natriuretic effect of calcitonin in man. *N. Engl. J. Med.* 284:681–88
8. Borle, A.G., Uchikawa, T. 1978. Effects of parathyroid hormone on the distribution and transport of calcium in cul-

tured kidney cells. *Endocrinology* 102:1725–32

9. Bourdeau, J. D., Burg, M. D. 1979. Effect of parathyroid hormone on calcium transport in the cortical thick ascending limb of Henle's loop. *Clin. Res.* 27:410A

10. Broadus, A. E., Mahaffey, J. E., Bartter, F. C., Neer, R. M. 1977. Nephrogenous cyclic adenosine monophosphate as a parathyroid function test. *J. Clin. Invest.* 60:771–83

11. Brunette, M. G., Chabardes, D., Imbert-Teboul, M., Clique, A., Montegut, M., Morel, F. 1979. Hormone sensitive adenylate cyclase along the nephron of genetically hypophosphatemic mice. *Kidney Int.* 15:357–69

12. Burnatowska, M. A., Harris, C. A., Sutton, R. A. L., Dirks, J. H. 1977. Effects of PTH and cAMP on renal handling of calcium, magnesium and phosphate in the hamster. *Am. J. Physiol.* 233:F514–18

13. Chabardes, D., Gagnan-Brunette, M., Imbert-Teboul, M., Gontcharevskaia, O., Montegut, M., Clique, A., Morel, F. 1980. Adenylate cyclase responsiveness to hormones in various portions of the human nephron. *J. Clin. Invest.* 65:439–48

14. Chabardes, D., Imbert, M., Clique, A., Montegut, M., Morel, F. 1975. PTH sensitive adenyl cyclase activity in different segments of the rabbit nephron. *Pfluegers Arch.* 354:229–39

15. Chabardes, D., Imbert-Teboul, M., Montegut, M., Clique, A., Morel, F. 1976. Distribution of calcitonin-sensitive adenylate cyclase activity along the rabbit kidney tubule. *Proc. Natl. Acad. Sci. USA* 73:3608–12

16. Costanzo, L. S., Windhager, E. E. 1978. Effect of parathyroid hormone and cyclic AMP on calcium and sodium transport in the distal tubule. *Kidney Int.* 14:638

16a. Czekalski, S., Loreau, N., Paillard, R., Ardaillou, R., Fillastre, J. P., Mallet, E. 1974. Effect of bovine parathyroid hormone 1–34 fragments on renal production and excretion of adenosine 3'5' monophosphate in man. *Europ. J. Clin. Invest.* 4:85–92

17. Dennis, V. W., Bello-Reuss, E., Robinson, R. R. 1977. Response of phosphate transport to parathyroid hormone in segments of rabbit nephron. *Am. J. Physiol.* 233:F29–38

18. Dennis, V. W., Brazy, P. C. 1978. Sodium, phosphate, glucose, bicarbonate and alanine interactions in the isolated proximal convoluted tubule of the rabbit kidney. *J. Clin. Invest.* 62:387–97

19. Dousa, T. P., Barnes, L. D., Ong, S. H., Steiner, A. L. 1977. Immunohistochemical localization of 3'5' cyclic AMP and 3'5' cyclic GMP in rat renal cortex, effect of parathyroid hormone. *Proc. Natl. Acad. Sci. USA* 74:3569–73

20. Evers, C., Murer, H., Kinne, R. 1978. Effect of parathyrin on the transport properties of isolated renal brush-border vesicles. *Biochem. J.* 172:49–56

21. Garg, L. C. 1975. Effect of parathyroid hormone and adenosine 3'5' monophosphate on renal carbonic anhydrase. *Biochem. Pharmacol.* 24:437–39

22. Gray, T. K., Munson, P. L. 1969. Thyrocalcitonin: evidence for physiologic function. *Science* 166:512–13

23. Greger, R., Lang, F., Marchand, G., Knox, F. G. 1977. Site of renal phosphate reabsorption. Micropuncture and microinfusion studies. *Pfluegers Arch.* 369:111–18

24. Grubb, S. A., Decker, S. A., Talmage, R. R. 1978. The effect of thyroidal calcitonin on post-prandial plasma calcium. *Fed. Proc.* 37:925

25. Harris, C. A., Burnatowska, M. A., Seely, J. F., Sutton, R. A. L., Quamme, G. A., Dirks, J. H. 1979. Effects of parathyroid hormone on electrolyte transport in the hamster nephron. *Am. J. Physiol.* 236:F342–48

26. Humes, H. D., Ichikawa, I., Troy, J. L., Brenner, B. M. 1978. Evidence for a parathyroid hormone-dependent influence of calcium on the glomerular ultrafiltration coefficient. *J. Clin. Invest.* 61:32–40

27. Ichikawa, I., Humes, H. D., Dousa, T. P., Brenner, B. M. 1978. Influence of parathyroid hormone on glomerular ultrafiltration in the rat. *Am. J. Physiol.* 234:F393–401

28. Iino, Y., Burg, M. D. 1979. Effect of parathyroid hormone on bicarbonate absorption by proximal tubules *in vitro*. *Am. J. Physiol.* 236:F387–91

29. Imbert, M., Chabardes, D., Montegut, M., Clique, A., Morel, F. 1975. Adenylate cyclase along the rabbit nephron as measured in single isolated segments. *Pfluegers Arch.* 354:213–28

30. Imbert, M., Chabardes, D., Morel, F. 1975. Hormone sensitive adenylate cyclase in isolated rabbit glomeruli. *Molec. and Cell Endocrinol.* 1:295–304

31. Jacobson, H. R. 1979. Altered permeability in the proximal tubule in response to cyclic AMP. *Am. J. Physiol.* 236:F71–79

32. Jacobson, H. R. 1979. Characteristics of volume reabsorption in rabbit superficial and juxtamedullary proximal convoluted tubules. *J. Clin. Invest.* 63:410–18

33. Kawamura, J., Daizyo, K., Hosokawa, S., Yoshida, O. 1978. Acute effects of salmon calcitonin on renal electrolyte excretion in intact, thyroparathyroidectomized and sulfacetylthiazole-induced uremic rats. *Nephron* 21:34–44

34. Kempson, S., Knox, F. G., Dousa, T. 1977. Enzyme changes in the renal cortex induced by low phosphate diet. *Kidney Int.* 12:563–70

35. Knox, F. G., Haas, J. A., Lechene, C. P. 1976. Effect of parathyroid hormone on phosphate reabsorption in the presence of acetazolamide. *Kidney Int.* 10:216–20

36. Knox, F. G., Osswald, H., Marchand, G. R., Spielman, W. S., Haas, J. A., Berndt, T., Youngberg, S. P. 1977. Phosphate transport along the nephron. *Am. J. Physiol.* 233:F261–68

37. Koide, Y., Kugai, N., Yamashita, K., Shimatzawa, E., Ogata, E. 1976. A transient increase in renal clearance of phosphate in response to continuous infusion of salmon calcitonin in rats. *Endocrinol. Jpn.* 23:295–304

38. Kretsinger, R. H. 1979. The informational role of calcium in the cytosol. *Adv. Cyclic Nucleotide Res.* 11:1–26

39. Kugai, N., Dorantes, L., Nissenson, R., Arnaud, C. D. 1978. Parathyroid hormone receptors and stimulation of renal cyclic 3'5' AMP *in vitro:* psysiologic relevance. *Adv. Exp. Med. Biol.* 103:537–42

40. Kuntziger, H., Cailla, H. L., Amiel, C., Delaugi, M. A. 1977. Renal tubular handling of 3'5' cAMP in normal and parathyroidectomized rat. *Adv. Exp. Med. Biol.* 81:75–77

41. Liang, C. T., Sacktor, B. 1977. Preparation of cortex basal lateral and brush border membranes. Localization of adenylate cyclase and guanylate cyclase activities. *Biochem. Biophys. Acta* 466:474–87

42. Linder, A., Tremann, J. A., Plantier, J., Chapman, W., Forrey, F. W., Haines, G., Palmari, G. M. 1978. Effects of parathyroid hormone on the renal circulation and renin secretion in unanesthetized dogs. *Min. Elect. Metab.* 1:55–65

43. Loreau, N., Cosyns, J. P., Lepreux, C., Verroust, P., Ardaillou, R. 1977. Renal calcitonin receptors and adenylate cyclase in rats immunized against tubular basement membrane. *Kidney Int.* 12:184–92

44. Loreau, N., Lajotte, C., Wahle, F., Ardaillou, R. 1978. Effects of guanyl nucleotides on calcitonin-sensitive adenylate cyclase and calcitonin binding in rat tubular membranes. *J. Endocrinol.* 76:533–45

45. Loreau, N., Lepreux, C., Ardaillou, R. 1975. Calcitonin sensitive adenylate cyclase in rat tubular membranes. *Biochem. J.* 150:305–14

46. Lorentz, W. B. Jr. 1974. The effect of cyclic AMP and dibutyryl cyclic AMP on the permeability characteristics of the renal tubule. *J. Clin. Invest.* 55:1250–57

47. Lorentz, W. B. Jr. 1976. Effect of parathyroid hormone on renal tubular permeability. *Am. J. Physiol.* 231:1401–7

48. Marx, S. S., Aurbach, G. D. 1975. Renal receptors for calcitonin: coordinate occurrence with calcitonin-activated adenyl cyclase. *Endocrinology* 97:448–53

49. Marx, S. J., Fedak, S. A., Aurbach, G. D. 1972. Preparation and characterization of a hormone responsive renal plasma membrane fraction. *J. Biol. Chem.* 247:6913–18

50. McKeown, J. W., Brazy, P. C., Dennis, V. W. 1979. Intrarenal heterogeneity for fluid phosphate and glucose absorption in the rabbit. *Am. J. Physiol.* 237:F312–19

51. McKinney, T. D., Myers, P. 1979. Effect of parathyroid hormone and dibutyryl-cyclic AMP on bicarbonate transport by proximal straight tubules. *Clin. Res.* 27:424A

52. Morel, F., Chabardes, D., Imbert, M. 1976. Functional segmentation of the rabbit distal tubule by microdetermination of hormone dependent adenylate cyclase activity. *Kidney Int.* 9:264–77

53. Nichols, G. A., Carnes, D. L., Anast, C. S., Forte, L. R. 1979. Parathyroid hormone-mediated refractoriness of rat kidney cyclic AMP system. *Am. J. Physiol.* 236:F401–9

54. Nissenson, R. A., Arnaud, C. P. 1979. Properties of the parathyroid hormone receptor-adenylate cyclase system in chicken renal plasma membranes. *J. Biol. Chem.* 254:1469–75

55. Pastoriza-Munoz, E., Colindres, R. E., Lassiter, W. E., Lechene, C. 1978. Effect of parathyroid hormone on phosphate reabsorption in rat distal convolution. *Am. J. Physiol.* 235:F321–30

56. Poujoel, P., Corman, B., Touvay, C., DeRouffignac, C. 1977. Phosphate reabsorption in rat nephron terminal segments. Intrarenal heterogeneity and strain differences. *Pfluegers Arch.* 371:39–44

57. Puschett, J. B., Zurbach, P. 1976. Acute effects of parathyroid hormone on proximal bicarbonate transport in the dog. *Kidney Int.* 9:501–10

58. Rocha, A. S., Magaldi, J. B., Kokko, J. P. 1977. Calcium and phosphate transport in isolated segments of rabbit Henle's loop. *J. Clin. Invest.* 59:975–83

59. Rodbell, M., Lin, M., Solomon, Y., Londos, C., Harwood, J. P., Martin, B. R., Rendell, M., Berman, M. 1975. Role of adenosine and guanine nucleotides in the activity and response of adenylate cyclase systems to hormones. *Adv. Cyclic Nucleotide Res.* 5:3–29

60. Rouse, D., Ng, R. C. K., Suki, W. N. 1980. Calcium transport in the pars recta and thin descending limb of Henle of the rabbit perfused *in vitro. J. Clin. Invest.* 65:37–42

61. Shareghi, G. H., Agus, Z. S. 1979. Phosphate transport in the light segment of the rabbit cortical collecting tubule. *Clin. Res.* 27:430A

62. Shareghi, G. R., Agus, Z. S. 1979. PTH sensitive magnesium transport in the rabbit cortical thick ascending limb of Henle. *Kidney Int.* 16:837

63. Shareghi, G. R., Stoner, L. C. 1978. Calcium transport across segments of the rabbit distal nephron *in vitro. Am. J. Physiol.* 235:F367–75

64. Shlatz, L. J., Schwartz, I. L, Kinne-Saffran, E., Kinne, R. 1975. Distribution of parathyroid hormone-stimulated adenylate-cyclase in plasma membranes of cells of kidney cortex. *J. Memb. Biol.* 24:131–44

65. Smith, J. M., Mouw, D. R., Vander, A. J. 1979. Effect of parathyroid hormone on plasma renin activity and sodium excretion. *Am. J. Physiol.* 236:F311–19

66. Sraer, J., Ardaillou, R., Couette, S. 1975. Increased binding of calcitonin to renal receptors in parathyroidectomized rats. *Endocrinology* 95:632–37

67. Sraer, J., Sraer, J. D., Chansel, D., Jueppner, H., Hesch, R. D., Ardaillou, R. 1978. Evidence for glomerular receptor for parathyroid hormone. *Am. J. Physiol.* 235:F96–103

68. Segre, G. V., Rosenblatt, M., Reiner, B. L. Mahaffey, J. E., Potts, J. T. 1979.

Characterization of parathyroid hormone receptors in canine renal cortical plasma membranes using a radioiodinated sulfur free hormone analogue. *J. Biol. Chem.* 254:6980–86

69. Stoll, R., Kinne, R., Murer, H., Fleisch, H., Bonjour, J. P. 1979. Phosphate transport by rat renal brush border membrane vesicles. Influence of dietary phosphate, thyroparathyroidectomy and 1, 25 dihydroxy vitamin D_3. *Pfluegers Arch.* 380:47–53

70. Suki, W. N. 1979. Calcium transport in the nephron. *Am. J. Physiol.* 237:F1–F6

71. Suki, W. N., Rouse, D. 1979. Heterogeneity of calcium transport in the medullary and cortical segments of the thick ascending limb of Henle. *Kidney Int.* 16:840

72. Suki, W. N., Rouse, D. 1980. Heterogeneity of calcium transport in the medullary and cortical thick ascending limb of Henle. Effect of calcitonin. *Clin. Res.* 28:536A

73. Talmage, R. V., Vanderwiel, C. J., Decker, S. A., Grubb, S. A. 1979. Changes produced in post-prandial urinary calcium excretion by thyroidectomy and calcitonin administration in rats on different calcium regimes. *Endocrinology* 105:459–64

74. Taylor, A., Windhager, E. E. 1979. Possible role of cytosolic calcium and Na-Ca exchanges in regulation of transepithelial transport. *Am. J. Physiol.* 235:F505–12

75. Ullrich, K. J., Rumrich, G., Kloss, S. 1977. Phosphate transport in the proximal convolution of the kidney. *Pfluegers Arch.* 372:269–74

76. Ullrich, K. J., Rumrich, G., Kloss, S. 1978. Phosphate transport in the proximal convolution of the rat kidney. II. Effect of extracellular and intracellular pH. *Pfluegers Arch.* 377:33–42

77. Wen, S. F. 1974. Micropuncture studies of phosphate transport in the proximal tubule of the dog. *J. Clin. Invest.* 53:143–53

78. Wolff, D. J., Brostrom, C. O. 1979. Properties and functions of the calcium-dependent regulator protein. *Adv. Cyclic Nucleotide Res.* 11:27–88

79. Wrenn, R. W., Currie, M. G., Biddulph, D. M. 1978. Influence of calcium, parathyroid hormone and ionophore A-23187 on cyclic nucleotide concentrations of isolated renal tubules. *Mol. Cell Endocrinol.* 10:263–76

Ann. Rev. Physiol. 1981. 43:597–609

THE RENAL KALLIKREIN-KININ AND PROSTAGLANDIN SYSTEMS INTERACTION

❖1332

Alberto Nasjletti and Kafait U. Malik

Department of Pharmacology, University of Tennessee Center for the Health Sciences, Memphis, Tennessee 38163

INTRODUCTION

In 1972 McGiff and associates (27) found that renal arterial infusion of bradykinin increases the concentration of a prostaglandin E-like material in the renal venous blood of the dog, indicating a relationship between kinins and renal prostaglandins. More recently, studies by Colina-Chourio and coworkers (10) in the perfused lapine kidney suggested dependency of prostaglandin release on intrarenal kinin generation leading to the proposal that the renal kallikrein-kinin and prostaglandin systems are coupled. This review analyzes the renal kallikrein-kinin and prostaglandin systems interaction and discusses the implication of that interaction with regard to the hemodynamic and excretory functions of the kidney.

THE RENAL KALLIKREIN-KININ SYSTEM

Kinins are polypeptides released from plasma protein precursor(s) by plasma and tissue enzymes termed kallikreins (7). Bradykinin and lysyl-bradykinin, the peptide products of plasma and glandular kallikreins respectively, increase the blood flow to the kidney and the excretion of salt and water (7, 40). A kallikrein that cleaves the decapeptide lysyl-bradykinin from a protein substrate, kininogen, occurs in the kidney and is released into urine (7, 36, 40). Renal and urinary kallikrein resemble each other, but both differ markedly from plasma kallikrein (7). Renal kallikrein is synthesized

597

0066-4278/81/0315-0597$01.00

by cellular elements of the cortex (36) where it is associated with the plasma membrane fraction (52). There is evidence that the active sites of the enzyme in dispersed cortical cells face the external environment, suggesting that renal kallikrein is an ecto-enzyme (8). Kallikrein is localized in the apical region of distal convoluted tubule cells (39) at which site it is released into the tubular fluid (43). Release of kallikrein into the renal vascular compartment and interstitium has also been suggested but is less well substantiated (7).

Kallikrein interacts with kininogen to generate lysyl-bradykinin intrarenally (7, 40). This event may be regulated by one or more kallikrein inhibitors found in the kidney (16) and in urine (41). The results of a study using the stop-flow procedure suggest that kinins first appear in the tubular fluid at the level of the distal nephron (44). Lysyl-bradykinin entering the tubular compartment is in part converted to bradykinin by an aminopeptidase, and large quantities of both peptides are found in urine (40). That urinary kinins originate intrarenally (33) in the distal nephron is well accepted, but information on the source of kininogen, and on the exact site(s) of kinin generation in the distal nephron, is scarce. Kininogen occurs in plasma, and in small amounts in urine and, possibly, in the kidney; two types have been described in plasma, one having high molecular weight, the other low (7, 40). It is conceivable, but as yet unproven, that low molecular weight kininogen filters in the glomeruli and escapes tubular reabsorption in the proximal tubules, reaching sites in the distal nephron where it is acted upon by urine kallikrein, or by kallikrein at the renal distal tubular cell surface. Less likely is the possibility that the interaction of kallikrein and its substrate occurs in the renal interstitium, and that the kinin subsequently escapes into the tubular fluid.

In setting the intrarenal level of kinins, enzymes termed kininases are of major importance (13). Probably the most abundant renal kininase is a peptidyl dipeptidase, kininase II, that inactivates kinins by cleaving C-terminal Phe-Arg (13). This enzyme, which also converts angiotensin I to angiotensin II, is associated primarily, but not exclusively, with cells of the proximal tubule (13, 52). That blockade of kininase II by specific inhibitors results in a substantial increase in the urinary excretion rate of kinins indicates that degradation of kinins by kininases is of major significance in determining the intrarenal level of kinins (33). It follows that the intrarenal activity of the kallikrein-kinin system—i.e. the concentration of kinins at specific effector sites—depends on the balance between kinin generating and degrading processes within the kidney. In turn, these processes are regulated by many factors including the availability of kininogen and the concentrations of kallikrein, kininases, and their respective inhibitors (7, 40, 41).

EFFECT OF KININS ON THE RENAL ARACHIDONATE-PROSTAGLANDIN SYSTEM

Cellular elements associated with the collecting tubules, the glomeruli, the medullary interstitium, and the blood vessels of the kidney have the capacity to synthesize prostaglandins (45). The production of prostaglandins by the kidney depends largely on the availability of nonesterified arachidonic acid (20). Arachidonic acid is released from membrane phospholipids by an acylhydrolase, presumably phospholipase A_2, and transformed by a cyclooxygenase to an endoperoxide intermediate which is the common precursor of thromboxane A_2 and of prostaglandins E_2, $F_{2\alpha}$, D_2, and I_2 (29).

Renal arterial infusion of bradykinin increases the release of renal prostaglandins (5, 10, 11, 20, 24, 27, 31, 32). Augmented release of prostaglandins from an organ denotes either enhanced biosynthesis or diminished degradation of prostaglandins because there is no appreciable storage of prostaglandins in tissues (29). The release of renal prostaglandins elicited by bradykinin is brought about by stimulation of synthesis rather than by inhibition of prostaglandin degradation. The following observations suggest that kinin-induced augmentation of renal prostaglandin synthesis is the result of stimulation of the deacylation process that makes available free arachidonic acid for conversion to cyclic endoperoxides. (*a*) The release of prostaglandins induced by bradykinin from the isolated perfused lapine kidney, and from lapine renomedullary interstitial cells grown in culture, is associated with release of arachidonic acid (20, 55); (*b*) renal arterial infusion of bradykinin causes augmentation of renal phospholipase activity in the rat (3); and (*c*) the phospholipase A inhibitor, mepacrine, inhibits the release of both arachidonic acid and PGE_2 elicited by bradykinin from the rabbit renomedullary interstitial cells (55). Nonetheless, it may be premature to exclude an additional effect of kinins on the microsomal enzymes that catalyze the conversion of arachidonic acid to prostaglandin endoperoxides and the subsequent metabolism of the labile intermediates. The deacylation reaction induced by bradykinin is highly selective in that it brings about release of arachidonic acid only (19). This suggests that the kinin either activates a specific lipase that distinguishes different fatty acids in the 2-position or, alternatively, that the lipase activated by the kinin is selectively compartmentalized with phospholipids containing arachidonic acid (19). The action of bradykinin to stimulate phospholipid deacylation and, consequently, the synthesis of prostaglandins may be limited by development of tachyphylaxis. For example, the effectiveness of bradykinin to release arachidonic acid (20) and prostaglandins (11, 27) from the kidney has been shown to diminish with time during continuous infusion of the kinin.

The range of products of arachidonic acid metabolism released by kinins from the kidney has not yet been fully established. McGiff and associates found that renal arterial infusion of bradykinin in the dog stimulates release into renal venous blood of a material that has chemical, chromatographic, and biological properties comparable to those of PGE_2 (27). Others confirmed this finding and also reported elevation of urine PGE_2 during infusion of the peptide (5, 10, 11, 20, 24). Recently, it was found that bradykinin also stimulates release of $PGF_{2\alpha}$ (11) and of PGI_2 (32) from the canine kidney. Interestingly, bradykinin, previously believed to release only PGE_2 from the isolated perfused rabbit kidney, was shown to release also thromboxane A_2 from the hydronephrotic lapine kidney (31), suggesting that the profile of prostaglandins released from the kidney by a kinin may vary with the experimental conditions. There is evidence that the predominant end-product of prostaglandin endoperoxide metabolism differs among the different cells and regions of the kidney (29)—e.g. PGE_2 and PGI_2 are major products of synthesis in the renal medulla and in the arterial blood vessels of the renal cortex, respectively (50, 53). Consequently, it is conceivable that kinins may promote synthesis of dissimilar prostaglandins in various cells types, and in the same cell type during varying experimental conditions.

THE RENAL KALLIKREIN-KININ AND PROSTAGLANDIN SYSTEMS INTERACTION

Evidence that the renal kallikrein-kinin and prostaglandin systems are interrelated comes from work defining (a) relationships between urinary excretion rates of kallikrein and prostaglandins, (b) the effect of alterations in the activity of the renal kallikrein-kinin system on renal prostaglandin production, and (c) the effect of prostaglandins and of prostaglandin synthesis inhibitors on the renal kallikrein-kinin system.

Relationship Between Urinary Kallikrein and the Urinary Excretion of Renal Prostaglandins

Several recent studies indicate associated disturbances in the activities of the renal kallikrein-kinin and prostaglandin systems in patients with Bartter's syndrome, and in subjects or animals receiving loop diuretics or sodium-retaining steroids. As prostaglandins in urine arise within the kidney, their rate of excretion is considered an index of renal prostaglandin production (11). Patients with Bartter's syndrome exhibit augmented urine PGE_2 excretion correlated positively with increased output of urinary kallikrein (17, 51). Similarly, the excretion into urine of both PGE_2 and kallikrein increases during the early phase following administration of loop diuretics (1, 37); in one study the rise in urine PGE_2 caused by furosemide (1 mg/kg, i.v.) in normal subjects was correlated positively with increments in urinary excretion of kinins and kallikrein (1). DOCA (5 mg/day), or aldosterone (0.25 mg/day), after a few days of treatment, increases the urinary output of both kallikrein and PGE-like material in the rat (35). Similarly, fluorocortisone (0.2. mg/day), which causes elevation of urinary kallikrein, also was reported to increase urine $PGF_{2\alpha}$ and PGE_2 excretion rate in humans (12).

Collectively, these observations relating the excretion rates of kallikrein and PGE_2 into urine suggest, but do not prove, that the renal kallikrein-kinin and prostaglandin systems are interrelated. For example, a positive relationship between urine PGE_2 and kallikrein is not always apparent. Normal subjects receiving DOCA (20 mg/day) for 10 days exhibit elevated urinary excretion of kallikrein but not of PGE_2 (54). Similarly, deprivation of dietary sodium for 12 days in the rat results in augmented kallikrein excretion while the urinary output of both PGE- and PGF-like material falls (34).

Effect of Alterations in the Activity of the Renal Kallikrein-Kinin System on Renal Prostaglandin Production

To investigate relationships between intrarenal generation of kinins and renal prostaglandins, Colina-Chourio and associates (10) studied the effect of kininogen, the inactive substrate of kallikrein, on prostaglandin release from the isolated lapine kidney perfused with Krebs solution. Kininogen, like bradykinin, was found to increase the venous and urinary efflux of prostaglandins, primarily of PGE_2-like material. Aprotinin, a kallikrein inhibitor, reduced the release of prostaglandin induced by kininogen but not that by bradykinin. This suggests that augmentation of renal prostaglandin production in response to kininogen is related to utilization of kininogen by renal kallikrein to generate a kinin that stimulates synthesis of renal prostaglandins. A corollary of this conclusion is that kinins generated within the kidney cause stimulation of renal prostaglandin production, which implies coupling of the renal kallikrein-kinin and prostaglandin systems (10).

Consonant with this conclusion are the results of a recent study of the effect of inhibition of peptidyl dipeptidase (kininase II or angiotensin I converting enzyme) on urine PGE_2 excretion in the rat pretreated with DOCA (4). Inhibition of this enzyme reduces intrarenal kinin degradation, resulting in increased kinin levels within the kidney reflected by augmentation of urinary kinin excretion (33, 38). Infusion of the peptidyl dipeptidase inhibitor Teprotide (SQ-20881, 1.2 mg/day, s.c., for 6 days) into rats pretreated with DOCA (5 mg/day for 10 days) increased urine PGE_2 excretion (4). This effect of Teprotide may relate to augmentation of renal prostaglandin production consequent to a rise in renal kinin levels. However, Teprotide does not increase urine PGE_2 in rats pretreated with the vehicle of DOCA only (4). Similarly, another inhibitor of peptidyl dipeptidase, Captopril, does not change urine prostaglandin excretion in the normal dog (38). Considering that blockade of this enzyme also results in lowering of plasma and tissue levels of angiotensin II (13), and that the latter stimulates prostaglandin synthesis (11), it is possible that in the normal dog and rat inhibition of peptidyl dipeptidase is not associated with elevated urine PGE_2 because the effect on renal PGE_2 production of an increase in kinins is offset by that of a reduction in angiotensin II. Such may not be the case in the DOCA-treated animal because the action of the steroid to suppress plasma renin, and consequently to reduce the formation of angiotensin, precludes any further lowering of angiotensin II levels by the inhibitor of peptidyl dipeptidase.

Additional evidence linking the renal kallikrein-kinin and prostaglandin systems comes from studies on the effect of kallikrein inhibition on urinary prostaglandin excretion. In the rat, daily administration of the kallikrein inhibitor, aprotinin, (100,000 units/day) reduced the urinary excretion of PGE_2 by 63% and 67% after one and three days of treatment; this was associated with decreased kallikrein activity in both urine and renal tissue (35). Similarly, aprotinin reduced urine PGE_2 excretion in rats that had been pretreated with DOCA to increase both renal kallikrein and basal renal PGE_2 production; the decrease in PGE_2 excretion caused by the enzyme inhibitor was correlated with reduction of kallikrein activity in both urine and the kidney (35). Aprotinin also reduced the urinary excretion rate of PGE_2 in the rat during acute saline loading, which increases the basal excretion of PGE_2, and in the non-volume expanded animal (23). Inasmuch as the effect of aprotinin in lowering urine PGE_2 excretion is most likely related to reduction of intrarenal kinin formation, these observations suggest that a product of renal kallikrein activity promotes production of PGE_2 by the kidney. That the renal kallikrein-kinin system also influences renal production of arachidonic acid metabolites other than PGE_2 is a distinct possibility that has not been addressed.

The sites and regions where the renal kallikrein-kinin and prostaglandin systems interact are not established nor is the route followed by lysyl-bradykinin to sites of prostaglandin synthesis. Since renal kallikrein is a cortical enzyme (7), it is conceivable that its peptide product promotes prostaglandin synthesis in renal cortical structures. Also, it is possible that lysyl-bradykinin produced in the distal nephron travels via the tubule to the renal medulla where the peptide stimulates production of prostaglandins in cellular elements associated with the collecting tubules, the medullary interstitium, and blood vessels. An additional possibility, suggested by the finding of small amounts of kallikrein in the medulla and papilla of the kidney, is that tubular fluid kallikrein crosses the collecting duct epithelium and enters the medullary interstitium to generate a kinin close to sites of prostaglandin synthesis in the renal medulla. An alternate route of transport of kallikrein and kinins via the blood stream to sites of prostaglandin synthesis in the renal medulla cannot be excluded.

Effect of Prostaglandins and of Prostaglandin Synthesis Inhibitors on the Renal Kallikrein-Kinin System

Because renal arterial infusion of PGE_1 elevates the urinary excretion of kallikrein in the dog, an involvement of prostaglandins in the release or activation of renal kallikrein was suggested (30). Consonant with this possibility are the following findings: (a) Treatment with an inhibitor of prostaglandin synthetase lowers urinary kallikrein excretion in patients with Bartter's syndrome (51); and (b) phospholipase A_2 activates a kallikrein-like esterase in suspended renal cortical cells (8). However, the rise in urinary kallikrein caused by administration of DOCA to normal subjects was not affected by indomethacin or ibuprofen (54). Further studies are needed to clarify a possible relationship between the arachidonate-prostaglandin system and the activation of renal kallikrein.

RENAL FUNCTION AS AFFECTED BY THE INTERACTION BETWEEN THE RENAL KALLIKREIN-KININ AND PROSTAGLANDIN SYSTEMS

The intrarenal infusion of the prostaglandin precursor, arachidonic acid, produces renal vasodilatation, diuresis, and natriuresis, which are consequences of augmented renal prostaglandin synthesis, most probably of PGI_2 and PGE_2 (49). PGI_2 and PGE_2, major end products of prostaglandin endoperoxide metabolism in the renal cortex and medulla (53), respectively, share the ability to increase renal blood flow and the excretion of water and sodium (6), and to reduce renal vascular reactivity (18, 48). Renal arterial infusion of bradykinin stimulates renal synthesis of PGE_2 and PGI_2, and this is associated with effects on renal hemodynamic and excretory functions similar to those of arachidonic acid, PGE_2, and PGI_2 (5). That many of the renal actions of kinins are reduced by inhibitors of cyclooxygenase suggests involvement of prostaglandins in the actions of the peptide.

Contribution of Renal Prostaglandins to Kinin Effects on Vascular Reactivity

Recent studies suggest that stimulation of renal prostaglandin synthesis by kinins results in reduced reactivity of the renal vasculature to sympathetic stimuli and angiotensin II. In the isolated lapine kidney perfused with Tyrode's solution, bradykinin at 1–100 ng/ml reduces the vasoconstriction produced by norepinephrine (50–75 ng) or by electrical stimulation of renal sympathetic nerves (3 Hz, 1 msec duration for 22 sec) and greatly enhances the renal output of a PGE-like material (25). Indomethacin (1 μg/ml) suppresses the basal and the bradykinin-evoked output of prostaglandins and significantly diminishes the inhibitory action of the peptide on the renal vasoconstrictor response to both adrenergic stimuli (25). Similar observations have been made in the in situ kidney of the dog. Renal arterial infusion of bradykinin at 10 ng/kg/min inhibits by 25–40% the lowering of renal blood flow elicited by sympathetic nerve stimulation or norepinephrine (47). Following inhibition of prostaglandin synthesis by sodium meclofenamate, the inhibitory action of kinin on adrenergically induced vasoconstriction is not apparent (47). Renal arterial infusion of bradykinin at 10 ng/kg/min also interferes with the vasoconstrictor effect of angiotensin II in the canine kidney (48). Pretreatment of the animals with sodium meclofenamate to inhibit prostaglandin synthesis results in blunting of the inhibitory action of the kinin (48).

Collectively, these observations suggest that bradykinin reduces the reactivity of the renal vasculature to pressor hormones by a mechanism related to prostaglandin synthesis. Consonant with this interpretation are observations that the major prostaglandins released from the kidney by bradykinin, PGE_2 and PGI_2, also attenuate angiotensin II and norepinephrine-induced vasoconstriction in the kidney (18, 48). From this it may be inferred that one or more prostaglandins produced by the kidney during infusion of bradykinin mediate(s) the action of the peptide in reducing the reactivity of the renal vasculature to angiotensin II and adrenergic stimulation.

Contribution of Renal Prostaglandin to Kinin Effects on Renal Hemodynamics

Inhibition of prostaglandin synthesis by indomethacin was reported to reduce the vasodilatory action of bradykinin in the isolated canine kidney perfused with blood (28), which implies contribution of prostaglandins to the action of kinin on renal hemodynamics. Contrasting with this finding, several other studies indicate that prostaglandin synthesis blockade does not attenuate the increase in renal blood flow induced by bradykinin in the dog (5, 14). Indeed, the vasodilatation elicited by bradykinin in the canine kidney and in the blood-perfused feline kidney was potentiated by inhibitors of prostaglandin synthesis in two studies (9, 24). It appears, then, that prostaglandins produced by the kidney during infusion of bradykinin in vivo do not contribute to the renal vascular actions of the peptide. This is intriguing because two of the arachidonic acid metabolites released from the kidney by bradykinin, i.e. PGE_2 and PGI_2, have a demonstrated capacity to increase renal blood flow (6, 49).

Contribution of Renal Prostaglandins to Kinin Effects on Renal Excretory Function

Bradykinin infused into the renal artery interferes with reabsorption of water and sodium causing, like PGE_2 and PGI_2, diuresis and natriuresis (5, 7, 33). Blockade of prostaglandin synthesis by indomethacin was reported to reduce the diuretic action of bradykinin in the isolated blood-perfused canine kidney (28), suggesting involvement of prostaglandins in the action of the peptide on water excretion. In contrast, the action of bradykinin infused intrarenally to increase urine volume in the pentobarbital anesthetized dog during water diuresis is not affected by prostaglandin synthesis blockade (5). As the kinin greatly increases the renal synthesis of PGE_2, failure to appreciate involvement of the prostaglandin in the kinin action may relate to the particular experimental conditions, i.e. water diuresis. PGE_2 is known to antagonize the tubular actions of vasopressin (15); it follows that the effect on urine volume of PGE_2 synthesis stimulation by a kinin is likely to be less apparent during water diuresis because plasma vasopressin levels are low.

Blockade of prostaglandin synthesis by sodium meclofenamate in the pentobarbital anesthetized dog during water diuresis was reported to suppress both the bradykinin-induced output of PGE-like substance and the associated natriuresis (5). As the inhibitor of cyclooxygenase does not affect the natriuresis induced by PGE_2, this observation suggests contribution of prostaglandins to the action of bradykinin in increasing urinary sodium. There is evidence that both bradykinin and PGE_2 increase urinary sodium excretion by interfering with sodium reabsorption by the distal nephron. Injection of either PGE_2 or bradykinin into surface convolutions of late proximal tubules in the rat inhibits the efflux of ^{22}Na in distal nephron segments (21, 22), which is consistent with reduction of tubular reabsorption. PGE_2 also inhibits sodium transport in isolated perfused segments of lapine cortical and medullary collecting tubules (46). It is possible, then, that PGE_2 mediates the kinin-induced natriuresis by reducing sodium reabsorption in the distal nephron.

Possible Physiological Significance of the Renal Kallikrein-Kinin and Prostaglandin Systems Interaction

Two major conclusions emerge from the preceding sections of this review: (a) Kinins generated within the kidney promote synthesis of renal prostaglandins; and (b) prostaglandins produced by the kidney during bradykinin infusion mediate the action of the peptide to increase urinary sodium excretion and to reduce the reactivity of the renal vasculature to both angiotensin II and adrenergic stimuli. Assuming that there are no differences in the effects of renal prostaglandin synthesis stimulation by the product of renal kallikrein and by exogenous kinins on the function of the kidney, it would be reasonable to propose that the renal kallikrein-kinin and prostaglandin systems interaction is a feature of mechanisms influencing renal hemodynamic and excretory functions. Positive evidence that such is the case is lacking, as yet, but several experimental observations are compatible with such a proposition.

Depending on the experimental conditions, the activity of vasoconstrictor systems, and the state of sodium balance, prostaglandins produced intrarenally may influence renal blood flow, its intrarenal distribution, the excretion of water and electrolytes, and renal vascular reactivity. This is inferred primarily from observations that blockade of renal prostaglandin synthesis is associated with: (a) lowering of renal blood flow during conditions that cause elevation of angiotensin II levels or of renal sympathetic activity (42); (b) augmentation of renal vascular reactivity to angiotensin II and adrenergic stimuli (2); (c) increased sensitivity to vasopressin (15); and (d) reduction of urinary sodium excretion (15). These findings are taken as evidence that prostaglandins produced by the kidney may influence its function by promoting vasodilatation, opposing the vasoconstrictor actions of angiotensin II and norepinephrine, antagonizing the actions of vasopressin on water reabsorption, and interfering with sodium reabsorption.

There is also evidence that the function of the kidney may be affected by alterations in the activity of the renal kallikrein-kinin system. The rise in intrarenal kinin levels following inhibition by Teprotide of kinin degradation is associated with renal vasodilatation, diuresis, and natriuresis (33). In contrast, inhibition of kallikrein by aprotinin decreases renal plasma flow, glomerular filtration rate, urine volume, and urinary excretion of sodium and potassium in the saline expanded rat, without affecting blood pressure (23). In another study, administration of aprotinin for 4 days to normal rats, or to rats pretreated with DOCA, resulted in reduced sodium excretion during the first 24–48 hr of treatment but not thereafter (35). Furthermore, bradykinin antibodies capable of blocking the biological actions of the peptide were reported to reduce the natriuretic response to saline loading in the rat (26). Collectively, the foregoing observations suggest that the renal kallikrein-kinin system influences renal hemodynamic and excretory functions by promoting vasodilatation and natriuresis. Involvement of prostaglandins in such events is a distinct possibility that needs to be fully evaluated.

ACKNOWLEDGMENTS

The authors extend their appreciation and apologies to the many researchers whose contributions to the literature were invaluable in the preparation of this manuscript but which, because of space limitations, could not be cited. We also thank P. Norton and B. Chandler for assistance and Dr. P. Baer for suggestions. A. Nasjletti and K. U. Malik are the recipients of USPHS Career Research Development Awards 1 K04 HL 00163 and 5 K04 HL 00142, respectively.

Literature Cited

1. Abe, K., Irokawa, N., Yasujima, M., Seino, M., Chiba, S., Sakurai, Y., Yoshinaga, K., Saito, T. 1978. The kallikrein-kinin system and prostaglandins in the kidney: Their relationship to furosemide-induced diuresis and to the renin-angiotensin-aldosterone system in man. *Circ. Res.* 43:254–60
2. Aiken, J. W., Vane, J. R. 1973. Intrarenal prostaglandin release attenuates the renal vasoconstrictor activity of angiotensin. *J. Pharmacol. Exp. Ther.* 184:678–87
3. Antonello, A., Tremolada, C., Baggio, B., Buin, F., Favaro, S., Piccoli, A., Borsatti, A. 1978. In vivo activation of renal phospholipase activity by bradykinin in the rat. *Prostaglandins* 16:23–29
4. Barr, J. G., Diz, D., Kauker, M. L., Nasjletti, A. 1980. Effect of SQ-20881 on urinary prostaglandin excretion in the conscious rat. *Fed. Proc.* 39(3):827 (Abstr.)
5. Blasingham, M. C., Nasjletti, A. 1979. Contributions of renal prostaglandins to the natriuretic action of bradykinin in the dog. *Am. J. Physiol.* 237:F182–87
6. Bolger, P. M., Eisner, G. M., Ramwell, P. W., Slotkoff, L. M. 1978. Renal actions of prostacyclin. *Nature* 271:467–69
7. Carretero, O. A., Scicli, A. G. 1980. The renal kallikrein-kinin system. *Am. J. Physiol.* 238:F247–55
8. Chao, J., Margolius, H. S. 1979. Studies on rat renal cortical cell kallikrein II. Identification of kallikrein as an ecto-enzyme. *Biochem. Biophys. Acta* 570:330–40
9. Chapnick, B.M., Paustian, P. W., Feigen, L. P., Joiner, P. D., Hyman, A. L., Kadowitz, P. J. 1977. Influence of inhibitors of prostaglandin synthesis on renal vascular resistance and renal vascular responses to vasopressor and vasodilator agents in the cat. *Circ. Res.* 40:348–57
10. Colina-Chourio, J., McGiff, J. C., Miller, M. P., Nasjletti, A. 1976. Possi-ble influence of intrarenal generation of kinins on prostaglandin release from the rabbit perfused kidney. *Br. J. Pharmacol.* 58:165–72
11. Dunn, M. J., Liard, J. F., Dray, F. 1978. Basal and stimulated rates of renal secretion and excretion of prostaglandins E_2 $F_{2\alpha}$, and 13,14-dihydro-15-keto F_α in the dog. *Kidney Int.* 13:136–43
12. Durr, J., Maron, H., Favre, L., Vallotton, M. B. 1979. Is the renal escape to mineralocorticoid mediated by prostaglandins in man? *Acta Endocrinol.* 91:Suppl. 225, p. 383
13. Erdos, E. G. 1979. Inhibitors of kininases. *Fed. Proc.* 38:2774–77
14. Feigen, L. P., Chapnick, B. M., Flemming, J. E., Kadowitz, P. J. 1978. Prostaglandins: Renal vascular responses to bradykinin, histamine, nitroglycerine. *Am. J. Physiol.* 234:H496–502
15. Fejes-Toth, G., Magyar, A., Walter, J. 1977. Renal response to vasopressin after inhibition of prostaglandin synthesis. *Am. J. Physiol.* 232:F416–23
16. Geiger, R., Mann, K. 1976. A kallikrein-specific inhibitor in rat kidney tubules. *Hoppe-Seyler's Z. Physiol. Chem.* 357:553–58
17. Halushka, P. V., Wohltmann, H., Privitera, P. J., Hurwitz, G., Margolius, H. S. 1977. Bartter's syndrome: Urinary prostaglandin E-like material and kallikrein; indomethacin effects. *Ann. Int. Med.* 87:281–86
18. Hedquist, P. 1979. Actions of prostacyclin (PGI_2) on adrenergic neuroeffector transmission in the rabbit kidney. *Prostaglandins* 17:249–58
19. Hsueh, W., Isakson, P. C., Needleman, P. 1977. Hormone selective lipase activation in the isolated rabbit heart. *Prostaglandins* 13:1073–91
20. Isakson, P. C., Raz, A., Denny, S. E., Wyche, A., Needleman, P. 1977. Hormonal stimulation of arachidonate release from isolated perfused organs. Relationship to prostaglandin biosynthesis. *Prostaglandins* 14:853–71

21. Kauker, M. L. 1977. Prostaglandin E_2 effect from the luminal side on renal tubular ^{22}Na efflux: tracer microinjection studies. *Proc. Soc. Exp. Biol. Med.* 154:274–77

22. Kauker, M. L. 1980. Bradykinin action on the efflux of luminal ^{22}Na in the rat nephron. *J. Pharmacol. Exp. Ther.* 214:119–23

23. Kramer, H. J., Moch, T., Von Sicherer, L., Dusing, R. 1979. Effects of aprotinin on renal function and urinary prostaglandin excretion in conscious rats after acute salt loading. *Clin. Sci.* 56:547–53

24. Lonigro, A. J., Hageman, M. H., Stephenson, A. H., Fry, C. L. 1978. Inhibition of prostaglandin synthesis by indomethacin augments the renal vasodilator response to bradykinin in the anesthetized dog. *Circ. Res.* 43:447–55

25. Malik, K. U., Nasjletti, A. 1979. Attenuation by bradykinin of adrenergically induced vasoconstriction in the isolated perfused rabbit kidney: Relationship to prostaglandin synthesis. *Br. J. Pharmacol.* 67:269–75

26. Marin-Grez, M. 1974. The influence of antibodies against bradykinin on isotonic saline diuresis in the rat: evidence for kinin involvement in renal function. *Pflügers Arch.* 350:231–39

27. McGiff, J. C., Terragno, N. A., Malik, K. U., Lonigro, A. J. 1972. Release of a prostaglandin E-like substance from canine kidney by bradykinin. *Circ. Res.* 31:36–43

28. McGiff, J. C., Itskovitz, H. D., Terragno, N. A. 1975. The actions of bradykinin and eledoisin in the canine isolated kidney: relationship to prostaglandins. *Clin. Sci. Mol. Med.* 49:125–31

29. McGiff, J. C., Wong, P. Y. K. 1979. Compartmentalization of prostaglandins within the kidney: implications for renal function. *Fed. Proc.* 38:89–93

30. Mills, I. H., Obika, L. F. O. 1977. Increased urinary kallikrein excretion during prostaglandin E_1 infusion in anesthetized dogs and its relation to natriuresis and diuresis. *J. Physiol. London* 273:459–74

31. Morrison, A. R., Mishikawa, K., Needleman, P. 1978. Thromboxane A_2 biosynthesis in the ureter obstructed isolated perfused kidney of the rabbit. *J. Pharmacol. Exp. Ther.* 205:1–8

32. Mullane, K. M., Moncada, S., Vane, J. R. 1980. Prostacycline release induced by bradykinin may contribute to the antihypertensive action of angiotensin-converting enzyme inhibitors. In *Adv. Prostagl. Thrombox. Res.* 7:1159–61

33. Nasjletti, A., Colina-Chourio, J., McGiff, J. C. 1975. Disappearance of bradykinin in the renal circulation of dogs: effects of kininase inhibition. *Circ. Res.* 37:59–65

34. Nasjletti, A., Malik, K. U. 1980. Interrelationship of the renal kallikrein-kinin and prostaglandin systems. In *Enzymatic Release of Vasoactive Peptides,* ed. F. Gross, and G. Vogel, pp. 323–34. NY: Raven

35. Nasjletti, A., McGiff, J. C., Colina-Chourio, J. 1978. Interrelations of the renal kallikrein-kinin system and renal prostaglandins in the conscious rat. *Circ. Res.* 43:799–807

36. Nustad, K., Vaaje, K., Pierce, J. V. 1975. Synthesis of kallikreins by rat kidney slices. *Br. J. Pharmacol.* 53:229–34

37. Olsen, U. B., Ahnfelt-Rone, I. 1976. Bumetanide induced increase of renal blood flow in conscious dogs and its relation to local renal hormones. *Acta Pharmacol. Toxicol.* 219–28

38. Olsen, U. B., Arrigoni-Martelli, E. 1979. The effects of kininase II inhibition by SQ 14225 on kidney kallikrein-kinin and prostaglandin systems in conscious dogs. *Eur. J. Pharmacol.* 54:229–34

39. Orstavik, T. B., Nustad, K., Brandtzaeg, P., Pierce, J. V. 1976. Cellular origin of urinary kallikrein. *J. Histochem. Cytochem.* 24:1034–39

40. Pisano, J. J., Corthorn, J., Yates, K., Pierce, J. V. 1978. The kallikrein-kinin system in the kidney. *Contrib. Nephrol.* 12:116–25

41. Ryan, J. W., Oza, N. B., Martin, L. C., Pena, G. A. 1979. Components of the kallikrein-kinin system in urine. *Adv. Exp. Med. Biol.* 120A:313–23

42. Satoh, S., Zimmerman, B. G. 1975. Influence of the renin-angiotensin system on the effect of prostaglandin synthesis inhibitors in the renal vasculature. *Circ. Res.* 36, 37: Suppl. I pp. 189–95

43. Scicli, A. G., Carretero, O. A., Hampton, A., Cortes, P., Oza, N. B. 1976. Site of kininogenase secretion in the dog nephron. *Am. J. Physiol.* 230:533–36

44. Scicli, A. G., Gandolifi, R., Carretero, O. A. 1978. Site of formation of kinins in the dog nephron. *Am. J. Physiol.* 234:F36–40

45. Smith, W. L., Bell, T. G. 1978. Immunohistochemical localization of the prostaglandin forming cyclooxygenase in renal cortex. *Am. J. Physiol.* F451–57

46. Stokes, J. B., Kokko, J. P. 1977. Inhibition of sodium transport by prostaglandin E₂ across the isolated, perfused rabbit collecting tubule. *J. Clin. Invest.* 59:1099–104

47. Susic, H., Nasjletti, A., Malik, K. U. 1980. Inhibition by bradykinin of the vasoconstrictor responses to sympathetic nerve stimulation and norepinephrine in the canine kidney: Relationship to prostaglandin synthesis. *Fed. Proc.* 39(3):997 (Abstr.)

48. Susic, H., Nasjletti, A., Malik, K. U. 1981. Inhibition by bradykinin of the vascular effects of pressor hormones in the canine kidney: Relationship to prostaglandins. *Clin. Sci.* In press

49. Tannenbaum, J., Splawinski, J. A., Oates, J. A., Nies, A. S. 1975. Enhanced renal prostaglandin production in the dog; effects on renal function. *Circ. Res.* 36:197–203

50. Terragno, N. A., Terragno, A., Early, J. A., Roberts, M. A., McGiff, J. C. 1978. Endogenous prostaglandin synthesis inhibitor in the renal cortex: Effects on production of prostacyclin by renal blood vessels. *Clin. Sci. Mol. Med.* 55:S199–202

51. Vinci, J. M., Gill, J. R., Bowden, R. D., Pisano, J. J., Izzo, J. L., Radfar, N., Taylor, A. A., Zusman, R. M., Bartter, F. C., Keiser, H. R. 1978. The kallikrein-kinin system in Bartter's syndrome and its response to prostaglandin synthetase inhibition. *J. Clin. Invest.* 61:1671–82

52. Ward, P. E., Erdos, E. G., Gedney, C. D., Dowben, R. M. Reynolds, R. C. 1976. Isolation of membrane bround renal enzymes that metabolize kinins and angiotensins. *Biochem. J.* 157:643–50

53. Whorton, A. R., Smigel, M., Oates, J. A., Frolich, J. C. 1978. Regional differences in prostacyclin formation by the kidney. Prostacyclin is a major prostaglandin of renal cortex. *Biochem. Biophys. Acta* 529:176–80

54. Zipser, R. D., Zia, P., Stone, R. A., Horton, R. 1978. The prostaglandin and kallikrein-kinin systems in mineralocorticoid escape. *J. Clin. Endocrin. Med.* 47:996–1001

55. Zusman, R. M., Keiser, H. R. 1977. Prostaglandin E₂ biosynthesis by rabbit renomedullary interstitial cells in tissue culture: Mechanism of stimulation by angiotensin II, bradykinin, and arginine vasopressin. *J. Biol. Chem.* 252:2069–71

Ann. Rev. Physiol. 1981. 43:611–24

ANTIDIURETIC HORMONE[1] ✦1333

Joseph S. Handler and Jack Orloff

Laboratory of Kidney & Electrolyte Metabolism, National Heart, Lung, and
Blood Institute, National Institutes of Health, Bethesda, Maryland 20205

This short review summarizes selected recent developments in our understanding of the mechanism of action of antidiuretic hormone (ADH). The subject has been reviewed in greater detail elsewhere (4, 22, 24–26, 30, 56).[2] After briefly considering the effects of ADH along the nephron, this review focuses on the control and the cellular mechanism of those effects that result in antidiuresis.

SITES OF THE EFFECTS ON TRANSPORT AND PERMEABILITY

In the limited range of mammalian species studied, ADH directly affects the glomerulus, medullary and cortical thick ascending limb, the connecting tubule, cortical and medullary collecting ducts, and papillary lining cells.

In the physiological concentration range ADH does not alter glomerular filtration rate (GFR) in mammals. Ichikawa & Brenner (27) found, however, that the glomerular ultrafiltration coefficient (K_f) fell as rats went from a state of water diuresis to a state of hydropenia. When a variety of manipulations were used to alter plasma ADH over a broad range, the inverse relationship between presumed plasma ADH concentration and K_f still held. Though one would expect the fall in K_f to result in a fall in GFR, virtually no change in either whole-kidney or single-nephron GFR was observed. The decrease in GFR was prevented by a concomitant rise in

---

[1] The US Government has the right to retain a nonexclusive, royalty-free license in and to any copyright covering this paper.

[2] The terminology is that used by Andreoli & Schafer (4). ADH connotes all species of antidiuretic hormone unless a specific analog is mentioned. P_f is the coefficient of hydraulic conductivity (cm · sec^{-1}) evaluated by measuring water flow along an osmotic gradient. PD_w is the coefficient of diffusional permeability to water (cm · sec^{-1}) evaluated by measuring the rate of exchange of isotopic water across a membrane. PD_i is the apparent diffusional permeability coefficient for the ith solute.

transcapillary hydraulic pressure difference. The rise in transcapillary pressure difference resulted from a fall in the hydraulic pressure in Bowman's space, a consequence of the ADH-elicited increase in reabsorption of water and fall in urine flow rate. The relationship between urine flow rate and proximal hydraulic pressure is believed to reflect the intrinsic resistance to the flow of tubule fluid in the loop of Henle and more distal segments. In this sense, the rise in transcapillary ultrafiltration pressure resulting from effects of ADH in the distal nephron would result in increased GFR were it not for the reduction in K_f, the direct effect of ADH on the glomerulus. In amphibia and reptiles, ADH causes a reduction of GFR thought to be the result of complete elimination of filtration in some nephrons rather than reduced filtration per nephron (27).

The role of cAMP in the glomerular effect of ADH is unclear. In the rat, intravenous infusion of dibutyryl cAMP lowers K_f (27). ADH, however, had only a small stimulating effect on adenylate cyclase activity of isolated rabbit glomeruli (29) and no effect in rat glomeruli (50, 53). ADH at 10^{-10} M causes contraction of cultured mesangial cells derived from rat glomeruli. The contraction occurs without a change in cAMP or cGMP levels, and may be analogous to the effect of vasopressin on vascular smooth muscle cells (5). Contraction of mesangial cells in situ could regulate the capillary surface area available for filtration and thereby regulate K_f.

ADH stimulates adenylate cyclase activity in the medullary and cortical thick ascending limb of some but not all mammalian species (36). In medullary thick ascending limb of the mouse (but not in rat or rabbit), the transport response to ADH is increased flux of chloride from lumen to blood surface and increased transepithelial electrical potential difference, lumen positive (49). There is no change in the permeability to water. ADH stimulates adenylate cyclase activity in the connecting tubule and in cortical and medullary collecting ducts of all mammalian species examined (36). The major effect, increased permeability to water, has been found only in collecting ducts (19, 37, 45), not in the connecting tubule (28). ADH also increases the permeability to water of the cells that line the papilla, their apical surface facing the urine in the renal pelvis. In the presence of dilute pelvic urine, these cells swell after the administration of ADH to the animal (8). Other effects of ADH on the cortical collecting duct include an increase in permeability to small moderately lipophilic solutes (2), a minor stimulation of sodium reabsorption (16), and no change in permeability to urea (P_{urea}) (19). Increased P_{urea} has been seen in some (37) but not all (45) studies of medullary collecting duct.

In many respects the skin and urinary bladder of some anurans and the distal nephron of the mammal respond similarly to ADH. There is a marked increase in permeability to water, to urea and similar small amides, to a variety of small moderately lipophilic molecules, and an increase in the rate of active sodium transport from urine to blood (see 4).

THE NATURE OF THE CHANGE IN PERMEABILITY TO WATER

It is convenient to consider the nature of the permeability changes elicited by ADH before discussing the intermediate steps involving cAMP. The development of ideas regarding the effect of ADH on the rate-limiting apical plasma membrane of responsive tissues has been reviewed in detail by Andreoli & Schafer (4). In brief, Koeford-Johnson & Ussing (33) applied Poiseiulle's Law to the flow of water along an osmotic gradient across toad skin, assuming that diffusional and hydraulic flow occur across the same aqueous channels. They reasoned that P_f/P_{D_w} would exceed 1.0 if there were pores and would increase as pore size increased. They observed that as the skin became permeable in response to ADH, P_f/P_{D_w} increased from 5.3 to 33.5. They computed that the hypothetical pore radius rose from 6 to 20 Å. Further studies with anuran skin and urinary bladder supported the pore-enlargement hypothesis. These included the demonstration of solvent drag for small solutes such as urea and acetamide, and the finding that the activation energy(E_a) for the diffusion of water across toad urinary bladder was 10 kcal • mole^{-1} (a value that might reflect the restriction of water movement by narrow channels) under basal conditions and fell to 4 kcal • mole^{-1} (the E_a of water diffusing in water) after ADH. Following the suggestion (10) that such quasi-porous behavior (i.e. $P_f/P_{D_w} > 1$) could be accounted for by unstirred layers next to the membrane, Hays and his colleagues (25) demonstrated that reduction of unstirred layers by vigorous stirring markedly reduced the P_f/P_{D_w} ratio of ADH-treated toad urinary bladder, eliminated solvent drag for urea, and resulted in E_a for the diffusion of water across the ADH treated toad urinary bladder that was clearly greater than that of water in solution and more like that of water permeation across restricted channels or across thin lipid membranes. Schafer, Andreoli, and their colleagues developed similar evidence for water permeation across ADH-treated cortical collecting ducts. They concluded that the increased water permeation occurred by means of a solubility-diffusion process through lipid regions of the apical plasma membrane (2, 4). Both groups concluded that intracellular constraints to diffusion could account for the fact that the observed ratio of P_f/P_{D_w} exceeded 1. [Please see (4) for references and a more detailed discussion of these ideas.] Subsequently, P_f and P_{D_w} were measured across gramicidin-A treated lipid bilayer membranes (47). Gramicidin-A in effect inserts into the hydrophobic lipid-membrane aqueous channels that are close to the size of the water molecule itself. In these membranes $P_f/P_{D_w} \cong 5$. A ratio as high as 5 was unexpected since wider nystatin and amphotericin B channels had $P_f/P_{D_w} = 3$. It was concluded that in such narrow channels water moves by single-file diffusion and that there were about five water molecules in single file in the gramicidin-A channel. It was noted that if the channels in the apical membrane of ADH-treated toad urinary bladder are as small as or smaller than a gramicidin-A channel (they might be since they exclude urea and Na^+), some portion of the $P_f/P_{D_w} > 1$ would be the result of single-file movement of water in the narrow channels.

In view of the ADH-elicited increase in diffusional permeability of toad urinary bladder to moderately lipophilic species, and evidence that in artificial lipid bilayers, P_{D_i} and P_{D_w} can be altered by altering lipid composition, it was proposed that ADH increases P_{D_w} (and P_{D_i}) of the apical membrane by altering the composition, or more likely, the arrangement of lipids in the membrane (4, 42). The proposal was reasonable in that the P_{D_w} of some lipid bilayers approaches that of the ADH-treated toad urinary bladder and cortical collecting duct. Finkelstein (14) questioned the suggestion that a solubility-diffusion mechanism could explain the increased permeability of ADH-treated membranes on the basis of studies with artificial lipid-bilayer membranes. By varying the composition and the temperature of the lipid membranes, he was able to vary their permeability to water and to nonelectrolytes such as butyramide over a 100-fold range. For each membrane, however, the ratio of P_{D_w} to permeability to butyramide and other solutes remained relatively constant. He proposed that in membranes where the ratio P_{D_w}/P_{D_i} exceeded the ratio seen in lipid bilayers, water must cross the biological membrane via aqueous pores. The ratio was exceeded even in unstimulated toad urinary bladder and was markedly exceeded in ADH-treated cortical collecting duct and toad urinary bladder. Therefore he proposed that ADH increased the number (or size) of aqueous channels.

Further evidence in support of the idea that vasopressin increases the number and/or size of aqueous channels in the apical membrane was provided by Gluck & Al-Awqati (17). Since protons travel in aqueous solution by jumping from one water molecule to another, they reasoned that if ADH induces aqueous pores, there should be a concurrent increase in proton conductance. On the other hand, if the increased permeability to water were the result of increased membrane fluidity, there should be little or no increase in proton conductance. In toad urinary bladder, ADH increased proton conductance along a hydrogen ion gradient from mucosal solution to serosal solution by 300%. In other experiments the increase in proton conductance was highly correlated with the increase in P_{D_w} and was not decreased by agents that inhibit the Na-transport or the urea-permeability response to ADH (17).

Considerable correlative evidence relates the appearance of intramembranous particle aggregates to the ADH-elicited water-permeability change. The aggregates, considered in detail elsewhere (59), were first described by Chevalier et al (9) in ADH-treated frog urinary bladder. They have been found in ADH-treated toad skin and urinary bladder. Somewhat similar aggregates have been seen in mammalian cortical collecting duct after ADH. The aggregates are seen in the P (protoplasmic) face of freeze-fracture preparations of the apical membrane. The particles are arranged in rows with a corresponding series of parallel grooves in the E (exoplasmic) face of the membrane. The appearance of aggregates in the apical membrane is independent of water flow per se; they appear in ADH-treated toad urinary bladders with or without an osmotic gradient. ADH increases the number of aggregates and their total area without altering their size distribution. There is a high correlation between the magnitude of the ADH-elicited water permeability and the number and area of aggregates. The aggregates are clearly unrelated to the sodium-transport or urea-permeability response (59). Particle aggregates similar to those in the apical membrane after ADH have been found in the membrane of intracellular vacuoles of unstimulated cells (26, 58), leading to the suggestion that the particle aggregates exist in a preformed state and are inserted into the apical membrane in response to ADH. This concept has been supported by freeze-fracture electron micrographs of intracellular membranes with particle aggregates apparently fusing with the apical plasma membrane in ADH-treated toad urinary bladders (38).

In reviewing the 25-year history of this subject, it is striking to see how experimental data at one time interpreted as strongly supporting a particular model for the apical membrane permeability barrier have been shown subsequently to be subject to a different interpretation (e.g. pore-like behavior resulting from unstirred layer effects discussed above). Recently Kachadorian et al (32) have questioned the interpretation that the high E_a for water diffusion across ADH-treated toad urinary bladder or cortical collecting duct reflects the E_a of the diffusion path for water movement across the membrane. They point out that manipulation of temperature in these studies could affect the permeability response to ADH as well as the interaction of water with the rate-limiting barrier. In view of the high correlation between permeability to water and the number of particle aggregates in the apical membrane after ADH, they factored P_f by aggregate frequency or cumulative aggregate area. The factoring brought the E_a for water flow of ADH-treated bladders down to a value like that of bulk water movement. The point was established further by eliciting the full water permeability response in the usual fashion at room temperature, fixing the bladder with glutaraldelyde by a method that preserves the water permeability for a few hours, and then measuring P_f at different temperatures. P_f across fixed bladders changed little with temperature, yielding E_a like that of viscous water flow. Although the interpretation of these experiments depends on the assumption that particle aggregates are intimately involved in the water-permeability response and in a sense reflect the area available for water flow, and that glutaraldehyde-fixed bladders retain their in vivo permeability to water, the theoretical objection is valid. Previous estimates of E_a may have reflected the E_a of steps in the permeability response to ADH rather than the E_a of water movement across the membrane.

At this time, most evidence favors the concept that the increased water permeability in response to ADH is the result of the appearance of very small aqueous channels in the apical membrane. The evidence that favors this idea is the marked ADH stimulation of PD_w compared to the modest increase in permeability to moderately lipophilic solutes (14), and the increased H^+ conductance after ADH (17). The particle aggregates may ultimately be shown to be directly involved in the pathway for water movement across the apical membrane.

ADH stimulates sodium transport from the apical to the basolateral surface of anuran skin and urinary bladder and across the isolated perfused cortical collecting duct (4). This effect in the collecting duct is small and transient (16). A third, apparently independent effect of ADH is an increase in the permeability of the apical membrane of anuran skin and urinary bladder to urea and related small amides (4). The independence of the water-permeability, sodium-transport, and urea-permeability responses has been demonstrated in a number of ways (24). There is evidence for at least three separate pools of cAMP (and therefore a separate ADH-sensitive adenylate cyclase) mediating each of the three responses in toad urinary bladder (24). This separation is difficult to conceptualize because at least two of the responses, and perhaps all three, occur in the granular cells of the bladder. If there are three ADH-sensitive adenylate cyclase systems and three pools of cAMP, interpretation of studies of cAMP metabolism in these cells is difficult.

The changes that result in increased permeability of the apical plasma membrane are associated with increased deformability of that membrane. Several years ago Grantham (18) demonstrated increased deformability of the apical membrane of medullary collecting duct cells after incubation with ADH or cAMP. Using a different technique, Dibona (11) has noted that when the epithelial cells of the toad urinary bladder are exposed to hypotonic solution only the basolateral membrane bulges as the cells swell. After exposure to vasopressin, the apical membrane bulges out as well. It remains to be determined whether ADH makes the apical membrane deformable because of a change in the composition or organization of the membrane or because of a change in the relationship between the apical plasma membrane and cytoskeletal elements.

The possibility that microtubules and microfilaments are involved in the water permeability response was suggested initially by Taylor and her associates (57). They found that incubation of the toad urinary bladder with colchicine and other agents that disrupt microtubules, or with cytochalasin-B, an agent that disrupts actin-like microfilaments, resulted in a reduction in the water-permeability response to ADH and to cAMP. Because studies with inhibitors do not establish a direct role as opposed to a permissive role for these cytoskeletal elements, the number of microtubules seen in thin-section electron micrographs of toad urinary bladder epithelial cells was assessed (44). After ADH there was a 30% increase (statistically significant) in the number of microtubules. Microtubules have been seen in the region of the apical membrane and associated with structures considered to be intracellular membranes containing particle aggregates fusing with the apical plasma membrane (38). Treatment with colchicine reduced the number of such fusion events in response to ADH. There was a parallel reduction in the number of particle aggregates in the apical membrane as well as a reduction in the water-permeability response. Treatment with cytochalasin-B inhibited the water-permeability response and reduced the number of apical-membrane particle aggregates without altering the number of membrane fusion events. On the basis of these observations it was suggested that microtubules are involved in the ADH-elicited fusion of particle-aggregate-containing cytoplasmic membranes into the apical plasma membrane. Microfilaments are not involved in the process of membrane fusion but in the movement of particle aggregates from the intracellular membranes to the apical plasma membrane after fusion (38). Confirmation of these studies will be important. There is an obvious need for direct evidence as to whether microtubules and microfilaments play a permissive role or are directly affected by elevation of cell cAMP levels. Finally, the nature of the particle aggregates and their exact role in the permeability change remain to be established.

Studies with metabolic inhibitors have shown that in toad urinary bladder energy derived from metabolism is required for the full water-permeability response to ADH and to cAMP (22), and for reversal to the impermeable state after removal of ADH (35). A host of agents including several thought to affect cytosolic calcium have been shown to alter the response to vasopressin, but these are not considered here.

REGULATION OF CELL cAMP

The permeability effects of ADH are initiated by interaction with specific receptors for the hormone in the basolateral plasma membrane of responsive epithelial cells. The interaction results in stimulation of adenylate cylase in that plasma membrane and elevation of the concentration of cAMP within the cell. On the basis of studies with other hormones in other tissues a scheme has emerged that may be general for hormone-receptor–adenylate cyclase interactions.

There are apparently three major units in the plasma membrane: (*a*) receptors for the hormone, (*b*) a guanine nucleotide binding regulatory protein, and (*c*) the catalytic unit of adenylate cyclase. Receptors are usually considered to be proteins that bind a specific hormone in a saturable fashion with an affinity appropriate for active concentrations of the hormone; they must be coupled in some fashion to the enzyme activated by the hormone. It is thought that in the absence of hormone, receptors are not coupled to adenylate cyclase. They may actually be mobile in the membrane. The guanine nucleotide binding protein is exposed to the cell interior and binds GTP and GDP. Depending on the bound nucleotide, the protein regulates the affinity of the receptor for hormone and couples the hormone-receptor complex to adenylate cyclase, activating the enzyme. The guanine nucleotide binding protein may also function as a GTPase. Fluoride and cholera toxin are thought to stimulate adenylate cyclase activity by affecting the guanine nucleotide binding protein. The model is considered further elsewhere (46).

Adenylate cyclase sensitive to ADH has been examined in detail by Jard and his colleagues (31) and by Hechter and his colleagues (7) in partially purified plasma membranes prepared from the renal medulla of pig and beef. Both groups prepared ^{3}H-labelled vasopressin of high specific activity and high chemical purity and compared binding of vasopressin with activation of adenylate cyclase under a variety of conditions. Vasopressin increased the maximal velocity of adenylate cyclase without changing the affinity of the enzyme for its substrate, Mg-ATP. The Km for Mg-ATP is about 0.1 mM, at least an order of magnitude lower than the cytosolic concentration of ATP. Thus, under normal circumstances, it is unlikely that cell ATP is a rate-limiting factor. In addition to forming the substrate with ATP, magnesium ions activate the enzyme. Ca^{2+} (undoubtedly acting at an intracellular site) inhibits the mammalian enzyme at all concentrations ($K_i = 10^{-5}$M) but is required in very low concentrations by the enzyme prepared from frog urinary bladder epithelial cells (31).

The binding affinity for ADH analogs is highest for the natural hormones, AVP and LVP, which are most active in stimulating adenylate cyclase (7, 31). The high affinity for AVP and LVP is the result of a low dissociation rate constant of hormone bound to receptor rather than a high association rate constant. This accounts for the longer half-life of the hormone-receptor complex for active hormones compared to hormones with a low affinity for the receptor. Stimulation of adenylate cyclase was proportional to the number of receptors occupied by ADH. The ADH concentration binding curve however was not superimposable on the ADH concentration–adenylate cyclase activation curve. The two functions saturated at the same concentration but the K_D for binding was higher ($\sim$ 10 nM) than the K_A for enzyme activation ($\sim$ 0.5 nM). In other words, a considerable fraction of maximal adenylate cyclase activation occurs when a relatively small fraction of binding sites are occupied by ADH. Both groups interpreted these observations as evidence for nonlinear coupling between receptors and adenylate cyclase. At low receptor occupancy, each receptor occupied by hormone may activate more than one adenylate cyclase molecule. The degree of this extensive coupling may depend on the length of time the receptor is occupied by hormone. Hormones with a lower affinity have concentration binding and activation curves that are superimposable; hormones with the lowest affinity (these would occupy receptors long enough to block binding of other hormone molecules, but not long enough to activate the enzyme) have reduced intrinsic activity or may act as competitive antagonists. Both groups (7, 31) appreciate the limitations of the techniques employed in the development of this model.

The concentration of cAMP in the cell also depends on the rate of its degradation catalyzed by cyclic nucleotide phosphodiesterase. The enzyme has been studied in homogenates of cortex and of medulla of mammalian kidney. Several forms of the enzyme appear in most tissues, including the kidney (55). It is likely that the form of the enzyme with a high affinity for cAMP ($K_A \sim 2$ μM) is involved in regulation of cell cAMP levels. Another form of the enzyme with a high affinity for cAMP is activated by low concentrations of cGMP, and a third form has a high Km for cAMP, a low Km for cGMP, and is activated by calmodulin plus calcium. In rat kidney cortex there is a liposomal protease that activates a calcium-independent cyclic nucleotide phosphodiesterase (55). It's physiological significance is unknown. The metabolism of cAMP in situ is subject to regulation. Adrenal streoid hormones affect cyclic nucleotide phosphodiesterase activity (see below). In addition, cAMP metabolism is affected by transepithelial sodium transport in toad urinary bladder (48) and in frog skin (30). With sodium-containing Ringer solution on both surfaces of the epithelium, cell cAMP levels rise transiently and then fall to a plateau slightly above control levels in response to ADH. If sodium transport is eliminated by the addition of amiloride or by the removal of sodium from the external medium, ADH elicits a greater increase in cell cAMP levels, which remain high until the hormone is removed. The mechanism of this effect is unknown.

The only mechanism by which cAMP has been shown to mediate the effect of hormones involves protein phosphorylation (39), catalyzed by the active form of cAMP-dependent protein kinase. The idea that cAMP elicits changes in membrane permeability by activation of phosphorylation of membrane proteins (or other proetins) is an attractive hypothesis but one with little direct support. The evidence has been reviewed recently (56).

CONTROL BY ENDOGENOUS FACTORS

Many factors have been shown to affect antidiuresis. Three of these, hormones or hormone-like substances, are considered here. Adrenergic agents affect water excretion. In frog skin, beta-adrenergic agents mimic the effect of ADH on water permeability (6). Alpha-adrenergic agents inhibit the response to ADH in frog skin (6) and in toad urinary bladder (22). The effect appears to be inhibition of the stimulation of adenylate cyclase since (a) the water-permeability response to cAMP is not affected by alpha-adrenergic agents, and (b) cAMP accumulation in response to ADH is reduced by alpha adrenergic agents (40). In mammals the injection of alpha-adrenergic agents inhibits, and beta-adrenergic agents enhance, antidiuresis. This is not a direct renal effect. It is the result of inhibition by alpha-adrenergic agents, and stimulation by beta-adrenergic agents, of ADH secretion (51).

Prostaglandin E inhibits the water-permeability response to ADH of toad urinary bladder (41) and of rabbit cortical collecting duct (20). Although it has not been demonstrated directly, it is generally accepted that PGE inhibits the stimulation of adenylate cyclase activity by ADH. The interpretation is based upon the observation that PGE does not inhibit the water-permeability response to cAMP (20, 41) and that ADH-elicited accumulation of cAMP in toad urinary bladder epithelial cells is reduced in the presence of low concentrations of PGE (15, 40). The suggestion that ADH-sensitive tissues may synthesize PGE and thus modulate the effect of the hormone (20) was supported by the demonstration that inhibitors of the biosynthesis of PGE (1, 15) and antagonists of PGE (1) enhance the water-permeability response of the toad urinary bladder to ADH. The biosynthesis of PGE (see 13) is generally regarded as involving two major steps. The first is the release of a precursor fatty acid (arachidonic acid is the precursor of PGE_2) from storage sites in lipids, catalyzed by an acylhydrolase. The second step involves molecular oxygen and an enzyme complex, termed prostaglandin synthetase. Using tracer and radioimmunoassay techniques, Zusman and his colleagues showed that ADH stimulates the biosynthesis of PGE in toad urinary bladder (61) and renal medullary interstitial cells in culture (60) by increasing the release of precursor (arachidonic acid), presumably by activating acylhydrolase activity. In toad urinary bladder, PGE biosynthesis and the water-permeability response are stimulated over the same ADH concentration range. In contrast to the permeability and transport effects of ADH, this effect is not mediated by cAMP (61). ADH may have a similar effect in mammalian kidney. The antidiuretic response to ADH is enhanced by inhibition of prostaglandin synthetase (3) as is the ADH-elicited accumulation of cAMP in renal medulla (34). ADH stimulates the urinary excretion of PGE by rats with pituitary diabetes insipidus (12). The site of biosynthesis of PGE that appears in mammalian urine remains to be identified. It is probably not medullary interstitial cells since stimulation of PGE production by these cells (in culture) requires very high concentrations of ADH and appears to be a response to the pressor activity of the hormone; PGE excretion appears to be a response to antidiuretic activity (12). Arachidonic acid cyclooxygenase, a component of prostaglandin synthetase, has been identified in the epithelial cells of mammalian collecting duct using fluorescent antibody techniques (12). Production of PGE by this segment has not been demonstrated directly. In this respect it would be of interest to know whether inhibitors of PGE biosynthesis enhance the water-permeability response of the isolated perfused cortical collecting duct to ADH as they do in toad urinary bladder. Vasopressin-prostaglandin interactions have been reviewed in detail recently (21).

Adrenal steroid hormones enhance the water-permeability response to ADH by three mechanisms. Two effects of the steroids have been identified in toad urinary bladder. One is inhibition of cyclic nucleotide phosphodiesterase activity (54). The second effect is inhibition of acylhydrolase activity, the rate-limiting step in PGE biosynthesis from endogenous stores of arachidonic acid (61). Neither of these effects of adrenal steroid hormones is unique to the toad urinary bladder. Adrenal steroid hormones have a similar effect in mammalian kidney. The ADH-elicited water-permeability response of the isolated perfused cortical collecting duct from adrenalectomized rabbits is markedly depressed (52). It can be restored in vitro by incubation with dexamethasone or aldosterone (52). As in the toad urinary bladder, the difference in effectiveness of mineralocorticoid and glucocorticoid hormones is not marked. A third effect of adrenal steroid hormones on the response to ADH involves receptors for ADH. Adrenalectomy reduces the adenylate cyclase reponse to ADH in rat renal cortex and medulla (43). The response to parathyroid hormone is unaltered. The reduced adenylate cyclase response to ADH appears to be the result of two effects, a reduction in the number of receptors for the hormone and reduced coupling of receptors to adenylate cyclase. Injection of aldosterone corrected only the defect in receptor number; injection of dexamethasone corrected both defects. Injection of corticosterone, the natural glucocorticoid in the rat, was without effect. Since aldosterone and dexamethasone were injected into the whole animal, it is not clear that their effects were directly on the kidney (43).

CONCLUDING REMARKS

In this brief review it has not been possible to summarize all of the interesting recent work on the effect of ADH on water permeability. Although emphasis was placed on studies employing more direct approaches, concepts summarized here will surely be modified. Knowledge of the biochemistry of prostaglandins continues to advance rapidly. Other prostanoids may be shown to be important in the response to ADH, and control mechanisms may be clarified. The availability of kidney-derived epithelial cells in culture that have ADH-sensitive adenylate cyclase (23) should facilitate studies of receptors for ADH and the activation of adenylate cyclase. More information about the permeability change itself may become available if suitable apical membrane vesicles can be prepared and if the particle aggregates can be isolated and studied. As in the past, foremost among the unknown are the steps by which elevation of cell cAMP content increases the water permeability of the apical plasma membrane.

Literature Cited

1. Albert, W. C., Handler, J. S. 1974. Effect of PGE$_1$, indomethacin, and polyphloretin phosphate on toad bladder response to ADH. *Am. J. Physiol.* 226:1382–86
2. Al-Zahid, G., Schafer, J. A., Troutman, S. L., Andreoli, T. E. 1977. Effect of antidiuretic hormone on water and solute permeation, and the activation energies for these processes in mammalian cortical collecting tubules. *J. Membr. Biol.* 31:103–29
3. Anderson, R. J., Berl, T., McDonald, M., Schrier, R. W. 1975. Evidence for an in vivo antagonism between vasopressin and prostaglandin in the mammalian kidney. *J. Clin. Invest.* 56:420–26
4. Andreoli, T. E., Schafer, J. A. 1976. Mass transport across cell membranes: the effects of antidiuretic hormone on water and solute flows in epithelia. *Ann. Rev. Physiol.* 39:451–500
5. Ausiello, D. A., Kreisberg, J. I., Roy, C., Karnovsky, M. J. 1980. Contraction of cultured rat glomerular cells of apparent mesangial origin after stimulation with angiotensin II and arginine vasopressin. *J. Clin. Invest.* 65:754–60
6. Bastide, F., Jard, S. 1968. Action of noradrenalin and oxytocin on the active transport of sodium and the permeability of frog skin to water. Role of cyclic AMP. *Biochim. Biophys. Acta* 150:113–23

7. Bergman, R. N., Hechter, O. 1978. Neurohypophyseal hormone-responsive renal adenylate cyclase. *J. Biol. Chem.* 253:3238–50
8. Bonventre, J. B., Karnovsky, M. J., Lechene, C. P. 1978. Renal papillary epithelial morphology in antidiuresis and water diuresis. *Am. J. Physiol.* 235:F69–76
9. Chevalier, J., Bourguet, J., Hugon, J. S. 1974. Membrane associated particles: distribution in frog urinary bladder epithelium at rest and after oxytocin treatment. *Cell Tiss. Res.* 152:129–40
10. Dainty, J. 1963. Water relations of plant cells. *Adv. Bot. Res.* 1:279–326
11. DiBona, D. R. 1979. Direct visualization of ADH-mediated transepithelial osmotic flow. In *Hormonal Control of Epithelial Transport, Vol. 85*, ed. J. Bourguet, J. Chevalier, M. Parisi, P. Ripoche, pp. 195–206. Paris: INSERM
12. Dunn, M. J. 1979. Renal prostaglandins: influences on excretion of sodium and water, the renin-angiotensin system, renal blood flow, and hypertension. In *Hormonal Functions of the Kidney*, ed. B. Brenner, J. Stein, pp. 89–114. NY: Churchill, Livingstone
13. Dunn, M. J., Hood, V. L. 1977. Prostaglandins and the kidney. *Am. J. Physiol.* 233:F169–84
14. Finkelstein, A. 1976. Nature of the water permeability increase induced by antidiuretic hormone (ADH) in toad uri-

nary bladder and related tissues. *J. Gen. Physiol.* 68:137–43

15. Flores, A. G. A., Sharp, G. W. 1972. Endogenous prostaglandins and osmotic water flow in the toad bladder. *Am. J. Physiol.* 223:1392–97

16. Frindt, G., Burg, M. B. 1972. Effect of vasopressin on sodium transport in renal cortical collecting tubules. *Kidney Int.* 1:224–31

17. Gluck, S., Al-Awqati, Q. 1980. Vasopressin increased water permeability by inducing pores. *Nature* 284:631–32

18. Grantham, J. J. 1970. Vasopressin: effect on deformability of urinary surface of collecting duct cells. *Science* 168:1093–95

19. Grantham, J. J., Burg, M. B. 1966. Effect of vasopressin and cyclic AMP on permeability of isolated collecting tubules. *Am. J. Physiol.* 211:255–59

20. Grantham, J., Orloff, J. 1968. Effect of prostaglandin E₁ on the permeability response of the isolated collecting tubule to vasopressin, adenosine 3',5'-monophosphate, and theophylline. *J. Clin. Invest.* 47:1154–61

21. Handler, J. 1981. Vasopressin-prostaglandin interactions in the regulation of epithelial cell permeability to water. *Kidney Int.* In Press

22. Handler, J. S., Orloff, J. 1973. The mechanism of action of antidiuretic hormone. In *Handbook of Physiology. Renal Physiology,* pp. 791–814. Washington DC: Am. Physiol. Soc.

23. Handler, J. S., Perkins, F. M., Johnson, J. P. 1980. Studies of renal cell function using cell culture techniques. *Am. J. Physiol.* 238:F1-F9

24. Hays, R. M., Carvounis, C. P., Franki, N., Levine, S. D. 1979. Water permeation in epithelial tissues: current concepts. See Ref. 11, pp. 281–88

25. Hays, R. M., Levine, S. D. 1974. Vasopressin. *Kidney Int.* 6:307–22

26. Humbert, F., Montesano, R., Grosso, A., deSousa, R. C., Orci, L. 1977. Particle aggregates in plasma and intracellular membranes of toad bladder (granular cell). *Experientia* 33:1364–67

27. Ichikawa, I., Brenner, B. M. 1977. Evidence for glomerular actions of ADH and dibutyryl cyclic AMP in the rat. *Am. J. Physiol.* 233:F102–17

28. Imai, M. 1979. The connecting tubule: a functional subdivision of the rabbit distal nephron segments. *Kidney Int.* 15:346–56

29. Imbert, M., Chabardes, D., Morel, F. 1974. Hormone-sensitive adenylate-

cyclase in isolated rabbit glomeruli. *Mol. & Cell. Endocrinol.* 1:295–304

30. Jard, S., Bockaert, J. 1975. Stimulus-response coupling in neurolypophysial peptide target cells. *Physiol. Rev.* 55:489–536

31. Jard, S., Roy, C., Barth, T., Rajerison, R., Bockaert, J. 1975. Antidiuretic hormone-sensitive kidney adenylate cyclase. *Adv. Cyclic Nucleotide Res.* 5:31–52

32. Kachadorian, W. A., Muller, J., Rudich, S. W. DiScala, V. A. 1979. Temperature dependence of ADH-induced water flow and intramembranous particle aggregates in toad bladder. *Science* 205:910–13

33. Koefoed-Johnson, V., Ussing, H. H. 1953. The contributions of diffusion and flow to the passage of D₂O through living membranes. *Acta Physiol. Scand.* 28:60–76

34. Lum, G. M., Aisenbrey, G. A., Dunn, M. J., Berl, T., Schrier, R. W., McDonald, K. M. 1977. In vivo effect of indomethacin to potentiate the renal medullary cyclic AMP response to vasopressin. *J. Clin. Invest.* 59:8–13

35. Masters, B. R., Fanestil, D. D. 1979. Metabolic dependence of the offset of antidiuretic hormone-induced osmotic flow of water across the toad urinary bladder. *J. Membr. Biol.* 48:237–47

36. Morel, F., Chabardes, D., Imbert-Teboul, M. 1978. Heterogeneity of hormonal control in the distal nephron. *Proc. VII Int. Congr. Nephrol.,* pp. 209–16

37. Morgan, T., Sakai, F., Berliner, R. W. 1968. In vitro permeability of medullary collecting ducts to water and urea. *Am. J. Physiol.* 214:574–81

38. Muller, J., Kachadorian, W. A., Di Scala, V. A. 1980. Evidence that ADH-stimulated intramembrane particle aggregates are transferred from cytoplasmic to luminal membranes in toad bladder epithelial cells. *J. Cell Biol.* 85:83–95

39. Nimmo, H. G., Cohen, P. 1977. Hormonal control of protein phosphorylation. *Adv. Cyclic Nucleotide Res.* 8:145–266

40. Omachi, R. S., Robbie, D. E., Handler, J. S., Orloff, J. 1974. Effects of ADH and other agents on cyclic AMP accumulation in toad bladder epithelium. *Am. J. Physiol.* 226:1152–57

41. Orloff, J., Handler, J. S., Bergstrom, S. 1965. Effect of prostaglandin (PGE₁) on the permeability of response of toad bladder to vasopressin, theophylline

and adenosine 3',5'-monophosphate. *Nature* 205:397–98

42. Pietras, R. J., Wright, E. M. 1974. Non-electrolyte probes of membrane structure in ADH-treated toad urinary bladder. *Nature* 247:222–24

43. Rajerison, R., Marchetti, J., Roy, C., Bockaert, J. Jard, S. 1974. The vasopressin-sensitive adenylate cyclase of the rat kidney: Effect of adrenalectomy and corticosteroids on hormonal receptor/enzyme coupling. *J. Biol. Chem.* 249:6390–400

44. Reaven, E., Maffly, R., Taylor, A. 1978. Evidence for involvement of microtubules in the action of vasopressin in toad urinary bladder. III. Morphological studies on the content and distribution of microtubules in bladder epithelial cells. *J. Membr. Biol.* 40:251–67

45. Rocha, A. S., Kokko, J. P. 1974. Permeability of medullary segments to urea and water: effect of vasopressin. *Kidney Int.* 6:379–87

46. Rodbell, M. 1980. The role of hormone receptors and GTP-regulatory proteins in membrane transduction. *Nature* 284:17–22

47. Rosenberg, P. A., Finkelstein, A. 1978. Water permeability of gramicidin-A-treated lipid bilayer membranes. *J. Gen. Physiol.* 72:314–50

48. Sapirstein, V. S., Scott, W. N. 1973. Cyclic AMP and sodium transport. Quantitative and temporal relationships in toad urinary bladder. *J. Clin. Invest.* 52:2379–82

49. Sasaki, S., Imai, M. 1980. Effects of vasopressin on water and NaCl transport across the in vitro perfused medullary thick ascending limb of Henle's loop of mouse, rat and rabbit kidneys. *Pflügers Arch.* 383:215–21

50. Schlondorff, D., Yoo, P., Alpert, B. E. 1978. Stimulation of adenylate cyclase in isolated rat glomeruli by prostaglandins. *Am. J. Physiol* 235:F458–64

51. Schrier, R. W., Berl, T., Anderson, R. J. 1979. Osmotic and nonosmotic control of vasopressin release. *Am. J. Physiol.* 236:F321–32

52. Schwartz, M., Kokko, J. 1980. The urinary concentrating defect of adrenal insufficiency: The permissive role of adrenal steroids on the hydroosmotic response across the rabbit cortical collecting tubule. *J. Clin. Invest.* 66:234–42

53. Sraer, J., Ardaillou, R., Loreau, N., Sraer, J. D. 1974. Evidence for parathyroid hormone sensitive adenylate cyclase in rat glomeruli. *Mol. Cell. Endocrinol.* 1:285–94

54. Stoff, J. S., Handler, J. S., Preston, A. S., Orloff, J. 1973. The effect of aldosterone on cyclic nucleotide phosphodiesterase activity in toad urinary bladder. *Life Sci.* 13:545–52

55. Strewler, G. J., Manganiello, V. C., Vaughan, M. 1978. Phosphodiesterase activator from rat kidney cortex. *J. Biol. Chem.* 253:390–94

56. Strewler, G. J., Orloff, J. 1977. Role of cyclic nucleotides in the transport of water and electrolytes. *Adv. Cyclic Nucleotide Res.* 8:331–61

57. Taylor, A., Mamelak, M., Reaven, E., Maffly, R. 1973. Vasopressin: possible role of microtubules and microfilaments in its action. *Science* 181:347–50

58. Wade, J. B. 1978. Membrane structural specialization of the toad urinary bladder revealed by the freeze-fracture technique. III. Location, structure and vasopressin dependence of intramembrane particle arrays. *J. Membr. Biol. Spec. Iss.* 281–96

59. Wade, J. B. 1981. Hormonal modulation of epithelial structure. *Curr. Top. Membr. Transp.* 13: In press

60. Zusman, R. M., Keiser, H. R. 1977. Prostaglandin E_2 biosynthesis by rabbit renomedullary interstitial cells in tissue culture: mechanism of stimulation by angiotensin II, bradykinin, and arginine vasopressin. *J. Biol. Chem.* 252:2069–71

61. Zusman, R. M., Keiser, H. R., Handler, J. S. 1978. Effect of adrenal steroids on vasopressin-stimulated PGE synthesis and water flow. *Am. J. Physiol.* 234:F532–40

Ann. Rev. Physiol. 1981. 43:625–36
Copyright © 1981 by Annual Reviews Inc. All rights reserved

CATECHOLAMINES AND THE KIDNEY: RECEPTORS AND RENAL FUNCTION

♦1334

Paul A. Insel and Marshall D. Snavely

Division of Pharmacology, Department of Medicine, University of California, San Diego, La Jolla, California 92093

INTRODUCTION

Catecholamines are involved in modulating a number of aspects of renal physiology, including renal blood flow, glomerular filtration, tubular transport, and renin and erythropoietin release. [reviewed in detail in (16, 17, 24, 26, 30, 31, 43, 63, 69)]. In this article we briefly consider effects of catecholamines on renal function and emphasize the need for better means of identification of renal adrenergic receptors, primarily through the use of radioligand binding techniques. Only the most rudimentary information exists regarding adrenergic receptors in the kidney. Thus, we wish to give the reader a framework with which to evaluate information likely to be forthcoming on renal receptors for catecholamines. For brevity's sake we have cited mostly reviews and work published since 1977.

ADRENERGIC RECEPTORS AND RENAL FUNCTION

General Aspects

Although we emphasize characterization of adrenergic receptors by using ligand binding techniques, meaningful use of such techniques requires measurement of physiological effects of receptor occupancy. Many investigators have attempted to identify properties of renal adrenergic receptors by defining changes in the contractile state of renal vessels, in glomerular or tubular function, or in secretion of hormones. Because of the complex interplay among such responses (e.g. changes in renal perfusion alter other responses), different experimental systems have often yielded conflicting results (69).

625

0066-4278/81/0315-0625$01.00

In considering effects of catecholamines on renal function it should be emphasized that NE[1] is the neurotransmitter released at postsynaptic sympathetic effector sites whereas EPI is the principal circulating adrenergic hormone. Unfortunately, investigators often administer adrenergic compounds in large, nonphysiologic doses and fail to consider the difference in tissue penetration between synthetic compounds and physiologically active amines.

An additional complexity is the presence of subclasses of adrenergic and dopaminergic receptors (8, 14, 15, 37, 44, 73). Such subclassifications derive from systematic patterns of rank order potency shown by a series of agonists or antagonists in physiological or radioligand binding studies. For α-adrenergic receptors, α_1 receptors are generally postsynaptic, and α_2 receptors are generally presynaptic sites that inhibit NE release (8, 37, 73). In addition to postsynaptic β_1- and β_2-adrenergic receptors, some β_2 presynaptic receptors may act to facilitate NE release (73). Dopaminergic receptors have also been subclassified; some (28), but not all (44), suggest that there are postsynaptic ("dopamine$_1$") and presynaptic ("dopamine$_2$") subclasses, the latter inhibiting NE release from sympathetic neurons. The naturally occurring adrenergic agonists, as well as the "classical" antagonists (e.g. phentolamine, propranolol), are nonselective, acting on both subclasses of a given type of receptor. Thus, the net effect of infusing EPI, for example, into the renal artery may involve the summation of α_1, α_2, β_1, and β_2 components at various sites in the kidney. This multiplicity of receptors and their subtypes contributes to the currently imprecise definition of the physiological role of catecholamines in regulating renal function.

Renal Hemodynamics

Catecholamines regulate renal hemodynamics predominantly via α-adrenergic-mediated vasoconstriction [perhaps by α_1-receptors (23)] and increased renal vascular resistance (10). Although contraction occurs along most portions of the intrarenal vasculature, differences in sensitivity to stimulation at certain sites have been noted (69). Whether such differences result from differences in α-adrenergic receptors in particular locations is unknown. Fluorescent histochemical studies indicate the presence of NE-containing fibers associated with the renal, arcuate, and interlobular arteries, as well as in peritubular and juxtaglomerular locations (5, 19). Only about one third of the cells of afferent and efferent arterioles are innervated (5). The sites at which such nerve fibers are allied with adrenergic receptors

---

[1]Abbreviations used in this review are: NE, norepinephrine; ISO, isoproterenol; EPI, epinephrine; PTH, parathyroid hormone; ADH, antidiuretic hormone; and cAMP, adenosine 3',5'monophosphate.

and the disposition of receptors in non-innervated cells remain to be determined. Although poorly defined as physiological modulators of renal perfusion, renal vascular α-adrenergic receptors have been implicated in decreasing renal blood flow or in altering intrarenal perfusion in several nonphysiological settings, such as hemorrhage, cardiac failure, liver disease, and hypertension (13, 69).

Alpha-adrenergic vasoconstriction predominates over β-adrenergic vasodilation in renal vessels, and β-adrenergic-mediated vasodilation is less in the kidney than in other vascular beds (10, 69). However, intrarenal vascular sites [for example, those modulating tubulo-glomerular feedback (74)] may be enriched in β-adrenergic receptors. In addition, whether renal vessels have functional α- and β-adrenergic receptor subtypes is thus far unresolved (23, 42).

Dopamine mediates a non-β-adrenergic renal arterial vasodilation at low doses (27, 29, 58) but an α-adrenergic-mediated vasoconstriction at higher doses (3). A physiological role for dopaminergic receptors in the renal vasculature remains largely conjectural, although the demonstration of dopamine-containing neuronal fibers at the vascular pole of the glomerulus is consistent with such a role (19). The site of dopamine's action on renal blood flow may not result from direct postsynaptic action but rather from a ganglionic and/or a presynaptic inhibition of NE release (46).

Renin Secretion

Catecholamines have important effects on the release of renin from renal juxtaglomerular (JG) cells (16, 56, 63). In vivo, direct actions of catecholamines on JG cells are difficult to separate from indirect effects due to alterations in vascular resistance and reabsorption of ions. In vitro experiments in which these variables were controlled have demonstrated that catecholamines increase renin secretion through activation of intrarenal β-adrenergic receptors (43, 52, 56, 63). Data from different sources suggest that these receptors are β_1 (35), β_2 (16), and "β-nonselective" (54). Definitive classification of the intrarenal β receptor mediating renin release must await further evidence. A rise in cAMP may mediate the β-agonist-stimulated renin release (36, 63), but other evidence indicates that calcium flux (33, 56, 57) and locally released prostaglandins (7) may be involved in this adrenergic response.

An intrarenal α-adrenergic receptor may also regulate renin release, though the physiological role of this receptor is ill-defined (8, 63). Studies have indicated that α_1-selective adrenergic agonists inhibit (52, 57, 77) and enhance (20) renin secretion. The reasons for these disparate results are unclear. Because α_2-selective agonists do not alter renin secretion in tissue slices, they probably inhibit renin release through central and presynaptic mechanisms (63). Thus the intrarenal α-adrenergic receptor regulating renin secretion appears to be of the α_1 type (8, 57).

Dopamine acts both in vivo and in vitro to increase renin secretion (61). Whether dopamine increases renin release via a dopaminergic or a β-adrenergic receptor is unresolved (30, 61).

Catecholamines and Renal Tubular Function

Denervation of the kidney leads to diuresis and natriuresis, as well as to decreased reabsorption of glucose, phosphate, urate, and other substances by the proximal tubule (31). Although it has not been proven that these effects result from loss of adrenergic regulation, sympathetic fibers have been shown to innervate both proximal and distal tubular cells (5). Current evidence indicates that low-level stimulation of renal nerves, either by direct electrical excitation or by reflex enhancement of nerve activity, increases the reabsorption of Na^+ and water by the proximal tubule (17, 26, 31, 59). Because these tubular effects can be separated from the renin-angiotensin system and prostaglandin synthesis, a direct action of catecholamines on the tubular cells can be inferred (18, 31).

The nature of the adrenergic receptor mediating tubular reabsorption is controversial. In addition to species differences, one explanation for the confusion is that in vivo experiments include the altered release of ADH from the posterior pituitary produced by systemically administered catecholamines (43, 64, 70). Generally, enhanced tubular reabsorption due to sympathetic nerve stimulation in vivo is blocked by α-adrenergic antagonists, thus implying that NE released from nerve terminals acts at a tubular α-adrenergic receptor (17, 18, 26, 31). Other studies in vivo suggest that a β-adrenergic receptor may regulate tubular reabsorption (26, 64). In isolated, perfused rat kidney and proximal tubular segments, addition of catecholamines apparently enhances Na^+ reabsorption via β-adrenergic receptors and inhibits fluid reabsorption via α-adrenergic receptors (6, 9). The nature of the adrenergic receptors acting on the sympathetically innervated distal tubular cells is poorly defined (17, 26, 64), as is the physiological role of adrenergic receptors in the non-innervated loop of Henle (4).

Dopamine appears to enhance Na^+ excretion through a complex interplay of CNS and poorly defined tubular actions (30, 64). In a recent review, Goldberg concludes that no available data prove a direct action of dopamine on renal tubular cells (30).

The effects of catecholamines on water excretion also demonstrate the difficulties involved in studying agents with multiple potential sites of action (43). Acting through baroreceptor pathways, α-adrenergic agonists stimulate and β-adrenergic agonists inhibit the release of ADH from the posterior pituitary (47, 62). In the kidney in some studies, catecholamines interact with ADH-sensitive portions of the nephron to enhance (β-adrenergic) or inhibit (α-adrenergic) cAMP generation in medullary or collecting duct preparations; effects of catecholamines on ADH-mediated inhibition of water excretion have been more difficult to document (12, 21, 62).

Other Functions

Release of kallikrein and erythropoietin and control of gluconeogenesis may also be regulated by adrenergic receptors (48, 49, 60). A β_2-adrenergic receptor has been implicated in modulating erythropoietin production, perhaps by regulating epithelial cells of the glomerular tuft (24, 41, 58). Renal gluconeogenesis, a process that is localized to proximal tubules and that may provide glucose to other portions of the nephron, is regulated by a number of factors, among them α-adrenergic receptors (48).

These functions, as well as other adrenergic effects on the kidney, may involve interaction of the catecholamines with locally produced prostaglandins (25). Relationships between prostaglandins and catecholamines are complex and include α-adrenergic stimulation of prostaglandin release (25), activation of adenylate cyclase by β-adrenergic agonists and certain prostaglandins [especially PGI_2, PGE's, and PGA_2 (22, 67)], alteration of NE release from sympathetic nerve terminals by prostaglandins (7, 25), and blockade of certain β-adrenergic effects (e.g. erythropoietin production) by inhibitors of prostaglandin synthesis (41). Variation in results among different species with different preparations, or when agents are given by different routes of administration (80), make it difficult to generalize about such prostaglandin-catecholamine interactions.

ADRENERGIC RECEPTORS AND SECOND MESSENGERS IN THE KIDNEY

In the kidney, β-adrenergic stimulation generally enhances cAMP generation. Studies in isolated glomeruli of rat (1, 45, 67), but not of rabbit (38), indicate slight β-adrenergic activation of adenylate cyclase, though this activation is far lower than that observed with other neurotransmitters and hormones (e.g. prostaglandins, histamine, and PTH) in such glomerular preparations.

Studies in renal tubules and collecting ducts indicate that hormone-stimulated adenylate cyclase and, presumably, hormone receptors are predominantly located in basal-lateral (anti-luminal) plasma membranes, whereas cAMP-dependent protein kinase is preferentially found on luminal (brush border) membranes (55). Beta-adrenergic-stimulated adenylate cyclase activity is distributed differently from activity stimulated by other hormones (ADH, PTH) and in the rabbit nephron is located only on four distal portions of the nephron: the "granular" portion of the distal convoluted tubule, "granular" and "light" portions of the cortical collecting duct, and on the medullary collecting duct (11, 51). Such results help to localize the β-adrenergic-stimulated adenylate cyclase activity that has been identified in cortical and medullary homogenates and plasma membranes (21, 55).

For α-adrenergic receptors, some (21, 62), but not all (11), workers report an inhibition of adenylate cyclase, although changes in K^+ or Ca^{2+} availability may be involved in α-adrenergic stimulation of renal gluconeogenesis (48, 66).

Dopamine enhances cAMP production from the kidney at sites that are not α- or β-adrenergic receptors (45, 53). Further characterization of this and other cyclase activities may be aided by using channel-forming antibiotics, such as alamethicin, which enhance adenylate cyclase activity in renal membranes (34), and by studies using more purified preparations of individual cell types from the kidney.

IDENTIFICATION OF ADRENERGIC RECEPTORS WITH RADIOLIGANDS

General Aspects

Use of radioligand binding techniques offers an important methodologic advance in defining the distribution, properties, and regulation of adrenergic and dopaminergic receptors in a wide variety of tissues [for reviews, see (14, 37, 39, 75, 78)]. The basic protocol involves incubation of tissue with radioligand in the absence ("total binding") or presence ("nonspecific binding") of a high concentration of a known agonist or antagonist and then separating bound and free radioactivity, generally by filtration over glass fiber filters. Subtracting "nonspecific binding" from "total binding" yields "specific binding," which is presumed to reflect interaction of the radioligand with the receptor of interest. The relative ease with which such experiments can be performed belies the numerous pitfalls that investigators can encounter in execution, analysis, and interpretation of radioligand binding studies. In view of the sites to which catecholamines might bind in addition to receptors (e.g. contaminating plasma proteins, tissue uptake sites, degradative enzymes, and transport systems), attempting to prove that radioactivity retained on a filter represents binding at a receptor site requires a variety of experiments. These include demonstration of appropriate kinetics (rates of association and dissociation) and saturability of binding, as well as stereoselectivity and rank order of potency of competitive binding to the sites by a series of agonists and antagonists. It is generally desirable to relate properties of radioligand binding to those of known biological activity in the same preparation (e.g. for β-adrenergic receptors, activation of adenylate cyclase). Unfortunately, investigators sometimes fail to demonstrate the characteristics required to be confident that bound radioligand is bound to the putative receptor. One problem has been the inappropriate choice of concentrations of agents to define "nonspecific" binding; propranolol, for example, at concentrations greater than 10 μM has well-known local anesthetic, membrane-perturbing properties.

Radioligand Binding Studies in the Kidney

Prior to reports of radioligand binding, Atlas et al injected rats with a fluorescent β-adrenergic blocking agent (9-aminoacridine-propranolol) in an attempt to identify renal β-adrenergic sites (2). This fluorescent derivative preferentially localized near the vascular pole of the glomeruli in association with afferent arterioles and to a lesser extent in proximal and distal convoluted tubules and collecting ducts. Unfortunately, detailed cellular localization could not be performed and propranolol incompletely blocked fluorescence intensity.

Two reports have appeared on identification of β-adrenergic receptors using radioligands—one on canine renal cortical plasma membrane (50) and the other on rat kidney particulates (79). The former study employed an inappropriately high concentration of propranolol (100 μM) to define nonspecific binding of the radioligand [^{3}H]dihydroalprenolol and failed to report competition by agonists for the binding sites. The latter study presented limited data validating the radioligand binding assay in the kidney. In our laboratory, we have recently used the β-adrenergic antagonist [^{125}I]iodohydroxybenzylpindolol in experiments with particulates prepared from rat renal cortex and have been able to further characterize this receptor; binding of this ligand is rapid, reversible, of high affinity, saturable, and stereoselective (72). In addition, [^{3}H]dihydroalprenolol has recently been used to identify putative β_1 receptors in membranes from rat renal tubular cells, although a high concentration of propranolol (5 mM) was used to define nonspecific binding in this study (25a).

For α-adrenergic receptors, radioligand binding has been reported by three different laboratories (40, 65, 68, 76). [^{3}H]clonidine and [^{3}H]para-aminoclonidine have been used to identify presumed α_2 receptors in guinea pig (40) and rat (65, 76) kidney. The nonselective α-adrenergic antagonist [^{3}H]dihydroergocryptine ([^{3}H]DHE) and the α_1-selective antagonist [^{3}H]WB4101 have also been used in rat kidney cortex to identify α-adrenergic receptors (76). In those studies no attempt was made to compare binding and physiological responses in the kidney. Nevertheless it was found that 6-hydroxydopamine treatment, which destroys sympathetic nerve terminals, had no effect on binding; this suggests a postsynaptic location for the bulk of the ligand binding sites. In addition, no kinetic measurements of association and dissociation of the ligand and the receptor were reported. In the rat kidney, the maximal number of [^{3}H]DHE binding sites was equal to the sum of the maximal number of binding sites as determined using [^{3}H]clonidine ($\sim$ 20% sites) and [^{3}H]WB4101 ($\sim$ 80% sites). As the latter ligand recognizes α_1 receptors and the former α_2, the data suggest that the predominant α-receptor in the rat kidney is α_1. Schmitz et al have examined binding of [^{3}H]DHE to rat kidney particulates and have found a similar rank order of potency for adrenergic agonists and antagonists in competing for the ligand binding sites and in altering α-adrenergic mediated renal vasoconstriction of isolated perfused kidneys (68). These and other results led Schmitz et al to conclude that the [^{3}H]DHE sites may correspond to postsynaptic sites mediating renal vasoconstriction (68). In other studies, Graham et al have found that the number of renal [^{3}H]DHE binding sites are increased in spontaneously hypertensive rats compared to controls (32).

For dopaminergic receptors, a recent abstract reports the use of [^{3}H]apomorphine to identify these receptors in canine renal cortex (71). The authors indicate that they have fulfilled a number of the requirements noted above to prove that these [^{3}H]apomorphine binding sites represent dopamine receptors.

SUMMARY AND CONCLUSIONS

Catecholamines are important modulators of several renal functions, including renal hemodynamics, proximal tubular reabsorption, and hormonal secretion (e.g. renin and erythropoietin). The nature of the class and subclass of adrenergic receptors mediating such actions, as well as the second messengers for these receptors, are as yet inadequately defined. Radioligand binding techniques are just beginning to be applied to renal preparations. As improved methodology for isolating and studying individual portions of the nephron is used together with such radioligand binding assays, the detailed localization and characterization of renal adrenergic receptors should be forthcoming. Application of these biochemical and cell-biological approaches to studying the multiplicity of renal sites that recognize catecholamines is likely to offer major conceptual advances in understanding the role of catecholamines in regulating renal physiology and in defining the role of changes in adrenergic receptors in a variety of settings demonstrating altered renal function.

ACKNOWLEDGMENTS

We thank the investigators who shared with us recent and unpublished results of studies in their laboratories: G. F. Di Bona, T. P. Dousa, G. M. Eisner, W. Ganong, L. I. Goldberg, R. M. Graham, and R. Schrier. Work in our laboratory is supported by an Established Investigatorship (PAI) and grants from the American Heart Association, National Science Foundation, and National Institutes of Health, and fellowships from the National Science Foundation and National Institutes of Health (MDS).

Literature Cited

1. Abboud, H. E., Shah, S. V., Dousa, T. P. 1979. Effects of biogenic amines and prostaglandins on cAMP and cGMP in isolated glomeruli. *Clin. Res.* 27:406A
2. Atlas, D., Melamed, E., Lahav, M. 1977. β-Adrenergic receptors in rat kidney: direct localization of a fluorescent β-blocker. *Lab. Invest.* 5:465–68
3. Augustin, H. J., Baumgarten, H. G., Huland, H., Leichtweiss, H. P. 1977. The vasoconstrictive effect of dopamine in the isolated, perfused rat kidney after catecholamine depletion. *Res. Exp. Med.* 170:1–15
4. Baines, A. D. 1978. Luminal volume and reabsorption in the loop of Henle: effects of blood pressure and noradrenaline. *Kidney Int.* 14:255–62
5. Barajas, L. 1978. Innervation of the renal cortex. *Fed. Proc.* 37:1192–201
6. Bello-Reuss, E. 1980. Effect of catecholamines on fluid reabsorption by the isolated proximal convoluted tubule. *Am. J. Physiol.* 238:F347–52
7. Berl, T., Henrich, W. L., Erickson, A. L., Schrier, R. W. 1979. Prostaglandins in the beta-adrenergic and baroreceptor-mediated secretion of renin. *Am. J. Physiol.* 236:F472–77
8. Berthelsen, S., Pettinger, W. A. 1977. A functional basis for classification of α-adrenergic receptors. *Life Sci.* 21:595–606
9. Besarab, A., Silva, P., Landsberg, L., Epstein, F. H. 1977. Effect of catecholamines on tubular function in the isolated perfused rat kidney. *Am. J. Physiol.* 233:F39–45
10. Buckley, N. M., Brazeau, P., Gootman, P. M., Frasier, I. D. 1979. Renal circulatory effects of adrenergic stimuli in anesthetized piglets and mature swine. *Am. J. Physiol.* 237:H690–95
11. Charbardés, D., Imbert-Teboul, M., Montegut, M., Clique, A., Morel, F. 1975. Catecholamine sensitive adenylate cyclase activity in different segments of the rabbit nephron. *Pfluegers Arch.* 361:9–15
12. Christensen, S. 1978. Dissociation between antidiuretic response and renal medullary cyclic AMP levels in the rat. *Pfluegers Arch.* 374:229–34
13. Click, R. L., Joyner, W. L., Gilmore, J. P. 1979. Reactivity of glomerular afferent and efferent arterioles in renal hypertension. *Kidney Int.* 15:109–15
14. Creese, I. 1980. Dopamine receptors: subtypes, regulation and localization. *Fed. Proc.* In press
15. Daly, M. S., Levy, G. P. 1979. The subclassification of β-adrenoceptors: evidence in support of the dual β-adrenoceptor hypothesis. In *Trends in Autonomic Pharmacology*, ed. S. Kalsner, pp. 347–86. Baltimore: Urban and Schwarzenberg. 498 pp.
16. Davis, J. O., Freeman, R. H. 1976. Mechanisms regulating renin release. *Physiol. Rev.* 56:1–56
17. Di Bona, G. F. 1977. Neurogenic regulation of renal tubular sodium reabsorption. *Am. J. Physiol.* 233:F73–81
18. Di Bona, G. F. 1978. Neural control of renal tubular sodium reabsorption in the dog. *Fed. Proc.* 37:1214–17
19. Dinnerstein, R. J., Vannice, J., Henderson, R. C., Roth, L. J., Goldberg, L. I., Hoffmann, P. C. 1979. Histofluorescence techniques provide evidence for dopamine-containing neuronal elements in canine kidney. *Science* 205:497–99
20. Donald, D. E. 1979. Studies on release of renin by direct and reflex activation of renal sympathetic nerves. *Physiologist* 22:39–42
21. Dousa, T. P. 1976. Drugs and other agents affecting the renal adenylate cyclase system. In *Methods in Pharmacology*, ed. M. Martinez-Maldonado, 4A:293–331. NY: Plenum. 385 pp.

22. Dousa, T. P., Shah, S. V., Abboud, H. E. 1979. Potential Role of cyclic nucleotides in glomerular pathophysiology. *Adv. Cyclic Nucleotide Res.* 12:285–99

23. Drew, G. M., Whiting, S. B. 1979. Evidence for two distinct types of postsynaptic α-adrenoceptor in vascular smooth muscle in vitro. *Br. J. Pharmacol.* 67:207–15

24. Fisher, J. W., Gross, D. M., Foley, J. E., Nelson, P. K., Rodgers, G. M., George, W. J., Jubiz, W. 1978. A concept for the control of kidney production of erythropoietin involving prostaglandins and cyclic nucleotides. *Contrib. Nephrol.* 13:37–59

25. Flamenbaum, W., Kleinman, J. G. 1977. Prostaglandins and renal function, or "A trip down the rabbit hole." *The Prostaglandins* 3:267–328

25a. Gavendo, S., Kapuler, S., Servan, I., Iaina, A., Eitan, B., Eliahou, H. 1980. β_1-adrenergic receptors in kidney tubular cell membrane in the rat. *Kidney Int.* 17:764–70

26. Gill, J. R., Jr. 1979. Neural control of renal tubular sodium reabsorption. *Nephron* 23:116–18

27. Goldberg, L. I. 1979. The dopamine vascular receptor. In *Peripheral Dopaminergic Receptors: Proc. Satel. Symp. 7th Int. Congr Pharmacol,* ed. J. L. Imbs, J. Schwartz, pp. 1–12. NY: Pergamon. 408 pp.

28. Goldberg, L. I., Kohli, J. D. 1979. Peripheral pre- and post-synaptic dopamine receptors: are they different from dopamine receptors in the central nervous system? *Comm. Psychopharmacol.* 3:447–56

29. Goldberg, L. I., Volkman, P. H., Kohli, J. D. 1978. A comparison of the vascular dopamine receptor with other dopamine receptors. *Ann. Rev. Pharmacol. Toxicol.* 18:57–79

30. Goldberg, L. I., Weder, A. B. 1980. Connections between endogenous dopamine, dopamine receptors, and sodium excretion: evidence and hypotheses. *Rec. Adv. Clin. Pharmacol.* In press

31. Gottschalk, C. W. 1979. Renal nerves and sodium excretion. *Ann. Rev. Physiol.* 41:229–40

32. Graham, R. M., Brabson, J., Sagalowsky, A., Stephenson, W., Pettinger, W. A. 1978. Increased renal alpha-adrenergic receptors in genetically hypertensive rats. *Clin. Res.* 26: 363A

33. Harada, E., Rubin, R. P. 1978. Stimulation of renin secretion and calcium efflux from the isolated perfused cat kidney by noradrenaline after prolonged calcium deprivation. *J. Physiol. London* 274:367–79

34. Herman, C. A., Zenser, T. V., Davis, B. B. 1980. Effects of alamethicin on hormonal activation of renal adenylate cyclase. *Biochem. Pharmacol.* 29:51–55

35. Himori, N., Izumi, A., Ishimori, T. 1980. Analysis of β-adrenoceptors mediating renin release produced by isoproterenol in conscious dogs. *Am. J. Physiol.* 238:F387–93

36. Hofbauer, K. G., Konrads, A., Schwartz, K., Werner, U. 1978. Role of cyclic AMP in regulation of renin release from the isolated perfused kidney. *Klin. Wochenschr.* 56(Suppl. 1):51–59

37. Hoffman, B. B., Lefkowitz, R. S. 1980. Radioligand binding studies of adrenergic receptors: New insights into molecular and physiological regulators. *Ann. Rev. Pharmacol. Toxicol.* 20:581–608

38. Imbert, M., Chabardés, D., Morel, F. 1974. Hormone-sensitive adenylate cyclase in isolated rabbit glomeruli. *Mol. Cell. Endocrinol.* 1:295–304

39. Insel, P. A. 1978. Membrane-active hormone: receptors and receptor regulation. In *International Review of Biochemistry, Vol. 20, Series II, Biochemistry and Mode of Action of Hormones,* ed. H. V. Rickenberg, pp. 1–43. Baltimore: University Park Press. 265 pp.

40. Jarrott, B., Louis, W. J., Sommers, R. J. 1979. Characteristics of [³H]clonidine binding to an alpha-adrenoceptor in membranes from guinea pig kidney. *Br. J. Pharmacol.* 65:663–70

41. Jelkmann, W., Brookins, J., Fisher, J. W. 1979. Indomethacin blockade of albuterol-induced erythropoietin production in isolated perfused dog kidneys. *Proc. Soc. Exp. Biol. Med.* 162:65–70

42. Kalsner, S., Chan, C. 1979. Adrenergic antagonists and the presynaptic receptor hypothesis in vascular tissue. *J. Pharmacol. Exp. Ther.* 211:257–64

43. Katz, A. I., Lindheimer, M. D. 1977. Actions of hormones on the kidney. *Ann. Rev. Physiol.* 39:97–134

44. Kebabian, J. W., Calne, D. 1979. Multiple receptors for dopamine. *Nature* 277:93–96

45. Kotake, C., Hoffmann, P. C., Goldberg, L. I. 1979. Dopamine and beta-adrenergic stimulation of adenylate cyclase in rat glomerular homogenates. *Fed. Proc.* 38:1655

46. Lokhandwala, M. F., Jandhyala, B. S. 1979. The role of sympathetic nervous system in the vascular actions of dopamine. *J. Pharmacol. Exp. Ther.* 210:120–26

47. McDonald, K. M., Kuruvila, K. C., Aisenbrey, G. A., Schrier, R. W. 1977. Effect of α and β adrenergic stimulation on renal water excretion and medullary tissue cyclic AMP in intact and diabetes insipidus rats. *Kidney Int.* 12:96–103

48. McDonald, D. W. R., Saggerson, E. D. 1977. Hormonal control of gluconeogenesis in tubule fragments from renal cortex of fed rats. *Biochem. J.* 168: 33–42

49. Mills, I. H., Obika, L. F. O., Newport, P. A. 1978. Stimulation of the renal kallikrein-kinin system by vasoactive substances and its relationship to the excretion of salt and water. *Contrib. Nephrol.* 12: 132–44

50. Montgomery, S., Jose, P., Spiro, P., Slotkoff, L., Eisner, G. M. 1979. Regional differences in the binding affinities of β-adrenergic receptors in the canine kidney cortex. *Proc. Soc. Exp. Biol. Med.* 162:260–63

51. Morel, F., Chabardés, D., Imbert, M. 1976. Functional segmentation of the rabbit distal tubule by microdetermination of hormone-dependent adenylate cyclase activity. *Kidney Int.* 9:264–77

52. Morris, B. J., Reid, I. A., Ganong, W. F. 1979. Inhibition by α-adrenoceptor agonists of renin release in vitro. *Eur. J. Pharmacol.* 59:37–45

53. Nakajima, T., Naitoh, F., Kuruma, I. 1977. Dopamine-sensitive adenylate cyclase in the rat kidney particulate preparation. *Eur. J. Pharmacol.* 41:163–69

54. Nakane, H., Nakane, Y., Roux, A., Corvol, P., Menard, J. 1980. Effects of selective and nonselective β-adrenergic agents on renin secretion in isolated perfused rat kidney. *J. Pharmacol. Exp. Ther.* 212:34–38

55. Osswald, H., Northrup, T. E. 1978. Renal adenylate cyclase systems. *Contrib. Nephrol.* 14: 74–86

56. Peart, W. S. 1978. Intrarenal factors in renin release. *Contrib. Nephrol.* 12:5–15

57. Peart, W. S. 1978, Renin release. *Gen. Pharmacol.* 9:65–72

58. Pendleton, R. G., Setler, P. E. 1977. Peripheral cardiovascular dopamine receptors. *Gen. Pharmacol.* 8:1–5

59. Prosnitz, E. H., Di Bona, G. F. 1978. Effect of decreased renal sympathetic nerve activity on renal tubular sodium reabsorption. *Am. J. Physiol.* 235: F557–63

60. Przala, F., Gross, D. M., Beckman, B., Fisher, J. W. 1979. Influence of albuterol on erythropoietin production and erythroid progenator cell activation. *Am. J. Physiol.* 346:H422–26

61. Quesada, T., Garcia-Torres, L., Alba, F., del Rio, C. G. 1979. The effects of dopamine on renin release in the isolated perfused rat kidney. *Experientia* 35:1205

62. Rayson, B. M., Ray, C., Morgan, T. 1978. A study of the interactions of catecholamines and antidiuretic hormone on water permeability and the cyclic AMP system in isolated papillae of the rat. *Pfluegers Arch.* 373:99–103

63. Reid, I. A., Morris, B. J., Ganong, W. F. 1978. The renin-angiotensin system. *Ann. Rev. Physiol.* 40:377–410

64. Roch-Ramel, F., Peters, G. 1979. Micropuncture techniques as a tool in renal pharmacology. *Ann. Rev. Pharmacol. Toxicol.* 19:323–45

65. Rouot, B. R., Snyder, S. H. 1979. [^{3}H]-para-amino-clonidine: a novel ligand which binds with high affinity to α-adrenergic receptors. *Life Sci.* 25: 769–74

66. Saggerson, E. D., Carpenter, C. A. 1979. Ouabain and K^+ removal blocks α-adrenergic stimulation of gluconeogenesis in tubule fragments from fed rats. *FEBS Lett.* 106:189–92

67. Schlondorff, D., Yoo, P., Alpert, B. E. 1978. Stimulation of adenylate cyclase in isolated rat glomeruli by prostaglandins. *Am. J. Physiol.* 235:F458–64

68. Schmitz, J. M., Salalowsky, A., Pettinger, W. A., Graham, R. M. 1980. α-Adrenergic receptors in the rat kidney: correlation of [^{3}H]dihydroergocriptine binding with α-adrenergic stimulation and inhibition of renal vasoconstriction. (Manuscript submitted)

69. Schrier, R. W. 1974. Effects of adrenergic nervous system and catecholamines on systemic and renal hemodynamics, sodium and water excretion and renin secretion. *Kidney Int.* 6:291–306

70. Schrier, R. W., Berl, T., Anderson, R. J. 1979. Osmotic and nonosmotic control of vasopressin release. *Am. J. Physiol.* 236:F321–32

71. Scott, C. K., Vanderwende, C. 1980. The identification of [^{3}H]apomorphine binding sites in dog renal cortex-membrane preparations. *Fed. Proc.* 38:1007

72. Snavely, M. D., Insel, P. A., 1980. Characterization of renal cortical beta-adrenergic receptors. *Pharmacologist* 22:284

73. Starke, K. 1977. Regulation of noradrenaline release by presynaptic receptor systems. *Rev. Physiol. Biochem. Pharmacol.* 77:1–124

74. Stowe, N., Schnermann, J., Hermle, M. 1979. Feedback regulation of nephron

filtration rate during pharmacologic interference with the renin-angiotensin and adrenergic systems in rats. *Kidney Int.* 15:473–86

75. Triggle, D. J., Moran, J. F. 1979. The identification and isolation of adrenergic receptors. See Ref. 15, pp. 387–409

76. U'Prichard, D. C., Snyder, S. H. 1979. Distinct α-noradrenergic receptors differentiated by binding and physiological relationships. *Life Sci.* 24:79–88

77. Vandongen, R., Strong, K. D., Poessé, M. H., Birkenhäger, W. H. 1979. Suppression of renin secretion in the rat

kidney by a nonvascular α-adrenergic mechanism. *Circ. Res.* 45(4):435–39

78. Williams, L. T., Lefkowitz, R. J. 1978. *Receptor Binding Studies in Adrenergic Pharmacology.* NY:Raven. 157 pp.

79. Woodcock, E. A., Johnston, C. I. 1980. Changes in tissue alpha-and beta-adrenergic receptors in renal hypertension in the rat. *Hypertension* 2:156–61

80. Zambraski, E. J., Di Bona, G. F. 1979. Interaction of adrenergic stimuli, prostaglandins and angiotensin II in the dog kidney. *Proc. Soc. Exp. Biol. Med.* 162:105–111

Ann. Rev. Physiol. 1981. 43:637–49

STEROID HORMONES AND THE KIDNEY

♦1335

Darrell D. Fanestil and Chun Sik Park

Division of Nephrology, Department of Medicine, University of California, San Diego, La Jolla, California 92093

Introduction

Steroid hormones appear to act generally by binding to a high-affinity, low-capacity, steroid-specific receptor protein in the cytoplasm of target cells. Translocation of the steroid-receptor complex to the nucleus induces the transcription of RNA, which results in the synthesis of proteins responsible for the physiological actions. In the kidney, receptors have been found for corticosteroids, estradiol, testosterone, and 1,25-dihydroxy-vitamin D_3. The most thoroughly studied of the hormones acting on the kidney are corticosteroids, especially aldosterone. We emphasize issues that are unresolved or need critical evaluation; we concentrate on corticosteroids. We discuss three areas of current interest: (*a*) steroid receptors; (*b*) the role of RNA, protein, and lipid synthesis; and (*c*) physiological effects.

Steroid Receptors

The soluble fraction of kidney cells (cytosol) contains distinct high-affinity, low-capacity receptors selective for all known classes of steroid hormones, as shown in Table 1. Progesterone is the sole exception to this generalization. Since progesterone antagonizes the action of mineralocorticoids (103) and since it competes with aldosterone (103), dexamethasone (104), and corticosterone (23) for their renal receptors, progesterone must interact with several proteins. However, specific binding of ^3H-progesterone in renal cytosol has never been reported (103). The binding of all other classes of steroids to renal cytosol is characterized by equilibrium dissociation constants (K_D, or the reciprocal of the affinity) of about nanomolar. The number of steroid-selective binding sites (N_{max}) varies from ∼15 (in the case of Type I receptor) to ∼900 (Type III receptor) fmol • mg^{-1} protein.

0066-4278/81/0315-0637$01.00

Table 1 Steroid hormone receptors in kidney[a]

| | Mineralocorticoid | | | Glucocorticoid | | | | Vitamin | | Sex steroids | | | |
| | Type I Aldosterone | | | Type II Dexamethasone/Triamcinolone | | | Type III Corticosterone | 1,25 Dihydroxy-Vitamin D3 | | Testosterone | | Estradiol | |
Species	Rat[21, 103]	Rabbit[61]	Human[62]	Rat[22, 24]	Rabbit[5]	Bovine[17f]	Rat[23]	Rat[14a]	Mouse[14c]	Mouse[13b]	Rat[4e]	Hamster[4e]	Human[11]
K_D (nM)[b]	0.5–3.0	3.0–3.7	0.5	4–5	3.3	3	3	0.2	0.34	1.7	.67	0.5	2.2
											10	20	
N_{max} (f mol·mg^{-1} protein)	17–22	15	4	160–246	160	210	900	50	–	56	87	29	34
											72	230	
Induced protein[c]	See Table 2			PEP carboxykinase Na$^+$,K$^+$-ATPase			?	Ca^{2+} Binding protein?[66]		β-glucuronidase[94] 20,000 dalton protein[97] 3α-OH-steroid oxidoreductase[101]	Ornithine aminotransferase[112]		
Physiologic action[d]	↓U$_{Na}$V, ↑U$_K$V, ↑U$_{H+}$V			gluconeogenesis			?	↑U$_{PO_4}$V; ↓U$_{Ca}$V		Renal growth	↓U$_{Na}$V[16]		

a Superscripts indicate references
b At 0°C in most but not all cases
c Not established in all cases
d Direct action on kidney not established in all cases
e Two classes of estradiol binding sites are probable, K_D and N_{max} for both classes of sites are given
f Triamcinolone but not dexamethasone measures Type II in bovine tissues[14]

The delineation of rat renal corticosteroid receptors into Type I or aldosterone receptors [selective for aldosterone > deoxycorticosterone (DOC) > corticosterone > progesterone > dexamethasone], Type II or glucocorticoid receptors [selective for dexamethasone and/or triamcinolone (6, 17) > corticosterone > DOC $\geqslant$ aldosterone $\geqslant$ cortisol > progesterone > estradiol = dihydrotestosterone] and Type III or corticosterone receptors (selective for corticosterone > cortisol > DOC > progesterone > aldosterone > dexamethasone) is based primarily upon these differential affinities for the various corticosteroids. Several areas remain for future clarification. First, aldosterone binds to two classes of receptors, distinguished by different K_{DS} and N_{max}s. The higher-affinity site, Type I, has a K_D for aldosterone of 0.8–3 nM and an N_{max} of 15–40 fmol $\cdot$ mg^{-1} protein (21, 103, 104). The lower-affinity site, presumably Type II receptor, has a K_D of 25–60 nM and an N_{max} of ~700 fmol $\cdot$ mg^{-1} protein. Clear demonstration that occupancy of either site by aldosterone results in a specific physiological action has not been achieved. The best evidence that occupancy of the higher-affinity of two receptors alters sodium transport was obtained in the urinary bladder of the toad, where the increase in sodium transport produced by the hormone correlated (albeit, nonlinearly) with occupancy of the higher-affinity of two receptors (18, 48).

Second, the functional significance of Type III receptor is not known. For example, dexamethasone, with less than 1/1000 the affinity of corticosterone for Type III receptors (23), elicits all known glucocorticoid responses in the kidney, presumably via Type II receptors. Of related concern is the similarity of Type III receptor with corticosterone binding globulin (CBG). The distinction of Type III from CBG is based on (a) differential occupancy after in vivo corticosterone (23), (b) different rates of dissociation of the steroid-protein complexes (23), (c) different sedimentation values (105), (d) the fact that only Type III receptors translocate ^{3}H-corticosterone to isolated cell nuclei (albeit, poorly) (23), (e) the finding of Type III sites in isolated kidney cells where CBG should have been removed during the isolation (105), and (f) localization of corticosterone by autoradiography to cortical and medullary collecting tubule cells after injection of ^{3}H-corticosterone (89). However, the autoradiographic study also found the steroid concentrated heavily in the cytoplasm of cells with lesser to minimal localization over cell nuclei. This contrasts sharply with the usual finding that steroid hormones are concentrated over nuclei with sparse localization in cytoplasm. Thus, corticosterone might not exert maximal nuclear translocation of the Type III receptor or, in other terminology (77), might be a suboptimal inducer. Therefore, other possibilities for Type III receptors need definitive evaluation: (a) Type III receptor could be CBG undergoing intracellular processing or degradation; (b) an unknown steroid might be the optimal inducer with corticosterone acting as a partial, physiological antisteroid; (c) since Type III receptors are in the same nephron segments responsive to aldosterone, the Type III receptor could be a pre- or post-processed Type I receptor; and (d) the physiologic function(s) (if any) mediated by Type III, quantitatively the greatest of the three types of corticosteroid receptors, remain(s) to be identified.

Localization of various classes of steroid receptors in specific nephron segments is currently being attempted. The identification of Type I receptors in rabbit kidney cortex and medulla (61) and preliminary autoradiographic localization in dissected, isolated distal convoluted and cortical collecting tubules (13) demonstrate that techniques are now available for precise localization of all classes of steroid hormone receptors in the nephron. Such information should, in turn, enable definition of the functional action of the hormones on those specific nephron segments demonstrated to contain receptor.

Moreover, two lines of evidence are consistent with the existence of an additional (Type IV) receptor. First, a canine kidney cell line, MDCK cells, contained a large quantity (N_{max} 25,000 fmol $\cdot$ mg^{-1}) of a protein with selectivity for deoxycorticosterone (DOC) > progesterone > aldosterone > corticosterone > cortisol = dexamethasone = none (60). This intracellular protein has a lower affinity ($K_D \sim 7 \times 10^{-8}$M) than do most classical steroid receptors (60). Suggestive, but equivocal evidence for nuclear translocation of DOC by this "receptor" was reported (60). Second, 16β-hydroxydehydroepiandrosterone (16β-OH DHEA) has negligible affinity for Type I (25, 36), Type II (25), and Type III (25) receptors. However, rat kidney cytosol contained a large amount (N_{max} 21,000 fmol $\cdot$ mg^{-1}) of a protein that bound radioactive 16β-OH DHEA with a relatively low affinity ($K_D \sim 3 \times 10^{-7}$ M)(63). These proteins binding DOC and 16β-OH DHEA are, therefore, distinguished from Type I–III by lower affinities and larger capacities and, in common with Type III, unknown function. Based on the large N_{max}, it is possible that the DOC- and 16β-OH-DHEA-binding proteins are the same; this possibility has not been evaluated.

The absolute dependence of the effects of a steroid hormone upon hormone-receptor interaction is best established with testosterone action on the mouse kidney. Androgenic steroids cause up to 50-fold increases in the activity of several enzymes in proximal tubular cells (95). All of these androgen-mediated responses are absent in kidneys of mice with the x-linked testicular feminization mutation, which results in absence of testosterone receptors (13b, 95). Localization of binding of testosterone and estradiol to specific nephron segments has not been achieved. The report that estradiol binding is concentrated in the medulla of human kidney (12) conflicts with the autoradiographic localization in proximal tubule (90).

Renal receptors for 1,25-dihydroxy-vitamin D_3 have been found in mouse and rat kidney (14a, 14c). The autoradiographic localization of this receptor in distal nephron, macula densa, and, surprisingly, in glomerular epithelial cells (90) challenges renal physiologists to find the functional consequences.

The Role of RNA, Protein and Lipid Synthesis

The dependence of the action of steroid hormones on RNA, protein, and lipid synthesis has been best studied with aldosterone. Briefly, the nucleus makes three types of RNA: ribosomal RNA (rRNA), transfer RNA (tRNA), and heterogenous RNA (HnRNA). HnRNA may be further processed in the nucleus into two types of messenger RNA (mRNA): (*a*) addition of adenines produces polyadenylated positive mRNA [poly A(+)RNA], which codes for most cellular and secretory proteins, and (*b*) nonpolyadenylated mRNA [Poly A(−)RNA], which codes for histones. Conflicting evidence concerning aldosterone stimulation of RNA synthesis obtained by earlier workers (reviewed in 58) might be explained in part by failure to examine specific classes of RNA. Thus an important recent series of studies in the urinary bladder of the toad reported that aldosterone increased the incorporation of radioactive precursors into 4S tRNA, 18S and 20S rRNA (108, 109), and poly A(+)RNA (108). The enhanced incorporation of uridine into tRNA has not been studied intensively, but may occur only 2–3 hr after addition of hormone (74, 109). On the other hand, increased incorporation of uridine and increased ^{14}C-methylation of 18S and 28S rRNA were evident after only 30-min exposure to aldosterone— i.e. the increased labelling of rRNA occurred prior to stimulation of Na$^+$ transport (109). However, increased synthesis of rRNA is apparently not a requisite for the increase in Na$^+$ transport that occurs in the 3 hr after addition of hormone. This conclusion is based on the finding that 3'-deoxycytidine produced marked inhibition of methylation of 18S and 28S rRNA but only minor, if any, inhibition of incorporation of uridine into polyA-(+)RNA and no significant inhibition of the action of aldosterone on Na$^+$ transport (76). In contrast, the synthesis of mRNA does appear to be necessary for the action of aldosterone. The hormone increased the incorporation of uridine into polyA(+)RNA with sedimentation values of 9–20S (108). Inhibition of formation of polyA(+)RNA by 70–80% with 3'-deoxyadenosine produced about 60% inhibition of the hormone's stimulation of Na$^+$ transport (73). Since a concentration of actinomycin D selected to produce comparable inhibition of uridine incorporation into polyA-(+)RNA produced complete blockade of stimulation of sodium transport, it was proposed that polyA(−)RNA (the synthesis of which is inhibited by actinomycin D but not by 3'-deoxyadenosine) is also required for full stimulation of Na$^+$ transport by aldosterone. This series of studies by Edelman, Rossier and colleagues (reviewed in 72) includes a number of important control experiments: Aldosterone stimulation of polyA(+)RNA synthesis was antagonized by a spirolactone (74, 75) but was not elicited by the inactive isomer, 17α-isoaldosterone (74). The fractional change in Na^+ transport produced by various additions of aldosterone or spirolactone singly or in combination was highly correlated with the simultaneously measured fractional change in incorporation of ^3H-uridine into 12S cytoplasmic polyA(+)RNA (75). The latter provides strong support for the sequential activation of RNA synthesis and sodium transport by aldosterone, although coordinate activation of parallel pathways is not totally eliminated. To recapitulate, aldosterone increases the incorporation of radioactive precursors into RNA characteristic of tRNA, rRNA, and mRNA. The early stimulation of Na^+ transport by the hormone depends upon synthesis of both types of mRNA [polyA(+)RNA and polyA(−) RNA] but not upon tRNA or rRNA. A requirement for tRNA and/or rRNA synthesis for sustained or later hormonal action remains possible. In this series of studies, the species of polyA(+)RNA altered by aldosterone were those sedimenting in the 9–20S region, usually peaking at 12S (75). This is at some variance with the peak at 22S recently reported for polyA-(+)RNA isolated from aldosterone-stimulated mitochondria-rich cells of toad urinary bladder (81). We note that mRNAs of 12S and 22S would code for proteins with approximate molecular weights of 32,000 and 150,000, respectively.

Evidence that aldosterone stimulation of Na^+ transport requires RNA synthesis contrasts with findings regarding aldosterone's effect on K^+ and H^+. Inhibition of RNA synthesis with actinomycin D in adrenalectomized animals inhibited the effect of the hormone on Na^+ excretion but not on K^+ (20, 55, 110) or H^+ excretion (55). The failure of inhibitors of RNA and protein synthesis to inhibit aldosterone stimulation of H^+ transport has been confirmed in the urinary bladder of the toad (59), where the inhibitors paradoxically mimicked the hormone by stimulating H^+ transport. Conflicting evidence exists concerning spirolactone: In the toad bladder spirolactone inhibited aldosterone stimulation of H^+ transport (59), but it stimulated H^+ transport in the turtle bladder (67). It is possible to construct a model whereby actinomycin D inhibits the synthesis of a depressor of H^+ transport and mimics aldosterone's stimulation of H^+ transport (59). However, there is no direct evidence for such a model, and stimulatory action of aldosterone on H^+ and K^+ transport by pathway(s) not involving RNA synthesis remains possible.

Inhibition of the antinatriuresis but not kaluresis caused by aldosterone also occurred with two analogs of riboflavin that inhibited flavin nucleotide synthesis (98). These analogs also inhibited aldosterone stimulation of ^{14}C-riboflavin incorporation into flavin nucleotides (98), an action of the hormone previously reported not to be blocked by actinomycin D (96). This presents a paradox: An agent that impaired antinatriuresis (actinomycin D) did not impair stimulation of flavin synthesis, whereas agents that impaired flavin synthesis did impair antinatriuresis.

This stimulation of flavin synthesis may be considered one of several enzyme activities altered by aldosterone. However, as shown in Table 2, some cases of enzyme change have yet to be confirmed (e.g. those in cAMP phosphodiesterase, phosphoprotein phosphatase). Contradictory reports exist in other cases (e.g. those of carbonic anhydrase, flavin dinucleotide synthesis). In some cases either the dose of aldosterone was so large that glucocorticoid action, possibly via occupancy of Type II receptor, was possible (Na^+,K^+-ATPase, cAMP phosphodiesterase) or the effect on the enzyme occurred long after the action of the hormone on electrolyte excretion [Na^+,K^+-ATPase (14b, 33), cAMP phosphodiesterase, and phosphoprotein phosphatase]. Only in citrate synthase did the increase in activity consistently occur with dose-response and time relationships that would enable it to mediate (some) early actions of aldosterone. The increase in renal citrate synthase activity elicited by 0.8 μg aldosterone/100 g rat was accompanied by a 55% increase in incorporation of methionine into the immuno-precipitated enzyme (51), providing impressive evidence that this may be an aldosterone-induced protein.

This synthesis of citrate synthase coincides with aldosterone-stimulated radioactive amino acid incorporation into protein with a molecular weight

Table 2 Aldosterone-induced changes in enzyme activity[a]

Enzyme	Tissue	Change (%)	Aldosterone dose[b]	Time[c]
Carbonic anhydrase	Mouse kidney[91,93]	60↑	2 μg/day	3 days
	Rat kidney[92]	50↓	0.05 μg/100 g	4 hr
Na^+, K^+-ATPase	Rat kidney medulla[33]	28↑	5 μg/100g × 6	24 hr
	Rat kidney medulla[14b]	12↑	100 μg/day	6 days
	Rat kidney[45]	15↑	20 μg/100 g	3 hr
	Toad bladder[37]	none	1000 nM	2.5 hr
Cyclic AMP phosphodiesterase	Toad bladder[86]	20↓	200 nM	24 hr
Phosphoprotein phosphatase	Toad bladder[56]	↑	>20 nM	10 hr
Flavin dinucleotide synthesis	Rat kidney[96]	20↑	2 μg/100 g	2 hr
	Rat kidney[19]	17↓	2 × 5 μg/day	3 days
	Rat kidney[98]	14↑	1.5 μg/100 g	3.5 hr
Citrate synthase	Toad bladder[42a]			
	Rat kidney[41,43]	20↑[43]	2 μg/100 g[43]	4 hr[43]
	Rat kidney cortex[51]	12↑	0.8 μg/100 g	3 hr
	Rat kidney medulla[51]	25↑	0.8 μg/100 g	3 hr

[a] Superscripts indicate references
[b] When indicated, dose is per 100 g body weight
[c] Time from first dose of hormone to sacrifice of preparation for enzyme assay

of ~ 31,000 (50) and would also correspond to a protein coded for by ~ 12S mRNA. Thus hormone-stimulated incorporation of amino acid into a 31,000 mol wt protein seems probable. As summarized in Table 3, aldosterone induction of proteins of other sizes has also been suggested, and much work remains to be done before consistently reproducible results are obtained. Not even the 31,000 (50) and 32,000 (82) mol wt proteins verify one another, because the 31,000 peak was probably citrate synthase from mitochondria and the 32,000 peak was putatively from plasma membrane (82). This area of investigation is in need of precise examination.

Other reports indicate that aldosterone action may involve altered lipid synthesis (44, 70). For example, (a) several changes occurred in the 30 min after introduction of hormone, including stimulation of synthesis, chain elongation, and desaturation of fatty acids (27); and (b) an inhibitor of the initial step in fatty acid synthesis and chain elongation inhibited the stimulation on Na^+ transport (54). Since inhibitors of RNA and protein synthesis blocked the hormonal alteration in lipid synthesis, the hormone may have induced proteins required for lipid metabolism, and the new lipids, in turn, may have increased Na^+ transport by altering the kinetic characteristics of one or more existing components of the Na^+ transport system. Recently, however, the inhibitor of lipid synthesis was reported to suppress the incorporation of four proteins (mol wt 170,000, 85,000, 32,000, and 6,000) into a membrane-rich fraction from toad bladder (82). Thus aldosterone may trigger synthesis of lipid and proteins, both being necessary for insertion of transport-altering proteins into cellular membranes.

Insertion of both lipids and proteins into cellular membranes, without equal removal of lipid and proteins from existing membranes, would result in an increase in cellular membrane. Indeed, Wade et al (102) reported that,

Table 3 Aldosterone-induced increase in proteins of specific size[a]

Investigators	Mol wt	Tissue	Aldosterone dose	Time[b]
Benjamin & Singer[9]	12,000	Toad bladder	1000 nM	0.5–4.5 hr
Scott & Sapirstein[83]	17–38,000	Toad bladder	20 nM	1–2 hr
Law & Edelman[50]	31,000	Rat kidney	0.8 μg/100 g[c]	1–3 hr
Scott et al[81]	12,000	Toad bladder	70 nM	0.75–3.75 hr
	85,000			
	170,000			
Scott et al[82]	6,000	Toad bladder	70 nM	0.75–3.75 hr
	32,000			
	85,000			
	170,000			

a Superscripts indicate references
b First time is the time after addition of aldosterone when radioactive amino acids were added; second time is time of termination of incubation.
c Per 100 g body weight

in rabbits, five mg DOCA for 11–18 days produced in cortical collecting tubules both an increase in transepithelial potential and a 100–150% increase in the baso-lateral area of principal (light) cells. Since 10 mg dexamethasone per day produced qualitatively similar effects, the relevance of these findings to mineralcorticoid action is obscure.

Physiological Effects

NA$^+$ METABOLISM The antinatriuresis and kaluresis produced by DOCA or aldosterone without changing renal plasma flow and glomerular filtration rate (7, 26, 71) provided evidence for a direct tubular action; the distal tubule is considered the main locus (35, 111). The distal tubule conventionally referred to in micropuncture was from the macula densa to the junction with another tubule. Based on recent criteria (30, 65, 87), this is a heterogeneous area that includes collecting tubules. In fact, studies with isolated perfused tubules of rabbit kidneys provided impressive evidence that mineralocorticoids increased the transtubular electrical potential (lumen negative) across cortical collecting, but not distal tubules (30, 31). More importantly, endogenous aldosterone or administered DOCA increased Na$^+$ reabsorption and K$^+$ secretion in the collecting tubules (68, 79), indicating the collecting tubule as a main site of action of mineralocorticoids. However, a few comments are in order. First, in earlier studies the transtubular electrical potential across cortical collecting tubules isolated from kidneys of rabbits fed an ordinary laboratory diet averaged about −25 to −35 mV (28, 88). Recently, though, such high values were measured only in tubules from animals with severe aldosteronemia; otherwise, the potential was close to zero or the polarity was reversed (30, 31, 68). The reason for the discrepancy has not been provided. Second, Gross & Kokko (31) found that in vitro aldosterone significantly increased the transtubular potential of collecting tubules, a finding Schwartz & Burg (79) failed to confirm. Third, in cortical collecting tubules from rabbits treated with a pharmacological dose of DOCA (5 mg/2 kg body weight) for 3 days, O'Neil & Helman (68) did not find a significant increase in transtubular potential, a disturbing finding since a single physiological dose of aldosterone can alter Na$^+$ excretion (20, 55). Finally, the absence of a change in the electrical potential of the distal tubule after introduction of aldosterone may not exclude action of aldosterone. Hierholzer & Wiederholt (34) found in rats that aldosterone normalized Na$^+$ transport in the distal tubule without changing the transtubular potential. Moreover, there is a poor correlation between the transtubular potential and Na$^+$ transport in collecting tubules (79). Therefore, a consensus has not been established regarding the actions of aldosterone on cortical collecting tubules and/or true distal tubules.

Similarly, studies on the papillary collecting duct have been controversial. Using the split-drop method, Uhlich et al (99) observed that adrenalectomy decreased volume absorption and reduced the transtubular concentration gradient for Na^+ in rat papillary collecting ducts. More recently, these investigators confirmed the prior finding and demonstrated that volume absorption was directly associated with Na^+ transport. Of particular importance were observations that volume absorption was restored in 3 hr by a single physiological dose of aldosterone and that aldosterone had an effect only on the fraction of Na^+ transport sensitive to amiloride (100). In sharp contrast, most studies with free-flow micropuncture and microcatheterization yielded negative results (32, 40). However, the calculation of Na^+ reabsorption between two puncture sites is affected not only by the segmental activity of Na^+ transport but also by unmeasured delivery of Na^+ from branching collecting ducts. Taking this and technical errors (40) into consideration, a need is apparent for more definitive study of aldosterone action on the papillary collecting duct. Controversies over the possible action of aldosterone on proximal tubular Na^+ transport have recently been reviewed (58).

Finally, interpretation of segmental changes in Na^+ transport produced by aldosterone throughout the nephron may be obscured or initiated by feedback regulatory loops within the intact nephron.

URINARY ACIDIFICATION   Administration of mineralocorticoids to normal subjects (53, 64, 107) or adrenalectomized animals (55, 78, 113) enhances urinary acidification. Mineralocorticoids appear to control urinary acidification via two mechanisms: H^+ transport and ammoniagenesis. Since normal bicarbonate reabsorption was found in adrenalectomized dogs with impaired urinary acidification, an effect of aldosterone on acidification in the proximal tubule appears excluded (47, 69). In accord with this conclusion, Hutler et al (39) reported that amiloride prevented or blocked the stimulatory effect of DOCA on acid excretion. Thus, aldosterone is generally thought to regulate H^+ secretion in the distal nephron, most likely in the collecting tubules. In toad and turtle urinary bladders, aldosterone stimulates H^+ secretion in vitro (3, 57, 59), where aldosterone modulates the rate of H^+ transport without affecting maximal H^+ concentration gradient (3). The increase in ammonia excretion produced by acid loading is depressed after adrenalectomy (38, 78, 113), indicating that corticosteroids likely have a direct effect on ammoniagenesis (38). Interestingly, mineralocorticoids and glucocorticoids may be equally effective (106, 107), but in most studies relatively high doses of mineralocorticoids were used and the issue of whether Type I or II receptor is responsible for ammoniagenesis warrants further study.

WATER METABOLISM   Limited capacity for dilution and concentration of urine is characteristic of adrenal insufficiency. Two mechanisms for the impaired dilution are postulated: an inappropriately high circulating level of antidiuretic hormone (ADH) (2, 13a, 84) vs increased tubular permeability to water independent of ADH (42, 52). These postulates were based on elevated (2, 13, 84) or normal ADH levels (42, 52) in adrenal insufficiency during water diuresis. Our brief literature survey revealed a distinct difference in the minimal urine osmolality at the peak of water diuresis: It was hypertonic or isotonic in studies that claimed elevated ADH (1, 2, 13a, 84, 98a) but was hypotonic in studies that claimed normal ADH (42, 52). Thus the circulating ADH level might be elevated or normal in adrenal insufficiency, depending on experimental conditions. The relative role of glucocorticoid vs mineralocorticoid in the impaired water diuresis of adrenal insufficiency is unclear.

The reduced urine concentrating ability in adrenal insufficiency (46) was ascribed to decreased papillary hypertonicity (15, 85). In rabbits after adrenalectomy, Schwartz & Kokko (80) recently observed a decreased maximal urine osmolality, and the hydroosmotic response of the cortical collecting tubules was decreased to ADH but not to cyclic AMP. Furthermore, the decreased hydroosmotic response to ADH was normalized by incubating the tubules with dexamethasone or aldosterone (5×10^{-11}M) or by an inhibitor of cyclic AMP phosphodiesterase. Schwartz & Kokko proposed that adrenal corticoids (both gluco- and mineralocorticoids) enhance urine concentration by inhibiting cyclic AMP phosphodiesterase.

Literature Cited

1. Ackerman, G. L., Miller, L. 1970. *J. Clin. Endocrinol. Metab.* 30:252–58
2. Ahmed, A. B., Gorge, B. C., Gonzalez-Auvert, C., Dingman, J. F. 1967. *J. Clin. Invest.* 46:111–23
3. Al-Awqati, Q., Norby, L. H., Mueller, A., Steinmetz, P. R. 1976. *J. Clin. Invest.* 58:351–58
4. Anderson, N. S. III, David, Y., Fanestil, D. D. 1979. *J. Steroid Biochem.* 10:123–28
5. Ballard, P. L., Baxter, J. D., Higgins, S. J., Rousseau, G. G., Tomkins, G. M., 1974. *Endocrinology* 94:998–1002
6. Barlow, J. W., Kroft, N., Stockigt, J. R., Funder, J. W. 1979. *Endocrinology* 105:827–34
7. Barger, A. C., Berlin, R. D., Tulenko, J. F. 1958. *Endocrinology* 62:804–15
8. Deleted in proof
9. Benjamin, W. B., Singer, I. 1974. *Science* 186:269–70
10. Deleted in proof

11. Bojar, H., Balzer, K., Dreyfurst, R., Staib, W., Wittliff, J. L. 1976. *J. Clin. Chem. Clin. Biochem.* 14:515–20
12. Bojar, H., Dreyfurst, R., Maar, K., Staib, W. 1977. *J. Clin. Chem. Clin. Biochem.* 15:319–21
13. Bonvalet, J. P., Farman, N., Vandewalle, A. 1979. *Colloq. INSERM* 85:113–20
13a. Boykin, J., DeTorrenté, A., Erickson, A., Robertson, G., Schrier, R. W. 1978. *J. Clin. Invest.* 62:738–44
13b. Bullock, L. P., Bardin, C. W. 1974. *Endocrinology* 94:746–56
13c. Bullock, L. P., Bardin, C. W. 1975. *Endocrinology* 97:1106–11
14a. Chandler, J. S., Pike, J. W., Haussler, M. R. 1979. *Biochem. Biophys. Res. Commun.* 90:1057–63
14b. Charney, A. N., Silva, P., Besarab, A., Epstein, F. H. 1974. *Am. J. Physiol.* 227:345–50

14c. Colston, K. W., Feldman, D. 1979. *J. Clin. Endocrinol. Metab.* 49:798–800
15. Cooke, R. C., Steenberg, R. W. 1973. *J. Lab. Clin. Med.* 82:784–92
16. DeVries, J. R., Ludens, J. H., Fanestil, D. D. 1972. *Kidney Int.* 2:95–100
17. Do, Y. S., Loose, D. S., Feldman, D. 1979. *Endocrinology* 105:1055–63
18. Farman, N., Kusch, M., Edelman, I. S. 1978. *Am. J. Physiol.* 235:C90–96
19. Fazekas, A. G., Sandor, T. 1976. *J. Steroid Biochem.* 7:29–32
20. Fimognari, G. M., Fanestil, D. D., Edelman, I. S. 1967. *Am. J. Physiol.* 213:954–62
21. Funder, J. W., Feldman, D., Edelman, I. S. 1973. *Endocrinology* 92:994–1004
22. Funder, J. W., Feldman, D., Edelman, I. S. 1973. *Endocrinology* 92:1005–13
23. Feldman, D., Funder, J. W., Edelman, I. S. 1973. *Endocrinology* 92:1429–41
24. Feldman, D., Funder, J., Loose, D. 1978. *J. Steroid Biochem.* 9:141–45
25. Funder, J. W., Robinson, J. A., Feldman, D., Wynne, K. N., Adam, W. R. 1976. *Endocrinology* 99:619–28
26. Ganong, W. F., Mulrow, P. J. 1958. *Am. J. Physiol.* 195:337–42
27. Goodman, D. B. P., Wong, M., Rasmussen, H. 1975. *Biochemistry* 14:2803–9
28. Grantham, J. J., Burg, M. B., Orloff, J. 1970. *J. Clin. Invest.* 49:1815–26
29. Deleted in proof
30. Gross, J. B., Imai, M., Kokko, J. 1975. *J. Clin. Invest.* 55:1284–94
31. Gross, J. B., Kokko, J. P. 1977. *J. Clin. Invest.* 59:82–89
32. Haas, J. A., Berndt, T. J., Youngberg, S. P., Knox, F. G. 1979. *J. Clin. Invest.* 63:211–14
33. Hendler, E. D., Torretti, J., Kupor, L., Epstein, F. H. 1972. *Am. J. Physiol.* 222:754–60
34. Hierholzer, K., Wiederholt, M. 1976. *Kidney Int.* 9:198–213
35. Hierholzer, K., Wiederholt, M., Holzgrove, H., Giebisch, G., Klase, R. M., Windhager, E. E. 1965. *Pflügers Arch.* 385:193–210
36. Higgins, J. R., Wambach, G., Kem, D. C., Gomez-Sanchez, C., Holland, O. B., Kaplan, N. M. 1977. *J. Lab. Clin. Med.* 89:250–56
37. Hill, J. H., Cortas, N., Walser, M. 1973. *J. Clin. Invest.* 52:185–89
38. Hulter, H. N., Ilnicki, L. P., Harbottle, J. A., Sebastian, A. 1977. *Am. J. Physiol.* 232:F136–46
39. Hulter, H. N., Licht, J. H., Sebastian, A. 1979. *Am. J. Physiol.* 236:F48–57

40. Jamison, R. L., Sonnenberg, H., Stein, J. H. 1979. *Am. J. Physiol.* 237:F247–61
41. Kinne, R., Kirsten, R. 1968. *Pflügers Arch.* 300:244–54
42. Kleeman, C. R., Czaczhes, J. W., Cutler, R. 1964. *J. Clin. Invest.* 43:1641–48
42a. Kirsten, E., Kirsten, R., Leaf, A., Sharp, G. W. G. 1968. *Pflügers Arch.* 300:213–25
43. Kirsten, R., Kirsten, E. 1972. *Am. J. Physiol.* 223:229–35
44. Kirsten, R., Nelson, K., Ruschendorg, U., Seger, W., Scholz, T. H., Kirsten, E. 1977. *Pflügers Arch.* 368:189–94
45. Knox, W. H., Sen, A. K. 1974. *Ann. N.Y. Acad. Sci.* 242:471–488
46. Kottke, F. J., Code, C. F., Wood, E. H. 1942. *Am. J. Physiol.* 136:229–43
47. Kurtzman, N. A., White, M. G., Rogers, P. W. 1971. *J. Lab. Clin. Med.* 77:931–40
48. Kusch, M., Farman, N., Edelman, I. S. 1978. *Am. J. Physiol.* 235:C82–89
49. Deleted in proof
50. Law, P. Y., Edelman, I. S. 1978. *J. Membr. Biol.* 41:15–40
51. Law, P. Y., Edelman, I. S. 1978. *J. Membr. Biol.* 41:41–64
52. Levi, J., Grinblat, J., Kleeman, C. R. 1973. *Israel J. Med. Sci.* 9:429–37
53. Liddle, G. W. 1958. *Arch. Intern. Med.* 102:998–1004
54. Lien, E. L., Goodman, D. B. P., Rasmussen, H. 1975. *Biochemistry* 14:2749–54
55. Lifschitz, M. D., Schrier, R. W., Edelman, I. S. 1973. *Am. J. Physiol.* 224:376–80
56. Liu, A. Y.-C., Greengard, P. 1974. *Proc. Natl. Acad. Sci. USA* 71:3869–73
57. Ludens, J. H., Fanestil, D. D. 1974. *Am. J. Physiol.* 226:1321–26
58. Ludens, J. H., Fanestil, D. D. 1976. *Pharmacol. Ther. B.* 2:371–412
59. Ludens, J. H., Vaughn, D. A., Fanestil, D. D. 1978. *J. Membr. Biol.* 40:199–211
60. Ludens, J. H., Vaughn, D. A., Mawe, R. C., Fanestil, D. D. 1978. *J. Steroid Biochem.* 9:17–21
61. Marver, D. 1980. *Endocrinology* 106:611–18
62. Matulich, D. T., Spindler, B. J., Schambelan, M., Baxter, J. D. 1976. *J. Clin. Endocrinol. Metab.* 43:1170–74
63. Matulich, D. T., Baxter, J. D., Gomez-Sanchez, C., Holland, O. B. 1979. *J. Steroid Biochem.* 10:285–89
64. Mills, J. N., Thomas, S., Williamson, K. S. 1960. *J. Physiol. London* 151:312–31
65. Morel, F., Chabardés, D., Imbert, M. 1976. *Kidney Int.* 9:264–77

66. Morrissey, R. L., Bucci, T. J., Empson, R. N. Jr., Lufkin, E. G. 1975. *Proc. Soc. Exp. Biol. Med.* 149:56–60
67. Mueller, A., Steinmetz, P. R. 1978. *J. Clin. Invest.* 61:1666–70
68. O'Neil, R. G., Helman, S. I. 1977. *Am. J. Physiol.* 233:F544–58
69. Perez, G. V., Oster, J. R., Vaamonde, C. A. 1976. *Nephron* 17:461–73
70. Rasmussen, H., Goodman, D. P. B., Max, E. 1977. In *Biochemistry of Membrane Transport*, ed. G. Semenza, E., Carafoli, pp. 470–80. Berlin-Heidelberg-New York: Springer
71. Roemmelt, J. C., Sartorius, O. W., Pitts, R. F. 1949. *Am. J. Physiol.* 159:124–36
72. Rossier, B. C. 1978. *J. Membr. Biol.* 40:187–97
73. Rossier, B. C., Gäggeler, H. P., Rossier, M. 1978. *J. Membr. Biol.* 41:149–66
74. Rossier, B. C., Wilce, P. A., Edelman, I. S. 1974. *Proc. Natl. Acad. Sci. USA* 71:3101–5
75. Rossier, B. C., Wilce, P. A., Edelman, I. S. 1977. *J. Membr. Biol.* 32:177–94
76. Rossier, B. C., Wilce, P. A., Inciardi, J. F., Yoshimura, F. K., Edelman, I. S. 1977. *Am. J. Physiol.* 232:C174–79
77. Rousseau, G. C., Baxter, J. D., Higgins, S. J., Tomkins, G. M. 1973. *J. Mol. Biol.* 79:539–54
78. Sartorius, O. W., Calhoon, D., Pitts, R. W. 1953. *Endocrinology* 52:256–65
79. Schwartz, G. J., Burg, M. 1978. *Am. J. Physiol.* 235:F576–85
80. Schwartz, M. J., Kokko, J. P. 1980. *J. Clin. Invest.* 66:234–42
81. Scott, W. N., Reich, I. M., Brown, J. A. Jr., Yang, C.-P. H. 1978. *J. Membr. Biol.* 40:213–20
82. Scott, W. N., Reich, I. M., Goodman, D. B. P. 1979. *J. Biol. Chem.* 254:4957–59
83. Scott, W. N., Sapirstein, V. S. 1975. *Proc. Natl. Acad. Sci. USA* 72:4056–60
84. Share, L., Travis, R. H. 1970. *Endocrinology* 86:196–201
85. Sigler, M. H., Forrest, J. N., Elkinton, J. R. 1965. *Clin. Sci.* 28:29–37
86. Stoff, J. S., Handler, J. S., Preston, A. S., Orloff, J. 1973. *Life Sci.* 13:545–52
87. Stokes, J. B., Tisher, C. C., Kokko, J. P. 1978. *Kidney Int.* 14:585–93
88. Stoner, L. C., Burg, M. B., Orloff, J. 1974. *Am. J. Physiol.* 227:453–59
89. Strum, J. M., Feldman, D., Taggart, B., Marver, D., Edelman, I. S. 1975. *Endocrinology* 97:505–16
90. Stumpf, W. F., Sar, M., Reid, F. A., Tanaka, Y., DeLuca, H. F. 1979. *Science* 206:1188–90
91. Suzuki, S., Ogawa, E. 1969. *Biochem. Pharmacol.* 18:993–1003
92. Suzuki, S., Ogawa, E. 1971. *Biochem. Pharmacol.* 20:2191–204
93. Suzuki, S., Ogawa, E., Inoue, Y. 1976. *J. Steroid Biochem.* 7:429–38
94. Swank, R. T. 1978. *Mol. Cell. Endocrinol.* 12:139–49
95. Swank, R. T., Davey, R., Joyce, L., Reid, P., Macey, M. R. 1977. *Endocrinology* 100:473–80
96. Tan, E. L., Trachewsky, D. 1975. *J. Steroid Biochem.* 6:1471–75
97. Toole, J. J., Hastie, N. D., Held, W. A. 1979. *Cell* 17:441–48
98. Trachewsky, D. 1978. *J. Clin. Invest.* 62:1325–33
98a. Ufferman, R. C., Schrier, R. W. 1972. *J. Clin. Invest.* 51:1639–46
99. Uhlich, E., Baldamus, C. A., Ullrich, K. J. 1969. *Pflügers Arch.* 308:111–26
100. Ullrich, K. J., Papavassiliou, F. 1979. *Pflügers Arch.* 379:49–52
101. Verhoeven, G., DeMoor, P. 1977. *J. Steroid Biochem.* 8:113–19
102. Wade, J. B., O'Neil, R. G., Pryor, J. L., Boulpaep, E. L. 1979. *J. Cell. Biol.* 81:439–45
103. Wambach, G., Higgins, J. R. 1978. *Endocrinology* 102:1686–93
104. Warnock, D. G., Edelman, I. S. 1978. *Mol. Cell. Endocrinol.* 12:221–33
105. Weiser, J. N., Do, Y. S., Feldman, D. 1979. *J. Clin. Invest.* 63:461–67
106. Welbourne, T. C. 1976. *Endocrinology* 99:1071–79
107. Welbourne, T. C., Francoeur, D. 1977. *Am. J. Physiol.* 233:E56–60
108. Wilce, P. A., Rossier, B. C., Edelman, I. S. 1976. *Biochemistry* 19:4279–85
109. Wilce, P. A., Rossier, B. C., Edelman, I. S. 1976. *Biochemistry* 15:4286–92
110. Williamson, H. E. 1963. *Biochem. Pharmacol.* 12:1449–50
111. Wright, F. S., Giebisch, G. 1978. *Am. J. Physiol.* 235:F515–27
112. Wu, C. 1978. *Biochem. Biophys. Res. Commun.* 82:782–86
113. Yoshimura, H., Fujimoto, M., Sugimoto, J. 1962. *Jpn. J. Physiol.* 12:143–59

SPECIAL TOPIC: NEURONAL PLASTICITY

Introduction, Gerald Fischbach,
Section Editor

"Plasticity" is one of those household words that is defined clearly enough in the dictionary but that has been hopelessly muddled by neuroneologists in different contexts. It has been applied to short-term (seconds to minutes) or long-term (hours to years) changes in the structure, function, and/or biochemistry of the nervous system. Plasticity, defined in such broad strokes, has been studied in developing and mature animals following imposed changes in neuronal activity and biochemical milieu, and also following trauma. The papers in this section illustrate a few topics of current interest.

Le Douarin, Smith & Le Lièvre summarize very new information concerning the determination of transmitter synthesis in neural crest derivatives. Zigmond & Bowers examine the influence of impulse and synaptic activity on certain identified proteins in mature excitable cells. Harris reviews recent literature on the role of activity in development from the unfertilized egg to the vertebrate visual cortex. Rogart discusses modulation of the number and distribution of voltage-sensitive sodium channels in peripheral nerves.

651

Ann. Rev. Physiol. 1981. 43:653–71

FROM THE NEURAL CREST TO ♦1336
THE GANGLIA OF THE PERIPHERAL
NERVOUS SYSTEM

N. M. Le Douarin, J. Smith, and C. S. Le Lièvre

Institut d'Embryologie du CNRS, 94130-Nogent-sur-Marne, France

In recent years, considerable effort has been expended in endeavors to elucidate the mechanisms underlying the transformation of undifferentiated and apparently identical neural crest cells into the various cell types constituting the peripheral nervous system (PNS). In particular, the diverse biochemical and structural modifications involved in the development of the autonomic nervous system (ANS) is being studied by an increasing number of workers [see (3, 4, 6, 31, 50) for references]. The ANS is especially suitable for investigations of this kind: Many autonomic ganglia can be dissected out cleanly, methods exist for their successful culture in vitro, and they are characterized by the synthesis and storage of two major neurotransmitter substances—acetylcholine (ACh) for parasympathetic and enteric neurons, and norepinephrine (NE) for nerve cells of the sympathetic ganglia—for the detection of which appropriate analytical techniques are available.

Furthermore, the very early steps of peripheral ganglion ontogeny are accessible to in vivo study, thanks to the existence of a stable cell marking technique that can be used to investigate the migration of their neural crest–derived precursor cells. Chimeric bird embryos can be constructed *in ovo* by grafting neural primordia of quails into chicks or vice versa; identification of the migration pathways and the final localization of the crest cells is possible by virtue of the distinctive differences in the structure of quail and chick interphase nuclei (28, 29). This technique has proved a useful tool for the analysis of early events in the constitution of the PNS. It has thus become apparent that the various cell types are not determined

653

0066-4278/81/0315-0653$01.00

in the neural crest; their differentiation appears to be the result of successive multi-cellular interactions.

LEVELS OF ORIGIN OF THE PERIPHERAL GANGLIA IN THE NEURAL CREST IN NORMAL DEVELOPMENT

The peripheral neurons arise from the neural crest [see (21, 64) for reviews]. Appropriate cell marking techniques have established precisely the site of origin along the neural axis of the different peripheral ganglia (reviewed in 30, 31, 31a). Systematic replacement of regions of the neural primordium (neural tube together with the neural folds) in a chick host by the corresponding portion from a quail donor (or vice versa) at the same developmental stage (grafts referred to as isotopic and isochronic) was followed by chimerism analysis of the host ganglia and paraganglia (34). Since these operations do not disturb significantly the course of development their results provide a reliable picture of the normal ontogenetic processes. In this way, several different levels of the neuraxis have been identified according to their role in the formation of the ANS (Figure 1). Similar studies, based on the use of either ^{3}H-thymidine-labelled neural crest or of the quail/chick system, have helped to clarify the rather more complex question of the development of sensory and autonomic ganglia in the head (24, 42, 44, 46).

MULTIPOTENTIALITY OF THE AUTONOMIC PRECURSOR POPULATION ALONG THE NEURAL AXIS

The heterogeneity of neural crest with respect to its fate as cholinergic parasympathetic and adrenergic sympathetic autonomic derivatives (Figure 1) suggested that the cells at each level of the crest were already determined before migration—i.e. that the crest was a mosaic-like structure made up of cells committed early to a given type of differentiation.

By changing the initial position of the crest cells along the neural axis before they started migrating, it could be shown that this interpretation was not correct. Both the cephalic and vagal neural crest, transplanted at the level of somites 18–24 ('adrenomedullary' level of the crest), provided adrenomedullary-like cells for the suprarenal paraganglia. Conversely, the cervicotruncal neural crest, grafted into the vagal region, colonized the gut and gave rise to cholinergic enteric ganglia (33, 35).

The latter finding was confirmed in a different experimental system. Culture of the hind-gut, taken from an embryo before it had received the ganglion precursor cells, on the chorio-allantoic membrane (CAM) for 7–10

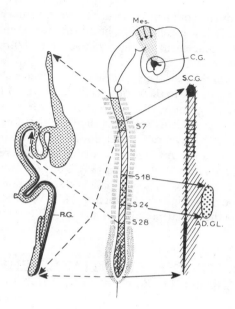

Figure 1   Levels of origin of sympathetic ganglia and plexuses, enteric and ciliary ganglia on the neural crest. The vagal level of the neural crest (from somites 1–7) provides all the enteric ganglia of the preumbilical gut and contributes to the innervation of the postumbilical gut. The lumbosacral level of the neural crest gives rise to the ganglion of Remak and some ganglion cells of the postumbilical gut (62). The ciliary ganglion arises from the mesencephalic crest (43). The sympathetic chain and plexuses are derived from the entire length of the neural crest posterior to the 5th somite, and the adrenomedullary cells originate from the level of somites 18–24. ADLG, suprarenal gland; SCG, superior cervical ganglion; S, somite; RG, ganglion of Remak; CG, ciliary ganglion; Mes, mesencephalic crest.

days resulted in apparently normal muscular development but a total absence of ganglia (60). When a fragment of a neural crest was associated with the aneural hind-gut before culture, enteric plexuses appeared, irrespective of whether the presumptive fate of the crest cells was to give rise to enteric ganglia or to sympathoblasts and adrenomedullary cells. The cholinergic nature of the ganglia formed in the culture was attested to by the presence of choline acetyltransferase (CAT) activity and high levels of acetylcholinesterase (AChE), while neither tyrosine hydroxylase, the key enzyme for CA synthesis, nor formol-induced fluorescence (FIF) of CA was detected.

Initial pluripotentiality of premigratory neural crest cells was also shown (45) in a study involving heterotopic transplantation of different regions of the cranial neural crest. When the forebrain crest, which normally never gives rise to neural elements, was grafted at the mesencephalic/metencephalic region, crest cells emigrated from their new position and responded to the mid/hindbrain environment by forming normal ciliary and trigeminal (sensory) ganglia. These ganglia were, however, absent when the reverse transplantation (i.e. replacement of diencephalic by mid/hindbrain crest) was performed.

Thus as a population the neural crest at each axial level can be considered as potentially able to give rise to the various cell types of the PNS. However, this does not necessarily imply that all regions of the crest are exactly equivalent. Indeed some evidence suggests they are not. For example, cephalic crest grafted at the level of somites 24–28 migrated into the dorsal mesentery and colonized the gut, whereas normal truncal crest derivatives are restricted to the dorsal trunk structures (35). Furthermore, trunk neural crest grafted in the place of metencephalic crest did not result in the development of a normal trigeminal ganglion (45). Whether these differences are related to the initial population size of the crest remains to be elucidated.

LABILITY OF THE DIFFERENTIATED PHENOTYPE OF NEURAL CREST-DERIVED GANGLION CELLS

Evidence for ganglion cell lability has been obtained from experiments in vivo and in vitro.

In Vivo Transplantation Experiments

PLASTICITY OF CHEMICAL DIFFERENTIATION IN AUTONOMIC AND SPINAL GANGLIA   Autonomic (ciliary and sympathetic chain) or sensory (DRG) ganglia, derived from quail embryo donors, were implanted into the dorsal trunk of a younger chick host embryo at the stage of neural crest cell migration and differentiation (32, 36, 38). The experiments were performed as described in the legend to Figure 2 and the evolution of the grafts was recorded by periodic histological observation of the chimeras. After the initial disaggregation of the implanted tissue, which occurred in a different manner for each type of ganglion, the cells of the graft migrated specifically in the host, reaching their definitive localization at around 6 days. The results are resumed in Figure 3.

Autonomic ganglion cells (both neuronal and satellite) became strictly localized in the autonomic structures of the host (sympathetic ganglia and plexuses, adrenal medulla, and enteric ganglia). Some cells of the grafted autonomic ganglion were also found in the rachidian nerves as Schwann cells. In contrast, the graft of sensory neurons resulted in the colonization of the host DRG in addition to the sympathetic and adrenomedullary host structures. Furthermore, associated FIF and Feulgen-Rossenbeck's tech-

QUAIL DONOR

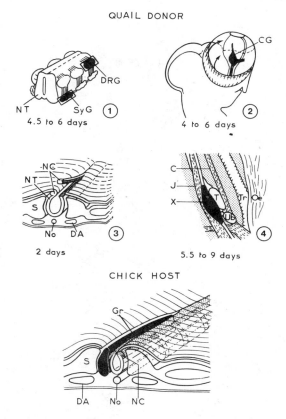

CHICK HOST

Figure 2 Diagram showing the different kinds of grafts of quail neural crest and neural crest–derived ganglia into a 2-day chick embryo as supernumerary structures. 1. Sympathetic chain ganglia (SyG) and dorsal root ganglia (DRG) are dissected out of 4.5–6-day embryos. NT, neural tube. 2. Ciliary ganglia (CG) are taken from 4–6-day quail embryos. 3. The trunk neural crest (NC) is cut out from 2-day quail embryos. (DA, dorsal aorta; No, notochord; S, somite). 4. The nodose ganglion (X), is dissected out of 5.5–9 day-quail embryos (C, carotid artery; J, jugular vein; Oe, esophagus; T, thyroid; Tr, trachea; Ub, ultimobranchial body). 5. The graft (Gr) is inserted into a slit made between somite and neural tube at the level of somites 18–24 of a chick embryo at stage 13.15 (18).

niques applied to embryos grafted with either sensory or autonomic ganglia showed that the quail cells found in the sympathetic plexuses and adrenal medulla were fluorescent.

These results led us to conclude that the observed distribution of implanted autonomic and sensory ganglion cells was the result of their differential "affinities" for the various neural crest cell target sites.

A model for cell line segregation during ontogeny of neural crest deriva-

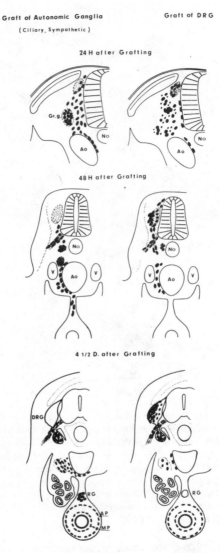

Graft of Autonomic Ganglia
(Ciliary, Sympathetic)

Graft of DRG

24 H after Grafting

48 H after Grafting

4 1/2 D. after Grafting

tives has been deduced from the above experiments (Figure 4). It occurs as a succession of binary choices and initially sets apart precursor cells with an "autonomic" determination that cannot, under our experimental conditions, take part in the constitution of DRG. This is true both for the neuronal and the satellite cell lines that derive from this autonomic precursor. In contrast, the cells present in the sensory ganglia during the first half of the developmental period seem to have, as a population, broader developmental capabilities, since grafting into a young host reveals "autonomic" potentialities in some of them. What is more, if we consider the expression of the final phenotype of the autonomic neurons in terms of transmitter synthesis, it is clear that at least some cells of the cholinergic ciliary ganglion can express adrenergic traits after being grafted in a younger host and becoming localized in the sympathetic ganglia and adrenal glands. It appears therefore that at least some decisions are labile and can be reversed.

NEURONAL POTENTIALITIES IN A NONNEURONAL CELL POPULATION DEMONSTRATED IN CHIMERIC NODOSE GANGLIA   One of the interesting problems raised by the histogenesis of peripheral ganglia concerns the segregation of the neuronal and satellite cell lines. If, as suggested in the model represented in Figure 4, this process occurs during the early steps of the formation of a ganglion, it is pertinent to ask whether presumptive satellite cells can change their differentiation pathway if they are subjected to major environmental changes during a critical stage of their development.

We decided to test this hypothesis on the nodose ganglion, which offers a very interesting model for this purpose inasmuch as the neurons are derived from the placode (local thickening of the dorsolateral ectoderm), whereas the satellite cells are of neural crest origin (C. Le Lièvre & N. Le Douarin, unpublished data). Owing to this mixed origin, it is possible to construct chimeric nodose ganglia of the vagus nerve in which the satellite cells are labelled by the quail nucleolus, while the neurons are of the chick type (Figure 5). Pieces of these ganglia were subsequently grafted as indicated in Figure 2. The evolution of the graft (taken from the donor at 5.5–9 days of incubation) was similar to that observed for the other types of peripheral ganglia. The interesting point is that the quail cells were

---

Figure 3   Localization of quail cells (black dots) after the graft of quail autonomic or sensory ganglia into chick embryos, 24 hr, 48 hr, and 4.5 days after grafting. In autonomic grafts the ganglion cells become dispersed in the host tissues and some are present for a while in the site where the host DRG is in formation. From 48 hr after grafting onward, the bulk of the grafted ganglion has disappeared and the quail cells become grouped along the ventral root, in the sympathetic ganglia and plexuses and in the adrenal medulla. Cells are no longer seen in the DRG area. In the case of ciliary ganglion grafts, quail cells migrate in the dorsal mesentery where they participate in the formation of the enteric plexuses.

In DRG grafts, necrosis is apparent within the first 24 hr after grafting (small dots represent pycnotic nuclei). Such necrosis, already in progress in the lateroventral part of the ganglion at the time of grafting, continues after grafting and contributes to the dispersion of ganglion cells. The latter aggregate with the host DRG but some also migrate ventrally and participate in the formation of autonomic adrenergic structures. (Ao, aorta; AP, Auerbach's plexus; Gr.g, grafted ganglion; MP, Meissner's plexus; V, vein.)

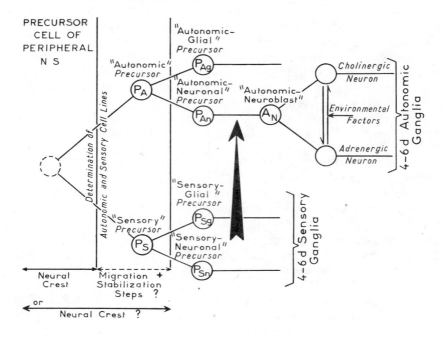

Figure 4 Segregation of the *autonomic* and *sensory* lines in the peripheral nervous system (NS). It is presented as an hypothesis that the sensory and autonomic lines are separated early (either in the neural crest itself or soon after cells have stopped migrating). The determination takes place in a precursor cell from which the satellite and the neuronal lines will respectively derive.

A succession of binary choices is responsible for cell line segregation. It seems that the choices may be for a while reversible after they have occurred. This was demonstrated for transmitter-related phenotype in autonomic neuroblasts which can be influenced by nonneuronal cells. Evidence is presented in this article that, in the nodose ganglion, cells with a glial fate may be induced toward the neuronal line. 'Autonomic' determination appears to be irreversible (see Figure 3) since no cells of grafted autonomic ganglia participate in DRG formation. In contrast, in the DRG, some cells can switch from sensory to autonomic when the ganglion is back-transplanted into a 2-day host.

subsequently found not only in the host DRG (a few only) and in the ventral rachidian roots and brachial nerves as Schwann cells, but also in the sympathetic ganglia and adrenal medulla. Some of the quail cells located in the adrenergic host structures contained CA. This shows that rhombencephalic neural crest cells, which do not normally contribute to the neuronal cell population in the nodose ganglion, can express such a phenotype if they are back-transplanted into the dorsal structures of a younger host. One can hypothesize that in contact with the neurons of placodal origin, neuronal potentialities are repressed in these cells, which then either remain undifferentiated or become engaged along the glial cell line differentiation

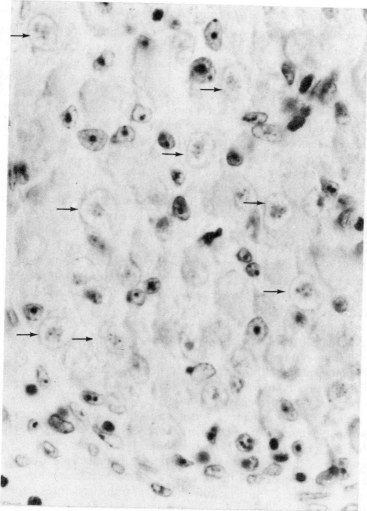

Figure 5 Chimeric nodose ganglion of an 8.5-day chick embryo. A quail rhombencephalic neural primordium has been isotopically and isochronically grafted on this embryo at the 10-somite stage. Neurons (→) have the chick clear nucleus; glial cells have the quail nucleus, which contains one or two masses of heterochromatin. Feulgen and Rossenbeck's staining. Magnification X 1100.

pathway. As a result of the cell dissociation that takes place after the graft of the ganglion in the chick host, the quail cells become isolated and can migrate anew; some stop in the sympathetic ganglia and the adrenal medulla of the host where they encounter the appropriate environment for the induction in them of the adrenergic neuronal phenotype.

In Vitro Cultures of Autonomic Ganglion Cells

The most abundantly documented example of the lability of the phenotype of developing neurons is provided by the superior cervical ganglion (SCG) of the neonatal rat in culture. The development of this ganglion in vitro is highly dependent on the conditions employed. Thus, when the ganglia are dissociated and grown under conditions in which most nonneuronal cells do not survive (39), the neurons continue to differentiate, acquiring many of the properties of mature adrenergic nerve cells—such as synthesis, storage, and release of norepinephrine (7, 39, 40, 53)—and may form adrenergic synapses with each other (55).

In marked contrast, dissociated neurons grown in the presence of nonneuronal cells, or medium conditioned by them, become primarily cholinergic (51, 52). CAT activity increases 100–1000-fold (52), while cytoplasmic vesicles change from the dense-core to the clear type (23). The extent of cholinergic differentiation is a function of the number of nonneuronal cells present or the concentration of conditioned medium added (52). The neurons form cholinergic synapses with each other (22, 49) and with target cells, such as skeletal myotubes or cardiac myocytes (16, 48). Similarly, explant cultures of SCG form predominantly cholinergic synapses with effector organs (20, 54).

By an ingenious use of single-cell cultures it was possible to confirm that the conversion from adrenergic to cholinergic metabolism is the result of a modification of the phenotype of individual cells (56). Furthermore, electrophysiological and ultrastructural evidence was obtained for the existence of 'dual-function' (cholinergic and adrenergic) neurons, possibly representing a transient, 'inter-phenotypic' state (16, 27).

These experiments provide clear evidence for the existence of an extrinsic factor capable of imposing a cholinergic phenotype on already differentiating, but obviously unstable, sympathoblasts. What is the evidence for the intervention of similar differentiation factors of nonneuronal origin during the normal development of the ANS? As will be discussed below, various attempts have been made to identify the dorsal trunk structures responsible for promoting adrenergic differentiation in neural crest derivatives.

TISSUE ORIGIN OF PUTATIVE FACTORS ELICITING ADRENERGIC DIFFERENTIATION IN VIVO

Potential adrenergic cells remain for a while in close contact with the neural tube and the somitic mesenchyme before differentiating in the latter. In the chick embryo, FIF of CA is first demonstrable at 3.5 days in the presumptive sympathoblasts of the primary sympathetic chains, located close to the notochord in the sclerotomal part of the somite (2, 9, 15, 26, 58). In contrast, it must be emphasized that neural crest cells, either before or during their dorso-ventral migration, never display CA-specific fluorescence [(2); our own observations].

Several workers have attempted to determine whether the notochord, the neural tube, and the somite influence the appearance of adrenergic phenotype. In a methodical study of sympathoblast differentiation involving culture of various tissue combinations on the CAM, Cohen (9) showed that trunk crest cells did not have to reach their normal destination dorso-lateral to the aorta in order to develop FIF. However, the presence of tissues normally encountered during the migration (neural tube and somites) was essential for the appearance of large numbers of FIF-positive cells. Cardiac or limb-bud mesenchyme was a poor substitute for somitic mesenchyme.

The interactions between neural tube, neural crest, and somite were examined further by Norr (47) in organ cultures. He confirmed that both neural tube and somites were necessary to obtain extensive sympathoblast differentiation (once again characterized by FIF). Results of trans-filter experiments led to the conclusion that the neural tube and notochord provoke a developmental change in somitic mesenchyme that then promotes differentiation of sympathoblasts.

The particular importance of the notochord was highlighted by the results obtained in our laboratory using a different experimental system, in which we looked for the appearance of CA in crest derivatives developing in the mesenchyme of the gut wall in the presence of neural tube and/or notochord (63). The aneural colorectum taken from a chick embryo at day 5 of incubation (i.e. prior the arrival of neural crest cells) was associated with quail neural crest of vagal or truncal origin and cultured for about 10 days on the chick CAM. Although many neurons developed and were distributed normally in submucosal and myenteric plexuses, none was fluorescent with the FIF method. If the tissue associations on the CAM included notochord, however, fluorescent neurons were observed in most cases. In more recent experiments (unpublished), we have noted that the extent of the appearance of adrenergic cells increases with the number of notochord explants associated.

In conclusion, somitic mesenchyme undoubtedly plays a role in eliciting the expression of adrenergic traits in neural crest derivatives, as shown by Cohen (9) and confirmed by our findings (below). However, the primordial role of notochord in this process is strongly suggested by its ability to permit the development of CA-containing cells in gut mesenchyme, which normally does not allow differentiation of the adrenergic phenotype.

If in vivo studies can help to identify the tissues that influence autonomic neuronal development, only an in vitro approach can lead to the isolation and characterization of the factor(s) involved. Thus a number of workers, including ourselves, have turned their attention to the culture of neural crest in vitro. As a first step, it was necessary to determine whether PNS phenotypes appeared in such cultures, and to what extent this differentiation was, in fact, dependent on nonneuronal cues.

DIFFERENTIATION OF NEURAL CREST CELLS IN VITRO

Crest cells migrate away from a neural primordium explanted in vitro (13). This phenomenon was exploited by Cohen & Konigsberg (11) to obtain viable primary cultures of quail neural crest. Cultures of trunk crest, prepared in this way, were shown to develop adrenergic properties spontaneously in medium supplemented with horse serum and embryo extract (10). Similarly, Greenberg & Schrier (17) have reported the differentiation of cholinergic properties in mesencephalic crest cultures derived in vitro from whole mesencephalon primordium.

Wishing to repeat these experiments, we argued that the momentary presence in vitro of the neural tube might influence subsequent crest cell differentiation—e.g. by production of extracellular material. To forestall this objection, we explanted neural crest obtained from both the cephalic and trunk levels by microdissection—i.e. at no stage was the neural tube introduced into the culture. Biochemical determination of neurotransmitter synthesis was used as an index of neuroblast differentiation [(65), M. Fauquet et al, unpublished data]. We could show that mesencephalic crest (a region from which the ciliary ganglion arises and that does not normally participate in adrenergic ganglion formation) cultured for 7 days developed both cholinergic and adrenergic traits. Cultures of trunk crest, although they always differentiated along the cholinergic pathway, virtually never developed CA-synthesizing cells when they were prepared from excised trunk neural fold explants. On the other hand, when trunk cultures were prepared from the total primordium, as in the experiments of Cohen, described above, adrenergic differentiation was observed in most cases.

A possible explanation for these results is that an early, albeit brief, contact between neural crest cells and the neural tube is sufficient to induce catecholaminergic differentiation in vitro. As for the apparent 'spontaneous' adrenergic differentiation of mesencephalic crest, there exists good evidence that mesencephalic crest is composed of a heterogeneous cell population, part of which is committed early to the formation of mesenchymal derivatives (37). Interaction between the latter and neuronal precursors may well account for the observed results. This interpretation received support from the fact that CA synthesizing ability appeared in trunk crest co-cultured with mesenchyme. Furthermore, the adrenergic differentiation already occurring 'spontaneously' in mesencephalic crest in vitro was markedly stimulated by co-culture with other embryonic tissues. This stimulatory effect, however, was not specific to somitic mesenchyme; embryonic chick heart and various other mesenchymes produced similar results. It seems clear, therefore, that neural crest cultures of this type cannot serve as a model for in vivo differentiation, since they permit the expression of phenotypes that do not occur during the normal course of events. They are nevertheless useful in revealing the *capabilities* of a crest population and, in this respect, confirm the pluripotentiality of the crest cell population along the neural axis already revealed by in vivo transplantation experiments.

On the other hand, certain normal developmental processes do not seem to take place in histiotypic cultures. This was particularly apparent in the report cited above (M. Fauquet et al, unpublished data): Although association of truncal neural crest with 2-day somites resulted in a certain 'primitive' degree of adrenergic differentiation, the extent of neuronal development was much greater when 3-day somitic mesenchyme, and, more specifically, the sclerotomal moiety (C. M. Cheney, J. W. Lash, personal communication.) of the somites, in which presumptive sympathoblasts have already migrated, was cultured (no exogenous neural crest was added). Although no CA synthesis could be detected before culture, as early as 20 hr after explantation, significant conversion of ^{3}H-tyrosine to NE was observed and, after 7 days in vitro, numerous FIF-positive ganglionic structures were visible. The most likely explanation of this result is that cellular interactions between the neural crest cells and the sclerotomal mesenchyme had already taken place at the time of explantation (i.e. between the migration phase and day 3 of development). One must conclude that specific developmental events, e.g. interactions with the neural tube and the notochord, 'condition' crest cells and somites in vivo between day 2 and 3 to a degree that does not seem to be easily reproducible in histiotypic cultures in vitro.

EVIDENCE FOR EARLY CHOLINERGIC TRAITS IN NEURAL CREST CELLS IN VIVO

The fact that cholinergic ganglia manifest appreciable ACh-synthesizing activity at the earliest stages of their existence (8, 36, 60) prompted us to investigate a possible expression of cholinergic properties in crest cells at an even earlier developmental stage, before the presumptive ganglioblasts aggregate.

The mesencephalic crest which we used for this study begins to migrate laterally from the mesencephalon at about 36 hr of incubation in the quail embryo. At this stage, it can be clearly seen as a sheet of cells on each side of the neural axis and can be excised microsurgically without great difficulty in a 'pure' state (i.e. free of contamination by the neural tube and surrounding mesenchyme) (65) while it is actually migrating. It was possible to show that isolated 'migrating' mesencephalic crest was able to synthesise ACh and contained CAT (61). The quantities measured were small, but significant; what is more, crest removed from mesencephalic neural folds (i.e. at an even earlier stage, when migration is only just beginning) could also make ACh, although somewhat less actively on a per cell basis. Thus long before reaching their target sites and even before being subjected to any influences from tissues encountered on the way, cholinergic properties are already apparent in the mesencephalic crest population. It was obviously impossible to ascertain whether all or only a fraction of the crest possessed cholinergic activity, but it is probable that the cells concerned include the presumptive neuroblasts of the ciliary ganglion.

These results immediately raise the question of whether an early ACh-synthesizing system is present in presumptive neuroblasts from other axial levels, including those that predominantly give rise to noncholinergic neurons. Although direct chemical analysis has not yet been possible (trunk crest contains many fewer cells than crest from the mesencephalic region), some (admittedly indirect) evidence suggests that a precocious cholinergic differentiation may indeed be common to crest cells from other sources. This evidence includes the fact that cultures of trunk crest invariably synthesized ACh (65) and the observation that crest cells from all axial levels contain AChE [(14); our unpublished results]. Further indications are provided by the finding of CAT activity in young sympathetic ganglia (19, 22, 41, 57). That not all of this is due to cholinergic preganglionic fibers is suggested by the facts that, first, CAT is detectable in the SCG of the 13-day mouse embryo—i.e. virtually as soon as the ganglion is formed (12)—and, second, that on culturing, although the enzyme activity declines during the first 2 days, a low residual level remains (12, 19, 22, 57). Furthermore, CAT and ACh have been detected in young sensory ganglia (25, 41). Additional evidence for intrinsic cholinergic activity in developing sympathoblasts was obtained in the experiments mentioned earlier, in which neuroblast differentiation was studied in isolated quail sclerotomes. Although no adrenergic differentiation could be identified in the freshly removed rudiments, the tissue, which was already seeded by crest cells, was able to convert ^{3}H-choline to ACh. This activity was maintained, even increasing somewhat, throughout the culture period while CA metabolism appeared.

CONCLUDING REMARKS

Neural Crest Cell Behavior

The experiments described in this article show that, although a regionalization can be recognized in the neural crest with respect to its fate as parasympathetic or sympathetic ganglia, a considerable homogeneity actually exists in the developmental capabilities of the crest cell population along the neural axis. The final localization of the precursors of the PNS depends on the pathways they follow after leaving the neural primordium. The sites of arrest for the precursors of the ANS, in the gut or in the adrenal medulla for example, are recognized equally well by crest cells arising from any region of the neural axis. Plexuses of Meissner and Auerbach of the gut can be formed by cells of the cephalic or truncal level of the crest just as they can by their normal vagal precursors.

The cell recognition mechanisms that probably account for the architectural arrangement of the ANS in the truncal area are 'memorized' in the crest-derived cells for a fairly long period during development: Quail ciliary or sympathetic ganglion cells grafted into a 2-day chick become distributed throughout the autonomic structures of the host and practically never form supernumerary ganglia located in abnormal sites. This is true even when the grafted ganglia are taken from embryos as late as 13 days of development [ciliary ganglion (see 65)].

The experiments involving back-transplantations of peripheral ganglia of quail into 2-day chick embryos strongly suggest that differences in cell membrane properties exist between autonomic and sensory ganglion cells as early as 4.5 days of incubation. This conclusion is based on the respective localization of autonomic and DRG cells implanted into a younger host. The results observed suggest that restrictions of developmental capacities take place early in autonomic cells whereas a broader range of differentiation can still be displayed by DRG under the same conditions.

The hypothesis that cell line segregation in the PNS involves a sequence of binary choices by precursors that are only partly committed to a particular pathway of differentiation led us to formulate the hypothesis that the satellite cells of the PNS ganglia possess repressed neuronal potentialities. The experiment with the chimeric nodose ganglion revealed that inducible neuronal traits are present in the nonneuronal population of this ganglion as late as 9 days of incubation. Although, owing to its mixed crest-placodal origin, the nodose ganglion is not strictly equivalent to the PNS ganglia of the trunk (which are entirely derived from the neural crest), this experiment raises a question concerning the interpretation of the results observed when the various other kinds of ganglia are back transplanted into a younger host. In particular when a developing cholinergic ganglion gives rise to adrenergic cells, the problem of whether the latter are derived from cholinergic neurons in which CA synthesis is induced or from a population of undifferentiated (or "satellite-like") cells is posed.

Chemical Differentiation

We have described how the first signs of adrenergic differentiation appear in crest-derived cells after they have undergone a phase of migration, during which the appropriate cellular interactions take place. In contrast, ACh-synthesizing ability is an initial property of at least some cells of the mesencephalic crest. Unlike the adrenergic phenotype, which can be revealed cytochemically with the FIF technique, the localization of cholinergic properties to individual cells is beset with practical difficulties. Whether or not the existence of cholinergic traits is common to early crest cells from all axial levels is thus still an open question. Nevertheless, the circumstantial evidence provided by the existence of ACh synthesis in developing sympathetic and sensory ganglia suggests that the phenomenon may well be widespread along the neural axis.

It is possible that early ACh synthesis by adrenergic ganglia reflects the presence there from the outset of a minority population of cholinergic cells, such as that previously demonstrated in various adult sympathetic ganglia (1, 5, 59). However, a plausible and ontogenetically more interesting theory is that all peripheral neuroblasts go through a cholinergic phase early in development, irrespective of their ultimate fate. Cholinergic neurons would result from the stabilization of this initial differentiation, perhaps via factors released by target organs, whereas alternative neuronal phenotypes would be acquired secondarily by neuroblasts subjected to the relevant environmental cues.

ACKNOWLEDGMENTS

The authors acknowledge financial support from the Centre National de la Recherche Scientifique, the Délégation Générale à la Recherche Scientifique et Technique, and U.S. National Institute of Health (Research Grant R01 DE0 4257 03 CBY).

Literature Cited

1. Aiken, J. W., Reit, E. 1969. A comparison of the sensitivity to chemical stimuli of adrenergic and cholinergic neurons in the cat stellate ganglion. *J. Pharmacol. Exp. Ther.* 169:211–23
2. Allan, I. J., Newgreen, D. F. 1977. Catecholamine accumulation in neural crest cells and the primary sympathetic chain. *Am. J. Anat.* 149:413–21
3. Black, I. B. 1978. Regulation of autonomic development. *Ann. Rev. Neurosci.* 1:183–214
4. Black, I. B., Coughlin, M. D., Cochard, P. 1979. Factors regulating neuronal differentiation. *Soc. Neurosci. Symp.* 4:184–207
5. Buckley, G., Consolo, S., Giacobini, E., Sjoqvist, F. 1967. Cholineacetylase in innervated and denervated sympathetic

ganglia and ganglion cells of the cat. *Acta Physiol. Scand.* 71:348–56
6. Bunge, R., Johnson, M., Ross, C. D. 1978. Nature and nurture in the development of the autonomic neuron. *Science* 199:1409–16
7. Burton, H., Bunge, R. P. 1975. A comparison of the uptake and release of [^{3}H] norepinephrine in rat autonomic and sensory ganglia in tissue culture. *Brain Res.* 97:157–62
8. Chiappinelli, V., Giacobini, E., Pilar, G., Uchimura, H. 1976. Induction of cholinergic enzymes in chick ciliary ganglion and iris muscle cells during synapse formation. *J. Physiol. London* 257:749–66
9. Cohen, A. M. 1972. Factors directing the expression of sympathetic nerve

traits in cells of neural crest origin. *J. Exp. Zool.* 179:167–82

10. Cohen, A. M. 1977. Independent expression of the adrenergic phenotype by neural crest cells *in vitro. Proc. Natl. Acad. Sci. USA* 74:2899–903

11. Cohen, A. M., Konigsberg, I. R. 1975. A clonal approach to the problem of neural crest determination. *Devel. Biol.* 46:262–80

12. Coughlin, M. D., Dibner, M. D., Boyer, D. M., Black, I. B. 1978. Factors regulating development of an embryonic mouse sympathetic ganglion. *Devel. Biol.* 66:513–28

13. Dorris, F. 1936. Differentiation of pigment cells in tissue cultures of chick neural crest. *Proc. Soc. Exp. Biol. Med.* 34:448–49

14. Drews, U. 1975. Cholinesterase in embryonic development. *Prog. Histochem. Cytochem.* 7:1–52

15. Enemar, A., Falck, B., Hakanson, R. 1965. Observations on the appearance of norepinephrine in the sympathetic nervous system of the chick embryo. *Devel. Biol.* 11:268–83

16. Furshpan, E. J., MacLeish, P. R., O'-Lague, P. H., Potter, D. D. 1976. Chemical transmission between rat sympathetic neurons and cardiac myocytes developing in microcultures: evidence for cholinergic, adrenergic, and dual-function neurons. *Proc. Natl. Acad. Sci. USA* 73:4225–29

17. Greenberg, J. H., Schrier, B. K. 1977. Development of CAT activity in chick cranial crest cells in culture. *Devel. Biol.* 61:86–93

18. Hamburger, V., Hamilton, H. L. 1951. A series of normal stages in the development of the chick embryo. *J. Morphol.* 88:49–92

19. Hill, C. E., Hendry, I. A. 1977. Development of neurons synthesizing noradrenaline and acetylcholine in the superior cervical ganglion of the rat *in vivo* and *in vitro. Neuroscience* 2:741–50

20. Hill, C. E., Purves, R. D., Watanabe, H., Burnstock, G. 1976. Specificity of innervation of iris musculature by sympathetic nerve fibres in tissue culture. *Pflügers Arch.* 361:127–34

21. Hörstadius, S. 1950. *The Neural Crest: Its Properties and Derivatives in the Light of Experimental Research.* London: Oxford Univ. Press. 111 pp.

22. Johnson, M., Ross, D., Meyers, M., Rees, R., Bunge, R., Wakshull, E., Burton, H. 1976. Synaptic vesicle cytochemistry changes when cultured sympathetic neurons develop cholinergic interactions. *Nature* 262:308–10

23. Johnson, M. I., Ross, C. D., Meyers, M., Spitznagel, E. L., Bunge, R. P. 1980. Morphological and biochemical studies on the development of cholinergic properties in cultured sympathetic neurons. I. Correlative changes in choline acetyltransferase and synaptic vesicle cytochemistry. *J. Cell Biol.* 84:680–91

24. Johnston, M. C., Hazelton, R. D. 1972. Embryonic origins of facial structures related to oral sensory and motor function. In *Third Symposium on Oral Sensation and Perception: the Mouth of the Infant,* ed. J. B. Bosma, pp. 76–97. Springfield, Ill: Thomas

25. Karczmar, A. G., Nishi, S., Minota, S., Kindel, G. 1980. Electrophysiology, acetylcholine and acetylcholinesterase of immature spinal ganglia of the rabbit —an experimental study and a review. *Gen. Pharmacol.* 11:127–34

26. Kirby, M. L. 1978. Drug modification of catecholamine synthesis and uptake in early embryo. *Brain Res.* 149:443–52

27. Landis, S. C. 1976. Rat sympathetic neurons and cardiac myocytes developing in microcultures: correlation of the fine structure of endings with neurotransmitter function in single neurons. *Proc. Natl. Acad. Sci. USA* 73:4220–24

28. Le Douarin, N. 1969. Particularités du noyau interphasique chez la caille japonaise (*Coturnix coturnix japonica*). Utilisation de ces particularités comme "marquage biologique" dans les recherches sur les interactions tissulaires et les migrations cellulaires au cours de l'ontogenèse. *Bull. Biol. Fr. Belg.* 103:435–52

29. Le Douarin, N. 1973. A biological cell labelling technique and its use in experimental embryology. *Devel. Biol.* 30:217–22

30. Le Douarin, N. 1976. Cell migration in early vertebrate development studied in interspecific chimaeras. In *Embryogenesis in Mammals,* Ciba Found. Symp., pp. 71–101. Amsterdam: Elsevier-Excerpta Medica, North-Holland

31. Le Douarin, N. 1980. Migration and differentiation of neural crest cells. In *Current Topics in Developmental Biology.* In press

31a. Le Douarin, N. M. 1980. The ontogeny of the neural crest in avian embryo chimeras. *Nature* 286:663–69

32. Le Douarin, N. M., Le Lièvre, C. S., Schweizer, G., Ziller, C. M. 1979. An analysis of cell line segregation in the

neural crest. In *Cell Lineage, Stem Cells and Cell Determination,* ed. N. Le Douarin, pp. 353–65. Amsterdam: Elsevier/North Holland

33. Le Douarin, N. M., Renaud, D., Teillet, M. A., Le Douarin, G. H. 1975. Cholinergic differentiation of presumptive adrenergic neuroblasts in interspecific chimaeras after heterotopic transplantations. *Proc. Natl. Acad. Sci USA* 72:728–32

34. Le Douarin, N., Teillet, M. A. 1973. The migration of neural crest cells to the wall of the digestive tract in avian embryo. *J. Embryol. Exp. Morphol.* 30:31–48

35. Le Douarin, N., Teillet, M. A. 1974. Experimental analysis of the migration and differentiation of neuroblasts of the autonomic nervous system and of neurectodermal mesenchymal derivatives, using a biological cell marking technique. *Devel. Biol.* 41:162–84

36. Le Douarin, N. M., Teillet, M. A., Ziller, C., Smith, J. 1978. Adrenergic differentiation of cells of the cholinergic ciliary and Remak ganglia in avian embryo after *in vivo* transplantation. *Proc. Natl. Acad. Sci. USA* 75:2030–34

37. Le Lièvre, C. S., Le Douarin, N. M. 1975. Mesenchymal derivatives of the neural crest: analysis of chimaeric quail and chick embryos. *J. Embryol. Exp. Morphol.* 34:125–54

38. Le Lièvre, C. S., Schweizer, G. G., Ziller, C. M., Le Douarin, N. M. 1980. Restrictions of developmental capabilities in neural crest cell derivatives as tested by *in vivo* transplantation experiments. *Devel. Biol.* 77:362–78

39. Mains, R. E., Patterson, P. H. 1973. Primary cultures of dissociated sympathetic neurons. I. Establishment of long-term growth in culture and studies of differentiated properties. *J. Cell Biol.* 59:329–45

40. Mains, R. E., Patterson, P. H. 1973. Primary cultures of dissociated sympathetic neurons. III. Changes in metabolism with age in culture. *J. Cell Biol.* 59:361–66

41. Marchisio, P. C., Consolo, S. 1968. Developmental changes of CAT activity in chick embryo spinal and sympathetic ganglia. *J. Neurochem.* 15:759–64

42. Narayanan, C. H., Narayanan, Y. 1978. Determination of the embryonic origin of the mesencephalic nucleus of the trigeminal nerve in birds. *J. Embryol. Exp. Morphol.* 43:85–105

43. Narayanan, C. H., Narayanan, Y. 1978. On the origin of the ciliary ganglion in birds studied by the method of interspecific transplantation of embryonic brain regions between quail and chick. *J. Embryol. Exp. Morphol.* 47:137–48

44. Narayanan, C. H., Narayanan, Y. 1980. Neural crest and placodal contributions in the development of the glossopharyngeal-vagal complex in the chick. *Anat. Rec.* 196:71–82

45. Noden, D. M. 1978. The control of avian cephalic neural crest cytodifferentiation. II. Neural tissues. *Devel. Biol.* 67:313–29

46. Noden, D. M. 1978. Interactions directing the migration and cyto-differentiation of avian neural crest cells. In *The Specificity of Embryological Interactions,* ed. D. Garrod, pp. 4–49. London: Chapman & Hall

47. Norr, S. C. 1973. *In vitro* analysis of sympathetic neuron differentiation from chick neural crest cells. *Devel. Biol.* 34:16–38

48. Nurse, C. A., O'Lague, P. H. 1975. Formation of cholinergic synapses between dissociated sympathetic neurons and skeletal myotubes of the rat in cell culture. *Proc. Natl. Acad. Sci USA* 72:1955–59

49. O'Lague, P. H., Obata, K., Claude, P., Furshpan, E. J., Potter, D. D. 1974. Evidence for cholinergic synapses between dissociated rat sympathetic neurons in cell culture. *Proc. Natl. Acad. Sci. USA* 71:3602–6

50. Patterson, P. H. 1978. Environmental determination of autonomic neurotransmitter functions. *Ann. Rev. Neurosci.* 1:1–17

51. Patterson, P. H., Chun, L. L. Y. 1974. The influence of non-neuronal cells on catecholamine and acetylcholine synthesis and accumulation in cultures of dissociated sympathetic neurons. *Proc. Natl. Acad. Sci. USA* 71:3607–10

52. Patterson, P. H., Chun, L. L. Y. 1977. The induction of acetylcholine synthesis in primary cultures of dissociated rat sympathetic neurons. I. Effects of conditioned medium. *Devel. Biol.* 56:263–80

53. Patterson, P. H., Reichardt, L. F., Chun, L. L. Y. 1975. Biochemical studies on the development of primary sympathetic neurons in cell culture. *Cold Spring Harbor Symp. Quant. Biol.* 40:389–97

54. Purves, R. D., Hill, C. E., Chamley, J. H., Mark, G. E., Fry, D. M., Burnstock, G. 1974. Functional Autonomic Neuromuscular Junctions in tissue culture. *Pflügers Arch.* 350:1–7

55. Rees, R., Bunge, R. P. 1974. Morphological and cytochemical studies of synapses formed in culture between isolated rat superior cervical ganglion neurons. *J. Comp. Neurol.* 157:1–11

56. Reichardt, L. F., Patterson, P. H. 1977. Neurotransmitter synthesis and uptake by individual rat sympathetic neurons developing in microcultures. *Nature* 270:147–51

57. Ross, D., Johnson, M., Bunge, R. 1977. Evidence that development of cholinergic characteristics in adrenergic neurons is age-dependent. *Nature* 267:536–39

58. Rothman, T. P., Gershon, M. D., Holtzer, H. 1978. The relationship of cell division to the acquisition of adrenergic characteristics by developing sympathetic ganglion cell precursors. *Devel. Biol.* 65:322–41

59. Sjöqvist, F. 1963. The correlation between the occurrence and localization of AChE-rich cell bodies in the stellate ganglion and the outflow of cholinergic sweat secretory fibres to the forepaw of the cat. *Acta Physiol. Scand.* 57:339–51

60. Smith, J., Cochard, P., Le Douarin, N. M. 1977. Development of choline acetyltransferase and cholinesterase activities in enteric ganglia derived from presumptive adrenergic and cholinergic levels of the neural crest. *Cell Different.* 6:199–216

61. Smith, J., Fauquet, M., Ziller, C., Le Douarin, N. M. 1979. Acetylcholine synthesis by mesencephalic neural crest cells in the process of migration *in vivo*. *Nature* 282:852–55

62. Teillet, M. A. 1978. Evolution of the lumbo-sacral neural crest in the avian embryo: origin and differentiation of the ganglionated nerve of Remak studied in interspecific quail-chick chimaerae. *Wilhelm Roux's Archiv Devel. Biol.* 184:251–68

63. Teillet, M. A., Cochard, P., Le Douarin, N. M. 1978. Relative roles of the mesenchymal tissues and of the complex neural tube-notochord on the expression of adrenergic metabolism in neural crest cells. *Zoon* 6:115–22

64. Weston, J. A. 1970. The migration and differentiation of neural crest cells. In *Advances in Morphogenesis,* ed. M. Abercrombie, J. Brachet, T. J. King, 8:41–114. NY: Academic

65. Ziller, C., Smith, J., Fauquet, M., Le Douarin, N. M. 1979. Environmentally directed nerve cell differentiation: *in vivo* and *in vitro* studies. *Prog. Brain Res.* 51:59–74

Ann. Rev. Physiol. 1981. 43:673–87
Copyright © 1981 by Annual Reviews Inc. All rights reserved

INFLUENCE OF NERVE ACTIVITY ❖1337
ON THE MACROMOLECULAR
CONTENT OF NEURONS AND
THEIR EFFECTOR ORGANS

Richard E. Zigmond and Chauncey W. Bowers

Department of Pharmacology, Harvard Medical School, Boston,
Massachusetts 02115

INTRODUCTION

The term "plasticity" is sometimes used to refer exclusively to anatomical changes in the nervous system that occur in response either to neural damage or to changes in an animal's environment. However, in a more general sense, the term can encompass long-term changes in the biochemical and electrophysiological properties of neurons that occur under these same circumstances. One experimental approach to the study of biochemical plasticity has been to ask what effects periods of "use" or "disuse" have on the biochemistry of neurons and their effector cells. Biochemical changes following repeated activation of a neural circuit have often been postulated to underlie long-term changes in an animal's behavior and physiology (e.g. learning, adaptation to environmental change) (see 44). Such activity-dependent changes have thus far been most successfully studied in the peripheral nervous system—particularly in skeletal muscle, the superior cervical ganglion, and the pineal gland. This brief review summarizes evidence that the level of neural stimulation of these tissues affects the concentrations of certain proteins important in regulating the tissues' function.

Regulation of Extrajunctional Acetylcholine Receptors
The vertebrate neuromuscular system has been particularly useful in demonstrating the influence of nerve activity on tissue biochemistry. Much of

673

0066-4278/81/0315-0673$01.00

the work using this system has been concerned with the spectrum of biochemical and electrophysiological changes that occur in skeletal muscle after denervation. The loss of muscle activity appears to be an important factor in many, if not all, of these denervation-induced changes (for review, see 30, 70). Perhaps the best-characterized phenomenon that occurs following denervation of vertebrate skeletal muscle is the 1000-fold increase in the extrajunctional sensitivity to acetylcholine (3, 10). Approximately one week is required for this response to develop fully (3, 56). This increase in sensitivity reflects an increase in the concentration of extrajunctional acetylcholine receptors (37) and occurs not only after denervation but also following chronic neuromuscular blockade with the nicotinic antagonist curare or following chronic conduction block in the motor nerves produced by a local anesthetic cuff (4, 56). These studies suggest that the denervation supersensitivity observed in skeletal muscle results from the loss of nicotinic cholinergic stimulation. However, supersensitivity can be completely reversed in one to two weeks by direct electrical stimulation of the denervated muscle cells (56), indicating that the loss of cholinergic stimulation following denervation affects the extrajunctional sensitivity via the cessation of muscle activity. Most of the manipulations of skeletal muscle that result in supersensitivity also produce a general atrophy of the muscle. However, atrophy of the muscle is probably not causally related to increases in extrajunctional receptor density since tenotomy of the rat soleus muscle, which results in severe atrophy without significantly decreasing neural stimulation (64), does not appear to result in increased extrajunctional receptors (56, 59).

The increase in the number of extrajunctional acetylcholine receptors after denervation reflects an increase in the rate of receptor synthesis with no change in receptor degradation (38, 55). Administration in vitro and in vivo of the RNA synthesis inhibitor actinomycin D or the protein synthesis inhibitor cycloheximide prevents the appearance of these extrajunctional receptors (29, 35). Thus the electrical activity of the muscle cell may regulate the appearance of extrajunctional acetylcholine receptors at the level of the genome.

The response of the denervated muscle to electrical depolarization is dependent on the total number of stimuli. Directly stimulating the denervated soleus muscle of the rat at high frequencies (e.g. 10 Hz) reduces the extrajunctional sensitivity more quickly than does stimulation at lower frequencies (57). However, frequencies as low as 0.01 Hz are capable of completely reversing the supersensitivity. The ability of low levels of activity to suppress extrajunctional sensitivity could account for the failure of other workers to measure appreciable supersensitivity following the immobilization of limbs or the isolation of motor neurons from supraspinal areas (32, 43, 85). Furthermore, these findings suggest that supersensitivity probably does not occur to any significant degree in normally functioning muscles even during periods of prolonged disuse. Apparently, changes in sensitivity in mature skeletal muscle only occur as a result of pathological conditions. However, cholinergic supersensitivity also occurs in development prior to innervation of skeletal muscle (26). The physiological significance of supersensitivity in either of these situations is unknown.

Lømo & Westgaard (57) further investigated the effects of muscle activity on extrajunctional sensitivity by determining whether, in addition to the total number of stimuli (muscle depolarizations), the temporal pattern of stimulation was a factor in controlling the decrease of supersensitivity in denervated soleus muscle. In order to separate the effects of the number of stimuli from the effects of the pattern of stimulation, different patterns were chosen with the same average frequency. Direct stimulation of denervated muscle with high frequency bursts was found to be more efficient at reducing extrajunctional sensitivity than was continuous stimulation. For instance, stimulation of the muscle at a frequency of 100 Hz for 1 in every 100 sec decreased the cholinergic sensitivity of the denervated soleus muscle nearly 3 times more quickly than did stimulation at 1.0 Hz continuously, in spite of the fact that the total number of stimuli applied per hour was exactly the same in each case. Since these experiments were performed on denervated muscle, it is clear that this influence of stimulation pattern on the muscle is not mediated by a synapse.

The effects of stimulation pattern in skeletal muscle are not restricted to denervation supersensitivity. Two distinct types of skeletal muscle have been described in mammals, fast-twitch and slow-twitch, based on their contractile properties and unique histologies (13, 25). It has been demonstrated by cross-innervation experiments that the particular nerve innervating a muscle determines to some extent the muscle type (14, 18). This influence of motor nerves on muscle cells is at least partly due to differences in the pattern and frequency of neural activity that occur in the different types of nerves (78). Further support for this mechanism was provided by the experiment of Lømo, Westgaard & Dahl (58) with the rat soleus muscle (a slow-twitch muscle). The denervated soleus muscle was stimulated at a frequency of 100 Hz for 0.5 sec in every 25 sec [100 Hz (0.5/25)] or 10 Hz for 10 in every 50 sec [10 Hz (10/50)]. Although both of these patterns provide the same numer of stimuli, only stimulation with the pattern 100 Hz (0.5/25) produced characteristics in the slow-twitch muscle resembling those of fast-twitch muscles. These alterations included changes in both the histological and contractile characteristics of the soleus muscle (58). Since the patterns, 100 Hz (0.5/25) and 10 Hz (10/50), are thought to resemble the electrical activity in the nerves for the fast- and slow-twitch muscles, respectively (31; also see 28), it is likely that the pattern of activity in motor neurons serves an important regulatory function in vivo.

Regulation of Tyrosine Hydroxylase

Tyrosine hydroxylase (TH) (tyrosine 3-monooxygenase, EC 1.14.16.2) catalyzes the first step in the synthesis of the neurotransmitter norepinephrine and is localized exclusively in peripheral and central adrenergic neurons and in the adrenal medulla. In 1969, Thoenen, Mueller & Axelrod (91) demonstrated that the activity of this enzyme was elevated in the rat superior cervical ganglion two days after the administration of the "sympatholytic" drug reserpine. Based on the finding that prior section of the preganglionic input to the superior cervical ganglion blocked the increase in TH activity, the authors hypothesized that reserpine produced a "reflex" increase in preganglionic nerve activity that resulted in increased TH activity (91).

The validity of this hypothesis rests on two assumptions. One is that reserpine administration increases the activity of neurons in the cervical sympathetic trunk, the preganglionic nerve innervating the superior cervical ganglion. The other is that this increase in nerve activity leads to an increase in TH activity. To date, electrophysiological studies on the effects of reserpine on preganglionic nerve activity have produced conflicting results (e.g. 27, 39, 79). However, since in addition to any possible effects on sympathetic nerve activity, reserpine has many other physiological and cellular effects [see (33) for further discussion of this point], it would be difficult to prove that TH activity is regulated by preganglionic nerve activity using this drug. Therefore, we decided to investigate the relationship between nerve activity and TH activity directly, using electrical stimulation. We have found that electrical stimulation of the preganglionic input to the rat superior cervical ganglion lasting from 10–90 min increases TH activity in the ganglion when assayed in vitro under "optimal conditions" (101). The increase in enzyme activity is maximal three days after the period of stimulation, and the magnitude of the increase depends on the duration of stimulation (15, 100, 101). When the cervical sympathetic trunk was stimulated at 10 Hz continuously for 30 or 60 min, TH activity was elevated by 32% and 73%, respectively. Stimulation for 90 min produced no further increase in enzyme activity, even though transmission through the ganglion was maintained throughout the period of stimulation (101). When 40 Hz trains of stimuli (on for 250 msec, off for 500 msec) were applied for 30 or 90 min, TH activity was elevated by approximately 50% and 100%, respectively. As suggested above, a convincing demonstration that this dependence of TH activity on preganglionic nerve activity accounts for the increases in TH activity seen after reserpine administration [and after a variety of other experimental manipulations, such as exposure of animals to a cold environment (90)] awaits electrophysiological verification.

When the preganglionic nerve was stimulated for 30 min once every 750 msec (an average frequency of 1.3 Hz), there was no change in TH activity (101). This finding suggests that the relatively slow (1–2 Hz) "spontaneous" firing rates recorded in preganglionic cervical sympathetic neurons (84) may not influence the activity of TH and may explain why decentralization of the ganglion leads to little, if any, change in this enzyme activity (101).

Immunoprecipitation experiments established that under stimulation conditions that produced a doubling in enzyme activity there was also a doubling in the amount of immunoreactive TH (102). Thus the increase in TH activity appears to be due to an increase in the number of enzyme molecules with no alteration in the activity of individual molecules. Whether this change is due to a change in the rate of synthesis or degradation of the enzyme or in both has not been determined. However, an increased rate of TH synthesis has been found in the adrenal medulla following "cold stress" (17).

The changes in TH after preganglionic nerve stimulation occur in the absence of changes in either total ganglion protein or in the activity of dopa decarboxylase, the second enzyme in the pathway of norepinephrine synthesis (15). However, the activity of dopamine-β-hydroxylase, the last enzyme in this pathway is also elevated (15). In the rat superior cervical ganglion TH is localized both in the principal neurons and in the small intensely fluorescent (SIF) cells; however owing to the larger number and size of the former, it is likely that most of the enzyme is localized in the principal neurons. The increase in enzyme activity produced by preganglionic stimulation can be prevented by pretreating animals with the nicotinic, ganglionic antagonists hexamethonium (16) and chlorisondamine (15). Administration of atropine and dihydroergotamine, muscarinic and α-adrenergic antagonists, respectively, has no effect (15). These pharmacological data indicate that the increase in ganglionic TH activity is primarily due to a change in the principal neurons, since transmission between preganglionic neurons and SIF cells is thought to be via muscarinic receptors (36).

Thus the increase in tyrosine hydroxylase activity following preganglionic nerve stimulation depends on increased nicotinic receptor stimulation in the postganglionic neurons. In an attempt to determine whether the role of nicotinic receptors was simply to increase the action potential frequency of the postganglionic neurons, the neurons were stimulated antidromically. Since antidromic stimulation did not increase TH activity, we have hypothesized that some effect of nicotinic receptor stimulation other than the triggering of action potentials is involved in the regulation of TH (16). The findings of Otten & Thoenen (66) that carbachol can increase TH in superior cervical ganglia in organ culture in the presence of tetrodotoxin lead to the same conclusion. While early experiments suggested that prolonged depolarization of ganglion cells with high K^+ in organ culture led to increased TH activity (60), this effect has now been attributed to the release of acetylcholine from preganglionic nerve terminals and the subsequent nicotinic stimulation of the ganglion (65). Thus the link between nicotinic receptor stimulation and increased TH activity remains to be elucidated.

Few studies have explored the physiological significance of increases in the amount of TH. The increase in TH activity found in cervical sympathetic ganglia two days after reserpine administration is followed two days later by an increase in enzyme activity in the heart (92). This delay is presumably due, at least in part, to the time required for axonal transport of the enzyme from cell bodies in the ganglia to terminals in the periphery. Since TH catalyzes the rate-limiting step in norepinephrine biosynthesis, increases in the amount of this enzyme in sympathetic nerve terminals may lead to increases in the rate of transmitter synthesis. Such an increase in catecholamine synthesis has been reported in the heart for one condition in which there is a long-term increase in TH activity (i.e. after phenoxybenzamine administration) (19).

Regulation of Serotonin N-Acetyltransferase

The activity of the enzyme serotonin N-acetyltransferase (NAT) (arylamine N-acetyltransferase E.C. 2.3.1.5) increases 50-100 fold every night in the pineal gland of the rat (22, 50). This enzyme, together with hydroxyindole-0-methyltransferase, catalyzes the synthesis of melatonin from serotonin (2, 96). Melatonin is thought to be the pineal hormone that mediates the effects of this gland on gonadal function (72, 87, 88). In all cases examined, changes in the activity of NAT parallel changes in melatonin synthesis (40, 71, 98).

The pineal gland of the rat is innervated primarily, if not exclusively, by neurons in the superior cervical ganglia (SCG) (45, 67), and the circadian variations in NAT activity are dependent on these neurons. Thus, removing the SCG or cutting the preganglionic trunks of the SCG abolishes the nocturnal increase in NAT activity (52). In addition, β-adrenergic agonists can stimulate NAT to peak nighttime levels in vivo and in vitro while propranolol, a β-adrenergic anatagonist, quickly reduces the high, nocturnal NAT activity in vivo (12, 23, 47, 74). The rapid decline ($t_{1/2} = 3$–5 min) in pineal NAT activity resulting from propranolol administration is identical to the decline observed when animals are exposed to light at any time during darkness (51).

Because of the pharmacological and anatomical evidence cited above, as well as the observation that the rate of turnover of pineal norepinephrine increases at night (11), it was hypothesized that an increase in the activity of the adrenergic neurons innervating the pineal gland causes the increased NAT activity observed during darkness (1, 46). Thus far there is a lack of convincing electrophysiological evidence that neural activity increases at night (62, 81, 82, 89). However, we have examined the possibility that increased sympathetic nerve activity can account for the circadian rhythm of NAT by electrically stimulating the cervical sympathetic trunk. An earlier study by Volkmann & Heller had shown that such stimulation could increase pineal NAT activity, but the increases produced were relatively small (maximum 3-fold) (94). We have now established that increased neural activity to the pineal gland is sufficient to stimulate NAT activity to peak nighttime levels (7, 8).

Bilateral stimulation of the cervical sympathetic trunk at a frequency of 5 Hz produces a linear increase in NAT activity that attains the peak nighttime level seen in intact rats within 3 hr. This corresponds to a 20–30-fold increase in NAT activity over the prestimulation values. It should be noted that in these studies, unlike the studies on TH, enzyme activity is measured immediately after the end of the stimulation period. The frequency range over which the NAT activity increases is narrow, giving little or no response at 1.0 Hz, a submaximal response at 2.5 Hz, and an essentially maximal response at 5 Hz (i.e. the effects of 10 Hz stimulation are not significantly different from those of 5 Hz stimulation). Similar results were obtained by stimulating the internal carotid nerve, the postganglionic trunk by which cells in the superior cervical ganglion innervate the pineal gland (7). These responses of NAT activity to nerve stimulation occur within the range of frequencies recorded in sympathetic neurons (e.g. 39, 41, 84), which suggests that electrical stimulation is mimicking physiologically relevant events. Cessation of stimulation leads to a rapid decrease in NAT activity with a $t_{1/2}$ of about 5 min, similar to the rate of decrease that occurs in response to light or propranolol administration (8).

The sensitivity of the nerve-pineal system to different patterns of stimuli can be determined in a manner similar to that described above for skeletal muscle. When the internal carotid nerves are stimulated at a frequency of 10 Hz for 2 in every 20 sec, the NAT activity increases to a level 60% greater than the activity after stimulation at 1.0 Hz continuously. In contrast, stimulation at 10 Hz for 1 in every 10 sec results in NAT activity equal to that measured after stimulation at 1.0 Hz continuously (7). Thus the pinealocytes and/or the sympathetic nerve terminals in the gland are sensitive to the temporal relationships between stimuli—i.e. the nerve-pineal system is not merely responding to the total number of stimuli in the internal carotid nerves. It should be noted that sympathetic neurons in vivo often exhibit high-frequency bursts of activity sometimes, though not always, in phase with respiratory or cardiac rhythms (39, 41, 42, 69). The data described above for stimulation of the internal carotid nerves suggest that such patterns of neural activity may be more efficient in stimulating the pineal gland (and perhaps other effector organs) than a continuous nonperiodic pattern would be.

The intracellular events mediating the increase in NAT activity in pineal cells have been studied using pharmacological techniques in vitro. Cyclic AMP (cAMP) seems to be the second messenger in this system since β-adrenergic agonists cause increases in cAMP concentrations (21, 86, 95) and since dibutyryl cAMP (dbcAMP) can mimic the effects of adrenergic stimulation on NAT activity (47). The effects of dbcAMP on NAT activity are consistent with earlier reports that this cAMP analog can increase the synthesis of melatonin from tryptophan in organ culture (48, 83). More recent evidence suggests that the abrupt decrease in NAT activity in response to propranolol administration may be due to a rapid decrease in the intracellular concentration of cAMP (49). Thus it appears that pineal NAT activity is controlled by the intracellular concentrations of cAMP. The mechanism of control by the nucleotide is unknown, though it may act via a cAMP-dependent protein kinase (34, 99) as it does in several other systems (53). The increase in NAT activity may be the result of increased synthesis of NAT molecules since the increases in enzyme activity can be blocked with protein synthesis or RNA synthesis inhibitors (23, 75). However, immunological precipitation techniques, similar to those utilized to study tyrosine hydroxylase, have not been applied to pineal NAT owing to the difficulties in isolating the NAT enzyme (5, 63). Thus it is not yet known whether an increase in the number of NAT molecules actually occurs during periods when NAT activity is increased.

Stimulation of the pineal β-adrenergic receptors results in a hyperpolarization of the membrane of the pineal cells (77). Administration of dbcAMP also causes a hyperpolarization of pineal cells (68). Exposure of pineal cells to ouabain or to a high concentration of potassium prevents both the hyperpolarization and the increase in NAT activity resulting from norepinephrine or cyclic nucleotide stimulation (68). Based on these findings, Klein and co-workers have hypothesized that the increase in membrane potential may mediate some of the events responsible for the norepinephrine-induced increase in NAT activity (68).

Using the increase in NAT activity as the response, it has been shown that denervation of the pineal gland leads to a supersensitivity to β-adrenergic agonists analogous in several respects to denervation supersensitivity at the neuromuscular junction (24, 74). In addition, the adrenergic sensitivity of the pineal gland shows a circadian variation that seems related to circadian fluctuations in neural stimulation of the gland (73). Thus the sensitivity of the gland to isoproterenol is higher at the end of the light period than at the end of the dark period, presumably because activity in the nerves innervating the pineal gland is suppressed by light. Part of this increased adrenergic sensitivity is probably due to the approximate doubling in the number of β-receptors on the pineal cells that occurs during the day (76). Whether this increase in receptor number is dependent on protein synthesis is not known. In addition, other factors distal to the receptors seem to play a significant role in the increased sensitivity to β-adrenergic agonists after decreased stimulation (74)—e.g. increased cAMP-dependent protein kinase activity (99). Thus, in addition to controlling the rate of synthesis of melatonin, neural stimulation may control the sensitivity of the pineal gland to further stimulation.

Summary and Discussion

The experiments summarized above present several examples of selective alterations in the protein composition of cells following changes in the activity of the neurons that innervate them. In the cases of the nicotinic cholinergic receptor in skeletal muscle and the β-adrenergic receptor in the pineal gland, decreased nerve stimulation produces an increase in the number of receptor molecules. In the case of the enzyme TH in the superior cervical ganglion, increased nerve stimulation leads to an increase in the number of enzyme molecules, and a similar mechanism is likely to hold for NAT in the pineal gland. In all four examples, the effects of presynaptic nerve stimulation on the biochemistry of the postsynaptic cell are mediated via the transmitter released by the presynaptic neuron—e.g. acetylcholine in the cases of the neuromuscular junction and the sympathetic ganglion, and norepinephrine in the case of the pineal gland. Such long-term actions of a neurotransmitter on the chemistry of postsynaptic cells are in marked contrast with the rapid effects (msec to sec) such compounds have on the ionic permeabilities of cells. These slower effects are more comparable to the effects of peptide and polypeptide hormones, such as TRH and prolactin, on the synthesis of specific proteins in their target cells (20, 93).

The immediate effect of acetylcholine's interaction with nicotinic receptors, both at the neuromuscular junction and in the superior cervical ganglion, is to depolarize the postsynaptic membrane triggering an action potential. The experiments described above indicate that an increase in action potential frequency in skeletal muscle is a sufficient stimulus for the

suppression of extrajunctional receptors, but that increased firing in ganglionic neurons is not sufficient to increase TH activity. Thus, even at synapses
where synaptic stimulation results in depolarization, direct postsynaptic
stimulation will not always mimic the effects of presynaptic stimulation. In
the pineal gland, the interaction of norepinephrine with β-adrenergic receptors produces a hyperpolarization of the pinealocytes. Whether this hyperpolarization is a sufficient stimulus to cause an increase in NAT activity has
not been established.

In the studies cited above, the magnitude of the effects of nerve stimulation are dependent both on the number of stimuli and, at least in some
instances, on the pattern of stimulation. It has long been known in a variety
of tissues, including striated muscle and sympathetic ganglia, that the pattern of neural activity is important in determining the immediate electrophysiological response to an individual stimulus (54, 61, 80, 97). The results
described in this review demonstrate that in skeletal muscle and pineal
gland, differently patterned stimuli also have different long-term biochemical consequences distal to or independent of electrophysiological changes.
Thus to relate the ongoing activity of neurons in vivo to biochemical events,
it is important to consider changes not only in the average frequency of
neural activity but also in the pattern of activity.

Most of the experiments reviewed here involve direct stimulation of
nerves and muscles. This raises the question of whether activity-dependent
changes in tissue biochemistry occur normally in the life of an organism.
Such changes have been most clearly demonstrated for the pineal gland
where daily variations both in postjunctional β-adrenergic sensitivity and
in NAT activity appear to be related to a circadian rhythm in sympathetic
nerve stimulation. On the other hand as already noted, only minor changes
in extrajunctional cholinergic sensitivity have been reported in adult skeletal muscle following large variations in muscle use, probably owing to the
extreme sensitivity of this system to low levels of activity. It remains to be
determined whether a physiological counterpart exists to the increase in TH
activity following nerve stimulation, but it may be that the increase in TH
following exposure of animals to a variety of forms of "stress" is due to an
increase in preganglionic nerve activity (90). In addition to their role in the
adult organism, activity-dependent mechanisms may explain certain
changes in tissue biochemistry during development following the onset of
neural transmission (e.g. increased TH and decreased extrajunctional nicotinic receptors) (6, 26).

The nighttime increase in NAT activity is accompanied by increases in
melatonin synthesis and secretion by the pineal gland. Thus the activity-
dependent regulation of NAT is probably at least one of the factors main-

taining the circadian rhythm in plasma melatonin. However, many questions remain concerning the physiological consequences of other biochemical effects resulting from periods of use or disuse. Even in the cases discussed above where there are changes in an enzyme catalyzing the rate-limiting step in the synthesis of a neurotransmitter (i.e. TH) or in the postsynaptic receptors for a neurotransmitter (i.e. nicotinic or β-adrenergic receptors), it must be demonstrated that such changes have physiological significance. Thus, while increases in TH activity may lead to an increased rate of norepinephrine synthesis, the effect of this increase on the amount of transmitter released, on the one hand, and on the magnitude of the postjunctional effect of nerve stimulation, on the other hand, remains to be established. In addition, while it is often tacitly assumed that an increase in postjunctional supersensitivity will increase tissue responsiveness to neural stimulation, increased responsiveness is usually tested only by exogenous application of an agonist. The importance of an increase in the number of postjunctional receptors to neural transmission at a particular junction will depend both on the safety factor for transmission at that junction and on the accessibility of the new receptors to neurally released transmitter. At the skeletal neuromuscular junction, for example, even if a large increase in extrajunctional receptors were to occur in innervated muscle, this biochemical change would presumably have little effect on synaptic transmission owing to the large safety factor at this synapse and to the high concentration of acetylcholinesterase, which ensures that little acetylcholine escapes from the junctional area. It is therefore important to determine, for each example of supersensitivity, whether the postjunctional sensitivity is increased to neurally released transmitter. This has only rarely been examined. The ultimate goal of the study of the activity-dependent regulation of specific proteins must be to relate these phenomena to the normal life of an organism by determining under what conditions such processes occur and what impact these biochemical changes have on synaptic efficacy and end-organ response.

ACKNOWLEDGMENTS

We would like to thank Drs. Gerry Fischbach, Ralph Loring, and Eric Frank for helpful discussions. Portions of this work were supported by NIH grant NS 12651 and a Grant-in-Aid from the American Heart Association with funds contributed in part by the Massachusetts Heart Association. R.E.Z. is a recipient of an NIMH Research Scientist Development Award (MH 00162) and C.W.B. is a trainee of the U.S. Public Health Service (NS 07009).

Literature Cited

1. Axelrod, J. 1974. The pineal gland: a neurochemical transducer. *Science* 184:1341–48
2. Axelrod, J., Weissbach, H. 1960. Enzymatic O-methylation of N-acetylserotonin to melatonin. *Science* 131:1312
3. Axelsson, J., Thesleff, S. 1959. A study of supersensitivity in denervated mammalian skeletal muscle. *J. Physiol. London* 147:178–93
4. Berg, D. K., Hall, Z. W. 1975. Increased extrajunctional acetylcholine sensitivity produced by chronic postsynaptic neuromuscular blockade. *J. Physiol. London* 244:659–76
5. Binkley, S., Klein, D. C., Weller, J. L. 1976. Pineal serotonin N-acetyltransferase activity: protection of stimulated activity by acetyl-CoA and related compounds. *J. Neurochem.* 26:51–55
6. Black, I. B. 1978. Regulation of autonomic development. *Ann. Rev. Neurosci.* 1:183–214
7. Bowers, C. W. 1980. *The anatomical organization of the cervical sympathetic nervous system and the influence of this system on the activity of arylamine: N-acetyltransferase in the pineal gland.* Ph.D. Thesis. Harvard University
8. Bowers, C. W., Zigmond, R. E. 1980. Electrical stimulation of the cervical sympathetic trunks mimics the effects of darkness on the activity of serotonin: N-acetyltransferase in the rat pineal. *Brain Res.* 185:435–40
9. Deleted in proof
10. Brown, G. L. 1937. The actions of acetylcholine on denervated mammalian and frog's muscle. *J. Physiol. London* 89:438–61
11. Brownstein, M., Axelrod, J. 1974. Pineal gland: 24-hour rhythm in norepinephrine turnover. *Science* 184:163–65
12. Brownstein, M., Saavedra, J. M., Axelrod, J. 1973. Control of pineal N-acetylserotonin by a beta adrenergic receptor. *Mol. Pharmacol.* 9:605–11
13. Buller, A. J., Eccles, J. C., Eccles, R. M. 1960. Differentiation of fast and slow muscles in the cat hind limb. *J. Physiol. London* 150:399–416
14. Buller, A. J., Eccles, J. C., Eccles, R. M. 1960. Interactions between motoneurones and muscles in respect of the characteristic speeds of their responses. *J. Physiol. London* 150:417–39
15. Chalazonitis, A., Rice, P. J., Zigmond, R. E. 1980. Increased ganglionic tyrosine hydroxylase and dopamine-β-hydroxylase activities following preganglionic nerve stimulation: Role of nicotinic receptors. *J. Pharmacol. Exp. Ther.* 213:139–43
16. Chalazonitis, A., Zigmond, R. E., 1980. Effects of synaptic and antidromic stimulation on tyrosine hydroxylase activity in the rat superior cervical ganglion. *J. Physiol. London* 300:525–38
17. Chuang, D. M., Costa, E. 1974. Biosynthesis of tyrosine hydroxylase in rat adrenal medulla after exposure to cold. *Proc. Natl. Acad. Sci. USA* 71:4570–74
18. Close, R. 1969. Dynamic properties of fast and slow skeletal muscles of the rat after nerve cross-union. *J. Physiol. London* 204:331–46
19. Dairman, W., Udenfriend, S. 1970. Increased conversion of tyrosine to catecholamines in the intact rat following elevation of tyrosine hydroxylase levels by administered phenoxybenzamine. *Mol. Pharmacol.* 6:350–56
20. Dannies, P. S., Tashjian, A. H. 1973. Effects of thyrotropin-releasing hormone and hydrocortisone on synthesis and degradation of prolactin in a rat pituitary cell strain. *J. Biol. Chem.* 248:6174–79
21. Deguchi, T. 1973. Role of the beta adrenergic receptor in the elevation of adenosine cyclic 3',5'-monophosphate and induction of serotonin N-acetyltransferase in rat pineal glands. *Mol. Pharmacol.* 9:184–90
22. Deguchi, T., Axelrod, J. 1972. Control of circadian change of serotonin N-acetyltransferase activity in the pineal organ by the β-adrenergic receptor. *Proc. Natl. Acad. Sci. USA* 69:2547–50
23. Deguchi, T., Axelrod, J. 1972. Induction and superinduction of serotonin N-acetyltransferase by adrenergic drugs and denervation in rat pineal organ. *Proc. Natl. Acad. Sci.*, 69:2208–11
24. Deguchi, T., Axelrod, J. 1973. Superinduction of serotonin N-acetyltransferase and supersensitivity of adenylcyclase to catecholamines in denervated pineal gland. *Mol. Pharmacol.* 9:612–18
25. Denny-Brown, D. 1929. The histological features of striped muscle in relation to its functional activity. *Proc. Roy. Soc. Ser. B* 104:371–411
26. Diamond, J., Miledi, R. 1962. A study of foetal and new-born rat muscle fibers. *J. Physiol. London* 162:393–408
27. Dontas, A. S. 1957. Effects of reserpine and hydralazine on carotid and splanchnic nerve activity and blood pressure. *J. Pharmacol. Exp. Ther.* 121:1–7

28. Eccles, J. C., Eccles, R. M., Lundberg, A. 1958. The action potentials of the alpha motoneurons supplying fast and slow muscles. *J. Physiol. London* 142:275–91

29. Fambrough, D. M. 1970. Acetylcholine sensitivity of muscle fiber membranes: mechanism of regulation by motoneurons. *Science* 168:372–73

30. Fambrough, D. M. 1979. Control of acetylcholine receptors in skeletal muscle. *Physiol. Rev.* 59:165–227

31. Fischbach, G. D., Robbins, N. 1969. Changes in contractile properties of disused soleus muscles. *J. Physiol. London* 201:305–20

32. Fischbach, G. D., Robbins, N. 1971. Effects of chronic disuse of rat soleus neuro-muscular junctions on postsynaptic membrane. *J. Neurophysiol.* 34:562–69

33. Fleming, W. W., McPhillips, J. J., Westfall, D. P. 1973. Postjunctional supersensitivity and subsensitivity of excitable tissues to drugs. *Rev. Physiol.* 68:55–119

34. Fontana, J. A., Lovenberg, W. 1971. A cyclic AMP-dependent protein kinase of the bovine pineal gland. *Proc. Natl. Acad. Sci. USA* 68:2787–90

35. Grampp, W., Harris, J. B., Thesleff, S. 1972. Inhibition of denervation changes in skeletal muscle by blockers of protein synthesis. *J. Physiol. London* 221:743–54

36. Greengard, P., Kebabian, J. W. 1974. Role of cyclic AMP in synaptic transmission in the mammalian peripheral nervous system. *Fed. Proc.* 33:1059–67

37. Hartzell, H. C., Fambrough, D. M. 1972. Acetylcholine receptors. Distribution and extrajunctional density in rat diaphragm after denervation correlated with acetylcholine sensitivity. *J. Gen. Physiol.* 60:248–62

38. Hogan, P. G., Marshall, J. M., Hall, Z. W. 1976. Muscle activity decreases rate of degradation of α-bungarotoxin bound to extrajunctional acetylcholine receptors. *Nature* 261:328–30

39. Iggo, A., Vogt, M. 1960. Preganglionic sympathetic activity in normal and in reserpine-treated cats. *J. Physiol. London* 150:114–33

40. Illnerova, H., Backstrom, M., Saaf, J., Wetterberg, L., Vangbo, B. 1978. Melatonin in rat pineal gland and serum; rapid decline after light exposure at night. *Neurosci. Lett.* 9:189–93

41. Janig, W., Schmidt, R. F. 1970. Single unit responses in the cervical sympathetic trunk upon somatic nerve stimulation. *Pflügers Arch.* 314:199–216

42. Janig, W., Szulczyk, P. 1980. Functional properties of lumbar preganglionic neurons. *Brain Res.* 186:115–31

43. Johns, T. R., Thesleff, S. 1961. Effects of motor inactivation on the chemical sensitivity of skeletal muscle. *Acta Physiol. Scand.* 51:136–41

44. Kandel, E. R. 1976. *Cellular Basis of Behavior.* San Francisco: Freeman, pp. 475–536

45. Kappers, J. A. 1960. The development, topographical relations, and innervation of the epiphysis cerebri in the albino rat. *Z. Zellforsch.* 52:163–215

46. Klein, D. C. 1974. Circadian rhythms in indole metabolism in the rat pineal gland. In *The Neurosciences Third Study Program,* ed. F. O. Schmitt, F. G. Worden, pp. 509–11. Cambridge, Mass: MIT Press

47. Klein, D. C., Berg, G. R., Weller, J. L. 1970. Melatonin synthesis: adenosine 3'5'-monophosphate and norepinephrine stimulate N-acetyltransferase. *Science* 168:979–80

48. Klein, D. C., Berg, G. R., Weller, J., Glinsmann, W. 1970. Pineal gland: dibutyryl cyclic adenosine monophosphate stimulation of labeled melatonin production. *Science* 167:1738–40

49. Klein, D. C., Buda, M. J., Kapoor, C. L., Krishna, G. 1978. Pineal serotonin N-acetyltransferase activity: abrupt decrease in adenosine 3'5'-monophosphate may be signal for "turnoff." *Science* 199:309–11

50. Klein, D. C., Weller, J. L. 1970. Indole metabolism in the pineal gland: a circadian rhythm in N-acetyltransferase. *Science* 169:1093–95

51. Klein, D. C., Weller, J. L. 1972. Rapid light-induced decrease in pineal serotonin N-acetyltransferase activity. *Science* 177:532–533

52. Klein, D. C., Weller, J. L., Moore, R. Y. 1971. Melatonin metabolism: neural regulation of pineal serotonin: acetyl coenzyme A N-acetyltransferase activity. *Proc. Natl. Acad. Sci. USA* 68:3107–10

53. Langan, T. A. 1973. Protein kinases and protein kinase substrates. In *Adv. Cyclic Nucleotide Res.* 3:99–153

54. Larrabee, M. G., Bronk, D. W. 1947. Prolonged facilitation of synaptic excitation in sympathetic ganglia. *J. Neurophysiol.* 10:139–54

55. Linden, D. C., Fambrough, D. M. 1979. Biosynthesis and degradation of acetylcholine receptors in rat skeletal mus-

cles. Effects of electrical stimulation. *Neuroscience* 4:527–38

56. Lømo, T., Rosenthal, J. 1972. Control of ACh sensitivity by muscle activity in the rat. *J. Physiol. London* 221:493–513

57. Lømo, T., Westgaard, R. H. 1975. Further studies on the control of ACh sensitivity by muscle activity in the rat. *J. Physiol. London* 252:603–26

58. Lømo, T., Westgaard, R. H., Dahl, H. A. 1974. Contractile properties of muscle: control by pattern of muscle activity in the rat. *Proc. Roy. Soc. Lond. Ser. B* 187:99–103

59. Lorkovic, H. 1979. Effects of motor nerve anesthesia and tenotomy on muscle membrane properties. *Pflügers Arch.* 379:89–93

60. Mackay, A. V. P., Iversen, L. L. 1972. Trans-synaptic regulation of tyrosine hydroxylase activity in adrenergic neurons: Effect of potassium concentration on cultured sympathetic ganglia. *Naunyn-Schmiedebergs Arch. Pharmacol.* 272:225–29

61. Martin, A. R. 1977. Junctional transmission II. Presynaptic mechanisms. In *The Handbook of Physiology*, Sect. I, Vol. 1, ed. E. R. Kandel, pp. 348–55. Bethesda, Md: Am. Physiol. Soc.

62. McClung, R., Dafny, N. 1975. Neurophysiological properties of the pineal body. *Life Sci.* 16:621–28

63. Namboodiri, M. A., Nakai, C., Klein, D. C. 1979. Effects of selected treatments on stability and activity of pineal serotonin N-acetyltransferase. *J. Neurochem.* 33:807–10

64. Nelson, P. G. 1969. Functional consequences of tenotomy in hind limb muscles of the cat. *J. Physiol. London* 201:321–33

65. Otten, U., Thoenen, H. 1976. Mechanisms of tyrosine hydroxylase and dopamine β-hydroxylase induction in organ cultures of rat sympathetic ganglia by potassium depolarization and cholinomimetics. *Naunyn-Schmiedebergs Arch. Pharmacol.* 292:153–59

66. Otten, U., Thoenen, H. 1976. Role of membrane depolarization in trans-synaptic induction of tyrosine hydroxylase in organ cultures of sympathetic ganglia. *Neurosci. Lett.* 2:93–96

67. Owman, C. 1964. Sympathetic nerves probably storing two types of monoamines in the rat pineal gland. *Int. J. Neuropharmacol.* 2:105–12

68. Parfitt, A., Weller, J. L., Sakai, K., Marks, B. H., Klein, D. C. 1975. Blockade by ouabain or elevated potassium ion concentration of the adrenergic and adenosine cyclic 3',5'-monophosphate-induced stimulation of pineal serotonin N-acetyltransferase activity. *Mol. Pharmacol.* 11:241–55

69. Passatore, M., Pettorossi, V. E. 1976. Efferent fibers in the cervical sympathetic nerve influenced by light. *Exp. Neurol.* 52:66–82

70. Purves, D. 1976. Long-term regulation in the vertebrate peripheral nervous system. *Int. Rev. Physiol.* 10:125–77

71. Ralph, C. L., Binkley, S., MacBride, S. E., Klein, D. C. 1975. Regulation of pineal rhythms in chickens: effects of blinding, constant light, constant dark, and superior cervical ganglionectomy. *Endocrinology* 97:1373–78

72. Reiter, R. J., Vaughan, M. K., Vaughan, G. M., Sorrentino, S., Donofrio, R. J. 1975. The pineal gland as an organ of internal secretion. In *Frontiers of Pineal Physiology*, ed. M. D. Altschule, pp. 54–174. Cambridge, Mass: MIT Press

73. Romero, J. A., Axelrod, J. 1974. Pineal β-adrenergic receptor: diurnal variation in sensitivity. *Science* 184:1091–92

74. Romero, J. A., Axelrod, J. 1975. Regulation of sensitivity to β-adrenergic stimulation in induction of pineal N-acetyltransferase. *Proc. Natl. Acad. Sci. USA* 72:1661–65

75. Romero, J. A., Zatz, M., Axelrod, J. 1975. Beta-adrenergic stimulation of pineal N-acetyltransferase: adenosine 3': 5'-cyclic monophosphate stimulates both RNA and protein synthesis. *Proc. Natl. Acad. Sci. USA* 72:2107–11

76. Romero, J. A., Zatz, M., Kebabian, J. W., Axelrod, J. 1975. Circadian cycles in binding of ³H-alprenolol to β-adrenergic receptor sites in rat pineal. *Nature* 258:435–36

77. Sakai, K. K., Marks, B. H. 1972. Adrenergic effects on pineal cell membrane potential. *Life Sci.* 11:285–91

78. Salmons, S., Sréter, F. A. 1976. Significance of impulse activity in the transformation of skeletal muscle type. *Nature* 263:30–34

79. Schmitt, H. 1968. Influence of reserpine and rescinnamine on the spontaneous and evoked sympathetic activity in rats. *Pharmacology* 1:25–32

80. Segundo, J. P., Perkel, D. H. 1969. The nerve cell as an analyzer of spike trains. In *The Interneuron*, ed. M. A. B. Brazier, pp. 349–90. Berkeley: Univ. California Press

81. Semm, P., Vollrath, L. 1979. Electrophysiology of the guinea-pig pineal organ: sympathetically influenced cells re-

sponding differently to light and darkness. *Neurosci. Lett.* 12:93–96

82. Shapiro, S., Silas, M. 1971. Effects of age, light, and sympathetic innervation on electrical activity of the rat pineal gland. *Brain Res.* 28:47–55

83. Shein, H. M., Wurtman, R. J. 1969. Cyclic adenosine monophosphate: stimulation of melatonin and serotonin synthesis in cultured rat pineals. *Science* 166:519–20

84. Skok, V. I. 1973. *Physiology of Autonomic Ganglia.* Tokyo: Igaku Shoin

85. Solandt, D. Y., Magladery, J. W. 1942. A comparison of effects of upper and lower motor neurone lesions on skeletal muscle. *J. Neurophysiol.* 5:373–80

86. Strada, S. J., Klein, D. C., Weller, J., Weiss, P. 1972. Effect of norepinephrine on the concentration of adenosine 3',5'-monophosphate of rat pineal gland in organ culture. *Endocrinology* 90:1470–75

87. Tamarkin, L., Hollister, C. W., Lefebvre, N. G., Goldman, B. D. 1977. Melatonin induction of gonadal quiescence in pinealectomized Syrian hamsters. *Science* 198:935–55

88. Tamarkin, L., Westram, W. K., Hamill, A. I., Goldman, B. D. 1976. Effect of melatonin on the reproductive systems of male and female Syrian hamsters: a diurnal rhythm in sensitivity to melatonin. *Endocrinology* 99:1534–41

89. Taylor, A. N., Wilson, R. W. 1970. Electrophysiological evidence for the action of light on the pineal gland in the rat. *Experientia* 26:267–69

90. Thoenen, H. 1975. Transsynaptic regulation of neuronal enzyme synthesis. In *Handbook of Psychopharmacology,* Vol 3, ed. L. L. Iversen, S. D. Iversen, S. H. Snyder, pp. 443–75. NY: Plenum

91. Thoenen, H., Mueller, R. A., Axelrod, J. 1969. Increased tyrosine hydroxylase activity after drug-induced alteration of sympathetic transmission. *Nature* 221:1264

92. Thoenen, H., Mueller, R. A., Axelrod, J. 1970. Phase difference in the induction of tyrosine hydroxylase in cell body and nerve terminals of sympathetic neu-

rones. *Proc. Natl. Acad. Sci. USA* 65:58–62

93. Turkington, R. W., Majumder, G. C., Kadohama, N., MacIndoe, J. H., Frantz, W. L. 1973. Hormonal regulation of gene expression in mammary cells. *Rec. Prog. Harm. Res.* 29:417–49

94. Volkman, P., Heller, A. 1971. Pineal N-acetyltransferase activity: effect of sympathetic stimulation. *Science* 173:839–40

95. Weiss, B., Costa, E. 1968. Selective stimulation of adenyl cyclase of rat pineal gland by pharmacologically active catecholamines. *J. Pharmacol. Exp. Ther.* 161:310–19

96. Weissbach, H. B., Redfield, B. G., Axelrod, J. 1969. Biosynthesis of melatonin: enzymic conversion of serotonin to N-acetylserotonin. *Biochim. Biophys. Acta* 43:352–53

97. Wiersma, C. A. G., Adams, R. T. 1950. The influence of nerve impulse sequence on the contractions of different crustacean muscles. *Physiol. Comp. Oecol.* 2:20–33

98. Wilkinson, M., Arendt, J., Bradtke, J., deZiegler, D. 1977. Determination of a dark-induced increase of pineal N-acetyltransferase activity and simultaneous radioimmunoassay of melatonin in pineal, serum, and pituitary tissue of the male rat. *J. Endocrinol.* 72:243–44

99. Zatz, M., O'Dea, R. F. 1976. Regulation of protein kinase in rat pineal: increased V_{max} in supersensitive glands. *J. Cyclic Nucleotide Res.* 2:427–39

100. Zigmond, R. E., Ben-Ari, Y. 1977. Electrical stimulation of preganglionic nerve increases tyrosine hydroxylase activity in sympathetic ganglia. *Proc. Natl. Acad. Sci. USA* 74:3078–80

101. Zigmond, R. E., Chalazonitis, A. 1979. Long-term effects of preganglionic nerve stimulation on tyrosine hydroxylase activity in the rat superior cervical ganglion. *Brain Res.,* 164:137–52

102. Zigmond, R. E., Chalazonitis, A., Joh, T. 1980. Preganglionic nerve stimulation increases the amount of tyrosine hydroxylase in the rat superior cervical ganglion. *Neurosci. Lett.* 20:61–65

Ann. Rev. Physiol. 1981. 43:689–710
Copyright © 1981 by Annual Reviews Inc. All rights reserved

NEURAL ACTIVITY
AND DEVELOPMENT

❖1338

William A. Harris

Department of Neurobiology, Harvard University Medical School, Boston, Massachusetts 02115 and Department of Biology, University of California, San Diego, La Jolla, California 92093

INTRODUCTION

Because nature is often conservative, the same electrical and chemical signals that the brain uses in its mature function may guide its development. This review by bringing together many different types of experiments (mostly recent) on different animals at different stages of development, supports the above notion. Experiments are discussed that examine the developmental roles of action potentials, slow changes in membrane potentials, steady transmembrane ionic currents, and neurotransmitters. Hormonal effects are not included although many developmentally important hormones are released by neural activity. Denervation studies are not discussed, except for those supported by demonstrations of a specific role for neural activity. I have also excluded nonelectrical or nontransmitter-related neurotrophic effects on development.

More than half a century ago, there were those who speculated on the role of neural activity in development (96, 183). Shortly thereafter, however, experiments in which animals were raised through embryogenesis in anesthetic solutions (80, 127) or with complete sensory deprivation (32, 45, 75, 205) resulted in few neural or behavioral deficits. Early reports on neurites orienting in electric fields (90) failed to be replicated (69, 97, 115). These studies cast doubt on a role for neural activity in development. For many years the issue appeared settled (199). The application of modern electrophysiology, pharmacology, culturing techniques, and genetic approaches, however, has reopened this question.

The organization of this review parallels the ontogeny of the organism. It starts with the unfertilized egg and progresses through embryogenesis, differentiation, function, and degeneration.

689

0066-4278/81/0315-0689$01.00

EGG MATURATION

In certain spherically symmetrical plant eggs, a steady and localized inward Ca^{2+} current has been measured; the point of current entry defines the primary axis of growth; an externally applied field, capable of inducing a comparable current, can cause this directed growth (93). Similarly in animals, steady inward Cl^- currents in frog oocytes correlate with the developing dorso-ventral axis of the egg (159). Progesterone, which leads to the rapid maturation of the oocyte, blocks this Cl^- current possibly by disturbing the Ca^{2+} gradient (159). The Ca^{2+} ionophore A23187 causes a Ca^{2+} influx, blocks the Cl^- current, and leads to oocyte maturation (159).

At fertilization, in both vertebrates and invertebrates, a fast depolarization of the egg membrane is caused by changes in Na^+, Ca^{2+}, K^+, or sometimes Cl^- permeabilities; this fertilization potential is necessary and sufficient for blocking further sperm penetration (42, 73). The entry of Ca^{2+} into the egg at fertilization can lead to an explosive release of Ca^{2+} from internal stores, activating mitosis (73, 157). Fertilization potentials, however, do not always lead to activation of the egg (73), which indicates separate controls for the two events.

Electrophysiological studies reveal nonlinearities in the current-voltage curves of many eggs; some oocytes and eggs have action potentials due to voltage sensitive Ca^{2+} and Na^+ channels; immature amphibian oocytes are electrically excitable, whereas mature eggs are not (73). Amphibian oocytes also have neurotransmitter-sensitive channels on their membranes; when acetylcholine (ACh) is applied iontophoretically, the membrane potential rapidly depolarizes owing to the opening of Cl^- channels; serotonin (5HT) and dopamine (DA) cause a hyperpolarization (104).

Between fertilization and the first cleavage in the frog egg, current enters at the animal pole and leaves at the equator; the point on the equator with the biggest potential difference from the animal pole correlates with the axis of eventual bilateral symmetry (24).

BLASTULA FORMATION

In sea urchins and frogs, during the first few mitoses current enters the prospective cleavage furrow during the ten minutes preceding cleavage initiation; after cleavage has begun, current leaves the same regions (93). These currents might be involved in blastokinesis, for it has been shown that there is Ca^{2+}-sensitive contractile machinery near the surface of amphibian eggs (65).

Endogenous levels of ACh and 5HT vary with the cell cycle during early cleavages in sea urchins (26). Antagonists or agonists to these and other transmitters (especially blockers of the catecholamine β-receptor) stop blastokinesis when externally applied at low concentrations (26–29, 44). The action of the antagonists can be overcome by exogenous application of the transmitter (26). 5HT, most extensively studied in this process, has been localized in the archenteron by fluorescence techniques (28) and by electronmicroscopic (EM) autoradiography to the yolk granules (52). At cleavage, many yolk granules break down, and the released 5HT can be found binding to microfilaments at the cleavage furrow (52), implicating 5HT in the contractile machinery of cleavage. 5HT and its antagonists also interfere with blastoderm formation in the chick when injected into the yolk of the 4-hr embryo (143).

As mitoses continue, the blastomeres remain electrically coupled (59, 144). This coupling is voltage sensitive: A 20 mV depolarization or hyperpolarization of a blastomere at the 32-cell stage in the amphibian can reduce the coupling coefficient from 0.8 to 0.1 (180). Thus endogenous changes in the potential of blastomeres might be used to uncouple cells as their specific fates are determined. This might be especially so in embryos such as the tunicate with a mosaic development of the blastula. In this animal electrophysiological studies show that primordial muscle cells in the blastula and throughout development remain electrically excitable, except that the Na^+ component of the action potential present in the egg eventually disappears leaving purely Ca^{2+} action potentials (132, 133, 186). Primordial nerve cells show the opposite changes—i.e. diminishing voltage-sensitive Ca^{2+} and increasing voltage-sensitive Na^+ conductance (S. Hagiwara, personal communication). Increasing the intracellular Ca^{2+} concentration in these embryos diminishes voltage-sensitive Ca^{2+} conductances and increases voltage-sensitive Na^+ ones (187).

From early to late blastula development the resting potential increases in echinoderms and amphibians from ~ -10 mV to ~ -50 mV (144, 192). In the echinoderm this has been shown to be partially an effect of doubling the K^+ permeability (192). In the amphibian blastula, junctional resistances increase, input resistance falls then increases, and the current-voltage curve remains linear (144).

GASTRULATION, INDUCTION, AND NEURULATION

Neurotransmitters appear to play a role in gastrulation movements. At gastrulation, endogenous levels of 5HT and ACh rise; 5HT antagonists, indolamine derivatives, antihistamines, lipid soluble cholinomimetics or cholinolytics, and blockers of catecholamine β-receptors interfere with the invagination of mesodermal cells in the sea urchin early gastrula; Similar effects are produced by blocking ACh and 5HT synthesis, and these effects as well as those caused by the antagonists can be counteracted with exogenously applied transmitters (72, 191). Serotonin antagonists applied to chick embryos at gastrulation interfere with primitive streak formation (143).

During gastrulation in the amphibian, the invaginating chordomesoderm induces the overlying ectoderm to become committed to a neural destiny. At this time neither the presumptive neural cells nor the underlying mesoderm is electrically excitable, though the two tissues are directly electrically coupled (196).

At midgastrula in the frog, Na^+ uptake increases 800-fold, and later at the neural plate stage Ca^{2+} uptake increases 22-fold (6). Neural induction is a Ca^{2+}-activated and Na^+-dependent process (5). Hybrid animals that consistently arrest at gastrulation show neither these increases in Na^+ and Ca^{2+} uptake nor signs of neural induction (6).

During neural plate formation (after primary induction) the membrane potential of the presumptive neural cells increases, probably owing to activation of the Na^+/K^+-ATPase pump (130). Addition of strophanthidine, which blocks the pump at this stage, causes gross abnormalities in the developing nervous system (130). Treatment of dissociated neural plate cells in culture with strophanthidine selectively reduces the number of neurons differentiating (130), an effect counteracted by increasing the external K^+ concentration to 100 mM (130).

K^+ has also been implicated in the earliest differentiation of neurons in a *Drosophila* mutant. The mutant *shibire*[ts] is a temperature-sensitive paralytic with pleiotropic defects in embryonic, larval, and pupal development, and neurophysiological defects in the larva and adult (152). The developmental defects can be mimicked by aminopyridines—potassium channel blockers (166). Thus the defect in neuromuscular transmission (89, 174) and the embryological defects may be caused by a common mechanism related to potassium channels. Cultures from gastrulae of *shibire*[ts] mutants show temperature-sensitive inhibition of neuron and muscle differentiation (25). The relatively short temperature-sensitive period for this effect begins several hours after the beginning of gastrulation (25).

Closure of the neural tube in amphibians is accompanied by a Ca^{2+} efflux (135) and can be disturbed by adding the Ca^{2+} ionophore A23187 (112). As the tube closes, it becomes uncoupled from the overlying epidermis, and its cells increase their membrane potentials again; occasional signs of regenerative electrical activity are seen (196). In the chick, the early neural tube contains and takes up catecholamines as demonstrated by fluorescence histochemistry. Treatment of chick embryos at this stage with α-methyltyrosine, a blocker of catecholamine synthesis, results in numerous archencephalic anomolies such as spina bifida, and abnormal flexures (111).

EARLY DIFFERENTIATION OF NEURONS: MITOSIS, NEURITES, AND EXCITABILITY

Perhaps the earliest step in neuronal differentiation is the final mitosis. This step has been shown to be affected in cultured neuroblastoma cells by applied neurotransmitters, including ACh, catecholamines, and prostaglandins. Addition of low concentrations of these substances to cultures prevents cell division and initiates neural differentiation: neurite outgrowth, excitability, and manufacture of transmitter (139, 153, 165). These effects are probably mediated through cAMP (64, 153, 165, 170). In the developing rat brain, neuronal differentiation and proliferation are inhibited by monoamine-depleting drugs (4, 109, 145, 146, 175, 204). ACh may be involved in the induction of differentiation in sympatheticoblasts, since treatment of chick embryos with anticholinesterases inhibits neurite outgrowth and eventually leads to the degeneration of neuroblasts in the lumbar sympathetic ganglia (82).

In some neuroblastoma lines, membrane hyperpolarization may induce differentiation, and depolarization may prevent it. Valinomycin, a K^+ ionophore, causes these cells to stop dividing, to send out neurites (100), and to become excitable (178). This effect is counteracted by raising external K^+ (100). Dorsal root ganglion cells seem to continue to divide in culture when K^+ is elevated (171). In CNS cultures, sustained depolarization by ouabain, a pump blocker, induces mitosis in fully mature neurons (36).

In amphibians and grasshoppers, the natural sequence of early neuronal differentiation has been studied electrophysiologically (66, 179). About two days after the final mitosis, the dorsal unpaired medial (DUM) neurons of the grasshopper begin to send out axons, and the cells become sensitive to applied transmitter (66). Electrical excitability of the axon then the soma develops four days later. Soon after the birth of Rohon-Beard (RB) neurons in *Xenopus,* neurites and electrical excitability develop nearly synchronously; chemosensitivity comes later (179). Thus the sequences of neurite outgrowth, chemosensitivity, and excitability are not entirely parallel in these two types of neurons.

An intriguing similarity in the early differentiation of excitability in DUM, RB, and other developing neurons (179) is that they start with Ca^{2+} or mixed (Ca^{2+}- and Na^+-dependent) action potentials and then later become purely Na^+-dependent (179). The role of the developmentally transient Ca^{2+} channels is not yet clear, but it is interesting to note that similar sequences of conductance changes occur in regenerating axon tips (128a).

NEUROTRANSMITTER PRODUCTION

The role of activity in neurotransmitter synthesis has best been studied in rat sympathetic neurons. (For more complete discussion see Zigmond & Bowers in this volume.) These cells of neural crest origin synthesize some catecholamine before they cease mitosis (162), but the choice of transmitter is not predetermined, as they may become either adrenergic or cholinergic depending on the environment (147). In cultures of dissociated sympathetic cells from newborn rats, the addition of medium conditioned by nonneural elements tends to make the cells cholinergic (147). This effect can be blocked by depolarizing the neurons with high K^+, veratridine (a sodium channel opener), or electrical stimulation (194, 195). The effect of conditioned medium can be strengthened by preventing depolarization with TTX (194). It has been shown that Ca^{2+} entry and possibly changes in cAMP are required if depolarization is to block the effect of conditioned medium (194, 195).

There are many examples of chronic depolarization increasing catecholamine synthesis in sympathetic neurons as a result of increased activity and production of tyrosine hydroxylase (TH) (142, 194). This effect can be shown transsynaptically by stimulating the cholinergic preganglionic fibers and is particularly strong in early development (14), although it is present in the adult (207). Cutting the preganglionic fibers, or blocking their postsynaptic action with ACh antagonists prevents this induction (14).

Transsynaptic induction of TH may not be the same as that studied in early sympathetic neurons undergoing transmitter choice, because high K^+ cannot induce TH in organ-cultured sympathetic ganglia that have previously been denervated (142), in the absence of Ca^{2+} (176), or in the presence of chlorisondamine, an ACh antagonist (142). Carbamylcholine, an ACh agonist that has no effect on transmitter choice (194), can cause TH induction in organ-cultured ganglia in the absence of Ca^{2+} but not in the absence of Na^+ (188). Finally, antidromic stimulation of the sympathetic nerve even in the presence of Na^+ does not induce TH (31). The initial transmitter choice may thus be affected by depolarization-stimulated Ca^{2+} entry, but the subsequent induction of TH in committed cells may involve receptor-stimulated Na^+ entry.

AXONAL NAVIGATION AND SYNAPTOGENESIS

The idea that growing axons orient along electric fields to reach their targets is old (183), as is the idea that these fields are generated by the neural elements themselves (96). Early studies in organ culture of neurites growing toward the anode (90) were possibly due to artifacts and were not repeatable

(69, 97, 115). More recently, however, there have been more convincing demonstrations of neuronal processes in culture growing towards the cathode when small steady fields of ~ 500 mV cm^{-1} were applied (94, 124).

A role of action potentials in axonal navigation and synaptogenesis has been ruled out by a number of experiments: (a) In the normal development of DUM neurons in the grasshopper, axons grow to their peripheral target before they become excitable (66). (b) In the filiform mutant of crickets, sensory axons that never carry impulses make functional connections with their central target neuron (9). (c) TTX-blocked autonomic fibers can sprout to form functional synapses on denervated heart ganglion cells (160). (d) In primary tissue culture, motoneuron axons can grow and make synapses on muscle in the continued presence of TTX (136). (e) Explants of developing rodent brain develop their normal synaptic connections in organ culture when grown in the presence of blocking does of xylocaine (38, 134) (f) Embryonically developing retinal ganglion cells from a species of salamander sensitive to TTX continually blocked by transplantation into another species that manufactures the toxin can nevertheless grow to and make synapses on their proper central targets (77). (g) Retinal ganglion cells of the rabbit continually exposed to TTX throughout synaptogenesis in the retina develop all connections responsible for their normal receptive field properties (D. Masland, personal communication).

In other experiments, synaptic transmission has been found not to be involved in axonal navigation and early synaptogenesis. This has been mostly investigated with cholinergic blockers in nerve muscle development in vitro (35, 39, 136), in chick embryogenesis (62, 141), and in nerve regeneration (48).

DIFFERENTIATION AND MAINTENANCE OF POSTSYNAPTIC PROPERTIES

The differentiation and maintenance of postsynaptic properties has been studied in vertebrate skeletal muscle. These muscles may differentiate into two main types, fast or slow, distinguished by a variety of properties including myosin-type, ribosomal activity, twitch speed, histochemistry, and metabolism [see (164) for references]. Recent evidence in rats suggests that both start as fast muscles in early development (164) and that a fast-to-slow transformation happens in some of them. Rat muscles can completely switch their "type," even in the adult, by cross-innervating fast and slow muscles (22, 33), implying that the nerve specifies the muscle type. In fact, the pattern of impulse activity that the nerve dictates to the muscle determines its type. This has been shown by the following results: (a) Slow muscles change into fast muscles with electrical stimulation of the slow nerve in a pattern that mimics the activity in fast muscle nerves, and vice-versa (167, 168, 184). (b) Fast muscles remain fast after cross-innervation when the foreign slow nerve is stimulated in the characteristic fast pattern (184). (c) Direct stimulation of denervated muscle in either the fast or slow pattern leads to the appropriate transformation (121). Cross-innervation does not change muscle type either in amphibians (34, 131) or adult birds (83), although it does in young chicks (206).

In invertebrates, a more complex situation is being studied. Both claws of a lobster begin to develop as cutters, with predominantly fast-muscle types (68). Later one claw develops into a large crusher with entirely slow muscle. Immobilization of either claw in the juvenile by tenotomy of the claw-closer muscle leads the unoperated claw to become a crusher (K. Kent, personal communication). Both claws are prevented from becoming crushers (i.e. both become cutters) when animals are raised in containers with smooth bottoms and no sand or gravel to manipulate [(107) and K. Kent, personal communication]. In the alpheid shrimp, the earliest hatchling has asymmetric claws, a snapper and a pincher, with radically different muscle types (129). When the nerve to the snapper is cut, the pincher transforms into a snapper (129). This transformation can be prevented by tenotomy or permanently closing the transforming pincher (129). Thus the pattern of activity from the periphery can influence, probably via central connections, the muscle type on the same or opposite side of the animal.

The distribution of membrane bound ACh receptors also is labile and dependent on innervation. During differentiation, dispersed clusters of ACh receptors on the surface of the muscle cell gather under the nerve terminal (1, 2, 12, 56a). Functional transmission is not needed for this process, as it can occur in the presence of ACh antagonists and TTX (1, 17, 18, 182, 193). However, the elimination of the extra receptors not at the nerve-muscle junction requires activity, since muscles grown in the presence of these blockers retain extrajunctional receptors (17, 18, 23). If adult muscle is denervated, extrajunctional receptors reappear (122). A similar effect has been seen in some neurons (102). Denervation of the muscle can be mimicked by blocking action potentials in the nerve with TTX or ACh antagonists (10, 149). These supersensitive muscles also develop TTX-insensitive Na^+ action potentials (156) and the ability readily to accept foreign innervation [(95), though see (13)]. All these immature properties are eliminated upon functional reinnervation or direct depolarization of the muscle (49, 95, 117, 118, 120). If the muscle is stimulated after denervation, all of the extrajunctional receptors are eliminated while receptors localized at the old endplate remain (55, 56). Contraction of the muscle may not be necessary to remove extrajunctional receptors, since natural fibrillation of denervated muscles cannot eliminate them (154) but submechanical threshold stimulation can (19, 70, 71).

Acetylcholinesterase (AChE), like AChR, is spread along the muscle surface early in development and later is found localized under the nerve-muscle junction (17, 67, 163). Unlike AChR, however, functional neuromuscular connections are needed to induce junctional AChE. Chick embryos developing in the presence of cholinergic blockers develop no junctional AChE (17, 67). Similarly, in culture junctional AChE does not develop in the presence of curare or TTX but appears upon removal of these toxins; muscle contractions and cGMP are implicated in this induction since direct stimulation of a muscle grown in the presence of curare will induce increases in cGMP and junctional AChE only if the muscle contracts; direct muscle stimulation in the presence of TTX will not raise cGMP levels or induce junctional AChE; finally, the induction of AChE can also be caused by the addition of cGMP to cultures of curarized muscles (163).

Upon denervation, junctional AChE declines, an effect that can be mimicked with blockers of neuromuscular transmission (47). This effect can be reversed by electrical stimulation of the muscle (119) or by foreign innervation of the muscle at an ectopic site (197). As with the AChR, the AChE "remembers" the site of the old endplate. A foreign nerve can leave an imprint on a muscle without itself inducing AChE (119). This was shown in the rat by transplanting a fibialis nerve to an endplate-free region of the soleus muscle after the host innervation had been removed. Before the foreign nerve could induce junctional AChE (i.e. 2 days later) it was cut. Now direct electrical stimulation of the muscle induced junctional AChE at the denuded foreign endplate (119).

MAINTENANCE OF PRESYNAPTIC PROPERTIES

Most of our information on the role of activity in the maintenance of presynaptic properties comes from studies of motoneurons. When their connections with the periphery are severed, vertebrate motoneurons go through a sequence of histologically defined changes called chromatolysis (116). A physiological correlate of chromatolysis in cat motoneurons can be seen in the shape of the action-potential—e.g. the duration of the after-hyperpolarization (a.h.p.) is decreased (103). This sign of chromatolysis can be caused by the reduction of muscle activity. This is known because (a) transection of the spinal cord anterior to the studied motor neuron (43), (b) TTX blockade of the peripheral nerve (43), and (c) chronically shortening the muscle (60) all cause the effect, which in turn can be prevented by (a) stimulation of the TTX-poisoned nerve distal to the block (43), (b) chronically lengthening the muscle after spinal transection (60), and (c) allowing a crushed nerve functionally to reinnervate the target (103). It is interesting to note that motoneuron properties return to normal even when reinnervation is to a foreign muscle of different "fast-slow" type (103). From these experiments it appears that a trophic factor originating from the muscle and dependent on muscle activity is sent back to the motoneuron preventing chromatolysis.

Another property of motoneurons dependent on activity is the efficacy of the sensory input from synergistic muscles. A TTX-cuff on a nerve will enhance the synaptic input to a motoneuron from its homonymous sensory fibers but will cause no change in the heteronymous synergistic input (61). This is different from a simple crushing of the peripheral nerve, which leads to enhancement of both homonymous and heteronymous sensory input (61). During normal development, neurons, like their terminals (see next section), are produced in overabundance; later many die (37, 85). This natural cell death has been seen in many systems to depend on the target area: Less target leads to more death, and vice-versa (37, 85). Recently, it has been shown in chick (105, 150, 151) and duck (40) motoneurons that this natural cell death can be completely prevented by blocking neuromuscular transmission with cobratoxin (150, 151), curare (151), botulinum toxin (151), or α-bungarotoxin (40, 105, 151). As soon as the treatment is stopped, however, precipitous motoneuron death ensues (40, 105, 151). It has been shown by horseradish peroxidase backfilling that all the motoneurons prevented from dying actually project to their target muscles (40). The postsynaptic blockers make it likely that the inactive muscle fibers keep the motoneurons alive. This anomalous survival is not a simple consequence of ineffective synapse elimination caused by these toxins (discussed below) since synapse elimination happens after the normal period of cell death (85).

SPROUTING AND SYNAPSE ELIMINATION

In the normal development of many parts of the nervous system, axon terminals, on first reaching the target area, produce an overabundance of connections. Later the extra synapses are eliminated (37, 66, 85, 91, 114). Both the initial "sprouting" of terminals and the subsequent elimination of extra synapses may be under the control of postsynaptic activity. This has been best studied in the neuromuscular system.

The blockade of nerve conduction with TTX (21) or of neuromuscular transmission with botulinum toxin (148) causes morphologically (21, 148) and physiologically (177) demonstrable sprouting of the motor nerve terminals. Direct muscle stimulation can prevent botulinum-induced sprouting (148). If a muscle is partially denervated, the remaining intact nerve fibers will sprout; this sprouting, too, can be prevented by direct stimulation of the partially denervated muscle, but it is not prevented by similar electrical stimulation of the intact nerve (20). Stimulation of the intact nerve may, in fact, accelerate sprouting (84). These results, imply that the lack of activity in denervated muscles may cause the nearby presynaptic terminals to sprout.

In the sensory innervation of rat skin it appears that sprouting of the high-threshold fibers to denervated areas of skin is greatly enhanced by occasional stimulation of the intact fibers either physiologically, with pinches, or centrally, with stimulating electrodes [(92) and J. Diamond, personal communication].

The normal elimination of extra synapses at the neuromuscular junction in normal development happens suddenly (161) but can be accelerated by direct stimulation of the nerve (137) or the muscle (138); or it can be delayed by tenotomy of the muscle (7, 158) or application of curare (181), lidocaine (8), or TTX (189) to the nerve. In the last case, synapse elimination begins normally but then is arrested. This implies that the failure of synaptic elimination may be due to the countereffect of TTX-induced sprouting (189). Again, these results show a role for muscle activity in elimination of synapses. Since upon depolarization muscle fibers secrete a protease at the neuromuscular junction (137), it has been proposed that activity-dependent elimination of synapses is caused by digestion of the terminals (137, 138).

Studies on retinal innervation of frog and fish tecta have shown that α-bungarotoxin, which may block the tectal ACh receptors, applied to small areas can cause morphological and physiological elimination of retinal terminals from the effected area (57, 169). This situation is obviously quite different from that in muscle. In the cat visual system impulse activity can be eliminated during early postnatal life by intraocular injections of TTX, and this treatment inhibits the retraction of lateral geniculate axon terminals involved in the postnatal segregation of ocular dominance columns. (M. Stryker, personal communication; and see below).

SENSORY DEPRIVATION

Much of our knowledge about the developmental consequences of sensory deprivation comes from studies in the mammalian visual system. Visual deprivation, either by dark-rearing or suturing eyes closed, does not prevent electrical activity. Recordings from visual brain areas of normal or dark-reared animals show spontaneous activity even in total darkness. Therefore the effects of deprivation are due to differences in the patterning or quantity of activity. Cats raised in total darkness have only minor histological abnormalities in the retina: Cells and synaptic layers are somewhat smaller (155, 198). Electrophysiologically, however, a deprived and normal retina are indistinguishable (D. Masland, personal communication). One destination of retinal ganglion cell axons is the lateral geniculate nucleus (LGN), which serves as a relay station to the visual cortex. Deprivation results in slight cell shrinkage in the LGN and the absence of one cell type (the Y-cells) (113, 173, 200). Except for the absence of Y-cells, the deprived LGN seems physiologically normal (173, 200).

Visual deprivation leads to more noticeable changes in the primary visual cortex. A large fraction of neurons of cats that have been binocularly deprived for several months neonatally lose many of their physiological properties; they become sluggishly and unselectively responsive to visual stimuli (201). If cats are raised in an environment that restricts their visual experience to vertical lines, then in the cortex only cells that respond well to verticals remain intact and the other cells become poorly responsive (185).

Monocular deprivation causes the visual cortex to become permanently dominated by the normal eye (201). Monocular deprivation causes this effect only during a critical period early in postnatal life (1–3 months), (87). Deprivation of the adult has no effect (87). LGN axons terminate in layer IV of the visual cortex. In normal animals, the right and left eyes, via the LGN, divide layer IV of the cortex into alternating bands or columns of ocular dominance (88, 172). In monocularly deprived animals, the "deprived" columns shrink while the "normal" columns expand (88, 172).

Most cells in the visual cortex (except those in layer IV) are binocular and respond to input from either eye. In monocularly deprived cats these cells respond to input from the normal eye only (201). If cats are raised with alternating occlusion of the two eyes (at 1 cycle every 20 sec to 1 cycle every 2 days) neither eye dominates the cortex. Instead cortical cells lose their binocularity, so that each cell responds through only one eye (16, 86). Similarly, if the animal is surgically induced to be crossed-eyed or wall-eyed, causing the two eyes to gaze in different directions, cortical cell binocularity is lost (86). Therefore, the preservation of cortical binocularity demands simultaneous activity from corresponding regions of both retinae.

Not all inputs from the deprived eye are eliminated from the cortex, but those that remain may be inhibited, as shown by the following results: (a) Bicuculine, an antagonist of the inhibitory neurotransmitter γ-amino butyric acid, when applied to the cortex of a monocularly deprived adult cat, causes some cells to become responsive to deprived eye stimuli (50). (b) Enucleation of the normal eye of an adult causes the same effect (101). Thus, besides the anatomical effect demonstrated in layer IV, there may be a subtler physiological effect: The normal eye may tonically inhibit the deprived eye's cortical input. This tonic inhibition cannot derive solely from action potentials in the retina of the normal eye because when these are blocked by raised intraocular pressure, little or no recovery of the deprived eye's input has been noticed in several experiments (15, 41, 79, 81). Curiously, it has recently been reported that eliminating action potentials in the normal eye with pressure blockade will temporarily reverse the effects of monocular deprivation only if the retrobulbar muscles of the normal eye are also blocked with anesthetic (41). Thus the tonic inhibition of the deprived eye necessitates a coordinated effort from two different sources of spontaneous activity—the retinal ganglion cells of the normal eye and the sensory cells innervating the extraocular muscles of the normal eye. Norepinephrine (NE) has also been implicated in visual deprivation effects since (a) intraventricular application of 6-hydroxydopamine, which kills noradrenergic (NE) cells, to a young kitten prevents some of the effects of monocular deprivation (98) and (b) local perfusion of NE to the brain of a kitten treated with 6-hydroxydopamine, or even to an adult cat, restores sensitivity to monocular deprivation (99).

Deprivation in the somatosensory system during an early critical period also causes changes in the physiology and morphology of the thalamus and cortex in the mouse (76, 202, 203) and of the wind-sensitive system of the cricket (125, 126). A similar critical period for deprivation exists in the avian auditory system (123).

CELL DEATH

The last phase in the natural progress of a neuron is degenerative. Too much physiological activity has been implicated in cell death in a number of systems. Muscles treated with anticholinesterases degenerate (3, 53, 54, 106, 108) and can be prevented from degenerating by cholinesterase reactivators (106). In *Drosophila* it has been possible to induce mutations for acetylcholinesterase (AChE) (74). While the condition is lethal in thoroughly mutant animals, mosaic flies with only part of the nervous system deficient in AChE may survive (74). Those portions of the nervous system deficient in AChE are compacted, possibly disorganized, and sometimes degenerative (74). Upon inactivation of the enzyme by heat treatment, adult *Drosophila* with temperature-sensitive alleles of the AChE gene show similar changes in the nervous system (J. Hall, personal communication). Kainic acid, a potent agonist for glutamate's transmitter function, appears to act as an exitotoxic agent, instantly killing cells with glutaminergic innervation (30, 140). Finally, too much light can cause degeneration of photoreceptors, especially in albino mammals (46, 110). In a *Drosophila* mutant, inherited retinal degeneration can be prevented by keeping the flies in the dark or by blocking the receptor potential with a no-receptor-potential mutation (78).

Examples of degeneration caused by too little activity can also be found in muscles. Atrophy results from lengthy disuse or blockade of neuromuscular transmission (51, 58, 62, 63). In cultures of embryonic spinal cord a certain class of large neurons can be selectively killed with TTX (11).

CONCLUSIONS

Many seemingly unrelated events in embryogenesis and in the postembryonic development of the nervous system are united in their dependence on electrical and neurotransmitter-mediated signals: signals that are more commonly associated with the function of the differentiated nervous system. A clue to the meaning of this unity in development and function was presented by McMahan (128) and Tomkins (190). Tomkins proposed that the signals the nervous system uses in its function, such as neurotransmitters, were first evolved as parts of a metabolic code in primitive, possibly unicellular, organisms. In these ancient forms of life the intracellular presence of modified amino acids (neurotransmitters) might have signalled certain metabolic needs. According to the theory, as organisms became multicellular and grew in complexity, these signals became intercellular, which allowed them gradually to evolve their present role. Thus the same signals the nervous system now uses in its mature function were used by primitive organisms that had not yet evolved nervous systems. I would like to advance a further hypothesis to explain the results presented in this review: The phylogeny an animal recapitulates in its ontogeny extends back to the egg and thus to the age of primitive unicellular organisms. If so, the role of electrical and neurochemical signals in the embryonic development of modern metazoans may harken back to primitive phylogenetic evolution and the original metabolic code.

ACKNOWLEDGMENTS

I thank P. Desan, J. Hall, P. Johns, and P. Sniderman for comments on the manuscript, and the Harvard Society of Fellows for support.

Literature Cited

1. Anderson, M. J., Cohen, M. W. 1977. Nerve-induced and spontaneous redistribution of acetylcholine receptors on cultured muscle cells. *J. Physiol. London* 268:757–73
2. Anderson, M. J., Cohen, M. W., Zorychta, E. 1977. Effects of innervation on the distribution of acetylcholine receptors on cultured muscle cells. *J. Physiol. London* 268:731–56
3. Ariëns, A. T., Meeter, E., Wolthins, O. L., van Benthen, R. M. J. 1960. Reversible necrosis at the end-plate region in striated muscles of the rat poisoned with cholinesterase inhibitors. *Experientia* 25:57–59
4. Baker, P. C., Quay, W. B. 1969. 5-hydroxytryptamine metabolism in early embryogenesis and the development of brain and retinal tissues. A review. *Brain Res.* 12:273–95
5. Barth, L. A., Barth, L. J. 1969. The sodium dependence of embryonic induction. *Dev. Biol.* 20:236–62
6. Barth, L. A., Barth, L. J. 1972. ^{22}Sodium and ^{45}Calcium uptake during embryonic induction in *Rana pipiens*. *Dev. Biol.* 28:18–34
7. Benoit, P., Changeux, J.-P. 1975. Consequences of tenotomy on the evolution of multiinnervation in developing rat soleus muscle. *Brain Res.* 99:354–58
8. Benoit, P., Changeux, J.-P. 1978. Consequences of blocking the nerve with a local anesthetic on the evolution of multiinnervation at the regenerating neuro-

muscular synapse of the rat. *Brain Res.* 49:89–96

9. Bentley, D. 1975. Single gene cricket mutations: Effects on behavior, sensory neurons and identified interneurons. *Science* 187:760–64

10. Berg, D. K., Hall, Z. W. 1975. Increased extrajunctional acetylcholine sensitivity produced by chronic postsynpatic neuromuscular blockade. *J. Physiol. London* 244:659–76

11. Bergey, G. K., MacDonald, R. L., Nelson, P. A. 1978. Adverse effects of tetrodotoxin on early development and survival of postsynaptic cells in spinal cord cultures. *Neurosci. Abstr.* 4:601

12. Bevan, S., Steinbach, J. H. 1977. The distribution of α-bungarotoxin binding sites on mammalian skeletal muscle developing *in vivo. J. Physiol. London* 267:195–213

13. Bixby, J. L., Van Essen, D. C. 1979. Competition between foreign and original nerves in adult mammalian skeletal muscle. *Nature* 282:726–28

14. Black, I. B., Coughlin, M. D., Cochard, P. 1979. Factors regulating neuronal differentiation. In *Aspects of Developmental Neurobiology,* ed. J. Ferrendelli, pp. 184–207. Bethesda: Soc. Neurosci. 389 pp.

15. Blakemore, C., Hillman, P. 1977. An attempt to assess the effects of monocular deprivation and strabismus on synaptic efficiency in the kitten's visual cortex. *Exp. Brain Res.* 30:187–202

16. Blasdel, G. G., Pettigrew, J. D. 1979. Degree of interocular synchrony required for maintenance of binocularity in kitten's visual cortex. *J. Neurophysiol.* 42:1692–710

17. Bourgeouis, J. P., Betz, H., Changeux, J.-P. 1978. Effects of the chronic paralysis of the chick embryo by flaxedil on the development of the neuromuscular junction. *C.R. Acad. Sci.* 286:773–76

18. Braithwaite, A. W., Harris, A. J. 1979. Neural influence on acetylcholine receptor clusters in embryonic development of skeletal muscles. *Nature* 279:549–51

19. Bray, J. J., Harris, A. J. 1975. Dissociation between nerve-muscle transmission and nerve trophic effects on rat diaphragm using type D Botulinum toxin. *J. Physiol. London* 253:53–77

20. Brown, M. C., Holland, R. L. 1979. A central role for denervated tissues causing nerve sprouting. *Nature* 282:724–26

21. Brown, M. C., Ironton, R. 1977. Motoneuron sprouting induced by prolonged tetrodotoxin block of nerve action potentials. *Nature* 265:495–97

22. Buller, A. L., Eccles, J. C., Eccles, R. M. 1960. Interactions between motoneurones and muscles in respect of the characteristic speeds of their responses. *J. Physiol. London* 150:417–39

23. Burden, S. 1977. Development of the neuromuscular junction in the chick embryo: The number, distribution, and stability of acetylcholine receptors. *Dev. Biol.* 57:317–29

24. Burr, H. S. 1941. Field properties of the developing frog's egg. *Proc. Natl. Acad. Sci. USA* 27:276–81

25. Buzin, C. H., Dewhurst, S. A., Seecof, R. L. 1978. Temperature sensitivity of muscle and neuron differentiation in embryonic cell cultures from the *Drosophila* mutant, *shibire*[ts1]. *Dev. Biol.* 66:442–56

26. Buznikov, G. A., Kost, A. N., Kucherova, N. F., Mndzhoyan, A. L., Suvorov, N. N., Berdysheva, L. V. 1970. The role of neurohumours in early embryogenesis. II. Pharmacological analysis of the role of neurohumours in cleavage divisions. *J. Emb. Exp. Morphol.* 23:549–69

27. Buznikov, G. A., Manukhin, B. N., Rakic, L. 1979. The sensitivity of whole, half, and quarter sea urchin embryos to cytotoxic neuropharmacological drugs. *Comp. Biochem. Physiol. C.* 64:129–36

28. Buznikov, G. A., Sakharova, A. V., Manukhin, B. N., Markova, L. N. 1972. The role of neurohumours in early bryogenesis. III. Fluorometric and histochemical study of serotonin in cleaving eggs and larvae of sea urchins. *J. Emb. Exp. Morphol.* 27:339–51

29. Buznikov, G. A., Zvezdina, N. D., Prokazova, N. V., Manukhin, B. N., Bergelson, L. D. 1975. Protection of sea urchin embryos against the action of some neuropharmacological agents and some detergents by endogenous gangliosides. *Experientia* 31:902–4

30. Campochiaro, P., Coyle, J. T. 1978. Ontogenetic development of kainate neurotoxicity: Correlates with glutamatergic innervation. *Proc. Natl. Acad. Sci. USA* 75:2025–29

31. Chalazonitis, A., Zigmond, R. 1980. Effects of synaptic and antidromic stimulation of the rat superior cervical ganglion on the long-term regulation of tyrosine hydroxylase activity. *J. Physiol. London.* 300:525–38

32. Chase, P. E. 1940. An experimental study of the relation of sensory control

to motor function in amphibian limbs. *J. Exp. Zool.* 83:61–93

33. Close, R. 1969. Dynamic properties of fast and slow skeletal muscle of the rat after cross-union. *J. Physiol. London* 204:331–46

34. Close, R., Hoh, J. F. 1968. Effects of nerve cross union on fast twitch and slow-graded muscle fibers in the toad. *J. Physiol. London* 198:103–25

35. Cohen, M. W. 1972. The development of neuromuscular connexions in the presence of D-tubocurarine. *Brain Res.* 41:457–63

36. Cone, C. D., Cone, C. M. 1976. Induction of mitosis in mature neurons in the central nervous system by sustained depolarization. *Science* 192:155–58

37. Cowan, W. M. 1978. Aspects of neural development. *Int. Rev. Physiol.* 17: 149–91

38. Crain, S. M., Bornstein, M. B., Peterson, E. R. 1968. Maturation of cultured embryonic CNS tissues during chronic exposure to agents which prevent bioelectric activity. *Brain Res.* 8:363–72

39. Crain, S. M., Peterson, E. R. 1971. Development of paired explants of fetal spinal cord and adult skeletal muscle during chronic exposure to curare and hemicholinium. *In Vitro* 6:373

40. Creazzo, T. L., Sohal, G. S. 1979. Effects of chronic injections of α-bungarotoxin on embryonic cell death. *Exp. Neurol.* 66:135–45

41. Crewther, D. P., Crewther, S. G., Pettigrew, J. D. 1978. A role for extraocular afferents in post-critical period reversal of monocular deprivation. *J. Physiol. London* 282:181–95

42. Cross, N. L., Elinson, R. P. 1980. A fast block to polyspermy in frogs mediated by changes in the membrane potential. *Dev. Biol.* 75:187–98

43. Czéh, G., Gallego, R., Kudo, N., Kuno, M. 1978. Evidence for the maintenance of motoneurone properties by muscle activity. *J. Physiol. London* 281:239–52

44. Deeb, S. S. 1972. Inhibition of cleavage and hatching of sea urchin embryos by serotonin. *J. Exp. Zool.* 181:79–86

45. Detwiler, S. R. 1947. Further observations on the function and posture of limbs following removal of the trunk neural crest in *Amblystoma. J. Exp. Zool.* 106:299–312

46. Dowling, J. E., Sidman, R. L. 1962. Inherited retinal dystrophy in the rat. *J. Cell Biol.* 14:73–109

47. Drachman, D. B. 1972. Neurotrophic regulation of muscle cholinesterase:

Effects of botulinum toxin and denervation. *J. Physiol. London* 266:619–27

48. Drachman, D. B., Singer, M. 1971. Regeneration of botulinum-poisoned forelimbs of the newt *Triturus. Exp. Neurol.* 32:1–11

49. Drachman, D. B., Witzke, F. 1972. Trophic regulation of acetylcholine sensitivity of muscle: effect of electrical stimulation. *Science* 176:514–16

50. Duffy, F. H., Snodgrass, S. R., Burchfiel, J. L., Conway, J. L. 1976. Bicuculline reversal of deprivation amblyopia in the cat. *Nature* 260:256–57

51. Eccles, J. C. 1941. Disuse atrophy of skeletal muscle. *Med. J. Aust.* 2:160–64

52. Emmanuelsson, H. 1974. Localization of serotonin in cleavage embryos of *Ophryotrocha labronica* La Greca and Bacci. *Wilhelm Roux's Arch.* 175:253–71

53. Engel, A. G., Lambert, E. H., Santa, T. 1973. Study of long-term anticholinesterase therapy. *Neurology* 23:1273–81

54. Fenichel, G. M., Kibler, W. B., Olson, W. H., Dettbarn, W.-D. 1972. Chronic inhibition of cholinesterase as a cause of myopathy. *Neurology* 22:1026–33

55. Fischbach, G. D., Cohen, S. A. 1974. Some observations on trophic interactions between neurons and muscle fibers in cell culture. *Ann. NY Acad. Sci.* 228:35–46

56. Frank, E. 1977. Formation and maintenance of neural connections. In *Function and Formation of Neural Systems,* ed. G. Stent, pp. 225–52. Berlin: Dahlem Konferenzen. 365 pp.

56a. Frank, E., Fischbach, G. D. 1979. Early events in neuromuscular junction formation in vitro. *J. Cell Biol.* 83:143–158

57. Freeman, J. A. 1977. Possible regulatory function of acetylcholine receptor in maintenance of retinotectal synapses. *Nature* 269:218–22

58. Freeman, S. S., Engel, A. G., Drachman, D. B. 1976. Experimental acetylcholine blockade of the neuromuscular junction, effects on endplate and muscle fiber ultrastructure. *Ann. NY Acad. Sci.* 274:46–59

59. Furshpan, E. J., Potter, D. D. 1968. Low resistance junctions between cells in embryos and tissue culture. *Curr. Top. Devel. Biol.,* 3:95–127

60. Gallego, R., Kuno, M., Núñez, R., Snider, W. D. 1979. Dependence of motoneurone properties on the length of the immobilized muscle. *J. Physiol. London* 291:179–89

61. Gallego, R., Kuno, M., Núñez, R., Snider, W. D. 1979. Disuse enhances synaptic efficiency in spinal motoneurones. *J. Physiol. London* 291:191–205

62. Giacobini, G., Filogamo, G., Weber, M., Boquet, P., Changeux, J.-P. 1973. Effects of a snake α-neurotoxin on the development of innervated skeletal muscles in chick embryo. *Proc. Natl. Acad. Sci. USA* 70:1708–12

63. Giacobini-Robecchi, M. G., Giacobini, G., Filogamo, G., Changeux, J.-P. 1975. Effects of the type A toxin from *Clostridium botulinum* on the development of skeletal muscles and their innervation in chick embryos. *Brain Res.* 83:107–21

64. Gilman, A. G., Nirenberg, M. 1971. Effect of catecholamines on the adenosine 3'5'-cyclic monophosphate concentrations of clonal satellite cells of neurons. *Proc. Natl. Acad. Sci. USA* 68:2165–68

65. Gingell, D. 1970. Contractile responses at the surface of an amphibian egg. *J. Emb. Exp. Morphol.* 23:583–609

66. Goodman, C. S., Spitzer, N. C. 1979. Embryonic development of identified neurones: differentiation of neuroblast to neurone. *Nature* 280:208–14

67. Gordon, T., Perry, R., Tuffery, A. R., Vrbová, G. 1974. Possible mechanisms determining synapse formation in developing skeletal muscles of the chick. *Cell Tissue Res.* 155:13–25

68. Govind, C. K., Lang, F. 1978. Development of the dimorphic claw closer muscle of the lobster. *Homarus americanus*. III. Transformation to dimorphic muscles in juveniles. *Biol. Bull.* 154:55–67

69. Gray, P. 1939. Experiments with direct currents on chick embryos. *Wilhelm Roux's Arch.* 139:732–79

70. Gruener, R., Baumbach, N. 1976. Muscle insensitivity to tetrodotoxin: induction by α-bungarotoxin and removal by submechanical threshold stimulation. *J. Neurobiol.* 7:513–19

71. Gruener, R., Baumbach, N., Coffee, D. 1974. Reduction of denervation supersensitivity of muscle by submechanical threshold stimulation. *Nature* 248:68–69

72. Gustafson, T., Toneby, M. 1970. On the role of serotonin and acetylcholine in sea urchin morphogenesis. Motility and contractions in gastrulation movements. *Exp. Cell Res.* 62:102–17

73. Hagiwara, S., Jaffe, L. A. 1979. Electrical properties of egg cell membranes. *Ann. Rev. Biophys. Bioeng.* 8:385–416

74. Hall, J. C., Greenspan, R. J., Kankel, D. R. 1979. Neural defects induced by genetic manipulation of acetylcholine metabolism in *Drosophila*. See Ref. 14, pp. 1–42

75. Hamburger, V., Wenger, E., Oppenheim, R. 1966. Motility in the chick embryo in the absence of sensory input. *J. Exp. Zool.* 162:133–60

76. Harris, R. M., Woolsey, T. A. 1979. Morphology of Golgi-impregnated neurons in mouse cortical barrels following vibrissae damage at different postnatal ages. *Brain Res.* 161:143–49

77. Harris, W. A. 1980. The effect of eliminating impulse activity on the development of the retino-tectal projection in salamanders. *J. Comp. Neurol.* 194:303–17

78. Harris, W. A., Stark, W. S. 1977. Hereditary retinal degeneration in *Drosophila melanogaster*. A mutant defect associated with the phototransduction process. *J. Gen. Physiol.* 69:261–91

79. Harris, W. A., Stryker, M. P. 1977. Attempts to reverse the effects of monocular deprivation in the adult cat's cortex. *Neurosci. Abstr.* 3:562

80. Harrison, R. A. 1904. An experimental study of the relation of the nervous system to the developing musculature of the frog. *Am. J. Anat.* 3:197–220

81. Hawken, M., Mark, R., Blakemore, C. 1978. The effects of pressure blinding in monocularly deprived kittens. *Arch. Ital. Biol.* 116:448–51

82. Hervonen, H. 1977. Effect of cholinesterase inhibitors on differentiation of cultured sympatheticoblasts. *Experientia* 33:1215–17

83. Hník, P., Jirmanová, I., Vyklicky, L., Zelená, J. 1967. Fast and slow muscles of the chick after nerve cross-union. *J. Physiol. London* 193:309–25

84. Hoffman, H. 1952. Acceleration and retardation of the process of axon sprouting in partially denervated muscles. *Aust. J. Exp. Biol. Med. Sci.* 30:541–65

85. Hollyday, M. 1980. Motor neurohistogenesis and development of limb innervation. *Curr. Top. Devel. Biol.* 15:181–215

86. Hubel, D. H., Wiesel, T. N. 1965. Binocular interaction in striate cortex of kittens reared with artificial squint. *J. Neurophysiol.* 28:1041–59

87. Hubel, D. H., Wiesel, T. N. 1970. The period of susceptibility to physiological effects of unilateral eye closure in kittens. *J. Physiol. London* 206:419–36

88. Hubel, D. H., Wiesel, T. N., LeVay, S. 1977. Plasticity of ocular dominance columns in monkey striate cortex. *Philos. Trans. R. Soc. London Ser. B* 278:377–409

89. Ikeda, K., Ozawa, S., Hagiwara, S. 1976. Synaptic transmission reversibly conditioned by a single gene mutation in *Drosophila melanogaster*. *Nature* 259:489–91

90. Ingvar, S. 1920. Reaction of cells to galvanic current in tissue cultures. *Proc. Soc. Exp. Biol. Med. NY* 17:198–99

91. Innocenti, G. M., Fiore, L., Camaniti, R. 1977. Exuberant projection into the corpus callosum from the visual cortex of newborn cats. *Neurosci. Lett.* 4:237–42

92. Jackson, P. C., Diamond, J. 1979. Is sensory nerve activity necessary for collateral sprouting in the skin of adult rats. *Neurosci. Abstr.* 5:628

93. Jaffe, L. F., Nuccitelli, R. 1977. Electrical controls of development. *Ann. Rev. Biophys. Bioeng.* 6:445–76

94. Jaffe, L. F., Poo, M. M. 1979. Neurites grow faster towards the cathode than the anode in a steady field. *J. Exp. Zool.* 209:115–28

95. Jansen, J. K. S., Lømo, T., Nicolaysen, K., Westgaard, R. H. 1973. Hyperinnervation of skeletal muscle fibers: dependence on muscle activity. *Science* 181:559–61

96. Kappers, C. U. A. 1917. Further contributions on neurobiotaxis. IX. An attempt to compare the phenomena of neurobiotaxis with other phenomena of taxis and tropism. *J. Comp. Neurol.* 27:261–98

97. Karssen, A., Sager, B. 1934. Sur l'influence du courant electrique sur la croissance des neuroblastes *in vivo. Arch. Exp. Zellforsch.* 16:255–59

98. Kasamatsu, T., Pettigrew, J. D. 1979. Preservation of biocularity after monocular deprivation in the striate cortex of kittens treated with 6-hydroxydopamine. *J. Comp. Neurol.* 185:139–62

99. Kasamatsu, T., Pettigrew, J. D., Ary, M. 1979. Restoration of visual cortical plasticity by local microperfusion of norepinephrine. *J. Comp. Neurol.* 185:163–82

100. Koike, T. 1978. Neurite formation and membrane changes of mouse neuroblastoma cells induced by valinomycin. *Biochim. Biophys. Acta* 509:429–39

101. Kratz, K. E., Spear, P. D., Smith, D. C. 1976. Posteritical-period reversal of the effects of monocular deprivation on the striate cortex cells in the cat. *J. Neurophysiol.* 39:501–11

102. Kuffler, S. W., Dennis, M. J., Harris, A. J. 1971. The development of chemosensitivity in extrasynaptic areas of the neuronal surface after denervation of the parasympathetic ganglion cells in the heart of the frog. *Proc. R. Soc. London Ser. B* 177:555–63

103. Kuno, M., Miyata, Y., Muñoz-Martinez, E. J. 1974. Properties of fast and slow alpha motoneurones following motor reinnervation. *J. Physiol. London* 242:273–88

104. Kusano, K., Miledi, R., Stinnakre, J. 1977. Acetylcholine receptors in the oocyte membrane. *Nature* 270:739–41

105. Laing, N. A., Prestige, M. C. 1978. Prevention of spontaneous motoneurone death in chick embryos. *J. Physiol. London* 282:33–34P

106. Landauer, W. 1976. Cholinomimetic teratogens. V. The effect of oximes and related cholinesterase reactivators. *Teratology* 15:33–42

107. Lang, F., Govind, C. K., Costello, W. J. 1978. Experimental transformation of muscle fiber properties in lobster. *Science* 201:1037–38

108. Laskowski, M. B., Olson, W. H., Dettbarn, W.-D. 1975. Ultrastructural changes at the motor end-plate produced by an irreversible cholinesterase inhibitor. *Exp. Neurol.* 47:290–306

109. Lauder, J. M., Krebs, H. 1978. Serotonin as a differentiation signal in early neurogenesis. *Dev. Neurosci.* 1:15–30

110. LaVail, M. M., Battelle, B. A. 1975. Influence of eye pigmentation and light deprivation on inherited retinal dystrophy in the rat. *Exp. Eye Res.* 21:167–92

111. Lawrence, I. E., Burden, H. W. 1973. Catecholamines and morphogenesis of the chick neural tube and notochord. *Am. J. Anat.* 137:199–208

112. Lee, H., Nagele, R., Karasanyi, N. 1978. Inhibition of neural tube closure by ionophore A23187 in chick embryos. *Experientia* 34:518–20

113. LeVay, S., Ferster, D. 1977. Relay cell classes in the lateral geniculate nucleus of the cat and the effects of visual deprivation. *J. Comp. Neurol.* 172:563–84

114. LeVay, S., Stryker, M. P. 1979. The development of ocular dominance columns in the cat. See Ref. 14, pp. 83–98

115. Levi, G. 1934. Explanation, besonders die Struktur und die biologischen Eigenschaften der in vitro gezüchten Zellen und Gewebe. *Ergebn. Anat. Entw. Gesch.* 31:125–207

116. Lieberman, A. R. 1971. The axon reaction: a review of the principal features of perikaryal responses to axon injury. *Int. Rev. Neurobiol.* 14:49–124

117. Lømo, T., Rosenthal, J. 1972. Control of ACh sensitivity to muscle activity in the rat. *J. Physiol. London* 221:493–513

118. Lømo, T., Slater, C. R. 1978. Control of acetylcholine sensitivity and synapse formation by muscle activity. *J. Physiol. London* 275:391–402

119. Lømo, T., Slater, C. R. 1980. Control of junctional acetylcholinesterase by neural and muscular influences in the rat. *J. Physiol. London.* 303:191–202

120. Lømo, T., Westgaard, R. H. 1975. Further studies on the control of ACh sensitivity by muscle activity in the rat. *J. Physiol. London* 252:603–26

121. Lømo, T., Westgaard, R. H., Dahl, H. A. 1974. Contractile properties of muscle: control by pattern of muscle activity in the rat. *Proc. R. Soc. London Ser. B* 187:99–103

122. Luco, J. V., Eyzaguirre, C. 1955. Fibrillation and hypersensitivity to ACh in denervated muscle: effect of length of degenerating nerve fibers. *J. Neurophysiol.* 18:65–73

123. Marler, P. R. 1977. Development and learning of recognition systems. In *Recognition of Complex Acoustic Signals,* ed. T. Bullock, pp. 77–96. Berlin: Dahlem Konferenzen. 404 pp.

124. Marsh, G., Beams, H. W. 1946. *In vitro* control of growing chick nerve fibers by applied electrical currents. *J. Cell Comp. Physiol.* 27:139–57

125. Matsumoto, S. G., Murphey, R. K. 1977. Sensory deprivation during development decreases the resposiveness of cricket giant interneurons. *J. Physiol. London* 268:533–48

126. Matsumoto, S. G., Murphey, R. K. 1978. Sensory deprivation in the cricket nervous system: evidence for a critical period. *J. Physiol. London* 285:159–70

127. Matthews, S. A., Detwiler, S. R. 1926. The reactions of *Amblystoma* embryos following prolonged treatment with chloretone. *J. Exp. Zool.* 45:279–92

128. McMahan, D. 1974. Chemical messengers in development: a hypothesis. *Science* 185:1012–21

128a. Meiri, H., Spira, M. E., Parnas, I. 1980. Membrane conductance and action potential of a regenerating axonal tip. *Science.* In press

129. Mellon, D., Stevens, P. J. 1979. Experimental arrest of muscle transformation and asymmetry reversal in Alpheid shrimp. *Neurosci. Abstr.* 5:254

130. Messenger, E. A., Warner, A. E. 1979. The function of the sodium pump during differentiation of amphibian embryonic neurones. *J. Physiol. London* 292:85–105

131. Miledi, R., Orkland, P. 1966. Effects of a "fast" nerve on "slow" muscle fibers in the frog. *Nature* 209:717–18

132. Miyazaki, S., Takahashi, K., Tsuda, K. 1972. Calcium and sodium contributions to regenerative responses in the embryonic excitable cell membrane. *Science* 176:1441–43

133. Miyazaki, S., Takahashi, K., Tsuda, K. 1974. Electrical excitability in the egg of the tunicate. *J. Physiol. London* 238:37–54

134. Model, P. G., Bornstein, M. B., Crain, S. M., Papas, G. D. 1971. An electron microscopic study of the development of synapses in cultured fetal mouse cerebrum continuously exposed to xylocaine. *J. Cell Biol.* 49:362–71

135. Moran, D. J. 1978. Calcium-mediated morphogenetic movements during neurulation. *Bioelectrochem. Bioenerg.* 5:473–77

136. Obata, K. 1977. Development of neuromuscular transmission in culture with a variety of neurons and in the presence of cholinergic substances and TTX. *Brain Res.* 119:141–53

137. O'Brien, R. A. D., Östberg, A. J. C., Vrbová, G. 1978. Observations on the elimination of polyneuronal innervation in developing mammalian skeletal muscle. *J. Physiol. London* 282:571–87

138. O'Brien, R. A. D., Purves, R. D., Vrbová, G. 1977. Effect of activity on the elimination of multiple innervation in soleus muscle of rats. *J. Physiol. London* 271:54–55P

139. Oey, J. 1975. Noradrenaline induces morphological alterations in nucleated and enucleated rat C6 glioma cells. *Nature* 257:317–19

140. Olney, J. V., Rhee, V., Ho, O. L. 1974. Kainic acid: a powerful neurotoxic analogue of glutamate. *Brain Res.* 77:507–12

141. Oppenheim, R. W., Pittman, R., Gray, M., Maderdrut, J. L. 1978. Embryonic behavior, hatching, and neuromuscular development in the chick following a transient reduction of spontaneous motility and sensory input by neuromuscular blocking agents. *J. Comp. Neurol.* 179:619–40

142. Otten, U., Thoenen, H. 1976. Mechanisms of tyrosine hydroxylase and dopamine-β-hydroxylase induction in organ cultures of rat sympathetic gan-

glia by potassium depolarization and cholinomimetics. *Naunyn Schmiedeberg's Arch. Pharmakol.* 292:153–59

143. Palén, K., Thörneby, L., Emmanuelsson, H. 1979. Effects of serotonin and serotonin antagonists on chick embryogenesis. *Wilhelm Roux's Arch.* 187:89–103

144. Palmer, J. F., Slack, C. 1970. Some bioelectric parameters of early *Xenopus* embryos. *J. Emb. Exp. Morphol.* 24:535–53

145. Patel, A. J., Bailey, P., Balázs, R. 1979. Effect of reserpine on cell proliferation and energy stores in the developing rat brain. *Neurosci.* 4:139–43

146. Patel, A. J., Béndek, G., Balázs, R., Lewis, P. D. 1977. Effect of reserpine on cell proliferation in the developing rat brain: a biochemical study. *Brain Res.* 129:283–97

147. Patterson, P. H. 1979. Environmental determination of neurotransmitter function. See Ref. 14pp. 172–83

148. Pestronk, A., Drachman, D. B. 1978. Motor nerve sprouting and acetylcholine receptors. *Science* 199:1223–25

149. Pestronk, A., Drachman, D. B., Griffin, J. W. 1976. Effect of muscle disuse on acetylcholine receptors. *Nature* 260:352–53

150. Pittman, R. H., Oppenheim, R. W. 1978. Neuromuscular blockade increases motoneurone survival during normal cell death in the chick embryo. *Nature* 271:364–66

151. Pittman, R., Oppenheim, R. W. 1979. Cell death of motoneurons in the chick embryo spinal cord. IV. Evidence that a functional neuromuscular interaction is involved in the regulation of naturally occurring cell death and stabilization of synapses. *J. Comp. Neurol.* 187:425–47

152. Poodry, C. A., Hall, L., Suzuki, D. T. 1973. Developmental properties of *shibire*[ts]: a pleiotropic mutation affecting larval and adult locomotion and development. *Dev. Biol.* 32:373–86

153. Prasad, K., Gilmer, K. N. 1974. Demonstration of dopamine-sensitive adenylate cyclase in malignant neuroblastoma cells and change in sensitivity of adenylate cyclase to catecholamines in 'differentiated' cells. *Proc. Natl. Acad. Sci. USA* 71:2525–29

154. Purves, D., Sakmann, B. 1974. The effect of contractile activity on fibrillation and extrajunctional acetylcholinesensitivity in rat muscle maintained in organ culture. *J. Physiol. London* 237:157–82

155. Rausch, E., Swift, H., Riesen, A. H., Chow, K. L. 1961. Altered structure and composition of retinal cells in dark-reared mammals. *Exp. Cell Res.* 25:348–63

156. Redfern, P., Thesleff, S. 1970. Action potential generation in denervated rat skeletal muscle. II. The action of tetrodotoxin. *Acta Physiol. Scand.* 82:70–78

157. Ridgway, E. B., Gilkey, J. C., Jaffe, L. C. 1977. Free calcium increases explosively in activating medaka eggs. *Proc. Natl. Acad. Sci. USA* 74:623–27

158. Riley, D. A. 1978. Tenotomy delays the postnatal development of the motor innervation of the rat soleus. *Brain Res.* 143:162–67

159. Robinson, K. R. 1979. Electrical currents through full grown and maturing *Xenopus* oocytes. *Proc. Natl. Acad. Sci. USA* 76:837–41

160. Roper, S., Ko, C.-P. 1978. Impulse blockade in frog cardiac ganglion does not resemble partial denervation in changing synaptic organization. *Science* 202:66–68

161. Rosenthal, J. L., Taraskevich, P. S. 1977. Reduction of multiaxonal innervation at the neuromuscular junction of the rat during development. *J. Physiol. London* 270:299–310

162. Rothman, T. P., Gershon, M. D., Holtzer, H. 1978. The relationship of cell division to the acquisition of adrenergic characteristics by developing sympathetic ganglion cell precursors. *Dev. Biol.* 65:322–41

163. Rubin, L. L., Schuetze, S. M., Weill, C. L., Fischbach, G. D. 1980. Regulation of acetylcholinesterase appearance at neuromuscular junctions *in vitro*. *Nature* 283:264–67

164. Rubinstein, N. A., Kelly, A. M. 1978. Myogenic and neurogenic contributions to the development of fast and slow twitch muscles in rat. *Dev. Biol.* 62:473–85

165. Sahu, S. K., Prasad, K. N. 1975. Effects of neurotransmitters and protoglandin E₁ on cyclic AMP levels in various clones of neuroblastoma cells in culture. *J. Neurochem.* 24:1267–69

166. Salkoff, L., Kelly, L. 1980. Aminopyridines mimic mutant *Drosophila* developmental defects. *Compar. Biochem. Physiol.* 65:59–63

167. Salmons, S., Sreter, F. A. 1976. Significance of impulse activity in the transformation of skeletal muscle type. *Nature* 263:30–34

168. Salmons, S., Vrbová, G. 1969. The influence of activity on some contractile characteristics of mammalian fast and slow muscles. *J. Physiol. London* 201:535–49

169. Schmidt, J. T. 1979. Movement of optic terminals in goldfish tectum after local pre- or postsynaptic blockade of transmission. *Neurosci. Abstr.* 5:635

170. Schubert, D., Tarikas, H., LaCorbiere, M. 1976. Neurotransmitter regulation of adenosine 3',5'-monophosphate in clonal nerve, glia, and muscle cell lines. *Science* 192:471–72

171. Scott, B. S. 1977. The effect of elevated potassium on the time course of neuron survival in cultures of dissociated dorsal root ganglia. *J. Cell Physiol.* 91:305–16

172. Shatz, C. J., Stryker, M. P. 1978. Ocular dominance in layer IV of the cat's visual cortex and the effects of monocular deprivation. *J. Physiol. London* 281: 267–83

173. Sherman, S. M., Hoffman, K.-P., Stone, J. 1972. Loss of a specific cell type from the dorsal lateral geniculate nucleus in visually deprived cats. *J. Neurophysiol.* 35:532–41

174. Siddiqi, O., Benzer, S. 1976. Neurological defects in temperature-sensitive paralytic mutants of *Drosophila melanogaster. Proc. Natl. Acad. Sci. USA* 73:3253–57

175. Sievers, J., Klemm, H. P., Jenner, S., Baumgarten, H. A., Berry, M. 1980. Neuronal and extraneuronal effects of intracisternally administered 6-hydroxydopamine on the developing rat brain. *J. Neurochem.* 34:765–71

176. Silberstein, S. D., Lemberger, L., Klein, D. C., Axelrod, J., Kopin, I. J. 1972. Induction of adrenal tyrosine hydroxylase in organ culture. *Neuropharmacology* 11:721–26

177. Snyder, W. D., Harris, G. L. 1979. A physiological correlate of disuse-induced sprouting at the neuromuscular junction. *Nature* 281:69–71

178. Spector, I., Palfrey, C., Littauer, U. Z. 1975. Enhancement of the electrical excitability of neuroblastoma cells by valinomycin. *Nature* 254:121–24

179. Spitzer, N. C. 1979. Ion channels in development. *Ann. Rev. Neurosci.* 2: 363–97

180. Spray, D. C., Harris, A. L., Bennett, M. V. L. 1979. Voltage dependence of junctional conductance in early amphibian embryos. *Science* 204:432–34

181. Srihari, T., Vrbová, G. 1978. The role of muscle activity in the differentiation of neuromuscular junctions in slow and fast chick muscles. *J. Neurocytol.* 7:529–40

182. Steinbach, J. H., Harris, A. J., Patrick, J., Schubert, D., Heinemann, S. 1973. Nerve-muscle interaction *in vitro. J. Gen. Physiol.* 62:255–70

183. Strasser, H. 1891. Alte und neue Probleme der entwicklungeschichtlichen Forschung auf dem Gebiete des Nerven Systems. *Ergebn. Anat. Entw.* 1:721–69

184. Streter, F. A., Gergely, J., Salmons, S., Romanul, F. 1973. Synthesis by fast muscle of myosin light chains characteristic of slow muscle in response to long-term stimulation. *Nature New Biol.* 241:17–18

185. Stryker, M. P., Sherk, H., Levithal, H. C., Hirsch, H. V. B. 1978. Physiological consequences for the cat's visual cortex of effectively restricting early visual experience with oriented contours. *J. Neurophysiol.* 41:896–909

186. Takahashi, K., Miyazaki, S., Kidokoro, Y. 1971. Development of excitability in embryonic muscle cell membranes in certain tunicates. *Science* 171:415–18

187. Takahashi, K., Yoshii, M. 1978. Effects of internal free Ca upon the Na and Ca channels in the tunicate egg analyzed by the internal perfusion technique. *J. Physiol. London* 279:519–49

188. Thoenen, H., Otten, U., Schwab, M. 1979. Orthograde and retrograde signals for the regulation of neural gene expression: The peripheral sympathetic nervous system as a model. In *The Neurosciences Fourth Study Program,* ed. F. Schmitt, F. Worden, pp. 911–28. Cambridge, Mass: M.I.T. Press

189. Thompson, W., Kuffler, D. P., Jansen, J. K. S. 1979. The effect of prolonged reversible block of nerve impulses on the elimination of polyneuronal innervation of newborn rat skeletal muscle fibers. *Neuroscience* 4:271–81

190. Tomkins, G. M. 1975. The metabolic code. *Science* 189:760–63

191. Toneby, M. 1977. Functional aspects of 5-hydroxytryptamine in early embryogenesis of the sea urchin *Paracentrotus lividus. Wilhelm Roux's Arch.* 181: 247–59

192. Tupper, J. T., Powers, R. D. 1973. Changes in ion permeability and membrane potential during early echinoderm development: Electrophysiological and tracer experiments. *J. Exp. Zool.* 184:353–63

193. Van Essen, D., Jansen, J. K. S. 1974. Reinnervation of the rat diaphragm during perfusion with α-bungarotoxin. *Acta Physiol. Scand.* 91:571–73

194. Walicke, P. A. 1979. *Role of calcium and cyclic AMP in the mechanism and developmental effects of neuronal activity.* PhD thesis. Harvard Medical School

195. Walicke, P. A., Campenot, R. B., Patterson, P. H. 1977. Determination of transmitter function by neuronal activity. *Proc. Natl. Acad. Sci. USA* 74:5767–71

196. Warner, A. E. 1973. The electrical properties of the ectoderm in the amphibian embryo during induction and early development of the nervous system. *J. Physiol. London* 235:267–86

197. Weinberg, C. B., Hall, Z. W. 1979. Junctional form of acetylcholinesterase restored at nerve-free end-plates. *Dev. Biol.* 68:631–35

198. Weiskrantz, L. 1958. Sensory deprivation and the cat's optic nervous system. *Nature* 181:1047–50

199. Weiss, P. 1941. Nerve patterns: the mechanics of growth. *Growth* 5:163–203 (Suppl.)

200. Wiesel, T. N., Hubel, D. H. 1963. Effects of visual deprivation on morphology and physiology of cells in the cat's lateral geniculate body. *J. Neurophysiol.* 26:978–93

201. Wiesel, T. N., Hubel, D. H. 1965. Comparison of the effects of unilateral and bilateral unit responses in kittens. *J. Neurophysiol.* 28:1029–40

202. Woolsey, T. A., Anderson, J. R., Wann, J. R., Stanfield, B. B. 1979. Effects of early vibrissae damage on neurons in the ventrobasal-thalamus of the mouse. *J. Comp. Neurol.* 184:363–80

203. Woolsey, T. A., Wann, J. R. 1976. Areal changes in mouse cortical barrels following vibrissal damage at different postnatal ages. *J. Comp. Neurol.* 170:53–66

204. Yew, D. T., Ho, A. K. S., Meyer, D. B. 1974. Effect of 6-hydroxydopamine on retinal development in the chick. *Experientia* 30:1320–22

205. Yntema, C. L. 1943. Deficient efferent innervation of the extremities following removal of neural crest in *Amblystoma. J. Exp. Zool.* 94:319–49

206. Zelena, J., Jirmanova, I. 1973. Ultrastructure of chicken slow muscle after nerve cross union. *Exp. Neurol.* 38:272–85

206a. Zigmond, R. E., Bowers, C. W. 1981. Influence of nerve activity on the macromolecular content of neurons and their effector organs. *Ann. Rev. Physiol.* 43:XXX–XX

207. Zigmond, R. E., Yehezkel, B.-A. 1977. Electrical stimulation of preganglionic nerve increases tyrosine hydroxylase activity in sympathetic ganglia. *Proc. Natl. Acad. Sci. USA* 174:3078–80

Ann. Rev. Physiol. 1981. 43:711–25

SODIUM CHANNELS IN NERVE AND MUSCLE MEMBRANE

♦1339

Richard Rogart

Department of Neuroscience, Children's Hospital Medical Center, Boston, Massachusetts 02115

INTRODUCTION

Nerve cells are able to transmit and store information in the form of action potentials (APs) because highly specialized membrane properties allow rapid and reversible changes in membrane permeability to specific ions. Nerve cells use metabolic work to generate ion concentration gradients across their membranes. Membrane permeability changes release this energy as transient changes in membrane potential, i.e. nerve impulses.

Studies of excitable membranes in the last decade have focused on the molecular structures responsible for membrane permeability changes, the "ion channels." They are the most important class of membrane protein for nerve function. Different types of ion channels provide neuron structures with the membrane properties needed for AP propagation along axons, impulse transmission across synapses, and integrative responses of nerve cell bodies to multiple inputs. Current study of ion channels seeks the key to individual nerve cell properties and the more complex cell-cell interrelations necessary for nervous system function. Such research has begun to provide a molecular description of nervous system function.

Nervous system development and plasticity must also depend on membrane properties and hence are ultimately determined by ion channels. Neurons undergo morphological differentiation, as well as adaptation of membrane functional properties to meet certain tasks. Control mechanisms must exist to regulate expression of excitability, to meet different physiological needs. These mechanisms allow a neuron to (*a*) specify synthesis of ion channels with different structural characteristics, suited to particular membrane functions, and (*b*) regulate the distribution and density of different types of ion channels in different portions of its membrane.

711

0066-4278/81/0315-0711$01.00

Using one voltage-gated channel, the sodium channel, this review examines the ways ion channels may be involved in nervous system differentiation and plasticity. In many excitable membranes, Na^+ channels carry the largest inward ionic current during an AP, and are therefore the membrane protein most directly responsible for membrane excitability. I review (a) the molecular architecture of Na^+ channels in nonmyelinated nerve axons, the simplest form of excitable membrane; and (b) excitable membranes where functional requirements have necessitated alteration of the pattern of excitability found in nonmyelinated axons.

Only limited aspects of the relationship between the Na^+ channel and nerve membrane differentiation are discussed here. Recent reviews are cited for further details.

MOLECULAR CHARACTERISTICS OF NERVE MEMBRANE

Conduction of the AP in nerve axons involves permeability changes to two ions, Na^+ and K^+. Using the "voltage clamp" in squid giant axon, Hodgkin & Huxley (24) showed that nerve membrane depolarization led to (a) a transient increase and then turn off or "inactivation" of Na^+ permeability, and (b) an increase in K^+ permeability after a delay, plateauing to a steady-state value. Hence, an AP results from a small depolarization that is rapidly amplified to a large depolarization by increasing Na^+ permeability. Sodium permeability then inactivates, and an increase in K^+ permeability repolarizes the axon.

We now have strong evidence that nerve membrane permeability changes occur at discrete sites, the ion channels. Technical advances have allowed direct measurements to greatly clarify our conceptual picture of the Na^+ channel. One early (1970) review of ion channels (22) summarized indirect estimates of Na^+ channel density and single channel conductance that differ from current values by one to two orders of magnitude. Techniques using a variety of toxin probes that interact with specific sites on the Na^+ channel, and electrophysiological measurement of "gating currents" and ion-current noise, have converged upon one conclusion—ion channels occupy little space in nonmyelinated nerve axon.

Small Nonmyelinated Nerve Fibers

Tetrodotoxin (TTX) and saxitoxin (STX), two small, naturally occurring neurotoxins (mol wt about 500) that act by binding to the Na^+ channel in a highly specific, one-to-one fashion (38), have provided the first and most widely used pharmacologic probes for the Na^+ channel. Moore, Narahashi & Shaw (39) first showed that the number of TTX binding sites could be quantitatively measured in lobster walking leg nerves, which contained a vast number of very small nonmyelinated nerve fibers. Their estimate of 13 toxin binding sites per μm^2 in nerve membrane was the earliest demonstration of the very low density of channels in nonmyelinated nerve axon. Their bioassay technique was, unfortunately, not sensitive to small changes in toxin concentration, and was too tedious to measure toxin binding over a concentration range sufficient to distinguish the specific saturable component of toxin binding to Na^+ channels. Hafemann (17) first radioactively labelled these toxins, using the Wilzbach method (i.e. exposing toxin to tritium gas for a prolonged period). Wilzbach-labeled toxins (*TTX and *STX) were highly successful for biochemical characterization of the toxin binding site [see (50) for review].

In several nerve bundles consisting of very small, nonmyelinated nerve fibers, Na^+ channel densities of 25–110 binding sites per μm^2 were determined (51,59). The sparsity of Na^+ channels is striking. For instance, in garfish olfactory nerve, there are about 36 Na^+ channels per μm^2. Along the axon length, channels are spaced by about 0.2 μm—a distance about equal to the fiber diameter. There are about 40,000 phospholipids per Na^+ channel, and Na^+ channels occupy only about 1/5 of one percent of total membrane surface area. An average flux of 60–110 sodium ions passes through a single Na^+ channel during an AP of 5–6 msec duration, i.e. about 10,000 ions per second (51). In contrast, the Na^+ pump transports, at most, only about 200 sodium ions per second outward across the axon. The considerably greater rate of ion flux across the Na^+ channel has provided the strongest evidence that ion transport occurs through pores, rather than via a carrier-mediated, enzyme-like mechanism.

The sparsity of Na^+ channels in nonmyelinated nerve also highlights the major difficulty in understanding nerve differentiation and plasticity in terms of changes in membrane functional properties. Although ion channels are the molecular structure most directly related to membrane function, they represent at the same time only a minute fraction of the total membrane. Hence, studies of nerve differentiation by morphological, biophysical, or biochemical means do not reflect changes in membrane functional properties; these techniques are insensitive to ion channel proteins. Hence new pharmacological and electrophysiological techniques, sensitive to the molecular events underlying nerve excitation, have been essential to further study of nerve membrane functional properties.

Although TTX and STX have been successful as Na^+ channel markers, certain technical difficulties have limited their usefulness: (a) Modification of these toxins tends to destroy biological activity, presumably because their small size requires most of their structure to be involved in channel binding. In contrast, biochemical study of the best-characterized ion channel, the acetylcholine-activated channel, has relied on probes like α-bungarotoxin, which binds nearly irreversibly and can be modified and labelled by conventional protein biochemistry techniques. (b) STX and TTX binding is rapidly reversible (K_{off} ranging from 10–120 sec), requiring experimentation under equilibrium conditions, preventing extensive washout of nonspecifically bound toxin. For nerve bundles with many small, nonmyelinated fibers, this has not posed a problem. They have enormous surface area (i.e. 6000 cm^2 membrane per tissue), with high specificity of toxin binding (K_t = 4 nM), and 100 toxin binding sites per μm^2. Thus with 90% of binding sites saturated, 90 pmoles toxin uptake per g tissue bound to Na$^+$ channels can be measured easily, accompanied by only 40 pmoles of toxin in the extracellular space (ecs) and in nonspecific binding. However, in preparations with 1/10 the surface area or channel density, or with modified toxins with 1/10 the affinity, it becomes difficult to measure binding of 9 pmoles of specific toxin uptake, particularly when accompanied by 20–40 pmoles of nonspecifically bound toxin. (c) The random, nonspecific nature of Wilzbach-labeling resulted in low specific activity (typically, only about one tritium incorporated into 300–600 toxin molecules) and extensive toxin degradation during labeling, incorporating substantial radioactivity into breakdown products. Levinson (32) first showed that even after careful purification, 70–95% of labelling remained in impurities, leading to increased nonspecific binding and a 3–20-fold underestimation of saturable toxin binding density [see (50) for review]. Subsequent studies have overcome these initial difficulties with a 300–900-fold improvement in label incorporation and an improved radiochemical purity, routinely assessed by direct measurement. Taking advantage of a novel chemical feature of saxitoxin, Ritchie, Rogart & Strichartz (52) were able to exchange-label two slowly exchanging methylene hydrogens with tritium, incorporating about one tritium in each toxin molecule. Chicheportice et al (10) were able to modify TTX while retaining substantial activity, allowing both radioactive labeling and synthesis of a photo-affinity label.

Squid Giant Axon

The molecular architecture of ion channels in nerve membrane has been electrophysiologically characterized most extensively in the squid giant axon. Comparative study of toxin binding site density was therefore highly desirable, despite the poor suitability of this preparation for measuring toxin uptake (fiber diameter 500 μm, and hence, only 80 cm^2 membrane per g tissue). Levinson & Meves (33) measured Wilzbach-labeled *TTX uptake by groups of 6–8 single axons of *Loligo forbesii;* Strichartz, Rogart & Ritchie (58) studied exchange-labeled *STX uptake by *Loligo pealii.* Results of 553 and 170 toxin binding sites per μm^2, respectively, were obtained. Although there is statistical uncertainty in both these measurements, they are in good agreement with electrophysiologic measurements (discussed below) and serve to reaffirm the sparsity of Na^+ channels in nonmyelinated nerve axon.

Electrophysiological Determination of Single Channel Properties

A nerve cell is capable of synthesizing several different types of ion channels, with structural components suited for different tasks. A fundamental goal of neurobiological research is to determine the molecular mechanisms of the various ion channels underlying excitation. Ultimately, a detailed molecular description of the Na^+ channel will require correlating its observed electrophysiological properties with three-dimensional structure of biochemically isolated channels. Identification of the various ion channel protein components that nerve cells synthesize will provide one part of a molecular description of nerve cell differentiation and plasticity. Unfortunately, neither an adequate biophysical description of Na^+ permeability based on physically realistic assumption of membrane protein behavior in a voltage field, nor a means of obtaining structural information about Na^+ channels is yet available. I do not discuss the structural make-up of the Na^+ channel here [for recent detailed reviews see (4,11,23,56,57)]. However, I can briefly summarize some Na^+ channel properties related to nerve differentiation and plasticity, determined from electrophysiological and biochemical studies.

Two exciting recent advances have been: (a) measurement of "gating currents," corresponding to movement of charged particles hypothesized by Hodgkin & Huxley to accompany ion channel opening and closing (2, 42), and (b) correlation of the noise present in ionic currents (representing statistical fluctuations in the number of opened channels) with single channel properties (41). Sodium channel density has been estimated at 180 and 500 channels per μm^2 in gating current measurements in giant axons from *Loligo forbesii* and *pealii* (5,30), respectively, and as 380 channels per μm^2 in noise measurements in *Loligo vulgaris* (12). Single channel conductance has been estimated as 5–15 pSiemens.

In the squid giant axon (and in nodes of Ranvier, discussed below) estimates of channel density from several different methods have shown quantitative agreement to within a factor of about 2–3. This variability is larger than the experimental error expected in each measurement and may reflect differing assumptions in different models of Na^+ channel function. Gating currents (the asymmetric component of charge movement that occurs with symmetrical hyperpolarization and depolarization of nerve membrane) allow Q_{max}, the total charge movement associated with opening all of the Na^+ channels, to be determined. Despite similar values for Q_{max} in *Loligo forbesii* and *pealii* (1600–2400 e/cm^2), divergent channel densities (180 and 500 channels/μm^2) resulted from assuming different values for charge per channel in different Na^+ channel models (5,30). Noise measurements estimated conductance of a single Na^+ channel (about 10 pS). Channel density is then calculated from estimated total membrane conductance, gNa. For the H–H formulation, since inactivation occurs independently and in parallel with activation (with exponential time course), by the time channel activation is complete, ½–⅔ of channels are "inactivated," so gNa is estimated as about 200–300% of observed peak membrane conductance. However, pharmacologic modifiers that remove or slow inactivation increase conductance by only 25%, rather than the expected 100–200%. Alternative models estimate gNa's 50–60% smaller. Hence, even determination of gNa remains controversial.

FUNCTIONAL SPECIALIZATIONS OF EXCITABLE MEMBRANES

In nonmyelinated nerve axons, a low density of Na^+ channels allows continuous propagation of APs over large distances. In a number of nerve and muscle cells, however, impulse transmission requires more complicated membrane permeability properties. Membranes where Na^+ channel density and distribution have been altered to suit specialized roles will be described.

Nerve Membranes

MYELINATED NERVE   In myelinated nerve, impulses "jump" from node to node across internodes insulated by myelin. Electrophysiologically, this "saltatory conduction" causes two observable alterations: (*a*) sodium currents at nodes are 10–100 times larger than in other nerves; and (*b*) internodes exhibit only passive properties. Both noise and gating current measurements revealed Na^+ channel densities in nodes of Ranvier that were considerably higher than other excitable membranes, with estimates ranging from 2000–5000 channels per μm^2 (10,43). Measurement of labeled toxin uptake in myelinated nerve was technically difficult, because the amount of exposed axonal membrane was very small (i.e. 8 cm^2 per g sciatic nerve). Ritchie & Rogart (49) were able to measure a clear saturable uptake of exchange-labeled *STX in rabbit sciatic nerve, and determined a toxin binding site density of 12,000 channels per μm^2 in rabbit node of Ranvier. Additionally, their studies comparing uptake in intact and homogenized, sonicated preparations showed that all of the Na^+ channels in a myelinated nerve were located at the node of Ranvier, while internodal axon had almost none. Freeze fracture studies (31,54) in myelinated nerve have also found intramembranous particles with a high density (1000–2000 particles per μm^2), with dense deposits of dye precipitating at nodal but not internodal axon. Thus an axon can establish an inhomogeneous distribution of Na^+ channels, and neurons must have control mechanisms for expression of excitability, allowing two alterations in axon membrane: (a) Na^+ channels can be packed into nodal membrane at a density 1–2 orders of magnitude higher than other excitable membranes, and (b) they can be restricted to a very small portion of the myelinated nerve axon, the nodal membrane.

As in squid giant axon, quantitative agreement between estimated nodal Na^+ channel density is good to within a factor of 2–3, which is larger than expected experimental error. Noise and gating-current measurements, even from the same laboratory, in the same species of frog, determined 2000 and 5000 Na^+ channels per μm^2 membrane, respectively (10,43). Sigworth (56) recently used ensemble averages of Na^+ currents to study Na^+ current noise in node of Ranvier, estimating only about half as many channels per node as stationary noise measurements (10). The differences among these estimates may help in developing a correct biophysical model of Na^+ channel function.

Nodal axon is apparently quite different from other excitable membranes, since a sizeable percentage of membrane area is occupied by Na^+ channels. Assuming a spherical Na^+ channel protein with an 80 Å diameter, a node with 12,000 channels per μm^2 has 60% of its area occupied by Na^+ channels, leaving little room for other essential membrane proteins. Although several approximations about Na^+ channel size and nodal membrane area make it unlikely that this estimate is quantitatively precise, it is interesting to contrast node membrane with two other membranes where proteins are found in high density. Rhodopsin (mol wt about 40,000) is found at an average density of 20,000 sites per μm^2 in rod outer segment and occupies 80–90% of membrane area (21); ACh-activated channels (mol wt about 250,000) found at a density of 20–25,000 per μm^2 in some synapses (36,46) are almost at the close packing density.

DEMYELINATED NERVE The finding that internodal axon in myelinated nerve has few, if any, Na^+ channels has profound implications for conduction in demyelinated nerve. Conduction block results not only from loss of insulating myelin sheath, but also from exposed axon membrane lacking excitability properties. However, by measuring membrane currents along lengths of single demyelinated axons in ventral root fibers (in vivo),

Bostock & Sears (7) have demonstrated that electrical excitability can return to exposed axon. Ten days after demyelination, they found stretches of axon with inward currents, indicating the presence of Na^+ channels. Rasminsky (53) studied "amyelinated" nerve fibers in a similar manner in 129 Redydy mutant mice with muscular dystrophy, and also found excitation along continuous stretches of excitable membrane.

Membrane properties in demyelinated nerve may also help to explain enigmas about the clinical course of multiple sclerosis (MS) patients, who experience multiple remissions and exacerbations of symptoms, which correlate poorly with anatomical findings. For instance, an MS patient will become blind after extensive demyelination of the optic nerve. Frequently, however, after several weeks, some vision recovers, despite persistent demyelination of axons for 3–4 mm and despite physiological predictions that these fibers should not conduct. A hypothesis to explain these findings proposes plasticity in membrane properties after nerve injury. (a) Exposed internodes are unable to support an action potential because they are devoid of Na^+ channels. (b) Remissions may reflect recovery of conduction due to new synthesis or spreading of Na^+ channels into internodal axon after demyelination, analogous to appearance of AChR receptors along the entire muscle surface after denervation (7,52).

MAMMALIAN MOTONEURONS   Efficacy of synaptic transmission in motoneurons has been shown to depend critically on location of a synapse on a dendrite, and on dendritic and motoneuron passive cable properties (see 25). Kuno & Llinas (31) found that mammalian motoneurons show plasticity in membrane properties after pathologic insult, which demonstrates another mechanism affecting synaptic efficacy. While convergence of impulses from 10–20 different afferent fibers is required to excite normal motoneurons, after axotomy "hot spots" of excitability, presumed to be membrane patches with high densities of Na^+ channels, allow a single afferent fiber to stimulate the motoneuron. Llinas & Nicholson (34) postulated "hot spots" of ionic channels to explain their intradendritic records in alligator Purkinje cells. These studies with axotomized motoneurons demonstrate that synaptic efficacy depends upon ion channel localization in dendrites. Furthermore, "hot spots" of excitability appear to be changeable in nerve cells, and so selective activation of synapses can occur. "Hot spots" with high densities of ACh-activated channels have been shown to play a prominent role in development of cholinergic synapses (see 14). "Hot spots" may be a powerful means for maintaining plasticity of synapses in the CNS. Appearance of Na^+ channel "hot spots" in denervated frog slow muscle fibers is discussed further, below.

Inhomogeneous distributions of Na$^+$ channels are also essential for normal motoneuron function. Dodge & Cooley (13) predicted by computer modelling that dendrites, soma, and initial segment would require different Na$^+$ channel densities—in particular, that initial segment would need a channel density approaching that at nodes of Ranvier in order to initiate the AP reliably despite heavy impedance loading imposed by both the cell soma and dendrites. Waxman & Quick (62) indeed showed staining of motoneuron initial segments with ferric cyanate, resembling that found at nodes. Traub & Llinas (60) have conducted a comprehensive simulation of motoneurons, using varying ionic conductances, and have been able to simulate many of the features of experimental recordings. These studies illustrate how higher-order neuronal function might depend on selective distribution and density of ion channels in various portions of neuronal membranes.

MAMMALIAN DORSAL ROOT GANGLION (DRG) CELLS   TTX-resistant APs were first described in denervated mammalian muscles by Redfern & Thesleff (48) in 1971. Studies attributing this to a population of TTX-resistant Na$^+$ channels in mammalian muscle are described below. Recent studies have demonstrated TTX-resistant Na$^+$ channels in vivo in mouse DRG cells (63) and in DRG cells maintained in tissue culture (37). These studies have shown that with maturation, the normal developmental sequence of DRG cells includes a progressive increase in TTX-sensitive Na$^+$ channels and disappearance of toxin-resistant channels. However, in cultured ganglion cells, TTX-resistant sodium currents remained unchanged even after prolonged periods. This study concluded that spinal ganglion neurons in tissue culture, separated from normal spinal cord neuronal input, remained functionally analogous to denervated muscle fibers, maintaining TTX-resistant Na$^+$ channels (15). TTX-resistant Na$^+$ channels appear to be related to normal neuronal and muscle development; their function requires further study.

Muscle Membrane

The amenability of muscle fibers to both electrophysiological and biochemical characterization has led to productive pursuit of excitability properties in muscle membrane. For instance, although frog sartorius muscle has considerably less surface area (450 cm^2 membrane per g muscle) than nerve bundles with small nonmyelinated fibers (6,000–65,000 cm^2 membrane per g), this disadvantage is easily offset by the availability of voltage clamp data to compare with pharmacological studies. Furthermore, several physiologic observations in muscle have generated interest in characterizing muscle membrane.

AMPHIBIAN MUSCLE   Almers & Levinson (3) measured TTX uptake in frog sartorius muscle, obtaining an estimate of 380 binding sites per μm^2 of muscle surface membrane. Combining their data with voltage clamp studies, they concluded that a single Na^+ channel has a conductance of about 1 pS. This provided early evidence that single channel conductance was 10–100-fold lower than previous estimates (22). Since membrane depolarization had no effect on toxin uptake, this study also confirmed that there was little interaction between the *TTX binding site and the "gating" portion of the channel.

Ritchie & Rogart (49) measured uptake of exchange-labeled *STX in both amphibian and mammalian muscle. They found a two-fold difference in saturable uptake of toxin in two very closely related varieties of the same frog, Southern and Northern *Rana pipiens*. Since average fiber diameter (about 60 μm) in the two species was the same, the difference in toxin uptake reflected differing binding site densities of 195 and 340 sites per μm^2 in Northern and Southern frogs, respectively. These studies underlined the difficulty in comparing electrophysiologic and pharmacologic studies in different preparations and suggested a possible explanation for varying estimates of single channel conductance.

T-TUBULE MEMBRANE   T-tubule membrane in muscle conducts the surface membrane AP to the sarcoplasmic reticulum, thereby providing excitation-contraction coupling. Jaimovich et al (26) were interested in contrasting the properties of T-tubular and surface muscle membrane. Since osmotic shock with high glycerol concentration electrically and physically dissociates T-tubule and surface membrane, they measured uptake of TTX in normal and osmotically shocked frog sartorius muscle. They found that total toxin uptake decreased by more than 50%, after glycerol treatment, and homogenization restored toxin uptake to the previous value. On the basis of these studies, they estimated 175 toxin binding sites per μm^2 in surface membrane, and 40–50 sites per μm^2 in T-tubule membrane, indicating a conductance of about 25% of surface membrane. Adrian & Peachey (1) and Campbell & Hille (8) also estimated the ratio of Na^+ channel density in T-tubule and surface membrane. Computer simulated APs have the shape of experimentally observed APs when T-tubule conductance is between 5 and 20% of surface membrane. This indirect method qualitatively confirmed different excitability properties in surface and T-tubule membrane.

DENERVATED MAMMALIAN MUSCLE   Innervation seems to play a crucial role in the changing properties of the Na^+ channel ionophore in mammalian muscle. TTX-resistant APs develop in denervated muscles (47), neonatal rat skeletal muscle (19), L6 myotubes in culture (45), and mechanically injured muscle fibers. Under these same conditions, ACh sensitivity and α-bungarotoxin binding, found only at the synaptic junction in normal muscle, cover the entire extrajunctional surface in noninnervated muscle.

Ritchie & Rogart (49) studied STX uptake in normal and denervated mammalian muscle to determine the effect of denervation on the normal population of toxin-sensitive Na+ channels. They found that actual channel site density, referred to surface membrane area, appeared unchanged by denervation, as did toxin affinity. Their study also quantitatively ruled out the hypothesis that muscle membrane changes in denervation reflected conversion of extrajunctional Na+ channels into ACh-activated channels. Hansen-Bay & Strichartz (18) examined binding of *STX to rat extensor digitorum longus (EDL) muscle and showed more directly that site density was not significantly altered by denervation. Again, no significant change in toxin affinity was found. Thus toxin-resistant APs in denervated muscle probably reflect the appearance of a new population of toxin-resistant Na+ channels. This explanation was also consistent with the observation (16) that protein synthesis inhibitors blocked development of toxin-resistant APs.

Voltage clamp studies (44) in denervated rat EDL muscle have indicated that 75% of the channels have a normal TTX sensitivity, while 25% are resistant to TTX block. In the presence of 1 μM TTX, about 10% of sodium conductance remains in denervated muscle; a significantly smaller fraction remained in normal, innervated muscle fibers. TTX-resistant Na+ channels had normal activation and inactivation kinetics.

One unexplained observation in denervated muscle is that dV/dt, the rate of rise of the AP, decreases by about 30%, despite addition of toxin-resistant channels to normal channels, increasing total sodium conductance. Thesleff (personal communication) has ruled out the possibility that passive electrical properties change in denervated muscle fibers. However, a change in channel distribution between surface and T-tubule membrane might explain this paradox. Unfortunately, it has not yet been possible to measure toxin binding in glycerol-shocked denervated muscles.

Various studies have recently found that not only innervation, but also brain and spinal cord extracts alone can influence the state of ACh-activated channels in cultured denervated muscle, causing increase and redistribution of channels. This has led to a major search for a "trophic factor" in nerve that influences muscle development (14,27,35,45). Recent studies of denervated mammalian muscle cells have found that similar exposure of muscle cells to "trophic factor" also leads to disappearance of TTX-resistant

Na$^+$ channels, indicating another parallel between these channels and ACh-activated channel properties in denervation (15,20,29,64).

FAST AND SLOW MAMMALIAN MUSCLE FIBERS   Comparing toxin uptake in EDL muscle (which consists primarily of fast muscle fibers), soleus muscle (with a larger proportion of slow muscle fibers), and diaphragm muscle, Hansen-Bay & Strichartz (18) obtained Na$^+$ channel densities of 557, 371, and 421 sites per μm^2, respectively, which agreed with measured AP dV/dt in fast and slow fibers. Rash & Ellisman (46) had previously noted particles in square arrays in freeze-fractured muscle membrane, in greater number in fast than in slow muscle fibers. Although association between these freeze-fracture particles and Na$^+$ channels is obviously premature, the results from these two studies are suggestive.

SLOW AMPHIBIAN MUSCLE FIBERS   The rectus abdominis muscle in frog maintains a sustained contracture in response to continuous depolarization. This property depends on a special type of "slow muscle fiber," which is unable to generate APs. However, after denervation these fibers regain the ability to conduct APs. RNA and protein synthesis inhibitors block the re-development of APs in these denervated fibers. These studies (55) provide another example of membrane properties that change upon pathologic insult. Studies of reinnervation of these fibers led to postulation of a "trophic factor" from slow-conducting axons that provided the signal for alteration of membrane properties, since denervated fibers exposed to slow-conducting axons changed their properties at the same time as fibers with reinnervated synapses (55).

Schalow & Schmidt (55) also examined the spatial distribution of excitability in denervated slow muscle fibers with AP mechanisms. Rather than uniform excitability over the entire fiber membrane, they found patches of membrane were capable of generating large inward sodium currents, providing another example of altered membrane properties at "hot spots" with high densities of ion channels.

Literature Cited

1. Adrian, R. H., Peachey, L. D. 1973. Reconstruction of the action potential of frog sartorius muscle, *J. Physiol. London* 235:103–31
2. Almers, W. 1978, Gating currents and charge movements in excitable membranes. *Rev. Physiol. Biochem. Pharmacol.* 82:96–190
3. Almers, W., Levinson, S. R. 1975. Tetrodotoxin binding to normal and depolarized frog muscle and the con-ductance of a single sodium channel. *J. Physiol. London* 247:483–509
4. Armstrong, C. M. 1975. Ionic pores, gates, and gating currents, *Q. Rev. Biophys.* 7:179–210
5. Armstrong, C. M., Bezanilla, F. 1977. Inactivation of the sodium channel. II. Gating current measurements. *J. Gen. Physiol.* 70:567–90
6. Deleted in proof
7. Bostock, H., Sears, T. A. 1978. The internodal axonal membrane: electrical

excitability and continuous conduction in segmental demyelination, *J. Physiol. London* 280:273–301

8. Campbell, D., Hille, B. 1976. Kinetic and pharmacological properties of the sodium channel of frog skeletal muscle. *J. Gen. Physiol.* 67:309–23

9. Catterall, W. A. 1980. Neurotoxins that act on voltage-sensitive sodium channels in excitable membranes. *Ann. Rev. Pharmacol. Toxicol.* 20:15–43

10. Chicheportiche, R., Balerna, M., Lombet, A., Romey, G., Lazdunski, M. 1979. Synthesis and mode of action on axonal membranes of photoactivable derivatives of tetrodotoxin, *J. Biol. Chem.* 254:1552–57

11. Conti, F., DeFelice, L. J., Wanke, E. 1975. Potassium and sodium ion current noise in the membrane of the squid giant axon. *J. Physiol. London* 248:45–82

12. Conti, F., Hille, B., Nonner, W., Neumcke, B., Stampfli, R. 1976. Measurement of the conductance of the sodium channel from current fluctuations at the node of Ranvier. *J. Physiol. London* 262:699–728

13. Dodge, F. A., Cooley, J. W. 1973. Action potential of the motoneuron. *IBM J. Res. Dev.* 17:219–29

14. Frank, E. 1979. Acetylcholine receptor clusters. *Nature* 278:599–600

15. Fukuda, J., Kameyama, M. 1980. Tetrodotoxin-sensitive and tetrodotoxin-resistant sodium channels in tissue-cultured spinal ganglion neurons from adult mammals. *Br. Res.* 182:191–97

16. Grampp, W., Harris, J. B., Thesleff, S. 1972. Inhibition of denervation changes in skeletal muscle fibers by blockers of protein synthesis. *J. Physiol. London* 221:743–54

17. Hafemann, D. R. 1972. Binding of radioactive tetrodotoxin to nerve membrane preparations. *Biochim. Biophys. Acta* 266:548–56

18. Hansen-Bay, C. M., Strichartz, G. R. 1980. Saxitoxin binding to sodium channels of rat skeletal muscles. *J. Physiol. London* 300:89–103

19. Harris, J. B., Thesleff, S. 1971. Studies on tetrodotoxin resistant action potentials in denervated skeletal muscle. *Acta Physiol. Scand.* 83:382–88

20. Hasegawa, S., Kuromi, H. 1978. Ventral part of spinal cord contains the neurotrophic factor for the action potential of cultured muscle. *Br. Res* 157:153–56

21. Heitzmann, H. 1972. Rhodopsin is the predominant protein of rod outer segment membrane. *Nature New Biol.* 235:114–15

22. Hille, B. 1970. Ionic channels in nerve membranes. *Progr. Biophys. Molec. Biol.* 21:1–32

23. Hille, B. 1976. Gating in sodium channels of nerve. *Ann. Rev. Physiol.*, 38:139–52

24. Hodgkin, A. L., Huxley, A. F. 1952. A quantitative description of membrane current and its application to conduction and to excitation in nerve. *J. Physiol. London* 117:500–44

25. Jack, J. J. B., Noble, D., Tsien, R. W. 1975. *Electric Current Flow in Excitable Cells.* Oxford: Clarendon Press

26. Jaimovich, E., Venosa, R. A., Shrager, P., Horowicz, P. 1976. Density and distribution of tetrodotoxin receptors in normal and detubulated frog sartorius muscle. *J. Gen. Physiol.* 67:399–416

27. Jessell, T. M., Siegel, R. E., Fischbach, G. D. 1979. Induction of acetylcholine receptors on cultured skeletal muscle by a factor extracted from brain and spinal cord. *Proc. Natl. Acad. Sci. USA* 76(10):5597–401

28. Kano, M., Suzuki, N., Ojimi, H. 1979. Neurotrophic effect of nerve extract on development of tetrodotoxin-sensitive spike potential in skeletal muscle cells in culture. *J. Cell. Physiol.* 99:327–32

29. Keynes, R. D., Rojas, E. 1974. Kinetics and steady state properties of the charged system controlling sodium conductance in the squid giant axon. *J. Physiol. London* 239:393–434

30. Kristol, C., Sandri, C., Akert, K. 1978. Intramembranous particles at the nodes of Ranvier of the cat spinal cord: A morphologic study. *Br. Res.* 142:391–400

31. Kuno, M., Llinas, R. 1970. Enhancement of synaptic transmission by dendritic potentials in chromatolysed motoneurones of the cat. *J. Physiol. London* 210:807–21

32. Levinson, S. R. 1975. The purity of tritiated tetrodotoxin as determined by bioassay. *Philos. Trans. R. Soc. Ser. B.* 170:337–48

33. Levinson, S. R., Meves, H. 1975. The binding of tritiated tetrodotoxin to squid giant axons. *Philos. Trans. R. Soc. Ser. B* 270:349–52

34. Llinas, R., Nicholson, R. 1971. Electrophysiological properties of dendrites and stomata in alligator Purkinje cells. *J. Neurophysiol.* 34:532–51

35. Markelonis, G., Oh, T. H. 1979. A sciatic nerve protein has a trophic effect on development and maintenance of skeletal muscle cells in culture. *Proc. Natl. Acad. Sci. USA* 76:2470–74

36. Matsuda, Y., Yoshida, S., Yonezawa, T. 1978. Tetrodotoxin sensitivity and Ca component of action potentials of mouse dorsal root ganglion cells cultured in vitro. *Br. Res.* 154:69–82

37. Matthews-Bellinger, J., Saltpeter, M. M. 1978. Distribution of acetylcholine receptors at frog neuromuscular junction with a discussion of some physiological implications. *J. Physiol. London* 279:197–213

38. Moore, J. W., Blaustein, M. P., Anderson, N. C., Narahashi, T. 1967. Basis of tetrodotoxin's selectivity in blockage of squid axons. *J. Gen. Physiol.* 50:1401–11

39. Moore, J. W., Narahashi, T., Shaw, T. I. 1967. An upper limit to the number of sodium channels in nerve membrane? *J. Physiol. London* 188:99–105

40. Deleted in proof

41. Neher, E., Stevens, C. F. 1977. Conductance fluctuations and ionic pores in membranes. *Ann. Rev. Biophys. Bioeng.* 6:345–81

42. Neumcke, B., Nonner, W., Stampfli, R. 1978. Gating currents in excitable membranes. In *Biochemistry of Cell Walls and Membranes II*, vol. 19, ed. J. C. Metcalfe, pp. 129–55. Baltimore: University Park Press

43. Nonner, W., Rojas, E., Stampfli, R. 1975. Displacement currents in the node of Ranvier: Voltage and time dependence. *Pfluegers Arch.* 209:176–92

44. Pappone, P. 1977. Voltage clamp experiments on normal and denervated rat skeletal muscle fibers. *Biophys. J.* 17:3a

45. Podleski, T. R., Axelrod, D., Ravdin, P., Greenberg, I., Johnson, M. M., Saltpeter, M. M. 1978. Nerve extract induces increase and redistribution of acetylcholine receptors in cloned muscle cells. *Proc. Natl. Acad. Sci. USA* 75:2035–39

46. Rash, J. E., Ellisman, M. H. 1974. Studies of excitable membranes I. Macromolecular specializations of the neuromuscular junction and the nonjunctional sarcolemma. *J. Cell. Biol.* 63:567–86

47. Rasminsky, M., Keamey, R. E., Aguayo, A. J., Gray, G. M. 1978. Conduction of nervous impulses in spinal roots and peripheral nerves of dystrophic mice. *Brain Res* 143:71–85

48. Redfern, P., Thesleff, S. 1971. Action potential generation in denervated rat skeletal muscle. II. The action of tetrodotoxin. *Acta Physiol. Scand.* 82:70–78

49. Ritchie, J. M., Rogart, R. B. 1977. Density of sodium channels in mammalian myelinated nerve fibers and nature of the axonal membrane under the myelin sheath. *Proc. Natl. Acad. Sci. USA* 74:211–15

50. Ritchie, J. M., Rogart, R. B. 1977. The binding of labeled saxitoxin to the sodium channels in normal and denervated mammalian muscle and in amphibian muscle. *J. Physiol. London* 269:341–54

51. Ritchie, J. M., Rogart, R. B. 1977. The binding of saxitoxin and tetrodotoxin to excitable tissue. *Rev. Physiol. Biochem. Pharmacol.* 79:1–50

52. Ritchie, J. M., Rogart, R. B., Strichartz, G. R. 1976. A new method for labeling saxitoxin and its binding to nonmyelinated fibers of the rabbit vagus, lobster walking leg and garfish olfactory nerves. *J. Physiol. London* 261:477–94

53. Rogart, R. B., Ritchie, J. M. 1977. Pathophysiology of conduction. In *Demyelinated Nerve Fibers*, ch. 10, ed. P. Morell, p. 353–82. NY: Plenum.

54. Rosenbluth, J. 1976. Intramembranous particle distribution at the node of Ranvier and adjacent axolemma in myelinated axons of the frog brain. *J. Neurocytol.* 5:731–45

55. Schalow, G., Schmidt, H. 1977. Effect of nerve length and temperature on the induction of action potentials in denervated slow muscle fibers of the frog. *Pfluegers Arch.* 372:17–22

56. Sigworth, F. J. 1979. *Analysis of nonstationary sodium current fluctuations in frog myelinated nerve.* Ph.D. Thesis, Yale University, New Haven, Conn.

57. Stevens, C. F. 1978. Interactions between intrinsic membrane protein and electric field—an approach to studying nerve excitability. *Biophys. J.* 22:295–306

58. Strichartz, G. R., Rogart, R. B., Ritchie, J. M. 1979. Binding of radioactively labeled saxitoxin to the squid giant axon. *J. Membr. Biol.* 48:357–64

59. Tang, C. M., Strichartz, G. R., Orkand, R. K. 1979. Sodium channels in axons and glial cells of the optic nerve of *Necturus maculosa.* *J. Gen. Physiol.* 74:629–42

60. Traub, R. D., Llinas, R. 1977. The spatial distribution of ionic conductances in normal and axotonized motoneurons. *Neuroscience* 2:829–49
61. Deleted in proof
62. Waxman, S. G., Quick, D. C. 1978. Intra-axonal ferric ion-ferrocyanide staining of nodes of Ranvier and initial segments in central myelinated fibers. *Br. Res.* 144:1–10
63. Yoshida, S., Matsuda, Y., Samejima, A. 1978. Tetrodotoxin-resistant sodium and calcium components of action potentials in dorsal root ganglion cells of the adult mouse. *J. Neurophysiol.* 41:1096–106
64. Ziskind, L., Harris, A. J. 1979. Reinnervation of adult muscle in organ culture restores tetrodotoxin sensitivity in the absence of electrical activity. *Dev. Biol.* 69:388–99

AUTHOR INDEX

(Names appearing in capital letters indicate authors of chapters in this volume.)

727

SUBJECT INDEX

A

Acetylcholine
  cGMP mediator of action of,
    450
  respiratory effects of, 127
ACTH
  endorphin release and, 272
  fetal production of, 147
    placental and, 177, 178
  placental synthesis of, 147
  tremor producing
    endorphins in, 270
Actomyosin
  smooth muscle content of
    regulation of, 519–527
Adenohypophysis
  endorphins in, 269–273
Adenosine
  cerebral ischemia and, 402
  heart content and role of,
    389, 390
  intestinal occlusion
    hyperemia, 410
  muscle work and, 389,
    390
Adenylate cyclase in nephron,
  569–579
  collecting tubules, 577–579
    isoproterenol effects in,
      578
    parathyroid hormone
      effects in, 579
    vasopressin effects in, 577,
      578
  distal convoluted tubules,
    575–577
    calcium excretion and,
      576, 577
    hormone actions on, 575
    rabbit studies of, 575, 576
    rat studies of, 576, 577
    regions of, 575
  hormone actions and, 569,
    570
  proximal tubule, 570–572
    adrenergic receptors in,
      571
    cAMP locations in
      nephron, 570, 571
    norepinephrine effects on,
      571
    parathyroid hormone and,
      570
    phosphate handling and,
      571
  thick ascending limbs,
    572–575
    calcitonin effect on, 574,
      575

calcium excretion in, 574
  medullary vs. cortical
    portions of, 572, 573
  parathyroid hormone
    effects on, 574
  vasopressin effects on, 573,
    574
  hormone actions on, 572
Adrenal gland, fetal, 141–158
  adrenal medulla in fetus,
    154–156
    catecholamine secretion
      regulation, 155, 156
    chromaffin tissue of, 154,
      155
    innervation effects on, 156
  adrenal steroid biosynthesis
    metabolism and regulation,
      143–154
    blood steroid
      concentrations and,
        146
    cortisol-cortisone
      conversion, 148, 152
    cortisol metabolism
      schema, 152, 153
    cortisol synthesis and, 145,
      146
    cortisone blood content in
      fetus, 147, 151
    dexamethasone effects,
      151, 154
    DHAS metabolism, 144,
      145
    DHAS role in fetus, 153
    DHAS synthesis, 143–145
    fetal ACTH role, 147–153
    fetal adrenal secretion of
      mineralocorticoids,
        147
    "fetoplacental unit", 145
    fibroblast and epidermal
      growth factors, 149
    onset of corticoid
      synthesis, 145
    pituitary-adrenal axis in
      human fetus, 147–153
    progesterone and steroid
      synthesis, 149
    prolactin production in
      gestation, 148
    schema of fetal adrenal
      hormone formation,
        146
    steroids secreted by fetal
      adrenal, 149
    transplacental passage of
      cortisol, 151
  fetal adrenal gland function,
    156–158

morphology and
    development, 141–144
    adrenarche, 143
    human adrenal, 142
    onset of hormone
      secretion, 143
    postnatal regression of,
      142, 143
    zones of, 141–143
Aldosterone
  antidiuretic hormone action
    and, 621
  birth changes and, 374
  enzyme activity changed by,
    643
  fetal adrenal synthesis of,
    147
  kidney receptors for, 639
  protein synthesis increased
    by, 644
  proximal tubule sodium
    transport and, 646
  RNA incorporation into, 647
  transtubular electrical
    potentials, and, 645
  urinary acidification and, 646
Allometric relations, 301, 302
Amiloride
  cell volume regulation
    blocked by, 499
Amines
  inhibition of cellular entry
    by, 248
Amino acids
  respiratory effects of, 130,
    131
Ammonia
  urinary acidification
    aldosterone and, 646
Androgen binding proteins,
  extracellular, 189–196
  androgen binding protein,
    192–196
    bidirectional secretion of,
      195
    chemical structure of, 192,
      193
    function of, 195, 196
    hormonal control of, 193,
      194
    identification and isolation,
      192, 193
    neonatal secretion of, 194
    Sertoli cell secretion of,
      194, 195
    species differences in, 192,
      193
    synthesis and metabolism
      of, 193–195

761

attached bridges and, 557, 558
invertebrate muscle structure, 558, 559
myosin heads and, 558, 559
nucleotide AMPPNP and, 558, 559
rigor changes in, 557–559
thin filament structure, 556, 557
actin helix pitch, 556, 557
actin subunits and, 556
calcium role in, 556
"steric blocking model", 556
tropomyosin and, 556
Myosin
constitution of, 532
organ distribution of, 523
phosphorylation of regulation by, 520–526
properties of phosphorylation and, 523, 524
see also Muscle X-ray physiology and cells

N

Naloxone
opiate receptor antagonism by, 128, 129
Neonatal systemic circulation, 371–380
birth changes in circulation, 371–373
organ blood flow and, 372, 373
pulmonary blood flow, 372
ventricular outputs, 372
blood flow to specific organs, 376–380
cerebral blood flow, 378
ductus arteriosus closure, 379, 380
myocardial blood flow, 379
renal blood flow, 376–378
vasoactive substances role, 373–376
arterial pressure and, 373, 374
circulating vasoactive substances, 373–376
local vasoactive substances, 376
neurohypophyseal hormones, 375
prostaglandins, 375–376
renin-angiotensin-aldosterone system and, 374
sympathico-adrenal system, 373, 374

thyroid hormones, 375
Neoplastic cells
adrenal cortex and, 144
Neoplastic sympathetic tumors
nerve growth factor and, 256
sodium channels in, 711–719
Nerve activity and
macromolecular content of neurons and effector organs, 673–683
extrajunctional acetylcholine receptors, 673–676
acetylcholine-sensitivity in denervated muscle, 674
denervated muscle stimulation, 674, 675
denervation atrophy of muscle, 674
skeletal muscle denervation, 674
serotonin N-acetyltransferase regulation, 678–681
cAMP mediating, 680
cervical sympathetic stimulation and, 679–681
melatonin as pineal hormone, 678
pineal beta-adrenergic receptors, 680
pineal denervation and, 681
pineal diurnal rhythm in, 678
pineal norepinephrine diurnal rhythm, 679
propanolol and, 678, 679
sympathetic innervation and, 678
tyrosine hydroxylase regulation, 676–678
acetylcholine release and, 678
"cold stress" and, 677
hexamethonium blocking of tyrosine hydroxylase, 677
increased nicotinic receptor stimulation and, 677
norepinephrine synthesis and, 678
reserpine increase in preganglionic activity, 676, 677
stimulation and increased tyrosine hydroxylase, 676, 677
Nerve fibers
axon conduction
temperature extremes and, 291–292

growth of
nerve growth factor and, 256
growth of
nerve growth factor and, 256
Nerve growth factor
placental content of, 179
sympathetic system development and, 257–259
adrenal medulla effects, 259
adrenergic vs. cholinergic functions, 260
antibodies to, 257
cell death inhibited by, 258
chemical differentiation of neurons, 259–261
chromaffin cells transformed, 259
fibers entering spinal cord, 258
neuronal circuits formation, 257
tissue culture studies of, 256, 257
sympathetic adrenergic neurons, 256
trophic effects of, 256
Nerve, vagus
pulmonary afferent types, 106–108, 113–115
respiratory control, 77, 78, 83–85
Nervous system and
poikilothermia temperature adaptation, 281–296
capacity adaptations, 282–287
behavioral aspects, 283–287
brain metabolism and, 282
conditioning of behavior, 286, 287
eel muscle and, 282
extreme temperature adaptation, 282, 283
metabolism, 281, 283
nervous system and temperature adaptations, 281–288
range of selected temperatures, 283, 284
social behavior and, 285
thermoregulation and, 283–287
resistance adaptation, 287–295
axon conduction and, 291, 292
behavior and, 287, 288

CUMULATIVE INDEXES

CONTRIBUTING AUTHORS, VOLUMES 38–42

CHAPTER TITLES, VOLUMES 39–43